LANCELOT HOGBEN

Science for the Citizen

The second of the
Primers for the Age
of Plenty

The third of the Primers in

Professor Hogben's famous series is

HISTORY OF THE HOMELAND

American title:

ENGLAND: A HISTORY OF THE HOMELAND

by Henry Hamilton, M.A., D.LITT

    Jaffrey Professor of Political Economy in the University of Aberdeen

The fascinating story of the British background arranged by subjects and including Food, Clothes, Health, the British Empire, the Rise of Capitalism, the Labour Movement and Education.

"Professor Hamilton is to be congratulated. . . . He traverses the social, economic and institutional history from the earliest times to the present day with skill and deep knowledge."—*Manchester Guardian*.

The pictures, maps and diagrams alone are an inexhaustible quarry.

Before that there was

THE LOOM OF LANGUAGE: A Guide to Foreign Languages for the Home Student by Dr. F. Bodmer, edited and arranged by Lancelot Hogben. It is already in its fifth printing.

and the first of the Primers was HOGBEN'S *own*

MATHEMATICS FOR THE MILLION

of which it was said:

H. G. WELLS: My deliberate opinion is that it is a great book, a book of first-class importance, and that it should be read by every intelligent youth from fifteen to ninety who is trying to get the hang of things in this universe.

NEW YORK HERALD TRIBUNE: This is a challenge to the intelligent modern to understand his world.

LANCELOT HOGBEN

Science for the Citizen

A Self-Educator based on the Social Background of Scientific Discovery

"Such philosophy as shall not vanish in the fume of subtile, sublime, or delectable speculation but shall be operative to the endowment and betterment of man's life."   FRANCIS BACON

ILLUSTRATED BY

J. F. HORRABIN

NEW EDITION
WITH A NEW CHAPTER ON ATOMIC ENERGY

London
George Allen & Unwin Ltd

FIRST PUBLISHED 1938

REVISED SECOND EDITION 1940

THIRD IMPRESSION (SECOND EDITION) 1941

FOURTH IMPRESSION (SECOND EDITION) 1943

FIFTH IMPRESSION (SECOND EDITION) 1944

SIXTH IMPRESSION (SECOND EDITION) 1945

SEVENTH IMPRESSION (SECOND EDITION) 1948

THIRD REVISED EDITION (EIGHTH IMPRESSION) 1951

FOURTH REVISED EDITION (NINTH IMPRESSION) 1956

Printed in Great Britain
by
Novello & Co. Ltd.
London

TO
HAROLD J. LASKI

FOREWORD TO THIRD EDITION

Science for the Citizen is partly written for the large and growing number of intelligent adults who realize that the *Impact of Science on Society* is now the focus of genuinely constructive social effort. It is also written for the large and growing number of adolescents, who realize that they will be the first victims of the new destructive powers of science misapplied. Since it is the first British handbook to *Scientific Humanism*, it has, inevitably, the glaring faults of any new thing. Education segregates the scientific specialist from those who study problems of government and social welfare. So like anyone else who, in this generation, might have attempted a task so ambitious, I have had to re-educate myself in the process of writing it.

Natural science is an essential part of the education of a citizen, because scientific discoveries affect the everyday lives of everyone. Hence science for the citizen must be science as a record of past, and as an inventory for future, human achievements. Inevitably it cannot be divorced from history, and my first duty is to acknowledge the patience with which my former colleagues of the history department in the London School of Economics responded to my requests for sources of information. Needless to say I am not competent to judge the reliability of the sources, which I have quoted at length when a personal statement of opinion would imply that I have sufficient first-hand knowledge to do so. For instance, this applies to some suggestive speculations concerning the dating of ancient monuments in Chapters I and IV. To avoid misunderstanding, let me warn the reader that different experts do not always share the same views on this topic, and the example cited in Chapter IV is not given because all authorities would agree with the date of the Pyramid to which Neuberger subscribes in his treatise on ancient technology. I have included it for reasons more fully stated below, in particular, because it gives the reader a clue to the way in which a hypothesis of this kind can be subjected to an independent test.

In the Victorian age big men of science like Faraday, T. H. Huxley, and Tyndall did not think it beneath their dignity to write about simple truths with the conviction that they could *instruct* their audiences. There were giants in those days. The new fashion is to select from the periphery of mathematicized hypotheses some half assimilated speculation as a preface to homilies and apologetics crude enough to induce a cold sweat in a really sophisticated theologian who knows his job. The clue to the state of mind which produces them is contempt for the common man. The key to the eloquent literature which the pen of Faraday and Huxley produced is their firm faith in the educability of mankind.

Because I share that faith I have not asked the reader to take any reasoning on trust. Since the reasoning used in science is often conducted with the sort of shorthand called algebra or illustrated by the sort of scale diagrams called geometry, a casual glance at isolated pages of this book might be discouraging to those who have been humiliated by the obstacles which early education places in our path. Fortunately the engaging illustrations of my friend and collaborator Horrabin are likely to remove the impression that this is like anything that the reader has learned at school. Beyond that let me say this. Anyone who has mastered the essence of the first half of *Mathematics for the Million*, or has once been through a course of elementary mathematics leading to a school-leaving certificate, will have nothing to be afraid of. The rest will be told and the reader will be reminded of what may have been long since forgotten.

The present edition contains many amendments of the earlier text suggested by readers who have kindly co-operated with the author in removing obscurities and correcting the inevitable misprints in so long a book. I have to thank Mr. Richard Knight for invaluable assistance in the preparation of a new chapter and in appropriate revision of the text with that end in view. My debt to various friends, in particular to Mr. Richard Palmer, Dr. Miller, and Mr. H. D. Dickinson who helped to see it through the press in its original form has been recorded in the foreword to the first edition. The kind consideration which the latter received from reviewers prompts me to remove one other possible source of misunderstanding. *Science for the Citizen* is written for citizens living in a society which has scarcely begun to see how science might be used for the satisfaction of human needs. As such it is a product of a particular human environment in which a particular aspect of the manifold truth needs special emphasis. In an Age of Peace and Plenty it might well be important to lay more stress on what is sometimes called the *disinterested* pursuit of truth. I have hinted in various places, as in the introductory remarks of Chapter XV, that the individual attitude of the investigator is an aspect of scientific progress with which we must always reckon. Today the great need is to emphasize how the capacities of individuals who can pursue science in the only way in which truly scientific knowledge can be advanced are continually thwarted by the lopsided encouragement of research in a society which consecrates its finest gifts to gigantic preparations for destroying human life. Time may come, and will come if this book helps to promote the outlook which these pages unfold, when it will no longer be necessary to emphasize this aspect of scientific progress. If that time comes it may be necessary to discourage the approach to, and to displace the method of, exposition which I believe to be right and necessary for my day and generation. If so, I who have not always shown charity to my predecessors, shall not be in a position to complain of harsh criticism in a footnote on popular science in the first half of the twentieth century.

LANCELOT HOGBEN

CONTENTS

PART I

The Conquest of Time Reckoning and Space Measurement

PART II

The Conquest of Substitutes

PART III
The Conquest of Power

PART IV
The Conquest of Hunger and Disease

PART V
The Conquest of Behaviour

PART I

The Conquest of Time Reckoning and Space Measurement

"THE progress of Greek civilization was dependent essentially on the change of slave-labour into free, a transformation not supposable without the employment of natural forces, applied to labour-saving machines. It is evident that, with the invention of a machine which will convert a given natural force (e.g. a falling weight of water) into an industrial force, performing the labour of twenty men, the inventor could grow rich and twenty slaves be set free; moreover, that the natural effect of the introduction of machines is an augmentation of the productive class, whence a greater number of inventors and increased production. But, in a slave-state, the application of natural forces and the substitution of machine labour for servile, is mainly impossible, for as, in such a state, the profits of the capitalist rest upon his slaves, he sees that the introduction of machines must imperil his resources, and when, as in Greece, the capitalists belong to the ruling class, the Government and people will combine to perpetuate the existing system, i.e. slavery—the Government with the seemingly-wise purpose of assuring subsistence to the labourers. Only the freeman, not the slave, has a disposition and interest to improve implements or to invent them; accordingly, in the devising of a complicated machine, the workmen employed upon it are generally co-inventors. The eccentric and the governor, most important parts of the steam-engine, were devised by labourers. The improvement of established industrial methods by slaves, themselves industrial machines, is out of the question."

LIEBIG

CHAPTER I

POLE STAR AND PYRAMID

The Coming of the Calendar

A MUCH abused writer of the nineteenth century said: *up to the present philosophers have only interpreted the world, it is also necessary to change it.* No statement more fittingly distinguishes the standpoint of humanistic philosophy from the scientific outlook. Science is organized workmanship. Its history is co-extensive with that of civilized living. It emerges so soon as the secret lore of the craftsman overflows the dam of oral tradition, demanding a permanent record of its own. It expands as the record becomes accessible to a widening personnel, gathering into itself and coordinating the fruits of new crafts. It languishes when the social incentive to new productive accomplishment is lacking, and when its custodians lose the will to share it with others. Its history, which is the history of the constructive achievements of mankind, is also the history of the democratization of positive knowledge. This book is written to tell the story of its growth as a record of human achievement, a story of the satisfaction of the common needs of mankind, disclosing as it unfolds new horizons of human wellbeing which lie before us, if we plan our new resources intelligently.

Whether we choose to call it pure or applied, the story of science is not something apart from the common life of mankind. What we call pure science only thrives when the contemporary social structure is capable of making full use of its teaching, furnishing it with new problems for solution and equipping it with new instruments for solving them. Without printing there would have been little demand for spectacles; without spectacles neither telescope nor microscope; without these the finite velocity of light, the annual parallax of the stars, and the micro-organisms of fermentation processes and disease would never have been known to science. Without the pendulum clock and the projectile there would have been no dynamics nor theory of sound. Without the dynamics of the pendulum and projectile, no *Principia*. Without deep-shaft mining in the sixteenth century, when abundant slave labour was no longer to hand, there would have been no social urge to study air pressure, ventilation, and explosion. Balloons would not have been invented, chemistry would have barely surpassed the level reached in the third millennium B.C., and the conditions for discovering the electric current would have been lacking.

For this reason the chapters which follow will not adopt the customary division of science into separate disciplines, such as chemistry or biology. The topics dealt with will be grouped under six main themes; the story of man's conquest of time reckoning and earth measurement, of material substitutes, of new power resources, of disease, of hunger, and of behaviour. When the language of mathematics is used, no advanced knowledge will be assumed, and it will present no difficulties if the reader is prepared to do a little work on the examples given. If difficulties arise the reader should not be too easily discouraged, or give up hope. If one chapter or page is difficult to follow, as likely as not the next will be especially easy. The most difficult ones come at the beginning.

If the execution of the task is novel, there is no originality in the conception. The reader who is tempted to think so should reflect on the words with which the great German chemist Liebig addressed the Royal Academy of Sciences at Munich in 1866. Speaking of the *Development of Ideas in Physical Science*, Liebig said:

The history of physical science teaches us that our knowledge of things and of natural phenomena has, for its starting point, the material and intellectual wants of man and is conditioned by both. . . . Man is not born acquainted with sensible objects and their properties and effects; these notions must be gained by experience. . . . All these conceptions have sprung or have been derived from sensible marks. . . . Since natural phenomena are interconnected like knots in a net, the investigation of particular phenomena evinces that they have in common certain conditions, which as remarked are active things. . . . Having the facts it is our subsequent business to establish their connexion. The facts themselves are obtained through sensual perceptions; when these are imperfect, so will be the knowledge reared on them. We can have no general theoretical propositions except by means of induction, and inductions can be framed only through sensual perceptions. . . . Manifestly therefore the truth of explanations does not depend on the principles of logic alone. . . . The first explanations can, manifestly, be neither definite nor limited, and they must change just in proportion as the facts are more distinctly ascertained and as the unknown ones belonging to the conception are discovered and incorporated in it. The earlier explanations are therefore only relatively false and the latter only therein truer that the contents of the conceptions of things are more comprehensive, determinate and distinct. . . . The conception of time which belongs to the composite notion of velocity was first developed fifteen hundred years after Aristotle. For short intervals the Greeks had not clocks or time measures. . . . Charlemagne's endeavours by the establishment of schools to elevate the intelligence of the rude and ignorant priesthood of the age could have no result, the soil on which culture thrives being not yet prepared. The development of culture, i.e. the extending of man's spiritual domain, depends on the growth of the inventions which condition the progress of civilization, for through these new facts are obtained. . . . Only the free man, not the slave, has a disposition and interest to improve implements or to invent them; accordingly, in the devising of a complicated machine, the workmen employed upon it are generally co-inventors. . . . Greek civilization travelled through the Roman Empire and the Arabians into every European country. . . . The members of the newly originated intellectual class were at first occupied in gaining possession of the treasures of ancient learning. . . . The position and employment of the learned of those times concurred in withdrawing them from contact with the productive classes. Accordingly the literature of that age gives no indication of the degree of the popular civilization and culture; for the knowledge circulating through the masses and absorbed into their thinking, a knowledge originating in their improved acquaintance with physical laws, was not yet stored up in books and was wholly foreign to the learned. . . . With the extinction of the slavery of the ancient world and the union of all the conditions for the evolution of the human mind, progress of civilization and culture is thenceforth assured, indestructible, imperishable. Most of the facts from which the investigator elaborated empirical ideas he had long since received from the metallurgists, the engineers, the apothecaries, and had resolved their inventions into conceptions which the producing classes received back . . . the craftsman, technician, agriculturalist, physician, as in Greece, ask counsel of the theorist. . . . The history of nations informs us of the fruitless efforts of political and theological powers to perpetuate slavery, corporeal and intellectual. Future history will describe the victories of freedom which men achieved through investigation of the ground of things and of truth, victories won with bloodless weapons and in a struggle wherein morals and religion participated only as feeble allies. . . .

THE BEGINNING OF SCIENCE

We start with the conquest of time and distance. That is to say, the kind of knowledge we need to keep track of the seasons and to find our where-abouts in the world we inhabit. One depends upon the other. Making a calendar and navigating a ship depend on the same kind of knowledge, and we shall not be able to keep the two issues apart. Much of the mystery which enshrouds contemporary discussion of Relativity will present no difficulty if the use of the ship's chronometer is grasped firmly at the outset. All measure-ments of time depend on making measurements in space, and localization in space depends on measurements of time.

We used to think of man as a tool-bearing animal, and to divide the pre-literate stage of his existence into an old stone age and a new stone age. We now know that the social achievements of mankind before the beginning of the written record include far more important things than the perfection of axes and arrowheads. Three discoveries into which he blundered many millennia before the dawn of civilization in Egypt, Sumeria, or Turkestan, are specially significant. With the aid of the dogs which followed him and prowled about his camp fires, he began to herd instead of to hunt. He learned to scatter millet and barley, to store grain to consume when there were no fruits to gather. He collected gold nuggets and bits of meteoric iron, and, it may be, noticed the formation of copper (see p. 360) from the green pigment that he used for adornment, when it was heated in the embers. The sheep is an animal with seasonal fertility, and cereal crops are largely annual. In domesticating the sheep and learning to sow cereals, man therefore made a fateful step. The recognition of the passage of time now became a primary necessity of social life. In learning to record the passage of time man learned to measure things. He learned to keep account of past events. He made structures on a much vaster scale than any which he employed for purely domestic use. The arts of writing, architecture, numbering, and in particular geometry, which was the offspring of star lore and shadow reckoning, were all by-products of man's first organized achievement, the construction of the calendar. Shakespeare anticipated Sir Norman Lockyer when he wrote: "Our forefathers had no other books but the score and the tally."*

Science began when man started to plan ahead for the seasons, because

---

* *Henry VI*, Act IV—score in this context is from the Anglo-Saxon *scora* meaning notches made on the tally stick.

planning ahead for the seasons demanded an organized body of continuous observations and a permanent record of their recurrence. In an age of wireless transmission, of mechanical clocks and cheap almanacs, we take time for granted. Before there were any clocks or simpler devices like the hour-glass or the clepsydra for recording the passage of time, mankind had to depend on the direction of the heavenly bodies, sun by day and the stars by night. Already in the hunting and food gathering stage the human race had probably learned to associate changes in vegetation, the mating habits of animals, and the recurrence of drought or floods, with the rising and setting

FIG. 1

The earliest geometrical problems arose from the need for a calendar to regulate the seasonal pursuits of settled agriculture. The recurrence of the seasons was recognized by erecting monuments in line with the rising, setting, or transit of celestial bodies. This photograph, taken at Stonehenge, shows how the position of a stone marked the day of the summer solstice when the sun rises farthest north along the eastern boundary of the horizon.

of bright stars and star clusters immediately before sunrise or in evening twilight. When the great agrarian revolution reached its climax in the dawn of city life, a technique of timekeeping emerged as its pivotal achievement. What chiefly remain to record the beginnings of an orderly routine of settled life in cities are the vast structures which bear eloquent witness to the primary social function of the priesthood as custodians of the calendar. The temple with its corridor and portal placed to greet the transit of its guardian star or to trap a thin shaft of light from the rising or setting sun of the quarter-days; the obelisk or shadow clock; the Pyramids facing equinoctial sunrise or sunset, the pole and the southings of the bright stars in the zodiac; the great stone circle of Stonehenge with its sight-line pointing to the rising sun of the summer solstice—all these are first and foremost almanacs in architecture. Nascent science and ceremonial religion had a common focus of social necessity in the observatory-temple of the astronomer-priest. That we still divide the circle into 360 degrees, that we

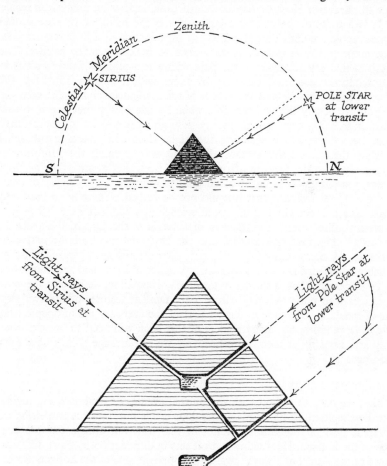

FIG. 2.—THE ASTRONOMICAL ORIENTATION OF THE GREAT PYRAMID

The Pyramid of Cheops and that of Sneferu are constructed on a common geometrical plan. The perimeter of the four sides, which face exactly the north, south, east, and west, has the same ratio to the height as the ratio of the circumference to the radius of a circle, i.e. $2 \times 3\frac{1}{7}$, or 2π. According to Flinders Petrie: "The squareness and level of the base is brilliantly true, the average error being less than a ten-thousandth of the side in equality, squareness, and level." According to *Neugebauer*, the rays of Sirius the dogstar, whose heliacal rising announced the Egyptian New Year and the flooding of the sacred river which brought prosperity to the cultivators, were perpendicular to the south face at transit, and shone down the ventilating shaft into the royal chamber while building was in progress. The main opening, and a second shaft leading to the lower chamber, conveyed the light of the Pole Star, which was then the star a in the constellation *Draco*, at its lower transit, three degrees below the true celestial pole.

reckon fractions of a degree in minutes and seconds, remind us that men learned to measure angles before they had settled standards of length or area. Angular measurement was the necessary foundation of timekeeping. The social necessity of recording the passage of time forced mankind to map out the heavens. How to map the earth came later as an unforeseen result.

It is a common belief that mathematics is the hallmark of science, and some people are apt to imagine that the introduction of a little mathematics into subjects like economics entitles them to rank as genuine science. The truth is that science rests on the painstaking recognition of uniformities in nature. In no branch of science is this more evident than in astronomy, the oldest of the sciences, and the parent of the mathematical arts. Between the beginnings of city life and the time when human beings first began to sow corn or to herd sheep, ten or twenty thousand years—perhaps more—may have been occupied in scanning the night skies and watching the sun's shadow throughout the seasons. Mankind was learning the uniformities which signalize the passage of the seasons, becoming aware of an external order, grasping slowly that it could only be commanded by being obeyed, and not as yet realizing that it could not be bribed. There is no hard and sharp line between the beginnings of science and what we now call magic. Professor Elliot Smith rightly says that magic is the discarded science of yesterday. The first priests were also the first scientists and the first civil servants. As custodians of the calendar, they created an organized body of reliable knowledge from the common experience of herdsman and cultivator.

To understand how a science of astronomy is possible, we have to acquaint ourselves with uniformities of nature, once familiar features of the everyday life of mankind. They are no longer part of the everyday life of people who live in large cities. So, many readers of this book will need to be told what they are. Looking at them retrospectively we can arrange them under four headings.

THE DIURNAL EVENTS

First we have to reckon with the diurnal events. At daybreak and nightfall the shepherd, as he stands at the door of his hut, sees the sun rising in different positions at different times of the year, but always towards one side of the horizon. He watches it, as it sets in different positions at different times of the year, but always towards the opposite side of the horizon. So he learns to distinguish an eastern horizon of sunrise and a western horizon of sunset. In the region north of the tropics, where the neolithic agrarian economy began, the sun travels over the heavens obliquely, so that the noon shadow is always on one side of the line joining the eastern and western horizons (Fig. 3). The sun's shadow shortens as day wears on till the sun itself is highest in the heavens, and then lengthens again as it points more and more towards the place of the rising sun. The noon or shortest shadow divided the working day of the cultivator into morning and afternoon. Fisher folk would be familiar with other time signals besides the daily changes of the sun and stars. They would see how high and low water at the tide marks would happen twice in a day and a night. Before there was any settled husbandry, hunting and food-gathering tribes had learned to recognize familiar star clusters, like the Dipper or Great Bear and Cassiopeia, when night fell; to know how they change their position like the sun as night goes on, and to notice how one star, the Pole Star, is always seen above the same point on the horizon, in the same place at sunset and at sunrise.

When men began to stick up poles or stone pillars to mark off the day by the direction and length of the shadow, they would notice that the noon

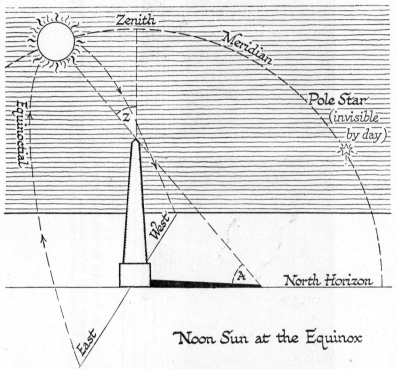

FIG. 3

The noon or shortest shadow of the Obelisk or shadow clock points due north towards the celestial pole. At the equinoxes (March 21st and September 23rd) the sun rises due east and sets due west, and the observer is at the centre of its semicircular track, called the *equinoctial* or celestial equator. The angle A which the sun makes with the horizon is called its *altitude*. The angle Z which it makes with the vertical is its *zenith distance*. The altitude of the Pole Star is very nearly constant, and on the equinoxes the z.d. of the noon sun is practically equal to the altitude of the Pole Star. Hence the plane of the equinoctial is at right angles to the axis which passes through the observer and the celestial pole. The stars and moon pass over the horizon in circular arcs parallel to that of the sun's transit, rising on the eastern side and setting on the western side of the meridian, or arc, which passes through the north and south points of the horizon, the pole, and the zenith directly overhead.

shadow always points to the same spot on the horizon, and that the Pole Star remains throughout the night exactly above it (Fig. 3). As the night passed they would see the other stars revolve about the Pole Star in an anti-clockwise direction, from east to west above it, like the sun. They would long since have known that star clusters nearest the pole, the "circumpolar" stars, never sink below the horizon, trailing from west to east below the pole,

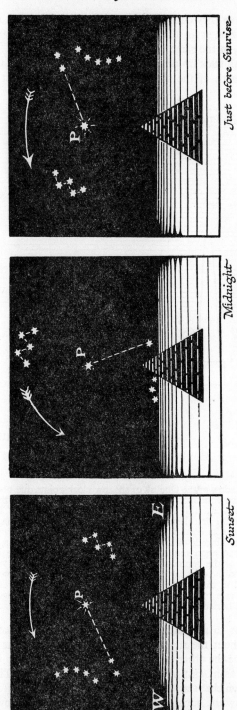

Sunset   *Midnight*   *Just before Sunrise*

FIG. 4.—THE NIGHTLY ROTATION OF THE STARS

Diagrammatic view as we might see the sky from the Pyramids today in late summer. The two constellations shown, being very near the pole, do not set below the horizon. Six months later Cassiopeia would be seen sinking after sunset and rising just before sunrise.

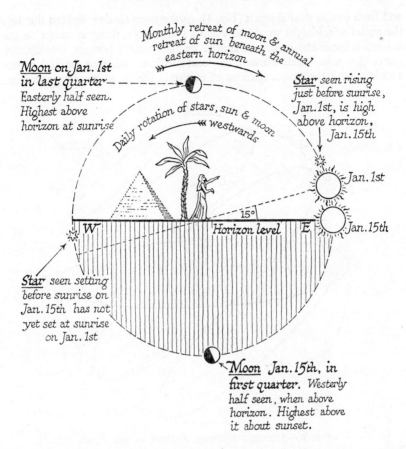

Monthly retreat of moon & annual retreat of sun beneath the eastern horizon

<u>Moon</u> on Jan. 1st in last quarter—
Easterly half seen. Highest above horizon at sunrise

Daily rotation of stars, sun & moon westwards

<u>Star</u> seen rising just before sunrise, Jan. 1st, is high above horizon, Jan. 15th

Jan. 1st

Jan. 15th

15°

W Horizon level E

<u>Star</u> seen setting before sunrise on Jan. 15th has not yet set at sunrise on Jan. 1st

<u>Moon</u> Jan. 15th, in first quarter. Westerly half seen, when above horizon. Highest above it about sunset.

FIG. 5.—THE CHANGING APPEARANCE OF THE HEAVENS

In twenty-four hours the whole dome of heaven, including the moon, sun, and fixed stars, rotates about an axis which joins the observer to the celestial pole, whose position is approximately marked by the Pole Star. With the exception of the "circumpolar" stars, which are too near the pole to dip under the horizon, the heavenly bodies all appear to rise upwards from the eastern boundary and to sink below the western boundary of the horizon plane. In this motion, called the apparent diurnal motion of the celestial sphere, the fixed stars retain the same position relative to one another, so that at any place the time between the risings or settings of any two stars and the direction in which any star is seen rising or setting are always the same. Relative to the rising of any fixed star, the moon and the sun each rise a little later on successive days. They thus seem to be slipping backwards below the eastern margin of the horizon plane. The sun takes 365¼ days to retreat eastwards till it is again in the same position relative to a fixed star, i.e. it slips under the horizon plane eastwards through approximately one degree per day. The moon takes 27⅓ days to do so, but, as the sun is slipping back, though more slowly, in the same direction it takes a little longer, namely, 29½ days (see p. 103), to return to the same position relative to the sun. In the figure new moon would occur about January 7th and the next new moon about February 5th. At last quarter the moon is 90° west of the sun, rising about midnight and reaching its highest point in the heavens about 6 a.m., when its easterly half is visible. At first quarter it sets about midnight, reaching its highest point in the heavens meridian transit) at about 6 p.m., when its westerly face is illumined.

and from east to west above it (Fig. 4). As the noon shadow divided the day, the signal of midnight would be when a star cluster, rising at sunset on the eastern horizon and setting at sunrise on the western horizon, was directly above the pole. These clusters or "constellations" received fanciful names redolent with the preoccupations of everyday life in an agrarian economy.

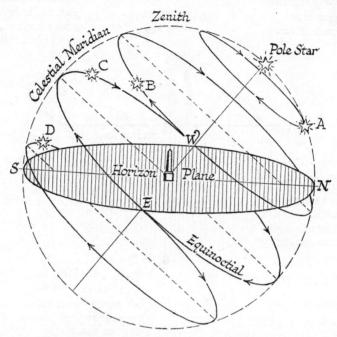

FIG. 6.—APPARENT DIURNAL MOTION OF THE STARS

The stars appear to describe circular arcs parallel to one another about an axis which joins the observer to the celestial pole. Those nearest the pole—the circumpolar stars, like A here seen at lower culmination, never sink below the horizon and may, therefore, be seen crossing the meridian below the pole. Other northerly stars, such as B, describe large arcs over the horizon and so remain *above* it more than 12 hours between rising and ·setting north of the east and west points. Stars (e.g. C) lying on the great equinoctial circle which cuts the east and west points (i.e. stars which rise due east and set due west) remain above the horizon for half the 24 hours of the diurnal cycle. Stars (like D) which lie south of the equinoctial rise and set towards the southern horizon and are *below* it more than 12 out of the 24 hours. The majority of stars in a northern latitude cross the meridian south of the zenith. Hence sailors speak of the transit of a star as its "southing."

Herdsmen watching the night pass would find it just as easy to recognize intervals of night time equivalent to the shadow hours of the day. The much despised yokel, who has not upholstered his brain with the urban super-stitions of all the ages, is often adept in using the star clock. A little practice while camping out is sufficient to enable you to tell the time by the stars with an error scarcely more than quarter of an hour.

Centuries before city life began, man had begun to fumble for a connected account of the regularities forced on his attention. He already knew that sun, moon, and stars partake of the same daily and nightly motion about one central point in the heavens. As they stand, the facts with which primitive man was familiar in his everyday life are capable of being looked at in two ways. When we are passing another train, we cannot at once tell whether we are at rest and the other one is in motion, or *vice versa*. So we cannot tell whether we are going east to meet the sun and rising stars, or whether they are moving west to meet us. In the train we can settle the issue by looking out of the opposite window. We put ourselves in the position of the man on the platform. Primitive man had no knowledge of what the two trains would look like from the platform. Having no other court of appeal, he inclined to his first impression that the sun and stars were rushing past him.

In the priestly lore of the earliest calendar civilizations the picture pieced together was something like this. The stars, moon, and sun were all on the surface of a great sphere, of which we only see one half at a time. The stars become visible when the sun is in the celestial hemisphere below our horizon (Fig. 5). The celestial sphere revolves around an axis joining the Pole Star (Fig. 6) to some fixed spot on the earth—the North Pole, as we call it today. It completes its revolution in a day and a night, revolving in an anti-clockwise direction from the standpoint of a person looking upwards towards the North Pole Star.

Although the facts are equally explicable on the alternative assumption that the stars are fixed and that the earth is revolving about the same axis in the opposite direction to the apparent revolution of the celestial sphere, the earlier and less sophisticated view embodied a tremendous gain. It involved the first step towards a world map. In counting the shadow hours and learning to use the star clock, man had begun to use geometry. He had begun to find his local bearings in cosmic and terrestrial space. An important step towards an art of measurement was made when men began to trace circles on the sand or the soft earth around the shadow pole to mark the moment when the shadow was shortest. In discovering the constant direction of the noon shadow pointing to the pole, they fixed two planes of reference. One is the *horizontal plane*, the north and south points of which divide the observer's terrestrial horizon into an easterly and a westerly half. The other was bounded by the great semicircle or *Meridian* of the heavens, with its highest point, the zenith, directly overhead (Fig. 3). The axle of the heavenly clock of star transit and shadow connected the Pole Star to the earthly pole in the meridian plane. Sun, moon, and stars are highest in the heavens where the circles they describe on the surface of the celestial sphere cut the meridian.

THE MONTHLY EVENTS

Strictly speaking in order of time, the first class of uniformities from which the measurement of time proceeded were in all probability the lunar phenomena, from which we got the grouping of days into months and weeks (quarter months). There are still backward peoples who have not learned to reckon in years of equivalent length. The recognition of the month is wellnigh universal even among hunting tribes with no settled agriculture. Moonlight is a circumstance of enormous importance in the everyday life of people who have crude means of artificial illumination. Even today in remote parts of the country the time of full moon is chosen for a long night journey.

An interval of roughly thirty days separates one full moon or new moon from another. The two half moons, the first "quarter" when waxing and the third "quarter" when waning, complete the division of the month into quarters, which roughly correspond to our week. Near the sea it is noticed that the tides are exceptionally high when the moon is invisible through the

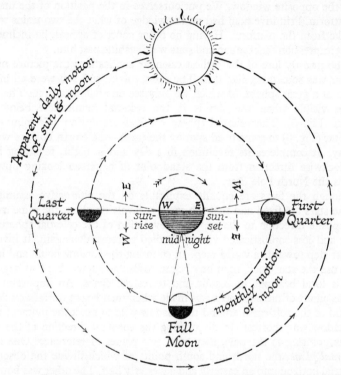

FIG. 7.—THE MONTHLY CYCLE OF THE MOON'S PHASES

whole night (new moon) and when it is full. At first and third quarter (half moons) the high-water mark is exceptionally low. The most important thing (Fig. 5) connected with the changing appearance of the moon is that as the moon waxes and wanes it rises towards the east a little later every day. At first quarter (Fig. 7) it is already high in the heavens at sunset, setting about midnight. The full moon rises about sunset, is at its highest about midnight, and sets towards sunrise. At the third quarter the waning moon does not rise till about midnight, is seen at its highest point ("crosses the meridian") about sunrise, and is visible during the morning by daylight.*

The moon seems to partake of the general motion of the celestial sphere,

* The relative times of setting and rising of the sun and moon depend partly on their declinations, as explained in Chapter II, and are different at different seasons. These remarks, like others on the next page, are only to be taken as a rough outline of what happens.

rising in the east and setting in the west. If it rises at the same time as a particular star cluster on a particular night in the month, the same constellation will rise a little earlier than the moon on the night following. A week later it would already be above the pole at moonrise. Thus the moon itself seems to be slipping backwards in the opposite direction to the apparent rotation of the sun and fixed stars, so that it gets back to where it was before after a definite interval of days and nights, i.e. what we call roughly a month. Alternatively we may say that it rotates round the earth in about a month in the same direction as the earth's axial or diurnal motion. Whichever way we look at it, the moon has a motion of its own, independent of the apparent motion of the fixed stars.

THE ANNUAL EVENTS

In regulating the seasonal requirements of a pastoral and grain economy, the determination of the year was of supreme importance. The continuity of careful observations which preceded, and the precision involved in settling the exact length of the year, entitle this achievement to be regarded as one of the half-dozen great cultural feats in the history of mankind. Since the Egyptian priests had already established a year of 365 days by 4241 B.C., we may conclude that the recognition of the year as a unit of time antedates the beginnings of the great calendar civilizations. Associated with the passage of the seasons in the everyday life of neolithic man, two classes of events contributed to the first crude appreciation of the year as a natural unit of time. One is concerned with the behaviour of the stars, the other with that of the sun's shadow.

The stars rise earlier every night. If a star is seen rising exactly at sunset on a particular day, it will be seen well above the horizon when the sun sets a few weeks later. If a star is in the west at sunrise and in the east at sunset in March, it will reach its highest point in the sky when the sun goes down, about three full moons later, i.e. at the end of June. After six months it will be already setting in the west at sunset, unless it is very near the pole. If it is a circumpolar star, as are those in the constellations of Cassiopeia and of the Great Bear in our latitude, it will be sloping down towards the northern horizon. A circumpolar star seen at midnight directly above the pole, will be seen directly below the pole ("lower culmination") at midnight six months later.

The majority of the stars are below the horizon at lower culmination. So they are only visible after nightfall during part of the year. At midwinter, in the latitude of London, Orion, with its three bright stars forming the belt, is visible most of the night, rising just after sunset and setting in the early morning hours before sunrise. By March 21st (vernal equinox) it has reached its highest point (crosses the meridian) in the heavens at sunset, and is seen setting about midnight. By midsummer it sets before sunset and has not yet risen by sunrise. So it is invisible in the summer sky.

All these appearances occur with perfect regularity after the lapse of the same number of full moons. Thus the sun's apparent position among the fixed stars is not constant. Since the stars rise earlier every day, the sun, while partaking of the apparent diurnal rotation of the celestial sphere, also seems to be *slipping back a little in the opposite direction,* like the moon only not so fast (Fig. 13). In the course of a year it slips back through complete circle to its original position. A common early estimate of the time taken to do so was twelve 30-day months or 360 days, hence the division of the great circle of the sun's track in the heavens into the three hundred and sixty degrees which have persisted to our own time. From the standpoint of an earth-observer, the constellations cross the meridian above the pole

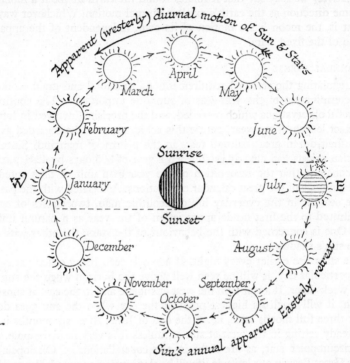

FIG. 8.—THE EGYPTIAN YEAR

This shows the rising of Sirius just before sunrise in July. By October it will rise 6 hours earlier towards midnight. By January it will rise about 12 hours earlier, i.e. *shortly after sunset,* and will be seen through the greater part of the night, setting before sunrise. By April it will rise towards noon and will set in the evening.

at night, when the sun occupies a position on the opposite side of the celestial sphere. When the sun is on the same great semicircle joining the celestial poles, they will pass over the horizon of the observer by day. Consequently they will not be visible to the naked eye, being screened by the brightness of the sun (Fig. 9).

The number of days which elapse between the rising of a star just before sunrise or its setting just before sunset on two successive occasions is the period in which the sun gets back to its same position relative to the fixed stars. The Egyptian year of 365 days was based on the *heliacal rising** of

* i.e. rising with the sun.

Sirius, the brightest star in the sky. Sirius is a winter star, rising at sunset about the beginning of January. Early in March it is already setting by midnight. After being invisible throughout the night in June, Sirius reappears

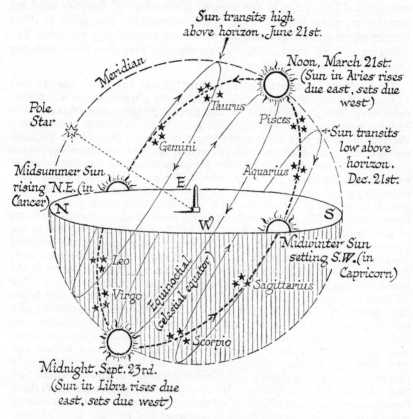

FIG. 9.—THE CHANGING HEAVENS

The successive positions of the sun in the heavens during its annual retreat below the eastern horizon in the circle called the *ecliptic* were mapped out by the ancient priest-hoods in milestones corresponding to the twelve months of the year. These mile-stones, the *zodiacal* constellations, were groups of stars whose rising and setting positions roughly corresponded to that of the sun at a particular season. Owing to the slow rotation (precession of the equinoxes) of the *equinoctial* circle about the ecliptic, the sun's position among the fixed stars at a particular season is not the same as it was in ancient times, here shown. When the sun occupies the position of Aries (i.e. is seen in the same direction as Aries would be seen if visible), it sets and rises with the latter, which is therefore invisible. A month later, when the sun is in Taurus, Taurus rises and sets with the sun and is invisible. Aries is seen rising just before sunrise where the sun rose a month earlier. When the sun was in Aries, Taurus would have been setting for about an hour after sunset where the sun would sink below the horizon a month later. The constellations corresponding to the sun's position during the summer months (Taurus and Virgo, Gemini and Leo, Cancer) had northerly risings and settings, describing large arcs and therefore remaining long above the horizon in the winter night sky. The constellations mapping out the sun's position in the winter months (Pisces and Scorpio, Aquarius and Sagittarius, Capricorn) have southerly risings and settings, describing short arcs above the horizon and being conspicuous during the short summer nights. (See also Figs. 138 and 166.)

on the eastern horizon a few minutes before sunrise on a day in July. This happened at the time when the flooding of the Nile brought assurance of food and prosperity to the Middle Kingdom. The advanced state of astronomical knowledge in the calendar civilizations of antiquity need not surprise us, when we take stock of the astronomical knowledge of living peoples whose cultural development is in other respects very primitive. The following extracts from Nilsson's* monograph *Primitive Time Reckoning* (pp. 109–143), are instructive:

Time-indications from the phases of the climate and of Nature are only approximate: they themselves, like the concrete phenomena to which they refer, are subject to fluctuation. . . . In general, primitive man takes no notice of these variations: the Banyankole, for instance, are indifferent as to whether the year is one or even three weeks longer or shorter, i.e. whether the rainy season opens so much earlier or later. The days are not counted exactly, but the people are content with the concrete phenomenon. More accurate points of reference are, however, especially desirable for an agricultural people, since, although the right time for sowing can be discerned from the phenomena and general conditions of the climate, yet a more exact determination of time may be extremely useful. The possibility of such a determination exists—and that at a far more primitive stage than that of the agricultural peoples—in the observation of the stars, and especially in the observation of the so-called "apparent" or, more properly, visible risings and settings of the fixed stars, the importance of which has already been explained. The observation of the morning rising and evening setting is extraordinarily widespread, but other positions of the stars, e.g. at a certain distance from the horizon, are also sometimes observed. The Kiwai Papuans also compute the time of invisibility of a star. When a certain star has sunk below the western horizon they wait for some nights during which the star is "inside"; then it has "made a leap," and shows itself in the east in the morning before sunrise. . . . Stellar science and mythology are therefore widespread among the primitive and extremely primitive peoples, and attain a considerable development among certain barbaric peoples. Although this must be conceded, some people are apt to think that the determination of time from the stars belongs to a much more advanced stage: it is frequently regarded as a very learned and very late mode of time-reckoning. Modern man is almost entirely without knowledge of the stars; for him they are the ornaments of the night-sky, which at most call forth a vague emotion or are objects of a science which is considered to be very difficult and highly specialized, and is left to the experts. It is true that the accurate determination of the risings and settings of the stars does demand scientific work, but not so the observation of the visible risings and settings. Primitive man rises and goes to bed with the sun. When he gets up at dawn and steps out of his hut, he directs his gaze to the brightening east, and notices the stars that are shining just there and are soon to vanish before the light of the sun. In the same way he observes at evening before he goes to rest what stars appear in the west at dusk and soon afterwards set there. Experience teaches him that these stars vary throughout the year, and that this variation keeps pace with the phases of Nature, or, more concretely expressed, he learns that the risings and settings of certain stars coincide with certain natural phenomena. . . . Just as the advance of the day is discerned from the position of the sun, so the advance of the year is recognized by the position of certain stars at sunrise

* *Acta Soc. Human. Litt. Lundensis*, 1920.

and sunset. Stars and sun alike are the indicators of the dial of the heavens. A determination of this kind, however, is not so accurate as that from heliacal risings and settings. Hence the latter pass almost exclusively or at least pre-eminently under consideration wherever, as in Greece, a calendar of the natural year is based upon the stars: sometimes, however, the upper culmination is given. . . . In order to determine the time of certain important natural phenomena it is therefore sufficient to know and observe a few stars or con-stellations with accuracy and certainty. The Pleiades are the most important. It has been asked why this particular constellation, consisting as it does of comparatively small and unimportant stars, should have played so great a part, and the answer is chiefly that its appearance coincides (though this is true of other stars also) with important phases of the vegetation. . . . An account of the Bushmen shows how extremely primitive peoples may also observe the risings of the stars, may connect them with the seasons, and—which is indeed somewhat rare—may even worship them. . . . Canopus and Sirius appear in winter, hence the cold is connected with them. . . . The Hottentots con-nect the Pleiades with winter. These stars become visible in the middle of June, that is, in the first half of the cold season, and are therefore called "Rime-stars," since at the time of their becoming visible the nights may be already so cold that there is hoar-frost in the early morning. The appearance of the Pleiades also gives to the Bushmen of the Auob district the signal for departure to the tsama field. . . . A tribe of Western Victoria connected certain con-stellations with the seasons. . . . The winter stars are Arcturus—who is held in great respect since he has taught the natives to find the pupae of the wood-ants, which are an important article of food in August and September—and Vega, who has taught them to find the eggs of the mallee-hen, which are also an important article of food in October. The natives also know and tell stories of many other stars. Another authority states that they can tell from the position of Arcturus or Vega above the horizon in August and October respectively when it is time to collect these pupae and these eggs. . . . For example, when Canopus at dawn is only a very little way above the eastern horizon, it is time to collect eggs; when the Pleiades are visible in the east a little before sunrise, the time has come to visit friends and neighbouring tribes. The Chukchee form out of the stars Altair and Tarared in Aquila a constellation named *pchittin*, which is believed to be a forefather of the tribe who, after death, ascended into heaven. Since this constellation begins to appear above the horizon at the time of the winter solstice, it is said to usher in the light of the new year, and most families belonging to the tribes living by the sea bring their sacrifices at its first appearing. . . . The South American Indians have much greater know-ledge of the stars, and in consequence frequently connect stellar phenomena, especially those of the Pleiades, with phases of Nature. In north-west Brazil the Indians determine the time of planting from the position of certain con-stellations, in particular the Pleiades. If these have disappeared below the horizon, the regular heavy rains will begin. The Siusi gave an accurate account of the progress of the constellations, by which they calculated the seasons, and in explanation drew three diagrams in the sand. No. 1 had three constellations:— "a Second Crab," which obviously consists of the three bright stars west of Leo, "the Crab," composed of the principal stars of Leo, and "the Youths," i.e. the Pleiades. When these set, continuous rain falls, the river begins to rise, beginning of the rainy season, planting of manioc. No. 2 had two con-stellations:—"the Fishing Basket," in Orion, and *kakudzuta*, the northern part of Eridanus, in which other tribes see a dancing implement. When these set, much rain falls, the water in the river is at its highest. No. 3 was "the Great Serpent," i.e. Scorpio. When this sets there is little or no rain, the water is at its lowest. The natives of Brazil are acquainted with the course of the constellations, with their height and the period and time of their appearance in, and disappearance from the sky, and according to them divide up their seasons. . . . In Africa also the observation of the stars, and above all the Pleiades, is widespread. In view of the dissemination of this knowledge all over the world it is making a quite unnecessary exception to state that it came into Africa from Egypt. Moreover, this assertion does not correspond with the facts, since among the Egyptians Sirius, and not the Pleiades, occupied the chief place. . . . The Melanesians of Banks Island and the northern New Hebrides are also acquainted with the Pleiades as a sign of the approach of the yam-harvest. The inhabitants of New Britain (Bismarck Archipelago) are guided in ascertaining the time of planting by the position of certain stars. The Moanu of the Admiralty Islands use the stars as a guide both on land and at sea, and recognize the season of the monsoons by them. When the Pleiades (*tjasa*) appear at nightfall on the horizon, this is the signal for the north-west wind to begin. But when the Thornback (Scorpio) and the Shark (Altair) emerge as twilight begins, this shows that the south-east wind is at hand. When the "Fishers' Canoe" (Orion, three fishermen in a canoe) disappears from the horizon at evening, the south-east wind sets in strongly: so also when the constellation is visible at morning on the horizon. When it comes up at evening, the rainy season and the north-west wind are not far off. When "the Bird" (Canis major) is in such a position that one wing points to the north but the other is still invisible, the time has come in which the turtles lay eggs, and many natives then go to the Los-Reys group in order to collect them. The Crown is called the "Mosquito-star," since the mosquitoes swarm into the houses when this constellation sets. The two largest stars of the circle are called *pitui* and *papai*: when this constellation becomes visible in the early morning, the time is favourable for catching the fish *papai*. The natives of the Bougainville Straits are acquainted with certain stars, especially the Pleiades: the rising of this constellation is a sign that the kai-nut is ripe: a ceremony takes place at this season. On Treasury Island a grand festival is held towards the end of October, in order—so far as could be ascertained—to celebrate the approaching appearance of the Pleiades above the eastern horizon after sunset. In Ugi, where of all the stars the Pleiades alone have a name, the times for planting and taking up yams are determined by this constellation. In Lambutjo the year is reckoned according to the position of the Pleiades. . . . When the stars indicate this or that event, the primitive mind, as so often happens, is unable to distinguish between accompanying phenomena and causal connexion; it follows that the stars are regarded as authors of the events accompanying their appearance, when these take place without the interference of man. So in ancient Greece the expressions (a certain star) "indicates" or "makes" certain weather were not kept apart, and the stars were regarded as causes of the atmospheric phenomena. A similar process of reasoning is not seldom found among primitive peoples, and a few instances have already been given, such as the warning-incantation of the Bushmen against Canopus and Sirius, the name given to the Pleiades among the Bakongo ("the Caretakers-who-guard-the-rain"), and the belief that the rain comes from them, the myth of the Euahlayi tribe that the Pleiades let ice fall down on to the earth in winter and cause thunderstorms, in other words send the rain, and the belief of the Marshall Islanders that the various positions of certain stars cause storms or good winds.

These extracts illustrate how familiar facts in the lives of food-gathering and primitive agrarian communities prepare the way for a fixed calendar and the emergence of a temple culture. The separation of a caste entrusted with the social responsibility of regulating the seasonal pursuits of a settled agrarian economy marks the beginning of written history. Only at this point does the need for a permanent record of events and measurements emerge. Here, also, we see history repeating itself—or if you prefer it— history at a standstill in backward cultures of the present day. Speaking of the time-keeping function of the priesthood in contemporary societies, Nilsson says (pp. 347–354):

As long as the determination of time is adjusted by the phases of Nature which immediately become obvious to everyone, anybody can judge of them, and should different people judge differently there is no standard by which the dispute can be settled, because the natural phases run into one another or are at least not sharply defined. The accuracy in determination demanded by time-reckoning proper is therefore lacking. Accuracy becomes possible as a result of the observation of the risings of stars, and this observation begins even at the primitive stage, but it is not a matter that concerns everyone. It requires a refined power of observation and a clear knowledge of the stars, so that the heavens can be known. This is especially the case with the commonest observations, those of the morning rising and evening setting. The observer must be able to judge, by the position of the other stars, when the star in question may be expected to twinkle for a moment in the twilight before it vanishes. The accuracy of the time-determination from the stars depends therefore upon the keenness of the observation. In this the individual differences of men soon come into play, along with a regular science which introduces the learner to the knowledge of the stars and its uses. Thus Stanbridge reports of the natives of Victoria that all tribes have traditions about the stars, but certain families have the reputation of having the most accurate knowledge; one family of the Boorung tribe prides itself upon possessing a wider knowledge of the stars than any other. . . . By the phases of the stars both occupations and seasons are regulated, and thus a standard is furnished by which to judge, and a limit is set to the indefiniteness of the phases of Nature. . . . The moon strikes the attention of everyone and admits of immediate and unpractised observation; at the most there may sometimes be some doubt for a day as to the observation of the new moon, but the next day will set all right. But because the months are fixed in their position in the natural year through association with the seasons, the indefiniteness and fluctuation of the phases of Nature penetrate into the months also, and are there even increased, for the reasons stated above. Cause for doubt and disagreement is given, the problem of the regulation of the calendar arises. Hence in the council meetings of the Pawnee and Dakota it is often hotly disputed which month it really is. So also the Caffres often become confused and do not know what month it is; the rising of the Pleiades decides the question. The Basuto in determining the time of sowing are not guided by the lunar reckoning, but fall back upon the phases of Nature; intelligent chiefs, however, know how to correct the calendar by the summer solstice. . . . The differences in intelligence already make themselves felt at an early stage, and are still more plainly shown when we come to a genuine regulation of the calendar. Some of the Bontoc Igorot state that the year has eight, others a hundred months, but among the old men who represent the wisdom of the people there are some who know and assert that it has thirteen. The further the calendar develops, the less does it become a common possession. Among the Indians, for example, there are special persons who keep and interpret year-lists illustrated with picture-writings, e.g. the calendrically gifted Anko, who even drew up a list of months. It is very significant that even where a complete calendar does exist, it will be found that this is not in use to its fullest extent among the people. . . . It follows that the observation of the calendar is a special occupation which is placed in the hands of specially experienced and gifted men. Among the Caffres we read of special "astrologers." Among the Kenya of Borneo the determination of the time for sowing is so

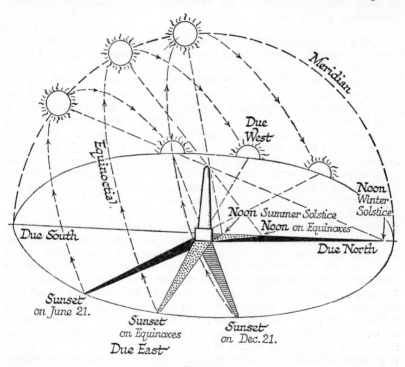

FIG. 10

This figure shows how the sun's apparent track in the heavens varies with the seasons. The noon shadow is shortest, i.e. the noon sun is highest, on June 21st. The noon shadow is longest, i.e. the noon sun is at its lowest, on December 21st. At the equinoxes, midway between, the sun rises due east and sets due west. Owing to distortion in a flat figure the winter noon shadow is longer than it should be. Sunset shadow, June 21st, points to where the sun rises, December 21st, and vice versa.

important that in every village the task is entrusted to a man whose sole occupation it is to observe the signs. He need not cultivate rice himself, for he will receive his supplies from the other inhabitants of the village. His separate position is in part due to the fact that the determination of the season is effected by observing the height of the sun, for which special instruments are required. The process is a secret, and his advice is always followed. It is only natural that this individual should keep secret the traditional lore upon which his position depends; and thus the development of the calendar puts a still wider gap between the business of the calendar-maker and the common people. Behind the calendar stand in particular the priests. But they are the most intelligent and learned men of the tribe, and moreover the calendar is peculiarly their affair if the development has proceeded so far that value is attached to the calendar for the selection of the proper days for the religious observances. Among the priests there is formed a special class whose duty it is to make observations and keep the calendar in order. Among the Hawaiians "astronomers (*kilo-hoku*)

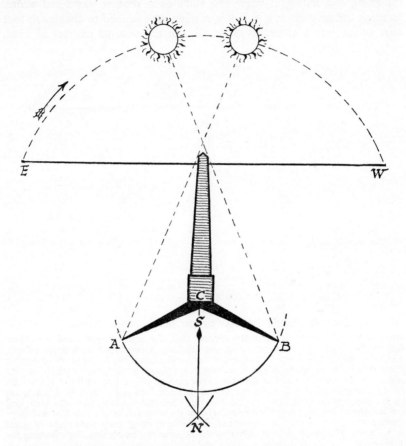

FIG. 11.—FIXING THE MERIDIAN IN ANCIENT TIMES

The method of equal altitudes was used to get the direction of the north point exactly The points at which this shadow just touched a circle traced on the sand around the shadow clock shortly before and after noon were noted, and the arc was bisected.

and priests" are mentioned; they handed down their knowledge from father to son; but women, *kilowahine*, are also found among them. Elsewhere the nobles appear alongside of the priests; thus in Tahiti it is the nobles who are responsible for the calendar, in New Zealand the priests. In the latter country there is said to have been a regular school, which was visited by priests and chiefs of highest rank. Every year the assembly determined the days on which the corn must be sown and reaped, and thus its members compared their views upon the heavenly bodies. Each course lasted from three to five months.

Wherever we find a calendar priesthood in existence among contemporary peoples in a backward state of culture, or in ancient civilizations as far removed as the Megalithic of Stonehenge and the Maya temples of Guatemala, knowledge of a second group of phenomena based on the sun's behaviour grows side by side with and tends to displace the reckoning of the year by the rising and setting of stars. The sun's noon shadow waxes and wanes. In using the noon shadow as a time marker, man learned to distinguish four days which have a characteristic relation to the seasonal changes of wind,

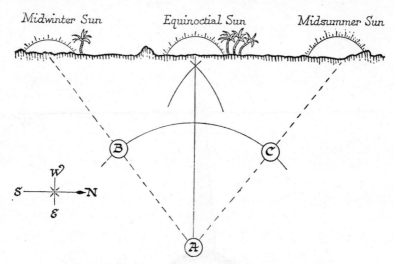

FIG. 12.—FIXING THE DAY OF THE EQUINOCTIAL FESTIVAL

Some early calendrical monuments suggest that the equinox was fixed by obser-vations on the rising or setting sun of the solstices (December 21st and June 21st), when the sun rises and sets at its most extreme positions towards the south and north respectively. In the figure, A and B are two poles placed in alignment with the setting sun of the winter solstice. The distance between A and C in line with the setting sun of the summer solstice is the same as the distance between A and B. Midway on its journey between the two extremes the sun rises and sets due east and west, and the lengths of day and night are equal. Hence these two days (March 21st and Sep-tember 23rd) are called the equinoxes. In ancient ritual they were days of great importance. The east and west points on the horizon can be obtained by bisecting the angle BAC.

rainfall, and warmth. The length of the day is longest when the noon shadow is shortest and the sun travels round the heavens perceptibly nearer the northern half of the horizon on the summer solstice (June 21st in our calendar) (Fig. 10). The length of the day is appreciably shortest when the noon shadow is longest and the sun rises and sets furthest towards the southern limit of the horizon on the winter solstice (December 21st). Midway between these two dates are two days on which the hands of the shadow clock describe a semicircle. On these two days, the vernal equinox (March 21st) and the autumnal equinox (September 23rd), day and night are of equal length. The sun rises exactly halfway between the north and south points of the horizon on the east side and sets exactly halfway between the north and south points of the horizon on the west side. Due east is the position of the rising sun on the equinoxes. Due west is the position of the setting sun on the same days. The surface bounded by the track of the equinoctial sun from the east and west points of the horizon gave the priestly custodians of the calendar a third plane of reference at right angles to the earth's axis (see Figs. 3, 6, and 9). It is called the celestial equator or *equinoctial*.

One of the earliest problems in the practical geometry of a calendar

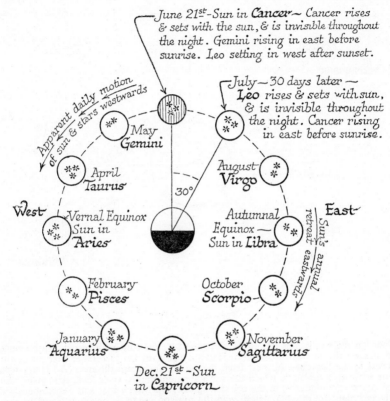

FIG. 13.—THE SUN'S (APPARENT) ANNUAL RETREAT THROUGH THE ZODIACAL CONSTELLATIONS

(The South Pole of the earth is nearest to you in the figure.)

priesthood arose in watching for the return of the equinoxes. One way in which the priests of antiquity fixed the exact direction of the meridian is shown in Fig. 11. With a sufficiently long piece of cord fairly high accuracy can be secured. Laying off the east and west points of the horizon to record the equinoxes was probably done in a similar way, two poles or stones being erected in line with the rising or setting sun of the summer solstice, and a third equidistant from one of them in line with it and the rising or setting sun of the winter solstice (Fig. 12). The sun of the equinoxes would rise and set along the line bisecting the angle between the sun's positions on the solstices. The Egyptians already recognized that this could also be done by making a line at right angles to the meridian. The division of the daily shadow path into hour angles was a later device probably of Babylonian origin, and betrays the early connexion between the art of space measurement and the social necessity of recording the passage of time. The division of the equinoctial half-circle into twelve divisions is not surprising. Of all integral sub-multiples of 360° the angle 15° is the smallest whole number which we can

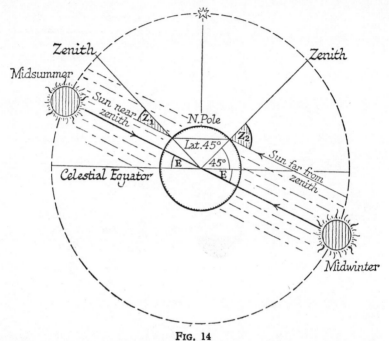

FIG. 14

Noon on the solstices at lat. 45° N. On June 21st the sun is highest in the heavens, i.e. nearest the zenith. Its zenith distance (Z_1) is least. On December 21st the sun is lowest in the heavens—furthest from the zenith. Its zenith distance (Z_2) is greatest. The angle E is the angle which the sun's apparent annual track (ecliptic) makes with the equator (equinoctial) of the celestial sphere. On March 21st and September 23rd day and night are of equal length, and the sun appears to lie on the celestial equator at noon. Note its zenith distance is then practically equivalent to the observer's latitude. (Compare Figs. 15 and 25.)

easily make by elementary methods of construction. By knotting cords at equal lengths we can peg out an equilateral triangle. Successive bisection of the angles of the equilateral triangle then gives 30° and 15°.

The phenomena of the rising and setting of stars show that the sun changes its position relative to the fixed stars, as if retreating *eastwards* through a complete circle in the celestial sphere. To account for the changing height of the noonday sun and the duration of the days and nights throughout the year, a second conception took shape. The sun appears to slip back through a track, the ecliptic, which is placed obliquely with reference to the polar axis (Figs. 9, 14). By about 3,000 B.C. we have ample evidence that the priests of Egypt had constructed simple instruments for measuring the angular direction of the stars, and were accustomed to watch for the moment when a star crosses the meridian, i.e. the great semicircle which cuts the north horizon, the Pole Star, the zenith vertically above the observer, and the south horizon. By noting the direction of the sun from the south horizon when it crosses the meridian at noon, they were able to identify the sun's annual track through a belt of twelve star clusters, called the Zodiac, corresponding to the twelve 30-day months of the Babylonian

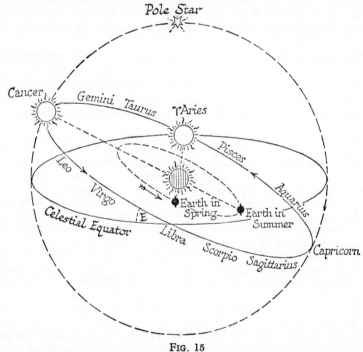

FIG. 15

If the stars are immensely distant the sun's apparent track through the ecliptic is equally explicable if we assume that the earth really moves annually round the sun with its North Pole always pointing towards the celestial pole and the plane of its equator always parallel to that of the celestial equator in an orbit which is oblique to the latter. (Compare Fig. 14.)

year (Fig. 13). The star clusters of the Zodiac are not systems of bodies with any known relation among themselves. They are simply signposts of the seasons. The times of rising and setting of a zodiacal constellation and its height above the southern horizon when it crosses the meridian correspond fairly closely with the times of sunrise and of sunset and with the height of the noon sun six months earlier or later (see Fig. 9). The names of the Zodiac star clusters are: Aries, Taurus, Gemini, Cancer, Leo, Virgo, Libra, Scorpio, Sagittarius, Capricornus, Aquarius, Pisces.

That two of these names are familiar to all of us draws attention to the far-reaching importance of the hypothesis which gradually developed from this foundation. It is true that all the facts are equally intelligible on another view, if we bear in mind what we now know about the immense distance of the fixed stars. The sun's apparent track through the ecliptic is also explicable if we assume that our train is moving and the sun's engine is at rest. All that we can see is compatible with the more sophisticated, and for the present purpose less straightforward, hypothesis that the earth pursues a slanting annual track around the sun with its polar axis always at the same angle to the ecliptic plane (Fig. 15). On either view we have made a very big advance in our knowledge of the earth through widening our knowledge of the heavens. We shall see this better when we have taken into account another class of events which clarified the recognition that our earth itself is a spherical body.

With regard to the formative influence which the calendar exerted in the early stages of civilization, the important point to grasp is that the determination of the year as the interval between successive summer or winter solstices or alternate equinoxes demands attention to measurement. Thus Nilsson, speaking of contemporary communities, says (pp. 311–318):

An observation of the annual course of the sun, therefore, unlike that of the stars—which everywhere, no matter where, can be performed immediately—demands a fixed place and special aids to determination. It follows that the observation of the solstices and equinoxes belongs to a much higher stage of civilization than does that of the stars. . . . It is used by the Eskimos, who have a very highly developed sense of place, and know how to make good maps. Moreover, where the sun in winter stands very low on the horizon, and for a time altogether disappears beneath it, the conditions are very favourable for the observation of its return. Older authors say that by the rays of the sun on the rocks the Eskimos can tell with tolerable accuracy when it is the shortest day; more recently we have been told of the Ammasalik that they can calculate beforehand the time of the shortest day—and that accurately to the day—not only from the solstitial point, but also from the position of Altair in the morning twilight. They begin their spring when the sun rises at the same spot as Altair. . . . The Incas erected artificial marks. There were in Cuzco sixteen towers, eight to the west and eight to the east, arranged in groups of four. The two middle ones were smaller than the others, and the distance between the towers was eight, ten or twenty feet. The space between the little towers through which the sun passed at sunrise and sunset was the point of the solstices. In order to verify this the Inca chose a favourable spot from which he observed carefully whether the sun rose and set between the little towers to east and west. For the observation of the equinoxes richly ornamented pillars were set up in the open space before the temple of the sun. When the time approached, the shadow of the pillars was carefully observed. The open space was circular, and a line was drawn through its centre from east to west. Long experience had taught them where to look for the equinoctial point, and by the distance of the shadow from this point they judged of the approach of the equinox. When from sunrise to sunset the shadow was to be seen on both sides of the pillar and not at all to the south of it, they took that day as the day of the equinox. This last account is for Quito, which lies just under the equator. At the spring equinox the maize was reaped and a feast was celebrated, at the autumn equinox the people celebrated one of their principal feasts. The months were calculated from the winter solstice. . . One would suspect that this Melanesian science, like the knowledge of the stars, is borrowed from the Polynesians: for the latter understood the annual course of the sun. In Tahiti the place of the sunrise was called *tataheita*, that of the sunset *topa-t-era*. The annual movement of the sun from the south towards the north was recognized, and so was the fact that all these points of the daily approach to the zenith lay in a line. This meridian was called *t'era-hwattea*, the northern point of it *tu-errau*, and the opposite point above the horizon, or the south, *toa*. According to other sources the December solstice was called *rua-maoro* or *rua-roa*, the June solstice *rua-poto*. The Hawaiians called the northern limit of the sun in the ecliptic "the black, shining road of Kane," and the southern limit "the black, shining road of Kanaloa." The equator was named "the bright road of the spider" or "the road to the navel of Wakea," equivalent to "the centre of the world." How the Polynesians came to recognize the tropics and the equator is unfortunately unknown, but certainly they did it like other peoples by observing the solstices and equinoxes at certain landmarks. . . . Agricultural peoples in particular have developed various methods of this kind. The rice-cultivating peoples of the East Indies use various methods in order to determine the important time of sowing. Of the observation of the stars we have already spoken. Among the Kayen of Sarawak an old priest determines the official time of sowing from the position of the sun by erecting at the side of the house two oblong stones, one larger and one smaller, and then observing the moment when the sun, in the lengthening of the line of connexion between these two stones, sets behind the opposite hill. The sowing-day is the only one determined by astronomical methods. In other respects the time-reckoning is a more or less arbitrary one, and is dependent on the agriculture. Of the hollows in a block of stone at Batu Sala, in the river-bed of the upper Mahakam, it is said that they originated in the fact that the priestesses of the neighbouring tribes used formerly to sit on the stone every year in order to observe when the sun would set behind a certain peak of the opposite mountain. This date then decided the time for the beginning of the sowing. . . . The Kenyah observe the position of the sun. Their instrument is a straight cylindrical pole of hardwood, fixed vertically in the ground and carefully adjusted with the aid of plumb-lines; the possibility of its sinking deeper into the earth is prevented. The pole is a little longer than the outstretched arms of its maker and stands on a cleared space by the house, surrounded by a strong fence. The observer has further a flat stick on which lengths measured from his body are marked off by notches. The other side has a larger number of notches, of which one marks the greatest length of the midday shadow, the next one its length three days after it has begun to shorten, and so on. The shadow is measured every midday. As it grows shorter after reaching its maximal length the man observes it with special care, and announces to the village that the time for preparing the land is near at hand. In Bali and Java the seasons are determined by the aid of a gnomon of rude construction, having a dial divided into twelve parts.

THE LOCAL EVENTS

In the priestly calendar lore, magic and genuine science were inextricably entangled. The social necessity of measuring time arises from the seasonal fertility of man's biological allies, and the earliest explanations of the celestial events were frequently mixed up with man's preoccupation concerning his own fertility. What are sometimes offered as rival explanations of early practices are really different ways of saying the same thing. The phallic tension of waking and the monthly cycle of a woman's life were closely associated with sunrise and lunar phenomena in the thought of primitive man. To say that an obelisk is a sundial, and to say that it is a phallic symbol involves no contradiction. Fertility and timekeeping were very closely connected in the same social context. Man had to be disciplined into the recognition that his own world is not the centre of the astronomical universe. He had to outgrow the belief that his own person is a sufficient model of natural processes in chemistry and biology. In psychology and social science he has

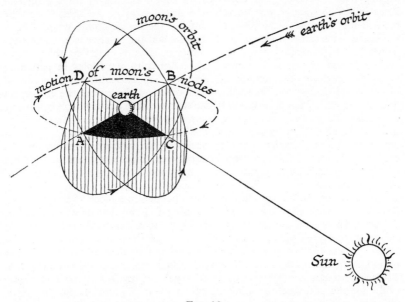

FIG. 16

Diagram to illustrate the slow retrograde motion of the moon's nodes. Two positions of the moon's orbit are shown, AB and CD, the latter position occurring about 4 or 5 years after the former. Eclipses take place when, as at node C (solar) or D (lunar), the place where the moon's orbit crosses the plane of the earth's orbit is in line with the earth and the sun; provided, of course, that the moon is also at the node. (The tilt of the moon's orbit in relation to the ecliptic is here much exaggerated.)

still to learn that individual preference is not a safe guide to the understanding of social behaviour.

As liaison officers to the celestial beings, the priests found it paid to encourage the belief that nature can be bought off with bribes like a big chief. One of their most powerful weapons was their ability to forecast eclipses (Figs. 17 and 18). Eclipses were indisputable signs of divine disapproval, and divine disapproval provided a cogent justification for raising the divine income tax. No practical utility other than the advancement of the priestly prestige and the wealth of the priesthood can account for the astonishingly painstaking attention paid to these phenomena. The moon's track lies very close to the ecliptic. If it moved exactly in the plane of the ecliptic, there would be a central eclipse of the sun every new moon, and a total eclipse of the moon every month, at the full. Careful measurement shows that its orbit is

FIG. 17

Total eclipse showing the sun's atmosphere just seen beyond the margin of the moon's disc (i.e. the sun's angular diameter is approximately the same as that of the moon).

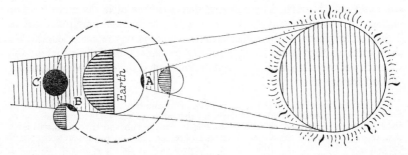

FIG. 18

Eclipses. A. total solar eclipse, C. total lunar eclipse, B. earth's shadow seen as moon is at beginning of a lunar eclipse.

inclined about 5° to the ecliptic (i.e. to the plane of the earth's orbit, as we now say). So the moon's path round the earth only cuts the earth's path round the sun (or the sun's apparent track round the earth) at two points called *nodes* (see p. 103), and an eclipse can only take place if the moon is at, or very near to, a node when the two nodes are in line with the sun and the earth. Relative to the fixed stars, the direction of the line which joins the nodes rotates slowly. The sun passes a particular node every 346·62 days. This is less than a year because the nodes are moving from east to west, and meet the sun before it completes its yearly circuit. So if earth, moon, nodes, and sun are in line at any time, they will be in line once more about eighteen years* later. More precisely this period is 18 years 11⅓ days. If an eclipse occurs on a particular date another one will occur at the same place 18 years 11⅓ days later. This cycle is still called the Saros, which is the name given to it by the Chaldean priests. It did not help people to arrange their meal-times and night journeys, to prepare for the lambing season, or to sow their crops. For the art of time reckoning the Saros had no particular use. Its discovery was prompted by a combination of super-stition and racketeering. Once made, it served to direct attention to two of the basic principles of scientific geography. Observation of eclipses in different places showed that solar time is local (see p. 78); and confirmed the belief that the earth is a spherical object (Fig. 18, B). The fact that lunar eclipses occur when the moon is practically in the ecliptic plane shows that the circular edge of the shadow on its face is the shadow of the earth itself.

As soon as trade intercourse began, many other facts helped the growth of this belief. When ships appeared in the Mediterranean, maritime people became accustomed to the sight of the mast sinking last below the horizon, or the mountain rising first as land was sighted (Fig. 19). Little later than 2000 B.C. Semitic traders were pushing north beyond the Mediterranean towards the Tin Isles, bringing back tales of the long summer days and the long winter nights of the northern regions. They told, too, how the aspect of the night sky changed. Stars low on the northern horizon became higher in the heavens as ships sailed into the northern seas. A fact most fatal to a flat earth view was that southern constellations disappeared entirely (Fig. 20) from view. To be sure, the belief that the earth is truly spherical (or nearly so) could only be settled by showing that a degree of latitude is the same distance if measured anywhere along any meridian of longitude, and a degree of longitude in the same latitude is always of the same length. We shall come to that later. Here it suffices to remark that the belief in the sphericity of the earth is of very great antiquity, and that there were a number of good reasons to support it.

* 19 revolutions of the line of nodes relative to the sun take 346·62 × 19 = 6585·78 days. 223 lunar months = 6585·32 days. So that after 18 years 11⅓ days the line of node will have performed 19 revolutions relative to the sun and the moon will have performed 223 revolutions almost exactly. Hence the sun and the moon will occupy the same position relative to the nodes at the end of this period as at the beginning. How the position of the moon's node in any particular month is found is ex-plained on p. 103. The rate of rotation is found by repeated observations of the same kind.

FIRST STEPS TOWARDS A WORLD MAP

The construction of the calendar taught mankind many lessons which were only fully assimilated when maritime trade developed. The phenomena on which we base the measurement of our fundamental units of time can only be explained if the spherical earth has a very definite orientation with respect to the celestial sphere. To begin with, we have already drawn the conclusion that there is one spot—the North Pole—which lies directly below the celestial pole or Pole Star. The plane of the ecliptic must cross the world at upper and lower limits defined by two belts where the sun will

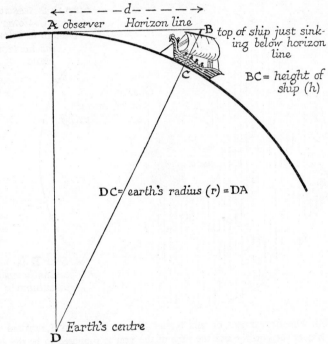

FIG. 19.—THE TANGENT OF THE HORIZON LINE

be at its zenith (i.e. exactly overhead) on the summer and winter solstices respectively (Fig. 14). These are the tropics. Within the tropical belt the direction of the sun's noon shadow will change twice in the course of the year, a fact which could be observed in the southernmost parts of Egypt. At the equinoxes the sun occupies the apparent position where the ecliptic cuts the celestial plane at right angles to the axis of the celestial sphere. This plane, the celestial equator, cuts the earth at a belt, where day and night are always equal and the sun is at its zenith on the equinoxes. Finally, the axis at right angles to the ecliptic through the earth's centre must trace out a belt north of which the sun never sets at midsummer. Men were beginning to grasp these truths firmly long before they had first-hand experience of them. In the fourth century B.C. the Greek materialist Bion taught the doctrine of the midnight sun in the Arctic Circle, which no ships had yet penetrated.

The accuracy with which the Egyptian priests determined the length of the year, as well as the orientation of their temple sites, bear witness to something more than the recognition of an orderly sequence of events in the day and night sky. At an early date they had already begun to recognize certain metrical uniformities. Simple devices for measuring the angular bearings of a star are dated as early as 3000 B.C. The local bearings of a heavenly body

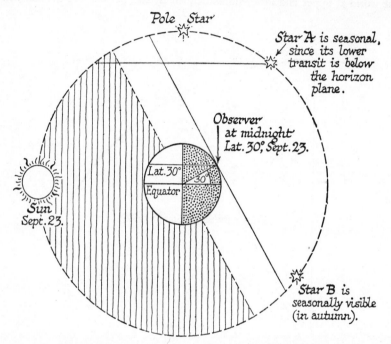

FIG. 20.—APPEARANCE OF THE NIGHT SKY IN DIFFERENT LATITUDES

The sun is over the equator and the time of the year is supposed to be the autumn equinox. At latitude 30° star A will be visible throughout the night in autumn and invisible at midnight in spring. At latitude 60° it will be seen crossing the meridian above the pole just south of the zenith at midnight in autumn, and will be visible throughout the spring night below the pole, making its lower culmination at midnight on the spring equinox. Star B will be visible at latitude 30° throughout part of

at any hour can be fixed by two angles. One is its *altitude* (angular height above the horizon), or its complement called the *zenith distance* (Figs. 3, 21, and 114). The other bearing is its angular distance east or west of a fixed point on the horizon. Measured from the north point eastwards it is called the *azimuth*. For measuring altitude (or Z.D.) and azimuth a simple instrument essentially like the sort of *astrolabes* or quadrants used in ancient times can easily be made from a large protractor for blackboard use, as in Figs. 22 and 115.

In taking the bearings of the stars in the night sky the two important principles which underlie the system of earth measurement by latitude and longitude were established long before the first star maps, described in the next chapter, were constructed. The first of these is implicit in the primitive art of telling the time by the stars. At a very early date the priestly custodians of the calendar were familiar with the use of simple mechanical devices for measuring short intervals of time. In principle they were analogous to the sand-glass which used to be sold to time the boiling of an egg. They could record the moment when some star crossed the meridian (i.e. when its

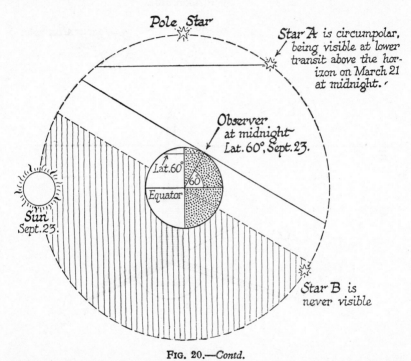

Pole Star

Star A is circumpolar, being visible at lower transit above the horizon on March 21 at midnight.

Observer at midnight Lat. 60°, Sept. 23.

Lat. 60

60

Equator

Sun Sept. 23.

Star B is never visible

FIG. 20.—*Contd.*

the night during autumn, crossing the meridian towards the southern margin of the horizon at midnight on the equinox. It will be invisible in the spring night. At latitude 60° it will never be visible, since its upper transit lies below the horizon plane. For the reasons explained on p. 58, with the aid of Figs. 29 and 30, the effective horizon may be drawn through the earth's centre parallel to the tangent of the horizon plane at the earth's surface. The part of the celestial sphere below the horizon is shaded.

azimuth is 0° or 180°) and the interval which elapsed before another star crossed it by measuring the outflow of sand or water from a vessel. Hence they knew that the interval is constant for any two stars chosen.

The stars appear to revolve uniformly around the pole, and their relative positions can be represented on semicircles radiating from the latter (see Fig. 48). The time which has elapsed since a star crossed the meridian can be measured by the angle through which its own celestial semicircle has rotated. Since the whole dome of heaven appears to rotate through 360° in 24 hours, an angle of 15°, i.e. 360° ÷ 24, between the celestial semicircles on which two stars lie is equivalent to a difference of an hour in their times of transit over the meridian. In the accompanying figure (Fig. 23) the star α in Cassiopeia (A) is roughly 30° from the furthermost of the five bright stars in the same constellation. So it takes about two hours for Cassiopeia to cross the meridian. The furthermost bright star (C) in the tail of the Great Bear is roughly 210° from α Cassiopeiae. The difference in hour angles is 210 ÷ 15 or 14 hours. That is to say, the tail star of Ursa Major crosses the meridian at its

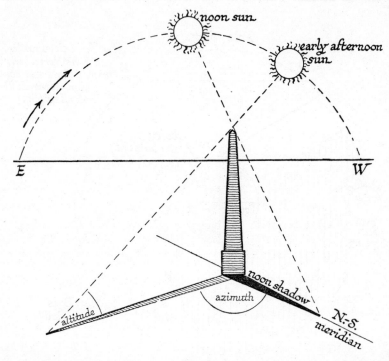

FIG. 21

The direction of a celestial body can be fixed by two angles, the angle it makes with the horizon or the vertical (altitude or zenith distance) and the angle it makes with the meridian (azimuth).

"upper culmination," roughly 14 hours after α Cassiopeiae. The hour angle differences of the stars give us an orderly picture of their appearance and disappearance on the horizon. The bright star Betelgeuse in the constellation of Orion is separated by an hour angle of nearly 6 hours from α Cassiopeiae. So when Cassiopeia is at its upper culmination, Betelgeuse will be rising almost exactly due east of the pole. See also Figs. 47, 48, and 49.

Lockyer (*Stonehenge and other Monuments*) reproduces a figure illustrating a "night dial" used in fourteenth-century England to tell the time at night by watching the rotation of the two stars (pointers) of the Great Bear in line with the Pole Star. It is essentially a movable arm which rotates on a dial, the centre of which is perforated (see Fig. 147, Chapter V). To use it, you would look at the Pole Star through this hole, move the arm in line with the pointers, and read off the time on the dial which could be calibrated like a planisphere (p. 94) for each day in the year. Hooke (*New Year's Day*) states that pictorial representations of crude night dials based on essentially the same principle come from ancient Egypt. The exactitude with which the priests of these early civilizations endeavoured to determine

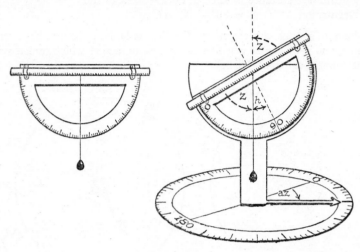

FIG. 22

A simple theodolite or astrolabe for measuring the angle a star (or any other object) makes with the horizon (altitude) or the vertical (zenith distance) can be made by fixing a piece of metal tube exactly parallel to the base line of a blackboard protractor, which you can buy from any educational dealer. To the centre point of the protractor fix a cord with a heavy weight (e.g. a lump of type metal which any compositor will give you free if you ask him nicely) to act as plumb line. The division opposite the cord when the object is sighted is its zenith distance (Z), and the altitude (h) is $90° - Z$. If you mount this to move freely on an upright wooden support which revolves freely on a base with a circular scale (made by screwing two protractors on to it) and fix a pointer in line with the tube, you can measure the azimuth (az) or bearing of a star or other object (e.g. the setting sun) from the north-south meridian. To do this fix the scale so that it reads 0° when the sighter is pointed to the noon sun or the Pole Star. This was a type of instrument used to find latitude and longitude in the time of the Great Navigations. You can use it to find the latitude and longitude of your house, or to make an ordnance survey of your neighbourhood.

the occurrence of celestial signals is illustrated by a Babylonian text which belongs to the time of Hammurabi. In it the heliacal risings of three constellations are given by *weight* (4 minas and 2 minas) corresponding to the outflow of water from a simple water clock or clepsydra analogous to the sandglass.

The construction of the Great Pyramid shows that the Egyptians made exact measurements of the position of the stars at transit as well as when rising or setting. Such observations entail the recognition of a second uniformity of measurement. This also was a very early discovery. When it crosses the meridian, the altitude of any star (or its Z.D.) is always the same at a particular place. Since the pole is fixed, we may also represent the position of a star in the heavens by the difference between its meridian altitude* (or Z.D.) and the altitude (or Z.D.) of the Pole Star. This difference is now called the *North Polar Distance*, and its complement is now called the *declination* of the star. Thus:

North Polar Distance = meridian altitude of star — altitude of Pole
or North Polar Distance = Z.D. of Pole — Z.D. of star
Declination = 90° — N.P.D.

Declination is thus the elevation of a heavenly body *above* the celestial equator, and is of course negative in the case of bodies which transit south of the celestial equator (Fig. 24).

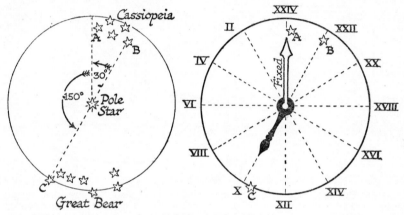

FIG. 23.—THE STAR CLOCK

Showing how the relative positions of the stars may be represented by the time interval between their transits over the meridian. The star A in Cassiopeia is almost directly above the pole, i.e. its hour angle is zero (= XXIV). The star C in the Dipper crossed the meridian ten hours earlier, i.e. its hour angle is X.

NOTE.—Since the celestial sphere rotates once in 24 hours the time which will elapse *before* a star crosses the meridian is the difference between 24 and its hour angle. Thus B in Cassiopeia will transit above the pole in 2 hours, and its hour angle is + 22 or — 2. The hour angle of C in the Dipper is + 10 or — 14.

The full significance of these facts did not clearly emerge until the study of the heavens received a new impetus in the great centres of Mediterranean shipping. As travel developed, the priestly lore of the calendar became the possession of Semitic trading peoples, who transmitted their knowledge to the Greek world. When astronomy ceased to be local and began to be international, observations made at different places could be compared. The result of this was another important discovery. Although the meridian altitudes vary from place to place, the N.P.D. of a star, like the difference in hour angle between any two stars, is the same everywhere (Fig. 24). Thus the position of the star in the heavens can be fixed for any observer by two coordinates—its hour angle difference referred to any one star and its N.P.D. (or declination). These two data are all that is required for constructing a

---

* Altitude, for this purpose, must be reckoned from the north point of the horizon. Zenith distances south of the zenith are reckoned as negative.

star map or planisphere. From the star map it was a very short step to the first world maps of latitude and longitude. The Alexandrian maps opened up vistas of unexplored territory waiting for the ships of Columbus, Amerigo Vespucci, and Magellan.

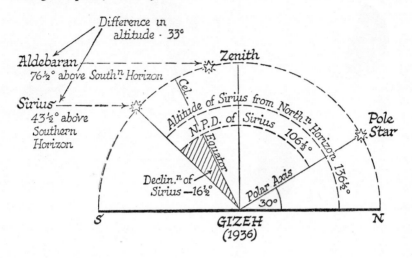

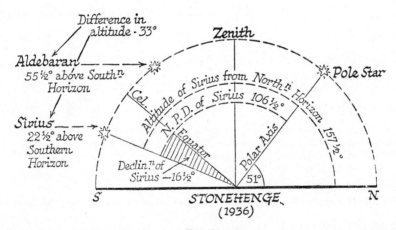

FIG. 24

The highest altitude of a star varies from place to place, but the difference between the highest altitudes of any two visible stars, i.e. the difference between their altitudes at meridian transit, is the same at all places. (The two stars chosen are Aldebaran and Sirius. They are drawn as if they crossed the celestial meridian at the same time. In reality Sirius transits about two hours later than Aldebaran.)

One class of measurements of great antiquity arose in connexion with the fixing of the year from the summer solstices. This was the determination of the "obliquity of the ecliptic," i.e. the angle which the sun's track in the zodiacal belt makes with the celestial equator. Chinese astronomers are said to have calculated the value correct within a quarter of a degree by as early

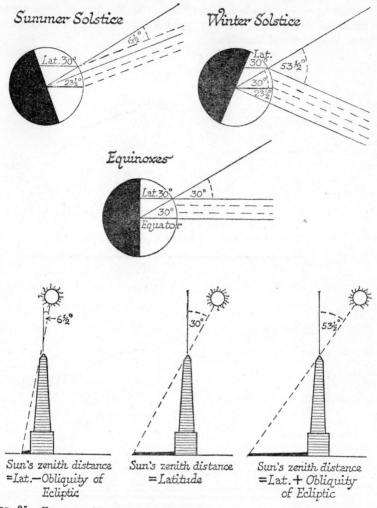

FIG. 25.—EGYPTIAN MEASUREMENT OF THE OBLIQUITY OF THE ECLIPTIC FROM THE SUN'S NOON SHADOW

At noon the sun is highest. The pole, the earth's centre, the observer, and the sun, are all in the same plane (or flat surface). On the equinoxes (March 21st and September 23rd) the sun's zenith distance at noon is the observer's latitude (30° at Memphis). If the obliquity of the ecliptic is E

$$L + E = \text{sun's zenith distance on winter solstice (December 21st).}$$
$$L - E = \text{sun's zenith distance on summer solstice (June 21st).}$$

So the obliquity of the ecliptic is

$$\tfrac{1}{2} \text{ (sun's z.d. on December 21st} - \text{sun's z.d. on June 21st).}$$

as 1000 B.C. The Egyptians and Babylonians almost certainly had an equally accurate estimate at a much earlier date. The accuracy of these early estimates was achieved by the large scale of the instruments used, and gives us some insight into the apparently pretentious dimensions of the great calendar monuments. Two obelisk measurements repeated over several years suffice (see Fig. 25) to give a very good mean value for the obliquity of the ecliptic. Unwittingly, as you will see from the same figure, those who first made these measurements also encountered another quantity. If Z_w is the sun's zenith distance on the winter solstice and Z_s is the sun's zenith distance on the summer solstice

$$\tfrac{1}{2}(Z_w + Z_s) = L$$

To them the quantity L was nothing more than the zenith distance (Fig. 26) of the noon sun on the equinoxes, hence a direct way of fixing the time of

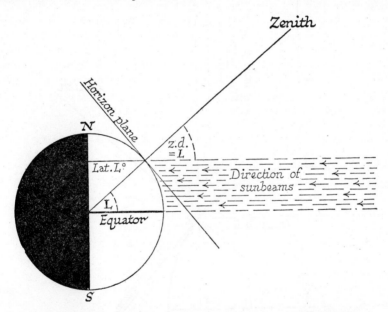

FIG. 26.—LATITUDE FROM SUN'S Z.D. AT NOON ON THE EQUINOXES

On March 21st and September 23rd day and night are of equal length throughout the world. So the sun lies above the equator. At noon the sun always lies over the line joining the north and south points of the horizon, i.e. the observer's meridian of longitude. So the sun, the poles, observer, zenith, and earth centre are all in the same flat slab (or "plane") of space. Since the edges of a sunbeam are parallel, the sun's z.d. at noon on the equinoxes is the observer's latitude.

a fertility festival which has persisted in the Lent observances of contemporary mythology. To us it is a fundamental physical constant. It is numerically equivalent to what we now call the *latitude* of the observer. You can find the latitude of your house within a quarter of a degree by observing the sun's altitude at noon on March 21st or September 23rd. There will be a slight error in all such calculations if you only make the observation on one occasion, because it will rarely happen that the exact moment at which the sun is above the equator will also be exactly noon at the place where you live. The very precise measurements of the ancients represented the average of many observations made repeatedly. The ecliptic angle which defines the latitude of the tropical belts is between 23° and 24°. At London (latitude 51° N.) the sun's zenith distance at midsummer is $51° - 23\frac{1}{2}° = 27\frac{1}{2}°$, and at midwinter $51° + 23\frac{1}{2}° = 74\frac{1}{2}°$. The sun's altitude at noon is $62\frac{1}{2}°$ ($90° - 27\frac{1}{2}°$) on June 21st. The midwinter noon sun is only $15\frac{1}{2}°$ ($90 - 74\frac{1}{2}°$) above the horizon. The Arctic Circle which defines the limit of the midnight sun on the summer solstice is at latitude $90° - 23\frac{1}{2}° = 66\frac{1}{2}°$ N.

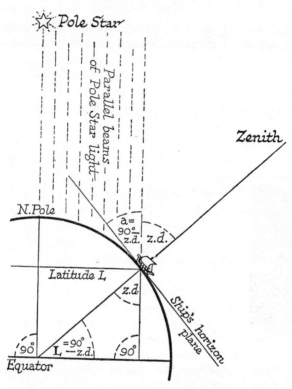

FIG. 27.—LATITUDE FROM POLE STAR

The altitude (horizon angle) of the Pole Star is the observer's latitude, both being equivalent to 90° – z.d. of Pole Star.

In making observations on the elevation of celestial bodies it is probable that the calendar-makers of the early Mediterranean civilizations had discovered another fact of great geographical importance. On the equinoxes the sun's zenith distance is the same as the mean nightly altitude of the Pole Star. This was actually the star α in the constellation Draco at the time when the Great Pyramid was built. The meaning of this is easy to see. On the equinoxes the sun is in the plane of the celestial equator. The direction of the Pole Star is at right angles to the celestial equator. You will therefore see (Fig. 27) that the elevation of the Pole Star above the horizon is the same as what we now call the latitude of the observer. In the northern hemisphere all you have to do to find the latitude of your house is to take the horizon angle of the Pole Star with a home-made instrument like the one in Fig. 22. You should not make an error of more than 1°. This tells you your distance from the equator or North Pole within 70 miles.

Certain geometric principles underlie all these early measurements, and play an important part in the later developments of the Alexandrian astronomy. Expressed in modern language, the first is that light rays from the heavenly bodies are parallel. At first sight this might seem a daring assumption. The fact is that the straight parallel edges of a beam of light were not laboratory curios to the first civilized men. In an age when there was no glass, and dust abounded, windows were high narrow slits to exclude wind and rain The sharp straight edge of a shaft of bright light piercing a narrow

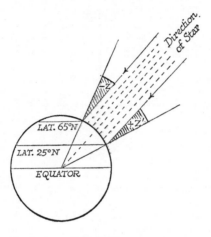

Fig. 28

The same star, whose declination is 45° North, as seen at transit from latitude 65° N., 20° south of the zenith (z.d. = − 20°) and from latitude 25° N., 20° north of the zenith (z.d. = + 20°).

orifice along a path of scintillating dust was one of the commonest facts of everyday life in ancient times. All the phenomena of shadow reckoning for timekeeping and architectural construction sustained the same belief.

Then there was the principle of tangency demonstrated by the shadow cast by curved vessels. One of the earliest geometrical principles used in astronomy was that the line joining the zenith to the observer must pass through the earth's centre, if produced far enough. This follows from the elementary principle that the line joining the centre of a circle to the point where the tangent grazes the boundary is at right angles to it. Since the edges of the beam of light are straight, the observer's horizon plane is tangential to the earth's curved face. The zenith axis is the direction of the plumbline. The lines joining the zenith and the earth's centre to the observer both make right angles with his horizon plane, and are therefore collinear. The pole, the zenith, and observer are all in the same plane, which we have called the meridian. The earth's centre is in this plane, and so is the earth's axis, i.e.

the line joining the pole to the earth's centre. This means that we can make
flat diagrams of the relations between an observer, a star, and the earth's
centre, traced on sand or drawn on paper, provided that everything (Fig. 41)
drawn is in the meridian plane at the same time. The direction of a star is
given by the angle it makes with the plane of the equator at the earth's centre.
As you will see from Figs. 28 and 31, this is the same as its *declination*, and
explains why the N.P.D. (hence also declination) is independent of the
observer's locality.

Another simple geometrical principle which was implicit in the earliest
attempts to diagrammatize the experiences which we have dealt with, is worth
mentioning, because there is an inescapable distortion in any diagram like
those in Fig. 20. The light beams of heavenly objects appear to be parallel

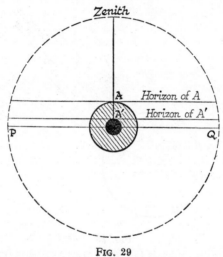

FIG. 29

If the size of the earth is very small compared with the distance of the stars, the
observer's horizon practically coincides with a plane through the earth's centre parallel
to the actual plane of the horizon. In other words, we see practically half the celestial
sphere at any moment

because they are very far away. This means that the celestial sphere is
immense compared with the earth. For practical purposes the observer's
north–south horizon line can be replaced by a parallel line in the meridian
plane drawn through the centre of the earth as in Figs. 29–30. So we actually
see half the celestial sphere, and the east and west points of the horizon are
in the same plane as the equator.

Such conceptions did not grow out of a preconceived system of logic.
It would be more correct to say that geometry grew out of them. Geometry
was largely the offspring of astronomy and its sister craft of architecture in
the calendar civilizations of the Mediterranean world. Admiration inspired
by Greek literature has fostered a legend which associates Greek metaphysics
with real or suppositious achievements of the Greeks in other domains.
Although Euclid takes us through twelve books before he arrives at the

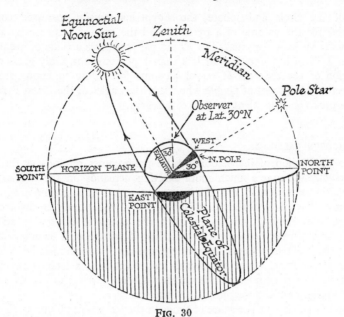

FIG. 30

For the reason explained in Fig. 29 the equinoctial or celestial equator cuts the horizon plane due east and due west.

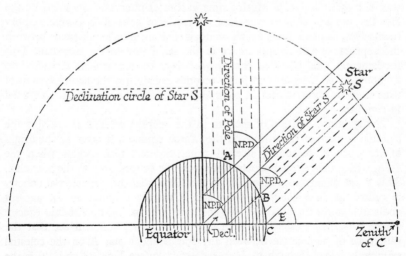

FIG. 31

The direction of a star as seen from the earth is everywhere the same as measured by the angle between it and the celestial pole, i.e. the difference (N.P.D.) between its z.d. (or altitude) and that of the pole when it crosses the meridian. The N.P.D. is the complement of the angle (*declination*) which the star beam makes with the plane of the equator as it passes over the observer's meridian. The declination is equivalent to the star's meridian zenith distance (E) as seen by an observer at the equator.

N.P.D. = star's zenith distance at North Pole
Decl. = star's zenith distance (E) at equator.

area of the circle and sphere, the Egyptians already possessed correct formulae for the volume of a pyramid and the area of a sphere by about 1500 B.C. (Moscow papyrus). The Rhind papyrus gives a value of π equivalent to $3 \cdot 16$ in our notation, or less than 1 per cent out. Only gross overvaluation of the contents of books accounts for failure to appreciate the intellectual equipment of people who made the angles of the Great Pyramid with a precision equivalent to $0 \cdot 06$ of a degree.

THE MODERN CALENDAR

The publication of international radio programmes reminds us that our own civilization makes much more exacting demands on the precision of calendrical practice than did the seasonal practices of a primitive agrarian economy. To a large extent the elaboration of the principles involved in modern time-keeping has arisen from the needs of navigation and, in particular, from the problem of determining longitude with accuracy at sea. Hence the theoretical explanation of present-day practice must be deferred to another context, where the reader may meet it at a later stage in our narrative. The remainder of this chapter will be devoted to a brief survey of the evolution of timekeeping in historic times.

There is no absolute measure of time. In the last resort all our mechanical instruments are checked against the same standard—the interval between two meridian transits of the same celestial body. To put the matter in another way, the possibility of measuring time in shorter intervals rests solely on the fact that we are able to construct devices like hour-glasses which empty themselves, or pendulums which swing, a constant number of times between the appearance and re-appearance of the same star on the meridian. This fundamental unit is called the *sidereal* day. Its mechanical division into 24 hours of 60 minutes and 3,600 seconds constitutes the actual system of time used in observatories in contradistinction to the system of time used in civil life.

The apparent position of the sun in the ecliptic, when it is crossing the celestial equator at some time on the March equinox, is taken as the origin of reference in reckoning sidereal time. Sidereal time begins when the point where the celestial equator intersects the ecliptic crosses the meridian. This point of intersection, which is the Greenwich of the celestial sphere, is called the *First Point of Aries*, and is usually denoted by the ancient zodiacal sign for the ram (Υ). We shall see later (p. 95) how to find exactly where it is. From what has been said on page 50, you will see that the difference of hour angle between any star B and a star A on the celestial semicircle traced through Υ from pole to pole (see Figs. 23 and 49) is the *sidereal time* at which the star B appears on the meridian. The star α in Cassiopeia is very close to the hour circle of Υ, and since the sun is always less than a degree from Υ at noon on the vernal equinox, noon March 21st is within 4 minutes $\left(= \dfrac{24 \times 60}{360} \right)$ of zero time on the sidereal clock. So the hour angle which separates a star from the first point of Aries is approximately the time which elapses between its meridian transit and that of α Cassiopeiae.

Although the sidereal day is the basic system of units and the one used in observatories, it is not suitable for everyday use. For everyday use the number assigned to an hour must correspond with our working, feeding, and sleeping habits. Everyday life was regulated by the solar day when sundials were used. The time of the day when the noon sun crosses the meridian, halfway between sunset and sunrise, always registers twelve o'clock on the sundial. Hour glasses or clocks, checked by the meridian transit of stars, register any number from 0 to 24 sidereal hours at solar noons between one vernal equinox and another. This is because the solar day is longer than the sidereal day. The sun, as we have seen, is continually slipping backwards in the ecliptic. In a year it gets back to where it was before. It has therefore receded 360°, which is the angle through which the stars rotate in one sidereal day. Thus the shadow clock loses one day per year. In an *average* day it loses

$$\frac{24 \times 60}{365} = 4 \text{ minutes (approximately)}$$

The day after the vernal equinox solar noon would register 0 hour 4 minutes instead of 0 hour on the sidereal clock. Fifteen days after the vernal equinox noon would be 1 hour by the observatory clock. At the end of three months, i.e. on June 21st, noon would occur at 6 o'clock by sidereal time.

The meridian transit of the sun gives us a *solar day*, which is approximately 4 minutes longer than the sidereal day. Unfortunately the exact length of the solar day is not constant. A clock or hour glass which always registers the same number of sidereal hours and minutes between successive transits of the same fixed star does not register exactly the same number of minutes from noon to noon on different days of the year. The social inconvenience of this fact is what forces us to take the sidereal day as the fundamental unit to which everything else is referred. If we agree to regard the diurnal rotation of the fixed stars as our best possible approximation to an absolute standard, the relative irregularity of the solar day can be explained as the result of several circumstances of which the two most important will be explained in Chapter IV. They are the *obliquity of the ecliptic*, and the form of the *earth's orbit*.

Owing to the obliquity of the ecliptic the sun's apparent annual motion is not in the same plane as its apparent diurnal rotation with the fixed stars. When it is "in Cancer" or "in Capricorn" it appears to be moving backwards in the ecliptic in a direction (Fig. 9) practically parallel to its apparent diurnal motion. In Aries or Libra its apparent path is very oblique. So even if the sun's apparent motion in the ecliptic were perfectly regular—or, as we now say, even if the earth moved in its orbit at a uniform speed—the shadow clock would not lose time at exactly the same rate throughout the seasons. Later we shall find that the angular velocity of the earth's orbital motion is not constant. Another fact, which did not emerge till it was possible to give a satisfactory account of the motions of the planets, is that the sun's apparent path is not exactly circular, though nearly so. According to what we now know (Chapter IV) the earth moves in a nearly circular ellipse, and the sun is not exactly at its centre. Even if it moved with constant speed in its track, it would not move in equal periods through exactly the same angular distance from the sun. What is constant is its "areal velocity," as Kepler discovered.

In antiquity there was no correspondence between short intervals of astronomical and civil time. The civil day was reckoned from noon to noon by the shadow clock, and when weight-driven and spring clocks began to be used in mediaeval times they were continually corrected by reference to the sundial. The use of the solar day as a unit was abandoned when the determination of longitude at sea emerged in the practice of navigation. Solar time is local. That is to say, noon does not occur simultaneously at places on different meridians of longitude, and the determination of longitude in the daytime is made possible by this fact (see p. 78). To do this we need to know when it is noon at some standard meridian (that of Greenwich is generally accepted). This would be simple enough if an accurate clock set by Greenwich time would always record noon when noon occurs at Greenwich. Since the solar day is not a fixed number of pendulum swings or hair-spring oscillations, the unit of time taken is the *mean* length of the solar day throughout the year. On any particular day noon by mean time is a few minutes (never more than 18) before or after true solar noon. The difference can be estimated by direct observation. It is tabulated in almanacs, being generally (though inappropriately) called the Equation of Time. The accompanying graph shows how it varies throughout the year (Fig. 32). It can be used to find sundial time at Greenwich if we have a reliable clock set to Greenwich mean time, and hence to compare sundial time at Greenwich with sundial time at any place to which the clock is taken. Likewise it can be used to set the clock to mean time by the sundial.

Applying the equation of time may be illustrated by reference to a discrepancy which sometimes puzzles people when they consult almanacs. Times of sunset and sunrise are always given in mean time to meet the requirements of mechanical clocks. On this account the lengths of morning and afternoon may differ by as much as half an hour, or a little more. On September 23, 1935, *Whitaker* gives the times of sunrise as 5.48 a.m. and sunset as 17.57 (i.e. 5.57 p.m.). This would make morning reckoned from mean noon $12 - 5.48 = 6$ hours 12 minutes, and afternoon $17.57 - 12.00 = 5$ hours 57 minutes, i.e. 15 minutes shorter than the morning. On the same day under "equation of time" we read "subtract from apparent time" (i.e. sundial time) "7 minutes 22 seconds." To the nearest half-minute therefore the mean time at true solar noon (which divides the day equally) was 11 hours $52\frac{1}{2}$ minutes a.m. This makes the times of morning (11 hours $52\frac{1}{2}$ minutes $-$ 5 hours 48 minutes) and afternoon (17 hours 57 minutes $-$ 11 hours $52\frac{1}{2}$ minutes) both the same, being 6 hours $4\frac{1}{2}$ minutes on that day. For the convenience of mechanized transport clocks are regulated to keep mean time for some standard locality like Greenwich or Paris. This avoids recourse to elaborate arithmetical corrections for differences of local time, when time-tables are revised. So sundial time may differ considerably from the time of a clock set by radio signal, when the correction for longitude and the equation of time are cumulative. Owing to the statutory introduction of Summer Time in England, an interval of about an hour and a half may separate the noon radio signal from sundial noon in Cornwall.

The problem of choosing a socially convenient unit for short periods of time only became important when civilization spread into the comparatively sunless northern hemisphere and portable mechanical clocks replaced the sundial. A much earlier dilemma arose in accommodating astronomical observations to social convenience when fixing the length of the year. For civil use a year must consist of a whole number of days. By refined astro-

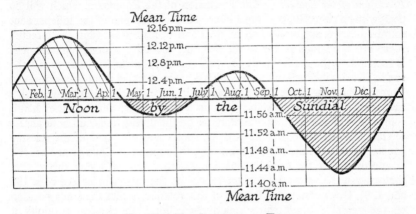

FIG. 32.—THE EQUATION OF TIME

The Equation of Time is the misnomer for the number of minutes which, on any particular day of the year, must be *added* to true solar time ("apparent" time) to give mean time, or, conversely subtracted from mean time to give sundial time. It has four seasonal phases. The first extends from December 25th to April 16th, with its maximum about February 12th, when it reaches 14 minutes 23 seconds. During this period the equation of time is positive. Thus sundial noon at Greenwich on February 12th occurs at 12 hours 14 minutes 23 seconds G.M.T. In the next phase from April 16th to June 15th, it is negative. The maximum is 3 minutes 47 seconds about May 15th. Thus on that date sundial noon at Greenwich occurs at 11 hours 56 minutes 13 seconds. From mid-June to September 1st the equation of time is again positive with a maximum of 6 minutes 22 seconds about July 25th. From September 1st till December 25th it is negative with a maximum about November 2nd, when it is necessary to subtract 16 minutes 22 seconds from sundial time to get mean time.

nomical measurement the year, as a record of seasonal events, is not an exact number of days. In order that the name or number assigned to a day may discharge its primary social use, it must keep pace with the seasons. Clearly it cannot do so if a year is always made up of the same number of days.

From direct observations of the heavens we can define the year in two ways. The *sidereal* year is based on the same principle as the Egyptian year, which was announced by the heliacal rising of Sirius. It is the time taken by the sun to get back to precisely the same position in the heavens as some fixed stars. In contradistinction to the sidereal or Pyramid year, the Stonehenge year was solar, and corresponds to what is now called the *tropical* year. The tropical year is equivalent to taking the average number of days between noon at two successive vernal equinoxes. Astronomers define it as the time taken for the sun to get back to the First Point of Aries, i.e. where the sun is at some time before or after noon on the vernal equinox. On any particular occasion the interval between noon on the first and the succeeding vernal equinox is necessarily a whole number; but since the sun will not generally be exactly over the equator exactly at noon on any particular equinox where the observations are made, successive observations do not average out as a whole number.

The average length of the solar or tropical year is not exactly the same as that of the sidereal year. The reason for this is a phenomenon known as the *Precession of the Equinoxes*. The Precession of the Equinoxes, which will be dealt with on page 219, is of great interest because it is one of the independent sources of evidence used to check the dates of historical events. The recurrence of the seasons is due to the fact that the sun's apparent annual path is inclined to the earth's axis, or, alternatively, the earth moves round the sun in an orbit inclined to its axis which is always parallel in any two positions. Through the seasons the Pole Star retains its fixed position. Hence the earth's axis itself does not appreciably shift in a single year. On the other hand, comparison of astronomical observations on the declinations and hour angles of stars, carried out over long periods, shows that the plane of the celestial equator like that of the moon's orbit (Fig. 16) appears to rotate on the ecliptic at approximately the same inclination. Another way of saying this is that the plane of the terrestrial equator rotates on the earth's orbit (see Figs. 138 and 139). One outstanding feature of this rotation is that the sun's position on the vernal equinox shifts round the ecliptic. In classical antiquity it occupied the same position in the heavens as the constellation of Aries. At the autumn equinox the sun was then in Libra. About 60 B.C. the sun's position at the equinoxes moved from Aries into Pisces and from Libra into Virgo. As a matter of fact we still speak of the First Point of Aries, though the sun is really in Pisces. On star globes the zodiacal signs, as used for months, no longer signify the actual constellation which is screened by the sun at that time. On December 21st the sun is now in Sagittarius and not in Capricorn; on June 21st it is in Gemini and not in the adjoining constellation of Cancer, as it was in ancient times. The phenomenon is generally said to have been discovered by Hipparchus, in 150 B.C., from comparison of earlier records with his own observations. According to Fotheringham's researches, it appears to have been elucidated at an earlier date (about 340 B.C.) by a Babylonian astronomer, Cidenas. The passage of seventy years brings about a shift of 1° in the position of the equinoctial sun in the zodiacal belt. A complete rotation is a matter of about 26,000 years.

Being at right angles to the plane of the equator the position of the celestial pole rotates very slowly round the pole of the ecliptic. We have spoken of the North Pole Star as if it were unchangeable and exactly located at the point round which the stars appear to revolve. It is a fortunate historical circumstance that there does happen to be a bright star practically at this point in our own time. There was also a bright star (α Draconis) very near it when the calendar cultures of the Nile and Mesopotamia flourished. Being fixed with reference to the earth the northern tunnel of the Great Pyramid always points near the celestial pole and not to any particular star that happens to be there. Today it nearly points to another bright star round which different circumpolar constellations revolve. Our own Pole Star (Polaris in Ursa Minor) at present describes a minute circle almost exactly one degree off the pole. That is to say, the maximum difference of two determinations of its altitude at any place is 2°. The average of two observations six months apart gives the correct position of the celestial pole, if we want an exact value for our latitude. On any one occasion we are not likely to be more than $\frac{1}{2}$° out, an error of only 35 miles, and therefore within sight of mountains on the sea horizon, when we are approaching land. There is no bright star near the south celestial pole.

Between 2000 B.C. and about A.D. 1000 there was no very bright star near the pole. We might perhaps go so far as to say that the approach of Polaris to the celestial pole was the herald of the Great Navigations.

Owing to *precession* the sidereal year gets out of step with the seasons in the course of centuries. The tropical year is about 20 minutes shorter than the sidereal year because the position of ♈ changes at the rate of 1 degree in 70 years (precession of the equinoxes). In mean solar units its exact length is 365 days 5 hours 49 minutes to the nearest minute. For keeping track of the seasons the tropical year is the proper astronomical unit because it is based on a seasonal event. The length of the civil year is adjusted to correspond with the tropical year by periodic insertion of extra days in the leap years. The leap year system is analogous to an earlier practice, employed when the calendar still retained its lunar function.

Since the Egyptians added five feast-days to twelve thirty-day months when they created the year of 365 days, it is probable that they first recognized a year of 360 days, or twelve 30-day months. There is evidence to show that the original length of the Chinese and the Sumerian year was also 360 days. While the Egyptian calendar discarded any attempt to keep the divisions of the year in step with the phases of the moon, the oriental civilizations were far less successful in devising a seasonal calendar. The mean length of the lunar month is almost exactly $29\frac{1}{2}$ days. To adjust the calendar to the phases of the moon the Babylonian priests introduced a regular alternation of 29- and 30-day months, with occasional intercalary months (or in our idiom "leap months"), to make up for the fact that the year of 12 lunar months is only 354 days. To desert nomads the moon as a traveller's beacon has more significance than the celestial signals of a settled agronomy. This may be why the Mohammedan calendar retained the Babylonian year of 354 days without any intercalation, so that each month goes through all the seasons in a generation. The early Hindu astronomers introduced a regular five-year cycle, in which an extra month was inserted in the second and fifth years. Greek calendrical practice did not break away from the attempt to square lunar with solar time reckoning. It made a good compromise by the introduction of a calendrical cycle due to Meton and Euctemon in 433 B.C. By intercalation of an extra month seven times in nineteen years, the beginning of a given named month did not suffer a seasonal shift of more than a day in two centuries.

A great deal of confusion arose in the ancient chronologies from attempts to conserve the more primitive use of the lunar cycle as a time unit. Even the Egyptian calendar must have been a month out after a lapse of about 120 years. Petrie remarks that "the cycle of 1,460 years in which the calendar shifted round the seasons enables the record of any seasonal event to be a control on chronology," and "the Berlin date" of 4241 B.C., which pushes back the origin of the Egyptian calendar to pre-dynastic times, is based on this fact. From texts extant in 2000 B.C. it appears that the Egyptian priests already recognized a "little year" or quadrennial cycle, analogous to our leap year, to compensate for the fact that their basic year of 365 days is roughly six hours too short. A brief and readable discussion of these early calendars is given in S. H. Hooke's book, *New Year's Day.**

When Julius Caesar came into power he found the Roman calendar in a state of hopeless confusion. Alexandrian astronomy had then reached a high level of attainment. On the advice of the Alexandrian astronomer Sosigenes, and in accordance with his suggestions, Caesar established in 45 B.C. what is known as the Julian calendar. With a trifling modification, this continues in use among all civilized nations. The Julian calendar discarded all consideration of the moon, and adopting 365¼ days as the true length of the year, ordained that every fourth year should contain 366 days. The extra day was inserted by repeating the sixth day before the kalends of March (our February 24th). Later the extra day became our February 29th. Caesar also transferred the beginning of the year to January 1st. Up to that time it had been in March. This is still indicated by the names of several of the months, e.g. September, the seventh month, etc. Caesar took possession of the month Quintilis, naming it July after himself. His successor, Augustus, in a similar manner appropriated the next month, Sextilis, calling it August.

The Alexandrian astronomers were not a priestly caste wedded to ceremonial practices. In acting on the advice of Sosigenes, Caesar took a step towards the secularization of the calendar. The complete secularization of the calendar did not come until after the invention of the clock. The next important reform was adopted for sacerdotal reasons rather than scientific or utilitarian convenience, when a civilization equipped with mechanical clocks was already outgrowing the need for a religion of saints' days. The sunnier Moslem world encouraged astronomical studies as a secular branch of learning after the decay of the Alexandrian culture. In spreading over the cloudier northern hemisphere the Christian priesthood associated the seasonal festivals of barbarian tribes with a newly-acquired equipment of saints, who replaced the star god Pantheon when Christianity became the State religion of a collapsing empire. The monasteries which tolled the bell for vespers became what the Egyptian priesthood had been, the official timekeepers. They were the custodians of the hour candle, and they nursed the invention of the weight-driven clocks, which were put up in churches two centuries before they came into secular use.

The fact that Christianity inescapably usurped the social function of the ancient priesthoods as the official timekeepers of civilization, when it became the imperial religion, explains the cordial encouragement which astronomy received from St. Augustine's teaching. Professor Farrington draws a sharp contrast between the words in which St. Augustine endorsed the position

* This account closely follows that of Russell, Dugan, and Stewart.

of astronomy in the curriculum of Christian education and his hostility to other branches of pagan science. In *de Doctrina Christiana* St. Augustine says:

A knowledge of the stars has a justification like that of history, in that from the present position and motion of the stars we can go back with certainty over their courses in the past. It enables us with equal certainty to look into the future, not with doubtful omens but on the basis of certain calculation, not

FIG. 33.—ALBRECHT DÜRER'S ADORATION OF THE LAMB

In this woodcut from Dürer's illustrations to the apocalypse (*Die heimlich Offenbarung Johannis*, 1498) the Paschal Lamb is superimposed on the noon sun in conformity to the astrological symbolism for the "Sun in Aries." The vernal equinox, when the sun enters Aries, was celebrated by fertility festivals in ancient times. In Christian ritual the Easter celebrations took their place, Easter being fixed with reference to the day when the sun enters the constellation of the Ram.

to learn our own future, which is the crazy superstition of pagans, but so far as concerns the stars themselves. For just as one who observes the phases of the moon in its course when he has determined its size today, can tell you also its phase at a particular date in past years or in years to come, so with regard to every one of the stars those who observe them with knowledge can give equally certain answers.

The last great reform was necessitated by the association of Easter cele-brations with the most ancient of the fertility festivals. Since the true length of the tropical year is a little less than 365¼ days (being 365 days 5 hours 48 minutes 46 seconds, or a little over eleven minutes less), the Julian year is too long. By the year A.D. 1582 the error had assumed theological dimen-sions. The spring equinox had fallen back to the eleventh of March instead of falling on the twenty-first, as it did at the time of the Council of Nice, A.D. 325. Under the advice of the distinguished astronomer, Clavius, Pope Gregory, therefore, ordered the elimination of ten days. The day following October 4, 1582, was called the fifteenth instead of the fifth. To prevent further displacement of the equinox, it was also decreed that thereafter only such century years should be leap years as are divisible by 400. Thus, 1700, 1800, 1900, 2100, and so on, are not leap years, while 1600 and 2000 are. The reformed calendar was immediately adopted by all Catholic countries, but the Greek Church and most Protestant nations refused to recognize the Pope's authority. In England it was finally adopted by an Act of Parliament passed in 1751. This provided that the year 1752 should begin on January 1st (instead of March 25th, as had long been the rule in England), and that the day following September 2, 1752, should be reckoned as the fourteenth instead of the third. There were riots in various parts of the country in consequence, especially at Bristol, where several persons were killed. Accord-ing to their slogan, they supposed that they had been robbed of eleven days, although the Act was carefully framed to prevent any injustice in the collec-tion of interest, the payment of rents, etc. The Julian calendar persisted in Russia until 1918, and in Rumania until 1919. When Alaska was taken over by the U.S.A. (1876) the official date had to be changed by only eleven days, one day being provided for in the alteration from the Asiatic reckoning to the American.

Professor Elliot Smith's assertion that the magic of today is the discarded science of yesterday is well illustrated by an illuminating study of the role of the zodiacal constellation Cancer in ancient social practices (D'Arcy Thompson, *Trans. Roy. Soc. Edinburgh*, XXXIX). "We err in my opinion," says Professor D'Arcy Thompson,

if we fail to recognize in this antiquated symbolism a deeper intention . . . I think we may discern that . . . these conventional but much varied collo-cations correspond in a singular and precise degree with natural groupings of constellations that are similarly figured and designated, and that the divinities with whom the emblems are associated had themselves a corre-sponding relation to the Signs of Heaven, where they had their places according to the doctrines of astrology, or which marked their festivals in the astronomic system of the sacred calendar. . . . We may abbreviate and sum-marize, as follows, the chief coincidences that have been related above: Cancer was domus Lunae, and the Crab is associated with the Moon on coins of Consentia, Terina, etc., with the lunar Diana of the Ephesians, and with various other images of the lunar goddess. Cancer was exaltatio Jovis, and the Crab is peculiarly associated with the Bird of Jove in the coinage of Agri-gentum, while the Aselli, individual stars of the same constellation, are mytho-logically associated with the same god. Cancer was sedes Mercurii, and the Crab is figured with the head of Hermes on coins of Aenus. Cancer rose with

Sirius, and there are dog-headed representations of both Mercury–Anubis and Luna–Hecate. Cancer marked the date of a festival of Pallas, and the Crab is figured with Pallas on coins of Cumae. Cancer is constellated with Hydra, simultaneously with part of which Virgo rose, and the Crab is associated with Hydra in the legend of Hercules, and hence with Lerna when the rites of the Virgo coelestis were performed. Cancer is in the neighbourhood of Corvus and Crater, and on coins of Mende the Ass is figured with the Raven and Cup. Cancer rose opposite to Aquila and Delphinus which set soon afterwards, and moreover, set precisely as the Dolphin rose; the Crab or the Ass is associated with the Eagle on coins of Agrigentum and Motya, and with the Dolphin on coins of Motya and Argolis. Cancer rose as Pegasus set, and the Crab is figured with the Horse on coins of Agrigentum. Cancer rose as the Southern Fish set, and the Crab and Ass are figured with the Fish on coins of Agrigentum and Cyzicus.

MEGALITHIC REMAINS

The conditions for fixing the year vary greatly in different parts of the world. Near the equator twilight is short, so that the interval between the visibility of a bright star and the moment of sunrise or sunset is small. On the other hand, the sun never rises or sets far north or south of the east and west point. Hence the determination of the year by heliacal rising or setting of bright stars is relatively easy, and the use of the solstice as a fixed point is relatively less convenient than it is in northerly latitudes like our own. At the latitude of Stonehenge twilight is prolonged, and the amplitude of the sun's shift between the solstices is large. On midsummer day it rises just over 40° north, and on December 21st 40° south of the east point, moving through an angle of over 80° in the course of the solstitial half-year. Hence it is not surprising to find evidence that megalithic monuments in northern Europe were set up to regulate a solar calendar.

Sir Norman Lockyer, who carried out an extensive survey (*Stonehenge and other British Stone Monuments*) of such remains in Brittany, Wales, Cornwall, and Dartmoor, distinguishes between three types of solar calendar. One is the solstitial calendar based on the midsummer (June 21st–June 21st) or mistletoe (December 21st–December 21st) year. One is the equinoctial (spring or autumn) year. The other is the "vegetative" year. In early Greek and Latin calendars the quarter days (about May 6th, August 6th, November 9th, and February 6th) are midway between a solstice and the ensuing equinox, and the beginning of the year was fixed in some of the Mediterranean cults at one of these dates, e.g. May 6th, by noting the position of the rising or setting sun when half the number of days (46) between the equinox and following solstice have elapsed. One advantage of a May (or August) year is that the same alignment serves to fix all four quarter days. If a line (Fig. 34) of stones is placed to greet the rising sun of June 21st, when the observer looks northward, it will also greet the setting sun of December 21st, when the observer looks southward. If a line is placed to greet the rising sun of May 6th, when the sun is still travelling northward, it will also greet the rising sun of August 6th on its return journey. Similarly, if the observer looks towards the southern horizon, it will equally well serve to fix the position of sunset on November 6th and February 6th. In northerly latitudes

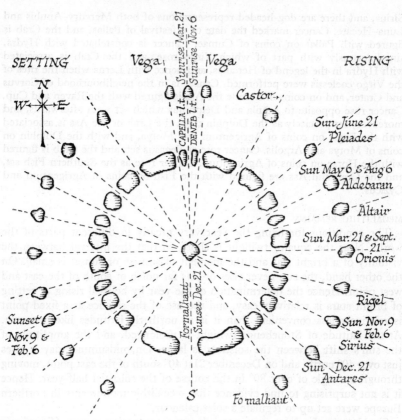

FIG. 34

Diagram to show how a double circle of stones arranged to sight the rising and setting of stars can be used to keep track of the seasons. The directions and times are calculated for today at about the latitude of Stonehenge where Vega just dips beneath the northern horizon and the star Capella never sinks below it. Vega setting in evening twilight in early March and rising in evening twilight in early April announces the coming and going of the vernal equinox, when Capella is seen skirting 7° above the north point of the horizon at lower transit in morning twilight. Castor setting in morning twilight in early March also warns the coming of the vernal equinox. Sirius rising, Altair and Fomalhaut setting in morning twilight in late August anticipate the onset of the autumnal equinox. The approach of midsummer day is announced by the Pleiades rising and Antares setting in morning twilight at the end of May. Midwinter is announced by Aldebaran setting in morning twilight in late November and the setting of the Pleiades and the belt of Orion with the rising of Antares in morning twilight in early December. Fomalhaut skirting the south point of the horizon in evening twilight about January 1st announces that the solstice is past. The November quarter-day is announced by Deneb skirting 5° above the north point of the horizon at lower transit in morning twilight.

where the sun is often obscured by rain or mist on any particular day of the year the advantages of this are obvious.

The megalithic relics of Northern Europe (stone circles, avenues or rows, monoliths or menhirs, dolmens) have remarkably constant features. From a study of the alignment of stone rows and avenues or neighbouring menhirs,

Lockyer found that a very large proportion are placed to greet the rising sun about May 6th, and, allowing for the slight change in the obliquity of the ecliptic in the course of the last five thousand years, he dates them about 1500 B.C. Associated with the solar alignments there are often found to be others which correspond to the rising or setting position of a bright star whose heliacal rising or setting at this date acted as a warning of the approach of the May new year's day. Since there are comparatively few bright stars which could serve the purpose, the established use of the same ones as signals of solar events in the Mediterranean cults leaves little doubt that the stone circle was a calendrical observatory, and the row or avenue leading to one was a *via sacra* for the ritual procession to watch the rising sun of the quarter day, or the heliacal rising and setting of the star (Pleiades, Sirius, Arcturus, etc.) which was the herald of its approach.

EXAMPLES ON CHAPTER I

1. With the aid of diagrams compare the behaviour of the sun's shadow at latitudes 70° N., 50° N., 10° N., and 0°, 10° S., 50° S., 70° S. throughout the seasons.

2. The star α in the constellation Ursa Major was seen at its lower culmination at midnight on September 4th. Later on it was seen due east of the Pole at 2 a.m. What was the date?

3. Given the obliquity of the ecliptic as $23\frac{1}{2}°$, find the sun's zenith distance on December 21st at a place where the altitude of the Polar Star is 51°.

4. The altitude of the Pole Star at a certain place is found to be 53°. Find the approximate date on which the sun's noon altitude was 60°, given the fact that the sun rose *earlier* on the previous day. (Use *Whitaker*.)

5. Imagine that you have been deported to an unknown destination at which you arrive after months of high fever. How would you be able to recognize (a) whether you were near the North Pole, the equator, the South Pole, the tropical belts; (b) how would you be able to locate your approximate position between these limits without any instruments; (c) how would you determine roughly the time of year?

6. What additional information could you gain, if you had a protractor, some string, and a few nails?

7. Suppose yourself in the same situation. You only recall the following geometrical theorems of your schooldays: (i) The theorem of Pythagoras, (ii) the angles at the base of an isosceles triangle are equal, (iii) the angle at the centre of a circle is twice the angle at the circumference subtending the same arc. How could you use these to make angles of 90, 45, 30, and 60 degrees round a shadow pole with a piece of cord and a peg? How would you proceed to obtain other angular divisions?

8. Assuming that you have done this, how would you find (a) your latitude, (b) the date, from observations of the sun's noon shadow?

9. How would you make an hour glass to record the time elapsing between the meridian transits of the stars?

10. Explain why leap years are inserted and what is meant by Greenwich mean time.

11. If Sirius transits $23\frac{1}{2}°$ above the southern horizon at lat. 50° N., show with a diagram like that of Fig. 24 at what latitude it will

(*a*) just graze the southern horizon at transit;
(*b*) transit $16\frac{1}{2}°$ south of the zenith.

12. If Aldebaran transits $12\frac{1}{2}°$ south of the zenith at latitude 29° N., at what latitude will it

(*a*) transit exactly overhead?
(*b*) transit 5° north of the zenith?
(*c*) just graze the northern horizon as a circumpolar star at lower culmination?

Test the rule that if the altitude is always measured from the northern horizon, the formula

$$\text{altitude} = 90° - (\text{zenith distance})$$

still holds good, if the zenith distance is *negative*, when a star transits south of the zenith.

13. Find the north polar distance of Aldebaran and the south polar distance of Sirius with diagrams like those in Fig. 24. Hence find with similar figures at what southern latitude

(*a*) Aldebaran ceases to be visible at all.
(*b*) Sirius becomes a circumpolar star of the south celestial hemisphere.

14. Find at transit the zenith distance of Sirius and Aldebaran at latitude 5° N. and latitude 5° S. and of Sirius at latitude $22\frac{1}{2}°$ S. Show that if (*a*) z.d. south of the zenith is negative, (*b*) declination south of the equator is negative, (*c*) latitude south of the equator is negative, the following formula applies to all situations:

$$\text{Declination} = \text{Latitude} + \text{zenith distance}.$$

15. Draw a figure to show the upper and lower transit of Sirius at 85° S. Show that in the southern hemisphere, where there is no bright star near the celestial pole, the latitude, i.e. elevation of the pole, is the mean altitude of a circumpolar star at upper and lower culmination reckoned from the southern horizon.

16. If solar time at Exeter is 14 minutes *behind* solar time at Greenwich, on what days of the year (see Fig. 32) will

(*a*) noon on the sundial at Exeter agree with broadcast time (G.M.T.) from Greenwich?
(*b*) noon on the sundial occur two minutes after broadcast noon?
(*c*) noon on the sundial occur twenty minutes after broadcast noon?

17. On November 5th the sun crosses the meridian at one o'clock G.M.T. At what time by a chronometer set to G.M.T. will it cross the meridian at the same place on February 5th, June 21st, and August 4th?

CHAPTER II

POMPEY'S PILLAR

The Science of Seafaring

IN the everyday life of mankind the first fact which led to the growth of an organized body of scientific knowledge was the fertility of the crops and flocks. The second was the freedom of the seas. From the first came the need for an organized calendar, from the second a system of earth survey. The following passage from Nilsson's monograph illustrates the same social needs at work in the culture of backward communities today:

The calendar and practical life become to some degree separated from each other; the first lays the principal emphasis upon the correct ordering of the series of days, which is of especial importance on religious grounds for the selection of days and the fixing of the right day for the religious observances; in practical life, however, the point of chief importance is to determine the times when the various occupations may be begun and sea-voyages undertaken, both of which depend upon the solar year, and for this the stars afford the best aid. Hence it happens that sometimes the reckoning by the stars appears, as one more profanely determined, in a certain opposition to the lunisolar reckoning, which has a more religious character. This happened in ancient Greece, where the stars served for the time-reckoning of sailors and peasants while the lunisolar calendar was developed and extended under sacral influence; the festival calendar, which was regulated and recorded by the moon, became the official civil calendar. It was only later that the stellar calendar was systematically brought under the influence of the fully developed astronomy and of the Julian calendar. In sailing, the stars afford to the primitive seafaring peoples the only means of finding their way when the land can no longer be seen. From the necessities of seafaring the greatly advanced knowledge of the stars possessed by the South Sea peoples has arisen; this is because practical ends are served not by a priestly wisdom, but by a profane. Nevertheless the knowledge of the stars is a secret which is carefully guarded in certain families, and kept from the common people—as is reported of the Marshall Islands. Among the Moanu of the Admiralty Islands it is the chiefs who are initiated by tradition into the science of the stars. On the Mortlock Islands, where the science of the stars is very highly developed, there was a special astronomical profession; the knowledge of the stars was a source of respect and influence, it was anxiously concealed, and only communicated to specially chosen individuals. Only a few can determine the hours of night by the stars. The Tahitian Tupaya, who accompanied Cook on his first voyage, was a man of this kind, specially distinguished for his nautical knowledge of the stars. The elements of the science, however, seem to have been pretty generally known, and from the Caroline Islands comes a curious account of a general instruction therein. It was first mentioned by the Spanish missionary Cantova in the year 1721, and was later confirmed by Arago. In every settlement there were two houses, in one of which the boys were instructed in the knowledge of the stars, and in the other the girls; only vague ideas were imparted, however. The teacher had a kind of globe of the heavens on which the principal stars were marked, and he pointed out to his pupils the direction which they must follow on their various journeys. One native could also represent on a table by means of grains of maize the constellations known to him. This is a nautical non-priestly astronomy, which has really little to do with calendrical matters in general, although as a matter of fact in the Carolines and the Mortlock Islands it has led to the naming of all months from constellations, and therefore to a systematic sidereal regulation of the calendar.

In ancient times transport by land involved a large initial outlay in making roads and a vast output of energy in carrying loads. Shipping dispensed with the need for roads and registered man's first tentative exploit in replacing the effort of man or beast by the forces of inanimate nature. The Semitic peoples of Asia Minor had established colonies throughout the Mediterranean world by the beginning of the second millennium B.C. Carthage was founded in the ninth century. By then ships had begun to track north towards the Tin Isles of the north. In the sixth century Carthaginian navigators had coasted along West Africa beyond the equator. From these Semitic peoples of Asia Minor the maritime Greeks of the seventh and sixth centuries B.C. absorbed the star lore of the ancient world and the geometrical principles of the calendar architecture. Their first two teachers of repute—Thales and Pythagoras—were both of Phoenician parentage. So was Anaxagoras, who brought astronomy from Miletus to the Court of Pericles. Pythagoras is said to have acquired in Egypt his knowledge of the obliquity of the ecliptic and the identity of the planets Mercury and Venus in their appearances as morning and as evening stars (see p. 184). According to Callimachus (cited by Diogenes Laertius), Thales determined the position of the stars in the Little Bear by which the Phoenicians guided themselves in their voyages. From Professor Taylor's studies on mediaeval pilot books it seems that a similar practice persisted in the Christian era. Fig. 67 shows how the relative positions of stars in the Little Bear were once used to estimate the error involved in determining latitude by the Pole Star, when it was not so near the true centre of the heavens as it is now. The orientation of two stars in the Little Bear above, below, east, or west of the true pole made it possible to apply the necessary correction, ranging from $-3\frac{1}{2}°$ to $+3\frac{1}{2}°$ in the fifteenth century.

Scientific geography starts with the exploration of the Mediterranean, and the determination of latitude, which probably antedates Greek civilization, arose by easy steps from the practice of navigating by the Pole Star. That maritime astronomy had reached a high level of precision before the great advances made by the Alexandrians is indicated by the reference to Pytheas in the following passage from Professor Farrington's *Science in Antiquity*:

. . . about 500 B.C. the Carthaginian, Hanno, coasted down the west coast of Africa as far as Sierra Leone, to within 8 degrees of the equator. Close on the heels of the Phoenicians followed their rivals, the Greeks. The effective discovery of the Black Sea was the work of the Greeks of Miletus. Exploration was begun about 800 B.C., and by 650 B.C. there was a heavy fringe of Greek colonies all round the Black Sea coast. It was for this city of explorers and merchants that Anaximander constructed his map. It was not from Miletus,

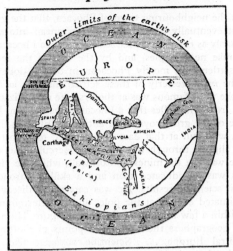

MAP OF THE WORLD BY HECATAEUS, 517 B.C. Showing the primitive ideas held at the time of Pythagoras. From Breasted's *Ancient Times*.

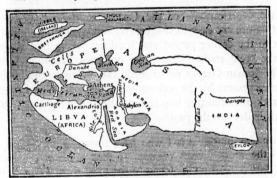

MAP OF THE WORLD ACCORDING TO ERATOSTHENES, ABOUT 250 B.C.

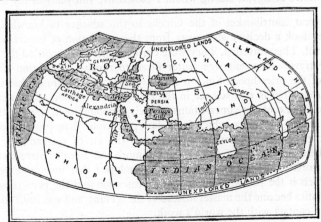

PTOLEMY'S MAP OF THE WORLD, ABOUT A.D. 200

FIG. 35

however, but from the neighbouring town of Phocaea, that the great enterprise was organized that eventually turned the Mediterranean into something like a Greek lake. Probably as early as 850 B.C. colonists from Phocaea occupied the Italian site of Cumae near Naples, and by the end of the seventh century numerous Greek settlements, mostly Phocaean in origin, dotted the western Mediterranean. The most westerly of these settlements was at Maenace, near Malaga in Spain, the most famous was at the first site of civilization in France, Marseilles. It was from Marseilles that a Phocaean sea-captain, Pytheas, about 300 B.C., made one of the great voyages of antiquity. Eluding the vigilance of the Carthaginians, who still at that date endeavoured to keep the Atlantic as their preserve, he slipped through the Pillars of Hercules and coasted north. His chief objective was the tin mines of Cornwall, which he visited and well describes. Pytheas was an educated man and a skilled astronomer, and his voyage was rich in scientific results. He was capable of discovering that the Pole Star is not situated exactly at the pole, and of determining the latitude of Marseilles to within a few minutes of the correct figure. His accurate observations gave later geographers their reference points in plotting the map of northern and central Europe. . . . Scientific voyagers like Pytheas were capable of calculating latitudes astronomically. Longitude, however, remained a matter of dead-reckoning.

The positive contributions of the Greeks to the advancement of new knowledge of nature are easy to exaggerate, and what useful discoveries they made belong to the earlier period and localities where they were in closest touch with the great trading centres of northern Palestine. It is only fair to say that the Ionian Greeks never made the claims to originality ascribed to their Attic successors by the lexicographers of later time. Democritus, the doyen of Greek materialism, has left us the following fragment which is eloquent of their debt to the past:

Of all my contemporaries it is I who have traversed the greater part of the earth, visited the most distant regions, studied climates the most diverse, countries the most varied, and listened to the most men. There is no one who has surpassed me in geometrical constructions and demonstrations, not even the geometers of Egypt, among whom I passed five full years of my life.

The great contribution of the Greeks to the advance of knowledge was that they took a decisive step away from the association of natural enquiry with ritual. They travelled. They were curious, and they recorded the results of their travels in a language better fitted to precise description than the scripts of the priesthood. Since it is always easier to separate what is mere magic from what is real science in the culture of foreigners, they were able to discard some of the superstitions of their schoolmasters. Eventually they fell victims to a practice which is no less pernicious than priesthood itself. As time passed the pursuit of science and the art of mathematics which should be its servant came to be regarded more and more as mere recreation for a leisured and litigious class. They developed that inveterate belief in logic which is the password of the legal profession and the peril of science. Mathematics became the master instead of the servant, and was itself sterilized by losing contact with the world's work.

It is sometimes suggested that naturalism and political philosophy flourished side by side as twin growths from the same soil of intellectual freedom. To a large extent they were chronologically and topographically separate. Aristotle, whose person symbolizes the fusion of positive science and political speculation, devoted much of his energy to verbal refutations of the sound experimental physics of his Ionian predecessors. Plato, who declared that all the works of Democritus ought to be burned, did not shrink from contemptuous references to astronomical observations or to the pioneer acoustical experiments of the Pythagoreans. The following (*Republic*, Book VII) is typical of the anti-scientific temper of Plato's teaching:

It makes no difference whether a person stares stupidly at the sky, or looks with half-shut eyes upon the ground; so long as he is trying to study any sensible object, I deny that he can ever be said to have learned anything, because no objects of sense admit the scientific treatment. . . . Do you not think that the genuine astronomer will . . . regard the heaven itself as framed by the heavenly architect? . . . But as to the proportion which the day bears to the night, both to the month, the month to the year, and the other stars to the sun and the moon, and to one another—will he not, think you, look down upon the man who believes such corporeal and visible objects to be changeless and exempt from all perturbations; and will he not hold it absurd to bestow extraordinary pains on the endeavour to apprehend their true relations?

We shall pursue astronomy with the help of problems just as we pursue geometry but we shall let the heavenly bodies alone, if it is our design to become really acquainted with astronomy and by that means to convert the natural intelligence of the soul from a useless into a useful possession. . . . You can scarcely be ignorant that harmony also is treated just like astronomy in this, that its professors like the astronomers are content to measure the notes and concords distinguished by the ear one against another, and therefore toil without result. Yes, indeed, they make themselves ridiculous. They talk about "repetitions" and apply their ears closely, as if they were bent on extracting a note from their neighbours; and then one party asserts that an intermediate sound can still be detected, which is the smallest interval, and ought to be the unit of measure; while the other party contends that now the sounds are identical—both alike postponing their reason to their ears. . . . They act like the astronomers, that is, they investigate the numerical relations subsisting between these audible concords, but they refuse to apply themselves to problems with the object of examining what numbers are, and what numbers are not, consonant, and what is the reason of the difference . . . a work useful in the search after the beautiful and the good, though useless if pursued with other ends.

From this morass of metaphysical disputation, into which the secular knowledge received by the Attic Greeks from their Ionian predecessors had fallen, the culture of classical antiquity was rescued by the brutal realities of war. The conquests of Alexander brought new opportunities of intellectual intercourse, new contacts with the world's affairs, and led to the foundation of a cosmopolitan centre of learning near the site of the greatest Egyptian triumphs of architecture and irrigation. Alexandria became a foremost centre of Mediterranean shipping. The daily record of a ship's progress which is put up in the saloon of a modern liner is part of the cultural debt which we

owe to the brilliant efflorescence of discoveries made in Alexandria during
the three centuries which preceded the beginning of the Christian era, and
the three centuries before Rome licensed the monks to loot the treasury of
pagan science.

We have seen that the cardinal achievement of the priestly culture of the
great calendar civilizations was the discovery of the year. The determination
of the year entailed careful daily measurement of the sun's shadow and the
bearings of the stars in the night sky. In making these measurements men
blundered into the recognition of certain physical constants which provide
a scientific basis for fixing our position in the universe of stars and upon
the earth's surface. Three fundamental relations to which we have already
directed attention are the altitude of the pole, the tilt of the plane of the sun's
apparent track on the equinoxes, and the inclination of the ecliptic to the
equator. The knowledge of these relations gives us all that we require to
estimate the northerly or southerly position of an observer with reference to
the poles or the equator, and divides the earth into three zones with characteristic seasonal phenomena on either side of the equator. These are the
frigid (Arctic or Antarctic), temperate, and tropical regions. A fourth
uniformity, the constant difference of hour angle between the transit of two
stars, gives us some of the information from which we can determine our
position east or west of any fixed line from pole to pole.

The full significance of none of these relations could emerge until it was
possible to draw comparisons between observations made at different places
and to sift what was purely local information about shadow, star bearings,
and seasons, from facts which are common ground to people inhabiting
different parts of the world. Without doubt by far the most difficult step in
this advance was to understand the geographical meaning of the time relations
between the transits of heavenly bodies. Today it is easy enough to establish
the fact that astronomical, e.g. solar, time is *local*. There is no difficulty in
determining within a minute the exact time at which the sun crosses the
meridian by means of a home-made apparatus like that shown in Fig. 22.
Noon for you will be the time when the zenith distance of the sun is least.
On four days of the year (April 15th, June 15th, September 1st, and December 25th—see Fig. 31) the correction (called the "equation of time") necessary
to make the length of the solar day bear a constant relation to the interval
between successive transits of the same star, vanishes. That is to say, 12 noon
G.M.T. is the true solar noon at Greenwich. If you live in Cornwall,
you will find that noon by your own sundial does not agree with a
watch set by the daily broadcast announcement of Greenwich time. Near
Land's End on these days noon will occur when the watch records the
time as 12.23.

The explanation of this fact is one which we generally learn in our schooldays. It is shown in Fig. 36. The earth rotates eastward to meet the rising
sun. If we are west of another place, we have farther to travel before the sun
crosses our meridian. The earth revolves through 360° in 24 hours, i.e. 15°
per hour, or 1° in 4 minutes. Hence, time is *local* reckoned from the transit
of a celestial body, whether it is *sidereal* time (reckoned from when ♈ crosses
our meridian) or solar time (reckoned from when the sun passes over our

meridian). That local noon is behind noon at another place, e.g. Greenwich, means that when it is noon at the latter we have still to go some distance before our meridian reaches the sun—or alternatively the sun has still to travel westwards some distance to reach our meridian. In other words, we are west of it. If local noon occurs 23 minutes after Greenwich noon, the earth has to rotate eastwards through an angle of $\left(\frac{23}{4}\right)° = 5\frac{3}{4}°$ to bring the sun to our meridian after crossing the meridian at Greenwich. This angle is our *west* longitude. So we have the following simple rule for determining

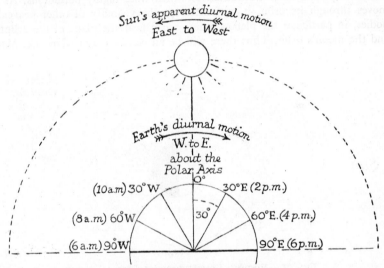

FIG. 36.—FINDING LONGITUDE

At noon the sun lies directly over the line joining the north and south points of the horizon, i.e. the meridian of longitude on which you are located. In the figure it is directly above the Greenwich meridian, and it is therefore noon at Greenwich. If you are 30° East of Greenwich the earth has rotated through 30° since your sundial registered noon. It has therefore made one-twelfth of its twenty-four-hourly revolution, so that it is now two o'clock by the sundial. If you are 60° West the earth has still to rotate 60° before the sun will be over your meridian, i.e. one-sixth of its twenty-four-hourly rotation; so your sundial will register 8 a.m.

longitude. If noon at a place B happens x minutes or y hours after noon at A, B is $\frac{x}{4}$ or $15y$ degrees west of A, and if noon happens at B x minutes or y hours before A, B is $\frac{x}{4}$ or $15y$ degrees east of A. Difference in longitude is the hour angle difference of the local transit of the sun across the meridian.

Simple as this is, it was a very difficult step to make in ancient times. Until there were wheel-driven clocks, there were no portable devices with which to compare solar time at two different places. Although the later Alexandrians had very elaborate water-clocks of much greater delicacy than the crude hour-glasses of an earlier period, and certainly no less accurate than the first mediaeval clocks which were driven by weights, they had no means of maintaining a continuous record of time over a long journey. The way in which they escaped from this limitation is not difficult to reconstruct, because we know the methods which were first used to determine terrestrial longitude. Although many of the hypotheses framed by the first civilized men about the influence of the heavenly bodies are now discarded as magical, they led people to observe phenomena which proved to be of great use to their successors in a different social setting. In particular the study of eclipses as events of august omen focussed close attention on the behaviour of the moon. Aside from eclipses, the moon's course displayed other circumstances which were highly portentous. As it moves through its orbit, it may intercept the visibility of other heavenly bodies, in particular the planets which move near the plane of the ecliptic and the moon's orbit. Thus there will be an *occultation* of Mars, i.e. Mars

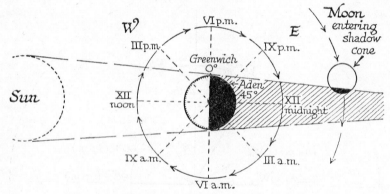

FIG. 37.—FINDING LONGITUDE BY A LUNAR ECLIPSE

The figure is drawn like Fig. 36 with the South Pole nearest to the observer, so that you see the meridians of the places named. The places themselves, being in the northern hemisphere, are not seen.

will disappear behind the moon's disc, from time to time, just as at times the sun would seem to move behind the moon's disc in a solar eclipse. The care bestowed on the study of eclipses and occultations has outlived confidence in the political and personal effects attributed to them. So also the usefulness of observations with the spectroscope may well outlast the wave theory of light and the ether. People observed them and were able to know when they would occur at a particular place. Anyone who possessed an hour-glass at another place could watch for them and record the interval which elapsed between an eclipse or occultation and the foregoing noon.

The illustration in Fig. 37 will make this clear. If a lunar eclipse is seen at 5.58 p.m. by Greenwich local time, you would see the moon's disc entering the earth's shadow cone at Aden just before nine o'clock (8.58) according to a watch set by the Aden sundial. You would therefore be (8.58—5.58)=3 hours in front of Greenwich time, and therefore you could conclude that Aden is $3 \times 15° = 45°$ East of Greenwich. The mariner who possesses an almanac giving the local time at which an eclipse or other celestial signal will occur at one place, can therefore obtain his longitude by recording the local time of its occurrence where he is. According to Marguet (*Histoire de la Longitude de la Mer au XVIII siècle en France*), Columbus looked out for a port of anchor at Haiti for observing at rest the conjunction of sun and moon on January 13, 1493. Bensaude (*L'Astronomie Nautique au Portugal à l'époque des grandes découvertes*) tells us that Amerigo Vespucci found the difference of longitude between Venezuela and Cadiz in 1499 by observation of a lunar eclipse.

In his book *The Geographical Lore of the Time of the Crusades*, J. K. Wright tells us how the Alexandrians, equipped with neither chronometers nor wireless signals, relied on this method of finding longitude to construct the first true maps:

Eratosthenes, Hipparchus, Pliny, and Ptolemy all understood that it may be found by observing the time of eclipses in different localities. Hipparchus believed that an extensive series of observations should be carried out in order to ascertain, by mathematical and astronomical means alone, latitudes and longitudes of a large number of places. To facilitate such a survey he prepared tables of lunar eclipses and tables to aid in the determination of latitudes, but the practical difficulties of the undertaking were too great and the work was never completed. In fact, throughout antiquity the total number of places whose position had thus been accurately determined probably does not exceed half a dozen, if it is as many. Pliny gives an account of two different occasions when observations were made of the same eclipse at two different places. He says that at the time of the battle of Arbela the moon was eclipsed at the second hour of the night, when at the same hour it was rising in Sicily. He also speaks of an eclipse of the sun that was seen in Campania between the seventh and eighth hours and in Armenia between the eleventh and twelfth, indicating a difference in longitude of four hours, or 60°. The actual distance is no more than half of this. Ptolemy also cites the eclipse of 331 B.C. as giving the distance between Carthage and Arbela. . . . Much greater accuracy was attained by the Arabs in their calculations of longitude and some of their figures were passed on to the Western world in astronomical tables during the twelfth and thirteenth centuries.

The use of eclipses depends on being able to reckon when the sun, the earth, and the moon will be in line with one another as seen at some particular place. This means being able to calculate the relative positions of the sun and moon as seen from the earth by analysis of recorded observations. An analogous method depends on the fact that the moon retreats in its monthly course through approximately $360 \div 30$, or 12 degrees a day. So its position with reference to the fixed stars changes appreciably in a couple of hours, even as judged by the use of very simple instruments. Thus the moon is a clock which registers short intervals of time. Once we have discovered how to map out the moon's relation to the apparent rotation of the fixed stars, there are two different ways in which the moon's motion may be used to compare local time with time at a standard observatory.

The discovery of how to map the position of the heavenly bodies was therefore a necessary preliminary to scientific earth survey. The wealth of astronomical knowledge amassed by the Alexandrian astronomers was not merely the by-product of idle curiosity, nor a lopsided hypertrophy of leisure. In constructing the first maps they were forced to rely on much more devious methods than we employ in an age of spring clocks. Getting a fairly good estimate of latitude inland in A.D. 1935 in the northern hemisphere is a very different thing from finding a latitude at sea on a particular day in the year 300 B.C. To begin with, there was no bright star very near to the celestial pole at that date. Even today the presence of Polaris 1° from the North Pole does not help navigation in the southern hemisphere. The sun is often obscured by cloud at noon so that it is highly unsatisfactory to rely on one or even two methods for finding one's bearings. The art of navigation, or of overland survey for imperialist campaigns, has to make use of all the relevant information which any visible celestial object can provide.

While important contributions to optics, mechanics, and medicine are to be credited to the Alexandrian culture, its supreme achievements are all related directly or indirectly to the discovery of a scientific basis for earth survey. Alexandria was a centre of maritime trade. It was also a cosmopolitan product of Greek Imperialism, and thereafter the cultural Mecca of the Roman Empire. Knowledge of latitude grew out of the mariner's practice of steering his course by the heavenly bodies and noticing the changing elevation of the Pole Star in coastal sailing northwards or southwards across the Mediterranean or beyond the Pillars of Hercules. Knowledge of longitude, as the previous citation suggests, came from the arts of war, and did not enter into the practice of navigation till a far later date. Estimates of long distances depended on information from imperialist campaigns. Scientific geography was in part a by-product of the practice of navigation, in part a by-product of imperial expansion; and it was made possible when the pre-existing lore of a ceremonial caste became the common possession of mankind. Brilliant innovations in mathematics arose in close relation to the same group of problems. The trigonometry of Archimedes and Hipparchus, the algebra of Theon and Diophantus, can be traced to the inadequacies of Platonic geometry and Greek arithmetic as instruments for handling the large-scale measurements which Alexandrian geodesy and astronomy entailed.

The principal discoveries which form the basis of the Ptolemaic system may be taken under four headings: the measurement of the size of the earth, the construction of universal star maps based on the principle of latitude and longitude, the introduction of latitude and longitude for terrestrial cartography, and the first estimates of the distances of the moon and sun from the earth.

THE SIZE OF THE EARTH

The first estimate of the earth's circumference was made by Eratosthenes (*c.* 250 B.C.). As librarian of Alexandria he had access to information from which he was able to compare the sun's altitude at two situations, one due south of the other (Fig. 38). On the summer solstice the noon sun was mirrored in a deep well near Syene just below the first cataract of the Nile on the tropic of Cancer. The noon sun was therefore at the zenith. On the same day at Alexandria, 500 miles due north, the obelisk shadow showed that the sun was $7\frac{1}{2}°$ from the zenith. Since the sun's rays are parallel, this

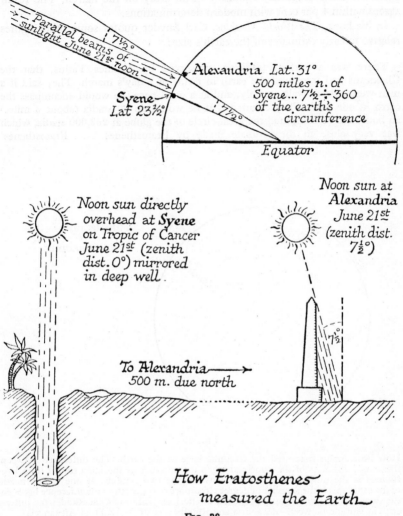

How Eratosthenes
measured the Earth

FIG. 38

Note that at noon the sun lies directly over the observer's meridian of longitude.
Syene and Alexandria have nearly the same longitude. So the sun, the two places,
and the earth's centre, may be drawn on the same flat slab of space.

means that the arc, or as we now say the difference of latitude, between
Syene and Alexandria is approximately $7\frac{1}{2}°$, i.e. $7\frac{1}{2} \div 360 = \dfrac{1}{48}$ of the
entire earth's circumference. Hence, the difference between Alexandria and
Syene (approximately 500 miles) is $\dfrac{1}{48}$ of the circumference of the globe. So
the earth's circumference is about $48 \times 500 = 24{,}000$ miles. The distance
was given in stadia (the length of the games stadium), and was probably

based on the average day's journey of an army on the march. The result agrees within 4 per cent with modern determinations.

In his book, *The World Machine*, Carl Snyder quotes some other figures relative to early estimates of the earth's size:

There was a curious tradition, preserved by Achilles Tatius, that the Chaldeans had measured the earth in terms of a day's march. They said if a man were able to walk steadily, and at a good pace, he would encompass the earth in one year. They counted that he would do 30 stadia (about 3 miles) an hour, and so computed the great circle of the globe at 263,000 stadia, which was very close to the estimate made by Eratosthenes. . . . Eratosthenes'

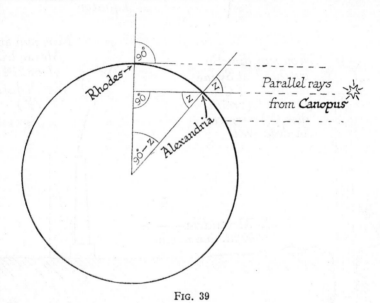

Fig. 39

How Poseidonius measured the circumference of the earth. The difference between the zenith distances of the same star when measured at its meridian transit from two stations is the difference of latitude between the two stations. If one is due north of the other this is the number of degrees in the arc of the earth's circumference between the two stations. Since Canopus grazed the horizon (Z.D.=90°) at Rhodes the difference in latitude between Alexandria and Rhodes was 90° − (Z.D. at Alexandria).

figure was 250,000 (or 252,000); Hipparchus wished to increase this to 275,000; Poseidonius to reduce it, fixing it at 240,000 stadia according to Cleomedes, at 180,000 according to Strabo. This last figure was that adopted by Ptolemy, and this and other errors of Ptolemy were the basis of Columbus' belief that India was near. Had he known the true distance, possibly he never would have sailed. . . . Is it the impression that we have here merely an intellectual conception—that the meaning of it in no wise came home to any of the ancients —that there was no vivid sense of new continents, new worlds to explore? Listen, then, to a passage of old Strabo; he is telling of the ideas of Eratosthenes, who, he says, held "that if the extent of the Atlantic Ocean were not an obstacle, we might easily pass by sea from Iberia (i.e. Spain) to India, still keeping in the same parallel (of the temperate zone), the remaining portion of which parallel, measured as above in stadia (252,000) occupies *more than a third* of the whole circle; since the parallel drawn through Athens, in which we have taken the distances from India to Iberia, does not contain in the whole 200,000 stadia."

To get his measured distance Poseidonius relied on mariners' estimates of a straight course northwards across the Mediterranean. Like that of Eratosthenes, his method depends on the fact that the difference of latitude between two places is equivalent to the difference of zenith distance or altitude of the same heavenly body when it crosses the meridian (Fig. 39).

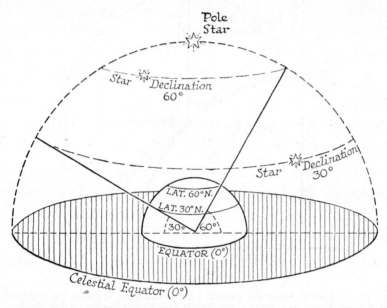

FIG. 40.—SMALL CIRCLES OF LATITUDE ON THE TERRESTRIAL AND OF DECLINATION ON THE CELESTIAL SPHERE

Just as latitude is the angle of elevation north of the equator of a point on the earth's surface, so declination is the angle of elevation north of the celestial equator of a point on the celestial sphere. Latitudes and declinations south of the equatorial plane are thus reckoned as negative.

Poseidonius measured the zenith distance of the star Canopus at Alexandria and on the island of Rhodes, situated roughly 350 miles north of the former. Canopus, after Sirius the brightest star in the sky, just grazes the horizon at Rhodes, and is invisible further north.

According to the best measurements, the earth's diameter is 7,900 miles along the polar axis and 7,926·7 miles across the equator. The geometric mean of the two is 7,913·3 miles. The flattening at the poles about which we heard so much at school amounts to a difference of less than fifty miles between the two axes. Thus the circumference along the Greenwich meridian is $\pi \times 7,913 \cdot 3 = 24,860$ miles, and along the equator, $\pi \times 7,926 \cdot 7 = 24,902$ miles. Once the size of the earth is known, it is an easy matter to calculate the distance which separates any two places, if their latitude and longitude are also available. The position of a ship at sea with reference to any port can be calculated within a few yards.

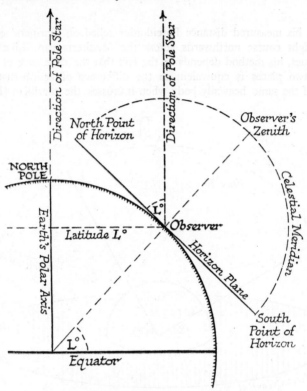

FIG. 41.—A Star at Meridian Transit Lies in the Same Plane as the Observer, the Earth's Poles, the Zenith, the South and North Points of the Horizon, and the Earth's Centre

A straight line which does not lie on some particular flat slab of space (or *plane*) can only cut it once. A straight line which passes through more than one point on a plane therefore lies on the same plane as the points through which it passes. The plane bounded by the observer's great circle of longitude and the earth's axis includes as points the earth's centre, observer, and the earth's poles. The line joining zenith and observer passes also through the earth's centre, i.e. through more than one point on this plane. Hence it lies wholly on the plane. The north and south points of the horizon lie in the same plane as the meridian of longitude through the observer. So south and north points, zenith, and observer, are all in the same plane with the earth's centre and poles. A circle can only cut a plane in which it does not itself lie at two points. The circle drawn through the north and south points and the zenith passes through more than two points in the same plane, and therefore lies wholly on it. So any point on this imaginary circle (the celestial meridian) is also on it.

THE CONSTRUCTION OF A STAR MAP

Today we are all brought up to use maps. An acquaintance with latitude and longitude is part of the equipment of a citizen for everyday life in an age of widespread communications over large distances. We shall therefore find it more easy to envisage the construction of a star map from what we have already learned in using an earth map. Imagine a long stick connecting the celestial sphere with the centre of the earth. If we rotate it (Fig. 48) in a great semicircle from pole to pole, it will trace out a meridian of longitude on the surface of the earth, and a corresponding semicircle which is called a meridian of *right ascension* on the celestial sphere. All observers on the same semicircle of longitude will have the same local time. They will all see any celestial body of the same right ascension crossing the meridian at the same moment. The difference between the longitudes of any two observers will be the hour angle difference between the corresponding semicircles of right ascension coinciding with their celestial meridians at the same moment. If we imagine the stick to rotate (Fig. 40) so that it always cuts the earth's surface

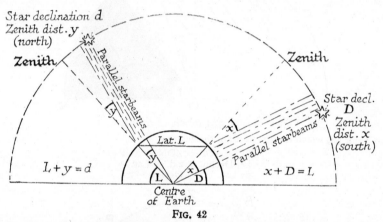

Fig. 42

Two stars in the northern half of the celestial sphere, one crossing the meridian north, the other south of the zenith. If the star crosses north: Declin. = Lat. of observer + meridian zenith distance. If it crosses south: Lat. of observer = Declination + meridian zenith distance, i.e. Declin. = Lat. of observer − meridian zenith distance. The first formula holds for all cases if we reckon as negative zenith distances south of the zenith, and latitudes or declinations south of the equator.

at the same distance from the equator, it will trace out a circle of latitude on the earth's surface, and a corresponding circle of *declination* on the celestial sphere. As the celestial sphere rotates around its axis in the plane of the equator, any heavenly body on this circle of declination will be seen exactly at the zenith when it crosses the meridian of any observer on the corresponding circle of terrestrial latitude. A star on any other declination circle will have the same meridian altitude for all observers on any one circle of latitude.

If the declinations and right ascensions of the stars are tabulated, we can use any one of them to find latitude (Figs. 42 and 43) or longitude. The practical advantage of this is that: (i) if we are travelling rapidly, we can check our position at frequent intervals, (ii) we are less dependent on continuously fine weather, (iii) we can make the necessary observations at any time between sunset and sunrise since there is always some star near the meridian. The construction of a rough star map which will give latitude and longitude within a degree is comparatively simple.

To get the declination of a star in the northern hemisphere, find its altitude (measured from the north point) when it crosses the meridian. This will be its maximum altitude taken at intervals of a minute round about the time when its azimuth is nearly zero. Subtract the local altitude of the Pole Star.

Fig. 43.—LATITUDE, DECLINATION, AND ZENITH DISTANCE, AT MERIDIAN TRANSIT
In both parts of the following figure, COP = ZON, since COP is the right angle between the celestial equator and the polar axis, and ZON is the right angle between the zenith and the horizon.

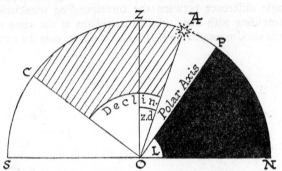

Star A transits north of the Zenith

For a star (A) which transits north of the zenith:

$$COP - AOP = ZON - AOP$$
$$\text{i.e. Declin.} = \text{z.d.} + \text{Lat.}$$
$$\text{or Lat.} = \text{Declin.} - \text{z.d.}$$

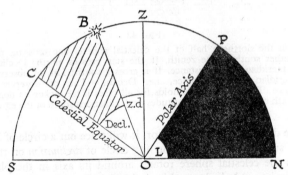

Star B transits south of the Zenith

For a star (B) which transits south of the zenith:

$$COP - ZOP = ZON - ZOP$$
$$\text{i.e. Declin.} + \text{z.d.} = \text{Lat.}$$
$$\text{or} \qquad \text{Declin.} = \text{Lat.} - \text{z.d.}$$

The first two formulae hold for both cases if zenith distances south of the zenith are reckoned as negative.

This gives us its angular distance from the Pole Star, i.e. its north polar distance within 1°. To the same order of precision the declination is 90° — N.P.D. (Fig. 24). The error is due to the fact that the Pole Star is not exactly located at the point round which the stars appear to revolve. Polaris itself describes a tiny circle of 1° round the true celestial pole. The mean of two determinations of the altitude of the Pole Star taken with an interval of six months at the same hour of the night gives a correct value. In principle this is what we should have to do, if we wanted to locate the pole of the southern hemisphere, because there is no bright star near it. There was no bright star very near the north celestial pole in the time of Hipparchus. The altitude of the celestial pole (P), whether south or north (Fig. 44), is simply the average of the altitude (A) of any circumpolar star at its upper culmination and the altitude (*a*) of the same star at its lower culmination, i.e.

$$P = \tfrac{1}{2}(A + a)$$

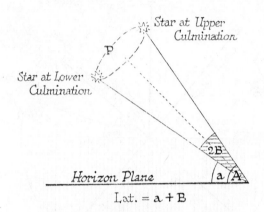

Lat. = a + B

FIG. 44

The celestial pole is half-way between the positions of a circumpolar star at its upper and lower culmination. Hence the angle (B) between the celestial pole and a circumpolar star is half the angle between its positions at lower and upper transit. So if the altitude of the star at lower transit is *a*, and at upper transit A, A = *a* + 2B. The observer's latitude is the altitude of the celestial pole.

$$\text{Lat.} = a + B = a + \tfrac{1}{2}(2B)$$
$$= a + \tfrac{1}{2}(A - a) = \tfrac{1}{2}(A + a)$$

Having got P, the south polar distance of any star whose meridian altitude is M, is M — P, and its south declination is

$$90° - \text{S.P.D.}$$

It will help you to visualize the meaning of declination if you see how the declination of a heavenly body affects its direction of rising, setting, transit, etc., by considering the appearance of the heavens at some particular latitude, e.g. Lat. 50° N. in Figs. 45 and 46. You see for instance that the plane of the midsummer sun's (declin. = + 23½°) apparent diurnal path cuts the horizon plane north of the midpoint between the north and south extremities of the horizon, so that the sun rises and sets north of the east and west points between March 21st and September 23rd and transits on June 21st 26½° south of the zenith. Between September 23rd and March 21st the declination is negative, being — 23½° on December 21st, and the sun rises and sets towards the south. It transits only 16½° above the horizon at Lat. 50° N. on December 21st.

Without making any measurements at all, you can get a good estimate of your latitude (L) if you know the stars by name and have an almanac at hand. The following simple deductions illustrated in Fig. 46 apply to latitudes north of

45° N. A corresponding figure will show you how to modify rules (*a*), (*b*) and (*c*) for latitudes farther south.

(*a*) If the declination of a star is greater than + L°, the star is circumpolar and transits north of the zenith.

(*b*) If the declination of a star is exactly + L°, it is circumpolar and transits at the zenith.

(*c*) If its declination lies between + L° and (90 − L)°, it is circumpolar and transits south. If its declination is exactly (90 − L)°, it just grazes the northern horizon at lower transit.

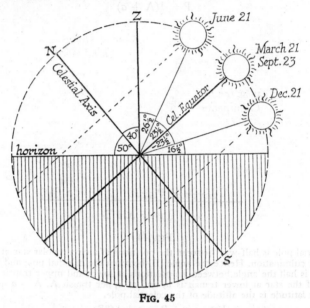

FIG. 45

The sun at latitude 50° N. transits on June 21st 26½° S. from the zenith and 63½° above the southern horizon. On December 21st it transits only 16½° above the southern horizon.

(*d*) If its declination lies between (90 − L)° and 0°, it rises and sets north of the east and west points of the horizon, and transits south.

(*e*) If its declination is exactly 0°, it rises and sets due east and west and transits south.

(*f*) If its declination lies between 0° and − (90 − L)°, it rises, sets, and transits towards the south.

(*g*) If its declination is exactly − (90 − L)°, it just grazes the southern horizon at upper transit.

It follows from these considerations that a table of declinations fixes your north latitude, if you can distinguish any star which transits at the zenith, any star which just grazes the northern horizon at lower transit, or any star which just grazes the southern horizon. In a similar way, you can find your south latitude if you live in the southern hemisphere. The previous figure (Fig. 45) shows you that the lengths of day and night are equal on the equinoxes, and that the lengths of night and day are reciprocally equivalent on alternate solstices. To get a picture of the rising and setting of a star at different times of the year, you need to know its R.A. and that of the sun. From the diagram you will see that if a star has south declination, it will never, at the latitude specified, be above the horizon for half its diurnal course, i.e. twelve hours. This means that if it is a winter star, it will traverse its complete course over the horizon in less time than the duration of darkness which is then greater than twelve hours.

To lay off the other coordinate of a star corresponding to longitude, we have to choose a base line in the heavens like the Greenwich meridian, which is usually taken as 0° for terrestrial position. The one chosen is the semi-

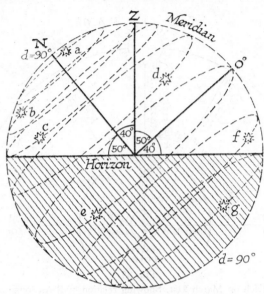

FIG. 46

At Latitude 50° N.

Star (a) declination greater than 50°, is circumpolar, and transits north of the zenith.
Star (b) declination exactly 50°, transits at the zenith and is also circumpolar.
Star (c) declination 40° (N.P.D. = 50°), transits south of the zenith at its upper culmination and just grazes the horizon at its lower.
Star (d) declination less than 40°, greater than 0°, transits south, rises in the north-east and sets in the north-west.
Star (e) declination exactly 0°, rises due east and sets due west, transits south.
Star (f) declination less than 0°, greater than − 40°, rises in the south-east, sets in the south-west and transits south.
Star (g) declination exactly − 40°, just grazes the horizon at transit.

circle of right ascension on which the sun lies at the exact moment when it crosses the equator on the vernal equinox (Figs. 47 and 48). Where the equinoctial intersects with the ecliptic in the spring position of the sun is called the First Point of Aries. This is the celestial Greenwich. The Right Ascension of a star is the hour angle which separates it from the Right Ascension circle which passes through the First Point of Aries. It is measured eastwards. So it is obtained by subtracting the time* at which the First Point of Aries crosses the meridian from the time at which the star under observation crosses the meridian. It is therefore usually given in hours rather than

* Strictly *sidereal* (see p. 60). The error in counting it as solar for short periods is neglected.

degrees (15° = 1 hour, or 1° = 4 minutes). This practice may at first confuse you, because degrees, like hours, are divided into minutes and seconds. So it is always important when speaking of seconds or minutes to make sure whether units of time or angular measure are being used. The signs ' and " are used for *angular* minutes and seconds.

For rough purposes the method of finding the R.A. of a star is therefore as follows. Determine the time at which any star crosses the meridian after

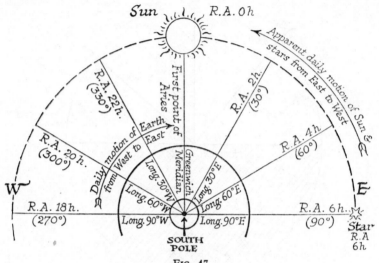

Fig. 47

Noon at Greenwich on March 21st. Showing relation of R.A., longitude, and time. At noon the R.A. meridian of the sun in the celestial sphere is in the same plane as the longitude meridian of the observer. If you are 30° W. of Greenwich the earth must rotate through 30° or $\frac{1}{12}$ of a revolution, taking 2 hours, before your meridian is in the plane of the sun's, or the sun must appear to travel through 30° before its meridian is in the same plane as yours. Hence your noon will be 2 hours behind Greenwich. A clock set by Greenwich time will record 2 p.m. when the sun crosses your meridian, i.e. at noon local time. If the date is March 21st when the sun's R.A. is zero a star of right ascension 6 hours will cross the meridian at 6 p.m. local time. If it crossed at 8 p.m. Greenwich time your clock would be 2 hours slow by Greenwich, so your longitude would be 30° W. The figure shows the anti-clockwise rotation of the stars looking *northwards*, so the south pole is nearest to you.

sunset on the vernal equinox. The sun is approximately at the First Point of Aries at noon on that day. So the number of hours which elapse between noon and the time when the star crosses the meridian after sunset is approximately its right ascension. If a star is not visible on the night following noon on the vernal equinox, we have only to compare its time of transit at a convenient season with that of one which is visible throughout the year, e.g. *a* in Ursa Major. If it transits before the standard star, we subtract the difference from the R.A. of the latter. If it transits later, we add the difference. If it rains or the sky is overcast on the night following the vernal equinox, we can use the sun as our standard star, taking its right ascension as 6 hours on June 21st, 12 hours on September 23rd, or 18 hours on December 21st, and so forth. Since the sun retreats eastwards through 360° in 365 days, its

R.A. increases from 0° at the vernal equinox to 360° at the next by roughly 1° per day.

Hence, if the R.A. of Betelgeuse is stated to be approximately 5 hours 50 minutes, this means that Betelgeuse transits 5 hours 50 minutes after the First Point of Aries (♈), or approximately at 5.50 p.m. on the day following the vernal equinox (Fig. 48). It will therefore be invisible at the time of transit since the sun has not quite set. A month earlier (30 days) the sun would not yet have reached ♈ in its annual retreat eastward in the ecliptic, and its R.A. would be 360° − 30° = 330° approximately, or in time units 22 hours. Thus the sun would transit 2 hours before ♈, and the star would

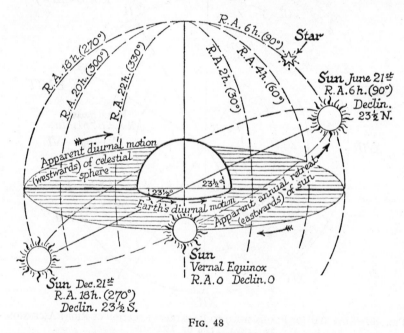

FIG. 48

The star shown (R.A. 6 hours) makes its transit above the meridian at noon on June 21st and midnight on December 21st, i.e. it is a winter star like Betelgeuse.

therefore cross the meridian 7 hours 50 minutes after the sun, i.e. at 7.50 p.m. A star will transit at midnight when its R.A. differs from that of the sun by 180°, or 12 hours. Hence Betelgeuse would transit at midnight when the sun's R.A. is 17 hours 50 minutes, i.e. when the sun's R.A. is about 10 minutes behind its R.A. on December 21st. Since 10 minutes in time represents $(10 \div 60) \times 15 = 2\frac{1}{2}°$, this is approximately $2\frac{1}{2}$ days before December 21st, i.e. about December 19th.

Alternatively you can look on the R.A. of a star as a way of determining local time at night. Thus, if the R.A. of Betelgeuse is given as 5 hours 50 minutes, and the date is November 1st, we can set a watch which has stopped by finding the moment at which it crosses the meridian. On November 1st, 39 days after the autumnal equinox (when the sun's R.A. is 12 hours or 180°) the sun's R.A. is approximately 219°, or $\left(12+\dfrac{39}{15}\right)$ hours = 14 hours 36 minutes. The sun therefore transits 24 hours − 14 hours 36 minutes = 9 hours 24 minutes before ♈, or 15 hours 14 minutes before the star. When Betelgeuse transits the local time is therefore 15.14 p.m., or 3.14 a.m. You will see from this that a single glance at a table of R.A. tells you whether a star

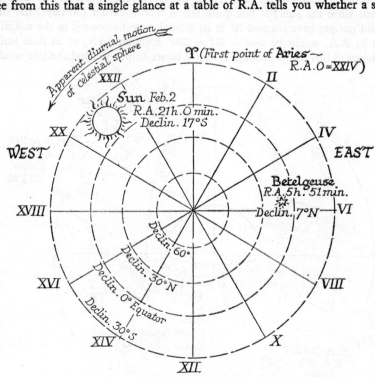

FIG. 49.—STAR MAP (OR PLANISPHERE) TO ILLUSTRATE RELATION OF RIGHT ASCENSION TO LOCAL TIME OF TRANSIT

If the sun's R.A. is x it transits x hours after the zero R.A. circle (through the First Point of Aries). If the star's R.A. is y, it transits y hours after ♈. The star therefore transits $y − x$ hours after the sun, i.e. its local time of transit is $(y − x)$. Hence

Star's R.A. − Sun's R.A. = Local time of transit

It may happen that the difference is negative, as in the example in the figure, the local time of transit being − 15 hours 9 minutes, i.e. 15 hours 9 minutes *before* noon which is the same as 8 hours 51 minutes after noon (8.51 p.m.). The figure shows that the sun transits 3 hours before ♈, and the star 5 hours 51 minutes after, making the time of transit as stated. The orientation is the same as in Fig. 47.

is in the ascendant in summer, winter, spring, or autumn. That the R.A. of Betelgeuse is 5 hours 50 minutes means that Betelgeuse occupies the same position in the celestial sphere as the sun does approximately 10 ÷ 4, or 2½ days before June 21st (when its R.A. is 6 hours), i.e. about June 19th. Hence it will transit 6 months later at midnight (about December 19th), and is a winter star.

In taking the position of ♈ as the sun's position at noon on the vernal equinox there is a small inaccuracy.* The way in which we actually determine the vernal equinox does not mean that the sun is exactly over the equator at local noon on that day. Hence the sun is not exactly at the First Point of Aries when it crosses the meridian. The vernal equinox is chosen as the day on which the sun at noon is nearer to the plane of the equator than it is on the day before or the day after. It is exactly at the First Point of Aries at some time on the vernal equinox, that is to say, within 12 hours before noon or after noon. Since it slips back eastwards at the rate of 1° per day of 24 hours, the method given does not involve an error of more than $\frac{1}{2}$° or 2 minutes of time in right ascension. The sun's right ascension at noon on the vernal equinox, therefore, lies between 23 hours 58 minutes and 0 hour 2 minutes. With home-made instruments we can be very well satis-

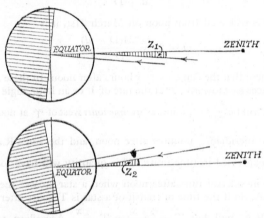

FIG. 50

The sun crossing the equator. Above just before March 21st, sun south of the equator. declination (noon z.d. of sun as seen by an observer at the equator) negative. Below just after March 21st declination positive.

fied with an error as small as this. It only involves an error of $\frac{1}{2}$° in longitude. At the equator that means a distance of roughly $(2\pi \times 4,000) \div (2 \times 360)$, or about 35 miles in a measurement round the earth.

For more accurate determination of the R.A. of a star we require to know when the sun "crosses the equator," i.e. when it is exactly at the point when the ecliptic intersects with the equinoctial. Over the equator the sun is highest at noon on the equinox, being *south* of the zenith (z.d. negative) on the day preceding the vernal equinox and *north* (z.d. positive) on the day following it (Fig. 50). Since the declination of a heavenly body is its z.d. in *meridian transit* at the equator, the declination changes from negative to positive through zero. The time at which the sun crosses the equator can be found approximately thus. Suppose the declination of the sun by z.d. at noon is known for the day before and after the equinox, so that:

Declination at noon March 20th $= -D$
Declination at noon March 22nd $= +d$

* See also footnote on p. 91.

In 48 hours the increase in declination is therefore:

$$d - (- D) = d + D$$

In t hours it is:

$$\frac{d + D}{48} \times t$$

If t hours after noon on March 20th is the time when the sun crosses the equator, the declination increases from $- D$ to 0 in t hours, i.e. the increase is D.

$$D = \frac{d + D}{48} \times t$$

$$t = \frac{48D}{d + D}$$

If the time is reckoned from noon on March 21st, it is

$$t - 24 = \frac{24(D - d)}{D + d}$$

Suppose, then, that the sun crosses x hours after noon. In these x ($= t - 24$) hours it advances east towards ♈ at the rate of $1°$ or an hour angle of 4 minutes per day, i.e. it will be $\frac{4x}{24} = \frac{x}{6}$ minutes in *time units* west of ♈ at noon. Therefore ♈ crosses the meridian $\frac{x}{6}$ minutes after noon, and the sun's R.A. at noon is $- \frac{x}{6}$ minutes expressed in time units. This quantity will have to be added to the difference in sidereal time after noon when a star crosses the meridian to get its true R.A. So if the time of transit of a star is T hours after noon on the equinox, its R.A. will be: $T + (- \frac{x}{6}) = T - \frac{x}{6}$. According to *Whitaker's Almanack*, 1934, the declinations of the sun at noon were:

March 20th — $19 \cdot 2$ minutes (angular units)
March 22nd $+ 28 \cdot 2$ minutes (angular units)

Hence the time after noon March 21st when the sun crossed was:

$$\frac{24(D - d)}{D + d} = \frac{-9 \times 24}{47 \cdot 4} = -4 \cdot 5 \text{ approx.}$$

i.e. the sun crossed the equator $4\frac{1}{2}$ hours before noon or at 7.30 a.m. on March 21st. Hence the time at which ♈ crosses the meridian is

$$\frac{4 \cdot 5}{6} \text{ minutes} = 45 \text{ seconds (approx.)}$$

before noon and the R.A. of the sun at noon is 45 seconds. This must be added to the time which elapses between noon and the next transit of a star to get its correct R.A. in time units.

It is important to bear in mind that mapping stars in this way is merely a way of telling us in what direction we have to look or to point a telescope in order to see them. The position of a star as shown on the star map has nothing to do with how far it is away from us. If you dug straight down following the plumbline, you would eventually reach the centre of the earth; and the bottom of a straight well, as viewed from the centre of the earth, if that were possible, would therefore be exactly in line with the top. It has the same latitude and longitude as the latter, though it is not so far away from the earth's centre. The latitude or longitude of the bottom of a mine is the latitude and longitude of the spot where the line joining it with the centre of the earth, if continued upwards, cuts the earth's surface. So the declination and right ascension of a star measure the place where the line joining the earth's centre and the star cuts an imaginary globe whose radius extends to the farthermost stars. In a total eclipse the sun and the moon have the same declination and R.A. just as the top and bottom of a mine have the same latitude and longitude. This means that the sun and moon are directly in line with the centre of the earth like the top and the bottom of a mine. If we are only concerned with the direction along which we have to look or tilt our telescope to see a star, we may therefore treat stars as if they were all placed on the surface of one and the same celestial sphere.

INTERPRETATION OF THE STAR MAP

Having determined the relative positions of a sufficient number of bright stars—Hipparchus tabulated 1,080 fixed stars in 150 B.C.—we can construct a star map like that of the northern celestial hemisphere in Fig. 51. Such a map or planisphere embodies in a compact form all the requisite data, set forth with more precision in nautical almanacs, for finding the position of a ship at sea.*

To find latitude from the declination of any star which is near the meridian at the time when we require to know where we are, we make use of the simple rule explained in Fig. 43, i.e.

Declination = Latitude + Z.D. or Latitude = Declination − Z.D.

To make this apply to all circumstances, it is necessary to reckon z.d. with opposite signs north and south of the zenith, and latitude or declination with opposite signs north and south of the equator. By agreement, north measurements are reckoned positive, south measurements negative. Thus, as you will see from Fig. 43, with northern latitudes we may distinguish three cases:

(a) Star north of the equator and zenith: Declination and z.d. both positive: $L = D - Z$

(b) Star north of equator, south of the zenith: declination positive, z.d. negative: $L = D + (- Z)$, $\therefore L = D - Z$

(c) Star south of the equator and zenith: declination and z.d. both negative: $L = (- Z) - (- D)$, $\therefore L = D - Z$

For latitudes south of the equator the three corresponding cases are:

(a) Star north of the equator: declination and z.d. both positive:
$$(- L) = Z - D, \qquad \therefore L = D - Z$$

* The first hint of such a model seems to have been given by the Athenian Eudoxus.

D

(*b*) Star south of the equator, north of the zenith: declination negative and z.d. positive: $(-L) = (-D) + Z$, $\therefore L = D - Z$

(*c*) Star south of equator and zenith: declination and z.d. both negative: $(-L) = (-D) - (-Z)$, $\therefore L = D - Z$

If we know the declination circle of any star on the star map, we have only to determine its zenith distance at meridian transit to obtain our lati-

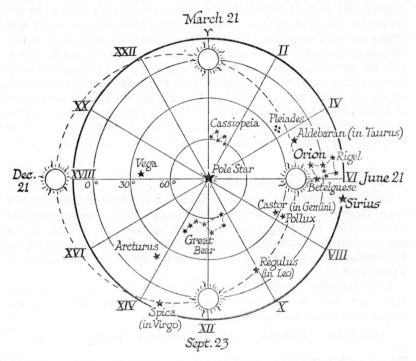

FIG. 51

Star map or planisphere showing the position of a few of the principal stars and constellations in the northern celestial hemisphere in circles of declination and radii of right ascension. The sun's track in the ecliptic and its position at the solstices and equinoxes are also shown.

tude. For example, on a certain night the altitude of the star *a* in Cassiopeia from the northern horizon was found to be 83° 10' at its upper culmination. The declination of *a* Cassiopeiae is given in the *Nautical Almanac* as 56° 11'. From the observed meridian altitude the zenith distance of the star at the ship's latitude is found to be 90° − 83° 10' = + 6° 50'. Since

Latitude = Declination − Z.D.

the latitude of the ship was

56° 11' − 6° 50' = 49° 21' N.

Now that we have clocks, the determination of longitude may be illustrated by the following example in which the data given are not very accurate. On January 21st the star Betelgeuse is seen crossing the meridian when the ship's chronometer (Greenwich Mean Time) registers 11.30 p.m. The R.A. of Betelgeuse is 5 hours 52 minutes (to the nearest minute). Hence Betelgeuse crosses the meridian 5 hours 52 minutes after ♈. If we are without an almanac we can make a rough estimate of our longitude as follows. On January 21st the sun has moved through $\frac{1}{12}$th of its apparent annual retreat since December 21st, when its R.A. is 18 hours. So the R.A. of the sun on January 21st is approximately 20 hours; and ♈ crosses the meridian 4 hours after the sun, i.e. at 4 p.m. Hence Betelgeuse crosses the meridian at 5 hours 52 minutes + 4 hours = 9 hours 52 minutes after local noon. So by local time its time of transit is 9.52 p.m. Neglecting the "equation of time," local time is therefore 1 hour 38 minutes or $1\frac{2}{3}$ hours behind Greenwich, and the ship is approximately $1\frac{2}{3} \times 15° = 25°$ W. of Greenwich.

The almanac for 1937 tells us that the sun's noon R.A. at Greenwich on January 21st is 20 hours 13 minutes. So its R.A. at 11.30 p.m. is about 20 hours 15 minutes; and the local time at which Betelgeuse transits is 3 hours 45 minutes + 5 hours 52 minutes, i.e. 9 hours 37 minutes. The almanac also states that we must *add* 11 minutes 24 seconds ("equation of time") to "apparent" (i.e. sundial) time to get mean time. We must therefore take away 11 minutes 24 seconds from the chronometer time to get true solar local time at Greenwich. Hence the Greenwich solar time of transit is 11 hours 19 minutes. Thus the ship's time is 11 hours 19 minutes −9 hours 37 minutes = 1 hour 42 minutes slow. Counting 4 minutes as equivalent to one degree a more accurate estimate of the longitude is therefore $\frac{102}{4} = 25\frac{1}{2}°$ W.

From these examples you will see that with modern methods of recording time, a ship's position can be determined at noon, sunset, midnight, and sunrise, or at any hour between sunset and sunrise, if the weather is fine. When the sky is overcast so that the familiar constellations are difficult to recognize, the star map also helps us to locate a particular star in a favourable position for observation, provided we already know our approximate bearings by a recent determination. In navigation the exact moment of transit of a star is not easy to record. It is usual to note the times when the star has the *same* altitude before and after transit, i.e. east and west of the meridian. The time of transit is midway between.

Looking at the map in Fig. 51 you will see that the summer star Arcturus of Browning's poem lies near the right ascension line XIV, i.e. it comes on the meridian about 2 a.m. on March 21st, about midnight April 21st, about 8 p.m. (or about sunset) on June 21st. On October 28th it is on the meridian about noon. So it will not be visible high in the heavens at any time on the latter date. To get a picture of its hours of rising and setting, we can make a rough construction by taking into account its declination circle (approximately 20°). The diagram (Fig. 52) shows that the sun rises and sets about 7 a.m. and 5 p.m. respectively Arcturus rises and sets at 4 a.m. and 8 p.m. respectively. So Arcturus will be visible in the eastern sky for three hours before sunrise and in the western sky after sunset.

The use of the star map to determine the azimuths of rising and setting, as also the times of rising and setting at different seasons, will be set forth more fully in Chapter IV, p. 196. The method of finding the moon's R.A. and declination on days of the month, when it does not transit after dark, will also be explained in the same context. What has been said about Arcturus suffices to illustrate the most characteristic features of the lunar cycle. The moon's R.A. increases by 360 degrees in a period a little less (Fig. 53) than an ordinary month reckoned from new moon to new moon. It has to move through a little more than 360° to catch up with the sun, because the sun's R.A. is slowly increasing at about one-twelfth the rate at which the moon recedes eastwards among the stars. If the moon's retreat eastwards occurred in the plane of the celestial equator, it would rise due east at noon, transit at 6 p.m. and set

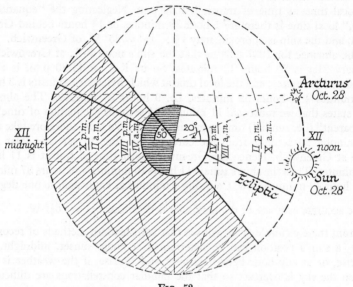

FIG. 52

Construction to show how the times of rising and setting of a star (Arcturus) can be deduced from its declination (20° N.) at a particular latitude (50° N.) on a particular day of the year (October 28th).

due west at midnight on the first quarter day; rise due east at 6 p.m., transit at midnight and set due west at 6 a.m. when full; rise due east at midnight, transit at 6 a.m. and set due west at noon on the last quarter day. The time and direction of rising and setting in the various phases of the moon vary from month to month because the moon retreats in an oblique path, like that of the sun, among the zodiacal constellations. As will be explained below (see also Fig. 53), the trace of the moon's cycle on the star map lies very close to the ecliptic. So the moon's cycle exhibits certain analogies with that of the sun.

In a northern latitude a star with north declination like Arcturus traces a wider arc above the horizon than a star with south declination like Sirius, the interval between rising and setting being more than 12 hours for a northerly and less than 12 hours for a southerly star. Since the sun remains longer above the horizon when it lies in the same direction as the northerly constellations of the Zodiac during the summer months, summer days are longer than those of the winter. When the sun is in Aries or Libra (using the terms in their historic sense, see p. 64), its declination is changing very rapidly. When in Cancer or Capricorn it is apparently retreating in a direction approximately parallel to the equator, and hence its declination is changing less rapidly. For this reason the length of day and night changes very little about the time of the solstices and more noticeably during spring and autumn, when the days are said to be "drawing out" or "drawing in."

Since the moon takes longer to get back to the same position relative to the sun (difference between sun's R.A. and moon's R.A. 360°) than to regain its former position among the fixed stars (moon's R.A. increased by 360°) the moon's station in the zodiacal belt at any particular phase (position relative to the sun) is not the same in two successive months, and since its northerly declination is increasing most rapidly when it is in Aries, the "moon day" is drawing out, i.e. the duration of its passage above the horizon is increasing most rapidly at this stage in its eastward retreat. This means that the time of rising on the succeeding night is not so much later as it would be if the moon retreated in a plane parallel to that of the equator. Conversely the interval between sunset and moonrise on successive nights increases rather quickly when the moon is in Libra, since the moon's declination is then decreasing most rapidly. Since full moon occurs when the moon's R.A. differs from that of the sun by 180°, the full moon is in Aries when the sun is in Libra, i.e. at the autumn equinox. About the full moon ("harvest moon") near the autumn equinox the time of moonrise changes very little on successive nights. So the interval between sunset and moonrise just after full moon changes very little, and there is a relatively long period during which the moon is high in the heavens for the greater part of the night.

Careful observation of the lunar cycle was a task of great social importance while calendrical practice adhered to the chimerical attempt to square the primitive lunar calendar of a hunting and food-gathering stage in social evolution with the stellar or solar calendar of a settled agrarian economy. The maritime Greeks (see p. 65) started off with a far more primitive calendar than that of the Egyptians; and this fact may have contributed to the fruitful fusion of navigational astronomy with calendrical practice. At a later date lunar tables had also to be composed for calculation of longitude. It will help you to understand how they are made, and, later on, to calculate the position of the planets, if you plot the moon's apparent track from one of the ephemerides sold for astrological amusement, or from *Whitaker's Almanack*, as in Fig. 53. This gives its position on the star map from January 3rd to 30th in the year 1894. New moon occurs when the moon's R.A. is the same as the sun's, full moon when it differs from that of the sun by 180°. We find from *Whitaker* that the moon and the sun have the same R.A. at some time between noon and midnight on January 7th of the month plotted in the figure. The following figures are for midnight, the values given in time units being turned into degrees, and obtained by taking the average for successive noons.

	Sun's R.A. (S) (midnight)	Moon's R.A. (M) (midnight)	Difference (S − M)
January 6th	$288\frac{1}{4}$	$287\frac{1}{4}$	+ 1
January 7th	$289\frac{1}{4}$	$300\frac{1}{4}$	−11

The sun's R.A. exceeded that of the moon by roughly 1° at midnight on the 6th. By midnight on the 7th the moon's R.A. exceeded the sun's by roughly 11°. Hence new moon occurred in the early hours of the morning

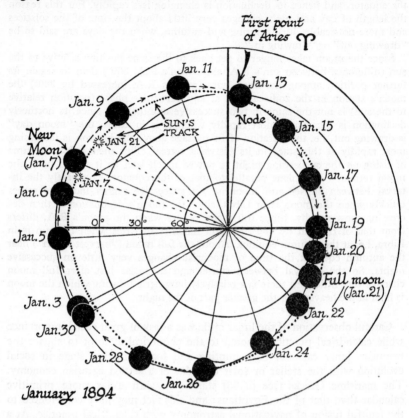

FIG. 53

The moon's course as represented in the star map in the course of a sidereal month (see text). The nodes occur at positions occupied by the moon late on January 13th and January 26th.

on January 7th. Full moon occurred soon after noon on January 21st. Thus using midnight values as before, *Whitaker* gives:

	Sun's R.A.	Moon's R.A.	Difference
January 20th	303¼	114½	+188¾
January 21st	304¼	130¾	+173½

The next new moon occurred in the evening of February 5th. Thus:

	Sun's R.A.	Moon's R.A.	Difference
February 4th	319¼	309½	+9¾
February 5th	320¼	321¾	−1½

This shows that the period which separates one new moon from the next is between 29 and 30 days. The average of many determinations shows that it is almost exactly 29½ days.

The interval between two new moons when the sun, moon, and earth are in the same line, is called the ordinary or *synodic* month. The synodic month is not the same as the time taken by the moon to revolve in its orbit. This time—the *sidereal* month—is the time in which the moon gets back to the same position with reference to the fixed stars, i.e. the time taken for its R.A. to increase by 360°, so that it has the same value. The synodic month is longer than the sidereal because the sun's R.A. increases in the course of the month. When the moon's R.A. is the same as what it was at the last new moon, the sun's R.A. is greater. Hence, the moon has to move farther to catch it up. The figure shows you that the sidereal month is just over 27 days. Daily record of its R.A. shows that values recur at average intervals of almost exactly 27⅓ days. The exact time at which the moon regains the same R.A. can be easily interpolated from daily records of its transit; and since we know the sun's daily change in R.A., we can easily deduce the exact time of the new moon. The exact time of recurrence of two new moons, i.e. the length of the synodic month, is connected with the length of the sidereal month by a very simple formula. The sun moves through 360° of R.A. in Y days (one *year*). The moon moves through 360° of R.A. in S days (one *sidereal* month) and *gains* 360° on the sun, so that they both have the same R.A. in M days (one *synodic* month). Thus,

in one day the sun's R.A. increases $\dfrac{360°}{Y}$

in one day the moon's R.A. increases $\dfrac{360°}{S}$

in one day the moon's R.A. gains on the sun's by $\dfrac{360°}{S} - \dfrac{360°}{Y}$

But in one day the moon gains in R.A. $\dfrac{360°}{M}$

$$\therefore \quad \frac{360}{M} = \frac{360}{S} - \frac{360}{Y}$$

$$\therefore \quad \frac{1}{M} = \frac{1}{S} - \frac{1}{Y}$$

If S is 27⅓ and Y is 365¼:

$$\frac{1}{M} = \frac{3}{82} - \frac{4}{1461}$$

$$M = 29\tfrac{1}{2} \text{ (approx.)}$$

The same figure also shows us the nodes where sun and moon have the same declination corresponding to the same R.A. Since eclipses can only occur if the moon is near a node, and when the sun's R.A. is the same as that of the moon (solar eclipse) or differs from it by 180° (lunar eclipse), we can calculate the time of eclipses by observations of this kind. Repeated records show that the position of the moon's node rotates along the ecliptic in accordance with the rule empirically discovered by the Sumerian priests (p. 46).

By knowing the exact length of the sidereal month we can calculate the time of an occultation. A star or planet will hide behind the moon's disc at the day and hour when its R.A. agrees with that of the moon and its declination does not differ from that of the moon by more than half the angular difference of the two edges of the latter. The angular diameter of the moon is almost exactly $\frac{1}{2}°$ (i.e. we have to turn a telescope through $\frac{1}{2}°$ to focus the two edges successively at the centre). To make such forecasts far ahead it is also necessary to take into account the rotation of the nodes. If we have tables of the moon's R.A. and declination on a given date at some stated longitude, we can compare the time of local noon with noon at the stated longitude by noting the interval which elapses between local noon and the time when the moon has the R.A. or declination tabulated for a particular hour.

The principle which was refined for use in British navigation by Newton, underlies the so-called "method of lunar distance." It is referred to in a twelfth-century treatise by the monk Gerard of Cremona, who translated several Arabic versions of the Alexandrian astronomical works. Gerard (cited by Wright, *Isis*, vol. v, p. 83) states:

When the moon is on the meridian, if you compare her position with that given in the lunar tables for some other locality, you may determine the difference in longitude between the place where you are and that for which the lunar tables were constructed by noting the differences in the position of the moon as actually observed and recorded in the tables. It will not be necessary for you to wait for an eclipse.

Portuguese ships, which carried Jewish astronomers schooled in the Arabic cartography, already practised this method in the fifteenth century. In an early sixteenth-century treatise on navigation elucidated by Professor E. R. G. Taylor, we find a reference to its use by the seamen of Dieppe. The passage is worth quoting, because it shows the eagerness with which mediaeval shipping everywhere made claim to astronomical science (cited from *Geographical Journal*, 1929):

The cartographical work of Jean Rotz is typical of the French school of the fourth and fifth decades of the sixteenth century (e.g. Desceliers, Vallard); nor is his treatise on Nautical Science unique, save in its survival. . . . The title runs: "Treatise on the variation of the magnetic compass and of certain notable errors of navigation hitherto unknown, very useful and necessary to all pilots and mariners. Composed by Jan Rotz, native of Dieppe, in the year 1542." . . . In a long and flattering preface to the King, the writer says that he comes before him not empty-handed, but bearing a book and an instrument for his acceptance: the book composed for all those who wish to taste the pleasant fruits of Astrology and Marine Science. . . . The third part treats of the construction and use of the instrument, which the inventor calls a Differential Quadrant. Actually it is one of the precursors of the theodolite, and a very elaborate one. The large magnetic compass set in the horizontal circle suggests a marine origin, and it may be compared with the contemporary instruments designed for taking horizontal bearings by such landsmen as the brothers Arsenius, which were orientated by tiny compasses inset on the margin. Like Waldseemuller's Polymetrum, Rotz' instrument could take a combined altitude 'and azimuth, but its prime purpose was for the accurate determination of the variation of the compass. . . . He gives two supposititious examples of longitude determination, as follows: "je dycts que le 15° de Janvier 1529, moy estant dessus la mer voulus scavoir la distance de mon meridien au meridien dulme." At sunrise, then, which occurred at eight o'clock, he took his astronomer's staff "dict par les mariners esbalester" and measured the distance between the sun and moon, finding it 41°. Two folios of complicated calculations follow, and finally, taking Ulm to be in 47° N., 30° 20′ E., the required longitude is found to be 180° E. of Ferro, i.e. somewhere east of the Moluccas. Using in the second example the moon and a fixed star, he says, "Moi estant sur la mer veulant scavoir la distance de mon meridien de Dieppe, premierement je rectifies mes ephemerides ou tables dalphonse au meridien de dieppe at puis je regard le vrai lieu de la lune pour ung certaine heure de la nuyt," namely ten o'clock, when he finds it 16° in Taurus, and determines its declination. He also finds the right ascension of the star Aldebaran "aprez toutes rectifications faictes destiez" 2° 18′ in Gemini, and its declination 15° 55′ N. "Et notte ycy ung poinct cest quil est necessite que tu rectifies ton heure par en moyen des equations des heures mis aux tables dalphonse ou aux ephemerides." Again, a couple of folios are occupied by computations, and the longitude works out as 229° 30′ E., or somewhere in mid-Pacific. . . . This Dieppe seaman had no reason to complain of his personal reward at the King's hands. He was taken into the royal service, and described himself as "servant of the King" in the Boke of Ydrography (written in English), the preparation of which was his first official duty. At Michaelmas in 1542, he received a payment of £20, being one-half of an annuity of £40, then a very considerable sum, while on October 7th of the same year he was granted papers of denization for himself, his wife and children.

CULTURAL FRUITS OF THE ALEXANDRIAN STAR MAPS

The star maps of Hipparchus (c. 150 B.C.) differed in one particular from those which are usually used today. They showed the star's position (see Chapter IV, p. 220) in circles like circles of declination drawn parallel to the ecliptic instead of the equator, and meridians radiating from the pole of the ecliptic plane. When the plane of the ecliptic is used instead of the equator, the angles corresponding to right ascension and declination are called celestial longitude and celestial latitude. The reason for choosing the ecliptic was that the moon and planets all revolve very nearly in the same plane as the sun's apparent track. The reason for preferring the equator is first that right ascension and declination are related in a simple way to longitude and latitude on the earth itself, and second that the determination of right ascension and declination involves no elaborate calculation when the times and altitudes of meridian transits have been recorded.

The first consideration was not obvious when star maps were introduced. Latitude and longitude were originally devised to describe the relative positions of objects on the celestial sphere. It was a short step to the recognition that the earth itself can be divided into similar zones with simple relations to the fixed stars. Marinus of Tyre is credited with the preparation of the first terrestrial map in which meridians of longitude and parallels of latitude were laid down. One immense cultural benefit of this was the extent to which it broadened man's knowledge of the habitable earth. You will appreciate this by comparing (Fig. 35) the world picture of the Greeks with that of Ptolemy (*c.* 200 A.D.), who garnered the fruits of Alexandrian astronomy in a work which usually bears the name of its Arabic translation. Jewish scholars, who sustained the traditions of the Moorish universities of Toledo, Cordova, and Seville, after the Christian conquerors had replaced the public baths by the odour of sanctity, handed on the Almagest to European navigators.

At first sight it might seem strange that in exploration the achievements of the Alexandrians and the Arabs, who kept astronomy alive in the dark ages of Faith, were so small as compared with those of their pupils in the fifteenth and sixteenth centuries. For several reasons there was an inescapable lag between the theoretical equipment which Alexandrian science bequeathed and its full use in navigation. One is that the Alexandrians had no convenient portable instrument for recording time. On land, crude measurements of longitude could be made by lunar methods with the help of hour-glasses or water-clocks. At sea, methods of determining longitude known in antiquity could not be used. The need for seeking out new methods did not become an acute technological problem so long as a large part of the globe could still be explored by sailing close to the coast.

In the great voyages associated with the names of the pharaoh Necho, and with the Carthaginian Hanno in antiquity, knowledge of latitude was adequate for the purpose of locating a place, because all the long distance expeditions of antiquity steered a northerly–southerly course along a coast-line. The same remark applies to the early expeditions of the Portuguese and Dieppe shipping guilds. The need to determine longitude became a real and acute one when the international exchange economy entered on its last phase at the end of the sixteenth century. Oarless ships then ventured out into the uncharted west far beyond the sight of land, equipped with wheel-driven clocks. To be sure, they were clumsy and inaccurate instruments according to our standards, yet an immense convenience when compared with hour-glasses. The ships of Columbus, Vespucci, and Magellan had to put into port to take a bearing in longitude. None the less, what observations they succeeded in recording introduced a new assurance into navigation and created the technological problem which in turn stimulated the development of optics, dynamics, and terrestrial magnetism.

A passage in Hakluyt's voyages is worth quoting to emphasize the importance of the new orientation which transatlantic navigation involved. It occurs in a letter of Thomas Stevens from Goa in 1579:

Being passed the line, they cannot straightway go the next way to the promontory; but according to the winde, they draw alwayes as neere South as they can to put themselves in the latitude of the point, which is 35 degrees and a halfe, and then they take their course towards the East, and so compasse the point. But the Winde served us so that at 33 degrees we did direct our course towards the point or promontory of Good Hope. You know that it is hard to saile from East to West or contrary, because there is no fixed point in all the skie, whereby they may direct their course, wherefore I shall tell you what helps God provided for these men. There is not fowle that appereth, or signe in the aire, or in the sea, which they have not written, which have made the voyages heretofore. Wherefore partly by their owne experience . . . and partly by the experience of others, whose books and navigations they have, they gesse whereabouts they be.

By this date longitudes are mentioned frequently in the records of English expeditions contained in Hakluyt's pages. Fifty years earlier it is clear that English seamen were only familiar with the determination of latitudes. The ensuing passage from a letter written in 1527 by Robert Thorne to Ley,

FIG. 54.—THE ASTRONOMER MAPPING THE HEAVENS
A woodcut from the title page of Messahalah, *De Scientia motus orbis,* printed by Weissenburger in 1504.

ambassador of Henry VIII to the Emperor Charles, points to considerations of high politics conspiring with mere convenience to promote the study of longitude:

Now for that these Islands of Spicery fall neere the terme and limites betweene these princes (for as by the sayd Card you may see they begin from one hundred and sixtie degrees of longitude, and ende in 215) it seemeth all that falleth from 160 to 180 degrees should be of Portingal: and all the rest of Spaine. And for that their Cosmographers and Pilots coulde not agree in the situation of the sayde Islandes (for the Portingals set them all within their 180 degrees and the Spaniards set them all without) and for that in measuring, all the Cosmographers of both partes, or what other that ever have bene cannot give certaine order to measure the longitude of the worlde, as they doe of the latitude; for that there is no starre fixed from East to West, as are the starres of the Poles from North to South, but all moveth with the mooving divine; no maner can bee founde howe certainely it may bee measured, but by conjectures, as the Navigants have esteemed the way they have gone.

The influence which Ptolemy's work exercised in the period which immediately preceded the Great Navigations may be illustrated by a passage from Roger Bacon's *Opus Majus,* cited by Professor E. R. G. Taylor*:

Again in the second book of the Almages he wrote that habitability is only known in respect of a quarter of the earth, namely that which we inhabit. . . . Whence it follows that the eastern extremity of India is a great distance from us and from Spain, since it is so far from the Arabian Gulf to India. . . . And so in the two quarters beyond the equinoctial (i.e. the equator) there will also be much habitable land.

In Pierre d'Ailly's *Imago Mundi* the passages which greatly influenced Columbus are mainly taken from Roger Bacon. In Roman Alexandria such possibilities could be entertained with a light heart. The temper of Bacon's times was different. To quote from Professor Taylor† once more,

many thinkers accepted the view found in the *De Situ Orbis* of Pomponius Mela, namely, that a habitable region, girt about by ocean, was to be found in each of the temperate zones, separated by a torrid zone impassable because of the heat. Supposing this to be the case, and that the Anticthones actually did exist, then these people were for ever cut off from the means of Salvation: it was for this reason that St. Augustine, in an oft-cited passage, condemned such a view as heretical.

Another fact in the everyday life of ancient times made it difficult to exploit the discoveries of Alexandrian astronomers to the fullest extent. Some celestial phenomena, e.g. the precession of the equinoxes or the motion of the moon's nodes, cannot be detected during short periods of observation without very accurate instruments such as we possess today. Although the first of these was discovered by Hipparchus, there were many others which escaped attention till modern times. Hence, astronomical tables, based on the principles we have dealt with so far, were liable to become out of date, i.e. inaccurate, in a comparatively short time. The older almanacs stood in need of constant revision. The introduction of printing into Europe on the threshold of the Great Navigations made it possible to maintain a fresh supply of almanacs for nautical use,‡ besides increasing the proportion of people who were able to use them and distributing the results of the latest calculations far and wide. Meanwhile the first printing presses were also busy with the distribution of commercial arithmetics which were replacing the laborious and devious methods of Greek arithmetic by the simpler modern system derived from the Arabs.

Two other cultural by-products of the Alexandrian star maps are of very

---

* *Scottish Geographical Magazine,* vol. xlvii, 1931, pp. 215–17.
† Ibid., vol. xlvii, 1931, p. 79.
‡ The following figures give the publication of almanacs for the years stated:

1448–58	..	..	.. 2	1468–78	..	.. 44
1458–68	..	..	.. 1	1479–88	..	.. 96
		1489–98	..	..	.. 110	

great significance for the subsequent advance of human knowledge. The method of Hipparchus essentially corresponds to the kind of graphical representation which mathematicians call polar coordinates, and flat maps of longitude and latitude essentially represent the more familiar way of plotting a graph in "Cartesian coordinates." From the Almagest mediaeval Europe learned graphical methods. In the fourteenth century Oresmus was giving lectures at Prague on the use of "latitudines and longitudines" to show the track of a moving point. Cartesian geometry emerged from the same social context as modern cartography. Alexandrian astronomy also precipitated a more decisive departure from the sterile tradition of Platonic geometry. From Euclid, the first teacher of Alexandrian mathematics, the Alexandrians had

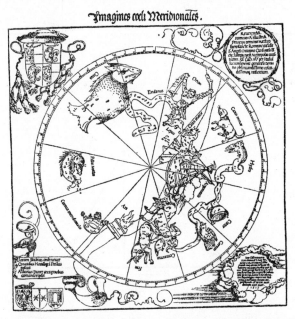

Fig. 55.—Albrecht Dürer's Woodcut of the Southern Celestial Hemisphere —from the Geographical Works of Johann Stabius, 1515, Professor of Mathematics at Vienna and Astronomer to the Emperor

Note Orion containing the bright stars Rigel and Betelgeuse, Canis minor with the bright star Procyon, Canis major with the brightest star Sirius, are visible in the latitude of London. Argo with Canopus, the second brightest star in the heavens, is not.

received Plato's idealistic doctrine that mathematics should be cultivated as an aid to spiritual refinement. The first measurements of celestial distances sufficed to show the clumsiness of the Platonic methods. The stubborn realities of the material world forced them to refinements which resulted in cultivating new methods. Hipparchus compiled the first trigonometrical table—a table of sines. Thenceforth Plato's geometry was an anachronism. With the aid of six or, at most, twelve of its propositions, we can build up the whole of trigonometry and the Cartesian methods. Unfortunately the curriculum of our grammar schools was designed by theologians and politicians who believed in Plato. So we continue to teach Euclidean geometry for the good of the soul. Since few normal people like what is good for them, this makes mathematics

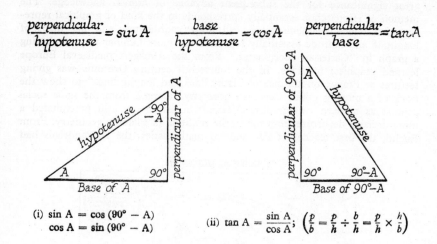

$$\frac{perpendicular}{hypotenuse} = \sin A \qquad \frac{base}{hypotenuse} = \cos A \qquad \frac{perpendicular}{base} = \tan A$$

(i) $\sin A = \cos (90° - A)$
    $\cos A = \sin (90° - A)$

(ii) $\tan A = \dfrac{\sin A}{\cos A}; \quad \left(\dfrac{p}{b} = \dfrac{p}{h} \div \dfrac{b}{h} = \dfrac{p}{h} \times \dfrac{h}{b} \right)$

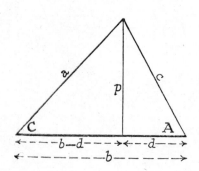

(iii)

$\sin A = \dfrac{p}{c} \qquad \therefore p = c \sin A$

$\sin C = \dfrac{p}{a} \qquad \therefore p = a \sin C$

$\therefore \quad c \sin A = a \sin C$

$\dfrac{\sin A}{a} = \dfrac{\sin C}{c}$

$\therefore \quad \sin A = \dfrac{a \sin C}{c}$

(iv)

$p^2 = c^2 - d^2$
$\quad = a^2 - (b - d)^2$
$\therefore \ c^2 - d^2 = a^2 - b^2 + 2bd - d^2$
$\therefore \quad c^2 = a^2 - b^2 + 2bd$

Since $\cos A = d \div c$, i.e. $d = c \cos A$

$\therefore \quad c^2 = a^2 - b^2 + 2bc \cos A$

or $\quad c^2 + b^2 - a^2 = 2bc \cos A$

$\therefore \quad \cos A = \dfrac{c^2 + b^2 - a^2}{2bc}$

FIG. 56.—THREE FUNDAMENTALS OF TRIGONOMETRY

If a right-angled triangle is completed about an angle A, the ratios of its sides severally (called sine A, cos A, and tan A) are given in tables. With the aid of these the remaining dimensions of *any* triangle can be found by applying the four rules of the figure if we know the length of one side and the size of two of its angles, or the length of two sides and the angle included, or the lengths of all three sides.

a most unpopular subject and effectually prevents the majority from ever finding out the immense usefulness of mathematics in man's social life. One result of not understanding how mathematics can be usefully applied is that many people do not realize when it cannot be usefully applied. Hence the delusion that a subject is entitled to rank as a science when it contains formulae.

THE SIZE OF THE MOON AND ITS DISTANCE FROM US

Trigonometry developed in connexion with the attempt to solve problems which had a very far-reaching influence upon human belief. The Alexandrians made the first estimates of the distance of the moon and the sun from the earth. Their measurement of the sun's distance involved that of the moon.

The principle involved in finding the distance of the moon is essentially

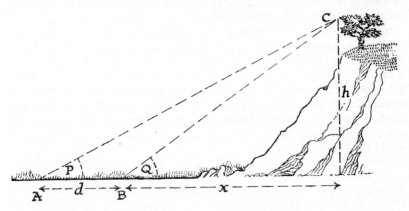

FIG. 57.—FINDING THE HEIGHT OF A CLIFF BY THE METHOD OF PARALLAX

$$\tan P = \frac{h}{x + d} \qquad\qquad \tan Q = \frac{h}{x}$$

$$\therefore x + d = \frac{h}{\tan P} \qquad\qquad \therefore x = \frac{h}{\tan Q}$$

$$d = h\left(\frac{1}{\tan P} - \frac{1}{\tan Q}\right) \qquad \therefore h = \frac{\tan P \tan Q}{\tan Q - \tan P} \cdot d$$

N.B.—The angle C is the *parallax* of the top of the cliff with reference to observers at A and B.

the same as that used for finding the height of a mountain peak. The method used for terrestrial objects, when we have tables of sines or tangents at our disposal, is shown in Fig. 57. The observer records the difference in direction of the object as seen from two situations at a measured distance apart. This difference of direction measured by the angle C is called the parallax of the object. So far we have assumed that the different angular positions of the celestial bodies, when observed at the same time in different places, are entirely due to the curvature of the earth, the direction of a star being fixed. In other words, it does not matter where we determine the R.A. and declination of a visible star. This is what we should expect if the stars are very remote. The nearest stars are too far away to make a difference of a thousandth of a degree. This is not true of the moon. Two simultaneous determinations of the moon's R.A. by observers situated at longitude 90° apart on the equator, or simultaneous determinations of declination by one observer at the equator and another observer at either of the poles, can differ by almost exactly one degree; and this difference is detectable with a comparatively crude instrument. In an age when the study of the moon's behaviour was important for regulating social festivals or night travel, and the study of solar eclipses and occultations had begun to assume a practical as well as a magical significance, differences of the moon's direction at different stations did not escape detection. They involve an appreciable correction in all calculations of the moon's position. The moon's position relative to a more distant celestial object is not quite the same as seen from two widely separated stations simultaneously. Consequently crude methods of determining longitude based on solar eclipses, occultations or lunar distances, can be somewhat inaccurate, unless a correction is made for the moon's parallax.

If we know the earth's radius we can calculate the distance between two observers at known latitudes and longitudes, and the parallax of the moon is all that is required to deduce its distance from the earth. The best method is to make simultaneous observations of the moon's zenith distance, when it crosses the meridian, at two stations on the same meridian of longitude at latitudes as far apart as possible. If the moon's rays were absolutely parallel, the south zenith distance at a given north latitude L when the moon's true declination (i.e. elevation from the plane of the equator) is D, would be (Fig. 58):

$$z = L - D$$

Actually the observed zenith distance Z is a little in excess of this by an angle p (called the *geocentric parallax* at L) representing the difference of direction of the moon as it would be seen simultaneously at L and at the earth's centre if we could get there. Thus,

$$Z = z + p$$

We have already seen (Fig. 28) that if the rays from a celestial body are perfectly parallel at two different latitudes, the difference of its zenith distances at two places is the difference of their latitudes, i.e.

$$L_1 - L_2 = z_2 - z_1$$

If one latitude is south of the equator, its sign is negative $(- L_2)$ and if the moon is seen south of the zenith at the northern latitude and north of the zenith at the southern, its zenith distance at the former is negative $(- z_1)$, and at the latter, positive $(+ z_2)$, so that

$$
\begin{aligned}
L_1 + L_2 &= z_1 + z_2 \\
&= (Z_1 - p_1) + (Z_2 - p_2) \\
&= (Z_1 + Z_2) - (p_1 + p_2)
\end{aligned}
$$

The quantity $(p_1 + p_2)$ is the moon's parallax P with reference to the two stations, so:

$$P = (Z_1 + Z_2) - (L_1 + L_2)$$

Turning to Fig. 59, you will see that if both stations are on the same longitude and both observations are made at the same time, the moon's distance (d) from the earth centre is the diagonal of a four-sided figure of which all four angles and two sides (equivalent to the earth's radius or approximately 4,000 miles) are known. Hence the quadrilateral can be constructed. Its remaining sides and the diagonal can be calculated by the fundamental relation (Fig. 56) between the sides and angles of any triangle, i.e.

$$\frac{\sin A}{a} = \frac{\sin B}{b} = \frac{\sin C}{c}$$

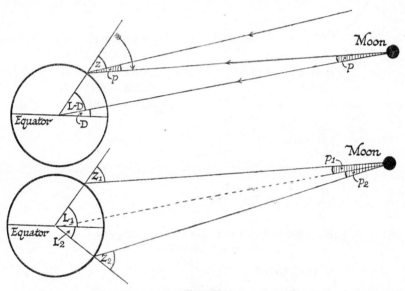

FIG. 58

The moon's *geocentric parallax*. If the moon's rays were truly parallel its direction at latitude $+ L$ would be the same as at the earth's centre, i.e. its zenith distance would be $z = L - D$. Actually (upper figure) the observed z.d. at transit for an observer at latitude L is greater by the angle p (geocentric parallax at L). This cannot be directly measured, but the sum $p_1 + p_2$ of the geocentric parallaxes of the moon for observers at two different latitudes ($+ L_1$ and $- L_2$) on the same longitude is

$$(Z_1 + Z_2) - (L_1 + L_2)$$

In this way the mean distance of the earth's centre from the moon is found to be approximately 240,000 miles, as shown in the legend attached to Fig. 59. Hipparchus gave the distance of the moon as between 67 and 78 radii (i.e. mean distance 72 radii or 280,000 miles). This is a tolerable approximation. His estimate of the sun's distance based on the study of eclipses was 13,000 earth radii or 51,000,000 miles, which is much too small, the correct distance being 92,000,000 miles.

The calculation of the moon's radius is easily deduced from this. The only new information required is the moon's angular diameter, i.e. the angular difference between the two edges of the moon. This is almost exactly half a degree. As shown in Fig. 60, the moon's diameter is therefore a little over 2,000 miles. It is almost exactly 2,160 miles, or three-elevenths that of the earth.

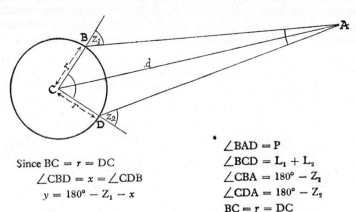

Since $BC = r = DC$

$\angle CBD = x = \angle CDB$

$y = 180° - Z_1 - x$

$\angle BAD = P$

$\angle BCD = L_1 + L_2$

$\angle CBA = 180° - Z_1$

$\angle CDA = 180° - Z_2$

$BC = r = DC$

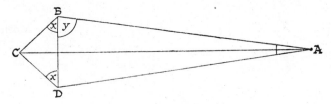

(i) In the $\triangle BCD$, $\angle x$, $\angle BCD$ and CB are known, and

$$\frac{\sin x}{r} = \frac{\sin BCD}{BD}$$

∴ BD is known

(ii) In the $\triangle ABD$, $\angle y$, $\angle BAD$ and BD are known, and

$$\frac{\sin BAD}{BD} = \frac{\sin y}{AD}$$

∴ AB is known

(iii) In the $\triangle ABC$, $\angle ABC$, BC $(= r)$ and AB are all known,

∴ $AC^2 = AB^2 + BC^2 - 2AB . BC \cos ABC$ (See Fig. 56)

∴ AC $(= d)$ is also known.

FIG. 59

The determination of the moon's distance, from the parallax of the moon with reference to two observers at different latitudes and the same longitude, as in Fig. 58, can be deduced from a simple geometrical construction.

One of the earliest Alexandrian astronomers, Aristarchus, made a rough estimate of the ratio of the sun's distance to that of the moon (Fig. 61). The method he used depends on the fact that the half moon at first quarter occurs a little earlier than the time when the moon's direction differs from that of the sun by 90°, and the half moon or third quarter occurs a little later than the time when the moon's direction differs from that of the sun by 270°. Aristarchus calculated that the ratio of the distances of sun and moon from the earth is about 20 : 1. In reality it is nearly 400 : 1. The reason for the inaccuracy is the extreme difficulty of ascertaining when exactly half of the moon's face is visible without the aid of the telescopic observations on the moon's mountains. However, the estimate of Aristarchus was a vast step beyond the boldness of Anaxagoras, who startled the court of Pericles by the suggestion that the sun might be as large as the whole mainland of Greece. In using mathematics to measure the heavens, Alexandrian astronomy

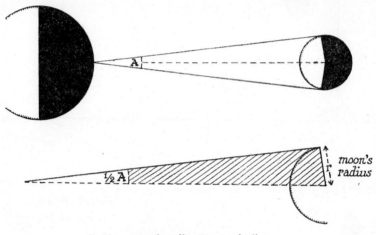

$$\sin \tfrac{1}{2}A = \text{moon's radius} \div \text{moon's distance}$$
$$\therefore \quad r = \sin \tfrac{1}{2}A \times 240{,}000$$

By observation the moon's angular diameter,
$$A = 31' 5''$$
$$\therefore \quad \tfrac{1}{2}A = 0° \ 16' \text{ approximately}$$
$$\therefore \quad \text{Moon's radius} = 240{,}000 \times \sin 0° \ 16'$$
$$= 240{,}000 \times 0\cdot0047$$
$$= 1{,}130 \text{ miles}$$
$$\text{Diameter} = 2{,}260 \text{ miles.}$$

FIG. 60.—THE MOON'S DIAMETER

disclosed a vision of grandeur concealed from the world view of Plato's idealism. Alexandrian sky measurement was the death knell of Plato's cosmology and of the ancient star god religions.

The sun's parallax is too small to be measured without the aid of good telescopes at observation stations separated by long distances. An alternative method which does not require the use of a telescope depends on observations of eclipse phenomena. If the time of greatest duration of a total lunar eclipse is known from repeated observations, the distance, radius and synodic period of the moon, and the earth's radius, give us all (Fig. 18) the necessary data for measuring the breadth of the earth's shadow cone where it is intercepted by the moon's orbit. In a solar eclipse the moon's edge just coincides with that of the sun, which therefore has approximately the same angular diameter. So the sun's radius and the earth distance are in the same ratio as the moon's radius and earth distance. The ratio of the earth's radius to the length of its own shadow cone is the same as the ratio of the sun's radius to the combined length of the earth's shadow cone and the sun's earth distance. Since the length of the shadow cone is easily calculated by similar angles if its breadth at any known distance from the earth is given, all the requisite data are supplied by eclipse measurements and the moon's parallax. Actually

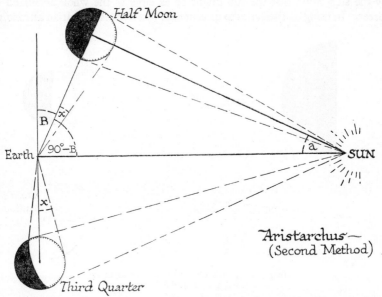

FIG. 61.—How Aristarchus Tried to Measure the Sun's Distance

Exactly at the first quarter or third quarter, *more* than half of the face of the moon is seen. Half moon occurs when the moon has still to move through an angle B before it is exactly at the first quarter. Aristarchus found that the delay between half moon and first quarter was six hours, so, if a lunar month is taken as 28 days, $B = \left(\dfrac{360}{4 \times 28}\right)^{\circ}$ = about 3°. In the half-moon position, lines joining the sun and the earth to the moon meet in a right angle. So $a = B = 3^{\circ}$ and $\sin 3^{\circ} = \dfrac{\text{Earth's distance from moon}}{\text{Earth's distance from sun}}$.

this method, which is referred to in the ensuing passage from Snyder's book, is extremely inaccurate because small errors of observation lead to large differences in the ratios determined from them:

The problem of the shadow cone, as is clear from the pages of Ptolemy, had been worked out by Hipparchus, apparently with great precision, but with the strange result of confirming the calculations of Aristarchus. He, too, found the distance of the sun about twenty times that of the moon, or from 1379 to 1472 half diameters of our globe. Ptolemy, a couple of centuries later, tries his hand at the matter, but with no better success; indeed, he reduces the distance to 1210 such half diameters. But with three distinct methods leading identically to the same result, there could now be little question of their truth. There seems, indeed, to have been no question for another seventeen centuries, and until Galileo and the telescope had come. Hipparchus' method—it is generally so styled—is reproduced with new proofs, but similar estimates, in the *De Revolutionibus* of Copernicus, A.D. 1543. The Theorem of Hipparchus gave not merely the relative but also the absolute measures of the solar and lunar distances, hence a direct measure of their size. Cleomedes tells us that Hipparchus computed the sun's bulk at 150 times that of the earth; Ptolemy made it 170 times. But Aristarchus, by what method he does not state, figured the diameter of the sun at between six and seven times that of the earth, hence about three hundred times its bulk. He sets the moon's diameter at one-third that of the earth—an error of but one-twelfth; admirable, if yet imperfect approximations. The march of the mind had begun! . . . There is, in an oddly-jumbled work, *Opinions of Philosophers*, attributed, with slight probability, to familiar old Plutarch, a paragraph which says that Eratosthenes had engaged the same problem. True to his love of concrete measures, he gives the distance of the moon at 780,000 stadia, of the sun at 804,000,000 stadia. Marvellous prevision of the truth! For though he makes the distance of the moon only about twenty earth radii—too small by two-thirds of the reality—his figure makes the sun's distance 20,000 radii, which, as nearly as we may estimate the stadium, was practically the distance that, after three centuries of patient investigation with micrometers and heliometers, is set down as the reality. . . . It is with a deepening interest, bordering even upon amazement, that we find yet another great investigator of antiquity announcing similar but quite distinct estimates. This was Poseidonius, the teacher of Cicero and of Pompey, one of the most contradictory of characters, now seeming but a merest polymath, now one of the most acute and original thinkers of that ancient day. We have already noted that his measure of the earth, adopted by Ptolemy, was the sustenance of Columbus. He had closely studied the refraction of light, and gives us a really wonderful calculation as to the height of the earth's atmosphere. In the pages of Cleomedes we learn that he equally attempted to establish the distance of the stars. He puts the moon at two million stadia away, the sun at five hundred million! This, on his earlier estimate of the earth's diameter, would place the moon at 52 radii of the earth, which would be nearer than the computations of Hipparchus. It would make the sun's distance 13,000 radii. If we take his later figure (180,000 stadia), the distance would become 17,400 radii, an estimate which, considering the necessarily wide limits of error, does not differ greatly from that of Eratosthenes, and equally little from the truth. Compare it with the thirteen *hundred* radii of his forerunners! Compare it with the notions of Epicurus, almost his contemporary, a very wise and large-minded man in his way, who yet believed that the sun might be a body two feet across!

The importance of science in the everyday life of mankind means more than making it possible for us to organize material prosperity. The advance of science liberates mankind from beliefs which sidetrack intelligently directed social effort. In the phraseology of the materialist poet Lucretius, science liberates us from the terror of the Gods. At a later date the scientific study of the heavens was destined to challenge the authority of custom-thought in a more spectacular context, by discrediting the biblical doctrine that the sun revolves round the earth. The view which is now held was recognized as a possible alternative by the Pythagorean brotherhoods and advocated by Aristarchus. For a very good reason it was rejected by Hipparchus, on whose teaching the Almagest is largely based. He did so, because no *parallax* of the sun could be detected.

Observations on the fixed stars made at different localities at the same time yield no appreciable difference in R.A. or declination. In other words, the fixed stars have no measurable *geocentric* parallax. Since even the moon's geocentric parallax is never a very big quantity, this would be quite intelligible on the assumption that they are much farther away than the moon. Aristarchus estimated that the sun was about 20 times as distant as the moon from the earth. When the moon's distance was found to be about 60 times the earth's radius, it appeared that the diameter of the earth's orbit must be more than a thousand times the diameter of the earth. The difficulty did not end here. If the earth moves round the sun, it must be nearer to any particular star at some seasons than at others. It still seemed

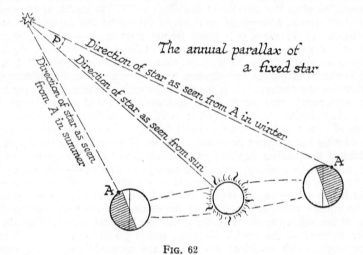

The annual parallax of a fixed star

Fig. 62

hard to believe that the stars are too far away to show any change of apparent direction when the earth is at opposite ends of its orbit (as in Fig. 62). With any instruments available before the nineteenth century, no *annual* parallax of the fixed stars could be detected. The refined methods we now have show that the heliocentric or annual parallax (P in Fig. 62) is never as much as one four-thousandth of a degree (0·78″ for the nearest star, *Proxima Centauri*). According to the only test which was known to the ancients, the doctrine of Aristarchus failed. On the evidence which their instruments yielded, the founders of the Ptolemaic system were right in putting the earth at the centre of the star map, where it is still convenient to leave it for the purposes of navigation and scientific geography.

Nowadays we often read dogmatic statements about the discredit into which Newton's system has fallen, and there is danger of losing sight of what is permanent in any useful hypotheses. Scientific hypotheses that yield a useful explanation of some facts of experience, are not relegated to the limbo of superstition whenever we discover—as we constantly do discover—

new facts which they do not explain. The Ptolemaic astronomy which provided the technological basis of the Great Navigations is still the most convenient representation of the apparent movements of the sun, moon, and fixed stars. It is the world view of the earth-observer, and as such remains the basis of elementary expositions on nautical astronomy after nearly two thousand years. Its greatest disadvantage—which eventually brought it into disrepute—is that it can give no reliable means of ascertaining the motions of another class of heavenly objects—the planets, which are not fixed in the heavens like the stars. If we use the methods of Chapter IV to plot the move-

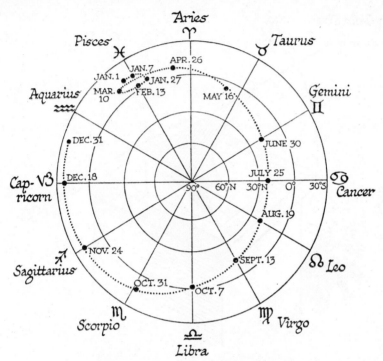

FIG. 63.—THE TRACK OF VENUS IN 1894

ments of a planet like Venus on the star map shown in Fig. 51, they do not conform to any simple rule. The nearer planets wander about the heavens, each in a seemingly capricious track, with no evident geometrical pattern. Their motions are easier to calculate if we put ourselves in the position of a sun observer.

We shall see later how Copernicus furnished the germs of a comparatively simple account of the way in which the planets move by discarding the belief that the earth is the centre of the universe. In the absence of satisfactory evidence for the annual parallax of the fixed stars (before about A.D. 1830), it is highly doubtful whether the usefulness of the Copernican doctrine for calculating the positions of the planets would have sufficed to overcome the combined authority of the Book of Joshua and the Almagest, had there been no new sources of information to discredit belief in the fixed position of the earth at the hub of the heavenly wheel. How the ancient astronomers attempted to explain the vagaries of the planets or "wanderers" of the heavens may best be dealt with when we come to the Copernican hypothesis. We shall first see how two devices prepared the way for its universal acceptance. The introduction of the telescope and the pendulum clock in the beginning of the seventeenth century registers an eventful phase in the conquest of

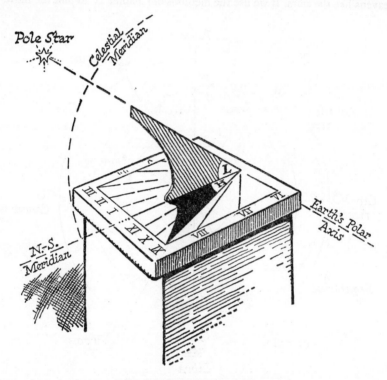

FIG. 64.—THE MOORISH SUNDIAL

distance and time. It is hardly too much to say that, with one exception, no other technical advances contributed so much to change the world picture of mankind between 4241 B.C. and A.D. 1800.

In the period which intervened, Arab astronomers and mathematicians, of whom Omar Khayyám was one of the most illustrious, blazed the trail for the new world outlook by more accurate measurements of the positions of the planets. A far more important Arabic contribution lay in devising simple rules of calculation. The use of mathematics in Alexandrian science was essentially *pictorial*. Mathematics was applied almost exclusively to astronomical data. The trigonometry of Hipparchus and the algebra of Diophantus, the last Alexandrian mathematician of importance, were imprisoned within the obscure number symbols of the Greek alphabet. By discarding the alphabet and adopting the Hindu *sunya* or zero, as we call it, the Arab mathematicians equipped us with an arithmetic which could accommodate a growing body of scientific measurements, and with an algebra which has extended the application of mathematics far beyond the confines of geometry.

Located in sunny regions, the ingenuity of the Islamic culture was not compelled to perfect mechanical devices for recording the time of day. The contribution of the Arab astronomers to the technique of recording time is now relegated to the status of a garden ornament. The ancient shadow clocks

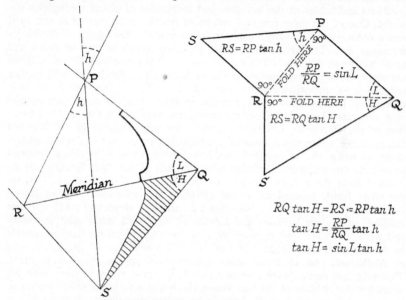

FIG. 65.—HOW TO CALIBRATE THE SUNDIAL.

A solid model of the sunbeam, style, and shadow, can be made by folding the upper figure SPQSR. The angle H is the shadow angle with the meridian; L the latitude of the place and the inclination of the style to the horizon plane; and h is the sun's hour angle. The figure shows that

$$\tan H = \sin L \tan h.$$

Thus to mark off the angle H corresponding to two o'clock (p.m.) or ten o'clock (a.m.), i.e. when $h = \pm (15 \times 2)° = \pm 30°$, at latitude 51° we have

$$\tan H = \sin 51° \tan 30°$$
$$= 0 \cdot 7771 \times 0 \cdot 5774 = 0 \cdot 4487$$

$\therefore$ from tables of tangents H = 24·15°.

did not record a constant hour at different seasons. The Arab sundial (Fig. 64) with its style set at an angle equivalent to the latitude and pointing due north marked out hours which were mechanically equivalent throughout the year. The only lasting importance of this invention, the theory of which is explained in Fig. 65, lies in the fact that the first mechanical clocks were checked by comparison with the readings of the dial.

The state of geographical knowledge available for navigational purposes in the time of the Crusades is indicated in the following passage from Wright's book already cited:

That the Saracens also were interested in the more strictly mathematical aspects of astronomical geography is emphatically proved by the fact that they undertook actually to measure the length of a terrestrial degree and thereby to determine the circumference of the earth. Some knowledge of this great work came to the Western world in our period through translations of the *Astronomy* of Al-Farghānī. . . . Astrology also necessitated this type of investigation. In order to cast a horoscope one must know what stars are overhead at a particular moment; and, to ascertain this, one must know latitude and longitude. In the Arabic astronomic works there occur rules for determining positions and tables of the latitudes and longitudes of places throughout the world. One of the most practical results of Arabic investigations in this field was a reduction of Ptolemy's exaggerated estimate of the length of the Mediterranean Sea. The Greek geographer gave the length as 62°, or about half again too long. Al-Khwārizmī cut this figure down to about 52°, and, if we are right in our interpretation of the available data, Az-Zarqalī still further reduced it to approximately the correct figure, 42°. . . . The results of these corrections became known in the medieval West. The Moslems, as a general rule, measured longitudes from the prime meridian which Ptolemy had used, that of the Fortunate Islands (now the Canaries), situated in the Western Ocean at the westernmost limit of the habitable earth; but individual writers came to make use of another meridian farther west, a meridian destined to become known to the Christian World as that of the True West, as distinguished from the supposed border of the habitable West. Abū Ma'shar, on the other hand, referred his prime meridian to a fabulous castle of Kang-Diz, far to the east in the China Sea . . . there is absolutely no doubt that methods of finding latitudes and longitudes were well understood in theory and were sometimes put to practical use. Rules are given for finding latitude in Az-Zarqalī's Canons, in Plato of Tivoli's translation of the Astronomy of Al-Battani, and in many other astronomical and astrological treatises. Two principal methods were recommended. You may either measure with the astrolabe the altitude of the sun above the horizon at noon at the spring or autumn equinox and find the latitude by subtracting this angle from 90° or you may measure the altitude of the celestial pole above the horizon, which is the same as the latitude. As to longitude, the fact that there are differences in local time between points east and west of each other was recognized and clearly explained by several writers of our age. The Marseilles Tables give a rule for finding longitude by the observation of eclipses. Roger of Hereford indicates that he himself, by observing an eclipse in 1178, ascertained the positions of Hereford, Marseilles, and Toledo in relation to Arin, the world centre of the Moslems.

The Marseilles tables mentioned in the foregoing passage seem to be the earliest astronomical tables in north-western Europe. Referring to their origin, Wright says:

Preserved in a twelfth-century manuscript of the Bibliothèque Nationale is a set of astronomical tables for Marseilles dating from 1140, the work of a certain Raymond of Marseilles. The Canons, or introductory explanation, of these tables are drawn largely from the astronomical Canons of Az-Zarqalī; the tables are an adaptation for the meridian of Marseilles of the Toledo Tables. Both Az-Zarqalī's Canons and the Toledo Tables, with their modifications like the Marseilles set, contained not a little incidental material of importance from the point of view of astronomical geography, including a

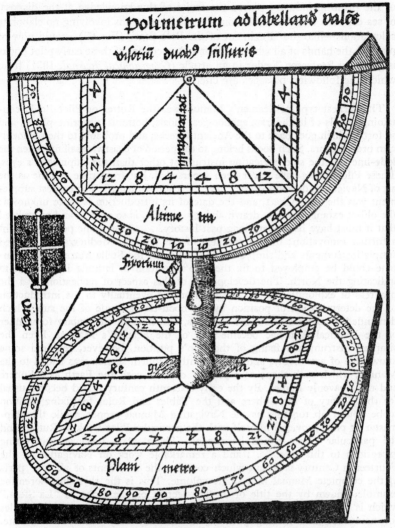

FIG. 66.—WALDSEEMULLER'S POLYMETRUM, FROM REISCH'S "MARGARITA PHILO-
SOPHICA," 1512

*(From "A Regional Map of the Early Sixteenth Century," by Professor E. G. R. Taylor,
Geographical Journal, Vol. LXXI, No. 5, May 1928.)*

list of cities with their latitudes and longitudes derived ultimately from Al-
Khwārizmi. That this material enjoyed wide popularity during our period
and later is proved by the existence of a large number of manuscripts. One
of the translations of Az-Zarqalī's Canons was done by the hand of the famous
Gerard of Cremona.

In the fifteenth century Portuguese and Spanish shipping enjoyed the
benefit of expert pilots schooled in the teaching which had been salvaged
from the wreckage of the Moorish universities in the Peninsula. The growth

of the printing industry placed the fruits of this knowledge at the disposal of sea captains with less erudition. Simple instructions involving no elaborate calculations—like the "Regiment of the Pole Star" (Fig. 67)—could now be put into the hands of all who could read. An account of these early pilot books is given by Professor Taylor in an article (*Geographical Journal*, 1931) from which the following passages are cited:

The earliest type of Seaman's Manual was the Rutter or Pilot Book, containing details of landmarks, anchorages, shoals, bottoms, watering-places, and so forth, which goes back to the Ancient Greeks, and probably to their Phoenician predecessors. Such books belong to the period of coastwise sailing, when the lode-line was the sole navigating instrument other than the shipmaster's eyes. These Pilot Books have never been superseded, but from time to time as the art of Navigation developed, they have been supplemented. The earliest supplement was the Pilot Chart, and the date of its introduction is quite unknown: the oldest extant example, drawn about A.D. 1300, is so perfect and so stylized that it must have had a very long past history. . . . The same period brought a further innovation: the astronomers of the Western Mediterranean devised simple instruments and simple methods whereby the Stella Maris or Tramontane could be employed to fix the ship's position in latitude in addition to indicating the North. The development of this aspect of navigation, and the progress of exploration across the equator, led eventually to the introduction of the determination of position by the noon-tide altitude of the sun, which demanded a calendar and a set of tables, and thus an elementary forerunner of the Nautical Almanac became part of the Seaman's Manual. Even the simplest instrumental fixing of the ship's position, however, required some knowledge of astronomy, and consequently a fourth section was added to the Manual, which took shape as a preface dealing with the Earth as a Sphere and the Heavenly Bodies. By the early sixteenth century it had become usual for the Theory of the Sphere and the Tables and Rules for fixing position to be bound up together as the Navigating Manual proper, while the shipmaster or pilot provided himself with the particular Pilot Book or Rutter, and the particular Chart which he needed. There were, however, interesting exceptions to this rule. . . . and a remarkable work on Navigation of the Fourteenth Century is extant which contains the rudiments of all four parts of the complete Manual in a single volume. This is the rhyming Florentine example, known by the title of its first section on the globe as "La Sfera," which is ascribed to Gregorio Dati. The second part, dealing with the rules for navigation and finding position, is naturally very crude at this date, while the chart (the third part) is drawn in sections, which are placed in the margins of the appropriate portions of the Rutter (the fourth part). . . . The Italian manuscript entitled "Brieve conpendio de larte del navegar," in the Society's Library, contains three out of the four parts of the complete Manual, namely, the section on the Sphere, the Rules and Tables, and the Chart; only the Rutter is absent, and certain supplementary notes and tables are inserted instead. . . . It was written by an Italian pilot, Battista Testa Rossa, whose patron was El Magnifico Marco Boldu, a member of one of the great ruling families of the Republic of Venice. It is dated 1557, when Battista had settled in London. . . . The section on the Sphere is of the simplest possible type, consisting of necessary definitions only, namely, of altitude, degree, horizon, zodiac, equinoctial line, declination, Circles, Poles, Tropics, seasons, longitude, latitude, parallels, meridians, hemisphere, zenith

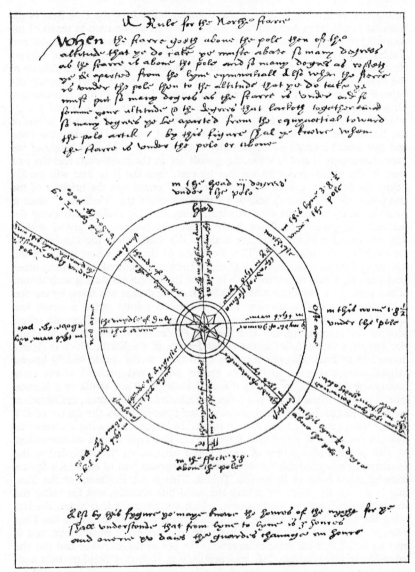

FIG. 67.—THE REGIMENT OF THE NORTH POLE

The star Polaris is only 1° off the true pole today. In mediaeval times Polaris revolved in a tiny circle 3° from the celestial pole as did α Draconis, when it was the guiding star of the Pyramid builders. Hence latitude by the altitude of the Pole Star might exceed or fall short of the true value by 3°. The pilot books gave instructions for making the necessary correction by noting the hour angle of the star β in the Little Bear. The positions of Polaris relative to the true pole were charted for eight positions of the "guards" (β and γ), so that naked eye observation sufficed to make a correction with an error less than half a degree.

Reproduced with Professor E. G. R. Taylor's permission, from her Tudor Geography 1485–1583 *(Methuen).*

and centre. A brief exposition of the changing altitude of the Pole Star as the traveller passes from Alexandria to Iceland, and its explanation in terms of the rotundity of the Earth, concludes the section. The second section, on Rules and Tables, opens with the Regiment of the North Pole, i.e. the number of degrees (from $\frac{1}{2}°$ to $3\frac{1}{2}°$) which must be added or subtracted from the observed altitude of the Pole Star, according to the position of the "guards," in order to obtain the latitude. "The guards" was the seaman's name for part of the constellation Ursa Minor, the two significant stars used as indicators being β and γ . . . when the guards are in the east and the forward star (of the guards) is east of the North Star, then the Pole Star, as it is called, will be $1\frac{1}{2}°$ below the Pole, and this must be added to the altitude, when the sum will be the height of the Pole above your horizon: when the guards are in the north-east, and the two stars of the guard, one with another by east, then the Pole Star will be $3\frac{1}{2}°$ below the Pole. . . . The "forward" or "fore" guard was the brighter of the two (i.e. β Ursae Minoris), and was sometimes called the "clock star," since it could be used to tell the time at night. Directions for making and using the balestilha or Jacob's Staff for these stellar observations are given, with a diagram to show how to add the scale to the Staff, while the quadrant and astrolabe are also mentioned. This Regiment of the North Star is one of the stereotyped Rules found in every Manual. Here it is followed, as in many other examples, by a rule to tell the time at night by the guards during each month of the year. . . . Now this makes it clear that the degree was taken by seamen as 70 Roman miles, equivalent to 64·4 English statute miles, a much less faulty figure than the $62\frac{1}{2}$ miles (of 5,000 feet), or alternatively 60 miles, adopted by cosmographers. The method of derivation, too, is made plain. Battista gives 25,200 miles as the circumference of the Earth, which is clearly derived from Eratosthenes's measure of 252,000 stadia (made widely known to navigators through Sacrobosco's Sphera which was prefixed to the early Portuguese Manuals), by taking the equivalent of 10 sea stadia to a Roman mile. The Portuguese league of 4 miles was adopted by all seamen, as Columbus mentions, and as Jean Rotz, too, makes clear; but in Spain the degree of $17\frac{1}{2}$ leagues was presently superseded by that of 16 leagues, reckoning according to Spanish use, only 3 miles to a league. . . . The next section of the Italian Manual consists of a couple of pages and a diagram on the Regiment of the Southern Cross, and then follows the most important part of all, which finds a place in every book of Rules and Tables. This is the Regiment of the Sun, that is to say, the rules for taking the noon-tide altitude, and for using the accompanying Table of Declinations, which are given for four years, the last being the Leap Year. A Calendar was combined with the tables for the First Year. . . . A few examples of latitude determination are worked out, and it may be noted that for solar observations the use of the astrolabe and not the balestilha is proposed. . . . It was probably in 1558 that Stephen Burrough visited the Casa de Contratacion in Seville, there to be greatly impressed by the meticulous care with which Spanish pilots were trained and examined. . . . So far as chart-making is concerned, Tudor England had nothing to set against the magnificent achievements of the Portuguese, Spanish, Italian, and French school of Cosmographer-Pilots.

A simple recipe analogous to the Regiment of the North Pole for use in southern latitudes is given in Hakluyt's *Voyages*. It refers to the *Southern Cross*, and is written by the mariner Edward Cliffe, who accompanied the consort ship of Drake in the 1577–9 expedition to the Strait of Magellan:

And thence we came along the coast being low sandie land till wee arrived at Cape Blanco. This Cape sheweth it selfe like the corner of a wall upright from the water, to them which come from the Northwardes: where the North Pole is elevated 20 degrees 30 min. And the Crociers being the guards of the South Pole, be raised 9 degrees 30 min. The said Crociers be 4 starrs, representing the forme of a crosse, and be 30 degrees in the latitude from the South Pole; and the lowest starre of the sayd Crociers is to be taken, when it is directly under the uppermost; and being so taken as many degrees as it wanteth of 30, so many you are to the Northwardes of Equinoctial: and as many degrees as be more than 30, so many degrees you are to the Southwards of the Equinoctial. And if you finde it to be just 30 then you be directly under the line.

THINGS TO MEMORIZE

1. North Polar Distance = Z.D. of Pole — Z.D. of star.
   Declination = 90° — N.P.D.
   Latitude = altitude of Pole = 90° — Z.D. of Pole.
   Declination = Z.D. + Latitude.
   Latitude = Declination — Z.D.
2. Zenith distances south of the zenith, and latitudes and declinations south of the equator are negative.
3. Sundial time + Equation of Time = Greenwich Mean Time.
4. Star's R.A. = *sidereal* time of transit of star = (approximately) *solar* time of star's transit — time of transit of ♈.
   Star's R.A. — Sun's R.A. = local (solar) time of transit (approximately).
5. See also Figs. 24, 43, 45 and 56.

EXAMPLES ON CHAPTER II

Use the graph in Fig. 32 for the "equation of time" correction.

1. What are the sun's declination and right ascension on March 21st, June 21st, September 23rd, and December 21st?

2. What *approximately* is the sun's R.A. on July 4th, May 1st, January 1st, November 5th? (Work backwards or forwards from the four dates given. Check by *Whitaker*.)

3. With a home-made astrolabe (Fig. 22) the following observations were made at a certain place on December 21st:

Sun's Zenith Distance (South)	Greenwich Time (p.m.)
74½°	12.18
74°	12.19
74°	12.20
73½°	12.21
73½°	12.22
74°	12.23
74½°	12.24

What was the latitude of the place? (Look it up on the map.)

4. Find the approximate R.A. of the sun on January 25th, and hence at what local time Aldebaran (R.A. 4 hours 32 minutes) will cross the meridian on that night. If the ship's chronometer then registers 11.15 p.m. at Greenwich, what is the longitude of the ship?

Examples continued on page 130

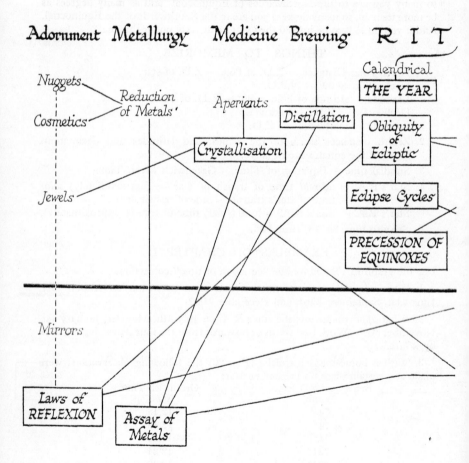

Adornment Metallurgy   Medicine Brewing   R I T

Nuggets

Cosmetics

Reduction of Metals'

Aperients

Distillation

Calendrical

THE YEAR

Obliquity of Ecliptic

Crystallisation

Jewels

Eclipse Cycles

PRECESSION OF EQUINOXES

Mirrors

Laws of REFLEXION

Assay of Metals

TIME

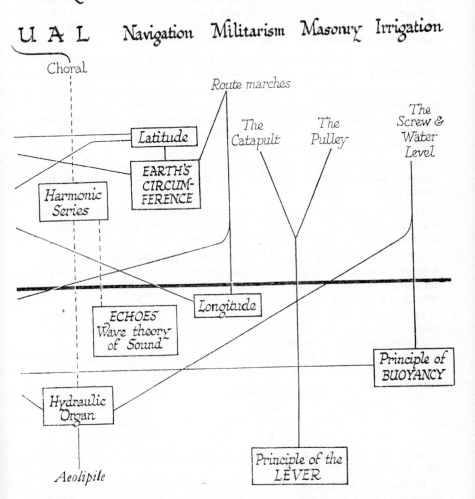

ANTIQUITY *(Below thick black line — Hellenistic)*

U A L Navigation Militarism Masonry Irrigation

Choral

Route marches

Latitude

The Catapult

The Pulley

The Screw & Water Level

EARTH'S CIRCUM-FERENCE

Harmonic Series

Longitude

ECHOES Wave theory of Sound

Principle of BUOYANCY

Hydraulic Organ

Aeolipile

Principle of the LEVER

CHART I

5. If the declination of Aldebaran is 16° N. (to the nearest degree) and its altitude at meridian transit is 60° from the southern horizon, what is the ship's latitude?

6. The R.A. of the star α in the Great Bear is nearly 11 hours. Its declination is 62° 5′ N. It crosses the meridian 4° 41′ north of the zenith on April 8th at 1.10 a.m. by the ship's chronometer. What is the position of the ship?

7. Suppose that you were deported to an island, but had with you a wrist watch and *Whitaker's Almanack*. Having set your watch at noon by observing the sun's shadow, you noticed that the star α in the Great Bear was at its lower culmination about eleven o'clock at night. If you had lost count of the days, what would you conclude to be the approximate date?

8. On April 1, 1895, the moon's R.A. was approximately 23 hours 48 minutes. Give roughly its appearance, time of rising, and transit on that date.

9. If the sun and the Great Bear were together visible throughout one, and only one, night in the year at some locality on the Greenwich meridian, how could you determine its distance from London, if you also remembered that the earth's diameter is very nearly 8,000 miles, and the latitude of London is very nearly 51°?

10. If you observed that the sun's noon shadow vanished on one day of the year and pointed south on every other, how many miles would you be from the North Pole?

11. On January 1st the sun reached its highest point in the heavens when the B.B.C. programme indicated 12.17 p.m. It was then 16° above the southern horizon. In what part of England did this happen?

12. The approximate R.A. and declination of Betelgeuse are respectively 5 hours 50 minutes and $7\frac{1}{2}$° N. If your bedroom faces east, and you retire regularly at 11 p.m., about what time of the year will you see Betelgeuse rising when you get into bed?

13. On April 13, 1937, the shortest shadow of a pole was exactly equal to its height, and pointed north. This happened when the radio programme timed for 12.10 p.m. began. In what county were these observations made?

14. With a home-made astrolabe the following observations were made in Penzance (Lat. 50° N., Long. $5\frac{1}{2}$° W.) on February 8th:

	Least Zenith Distance	Greenwich Mean Time
Betelgeuse	$42\frac{1}{2}$° S.	9.9 p.m.
Rigel	$58\frac{1}{2}$° S.	8.24 p.m.
Sirius	$67\frac{1}{2}$° S.	10.0 p.m.

Find the declination and R.A. of each star, and compare your results with the table in *Whitaker's Almanack*.

15. By aid of a figure show that if the hour angle (h) of a star is the angle through which it has turned since it crossed the meridian (or, if the sign is minus, the angle through which it must turn to reach the meridian),

R.A. of star (in hours) = Sun's R.A. (in hours) — (hour angle in degrees ÷ 15) + *local* time (in hours).

CHAPTER III

SPECTACLES AND SATELLITES

The Trail of the Telescope

AMONG writers who are not familiar with the history of science, it has been
the fashion to speak of the great intellectual awakening of the fifteenth and
sixteenth centuries as if it were closely connected with the artistic Renaissance
of Italy under Byzantine influence. The truth is that the advance of science
owed very little to the influx of classical models and classical texts from the
Eastern Empire. The fruits of Alexandrian science were harvested by the
Arab conquerors of Spain; and the diffusion of the Arabic learning into
northern Europe was largely due to the influence of Jewish physicians who
founded the medieval schools of medicine, and to the development of scientific
navigation before the tradition of the Moorish universities had been finally
extinguished. Two features of Catholic tradition and organization forced
the universities of western Christendom to open their doors to the Moorish
learning. One, which will be discussed in Chapter XVI, was the humanitarian ideology which prompted the monastic orders to found hospitals and
seek the assistance of experienced physicians. The other, which encouraged
monks like Gregory of Cremona or Adelard of Bath to visit the universities
of Spain during the Moorish occupation, was the social function of the
priesthood as custodians of the calendar. In conformity with their rôle as
timekeepers, the Augustinian teaching had endorsed astronomy as a proper
discipline of Christian education. So although the patristic influence was
mainly hostile to pagan science, clerical education was not completely in-
accessible to influence from the non-Christian world.

A substantial link between Moorish science and the medieval universities
of Christendom already existed when the growth of mercantile navigation
renewed the impetus to astronomical discovery. About 1420 Henry, then
Crown Prince of Portugal, built an observatory on the headland of Sagres,
one of the promontories which terminate at Cape St. Vincent, the extreme
south-west point of Europe. There he set up a school of seamanship under
one Master Jacome from Majorca, and for forty years devoted himself to
cosmographical studies while equipping and organizing expeditions which
won for him the title of Henry the Navigator. For the preparation of maps,
nautical tables, and instruments, he enlisted Arab cartographers and Jewish
astronomers, employing them to instruct his captains and assist in piloting
his vessels. Peter Nunes declares that the Prince's master mariners were well
equipped with instruments and those rules of astronomy and geometry
"which all map-makers should know." The development of astronomy once
more became part of the everyday life of mankind, and the new impetus
it received from the growth of maritime commerce was reinforced by the
introduction of two new technical inventions which emerged from the
world's everyday work in a different social context.

One of these was the invention of spectacles. Although devices of one kind or another for magnifying objects are of considerable antiquity, there does not seem to have been any general use of them in everyday life till the close of the Middle Ages. The Moorish savant Al Hazen appears to have observed the magnifying power of the segment of a glass sphere (*Opticae thesaurus*, vii, 48); and Roger Bacon explained in his *Opus Majus* (1266) how to magnify writing by placing the segment of a sphere of glass on the book with its plane side downwards. One of the earliest examples of the application of the principle is provided by a portrait of Cardinal Ugone in a church fresco

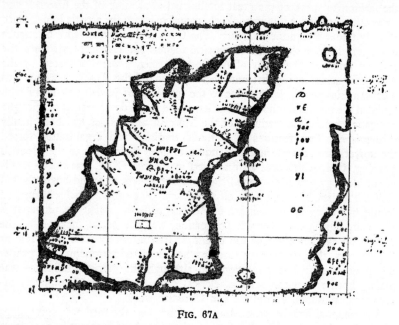

FIG. 67A

Ptolemy's Map of Ireland showing what the Great Navigations owed to Alexandrian Cartography. Note the lines of latitude and longitude.

at Treviso. This was painted in 1352. It shows two mounted lenses with their handles riveted together and fixed before the eyes. In Dobell's book, *Anthony Leeuwenhoek and His Little Animals*, the actual inventor of spectacles is said to be a Florentine about A.D. 1300. The invention was popularized by the monks, notably through the private labours of de Spina of Pisa for the help of "poor blind men." The compound microscope appears to have been invented at the same time as the telescope, possibly, according to Professor Wolf, a little earlier. It is mentioned in a letter dated 1625 by Giovanni Fabri, who uses the word. Pictures made with the help of the microscope by Stelluti were published (1630) in an Italian edition of Persius. Between 1650 and 1670 microscopic observations were published by Borel, Power, Hooke, and Leeuwenhoek. With the growth of literacy, the universal tendency to long sight as age advances found expression in a new social demand. The introduction of spectacles involved no theoretical discovery about phenomena with which Alexandrian and Arab astronomers were not fully conversant (see p. 141). It is therefore more reasonable to suppose that introduction of paper, the invention of printing, and the use of books in the fifteenth century stimulated the demand for eye glasses. The trade increased during the sixteenth century, especially in Italy and in south Germany. By 1600 opticians were to be found in most of the larger towns on the continent.

Two inventions which are signposts in the history of science, one in physics, one in biology, came as quite fortuitous by-products of the new industry. The name telescope was first adopted by Galileo in 1612. The first one was invented in Holland about 1608. The credit has been attributed variously to Hans Lippershey and Zacharias Jansen, spectacle makers in Middleburg, and to James Metius of Alkmaar (brother of Adrian Metius, the mathematician). On October 2, 1608, the assembly of the States-General at The Hague considered a petition of Hans Lippershey, inventor of an instrument for seeing at a distance. On October 9th, 900 florins were voted for it. On December 15th they examined, and voted 900 florins for, a binocular instrument made by Lippershey. Descartes attributed the invention of the telescope to Metius, who presented a petition later. The story goes that the discovery was made by holding two pairs of spectacles some distance apart and noticing that a neighbouring spire was brought nearer to view. In his *Nuncius Siderius* Galileo states that when he was in Venice about May 1609 he heard that a perspective instrument for making objects appear nearer and larger had been invented. Returning to Padua, he made his first telescope by fixing a convex lens in one end of a leaden tube and a concave lens in the other end. Then he made a better one, went to Venice, and presented the instrument to the Doge Leonardo Donato. His first telescope magnified 3 diameters. He soon made others which magnified 8 diameters, and finally one that magnified 33 diameters. Kepler devised an alternative form using a convex eyepiece.

The three years which followed the patents of Lippershey and Jansen were eventful. Kepler's account of the motion of Mars appeared in 1609. His telescope was constructed in 1611. Eight years later he was able to announce his complete vindication of the fundamental doctrine of Copernicus and his epoch-making laws of the solar system. Meanwhile Galileo had observed the motion of the sun's spots and had seen the moons of Jupiter. Galileo's discovery was partly important because it deprived the geocentric view of the universe of the inherent plausibility it enjoyed before people realized that there were other worlds with satellites circling about them. The Inquisition rightly judged the psychological effect of the new realization that our own small world is not a unique one. How the tract on the moons of Jupiter became the field of one of the most decisive battles between science and priestly superstition is a story too familiar to merit repetition.

The telescope has a threefold significance for the age of the Great Navigations. The determination of longitude for westerly sailing had become a technical issue of cardinal importance, and on this account astronomy retained its place as the queen of the sciences till the end of the eighteenth century. At a time when the only method of determining longitude was based on the use of celestial signals (eclipses and conjunctions), celestial signals were events of vital significance for the world's work; and the discovery of Jupiter's moons brought a new battery of celestial signals to the aid of seafaring and scientific geography (see p. 315, Chapter VI). More directly the telescope was of value to the mariner as a "spy glass." A less obvious use is related to one of the pivotal inventions in the history of mankind. The age of the Great Navigations was a period of revolutionary and imperialist wars in which success depended on exploiting the new technique of artillery. The demands of marksmanship called for accurate and immediate devices for surveying (see Fig. 149) and sighting distant objects. Galileo was not slow to recognize the possibilities of the telescope for navigation. Indeed, he offered his

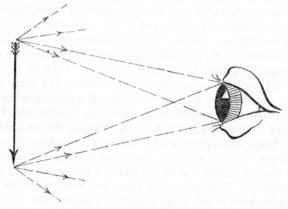

FIG. 68

As the edges of a beam seen emerging from a slit are always straight, we can look upon a shaft of light as made up of bundles of straight shafts or rays, which Alexandrian astronomers represented by geometrical lines or "rays." Light rays falling upon a surface which is opaque are scattered in all directions. When we look at anything only a few rays are able to enter the eyeball.

invention consecutively to the Catholic Emperor and to the opposing Protestant democracy in letters adapted to the convictions of both parties.*

The invention of the telescope is an instructive episode, if we are disposed to interpret the progress of human knowledge as an unbroken chain of theoretical principles due to the exercise of mere curiosity by a few exceptionally gifted individuals. The fundamental laws of magnification were familiar to the Alexandrians. Euclid composed a work on the geometrical principles of reflection, and Archimedes is credited with constructing concave mirrors for use as burning-glasses. Ptolemy investigated refraction, i.e. the bending of a beam of light in passing from one medium to another, and actually discussed the effect of atmospheric refraction in distorting the apparent position of objects on the horizon. Al Hazen, an Arab physician who lived about A.D. 1000, gave a correct account of the structure of the eye, contested Plato's idealism, which made it the source of illumina-

* Letters cited in Bernal's admirable book *The Social Function of Science* correct a confusion in the first edition of this one.

tion, and appears to have recognized it as what we should now call a camera. There was no further development of the subject till the invention of the telescope. The design of better telescopes immediately created two needs. The need for more definite theoretical principles of guidance in attaining high magnification led inevitably to a more precise statement of the law of refraction by Kepler, Snell (1621), and Descartes (1637). The need to eliminate the coloured fringe which blurs the outline of an image obtained with simple lenses led Newton to the study of the spectrum.

A number of circumstances conspired to encourage the experimental study of light at an early stage in human knowledge. Out of the quagmire of Greek idealism there had emerged one very pertinent issue. How can we tell when our senses deceive us? From the very dawn of civilization—possibly earlier than any cities—man had become accustomed to the use of the mirror as an aid to adornment. Earlier still he had puzzled about reflections seen in pools. Things do not always seem to be where they are—or to be the right way up. Early interest in such illusions is illustrated by the trick of the disappearing coin, which was correctly interpreted by Ptolemy as an effect due to the bending outwards of light when it passes from water into air, as shown in Fig. 69. Optical illusions, which possibly enjoyed a place in the priestly magic, assumed a special practical importance in an age when people were intensely interested in the heavenly bodies and were beginning to have a scientific knowledge of them.

There are several very striking optical illusions in the everyday life of people who watch for the rising and setting of the sun and moon. When near the horizon the sun and moon appear to be much larger than when seen high in the heavens. When seen rising behind a hill they seem to move much more rapidly than they do when they are above us. Measurement of the sun's or moon's angular diameter by an instrument, or of their bearings when rising and setting do not confirm our first impressions. Al Hazen was among the first to realize what we know to be a correct explanation of the deception. Our estimates of sizes and distances near the horizon are peculiar because we adopt comparatively near terrestrial objects as our standard of comparison. In learning to use the astrolabe or quadrant, men were taking the first eventful step of manufacturing social sense organs which do not deceive us in arranging the conduct of everyday life. One important fact in connexion with the early development of what we now call geometrical optics is that the kind of mathematics which developed in connexion with astronomy is specially useful for measuring the elementary properties of light.

The Narcissus myth still pursues us in everyday life from the moment we get up in the morning and shave or powder before a mirror. It no longer provokes among sensible people the mystification which led early philosophers to devise the false antithesis of appearance and reality. Today the experience of photography is enough to dispose of Plato's belief that the eye sends forth light. Appearance is part of the reality which includes a correct account of how our sense organs do their work. We know enough about the sense organs to see clearly what early science could only grope after in the dark. Vision is not merely a static copy of the changing world. We have to learn to use our eyes as we have to learn to use any other instrument.

Our estimates of distance, direction, and position do not merely depend on what the retina of the eye tells us. They involve complex movements of the muscles that move the lens of the eye, of the muscles that change its curvature and of the muscles that wield the eye itself in its socket, together with movements of the muscles of the neck and limbs and all the signals which these muscles send to the brain when they move. We learn to co-

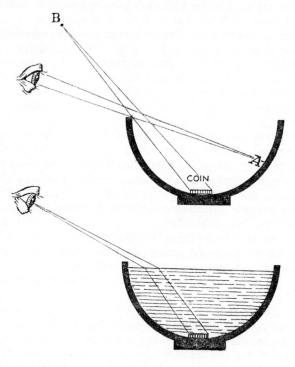

FIG. 69

The disappearing coin trick is of very great antiquity and provided the Alexandrian astronomers with a correct explanation of certain astronomical phenomena, such as why the apparent time of setting of the sun is a little later and its apparent rising a little earlier than expected from calculations as given in Chapter IV, p. 197. When the vessel is empty the eye cannot see deeper than the level of A, and the coin can only be seen if the head is raised till the eye is at B. If water is poured into the vessel the coin at the bottom becomes visible. When the sun is just below the horizon in the geometrical sense sunbeams passing from rarefied space into the denser atmosphere of the earth are bent downwards, so that the sun remains visible for a short while after it is actually below the level of the horizon, just as the coin is visible in the lower figure though below A.

ordinate our bodily movements with those of our eye muscles and with the pattern of light on the retina from the common experience of everyday life.

Part of our everyday experience is that a beam of light has a straight edge, or to use a customary figure of speech, "light travels in straight lines." We learn to *put* things "in line." The delicate adjustment which makes us able to grasp a thing by seeing it, or to direct our gaze to the thing we touch, is easily upset. By a simple device shown in Fig. 70 we can direct our eye movements so that we infer a set of lines which are really parallel to look as if they converge or diverge. By using mirrors, or looking at an object immersed in a different medium from that in which we usually see it, we can make a beam of light change its course from an uninterrupted straight line. So our eyes lead us to make judgments that do not agree with those which we are led to make when we also use our organs of touch. In such situations we call what we see an *image* of the thing or *object* as we see it when the testimony of all our sense organs agrees. *Real* images which can be

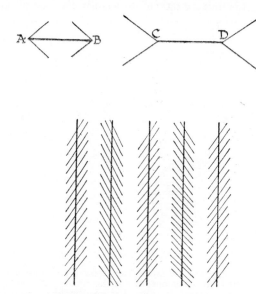

FIG. 70.—TWO OPTICAL ILLUSIONS

Judgments of vision do not merely depend on the static picture focussed on the retina at a given instant of time. They involve active movements of the eye muscles. If these movements are biassed our geometrical judgments go awry. Thus the two lines AB and CD in the upper half of the figure are the same size, and the vertical lines in the lower half are all parallel. You can see that they are, if you half shut your eyes.

caught on a screen are distinguished from *virtual* images which cannot. The image on the ground glass of a camera or the image of the sun focussed with a burning-glass are familiar examples of the former. Reflections in flat mirrors are familiar examples of virtual images.

The elementary principle that "light travels in straight lines" was implicit in all the astronomical lore of the ancient world. So was one of its consequences on which, as we shall see later on, depends our knowledge that the earth's path around the sun is not a perfect circle, as Plato believed. The apparent size of a body depends on the angle which light reflected from its outermost edges makes with the eye of the observer. We call this angle the angular diameter. Fig. 71 shows the same spherical object drawn at two different distances from the eye. When it is nearer, the angular *diameter* is larger than when it is far away. The sine of half the angular diameter is the ratio of its radius to its distance from the observer. When the angle is very small the ratio of two radii is not appreciably different from the ratio of the two angular diameters (Fig. 71, legend). Hence the apparent length of the radius of a circular or spherical body seen in different situations is inversely proportional to the distance. When we magnify a body by a mirror or a lens we change the path of the light coming from it so that the angle between the beams or "rays" converging on the eye is increased. The magnification of a very distant object is thus the ratio of the angular diameter of this seemingly

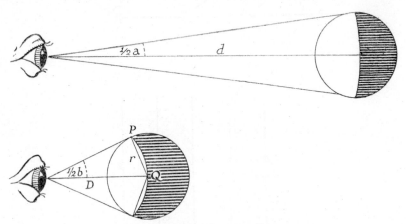

FIG. 71.—APPARENT SIZE AND DISTANCE

The same object seen near and far away. The angles a and b are called its *angular diameters* as seen in the two situations. If r is the actual radius and d the distance, $\sin \frac{1}{2}a = r \div d$, and $\sin \frac{1}{2}b = r \div D$. When very small angles are measured in circular measure (i.e. ratio of the arc to the radius of the circle of whose circumference it is part), $\frac{1}{2}a = \sin \frac{1}{2}a = PQ \div d$ and $\frac{1}{2}b = PQ \div D$ (see Fig. 213). Hence $\frac{a}{b} = \frac{D}{d}$.

nearer image to the angular diameter of the object seen without the instrument.

Modern telescopes use curved mirrors as well as lenses for magnification. Two experimental laws are sufficient to deduce the essentials for designing mirrors and lenses so as to produce a known degree of magnification, whether in constructing a telescope, prescribing the right spectacles or for the variety of other uses to which magnifying devices are now put in everyday life. The fundamental law of reflection is that when a shaft of light strikes a flat polished surface it is bent outwards in the same plane, making equal angles with an imaginary perpendicular drawn where it hits the mirror, as seen in Fig. 72. That this is approximately true is easily seen when a bright shaft of light falls through dusty air on a polished surface. It can be tested more precisely by the use of pins and a mirror placed edgewise on a sheet of paper as explained in Fig. 73. The Alexandrian astronomers were familiar with the

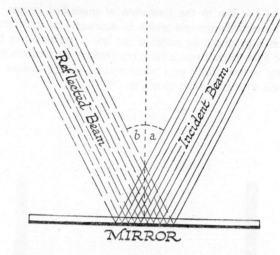

FIG. 72

The fundamental law of reflection is that a beam of light incident on a flat surface is
reflected in the same plane so that the angle of incidence (*a*) is equal to the angle of
reflection (*b*).

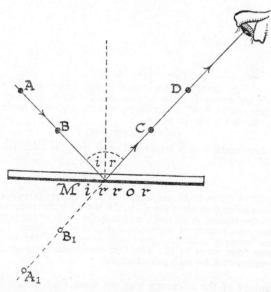

FIG. 73

A simple way of testing the law of reflection is to fix two pins, A and B, in front of a
mirror placed edgewise on a piece of paper. By moving the head from side to side, a
point is found at which the "virtual" images, A_1 and B_1 are in line. Two pins, C and D,
are now placed in line with A_1 and B_1. Lines can then be drawn through the pin
holes and the angles *i* and *r*, formed with the perpendicular are found to be equal.

application of the law to the formation of magnified images by curved surfaces. The second principle which is necessary for understanding how magnification is produced by lenses is the law of refraction or the bending of a beam of light when it passes from one transparent medium into another. This bending is beautifully seen when a shaft of light passes through an aquarium tank with glass sides as in Fig. 74.

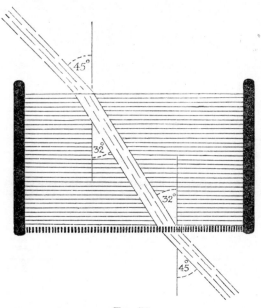

FIG. 74

The refraction of light inwards when a beam of light passes into an aquarium tank filled with water and outwards when it passes into the air again. Passing from air to water the incident angle $i = 45°$ in the figure, and the angle of refraction (r) is given by Snell's law, viz. $\sin i = \sin r \times R$, i.e.

$$\sin r = \sin 45° \div R.$$

Very accurate determination of R for air and water gives the value $1 \cdot 3$ or 4/3. From the tables $\sin 45° = \cdot 7071$.

$$\sin r = \cdot 7071 \div \frac{4}{3} = \cdot 5303.$$

Tables give $\sin 32° = \cdot 5299$. So r is very nearly 32°. In using the formula remember that R is 4/3 for light passing *from* air *to* water, i.e. if R is 4/3, i is always the angle which the ray makes with the vertical in air and r is always the angle which it makes with the vertical in water, irrespective of the actual direction of the beam. If, however, we apply the terms "angle of incidence" and "angle of refraction" literally, then R is 3/4 for light passing from water to air. The first convention saves us the trouble of recording two values of R for each pair of media.

The technology of the telescope was not what first directed attention to it. In contradistinction to the physiological distortion of objects seen near the horizon, when viewed with the unaided eye, another class of optical puzzles arises in the study of celestial phenomena, especially in connexion with a practical problem on which the collection of fines from motorists depends today. As you know, lighting-up time is fixed when "civil twilight" ends, and this rests on calculation of the times of rising and setting of the sun. From geometrical principles outlined on p. 99 and explained more fully in the next chapter, the times of rising and setting of a heavenly body are calculable from their position (R.A. and Declination) in the celestial sphere. Such calculations do not exactly correspond to the observed times of visibility at the horizon level unless a small correction is made for an illusion which depends on the fact that light is bent inwards on passing from empty space into the earth's atmosphere. The amount of this bending depends on the angle from which the object is seen, and has nothing to do with the imperfection of the eye as a physical instrument. So observations on the direction of the sun, moon, or stars, viewed near the zenith, do not accurately correspond to observations made near the horizon. To put the matter in another way, the sun is not geometrically in line with the horizon edge at the moment when it is seen setting. It is already a little below it, as the penny is a little below the line joining the edge of the basin to the eye in the disappearing coin trick.

The astronomers of Alexandria were fully conversant with the existence of refraction, and realized that it provided the explanation of the disappearing coin illusion, and why bodies immersed in water seem to be nearer to the surface than we find them to be when we try to grasp them. The attempt to find a correction for "atmospheric refraction" led Ptolemy of Alexandria to make the first extensive physical experiments in which numerical measurements were recorded to discover the amount of bending. In his experiments he studied the passage of light from air to water, from air to glass, glass to water, and vice versa. For water and air, he used a piece of apparatus essentially like that shown in Fig. 75. Although Ptolemy obtained numerical data good enough for making an empirical correction for the bending of light in passing from one medium to another, his results were not accurate enough to display the simple geometrical rule which more careful observation might have disclosed. Though atmospheric refraction does not affect observations on the time of transit, it does affect observation of the exact time when a heavenly body is seen in a given position east or west of the meridian. When the invention of the telescope revived interest in optical phenomena, interest in atmospheric refraction was renewed by the attempt to make accurate determinations of the moon's R.A. and the positions of the planets by observations when they are not on the meridian with the help of methods explained in the next chapter.

THE NATURE OF A SCIENTIFIC LAW

There is much misunderstanding concerning the meaning of a scientific law. So it may be well at this stage to illustrate the meaning, scope, and method of arriving at the law of refraction by using the first recorded body of numerical data in the history of experimental science. By referring to Figs. 74 and 75 you will see what is meant by the angle of the incident ray (*i*) and the angle of the refracted ray (*r*) when light passes from air into water. The terms are relative to the direction from which we are supposed to view the source of light. If light passes from water to air it is bent outwards and the incident angle is the smaller of the two. If light passes from air to water it is bent inwards and the angle of refraction is the smaller. The figures obtained in one of Ptolemy's experiments* are given in the two left-hand columns of the succeeding table.

Angle of Incidence (i)	Angle of Refraction Observed (r)	Calculated by Proportional Parts	Percentage Error
0°	0°		
10°	8°	7¾°	3·1
20°	15½°	15¼°	1·7
30°	22½°	22¼°	1·1
40°	29°	28¾°	0·9
50°	35°	34¾°	0·7
60°	40½°	40¼°	0·6
70°	45½°	45¼°	0·6
80°	50°		

Suppose we are satisfied that every one of the figures in this table is correct. That is to say, repeated observations agree. We can use the figures in one of three ways to calculate how much a ray entering water will be bent. The first is arithmetical, and is called the method of proportional parts. To find the angle of refraction when the incident angle is 22° we should refer to the observed values tabulated as above, finding that the two nearest figures for the incident ray are 20° and 30°. An incident ray of 22° is obtained by adding $\frac{2}{10}$ or $\frac{1}{5}$ of the interval (10°) between 20° and 30° to the former figure. The corresponding angles of the refracted ray are 15½° and 22½°, the interval being 7°. Adding $\frac{1}{5} \times 7$ to 15½ we get 16·9. To see how far this procedure is satisfactory we may compare the values of the refracted angle in Ptolemy's experiment calculated on the same assumption with the values he actually obtained. Thus 10° is half the interval between 0° and 20° and the corresponding angles of refraction are 0° and 15½°. Half the interval between 0 and 15½ is 7¾ instead of 8 as the experiment gives. We then get the values given in the third column. The fourth column, showing the percentage error of the calculated as compared with the observed value, indicates that the greatest discrepancy is 3·1 per cent, the average being 1·2 per cent. For incident angles between 0° and 70° we might reasonably conclude that such calculations would not generally lead us to make an error much larger than 3 per cent, and rarely if at all more than 4 per cent. A second way of using the information provided in the table would be to plot the values on squared paper, draw a smooth curve as nearly as possible through them, and read off the values which we wish to find out. Either of these methods can be made more accurate by including as many observations as we care to make in our table or graph of recorded results, and both are open to the objection that we have to refer to the original data whenever we wish to make a calculation.

The third method of using the data is to find some simple expression from which all the observed values can be inferred with a fairly high degree

* As given in the translation cited by Brunet (*Histoire des Sciences: Antiquité*).

of precision. Once we have found such an expression and ascertained how big an error can arise in using it, we have no need to refer again to the original data. *Such an expression is the sort of condensed statement of observed truths known as a scientific law.* Ptolemy did not himself succeed in detecting any simple rule of this kind connecting the numbers he obtained. The truth is that his observations on bending of the smaller and larger angles (10°, 20°, and 80°) were not very accurately made. With a device like the one in Fig. 75

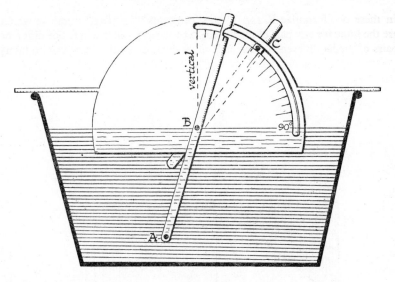

FIG. 75

A simple apparatus for finding the law of refraction, which can be made with a fret-saw from three-ply wood. At A, B, C nails project. When one bar is held in any position the other is rotated till all three projecting nails appear to be in line. From the graduated scale of degrees, the "angle of incidence," i.e. the angle light makes with the vertical in air, given by the bar BC, can be compared with the "angle of refraction," i.e. the angle light makes with the vertical in water, made by the bar AB.

In this instance the source of light is the light reflected from the bottom pin A, and a ray following the path AB is refracted outwards in air along the path BC to the observer's eye. It is immaterial which we call the angle of incidence and the angle of refraction as long as we always keep one term for the angle of the light ray in air and the other for the angle of the light ray in water. Literally speaking the latter is the incident ray in this case, but the law is usually stated as for light travelling in the opposite direction, in which case the terms have the meaning given above.

a schoolboy can get data which agree more closely with careful observations carried out with good instruments.

In seeking for a simple formula connecting two sets of numbers such as those in the first left-hand column (*i*) of the preceding table and the corresponding figures in the next column (*r*) the investigator may be guided by the shape of a curve based on his observations, or by analogy between the process that he is studying and some other process for which he already knows a satisfactory law. He may have to try several ways of stating the connexion before he finds one that is satisfactory. Kepler proposed the formula:

$$i = \frac{Kr \cos r}{K \cos r - (K - 1)}$$

Snell and Descartes gave the law as:

$$\sin i = R \sin r$$

In these two formulae K and R are "constants," i.e. fixed numbers which are the same for any pair of media, e.g. air to water, water to air. For different pairs of media different values of R or K must be used. These can be tabu-

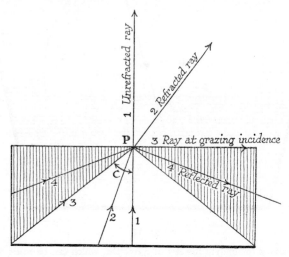

FIG. 76.—LIMITS OF REFRACTION

Four rays from the bottom and sides of a vessel converging at the same point P.

1. (angle of refraction zero) is not bent, when passing out into air.
2. (angle of refraction less than critical angle, C) bent towards the surface on emerging into air.
3. (angle of refraction equal to the critical angle) emerging ray just grazes the surface.
4. (angle of refraction greater than the critical angle) does not emerge but is reflected downwards.

lated in a short list of *refractive indices*. This dispenses with the need for constant reference to all the original experiments carried out to ascertain the law.*

Having found a formula which seems to connect two sets of measurements in a physical experiment the first thing is to ascertain how well it fits them. As Ptolemy's figures for smaller and larger angles do not agree with careful

---

* In using them, of course, we must remember, that in passing from water to air instead of air to water, *i* will be the angle which the beam makes with the vertical in water and *r* will be the angle it makes with the vertical in air. The values of R are usually tabulated for light passing from the lighter to the heavier medium. Otherwise the reciprocal of the tabulated value is used. See also p. 148.

observations which any competent person can make, we may shorten his table to illustrate how this is done. In Kepler's and Snell's laws K and R are constants for a given pair of media. How far this statement is true is seen from the following table which you will find it instructive to check. For instance, on looking up sin 20° in tables of sines it is found to be 0·342 and sin $15\frac{1}{2}$° = 0·267, so that by Snell's formula R = 0·342 ÷ 0·267 = 1·28.

i	r	Kepler's formula $K = \dfrac{i}{i + (\cos r)(r - i)}$	Snell's formula $R = \dfrac{\sin i}{\sin r}$
20	$15\frac{1}{2}$	1·28	1·28
30	$22\frac{1}{2}$	1·30	1·31
40	29	1·32	1·33
50	35	1·33	1·34
60	$40\frac{1}{2}$	1·33	1·33
70	$45\frac{1}{2}$	1·33	1·32

Having done this to find a representative value of the physical constant characteristic of the substances which we are using, we have next to test the accuracy of the law we propose to use. Taking the mean of the values in the last table as representative, K = 1·32 in Kepler's law and R = 1·32 for Snell's law applied to water and air, we may check the accuracy of each law by comparing values of r calculated by the formula with values actually observed. For instance, by Snell's law, sin r = sin i ÷ R. If i is 70°, sin i = 0·9397 and sin r = 0·9397 ÷ 1·32 = 0·7119. The tables give 0·7119 as sin 45·38°, so the calculated value of r, (45·38°), differs from the observed ($45\frac{1}{2}$°) by 0·12°, and an error of 0·12 on $45\frac{1}{2}$ is 0·3 in a hundred or less than 0·5 per cent. Making a table of the percentage errors obtained in calculating values of r from values of i by the two laws we get the following:

i Observed	i Calculated from r by Kepler's Law	Percentage Error	r Observed	r Calculated from i by Snell's Law	Percentage Error
20	20·71	3·6	$15\frac{1}{2}$	15·02	3·1
30	30·51	1·7	$22\frac{1}{2}$	22·27	1·0
40	40·12	0·3	29	29·15	0·5
50	49·71	0·6	35	35·47	1·3
60	59·46	0·9	$40\frac{1}{2}$	41·00	1·2
70	69·56	0·6	$45\frac{1}{2}$	45·38	0·3

Mean percentage error 1·3   Mean percentage error 1·2

Taking the facts as they stand, i.e. assuming that Ptolemy's data are as accurate as we can make them by using the best instruments and the most careful record of our readings, we see that between 20° and 70° we can calculate the angle of refraction correct within 3 per cent, or within half a degree, by using Snell's law. Clearly, also, there is not much to choose between the accuracy of the two laws with only this information to guide us. To decide in favour of one or the other we may next compare the results of applying both laws to other media, e.g. water and glass, or glass and air, or, using the same apparatus as before, air and paraffin, air and alcohol, air and glycerine, or water and olive oil. It might happen that the average error was much larger for some media than for others, using one law, while the other gave results of equal consistency. We should then have a reason for deciding in favour of the latter. It might happen that the differences between observed results and values calculated by either law were never greater than the accuracy with which we could make the observations. For instance, it might happen that repeated observations would not agree within half a degree, and that both sets of calculated values would not differ from the observed average values by more than half a degree. Either law would then be a safe guide to correct conduct, and our

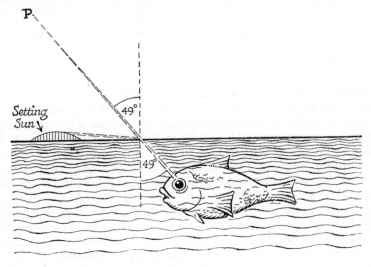

FIG. 77

One queer thing about the fish's heaven is not mentioned in Rupert Brooke's poem. The sun sets in the heaven of the fish at an angle of 49° instead of 90° from the zenith and the whole terrestrial world which is visible to the fish is compressed in a cone of which the apex is $2 \times 49°$. When the sun is just dipping on the horizon its rays enter the water at nearly 90° from the vertical, being then bent to 49° from the vertical. The result is that the sun appears to be at P.

only reason for preferring one to the other would be that using it involved less effort.

In this case Snell's law is the simpler of the two. That is to say, we can calculate more quickly with it. However, it should not be regarded as the true law of refraction merely because it is simple. It is more true if it yields results which agree more closely with observed facts. Even if it were less accurate than Kepler's law we might still use it in certain situations. If you only want to know the angle of refraction within a degree, a law which tells you how to calculate it with an error of half a degree is just as good as a law which tells you how to calculate it within a hundredth of a degree. So if the first happens to involve less effort spent in calculation you will naturally prefer it to the second. In testing a law there is another important thing to remember. Our table shows how the law helps us to calculate the angle of refraction for incident angles between 20° and 70°. Would it be true from

0° to 20° or from 70° to 90°? The data do not tell us. But two simple experiments suffice to show that Snell's law holds good at the extreme limits. A beam of light passing vertically downwards is not displaced to the right or left, i.e. when $i = 0$, $r = 0$. Snell's law gives $\sin r = 0 \div R = 0$, i.e. $r = 0$. If a beam of light just grazes the surface of the water the angle of incidence is 90°. Snell's law shows that $\sin r = \sin 90° \div R = \dfrac{1}{R}$. Taking the mean given above, $\sin r = 1 \div 1 \cdot 32 = 0 \cdot 7576$. The tables tell us that $0 \cdot 7576$ is the sine of $49\frac{1}{4}°$ or 49° to the nearest degree. This means that a beam of light coming from air into water cannot be bent in so that the angle of

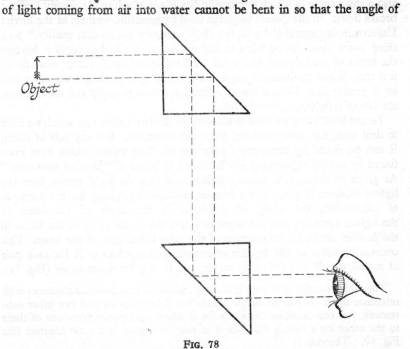

FIG. 78

Two prisms (with angles 90°, 45°, 45°) arranged as in the figure constitute the essential parts of a periscope. Parallel rays from the object enter the first face at right angles and are not refracted. The unrefracted ray strikes the slanting surface at 45° from the vertical. This is greater than the critical angle for air and glass so the ray does not pass out into the air. It is reflected downwards.

refraction is more than 49° (i.e. bent downwards $90° - 49° = 41°$) as shown in Fig. 76. Conversely if a beam of light in water is inclined to the vertical at 49°, ($r = 49°$), it will be bent outwards so much that it will just graze the surface as it passes into air, and if the "angle of refraction" in water is greater than 49° a beam of light will not pass out into air at all. It will be totally reflected backwards at the surface (Fig. 76). This is called the *critical angle*, and can be determined very accurately in agreement with Snell's law. For air into flint glass the value of R is $1 \cdot 65$ and $(1 \div 1 \cdot 65) = 0 \cdot 606 = \sin 37°$ (nearly). So the critical angle for flint glass is 37°. Thus a prism with angles 45°, 45° and 90° can be used as a perfect mirror if placed as in Fig. 78. Prisms are used as reflectors in binoculars and periscopes.

The main point to grasp about a scientific law based on measurements is that it is: (*a*) a condensed statement of observed facts to use as a guide for practical conduct, (*b*) the most economical way of getting a result as accurately as we need it. So to say that a law has been superseded does not mean that it is wrong in an absolute sense. It is wrong to go on using a law when it is no longer sufficiently accurate for our needs, especially when we can summarize what is known in a way which is sufficiently precise for use. Right and wrong in the domain of scientific laws is partly judged in its historical context, as believers judge the family life of the patriarchs. There is also a third sense in which a scientific law is not absolute. At certain limits it breaks down. In the quaint language used by scientific workers of the Soviet Union this is expressed by saying that "quantity passes into quality." So a third point about using a law is that we are not entitled to apply it beyond the limits of the original data until we have ascertained within what limits it is true. When the incident angle of a beam of light passing *from* water *into* air is greater than 49° the law of refraction ceases to apply and another law, the law of reflection, has to be used.

To use Snell's law we need to know R for the two substances which we have to deal with, e.g. water and air, glass and water, etc. For any pair of them, R can be found by experiment once for all. The values which have been found by careful experiment are tabulated in books of "physical constants." As given in them, it is usually understood that the light passes *from* the lighter medium (e.g. air) *to* the heavier medium (e.g. glass). So, for purposes of calculation, the angle of incidence is the angle of the beam in the lighter medium, and the angle of refraction is the angle of the beam in the heavier medium, irrespective of the actual direction of the beam. This convention saves us the trouble of recording two values of R for each pair of media, e.g. $R = \frac{4}{3}$ for air to water, and $R = \frac{3}{4}$ for water to air (Fig. 74).

The tables usually give only refractive indices of transparent substances with reference to air. If you know the figures for R between air and two other substances, you can calculate the value for R when light passes from one of them to the other by a simple rule which is easy to expose in a scale diagram like Fig. 80. The rule is

$$R \text{ (B to C)} = R \text{ (A to C)} \div R \text{ (A to B)}$$

Thus for air to flint glass, R is given in the tables as 1·65. For air to water it is 1·33. Hence for water to flint glass it is $1·65 \div 1·33 = 1·24$.

ACCURATE DETERMINATION OF THE REFRACTIVE INDEX

From what has been said, it is clear that we need better data than the ones which Ptolemy recorded to decide between the merits of Kepler's formula and Snell's law. With properly constructed instruments it can be shown that the latter is more accurate. The value of R (or the *refractive index*) of substances does not vary more than 0·01 per cent when calculated according to Snell's law.

One method of determining R for different substances is illustrated in Fig. 79. Another is shown in Figs. 80 and 81. When light passes through a transparent substance the emergent beam is parallel to the incident beam, if

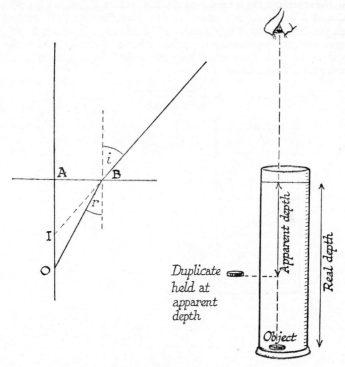

FIG. 79

One way of testing Snell's law or of finding the Refractive Index (R) for a liquid is to compare the actual depth of an object immersed in a tall cylinder of the liquid with its apparent depth judged by holding a duplicate outside the cylinder in such a position that both the immersed object and its duplicate appear at the same level when the head is moved from side to side. If Snell's law is true:

$$R = \frac{\text{real depth}}{\text{apparent depth}}$$

In the diagram O is an object immersed. The ray OB makes the angle r with the vertical and is bent outwards making the angle i with the vertical on passing into air, so that the object appears as if it were at I. By parallels

$$= \angle AIB \quad \text{and} \quad r = \angle AOB$$

$$\sin AIB = \frac{AB}{IB} \quad \text{and} \quad \sin AOB = \frac{AB}{OB}$$

$$\frac{\sin i}{\sin r} = \frac{\sin AIB}{\sin AOB} = \frac{OB}{IB}$$

When we are looking downwards the angles i and r are very small, so that

$$\frac{BO}{BI} = \frac{AO}{AI} = \frac{\text{real depth}}{\text{apparent depth}}$$

For water $R = 1\frac{1}{3}$ so that the apparent depth is three quarters of the real depth. This is the reason why a spoon appears to be bent when half immersed in water. Every point immersed in the water appears to be only $\frac{3}{4}$ as low down as we expect it to be.

the two opposite faces are also parallel. If the faces are inclined, like those of a *prism*, the emergent ray is bent inwards. For reasons shown in Figs. 80 and 81 the value of R is related in a simple way to the inclination A of the two faces through which the beam of light passes, and to the angle D, which the emergent ray makes with the ray entering the prism when both are inclined at the same angle (x) to the faces from which they respectively emerge or at which they enter the prism. This relation is:

$$R = \frac{\sin \frac{1}{2}(A + D)}{\sin \frac{1}{2}A}$$

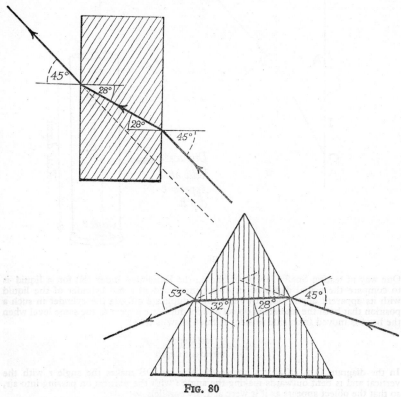

FIG. 80

Refraction of pure light of one colour through a prism of 60°. The refractive index (R) of the glass is $1 \cdot 5$. So if the incident ray (in air) is 45°,

$$\sin r = \sin 45° \div 1 \cdot 5 = 0 \cdot 707 \div 1 \cdot 5 = 0 \cdot 47.$$

Since $\sin 28° = 0 \cdot 47$ the angle of refraction at the first face is 28°.

To find the angle D for a prism with faces inclined at an angle A an instrument called a spectrometer is used. This consists of a source of light, which projects a thin beam on to the prism and telescope, both capable of revolving on a turntable with a graduated scale to record the angle. All that is necessary is to find the position in which the telescope and the source of light point at equal angles to the two prism faces while the telescope receives the beam. To find the refractive index of a solid substance, a prism made of it is used.

To find that of a liquid a hollow prism with thin glass sides is filled with it. The precision of the law can be tested by the consistency of results obtained when prisms with faces inclined at different angles are used.

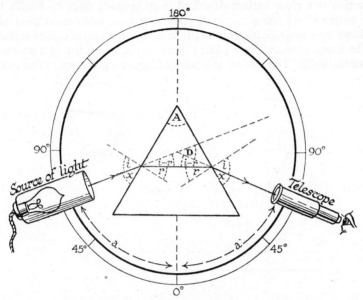

FIG. 81.—ACCURATE DETERMINATION OF REFRACTIVE INDEX. DIAGRAM OF SPECTROMETER

The prism (upper figure) is set so that the two faces which enclose A are equally inclined to the line joining 0° to 180° on the scale. The source of light and the telescope are moved till the telescope receives the beam while they are inclined at equal angles a to this line. The angle of deviation (D) is then $180° - 2a$

The beams entering and leaving the prism, then make equal angles (x) with the two faces which enclose the angle A, and $i = 90° - x$

Since the $\angle D =$ the sum of the two interior opposite angles, each $(i - r)$

$$D = 2(i - r) \quad \therefore \quad i = \tfrac{1}{2}D + r.$$

Since the $\angle A$ and the two base angles, each equal to $x + (i - r)$, make up 2 right angles

$$\therefore \quad A + 2(x + i - r) = 2(90°)$$
$$\therefore \quad A + 2(90° - i + i - r) = 2(90°)$$
$$\therefore \quad r = \tfrac{1}{2}A$$
$$\therefore \quad R = \frac{\sin i}{\sin r} = \frac{\sin \tfrac{1}{2}(A + D)}{\sin \tfrac{1}{2}A}$$

DESIGNING MIRRORS

The social conduct for which the laws of reflection and refraction provide us with guidance includes designing mirrors for shaving, or as reflectors for lamps, for searchlights, for telescopes and for periscopes; prescribing lenses for spectacles; or combining lenses in cameras, in magic lanterns, in telescopes, in microscopes, and in various surgical devices like the laryngoscope and auroscope; also designing prisms for spectroscopes, for periscopes and for binoculars. Designing lenses of the right curvature to produce magnification involves a knowledge of refraction at curved surfaces, in contradistinction to refraction at a plane surface described in its simplest form by Snell's law. The nature of refraction at curved surfaces is more easily understood when we know how magnification can be produced by reflection at curved surfaces.

The image produced by a plane mirror cannot be caught on a screen. It is a *virtual* image. To represent it in a scale diagram we have only to remember

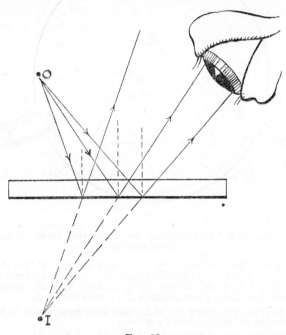

FIG. 82

I is called the *virtual image* of the object O, because it merely represents the point from which the reflected rays entering the eyeball *appear* to diverge. This point lies as far behind the mirror as the object does in front of the mirror. A virtual image cannot be caught on a screen. A *real* image (pp. 156, 157) can.

that the only "rays" of light visibly reflected from any point on an object (Fig. 68) are those which do not diverge by more than the width of the pupil where they enter the eye. This means that to represent the image of any point of an object placed before a mirror we only need to follow the path of any two rays which enter the eye and trace them backwards to the point from which they appear to diverge. Using this method (Fig. 82) shows us that the image of a point at a certain distance in front of a mirror is situated at the same distance behind it. By tracing out the course of two rays from each of the three corners of an L-shaped figure, as in Fig. 83, we also see that the virtual image is upright and reversed from left to right. To put the issue in another way, the image of a page of print seen in a mirror resembles the appearance we should see if we were looking at the script *through* a transparent page. The method of reconstructing the image by representing small beams of light or "rays" reflected from its edges as geometrical lines therefore agrees with the three most familiar characteristics of reflection from a flat surface like a hand mirror or a pool of water.

If a mirror is flat, it is immaterial whether we say that the angles which the incident and reflected rays make with the perpendicular (normal) to the surface or to the surface itself are equal; but it is more convenient to define their relation in terms of *zenith distance* than in terms of *altitude* when the reflecting surface is not flat. In applying the fundamental law of reflection to mirrors with curved surfaces such as form a slice from the surface of a sphere, the Alexandrian astronomers used the reasoning which they had

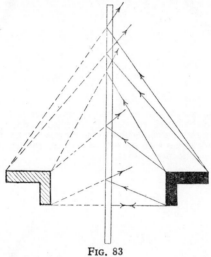

FIG. 83

By considering the points from which any pair of rays appear to diverge when an angular object is placed before a mirror we can see why the image is reversed from left to right.

learned to use in dealing with the observer's horizon. We can look on the immediate neighbourhood of the place where a ray of light strikes a spherical surface as a little patch of flat earth. That is to say, the ray is reflected as it would be if it struck a flat mirror placed in the plane which is *tangential* to the surface at the point where it strikes. A line which joins the point where the tangent plane grazes the surface to the centre of the imaginary sphere from which a concave or convex mirror is supposed to have been sliced off as in Fig. 84 must strike the tangent plane at right angles. If a ray does so, the angles of incidence and reflection are equal. So a ray passing along the line which joins any point on an object to the "centre of curvature" of a spherical mirror is reflected back on its own path. Any other one is reflected in the same plane so that the angle the reflected ray makes with the line joining the point, where it strikes to the centre of curvature, is equal to the angle which the incident ray makes with the same line. Rays that fall parallel to the line which joins the centre of the mirror to the centre of curvature are reflected so that they either converge towards (concave

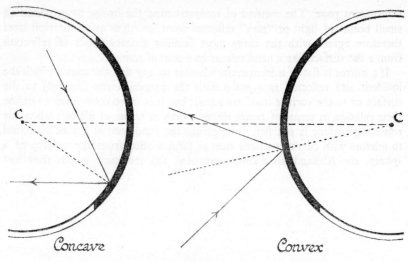

FIG. 84

A concave or convex mirror can be looked on as a slice from a sphere silvered or polished on the inside or outside respectively. The line joining a point on the surface of a sphere to its centre is perpendicular to the tangent. So the incident and reflected ray make equal zenith angles with the line which joins the centre of curvature to the point from which the incident ray is reflected.

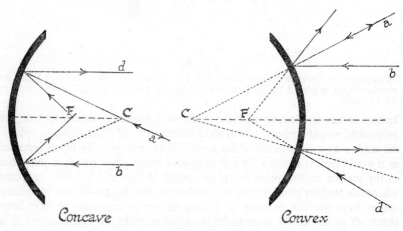

FIG. 85

The two rules which suffice for representing the image formed by an object placed before a concave and convex mirror are:

(1) A ray (*a*) which strikes the mirror so that it passes through or is directed towards the centre of curvature is reflected back along its own path.

(2) A ray (*b*) which runs parallel to the optical axis of the mirror is reflected back so that it passes through (concave mirror) or appears to come from (convex mirror) the focus. Conversely, a ray (*d*) coming from the focus (concave mirror) or proceeding towards it (convex mirror) is reflected parallel to the optical axis. The *optical axis* is the line which joins the centre of curvature to the centre of the mirror.

surface) or appear to diverge from (convex surface) the neighbourhood of a point called the *Focus* between the centre of curvature and the mirror itself. If the distance between the centre of curvature and the mirror is large compared with the diameter of the latter, the distance of the focus from the mirror (the focal length) is approximately half the distance (radius of curvature) from the mirror to the centre of curvature as in Fig. 85.

If the curvature of a concave or convex mirror is measured we can therefore reconstruct the position of the image when the object is placed at a measured distance from it by tracing the path of two rays from each of several points at the boundary of the object. For practical purposes the two end points are enough. One ray from each point is in the same straight line which joins it to the centre of curvature. This is reflected back along its own path. The other is parallel to the optical axis and is reflected back so

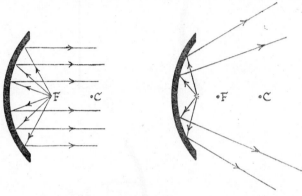

FIG. 86

Rays parallel to the optical axis converge to the focus of a concave mirror which can therefore be used like a lens as a burning-glass. Rays which come from the focus are reflected parallel to the optical axis. If they come from a point between the focus and the mirror they diverge on reflection. This is how mirrors are used on lamp reflectors or in headlights to produce a diverging beam of light.

that it diverges from (convex mirror) or converges towards (concave mirror) the focus (Fig. 86).

The image produced by a convex mirror has the same general characteristics wherever the object is put. It is an upright virtual image reversed from left to right like the image formed at a plane surface, differing only in so far as it is always *smaller* (Fig. 87, *a*) than the object. This compresses a larger visible field into a smaller space. So such mirrors are used as reflectors for motor-cycles and cars to display objects approaching from behind. If an object is placed between the focus and surface of a concave mirror (Fig. 87, *b*) an upright virtual image reversed from right to left is also obtained. Instead of being diminished the image appears to be larger than the object. Everyone who has used a shaving mirror, which belongs to this class, knows that the image enlarges as the face recedes till a certain distance is reached when no clear image is seen. This point is the focus. If an object (Fig. 88) like a candle burning in a darkened room is placed beyond the focus of a concave lens tilted a little, we can focus a *real* and *inverted* image on a screen, e.g. a piece of paper. If the object is between the focus and the centre of curvature a clear enlarged image is obtained when the paper is placed a certain distance beyond the centre of curvature. If the object itself is placed beyond the centre of curvature the screen must be held in some position between the centre of curvature and the focus to get a clear image, which is then seen to be smaller than the object. Concave mirrors are used in astronomical telescopes. The object is at a great distance. So an image is formed very near the focus, where it is studied with a lens combination called an eyepiece.

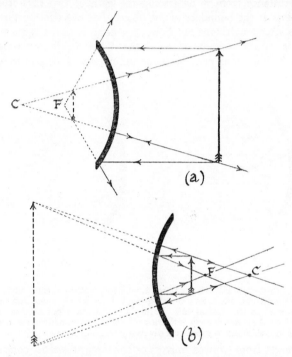

FIG. 87

(*a*) The virtual upright diminished image produced by putting an object before a convex mirror as in using one for sighting objects in the rear of the motor-cycle.

(*b*) The virtual upright enlarged image when an object is placed within the focal distance of a concave (e.g. shaving) mirror.

By applying the two simple rules given in the legend of Fig. 85 we can make a scale diagram (Fig. 89) of the position of the real image and the object, and thus calculate the centre of curvature of the mirror or its focal distance. Having done this we can make a scale diagram for the size and position of the image when the object is placed in another position. The results can readily be checked. Having justified the method we are not bound down to drawing a scale diagram to get similar results. The geometry of the scale diagram shows us how to calculate the magnification and position of the image by the simple formulae explained in Fig. 90. From these formulae we can deduce what curvature is necessary in designing a mirror to give a suitable magnification at a convenient distance for shaving.

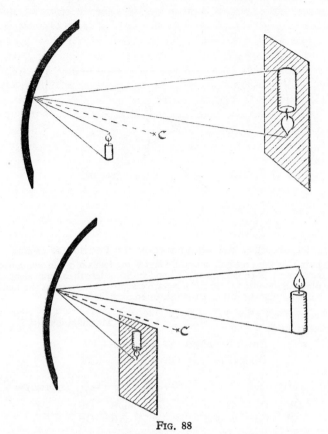

FIG. 88

The real inverted image of an object placed beyond the focus of a concave mirror may be enlarged if the object is within the radius of curvature, or diminished if beyond.

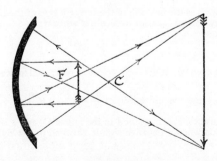

FIG. 89

The real image produced when an object is placed between the focus and centre of curvature of a concave mirror. If the arrows are reversed the figure also illustrates the case where the object is placed beyond the centre of curvature. Most optical diagrams are reversible in one way or another.

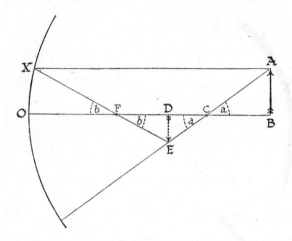

FIG. 90.—FORMULA FOR MAGNIFICATION AND POSITION OF IMAGES

In this diagram C is the centre of curvature and F the focus of a concave mirror. Its radius of curvature r is equivalent to OC and its focal length is equivalent to OF. When the object is between O and F a negative sign which precedes the numerical value of v indicates that the distance v is measured to the left of O.

Size of object AB = XO (approx.)

Size of image = DE

Magnification $= \dfrac{DE}{AB}$

Distance of object OB $= u =$ CB $+ 2f$

Distance of image OD $= v = 2f -$ CD

(i) $\dfrac{AB}{CB} = \tan a = \dfrac{DE}{DC}$

$\therefore \dfrac{DE}{AB} = \dfrac{DC}{CB} = \dfrac{2f - v}{u - 2f}$

(ii) $\dfrac{DE}{DF} = \tan b = \dfrac{XO}{OF}$ (approx.) $= \dfrac{AB}{OF}$

$\therefore \dfrac{DE}{AB} = \dfrac{DF}{OF} = \dfrac{v - f}{f}$

Combining (i) and (ii) $\dfrac{v - f}{f} = \dfrac{2f - v}{u - 2f}$. $\therefore uv - uf - 2fv + 2f^2 = 2f^2 - fv$

$\therefore uv - fv = uf$

$\therefore v = \dfrac{uf}{u - f}$ (iii)

Formula (iii) which gives the position of the image if that of the object and the focal length ($\frac{1}{2}r$) are already known is easier to recall, if written:

$$\frac{1}{v} + \frac{1}{u} = \frac{1}{f} \quad \text{(iv)}$$

The linear magnification (ii) is $(v - f) \div f = \dfrac{v}{f} - 1$; and since (iv) may also be written as: $\dfrac{v}{f} = \dfrac{u + v}{u}$ the magnification is: $\dfrac{u + v}{u} - 1 = \dfrac{v}{u}$.

If the mirror is convex OF is measured to the left of O, and a similar figure shows that formula (iii) holds when a negative sign is attached to the right numerical value for f.

COMBINING LENSES

The rules which have been given for finding what sort and size of image is produced by an object placed at a known distance from a mirror, or where the image is situated, can all be demonstrated by means of a simple optical bench (Fig. 91) which can also be used to make similar experiments with lenses. Most lenses used in optical instruments are of two general classes (Fig. 92), *diverging* lenses, which direct the path of a beam parallel to the optical axis

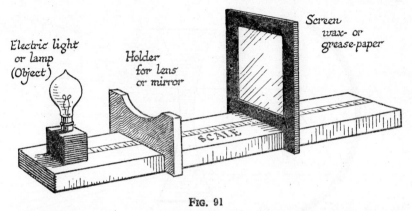

FIG. 91

Home-made bench for measuring position and size of real image formed by converging lens or (with holder and lamp reversed) concave mirror.

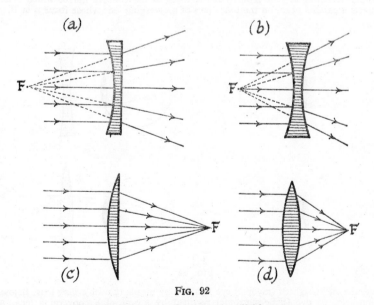

FIG. 92

Diverging lenses: (*a*) planoconcave; (*b*) biconcave.
Converging lenses: (*c*) planoconvex; (*d*) biconvex.
F is the focus in each case.

away from a point called the focus situated on the same side of the lens as the source of light, and *converging* lenses, which bring the rays to a focus on the side remote from the source, as when we use a lens to burn a hole in a piece of paper. One aspect of a converging lens is always convex. The other aspect may be convex, flat, or concave. If concave, the curvature of the concave side is less than the curvature of the convex. One side of a

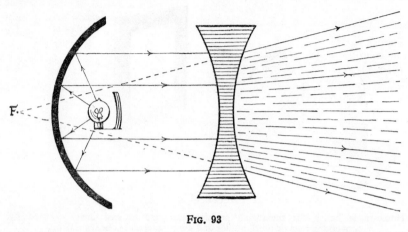

FIG. 93

A simple *Search-light*. The lamp is at the focus of the concave mirror which hence reflects a parallel beam on the inner face of a diverging lens whose focus is at F.

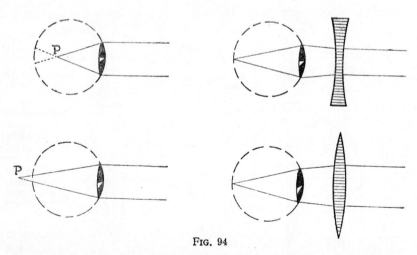

FIG. 94

Above, the short-sighted (myopic) eye rectified by means of a diverging lens. Below, the long-sighted eye (hypermetropic) rectified by means of a converging lens. A third common defect "astigmatism" is due to unequal curvature of the refractive surfaces in different planes. This is corrected by a cylindrical lens, i.e. a lens cut from the side of a cylinder, so that it produces convergence in one plane, but not in the plane at right angles to it.

diverging lens is always concave. The other may be flat or convex with a curvature less than that of the concave side.

Converging lenses, as their name suggests, make the rays of a beam converge as they emerge. Diverging lenses do the opposite. The eye, as Al Hazen was first to recognize, is a tiny camera with a translucent lens which produces an image on the sensitive layer or retina. When it functions properly it can be focussed for near and far objects by muscles which change the curvature of the lens. This adjustment is rarely perfect, and most people are a little "short-sighted" or "long-sighted." In short-sighted people light from a distant source is brought to a focus in front of the retina, and a

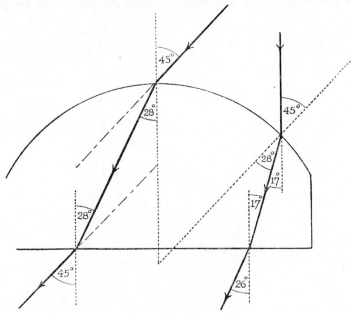

FIG. 95

This shows that a ray striking the edge of a convex surface is bent towards the optical axis (converging lens) after refraction. To make the construction all we need to know is the "refractive index" (R) of the glass. This is taken to be 1·5. Thus if the incident angle in air is 45°,

$$\sin r = \sin 45° \div 1·5 = 0·7071 \div 1·5$$

Hence r is found to be 28° from tables of sines. Notice that the direction of the ray which strikes the centre of the surface of the lens is unchanged when it emerges. If the lens is thin, with a large radius of curvature, this ray which strikes the centre of the surface may be considered to pass approximately through the centre of the lens itself.

diverging lens is necessary to make the rays converge more gradually as in Fig. 94. In long-sighted people, whose difficulty does not arise from the common failure of accommodation at an advanced age, the reverse is true. The eye is too short, and a suitable converging lens makes rays which enter it converge on the retina.

Why light is bent in this way, when it is refracted at a curved surface, is seen in the next two figures (Figs. 95 and 96). A geometrical device similar to that for curved mirrors can be used to trace out the path of a ray through a lens. The angles of incidence and refraction are measured from the line drawn perpendicular to the tangent at the point where the ray strikes the curved surface. The use of a lens as a burning-glass shows that parallel rays are brought to a sharp focus by a good lens of small curvature, and Figs. 95 and 96 show that the direction of any ray which strikes the centre of a lens is not changed when it emerges. If we know the focal distance of a lens the position and size of an image can be reconstructed by tracing the path of two rays from any point on the object. One is a ray which is parallel to the optical axis of the lens before it strikes the latter. This ray passes

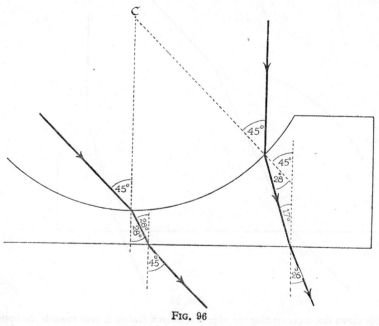

FIG. 96

This shows why a ray striking the edge of a concave surface is bent away from the. optical axis (diverging lens) after refraction. The construction is made in the same way as that of the previous figure.

through the focus of the lens if the latter belongs to the converging type. Otherwise it appears to diverge *from* the focus. The other ray passes through the centre of the lens. Its direction remains unchanged.

Diverging lenses are like convex mirrors. The image (Fig. 97) is always upright, and diminished in size. It is a virtual image. That is to say, it appears to be on the same side of the lens as the object and cannot be focussed on a screen. An upright virtual image is also obtained with a converging lens if the distance between the object and the lens is less than the focal distance of the latter. Instead of being diminished it is then magnified. This is what happens when we look at small print with a "magnifying glass." If an object is placed on one side of a converging lens, we can also focus a *real* image of it on a screen placed on the other side of the lens when the distance of the object from the lens is greater than the focal distance. As with a concave mirror, the real image is inverted, enlarged if the distance of the object is less than twice the focal distance and diminished if the distance of the object is more than twice the focal distance (Fig. 98). A camera is simply a box with a converging lens placed at the correct distance to focus a real image of distant objects on a

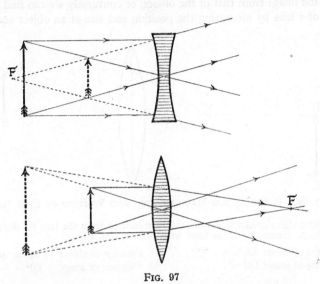

Fig. 97

Above, the image formed by a diverging lens. This is always virtual, erect, and diminished. Below, the image which is formed by a converging lens when the object is not further away than the focal distance of the lens. The image is then virtual, erect, and enlarged.

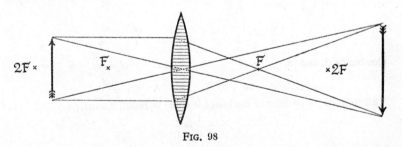

Fig. 98

When the object is separated from a converging lens by a distance greater than the focal distance, an image is formed on the opposite side of the lens and can be caught on a screen suitably placed. This *real* image is always *inverted*. If the object lies beyond 2F the image is diminished. If the object lies between F and 2F the image is enlarged. This is the principle on which the "magic-lantern" or cinema works.

photographic plate. For landscapes, the distance of the lens need not be adaptable. All rays from a very distant source are practically parallel, and converge so that the image is formed very slightly beyond the focus of the lens. So the distance between lens and plate is practically equivalent to the focal distance of the lens. To find the focal distance of a convex lens, we only have to find where a screen must be put on one side of it in order to get the clearest image of a very distant object.

Having found the focal length of a lens we can calculate the position and size of the image from that of the object, or conversely we can find the focal length of a lens by measuring the position and size of an object and its real

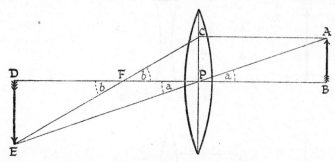

FIG. 99.—FORMULAE FOR MAGNIFICATION AND POSITION OF LENS IMAGE

The positive sign signifies that a distance is measured from the lens on the *same* side as the object. Hence, if f is the focal length of the lens, $PF = -f$

Size of object $AB = o = CP$ Distance of object $= BP = +u$
Size of image $DE = i$ Distance of image $= DP = -v$

(i) $\dfrac{CP}{FP} = \tan b = \dfrac{DE}{DP - FP}$

$\therefore \dfrac{o}{-f} = \dfrac{i}{-v - (-f)}$ $\therefore \dfrac{o}{i} = \dfrac{f}{v - f}$

(ii) $\dfrac{AB}{BP} = \tan a = \dfrac{DE}{DP}$

$\therefore \dfrac{o}{u} = \dfrac{i}{-v}$ $\therefore \dfrac{o}{i} = \dfrac{u}{-v}$

Combining (i) and (ii) $\dfrac{f}{v - f} = \dfrac{u}{-v}$ $\therefore -vf = uv - uf$

$\therefore uf = uv + vf$ $\therefore v = \dfrac{uf}{f + u}$

This formula for position of the image is easier to recall, if written:

$$\frac{1}{v} - \frac{1}{u} = \frac{1}{f}$$

Linear magnification is $\dfrac{i}{o} = \dfrac{v - f}{f} = \dfrac{-f}{f + u}$ or, from (ii), $\dfrac{i}{o} = \dfrac{-v}{u}$

image, by a simple scale diagram like the ones shown in Figs. 97 and 98. Alternatively, the calculation can be made from a formula which can be simply deduced from the geometrical relations of the diagram, as shown in Fig. 99. The truth of the rules applied in either way can be easily established by simple experiments with an optical bench like the one in Fig. 91. Their practical use lies in finding what magnification can be got from combinations of lenses in instruments like the telescope and microscope.

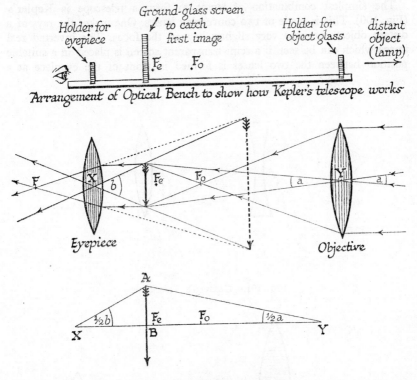

FIG. 100.—KEPLER'S TELESCOPE

Rays coming from the distant object converge to points on the real inverted image which would be seen if a screen were placed between the objective and eyepiece. From each of these points a *cone of rays* then diverges again. From these we can select two for graphical representation, one going through the centre of the eyepiece unbent, one parallel to the optical axis; so do not be misled into thinking that the rays drawn from the objective to the first image are bent at the latter. The ray passing through the centre of the eyepiece would not exist in a telescope having the precise proportions shown. It is put in as a sample to find the apparent origin of the rays that *do* exist, i.e. the virtual image. The focus of the objective is F_0. That of the eyepiece is F_e. In the figure the object is not very distant and the real image is formed beyond F_e. Where the object is at a considerable distance the real image falls almost at F_0 and the lenses are brought together so that F_0 and F_e practically coincide. The magnification is the ratio of the angular diameters: $\dfrac{b}{a} = \dfrac{\frac{1}{2}b}{\frac{1}{2}a}$. If the angles are small as stated on p. 138,

$$\frac{\frac{1}{2}b}{\frac{1}{2}a} = \frac{\tan \frac{1}{2}b}{\tan \frac{1}{2}a}$$

When F_0 and F_e are very close, so that the first image is only just beyond the focal distance of the objective and just inside the focal distance of the eyepiece (lower figure)

$$\frac{\tan \frac{1}{2}b}{\tan \frac{1}{2}a} = \frac{AB}{BX} \div \frac{AB}{BY} = \frac{BY}{BX}$$

i.e. the magnification is

$$\frac{\text{Focal distance of objective}}{\text{Focal distance of eyepiece}}.$$

The simplest combination of lenses to form a telescope is Kepler's (Fig. 100). This is made of two converging lenses. One makes the rays of a distant object converge very slightly beyond the focus. The inverted real image which can be seen if a semi-transparent screen is placed in a suitable position between the two lenses is formed in front of the eyepiece at a

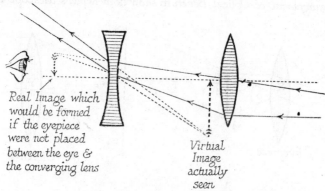

Real Image which would be formed if the eyepiece were not placed between the eye & the converging lens

Virtual Image actually seen

FIG. 101.—GALILEO'S TELESCOPE

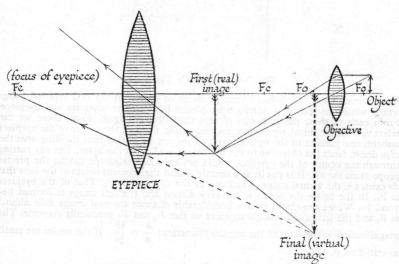

(focus of eyepiece) Fe

First (real) image

Fe　Fo

Fo

Object

Objective

EYEPIECE

Final (virtual) image

FIG. 102.—THE MICROSCOPE WITH SIMPLE EYEPIECE

distance slightly less than its focal distance. Where the rays would converge to form an image if a screen were present, they diverge again in all directions, as from the edges of an illuminated object. So the result is the same as if a real object were placed within the focus of the eyepiece, i.e. a magnified virtual image is produced. Kepler's arrangement therefore gives an inverted image. Hence though useful for astronomical purposes it is not suitable for viewing landscapes or the actors on a stage. For the reasons illustrated in Fig. 100 the magnification is the ratio of the angular diameter (*b*) of the virtual image and the angular diameter (*a*) of the object as seen without the telescope. This is the ratio of the focal distances of the far lens and the eyepiece.

The simplest type of combination which gives an upright image is Galileo's (Fig. 101). This is the type of arrangement used in opera-glasses. The eyepiece is a diverging lens. In ordinary circumstances a diverging lens produces a diminished upright image which appears to be situated on the same side of the lens as the object. This is because rays diverging from the object are

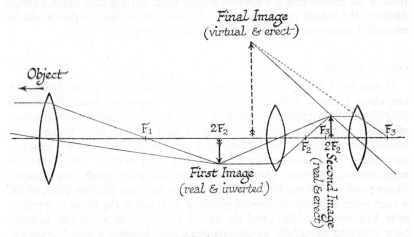

FIG. 103.—THE INVERTING EYEPIECE

A telescope made of converging lenses can be made to give an erect image by using a third lens. If the first real image formed near F_1, the focus of the objective, is made to fall at a distance equivalent to twice its focal length from the second lens, a real image which is an inversion of the first image, equivalent in size to it, is formed at the same distance from the second lens on the opposite side. This image is, therefore, the same way up as the object. If it is formed at a distance just a little less than the focal distance of the third lens, a magnified virtual and erect image is seen by the eye.

made to diverge more so that they seem to come from nearer the lens (Fig. 97). In the telescopic arrangement the diverging lens is placed between the converging lens and the position where the real image would be formed if the eyepiece were not there. These rays, converging to the focus of the converging lens, are made to diverge so that they appear to come from a virtual image larger than the real image which would otherwise be formed. This virtual image is an inversion of the latter, and since the latter is itself inverted, the result is an upright image of the object seen.

The microscope (Fig. 102) is essentially like Kepler's telescope. The object is placed at a distance from the "objective" greater than—but less than *twice*—the focal distance of the latter (see Fig. 98). So a real, enlarged, and inverted image is formed in front of the eyepiece at a distance less than the focal distance of the eyepiece. The real image produced by the objective is seen as a virtual image which is magnified still further. Any two lenses of different focal distances can be used as a microscope or telescope according as we use the lens of greater or smaller focal distance as the eyepiece.

A microscope of two- converging lenses like a telescope of the same type produces an inverted image. One way of avoiding this is the use of a compound eyepiece (Fig. 103) consisting of two lenses. If one is placed so that the focus of the objective is separated from it by a distance equivalent to twice its focal distance, the first or real image is replaced by a second reversed real image of the same size. The lens nearest the eyepiece gives a magnified virtual image of the second real image. If the first real image is formed in front of the second lens at a distance greater than, but less than twice, its focal distance, the second real image will be larger than the first, so that it will be magnified successively by the two lenses of the eyepiece.

COLOUR FRINGES

If you make a simple Kepler's telescope or a microscope by combining two cheap lenses of different focal distance, as explained, you will have no difficulty in discovering why scientists were forced to bother about the nature of colour, when instruments to produce high magnification began to be manufactured. Any image formed by a combination of ordinary lenses is surrounded by a coloured fringe which blurs the outline. The higher the magnification, the more troublesome is the distortion which this coloured fringe produces. People had long been familiar with the rainbow effect which is seen when light shines through pieces of glass cut in the shape of a prism, as in Venetian chandeliers and the like. A phenomenon which had hitherto been accepted thankfully as an ornament now became a social nuisance. Men who were active in advancing the study of astronomy, among whom Newton was foremost in the seventeenth century, were compelled to investigate colours. For the observations which led Newton to advance the views· now accepted no technique which was not available to the scientists of the Hellenistic age was necessary. What was new was *a new social need*. To make good telescopes it was essential to get rid of the coloured fringe.

Nature, as Bacon taught, can only be commanded when we have first learned to obey her. To get rid of the coloured fringe we have to understand in what circumstances it is produced. If a parallel beam of sunlight shining through a slit (or of a lamp focussed with a converging lens) strikes the face of a glass prism, one of two things may happen. It may be bent so that it strikes a second face, making an angle with the vertical greater than the critical angle, so that it is totally reflected as in Fig. 76. Otherwise it passes through the prism, without reflection at one of its faces, as a beam with diverging edges. If this diverging beam falls on a plane surface it produces a spectrum, a series of bright colours: violet, blue, green, yellow, and red (Fig. 104). If part of this coloured beam is allowed to pass through a second prism, the only colours which appear in the second spectrum will be those which are allowed to strike the second prism. The spectrum cast by a prism can be recomposed into white light by passing it through a second inverted prism (Fig. 106) or by bringing the rays to a focus with a lens.

Such simple experiments show that ordinary white light can be decomposed into different sorts of light, which we recognize by their colour. What our senses recognize as *white* light is not merely complex. It is not necessarily built up in the same way. It can be produced by combining the pure coloured lights of the spectrum in various ways. Superimposing the pure coloured lights of the spectrum (with the right degree of brightness) leads to surprising results. The combination of blue and yellow gives white. So what we recognize as white light may be made of all the coloured lights of the spectrum, or of a mixture of blue and yellow alone. Green and red give yellow. So what we recognize as yellow may be either pure spectral light

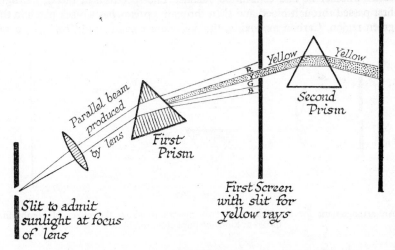

FIG. 104

Newton's classical experiment in which a spectrum was formed on a screen with a slit, which could be adjusted to admit only light of a particular region (e.g. yellow) of the spectrum. The colour of the pure "monochromatic light" which passed through the slit could not be changed by a second prism.

which cannot be decomposed, or a mixture of green and red, which can be split into its constituents with a prism. Blue and red give magenta. Magenta and green give white.

These combinations are not what we should expect from the visible results of mixing paints. For instance, blue and yellow dyes usually produce green when mixed. If we let light pass through a solution of blue dye before it strikes a prism it is nearly always found that the spectrum consists of a certain proportion of green rays as well as of blue. The dye fails to transmit, i.e. it "absorbs," red and yellow rays. A convenient arrangement for examining light transmitted through a prism is called a spectroscope. A yellow dye need not be yellow because it absorbs all light except spectral yellow. It may be yellow because it transmits red and green, absorbing all other colours. When such a yellow is mixed with blue the blue half of the mixture absorbs yellow and red rays. The yellow half absorbs blue rays, leaving nothing but green to be transmitted. In the same way a visibly red substance may be red, like

F*

the ruby lamp of the dark-room, because it absorbs all rays except those at the red end of the spectrum, or it may also be red because, like blood, it absorbs green light. Of the four principal colours we have left blue, yellow, and red when green is eliminated. Since blue and yellow give white, the effect is red.

The spectroscope is used in modern chemistry to detect differences which are not recognizable by the eye, and so to distinguish substances which at first sight seem to be physically alike in spite of their different chemical properties. If a man poisoned with strychnine or cyanide were afterwards placed with his head in a gas oven, the examination of a single drop of his blood would settle whether he had committed suicide. The spectrum of blood, i.e. light first passed through blood and then through a prism, has a black patch in the green region. Carbon monoxide, the poisonous constituent of coal gas, com-

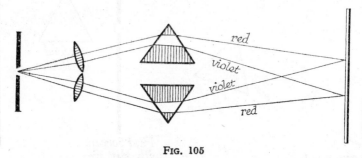

FIG. 105

An arrangement for superimposing two spectra to show the effect of combining different kinds of pure coloured light.

bines with the red pigment of blood, driving out oxygen. The resulting combination is also red, but the size and position of the black patch in the green region of its spectrum are not the same as for healthy blood.

You will see from Fig. 104 that when white light passes through a prism the rays at the red end of the spectrum are bent less than the rays at the blue end. Consequently magnification with a simple lens must always produce an image with a coloured fringe, where rays of complementary colours do not overlap and neutralize each other. When Newton set out to investigate the formation of coloured fringes, glass of quality sufficiently good for making lenses was a rarity. Italian glass-makers came to England in the middle of the seventeenth century, and flint glass, the best glass suitable for making the simple optical instruments used in Newton's time, was evolved in England about the same time. Since a lens of one and the same material must necessarily produce coloured fringes, the first effect of Newton's discoveries about the spectrum was to discourage further attempts to improve the magnifying power of the telescope by combinations of lenses. Newton designed a lens-mirror combination with which he could see the moons of Jupiter and the horns of Venus, and for a generation astronomers relied on further improvement by grinding good concave mirrors. During the eighteenth century the variety and quality of glass improved. The problem which defeated Newton was solved by practical instrument manufacturers, of whom Dollond was the successful competitor for the patent rights issued in the latter half of the eighteenth century.

This was possible, because another good quality glass was now available. The length of the spectrum produced by prisms of different kinds of glass varies considerably. For instance, if made of "crown glass" (calcium with potassium or sodium silicates), a prism of some particular size and shape produces a much shorter spectrum than one of the same dimensions made from "flint glass" (lead and potassium silicates). On the other hand, the magnifying power of lenses made of glass of two different kinds does not vary very much. This fact makes it possible to get high magnification without "chromatic

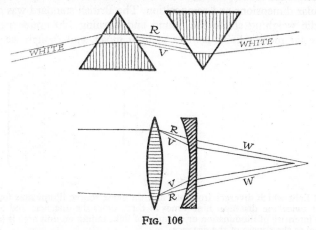

FIG. 106

Correcting chromatic aberration of lenses. A second prism placed as in figure neutralizes the dispersion of white light produced by the first. If the first prism is of crown glass, a *flatter* prism of flint glass suffices to neutralize the dispersion. In the same way a diverging lens of flint glass can neutralize the coloured fringe (RV) produced by a converging lens of crown glass. A flint glass lens which does this will be one of low diverging power as compared with the converging power of the crown glass lens. Hence the combination is itself a converging lens.

aberration," i.e. formation of coloured fringes which blur the outline of the image seen through a telescope or microscope. Modern instruments use Dollond's "achromatic" lenses formed by sticking together a crown glass converging lens of high curvature and a flint glass diverging lens of low curvature. The curvature of the flint glass lens is sufficient to neutralize the spectral "dispersion" of the crown glass lens in the same way as one prism can neutralize another (Fig. 106), without being sufficient to neutralize the magnifying power of the combination.

INTENSITY OF LIGHT

So soon as people were forced to an active interest in the nature of colour, the problem of measuring the intensity of a source of light acquired a new importance. If we match things by daylight our judgments do not agree with the result of matching the same things by artificial light. Nowadays we explain this by saying that electric light or gas light contains *more* red or yellow light than sunlight. The conditions of urban life in northern climates, the multiplication of sources of illumination and artificial dyes have compelled us to set up a standard of measurement by which we can tell how much light we get for the money we spend on illuminating our streets and dwellings, and how different shades of pigment harmonize. The principle used in determining the candle power of an electric light bulb is a simple application of Alexandrian optics. The only evident reason why antiquity did not bother to measure light is that antiquity had no need to do so.

Intensity of ordinary white light is measured nowadays by comparison with a standard source of illumination. The first standard set up was a candle of particular dimensions and composition. The British standard was a sperm wax candle weighing six to the pound and burning 120 grains per hour. There are far more reliable sources of light today, and though we use the

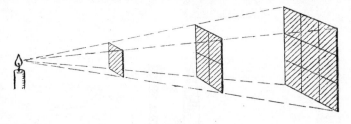

FIG. 107

A beam of light which diverges from one and the same source illuminates four times the area at twice the distance, nine times at three times the distance, and so forth. Hence the intensity of illumination or quantity of light falling on unit area is inversely proportional to the square of the distance.

term candle power, the actual physical standard used is not a candle. One of the best is a specially constructed burner for a constant mixture of air and pure pentane (the chief constituent of gasoline) arranged to give a flame of fixed dimensions. This is defined as a candle power of ten. To find the candle power of any other source of light by comparison we compare the distances at which the standard and the source of unknown candle power produce the same brightness. One way is to place them on opposite sides of a paper screen with a grease spot which makes the paper translucent in the middle. When the amount of light reflected from the opaque part and transmitted through the grease spot is equal on both sides, the outline of the grease becomes invisible. Another way is to compare the distances at which two shadows cast by the same object on the same screen, when the two sources of light are not quite in the same straight line with the object, look equally dark. From the elementary principle that "light travels in straight lines," it follows (Fig. 107) that the brightness of a source of light, i.e. the amount of light which falls on the same amount of surface, is inversely proportional to the square of the distance. So, if the distance of the source from the grease spot or shadow-screen of the "photometer" is three times the distance of the other, and the grease spot is invisible or the shadows are matched, its candle power is nine times as great.

INVISIBLE LIGHT

One of the earliest optical phenomena which attracted interest was the intense heat produced at the focus of a concave mirror when a parallel beam of sunlight strikes it. One legend credits Archimedes with applying the principle in naval warfare by attempting to set fire to enemy ships with large metallic mirrors. The analogous experiment for setting fire to a dry leaf or a piece of paper with a magnifying glass is one which most of us have carried out in our schooldays. The most celebrated burning-mirrors were made about the time of Newton's work on the spectrum by Tchirnhausen, who, with a large copper concave mirror, used the sun's rays to boil a kettle of water and to melt a hole in a coin.

Such phenomena force us to examine more closely what we mean by *light* rays. Ordinarily we recognize a beam of light by its effect on our eyes. The spectrum teaches us that unaided vision does not distinguish between colours which are found to be different when examined with a prism. Our eyes are not perfect instruments for recognizing when things are alike and when they are different. So we have to look for a new way of defining colour. The physicist says that things are of the same colour when they absorb rays of the same part of the spectrum. If our eyes are faulty as a means of recognizing colour, our judgments may also be faulty when we say that a beam of *light* can boil a kettle or blur a photographic plate. Some people are colour-blind in the sense that they cannot distinguish between green and red. It is easy to show that the distinction which the rest of us recognize is a real one. White light shining through a piece of red glass which absorbs all rays except red, as does the ruby lamp of the dark room, will not spoil a photographic plate. White light shining through a piece of green glass does so. Just as the effects which we observe in mixing colours cannot be explained by sticking to the belief that two colours are the same if the eye detects no difference, so the physical effects which we ascribe to "light" do not correspond perfectly with what we are able to recognize at first sight. In a certain sense we are all colour-blind.

The discovery that this is so was not made till more than a hundred years after Newton's work on the spectrum, when the blackening of silver chloride in sunlight was first studied. This effect of a visible source of light on silver salts is the basis of modern photography. We thus know of two physical effects other than what we see directly when light shines. A source of light can be used to produce heat or to produce chemical change. Neither of these effects corresponds exactly with what we usually recognize as light, i.e. the visible limits of the spectrum at the red and violet ends. If we move a sensitive thermometer along a spectrum thrown on a screen it detects heat above the visible limit of the red end of the spectrum and registers very little effect in the visible violet. An ordinary photographic plate is affected very little by the red rays, and is blurred *beyond* the limits of the visible violet end of the spectrum. If the spectrum is thrown on the screen vertically, the thermometer registers no heat when moved sideways beyond the visible limits, which are sharply defined. This points to the conclusion that the photographic plate can be affected by light which is more highly refracted than light which we see directly, and that heating can be produced by light which is less highly refracted than light which we see directly.

To avoid using the word *light* in an unfamiliar sense, you may prefer to speak of three kinds of "radiation," visible radiation, invisible "infra-red" radiation which is recognizable by its heating effect, and "actinic" or ultra-violet radiation which is recognizable by its chemical effect on silver salts. All three sorts of "radiation" have four characteristics of visible light. First, they can be communicated through empty space. That is to say, the effects which we describe as characteristic of a certain kind of radiation occur when the source is separated by a vacuum from the thing it influences. Second,

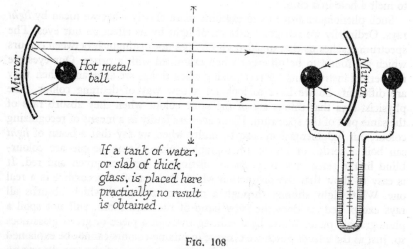

FIG. 108

A hot metal ball is placed at the focus of a concave metallic mirror. The black bulb of a sensitive thermometer placed at the focus of a second mirror registers a rise of temperature. In the type of thermometer shown (an "air thermometer") the two blackened bulbs contain air. The expansion of the air in one bulb forces the fluid in the corresponding limb downwards. Unless the metal ball which is the source of radiation is nearly incandescent, no effect will be registered while a slab of glass is held between the two mirrors.

they display the phenomenon of refraction, as the spectrum experiment shows. Third, they are reflected according to the same laws as light (see Fig. 108). Finally, they are obstructed by a black surface. If actinic rays fall on a black surface they are not reflected or scattered. Hence the image of a black object does not darken silver salts. That is why the photographic plate is a "negative." The absorption of heat rays is illustrated by the arrangement on the left-hand of Fig. 109, which also shows (right-hand) that a black surface emits heat radiation better than a white one.

The absorption or obstruction of radiation by a black body is always accompanied by rise of temperature, the effect being specially pronounced in the red end of the visible spectrum and the region of the radiations which are less highly refracted. We call the infra-red rays heat rays when the production of heat is their most striking effect. Nowadays, we know chemical reactions which are sensitive to these rays, just as the silver bromide of the ordinary photographic plate is sensitive to actinic rays and to visible rays in the blue end of the spectrum. Such reactions form the basis of infra-red photography. Aside from the specific physical effects mentioned, and the extent in which they are refracted, different sorts of radiation differ considerably in the ease with which they pass through different substances. Some kinds of glass are comparatively opaque to the invisible ultra-violet rays, which affect the photographic plate. This fact is of biological importance because some chemical reactions which occur in the animal body depend on ultra-violet light. The invisible heat rays of the infra-red spectrum pass through glass, otherwise we should not be able to recognize them. There

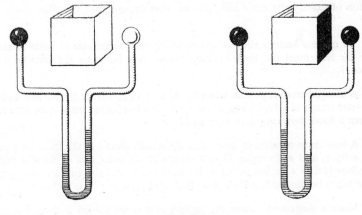

FIG. 109

A metal box filled with boiling water can be used as a source of heat radiation. If the box is uniformly white, the black bulb of an air thermometer of which the other bulb is unblackened registers greater absorption of heat. If one face of the box is black more heat is radiated from it.

are other heat rays which do not pass through glass. A body which is heated to incandescence soon ceases to give off heat rays which pass through glass when it cools beyond the temperature at which it just ceases to be visible, although (as the experiment of Fig. 109 shows) heat rays can be detected from a metal box filled with boiling water. Thus a greenhouse is a heat trap. It admits all radiations which pass through glass. These are absorbed, producing a rise in temperature, which leads to the production of heat rays, which cannot pass through glass. Dry air is highly transparent to the heat rays. Water which permits visible light to pass through it with hardly any loss is relatively opaque to invisible heat rays, especially if a little alum is dissolved in it. Some substances which obstruct visible light are readily penetrated by invisible radiation. The X-rays of medical diagnosis are ultra-violet rays which can penetrate the tissues of the human body sufficiently well to act upon an ordinary photographic plate.

EXAMPLES ON CHAPTER III

(These can be answered by making scale diagrams on graph paper)

1. A concave mirror is 10 inches wide and ¼ inch deep in the centre (neglecting the thickness of the glass). How far away must the chin be held to obtain the best magnification for shaving?

2. An extensible camera gives a clear image of a distant landscape when the lens is 8 inches from the ground-glass screen. How far must the screen be extended to get a good photograph of the page of a rare book placed 2 feet from the lens?

3. At what distance from the lens should the book be placed to get a reproduction of exactly the same size, and at what extension of the plate from the lens?

4. To make a lantern slide of the same object quarter size at what distance from the lens must the book be placed, and how far must the plate be from the lens?

5. A camera extends so that when the lens is 1½ feet from the screen it gives a life-size image of a bird's egg in the nest. At what length must it be focussed to snap a hawk hovering high overhead?

6. A headlamp consists of an electric light bulb placed at the focus of a concave mirror, and a diverging lens 9 inches in diameter and of focal distance 12 inches placed 4 inches in front. By how much will the angular divergence of the beam be diminished if the lens is shifted forwards by 2 inches?

7. Make a diagram to show the images of a point placed midway between two mirrors, and confirm your conclusion by standing between two. How is it that the moon's image is replaced by a band of light when the sea is covered by ripples? Find the distance between the third and fourth image seen in each of two mirrors 10 feet apart with an intervening object 7 feet from one of them.

8. Draw a diagram of the images formed by an object equidistant between two mirrors inclined (*a*) at 90°, (*b*) at 60°. How many images are formed in each case?

9. A glass vessel 8 inches deep is filled with

    (*a*) methyl alcohol, whose index of refraction is 1·332.
    (*b*) carbon bisulphide, whose index of refraction is 1·63.
    (*c*) Canada balsam, whose index of refraction is 1·52.
    (*d*) ethyl ether, whose index of refraction is 1·352.

What is the apparent depth in each case?

10. What is the apparent maximum north polar distance of any star ever visible to a fish in the River Thames (Lat. 51°)?

11. If the index of refraction from empty space to air is 1·0003, find the true elevation of the sun above the horizon plane when the observed altitude is 45°. (Assume that the earth is approximately flat.)

12. If a long-sighted person cannot see objects nearer than 50 cm. distinctly, find the focal length of a spectacle lens which will enable him to see objects as near as 25 cm. (clue—the lens must be capable of forming an image at 50 cm. of an object placed 25 cm. from it). Will the lens be converging or diverging?

13. A short-sighted person cannot see clearly beyond 30 cm. from the eye. What kind of lens must be used to enable him to see distant objects, and what will be its focal length?

14. A myopic patient can see print best at 12 cm. Find the focal length of a spectacle lens to extend his range to 30 cm.

15. In the practice of the optician the power of a lens of 1 metre focal length is said to be one diopter, that of a lens of 50 cm. focal length 2 diopters, etc. The + sign indicates a converging, the − sign a diverging lens. Give the results of the three last examples in diopters with the appropriate sign.

16. Explain why the sun looks red in a fog. How would the penetration of an arc lamp be affected by enclosing it in red glass?

17. If a prism is made of crown glass whose refractive index is 1·523, to what angle must it be ground to give a minimum deviation of 25°?

18. With the spectrometer method of Fig. 81 the minimum deviation for sodium light is 29° 32′ with a prism whose angle is 44° 46′. Find the refractive index of the glass for sodium light.

19. White light falls at right angles to one face of a prism whose vertex is 25°. For the end rays of the spectrum the glass of which it is made has refractive indices 1·61 and 1·63. What is the angle of divergence between the visible limits of the spectrum?

20. If the light of the sun is passed through a small hole on to a screen, an image of the sun is formed, but if the aperture is a large one, an image of the aperture is formed. Make a diagram to explain this. In a pinhole camera the screen is placed 6 inches from the hole. If the camera is at a distance of 50 feet from a tree 20 feet high, and is on the same level as a point half-way up the tree, what will be the height of the image?

21. Find the number of candles which at a distance of 420 cm. will give the same illumination as one candle of the same make placed at a distance of 60 cm.

22. If two electric glow lamps of 30 and 16 candle power are placed 120 cm. apart at the same height, at what points on the line through their centres do they give the same illumination?

23. By means of the grease-spot photometer (p. 172) the intensities of two glow-lamps are compared. The outline of the grease spot disappears when the photometer is 83 cm. from one lamp and 53 cm. from the other. On interchanging the lamps, and adjusting the photometer till the grease spot disappears, the distances are now 50 cm. and 77 cm. Find the ratio of the intensities of the lamps.

24. The illumination produced by the light of the full moon falling perpendicularly on a screen is the same as that of a standard candle at a distance of 4 feet. What is the candle power of the moon, its distance from the earth being 240,000 miles?

THINGS TO MEMORIZE

1. Law of Reflection. Angle of incidence = Angle of reflection.

2. Snell's Law of Refraction. Sin i = R sin r

3. Spherical Mirrors. $\dfrac{1}{v} + \dfrac{1}{u} = \dfrac{1}{f} = \dfrac{2}{r}$

   Linear magnification = $\dfrac{v}{u}$

4. Lenses. $\dfrac{1}{v} - \dfrac{1}{u} = \dfrac{1}{f}$. Magnification = $\dfrac{-v}{u}$

CHAPTER IV

THE WORLD ENCOMPASSED

The Decline of Mere Logic

THE year 1543 was notable in the history of human knowledge for the publication of the *De Revolutionibus* by Copernicus and the *De Fabrica Humani Corporis* by Vesalius. One marks the beginning of a new epoch in man's understanding of inanimate nature, the other marks the beginning of a new epoch in man's understanding of his own nature. There were abundant reasons why the opening years of the sixteenth century of our own era should have been signalized by a great advance in the study of the heavens. In the three-quarters of a century which preceded the work of Copernicus, navigation had rapidly attained a level far above any of the achievements of antiquity. Mechanical clocks were becoming available for astronomical observatories. Printing made possible the distribution of new information and old sources. In this situation a more exact knowledge of the position of the planets had an immediate practical importance which has been explained in Chapter II (p. 106). Although mechanical ingenuity had solved the problem of making standard (e.g. Greenwich) time portable in countries where sunlight is scarce, the clock was as yet—and was to remain for a long time to come—incapable of recording standard time over a long voyage. So measurement of longitude was still contingent on more precarious sources of information, as, for instance, the occultation of a planet by the moon's disc, symbolically represented by the Turkish national emblem.

The view which put the sun at the centre of the solar system was not new. It had been anticipated by Aristarchus—perhaps likewise by the Pythagorean brotherhoods a century earlier. It had been rejected by Hipparchus because there was no direct evidence for the annual parallax of a fixed star or for the earth's diurnal rotation. The parallax of a fixed star was not detected till three hundred years after the death of Copernicus, and the retardation of the pendulum at low latitudes (see p. 288), the first terrestrial experience pointing to the earth's axial rotation, was not recorded till fifty years after Kepler's successful exposition of the heliocentric doctrine. In this chapter and the next one we shall see why the Copernican view was bound to engage a sympathetic hearing among those equipped to understand it, in spite of the absence of new evidence to meet the seemingly decisive objections which could still be urged against it.

The invention of wheel-driven portable clocks made the determination of longitude at sea a technical possibility which began to be recognized in the fifty years that preceded the work of Copernicus and became a topic of absorbing interest in the half century which followed its publication. Before the modern chronometer came into use the two most simple methods were the observation of eclipses and occultations of the planets by the moon's disc. Aside from occultations, when the declination as well as the R.A. of the moon and a planet are identical (within about a quarter of a degree), the astrological lore of the medieval world attached considerable importance to the times when the R.A. of a planet is the same as that of the moon or sun (conjunction) and when they differ by 180° (opposition). The times of conjunctions and oppositions were therefore recorded in all ephemerides and in almanacs, before tables giving the daily variation of the moon's R.A at a given station were available for the method of lunar distances.

Amerigo Vespucci (Fig. 110) is said to have found his longitude when his ship was in latitude 10° N. from the following observations. At 7.30 p.m. by local time, i.e. 7½ hours after local noon, the moon was 1° E. of Mars. At midnight (local time) it had travelled to 5½° E. of Mars. Thus the moon had moved through 4½° in the same number of hours. So it would have been in conjunction with Mars at approximately 6.30 p.m. local time. On the

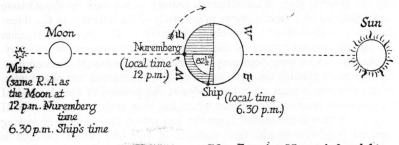

FIG. 110.—How Amerigo Vespucci Found His Longitude by a Conjunction of the Moon and Mars

When the R.A. of the moon is the same as that of a planet they are said to be in *conjunction*. If their declination is also the same, the planet will be occulted by the moon's disc. If the declination differs by a small angle it is still possible to gauge when the R.A. of the two is the same by the naked eye. The exact moment of the conjunction can be determined by successive observations of their local co-ordinates (azimuth and zenith distance). From these the R.A. can be calculated by the spherical triangle formula given on page 195.

same date his almanac prepared by Regiomontanus recorded a midnight conjunction of Mars at Nuremberg. So when the time at Nuremberg was 12 p.m. it was 6.30 p.m. at the ship's position. Local time was 5½ hours behind Nuremberg. Hence, he calculated that the ship was 5½ × 15° = 82½° west of Nuremberg. In addition to this example, Marguet (*Histoire de la Longitude de la Mer*, etc.) cites others. Columbus sought a port to observe the time of opposition of Jupiter and the moon in the 1493 voyage. In February and April of 1520 Andres de San Martin, the "best trained pilot" of Magellan's expedition, observed conjunctions of planets "according to the instructions of Faleiro who had composed *a treatise on longitudes for the special use of this expedition.*"

The words in italics show that mapping out the track of the planets was no longer a merely academic issue. It was a substantial problem of technology in the age of the great navigations. So the announcement of the doctrine of

Copernicus fulfilled an immediate social need. Not less important is the fact that the invention of spectacles proved to be the midwife of an instrument which weakened the inherent plausibility of the opposing view. The telescope revealed the planets as bodies with phases like the moon (Fig. 111), shining with reflected light like ourselves, enjoying night and day as we do, and having moons revolving round them like our own. Observations on the sun's spots showed that the sun rotates about its own axis. So there is nothing outrageous in supposing that we may do the same.

FIG. 111.—THE PLANETS' PHASES, MARS ABOVE, VENUS BELOW

Hitherto very little has been said about the motion of the planets. The account of the heavenly bodies given in the first two chapters was mainly concerned with the apparent motion of the sun and the fixed stars. While observing the stars, which seem to maintain the same relative positions in the uniform rotation of the heavenly sphere, the priestly astronomers of Egypt and Sumeria, and, it may be added, those of the calendar civilizations of Central America, recognized other bodies which do not have a fixed position in the celestial sphere, nor retreat steadily among the fixed stars in one direction like the sun and moon. Five of these bodies, Mercury, Venus, Mars, Jupiter, and Saturn, were known to the ancients. The extreme brilliancy of two of them—Jupiter and Venus—sufficiently explains the attention which their vagaries attracted. Three of them might be seen at some periods on the meridian in the course of the night. At such times nightly comparison showed that they seemed to be retreating slowly in the direction opposite to the sun's annual or the moon's monthly motion. The other two, namely Mercury and Venus, are never seen throughout the whole of any night. Each may be seen alternately as an evening star setting within three hours after sunset or as a morning star rising shortly before daybreak. The brightness of Venus makes it conspicuous in the twilight almost as soon as the sun sets and long before the brightest fixed stars are visible.

Owing to the brightness of the planets it is easy to recognize—in fact, difficult to avoid noticing—that their position among the fixed stars changes. During one month a planet may be east of a particular star, and may rise or set farther south. Next month it may be seen west of the same star, rising or setting perhaps farther north. Thus the R.A. and declination of a planet can be seen to change without recourse to measurement. The same times of rising and setting or of the meridian transit of any fixed star recur after a year. So the history of any fixed star in the course of one year is the same as its history in the preceding or succeeding year. This is not true of the planets. For instance, if you had watched for Venus month by month during 1934 and 1935 with the naked eye, you could have recorded its history as follows. In January 1934 Venus was a brilliant object setting in the early evening sky. At the beginning of February it was invisible. By the beginning of March it was a morning star rising within an hour before sunrise. In May it was still a morning star rising just before daybreak, and might be just visible before daybreak in June, July, August, and September. In October and November it was not visible. At the end of December it was visible just after sunset, as also in January 1935. In February 1935 it was a bright star in the evening sky for about two hours after sunset, remaining a conspicuous evening star till August, and in September again invisible (see also Fig. 63). The history of Mars during the same period was briefly (Fig. 112) as follows: in January and February 1934 Mars might be just visible for a short while after sunset. During March, April, May, and June, it would be hardly visible at any time. In July it would be visible before sunrise in the early hours, rising soon after midnight from August to December, but never on the meridian before the morning twilight. In January 1935 it rose before midnight and crossed the meridian before morning twilight. By April it was rising before sunset, crossing the meridian about midnight. By the end of June it was setting just before midnight, and had passed the meridian at sunset. It remained an evening star, being still just visible in twilight after sunset from September to December.

Each planet has its own cycle or synodic period in which it gets back to the same position relative to the earth and the sun. That of Venus is 584 days. If you look up *Whitaker's Almanack* for 1934 and 1935 you will see that on March 12, 1934, the R.A. of Venus, then at greatest brilliance, was 2 hours 37 minutes behind the sun, and it was then a morning star. Its R.A. was 2 hours 30 minutes behind the sun on October 13, 1935, 2 hours 38 minutes on October 18th, and 2 hours 43 minutes on October 23rd. So it had returned to its original position with reference to the earth and sun (see Fig. 63) on October 17th, 584 days later. The interest which was excited by the cycles of the planets in the priestly cultures of antiquity is illustrated by the following citation from a recent account of the calendar of the extinct Maya civilization of Central America. The Maya calendar contained five different long cycles, a year of 365 days, a year of 360 days, a period of 260 days, a lunar year based on the lunar month, and the Venus cycle. According to the source cited:*

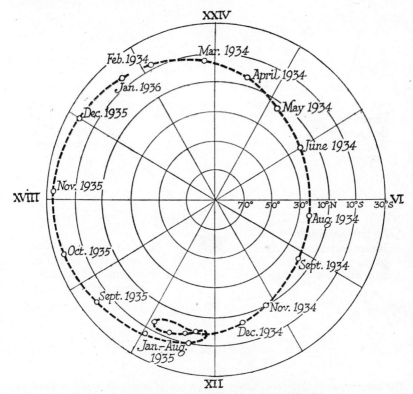

FIG. 112.—THE TRACK OF MARS IN 1934–35

The planet Venus was the object of an important cult. The revolution of Venus occupies a little less than 584 days; five of these Venus years equalled eight mean solar years (584 × 5 = 2,920, 365 × 8 = 2,920). The Mayas, however, were well aware that the Venus year was actually less than 584 days. They knew its length to the second decimal point. The actual period is 583·92 days, and to correct this error the Mayas dropped four days at the end of every sixty-one Venus years, and at the end of every three hundred Venus years eight days were dropped. This system was so accurate that had the Maya Venus calendar continued to function uninterruptedly up to the present day, the error over this period of over a thousand years would not have amounted to more than

* Field Museum of Natural History, leaflet No. 25, pp. 57–8.

a day. Such an accurate knowledge of the cycle of Venus, the revolutions of which are by no means regular, points to centuries of sustained observations. Up to the present, no deity in the Maya pantheon has been satisfactorily identified with Venus. In Mexico, however, Quetzalcoatl was closely associated with Venus as the Morning Star. In addition to Venus, the planets Mars, Mercury, and Saturn, were closely observed, and their phases accurately calculated. When one recollects that the Mayas were dependent solely on the naked eye for

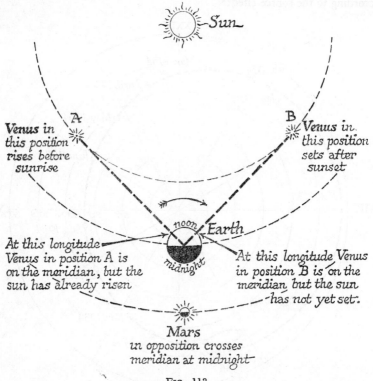

FIG. 113

The inferior planets, Mercury and Venus, have always passed the meridian when they become visible or have not yet reached it when they cease to be visible. Since it is customary to represent east on the right-hand side of a map, and also because the horizon plane rotates eastwards to meet the sun, the figure is drawn so that the South Pole is nearest an extra-terrestrial observer. Venus is at maximum elongation west of the sun as a morning star, and east of the sun as an evening star.

their observations, one is astounded at the grasp they had on the movements of the heavenly bodies. In various cities regular lines of sight existed for the observation of the equinoxes, solstices, and other important points of the tropical year, notably at Uaxactun, Copan, and Chichen Itza.

The precise positions of the inferior planets Mercury and Venus, which are only visible as morning or evening stars, cannot be gauged by the methods which we have mentioned in Chapter II. Since they never cross the observer's meridian by night (Fig. 113), we cannot find the R.A. or declination of either of them by recording the time and zenith distance at meridian transit. To trace out the motions of the planets we have to know how to calculate the right ascension or declination of a heavenly body from observations upon its position when it is not on the meridian. Even for mapping daily the entire course of the moon's monthly cycle, the methods which we have used so far are not wholly sufficient, because on several days the moon will not be visible at its time of transit. It is not necessary to watch for the time of transit of a celestial body to determine its co-ordinates in the celestial sphere (R.A. and declination). With the help of spherical trigonometry we can find the R.A. and declination of a heavenly body, if we know the local time and the local co-ordinates (azimuth, altitude, or zenith distance) and latitude. Con-

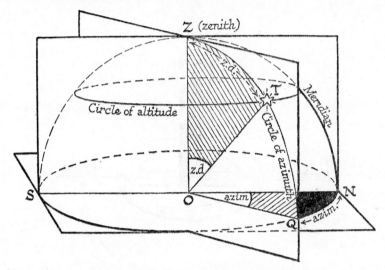

FIG. 114.—LOCAL CO-ORDINATES OF A STAR

The horizon bearing or altitude is 90° − z.d. The zenith distance z.d. is measured by the arc TZ or the flat angle ZOT in the azimuth plane. The meridian bearing or azimuth is the arc NQ which in degrees is the flat angle NOQ or the angle between the meridian plane NZS and the azimuth plane ZOQ.

versely, the navigator need not wait for a heavenly body to cross the meridian to find his latitude provided that he has a star map, or an almanac giving tables of the declination of the stars.

The local co-ordinates of a star when it is not on the meridian have already been defined on page 48, and will be understood with the help of Figs. 114 and 115. In Chapter II we have seen how to represent the position of a star in the heavenly sphere by small circles of declination parallel to the celestial equator and great circles of R.A. intersecting at the celestial poles. Such a map is true for all places, and relevant to any time of the year. At any fixed moment at a particular place we can represent the position of a star by small circles of *altitude* parallel to the circular edges of the horizon and great circles of *azimuth* intersecting at the zenith (Fig. 114). The altitude circles are numbered by their angular elevation above the horizon plane, just as declination or latitude circles are numbered by their elevation above the equator plane. An azimuth circle is numbered in degrees off the meridian by joining to the observer the ends of an arc on the horizon plane intercepted by the meridian and the azimuth circle, in just the same way as a circle of longitude is numbered by the angle between the end of an arc of the equator intercepted by it, the centre of the earth, and the point where the equator is cut by the Greenwich meridian. The azimuth of a star is therefore its east/west bearing with reference to the meridian. If you have mounted your home-made astrolabe or theodolite of Fig. 115 to revolve vertically on a graduated base

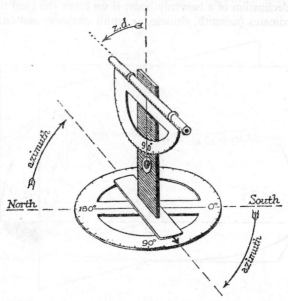

FIG. 115.—HOME-MADE APPARATUS FOR MEASURING AZIMUTH AS WELL AS Z.D., OR ALTITUDE OF A STAR

The materials are three blackboard protractors (you can make these with a fretwork set), a piece of iron tube (gas pipe), and a plumb-line. The object at which the instrument points has azimuth 70° East of North.

set so that 0° points due south or north, the azimuth of a star is the angle through which you have to turn the sighting tube (or telescope) on its base, and the altitude is obtained by subtracting from 90° the zenith distance. If the protractor is numbered reversibly from 0° to 90° and 90° to 0°, you can, of course, read off the altitude at once.

In a modern observatory the declination or R.A. of a heavenly body can be found when it is not on the meridian with an instrument called an equatorial telescope. A simple type of equatorial telescope can be made by fixing a shaft pointing straight at the celestial pole and mounting a telescope (or a piece of steel tube) so that it can rotate at any required angle about the shaft itself as axis (Fig. 116). If the telescope is now clamped at such an angle as to point to a particular star, we can follow the course of the star throughout the night by simply rotating it on its free axis without lowering it or raising it. If it is set very accurate modern clockwork so that it can turn through 360° in a sidereal day (i.e. the time between two meridian transits of any star whatever), it will always point to the same star. Since it rotates about the celestial axis the tilt of the telescope is the polar distance of the star, and if the clock is set at 0 (= XXIV) hours when the First Point

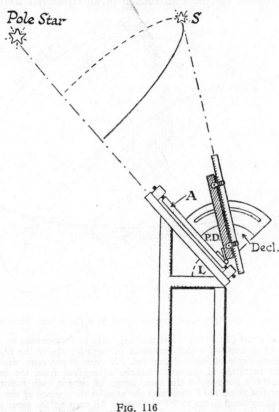

FIG. 116

A simple "equatorial" made with a piece of iron pipe and wood. The pipe which serves for telescope rotates around the axis A fixed at an angle L (latitude of the place) due north. When it is clamped at an angle PD (the "polar distance" of the star or 90° — Declin.) you can rotate it about A as the star (S) revolves, keeping S always in view.

of Aries crosses the meridian, the R.A. of the star is the sidereal time at which the telescope lies vertically above its axis of rotation. If you compare Figs. 116 and 117 you will therefore find little difficulty in seeing how it is possible to measure the celestial co-ordinates of a heavenly body at times when its transit is invisible, and if you are satisfied that it can be done, the next few pages can be deferred till you have read the ensuing sections on the hypotheses of Copernicus and Kepler. On the other hand, you will find it beneficial to work through it, when you have done so, if you wish to understand the final section of this chapter on the dating of ancient monuments.

THE SPHERICAL STAR TRIANGLE

In the time of Copernicus and Kepler it was not possible to make clocks sufficiently reliable for the construction of an equatorial instrument, and

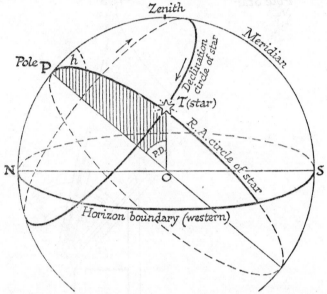

FIG. 117.—APPARENT ROTATION OF THE CELESTIAL SPHERE

The position of a star (T) in the celestial sphere may be represented by a point where a small circle of declination which measures its elevation above the celestial equator intersects a great circle of Right Ascension. All stars on the same declination circle must cross the meridian at the same angular divergence from the zenith and are above the observer's horizon for the same length of time in each twenty-four hours. The arc PT or flat angle POT measures the angular divergence of the star from the pole (polar distance) and hence is 90° − Declin. All stars on the same great circle of R.A. cross the meridian at the same instant. The angle between two R.A. circles measures the difference between their times of transit. The angle h measured from the meridian westward between the plane of the meridian and the R.A. circle of the star is the angle through which it has rotated since it last crossed the meridian. If the angle is 15° it crossed the meridian one hour ago. So h is called the hour angle of the star. If the hour angle is h degrees, the star made its transit $h \div 15$ hours previously. The hour angle is usually expressed in time units.

the determination of Declination or R.A. from measurements off the meridian could only be accomplished by a more devious method which calls for some knowledge of spherical trigonometry. This will now be explained. Figures traced out on the surface of a sphere are called spherical figures. Thus two parallels of latitude and two meridians of longitude enclose a spherical quadrilateral. The peculiarity of such figures is that all their dimensions are measured in fractions of the circumference of a circle, i.e. in degrees. If three

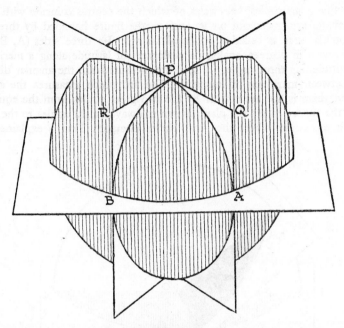

FIG. 118.—INTERSECTING FLAT PLANES ON WHICH THREE GREAT CIRCLES
OF A SPHERE LIE

This shows a globe in which three flat planes have been sliced through two meridians of longitude (along PA and PB), and through the equator (AB). Each of these planes cuts the surface of the terrestrial sphere in a complete circle, the centre of which is the centre of the sphere. Where they intersect on the surface they make the corners of a three-sided figure of which the sides are all arcs of *great circles,* i.e. circles with the same centre and the same radius as the sphere itself. Such a figure is called a spherical triangle. It has three sides, PA, PB, and AB, which we shall call *b* (opposite B), *a* (opposite A), and *p*. It has also three angles B, A, and P (PBA, PAB, and APB). What you already know about a map will tell you how these angles are measured. The angle APB is simply the difference of longitude between the two points A and B marked on the equator, and it is measured by the inclination of the two planes which cut from pole to pole along the axis of the globe. You will notice therefore that, since the earth's axis is at right angles to the equator plane, the plane of AB is at right angles to the plane of PA and of PB; and since we measure angles where two great circles traced on a sphere cut one another by the angle between the planes on which the great circles themselves lie, the spherical angle PAB is a right angle, and so is PBA. Thus the three angles of the spherical triangle are together greater than two right angles, an important difference between spherical triangles and Euclid's triangles. In practice, of course, it is a lot of trouble to draw a figure like this. So we measure the angles in one of three other ways which only involve flat geometry, which we have already learnt. These are:

(*a*) The geometry method: The angle BPA between the spherical sides PB and PA is the same as *the flat angle RPQ between the tangents* RP and QP which touch PB and PA at their common point, i.e. the "pole" P of the equatorial circle.

(*b*) The geography method: Remembering that BPA is simply the number of degrees of longitude between A and B, you will see that it is simply *the number of degrees in the arc cut off where the great circles on which PB and PA lie intersect any circle of latitude,* i.e. any circle *of which the plane is at right angles to the line joining the two poles where the great circles intersect above and below.*

(*c*) The astronomy method: This is illustrated in the next figure.

intersecting *great* circles, i.e. circles of which the centres coincide with that of a sphere, are traced out on its surface, the figure bounded by three of their circular arcs is called a spherical triangle. Its three sides (A, B, C) are measured in degrees, analogous to degrees of latitude along a meridian of longitude. Its three angles (*a*, *b*, *c*) are measured like the angular difference between meridians of longitude. The arc which measures the angle between them is the arc cut off by the two great circles from the equator where the sphere meets the plane drawn midway at right angles to the axis through the points where the great circles intersect. This is explained in

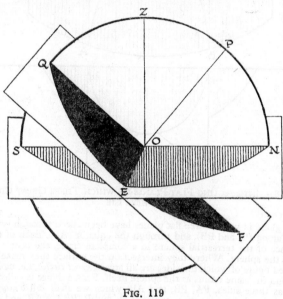

FIG. 119

The angle QES between the arcs QE and SE is the angle QOS between their intersecting planes, and

$$QOS = 90° - QOZ$$
$$POZ = 90° - QOZ$$

So *the angle between two spherical arcs is the angle between the poles of the great circles on which they lie.*

Figs. 118 and 119. You will not find it difficult to visualize the meaning of a spherical triangle if you think about one of the most elementary problems of navigation, calculating the shortest course of a ship between two ports. The shortest course on the earth's spherical surface is the flattest arc which can be traced between two places. The flattest arc is the arc of the circle of largest radius, i.e. that of the sphere itself. Hence the shortest course is the arc of a great circle. This forms one side (Fig. 122) of a spherical triangle of which the other two arcs are two meridians of longitude—also great circles. The length of these two arcs (Fig. 122) is known if the latitude of each port is known, and the angle between them is the difference of longitude. So finding a ship's course is finding the length of the third side of a spherical

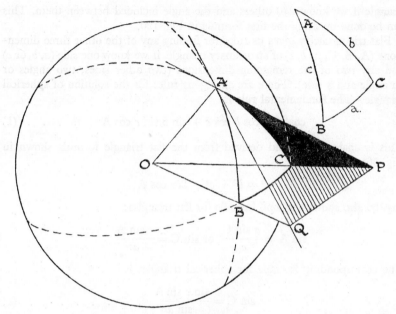

FIG. 120

With the aid of the key shown in the next figure the two fundamental formulae for
the solution of spherical triangles such as ABC in this one can be deduced from the
formulae for solving flat triangles given in Fig. 56, Chapter II.

$$PQ^2 = PO^2 + QO^2 - 2PO \cdot QO \cos a$$
$$PQ^2 = PA^2 + QA^2 - 2PA \cdot QA \cos A$$
$$\therefore \quad (PO^2 - PA^2) + (QO^2 - QA^2) - 2PO \cdot QO \cos a + 2PA \cdot QA \cos A = 0$$
$$\therefore \quad 2PO \cdot QO \cos a = 2AO^2 + 2PA \cdot QA \cos A$$

Divide through by 2PO . QO, then

$$\cos a = \frac{AO}{PO} \cdot \frac{AO}{QO} + \frac{PA}{PO} \cdot \frac{QA}{QO} \cos A$$
$$= \cos POA \cos QOA + \sin POA \sin QOA \cos A$$
$$= \cos b \cos c + \sin b \sin c \cos A$$

The formula for getting the third side (a), when you know the other two (b and c)
and the included angle A, is, therefore:

$$\cos a = \cos b \cos c + \sin b \sin c \cos A \quad \text{(i)}$$

$$\therefore \quad -\cos A \sin b \sin c = \cos b \cos c - \cos a$$
$$\therefore \quad \cos^2 A \sin^2 b \sin^2 c = \cos^2 b \cos^2 c - 2 \cos a \cos b \cos c + \cos^2 a$$

Now make the substitution $\cos^2 A = 1 - \sin^2 A$, etc.

$$(1 - \sin^2 A) \sin^2 b \sin^2 c = (1 - \sin^2 b)(1 - \sin^2 c)$$
$$- 2 \cos a \cos b \cos c + (1 - \sin^2 a)$$
$$\therefore \quad \sin^2 b \sin^2 c - \sin^2 A \sin^2 b \sin^2 c = 1 - \sin^2 b - \sin^2 c$$
$$+ \sin^2 b \sin^2 c - 2 \cos a \cos b \cos c + 1 - \sin^2 a$$

After taking away $\sin^2 b \sin^2 c$ from both sides this becomes

$$- \sin^2 A \sin^2 b \sin^2 c = 2 - \sin^2 a - \sin^2 b - \sin^2 c - 2 \cos a \cos b \cos c$$

Just by looking at this you can see that the right-hand side would be the same if
we had started with

$$\cos c = \cos a \cos b + \sin a \sin b \cos C$$

in which case we should have found

$$- \sin^2 C \sin^2 a \sin^2 b = 2 - \sin^2 a - \sin^2 b - \sin^2 c - 2 \cos a \cos b \cos c$$

Hence we can put

$$- \sin^2 C \sin^2 a \sin^2 b = - \sin^2 A \sin^2 b \sin^2 c$$

Dividing by $- \sin^2 b$, we get

$$\sin^2 C \sin^2 a = \sin^2 A \sin^2 c$$
$$\therefore \quad \sin C \sin a = \pm \sin A \sin c$$
$$\text{or} \quad \sin C = \pm \frac{\sin A \sin c}{\sin a} \quad \text{(ii)}$$

triangle if we know two others and the angle included between them. This can be done by using the first formula in Fig. 120.

Flat trigonometry gives us rules for finding any of the other three dimensions (A, B, C, *a*, *b*, *c*) of an ordinary triangle, if we know one side (*a*, *b*, or *c*) and any two of the remaining dimensions (two other sides, two angles or an angle and a side). There are analogous rules for the solution of spherical triangles. The fundamental rule is

$$\cos a = \cos b \cos c + \sin b \sin c \cos A \quad \ldots \quad \ldots \quad (1)$$

This is analogous to and derived from the flat triangle formula shown in Fig. 56:

$$a^2 = b^2 + c^2 - 2bc \cos A$$

Fig. 56 also shows a second formula for flat triangles:

$$\sin A = \frac{a \sin C}{c} \quad \text{or} \quad \sin C = \frac{c \sin A}{a}$$

The corresponding formula for spherical triangles is

$$\sin C = \frac{\sin c \sin A}{\sin a} \quad \ldots \quad \ldots \quad \ldots \quad (2)$$

With the aid of a paper model as directed in Figs. 120 and 121 you will be able to overcome the difficulties of envisaging figures drawn on a sphere, and to see how the formulas for solution of spherical triangles follow from those for flat triangles. To apply them correctly you will need to recall some of the more elementary formulae in flat trigonometry* and the convention that angles measured east of a line of reference are negative. You will probably find it helpful to practise the use of the first formula by examples like the one shown in Fig. 122. Most atlases give the length of the ship's course between large ports, and you can therefore check your answer. The distances are usually given in sea miles (1 of the earth's circumference, i.e. a great circle of the terrestrial globe is 360×60 sea miles).

To find the R.A. of a star off the meridian it is first necessary to find its declination with the cosine formula (1). The local position of every star at any instant can be placed at the corner of a spherical triangle (Fig. 123) like the Bristol-Kingston triangle of Fig. 122. One side (*b*), like the polar distance of Kingston, is the arc between the celestial pole and the zenith along the prime meridian. The elevation of the pole is the latitude (L) of the observer. So $b = 90° - L$. One side (*c*), like the polar distance of Bristol, is the arc between the star and the zenith on its own great circle of azimuth. This arc is its zenith distance (*c* = z.d.). The angle A between its azimuth circle and the prime meridian which cuts it at the zenith is its azimuth (A = azim.). Between the ends of these two arcs passes the great circle of

* $\sin A = \cos (90° - A), \cos A = \sin (90° - A)$
  $\sin A = -\sin (-A) = \sin (180° - A)$
  $\cos A = \cos (-A) = -\cos (180° - A)$
  $\cos (180° \pm A) = -\cos A; \sin (180° \pm A) = \mp \sin A$

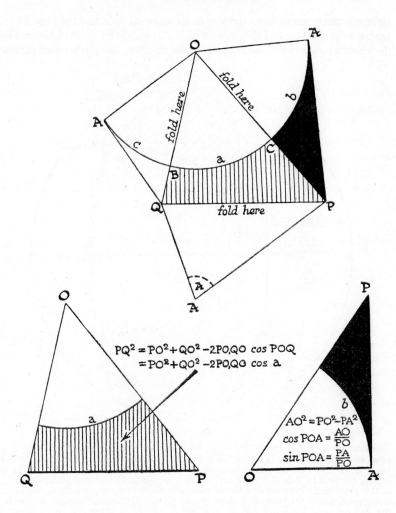

$$PQ^2 = PO^2 + QO^2 - 2PO.QO \cos POQ$$
$$= PO^2 + QO^2 - 2PO.QO \cos a$$

$$AO^2 = PO^2 - PA^2$$
$$\cos POA = \frac{AO}{PO}$$
$$\sin POA = \frac{PA}{PO}$$

$$PQ^2 = PA^2 + QA^2 - 2PA.QA \cos PAQ$$
$$= PA^2 + QA^2 - 2PA.QA \cos A$$

$$AO^2 = QO^2 - QA^2$$
$$\cos QOA = \frac{AO}{QO}$$
$$\sin QOA = \frac{QA}{QO}$$

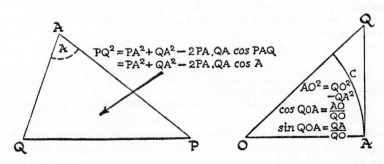

Fig. 121

Paper model key to the geometrical relations of the previous figure (Fig. 120).

right ascension which joins the star to the celestial pole, and the length of the arc between the star and the pole on its R.A. circle is its polar distance. Since the celestial pole is 90° from the celestial equator, the star's polar distance,

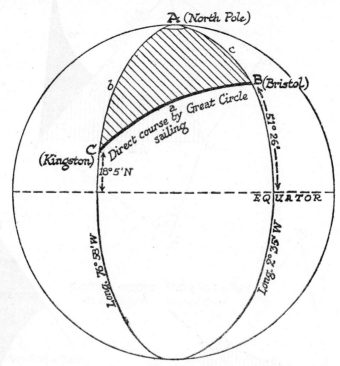

FIG. 122

The latitude of Bristol is 51° 26′ N. of the equator, and therefore 38° 34′ from the pole, along the great circle of longitude 2° 35′ W. The latitude of Kingston is 18° 5′, i.e. it is 71° 55′ from the pole along the great circle of longitude 76° 58′ W. The arc joining the pole to Bristol (c), the arc joining the pole to Kingston (b), and the arc (a) of the great circle representing the course from Bristol to Kingston form a spherical triangle, of which we know two sides (b and c), and the included angle A, which is the difference of longitude 76° 58′ − 2° 35′ = 74° 23′ between the two places. So we can find a from the formula (i) in Fig. 120 by putting

$$\cos a = \cos 71° 55′ \cos 38° 34′ + \sin 71° 55′ \sin 38° 34′ \cos 74° 23′$$

From the tables:

$$\cos a = 0\cdot3104 \times 0\cdot7819 + 0\cdot9506 \times 0\cdot6234 \times 0\cdot2692$$
$$= 0\cdot4022$$

Thus a is approximately $66\frac{1}{3}°$ of a great circle, i.e. a circle of the earth's complete circumference. The length of one degree of the earth's circumference is approximately 69 miles. So the distance is approximately

$$66\tfrac{1}{3} \times 69 = 4,577 \text{ land miles } (3,980 \text{ sea miles})$$

which is the third side of our spherical triangle, is the difference between one right angle and its declination ($a = 90°$ − declin.). Applying the formula we have

$$\cos (90° - \text{declin.}) = \cos (90° - \text{lat.}) \cos \text{z.d.}$$
$$+ \sin (90° - \text{lat.}) \sin \text{z.d. } \cos \text{azim.}$$

This may be written

$$\text{sin declin.} = \text{sin lat. cos z.d.} + \text{cos lat. sin z.d. cos azim.}$$

In applying this you have to remember that we have reckoned azimuth westward from the north point. The azimuth is reckoned positive west and negative east of the north point. If the star transits south of the zenith, the azimuth $\pm$ A reckoned west or east of the south point is equivalent to $180° \mp$ A from the north point. Since cos $(180° \pm A) = -$ cos A, cos (azim.) is always

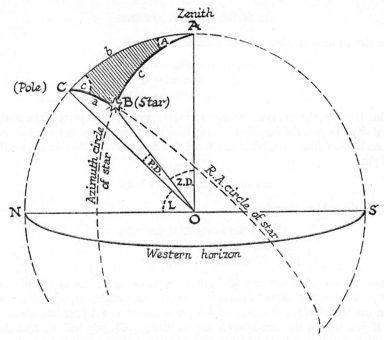

FIG. 123.—THE STAR TRIANGLE

of the opposite sign, if reckoned from the south point, and the formula becomes:

$$\text{sin declin.} = \text{sin lat. cos z.d.} - \text{cos lat. sin z.d. cos azim.}^*$$

This means that if you know the azimuth and zenith distance of a heavenly body at one and the same time, you can calculate its declination without waiting for it to reach the meridian. You cannot get the latitude of the place from an observation on a star of known declination directly by using the same formula; but if you have the z.d. and azimuth of any two stars taken at one

* When a star is crossing the meridian its azimuth is zero or 180° and since cos 0 = 1 and cos 180° = — 1, sin declin. = sin lat. cos z.d. $\pm$ cos lat. sin z.d.
Since sin $(A \pm B)$ = sin A cos B $\pm$ cos A sin B

$$\text{sin declin.} = \text{sin (lat.} \pm \text{z.d.)}$$

This is the formula given in Fig. 41 when no sign is attached to the z.d.

and the same place, you can calculate its latitude provided you have an almanac or star map to give the declination of the stars. In general the arithmetic takes less time than waiting about for one bright and easily recognized star to cross the meridian.

Another application of the formula just derived gives the direction of a heavenly body when rising or setting at a known latitude, or conversely the latitude from the rising or setting of a star. At the instant when a heavenly body is rising or setting its zenith distance is 90°. Since cos 90° = 0 and sin 90° = 1, the formula then becomes

$$\text{sin declin.} = \text{cos lat. cos azim.}$$

On the equinoxes when the sun's declination is 0°,

$$\text{cos lat. cos azim.} = 0$$
$$\therefore \quad \text{cos azim.} = 0$$
$$\therefore \quad \text{azim.} = \pm 90°$$

That is to say, the sun rises due east and sets due west in all parts of the world that day. To find the direction of the rising or setting sun at latitude $51\frac{1}{2}°$ N. (London) on June 21st, when the sun's declination is $23\frac{1}{2}°$ N., we have only to put

$$\text{sin } 23\frac{1}{2}° = \text{cos } 51\frac{1}{2}° \text{ cos azim.}$$

From the tables, therefore:

$$0 \cdot 3987 = 0 \cdot 6225 \text{ cos azim.}$$
$$\therefore \quad \text{cos azim.} = 0 \cdot 6405$$
$$\text{azim.} = \pm 50\frac{1}{8}°$$

Thus the sun rises and sets $50\frac{1}{8}°$ from the meridian on the north side, or $90° - 50\frac{1}{8}° = 39\frac{7}{8}°$ north of the east or west point. Conversely, of course, you can use the observed direction of rising and setting to get your latitude.

If you look at the star triangle shown in Fig. 123, you will see that the angle C between the arc which represents the star's polar distance and the arc b, which is the angle (90° − lat.) between the observer and the earth's pole, is the angle through which the star has rotated since it was last on the meridian. Since the celestial sphere appears to rotate through 360° in 24 hours, i.e. 15° an hour, this angle C is sometimes called the hour angle of the star, because you can get the time (in hours) which has elapsed since the star made its transit by dividing the number of degrees by 15. If you know when the star crossed the meridian by local time, you also know how long has elapsed since the sun crossed the meridian because time is reckoned that way, and if you know the sun's R.A. on the same day, you know how long has elapsed since ♈ crossed the meridian. Thus all you have to do to get the star's R.A. is to add the sun's R.A. to the star's time of transit.

So to get the star's R.A. from its altitude and azimuth at any observed time, we need to determine one of the other angles of a spherical triangle of which we already know two sides and the angle between them. This is done by the second formula which tells us that:

$$\sin C = \frac{\sin A \sin c}{\sin a}$$

In our original triangle of Fig. 123, A is the azimuth, c is the zenith distance, and a the polar distance $(90° - \text{declin.})$ of the star, i.e. $\sin a = \cos \text{declin.}$ Hence

$$\sin \text{hour angle} = \frac{\sin \text{azim.} \sin \text{z.d.}}{\cos \text{declin.}}$$

As stated already, the azimuth is reckoned positive *west* and negative *east* of the north point. Since $\sin(-A) = -\sin A$, the sine of the azimuth is negative if the star has not yet reached the meridian. If it transits south of the zenith its azimuth A east of the south point is equivalent to $(180° + A)$ measured west of the north point. Since $\sin(180° + A) = -\sin A$, the sine of the azimuth is also negative if measured east of the south point.

Suppose that the star Betelgeuse in Orion is found to have the hour angle $10°$ when it is west of the meridian at 8.40 p.m. local time. It crossed the meridian $\frac{10}{15}$ hour = 40 minutes before, i.e. at exactly eight o'clock, and its R.A. is greater than that of the sun by 8 hours. If the sun's R.A. on that day were 21 hours 50 minutes, the sun would transit 2 hours 10 minutes before ♈, i.e. ♈ would transit at 2.10 p.m., and Betelgeuse 8 hours 0 minutes -2 hours 10 minutes = 5 hours 50 minutes after ♈. So its R.A. would be 5 hours 50 minutes.

The same formula also tells you how to calculate the time of rising and setting of stars in any particular latitude. At rising or setting the z.d. of a heavenly body is $90°$, and $\sin 90° = 1$. So the formula becomes

$$\sin \text{hour angle} = \frac{\sin \text{azim.}}{\cos \text{declin.}}$$

The azimuth of a rising or setting star can be found from the formula already given, i.e.

$$\cos \text{azim.} = \frac{\sin \text{declin.}}{\cos \text{lat.}}$$

As an example we may take the time of sunrise on the winter solstice in London (Lat. $51\frac{1}{2}°$). By the last formula the azimuth of the rising and setting sun is $50\frac{1}{8}°$ from the south point on the winter solstice. So at sunset

$$\sin \text{hour angle} = \frac{\sin 50\frac{1}{8}°}{\cos(-23\frac{1}{2}°)}$$
$$= \frac{0\cdot 7679}{0\cdot 9171}$$
$$= 0\cdot 8373$$

For sunrise the azimuth will be east, therefore of *negative* sign, and the result is $-0\cdot 8373$. Since $0\cdot 8373$ is the sine of $56° \, 51'$, the time which elapses between setting or rising and meridian transit (i.e. noon, since it is the sun with which we are dealing) is $(56\frac{5}{6} \div 15)$ hours, i.e. 3 hours 47 minutes. Thus sunrise would occur at 8.13 a.m., and sunset at 3.47 p.m. Daylight lasts roughly $7\frac{1}{2}$ hours. This calculation differs by about 6 minutes from the value given in *Whitaker*. This is partly due to approximations made in the arithmetic, and partly due to other things about which you need not worry, because you will not find it difficult to put in the refinements when you understand the basic principles.

The same formula would apply to calculating the times of sunset or sunrise on June 21st, when the lengths of day and night are reversed. Since sin C = sin $(180° - C)$, $0 \cdot 8373$ may be either sin 56° 51' or sin $(180° - 56° 51')$, i.e. sin $(123° 9')$. Fig. 124 shows you at once which value to take. An equatorial star rising due east passes through 90° in reaching the meridian. A star south of the equator passes through a smaller and a star north of the equator through a larger arc. So if *the declination of a heavenly body is north (like the sun on June 21st), we take the solution as sin* $(180° - C)$, *and if south as sin C*. Thus the hour angle of sunrise and sunset on June 21st would be $(123\frac{1}{8} \div 15)$ hours = 8 hours 13 minutes, i.e. sunrise would be at 3.47 a.m. and sunset at 8.13 p.m. solar time.*

The following data, determined by a home-made instrument like the one shown in Fig. 115, illustrate how you can find the position of any star on the star map or make your own star map from observations off the meridian. At 9.5 p.m. (G.M.T.) near Exeter (Lat. 51° N. Long. $3\frac{1}{4}$° W.) the bright star Procyon in Canis Minor was seen on February 10th at 49° below the zenith and $28\frac{1}{2}$° *east* of the *south* point. The star transits south of the zenith, so we use the difference formula. From tables of sines and cosines we get

$$\text{sin declin.} = \sin 51° \cos 49° - \cos 51° \sin 49° \cos 28\tfrac{1}{2}°$$
$$= 0 \cdot 7771 \times 0 \cdot 6561 - 0 \cdot 6293 \times 0 \cdot 7547 \times 0 \cdot 8788$$
$$= 0 \cdot 0925$$
$$\therefore \text{declination} = 5° \ 18'$$

Since the star is east of the meridian its hour angle is negative, and

$$\text{sin (hour angle)} = -\frac{\sin 49° \sin 28\frac{1}{2}°}{\cos (5° \ 18')}$$
$$= -\frac{0 \cdot 7547 \times 0 \cdot 4772}{0 \cdot 9957}$$

$$\text{Hour angle} = -21\tfrac{1}{5}°$$

In time units $21\frac{1}{5}$° is 1 hour 25 minutes, and since the sign is negative, this means that the star will transit 1 hour 25 minutes *later*. On February 10th (39 days before March 21st) the sun's R.A. is about 21 hours 35 minutes. Under "equation of time" *Whitaker* states that we must add $14\frac{1}{2}$ minutes to apparent (sundial) time to get mean time. Hence the time of observation was (9 hours 5 minutes − 0 hours $14\frac{1}{2}$ minutes) = 8 hours $50\frac{1}{2}$ minutes Greenwich sundial time. Since Exeter is $3\frac{1}{4}$° W., the Exeter time is 13 minutes slow by Greenwich (i.e. it is 11.47 a.m. at Exeter when it is noon at Greenwich).

---

* The remarks here made apply to the northern hemisphere, where the bulk of the world's population lives at present. Australians and New Zealanders will not need to be told how to make the necessary adjustments.

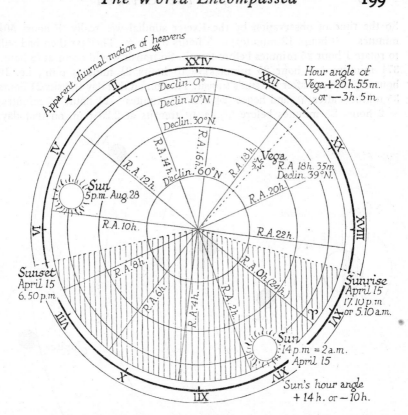

FIG. 124.—RELATION BETWEEN R.A., HOUR ANGLE OF A STAR, AND LOCAL TIME

About April 15th and August 28th the sun's declination is a little less than 10° N. and its hour angle of rising and setting is ± 103°. The shaded area is the arc of the sun's path below the horizon on the earlier date when its R.A. is 1 hour 30 minutes. The time is (April 15th) 2 a.m. (14 p.m.). So the sun's hour angle is + 14 hours or − 10 hours. The sun will transit 10 hours hence; ♈ will transit 10 hours −1 hour 30 minutes or 8 hours 30 minutes hence. Vega's R.A. is 18 hours 35 minutes, hence it transits 18 hours 35 minutes after ♈ and 5 hours 25 minutes before ♈. Therefore Vega will transit 8 hours 30 minutes −5 hours 25 minutes or 3 hours 5 minutes hence, and the hour angle of Vega must be − 3 hours 5 minutes or + 20 hours 55 minutes. The formula for the star's R.A. if its hour angle at a given instant of solar time is known is therefore derived as follows:

$$\text{sun's hour angle} - \text{star's hour angle} = \text{star's R.A.} - \text{sun's R.A.}$$

$$\therefore \quad \text{Solar time} - \text{star's hour angle} = \text{star's R.A.} - \text{sun's R.A.}$$

$$\therefore \quad \textit{star's R.A.} = \textit{sun's R.A.} + \textit{solar time} - \textit{star's hour angle.}$$

Thus, if Vega's hour angle is + 20 hours 55 minutes or − 3 hours 5 minutes at 14 p.m. when the sun's R.A. is 1 hour 30 minutes

R.A. of Vega = 1 hour 30 minutes + 14 hours 0 minutes − − 3 hours 5 minutes)
= 18 hours 35 minutes

Or using positive quantities only

= 1 hour 30 minutes + 14 hours 0 minutes − 20 hours 55 minutes
= − 5 hours 25 minutes = + 18 hours 35 minutes

So the time of observation by the Exeter sundial was really (8 hours 50½ minutes — 0 hours 13 minutes) = 8 hours 37½ p.m. The star then had still to rotate 1 hour 25 minutes before transit. So transit would occur at (8 hours 37½ minutes + 1 hour 25 minutes) = 10 hours 2½ minutes p.m., i.e. 10 hours 2½ minutes after the sun's transit. The sun on that day transits 21 hours 35 minutes after ♈, and hence (24 hours 0 minutes —21 hours 35 minutes) = 2 hours 25 minutes before ♈, i.e. ♈ transits at 2.25 p.m. on that day.

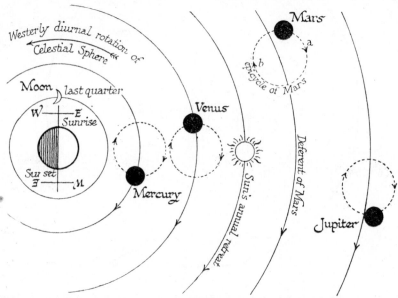

FIG. 125

In Ptolemy's system four classes of motion were recognized:

(i) The diurnal rotation of the whole heavenly sphere *from east to west*. In this motion the stars maintain a constant position relative to one another. A heavenly body (moon, star, or planet) west of the sun rises before sunrise. A heavenly body east of the sun sets after sunset. In the position here drawn, Venus and Mars are seen as "morning stars," Mercury and Jupiter as "evening stars."

(ii) The daily *increase* of the moon and sun in R.A. as they retreat from west to east.

(iii) Two independent motions of each planet, one the epicyclic orbit of the planet about an imaginary fixed point, the other the deferent orbit of this fixed point around the earth as world centre. The deferent motion was analogous to the daily increase of the sun's or moon's R.A. The epicyclic motion might have, e.g. when Mars is at (*a*), the same direction, or, e.g. when Mars is at (*b*), the opposite direction to the deferent motion. Hence planets may have alternate periods in which the R.A. increases daily and slowly diminishes.

Hence the star's transit was (10 hours 2½ minutes — 2 hours 25 minutes) =7 hours 37½ minutes after ♈, i.e. the R.A. of Procyon is 7 hours 37½ minutes if the observations were correct. With the best instruments the value given is 7 hours 36 minutes.

THE ALEXANDRIAN VIEW OF PLANETARY MOTION

When these methods are applied to the observation of the position of the planets day by day over a period of years, the latter are all found to be alike in one respect. Each planet exhibits long periods in which its R.A. increases steadily like the R.A. of the sun or moon, alternating with shorter periods in which its R.A. diminishes at a slower rate, so that it appears to pause and double on its course at regular intervals. The times when a superior planet* like Mars transits near midnight and is visible throughout the night correspond to the times when its apparent motion is retrograde, or in the opposite direction to the annual motion of the sun and the monthly motion of the moon among the fixed stars. At the time when the motion of such a

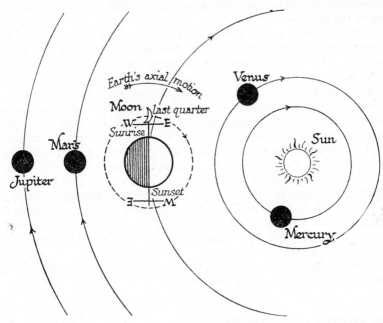

FIG. 126

In the Copernican system only three classes of motion need be recognized:
(*a*) the earth's diurnal motion about its own axis from *west to east,* (*b*) the moon's orbital motion from west to east, (*c*) the orbital motion of all planets (including the earth) from west to east. In the positions here shown Mars and Jupiter are in opposition, i.e. on the meridian at midnight. Mercury is at its extreme easterly position (maximum elongation) as an evening star. Venus is at its extreme westerly position (maximum elongation) as a morning star. Neither of them can ever be seen on the meridian after dark.

planet is most rapidly direct it is invisible. That is to say, it rises and sets about the same time as the sun. Thus there is a very close connexion between the apparent movements of the planets and their position relative to the sun, as we see them. This connexion was recognized by the Egyptians, who believed that the whole celestial sphere, including the sun, rotated around the earth as the centre, and that the planets rotated round the sun as the moon rotates around the earth. They placed the orbits of Mercury and Venus cor-

* I.e. a planet whose orbit lies outside that of the earth.

rectly between the sun and the earth. This explained why Mercury and Venus can never be seen throughout the whole night, since they can never be above the side of the earth opposite to that which is illuminated by the sun's rays. The theory which Hipparchus, and later Ptolemy, took from Apollonius was a decidedly backward step. Each planet (Fig. 125) moved around an imaginary centre in an orbit called its *epicycle*. Each imaginary centre was placed at the end of an imaginary or *deferent* spoke rotating round the earth itself. While accounting for the retrograde and direct motion of the planets, the theory of epicycles could recognize no significance in the connexion between the different phases of a planet's motion and its position relative to that of the sun.

Its great defect was that it made the geometry of the heavens a good deal more complicated than the alternative view that the planets revolve around the sun; and the more accurate observations, which had been accumulated by the Arabian astronomers in the period which followed, made increasing demands upon mathematical ingenuity, as new epicycles were added to accommodate the theory with the facts. Copernicus, as we have seen, began his work when the forecasting of planetary occultations was becoming a matter of practical moment, and the possibilities of further improvement on the Ptolemaic system had been exhausted. There remained the alternative of starting from fresh assumptions. Copernicus went back to the doctrine of Aristarchus and put the sun at the centre of the whole planetary system, including the earth as a planet (Fig. 126). Having no telescopic information to reveal their different sizes as seen at different phases, he stuck to the idealistic belief that each planet moves in the most perfect plane figure, the circle. This assumption is so nearly true of Venus and Mars that it does not involve very serious inaccuracies, and makes it easier to understand how the position of a planet is calculated. So we may here suppose that the orbits of Venus and Mars are circles.

THE HYPOTHESIS OF COPERNICUS

The hypothesis which Copernicus adopted may be summarized under four headings:

(1) The apparent diurnal rotation of the celestial sphere is due to the complete rotation of the earth about its polar axis in a period of 24 hours.

(2) The moon revolves around the earth in a period of $27\frac{1}{3}$ days.

(3) The earth and the planets revolve in circular orbits about the sun in the same direction as the earth's diurnal motion.

(4) The orbits of Mercury and Venus lie between the sun and that of the earth, while the orbits of Mars, Jupiter, and Saturn, lie beyond the earth's orbit.

The tracks of the planets lie close to the ecliptic. So it is better to calculate their positions in celestial longitude and latitude (see p. 220) as Copernicus did. For the purpose of grasping the principles employed in tracing out their orbits it will be sufficient for our purpose if we use right ascension to measure their angular displacements. This is equivalent to projecting their movements on to the plane of the celestial equator.

The first thing to notice (Fig. 127) is that it does not make any difference

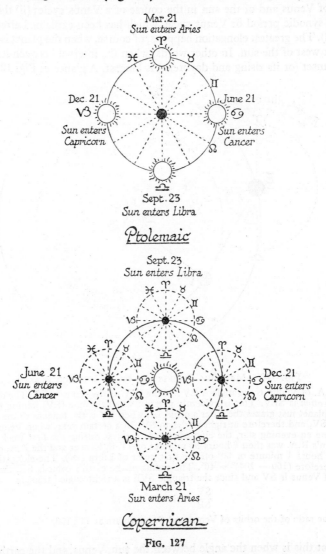

Mar. 21
Sun enters Aries

Dec. 21
Sun enters Capricorn

June 21
Sun enters Cancer

Sept. 23
Sun enters Libra

Ptolemaic

Sept. 23
Sun enters Libra

June 21
Sun enters Cancer

Dec. 21
Sun enters Capricorn

March 21
Sun enters Aries

Copernican

FIG. 127

Since the earth and sun are very close relative to the distance of the fixed stars (i.e. the annual parallax of a star is very small) the direction of the stars may be measured either from the earth as centre (Ptolemaic) or the sun as centre (Copernican) without making much difference.

to the measurement of the sun's R.A. whether we put the earth or the sun at the centre of the star map. To calculate the position of a planet according to the Copernican hypothesis we need to know two things, (*a*) its distance relative to the sun; (b) its sidereal period (P), i.e. the time which it takes to go round the sun. In the case of the inferior planet Venus, all we need to know is (i) the greatest elongation, i.e. the greatest difference between the R.A. of Venus and of the sun in the course of a Venus cycle; (ii) the length of the synodic period or Venus cycle, which has been explained already (see p. 182). The greatest elongation happens, of course, when the planet is farthest east or west of the sun. In other words, when the interval between its setting and sunset (or its rising and daybreak) is longest. A glance at Fig. 128 shows

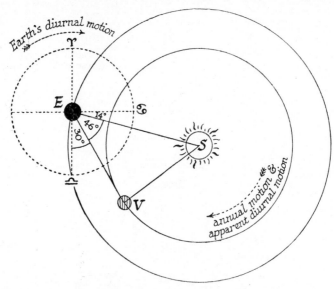

FIG. 128.—MAXIMUM ELONGATION OF AN INFERIOR PLANET

The R.A. of Venus is the angle ♈EV and the R.A. of the sun is ♈ES. The difference or *elongation* is SEV. This is evidently greatest when the line (EV) joining the earth to the planet just grazes the latter's orbit, i.e. when EV is the tangent to the circle of radius SV, and therefore at right angles to SV. In a certain year, when Venus was at that time an evening star, the elongation was greatest during the first week in July. The sun's R.A. was then 6 hours 55 minutes or 14° in Cancer and the R.A. of Venus was 10 hours 1 minute or 30° off the first point of Libra (♎). The elongation SEV was therefore (150 − 104)° = 46°. The radius of the earth's orbit is SE, that of the orbit of Venus is SV and since the triangle SVE is a right-angled triangle

$$\frac{SV}{SE} = \sin 46° = 0.72$$

Thus the ratio of the orbits of Venus and the earth are as 72 : 100.

you that this is when the angle between the sun, Venus, and the earth (SVE) is 90°. The same figure (Fig. 128) shows that the angle between the sun, the earth and Venus (SEV) is the difference between the sun's R.A. and that of Venus, i.e. the elongation of the planet. So at maximum elongation the sun, the earth and Venus form a right-angled triangle in which

$$\sin SEV = \frac{SV}{SE}$$

i.e.

$$\text{sin (maximum elongation)} = \frac{\text{radius of the orbit of Venus}}{\text{radius of the earth's orbit}}$$

The greatest possible angle between the sun and Venus is roughly 46°.*
Since sin 46° = 0·72, the ratio of the earth's distance from the sun to that

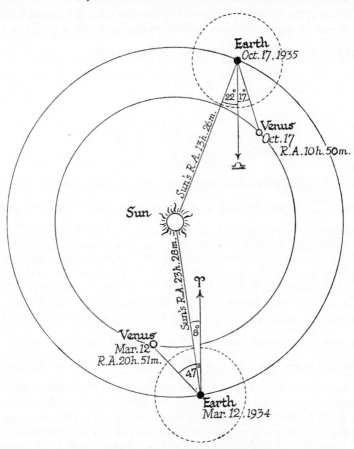

FIG. 129.—THE VENUS CYCLE

On March 12, 1934, the sun's R.A. was 352°, being then 39° greater than that of
Venus which was thus a morning star, rising before the sun. On October 17, 1935,
584 days later the sun's R.A. was 202°, being again 39° in excess of the R.A. of Venus.

of Venus is 100 : 72. Hence you can take the first step in drawing a scale
map for showing the relative positions of the earth and Venus by describing
two circles of radii in the ratio 100 : 72 with the sun as centre.

According to the hypothesis we are now adopting, the earth moves round

* This is not exactly the same as the greatest difference in R.A. For simplicity we
here neglect the fact that Venus and the sun do not usually have the same declination.

the sun through $\frac{360}{365}$ degrees per day. Suppose Venus moves through $\frac{360}{V}$ degrees per day. This means that Venus takes V days to go round the sun. It therefore gains $\left(\frac{360}{V} - \frac{360}{365}\right)$ degrees per day. We have seen (p. 183) that

the Venus cycle, i.e. its *synodic period* or the time taken for the earth, the sun and Venus to regain the same relative positions, is 584 days. Thus Venus gains 360° in 584 days or $\frac{360}{584}$ degrees per day, so that

$$\frac{360}{584} = \frac{360}{V} - \frac{360}{365}$$

$$\frac{1}{V} = \frac{1}{584} + \frac{1}{365} = \frac{13}{2920}$$

$$V = 225 \text{ days}$$

Thus the sidereal period of Venus is 225 days. In other words, Venus rotates through $\frac{360}{225}$ degrees per day. You can now see whether the hypothesis is satisfactory by observing the R.A. of Venus on any particular day (Fig. 130) and calculating what it will be at some later date. Seventy-five days later Venus will have moved through 120° and the earth through 74° According to *Whitaker* on September 23, 1934, when the sun's R.A. is 180 (in degrees), the R.A. of Venus was 11 hours 8 minutes or 167°, i.e. Venus was 13° west of the sun and just about at the end of its period as a morning star. Seventy-five days later, December 7th, Venus would have revolved through $\frac{75}{225} \times 360° = 120°$ and the earth would have revolved through $\frac{75}{365} \times 360° = 74°$: i.e. the sun's R.A. has increased by 74°, and is now 254°. If you now draw Venus and the earth in their new positions on your scale map, you will find that the R.A. of Venus is now a little greater than that of the sun. Venus is beginning to be an evening star. The angle between Venus, the earth and the sun (the elongation of Venus) is 5°. According to *Whitaker*, the difference between the R.A. of Venus and the sun on December 7th was 0 hours 19 minutes 37 seconds, or 5°.

The case of a superior planet like Mars can be dealt with in this way (Fig. 131). First find the length of the Mars cycle, i.e. the *synodic* period which elapses between two successive occasions when Mars, the sun, and the earth occupy the same relative positions. This is easily done by noting when Mars is in opposition, i.e. when it is on the meridian at midnight, and counting the number of days which intervene before its next midnight meridian transit. If you refer to *Whitaker*, you will see that Mars was in opposition (midnight meridian transit) on March 1, 1933, and it was next in opposition on April 6, 1935, 766 days later. This makes the Mars cycle 766 days. So, if P is the length of the sidereal period

$$\frac{1}{P} = \frac{1}{365} - \frac{1}{766} = \frac{1}{697}$$

The earth gets back to its original position (E_1) after $365\frac{1}{4} \times 2 = 730\frac{1}{2}$ days. To the nearest day this is 34 days *after* Mars completes a sidereal period of 697 days. At the end of a sidereal period of Mars, the earth is therefore 34° west of the position which it occupied at the beginning. If we now find the R.A. of Mars, we know its elongation, the angle SE₂B, as in Fig. 131.

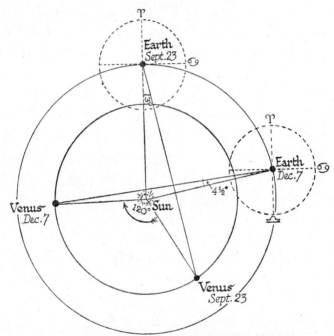

FIG. 130.—CHECKING THE COPERNICAN HYPOTHESIS

Since the sidereal period of Venus is 225 days, Venus goes through 120° in 75 days, the interval between September 23rd and December 7th. On September 23, 1934, the R.A. of Venus was 11 hours 8 minutes or 13° less than that of the sun (12 hours or 180°). On December 7th the R.A. of Venus, which has advanced through 120° of its orbit, will be found to be 4¼° in excess of the sun (253¼°). Thus its R.A. is 258° or 17 hours 12 minutes.

Since Mars was in opposition when the earth was at E_1, it was then situated somewhere on the line SE₁A. After 697 days it is somewhere on the line E₂B. According to the Copernican view, it is presumably in the same place once more. So it must be at M where these two lines intersect. Hence we can now put the orbit of Mars on the scale map by drawing a circle of radius SM. The radius of its orbit is then found to be 1·52 times that of the earth's orbit.

The reasoning given above and the figure based on it (Fig. 131) need qualifying. The synodic period is not absolutely constant. The *average* length of the Mars cycle is nearly 780 days, and the sidereal period is therefore 687 days. Hypothesis and observation can be tested in the same way for Mars and Venus. The only thing which remains to be explained is the retrograde movement which the planets show. As stated, the R.A. of a superior planet like Mars diminishes daily when it is visible during the greater part of the night, i.e. about the time when it is in opposition. Fig. 132 shows you how

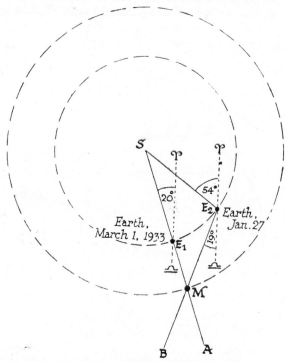

FIG. 131.—THE ORBIT OF A SUPERIOR PLANET

About March 1, 1933, Mars is in opposition, the sun being roughly 20° from the First Point of Aries. So it lies somewhere on the line SE₁A. By January 27, 1935, Mars has returned to the same position in its orbit. The sun's R.A. is now about 54° west of ♈ and the R.A. of Mars is 13 hours 15 minutes, i.e. it is 19° in Libra. It now lies somewhere on the line E₂B. The radius of the circle drawn through M where E₁A and E₂B cut is 1·52 times SE₁ or SE₂, the radius of the earth's orbit. Hence Mars is one and a half times as far away from the sun as the earth is.

this happens. The sidereal period of Mars itself is a little less than twice that of the earth (687 : 365). For simplicity, consider an imaginary planet M which revolves like Mars in an orbit 1½ times the width of the earth's orbit, taking exactly twice as long as the earth to make a complete revolution. So, if the earth goes through 40°, the imaginary planet goes through 20° in the same time. On the left, the earth is shown in two positions at the beginning of March and the middle of April. In the first it is approaching, in the second at opposition. You will see that the R.A. of the planet changes from 180° + a (a off the first point of Libra) to 180° + b. Since b is manifestly smaller than *a*, the R.A. of the planet is diminishing daily at this stage in its course. On the right, the planet is approaching conjunction. It is just seen after sunset at M_a and is totally obscured by the sun when it has moved on through 20° to M_b. Meanwhile the earth moves from E_a to E_b through 40°. At M_a the planet is in Pisces, at M_b in Aries, and its R.A. is therefore *increasing* daily.

Before dealing with the imperfections of the Copernican hypothesis one result may be pointed out. Early estimates of the sun's distance like that of Hipparchus were very inaccurate. Owing to its great distance the sun's

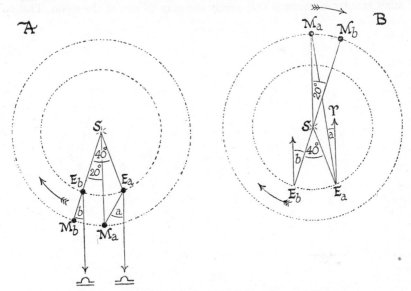

FIG. 132.—RETROGRADE AND DIRECT MOTION OF A PLANET

The outer planet M takes twice as long to traverse its orbit as the inner one E. Hence when E goes through 40°, M rotates through 20°. Their relative motions resemble what a passenger in one train would experience if travelling in a circular track concentric with another one on which a train was also moving. When E and M are close they are travelling in the same direction and E is gaining on M. The motion of M is then retrograde, i.e. the R.A. of M is decreasing. When M and E are in opposite side of their orbits they are travelling in opposite directions and both motions make the R.A. increase. So the motion is *direct*.

parallax is only about 9″ or $\frac{1}{400}$ of a degree. The Copernican hypothesis gives us a simple way of estimating the sun's distance without recourse to the direct measurement of such a small quantity. Having now made a scale map (Fig. 133) of the orbits of the planets by combining Fig. 128 with Fig. 131 and others like them, we can at once deduce the distance between the sun and any planet if we can find the actual distance between any points on our scale. Thus we can use the parallax of the *nearest* planet to get the sun's parallax. For instance, the distance between the earth and Venus when the latter crosses the sun's disc is $\dfrac{100 - 72}{100}$ times or only about a quarter of the distance between the earth and the sun. A minor planet Eros discovered in the latter half of the nineteenth century comes within a distance equivalent to a sixth of the radius of the earth's orbit. By determination of the parallaxes of near planets like Eros, Venus, and Mars, we know the sun's parallax with great accuracy and the average distance deduced is about 93 million miles. This estimate agrees very closely with two other estimates based on the optical phenomena of aberration and line spectra (see Chapter VI). A fairly close approximation to the diameter of the sun can be got without telescopic equipment. Since the moon's disc just covers the sun in a total eclipse, the sun's angular diameter is very nearly the same as that of the moon. That is

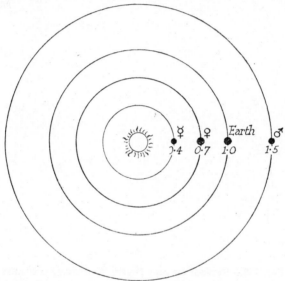

FIG. 133.—SCALE DIAGRAM OF THE ORBITS OF THE FOUR INNER MAJOR PLANETS

to say, it is roughly half a degree. So the sun's diameter calculated in the same way as the moon's is between three-quarters of a million and one million miles.

THE IMPERFECTIONS OF THE COPERNICAN HYPOTHESIS

Calculations based on the Copernican assumption that the orbits of the planets are circular do not yield conclusions which are sufficiently accurate. Detectable errors were recognized before the advent of the telescope and all the refinements of measurement which followed it. An immense array of new data about the planet Mars collected by Tycho Brahe in the latter half of the sixteenth century made it possible to analyse the movement of Mars more thoroughly than Copernicus or his predecessors had done. If, instead of determining the radius of the orbit by drawing a circle through the point M where E_1A and E_2B intersect in Fig. 131, we note the successive positions of the earth after several complete sidereal cycles beginning on different dates,

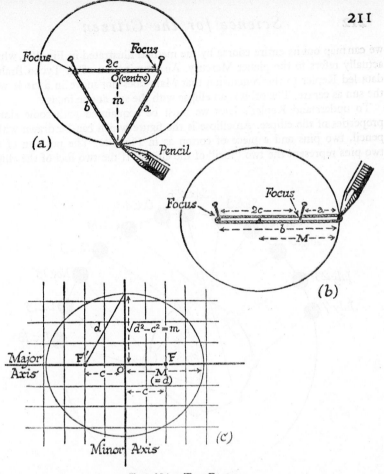

FIG. 134.—THE ELLIPSE

Since the loop is of fixed length, the sum of the distances a and b of any point from the two foci is the same. Half the sum is d in the diagram, i.e. $a + b = 2d$

The ellipse is symmetrical about two unequal diameters. One, called the *minor axis*, at right angles to the line between the foci, joins the opposite points where $a = b = d$. If m is half the minor axis Fig. (c) shows you that

$$m^2 = d^2 - c^2 \qquad \cdots \qquad \text{(i)}$$

The other, called the *major* axis, is a continuation of the line joining the two foci. You will see from the diagram, in which half the major axis is called M, that

$$M = a + c \quad \text{and} \quad M = b - c$$
$$\therefore \quad 2M = a + b = 2d$$
$$M = d \qquad \cdots \qquad \text{(ii)}$$

We call the ratio of c, the distance between the centre and the focus, to d, the distance along the major axis from the centre to the boundary, the *eccentricity* of the ellipse, i.e.

$$e = \frac{c}{d} \quad \text{or} \quad c = de$$
$$\therefore \quad m^2 = d^2 - (de)^2$$
$$= d^2 (1 - e^2) \qquad \cdots \qquad \text{(iii)}$$
$$\text{Combining (ii) and (iii)} \quad m^2 = M^2 (1 - e^2)$$
$$\therefore \quad e = \sqrt{1 - \frac{m^2}{M^2}}$$

we can map out its entire course by the method illustrated in Fig. 135, which actually refers to the planet Mercury. An examination of all Tycho Brahe's data led Kepler to the conclusion that Mars does not move in a circle with the sun as centre. The orbit is an ellipse with the sun at one focus.

To understand Kepler's laws we must be acquainted with some simple properties of the ellipse. An ellipse is the figure which can be drawn with a pencil, two pins and a piece of cotton as in Fig. 134. The position of the two pins represent the two "foci" of the ellipse. If the two foci of the ellipse

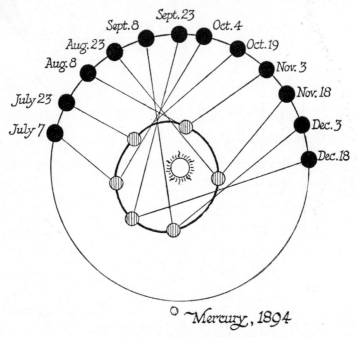

Fig. 135.—The Orbit of Mercury

are very close together it becomes undistinguishable from a circle. The connexion between the circle and the ellipse is brought out more precisely by the index known as eccentricity (e). The broadest diameter of an ellipse is called its major axis. The narrowest is called the minor axis. The two foci lie on the major axis. If we measure along the major axis the distance of either focus from the boundary in both directions, the ratio of the difference between the greater and smaller distance to the length of the major axis is called the eccentricity of the ellipse. If its eccentricity is 0, the two foci coincide and an ellipse becomes a true circle. The geometry of the ellipse (Figs. 134 and 136) shows that e can also be defined as:

$$\sqrt{1 - \left(\frac{\text{minor axis}}{\text{major axis}}\right)^2}$$

So if we say that the eccentricity of the orbit of Mercury is $0 \cdot 2$, we mean that

$$(0 \cdot 2)^2 = 1 - \left(\frac{\text{minor axis}}{\text{major axis}}\right)^2$$

i.e. the minor axis and major axis are in the ratio 49 : 50. Since the eccentricity of the orbit of Mercury is more than twice that of any of the other major planets (except the newly discovered planet Pluto) it is clear that the

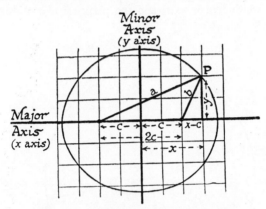

FIG. 136.—THE EQUATION OF THE ELLIPSE

$$a^2 = y^2 + (x + c)^2 = y^2 + x^2 + 2cx + c^2 \quad \cdot \quad \cdot \quad \cdot \quad \cdot \quad \textbf{(iv)}$$
$$b^2 = y^2 + (x - c)^2 = y^2 + x^2 - 2cx + c^2 \quad \cdot \quad \cdot \quad \cdot \quad \cdot \quad \text{(v)}$$

Adding the left-hand side of (iv) to the left-hand side of (v) and the right-hand side of (iv) to the right-hand side of (v), we get

$$a^2 + b^2 = 2y^2 + 2x^2 + 2c^2$$
$$= 2y^2 + 2x^2 + 2d^2e^2 \quad \cdot \quad \cdot \quad \cdot \quad \cdot \quad \cdot \quad \text{(vi)}$$

Subtract (v) from (iv):

$$a^2 - b^2 = 4cx = 4dex$$

Since

$$a^2 - b^2 = (a + b)(a - b)$$
$$\therefore \quad (a + b)(a - b) = 4dex$$
$$2d(a - b) = 4dex$$
$$a - b = 2ex$$
$$\therefore \quad (a - b)^2 = 4e^2x^2$$
$$\text{or} \quad a^2 - 2ab + b^2 = 4e^2x^2 \quad \cdot \quad \cdot \quad \cdot \quad \cdot \quad \cdot \quad \text{(vii)}$$

Take (vii) from (vi):

$$2ab = 2y^2 + 2x^2 - 4e^2x^2 + 2d^2e^2 \quad \cdot \quad \cdot \quad \cdot \quad \cdot \quad \cdot \quad \text{(viii)}$$

Add (viii) and (vi):

$$a^2 + 2ab + b^2 = 4y^2 + 4x^2 - 4e^2x^2 + 4d^2e^2$$
$$(a + b)^2 = 4y^2 + 4x^2 (1 - e^2) + 4d^2e^2$$

But (Fig. 134)

$$(a + b)^2 = (2d)^2$$

$$\therefore \quad 4d^2 = 4y^2 + 4x^2(1 - e^2) + 4d^2e^2$$
$$d^2 = y^2 + x^2(1 - e^2) + d^2e^2$$
$$d^2 - d^2e^2 = y^2 + x^2(1 - e^2)$$
$$1 = \frac{y^2}{d^2(1 - e^2)} + \frac{x^2}{d^2}$$

From (ii) and (iii)

$$1 = \frac{y^2}{m^2} + \frac{x^2}{M^2}$$

Copernican doctrine of circular orbits is not very wide of the mark. The eccentricities of the orbits of Venus and Mars are respectively 0·007 and 0·093. So the orbit of Venus is very nearly a perfect circle.

In his first study on Mars, Kepler had to work on the assumption that the earth's orbit is practically circular. By good fortune it happens to be so. The eccentricity of the earth's orbit is only 0·017. So the orbit of Mars is decidedly more flattened. With the aid of Figs. 134 and 136, which give the Cartesian equation of the ellipse, you will be able to see how Kepler's first law can be tested. Having made a graph of the actual positions, measure the greatest width (major axis) and the perpendicular width through the

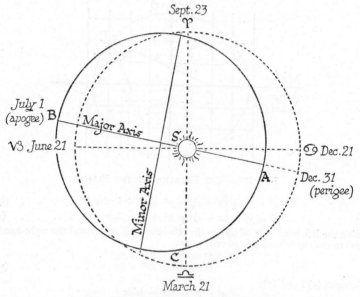

FIG. 137.—PLOTTING THE EARTH'S ORBIT
The dates of perigee and apogee are Kepler's. They are now about 3 days later.

midpoint of the longest diameter. This will be the minor axis. Fig. 136 shows you that, if an ellipse is drawn with the minor axis lying along the y and the major axis along the x reference lines,

$$1 = \frac{y^2}{m^2} + \frac{x^2}{M^2}$$

From this you can tabulate corresponding values of x and y, since m and M are known. If Kepler's first law is a good one, the points deduced from the equation should lie closely in the same curve as those based on direct observation. Having satisfied himself that the figure was not a true circle, Kepler explored nineteen hypotheses before he found one which was entirely satisfactory.

The publication of Kepler's analysis of the orbit of Mars was immediately followed by the invention of the telescope. With new optical equipment it was now possible to measure smaller angles. With refined measurement the angular diameter of the sun is seen to vary appreciably in the course of a year. That is to say, the earth is nearer to the sun at some times than at others. The distance at any time is inversely proportional to the apparent size. So if we make a date circle along the radii of which the earth lies at different times of the year, as in Fig. 137, we can measure off distances proportional to the actual distance of the sun on any day. If we first measure off SA as the earth's distance on December 31st (when the earth is nearest to the sun), and observe that the sun's angular diameter is *x* times as large on December 31st as on July 1st, the earth's distance SB on July 1st, is SA ÷ *x*. In this way we can plot out the earth's orbit from day to day. Although it is very nearly circular—far more so than the accompanying figure would suggest—it is easy to detect that the earth does not move in a circle with the sun as centre. If you draw a series of ellipses of different eccentricities by the method shown in Fig. 135, you will find that the foci can be relatively far apart without producing a very noticeable departure from the shape of a circle. If the foci are far apart either of them must be decidedly nearer to one end of the major axis than to the other. Measurement of the form of the earth's orbit shows that the sun is at one focus of an ellipse. Although the ellipse is very nearly circular, the extreme distances of the earth from the sun differ by quite a considerable quantity, namely three million miles.

KEPLER'S LAWS

Tycho Brahe had refused to accept the Copernican view. Rejecting the Ptolemaic epicycles which gave no account of the relation of the behaviour of the planets to their propinquity to the sun, he adopted a compromise essentially the same as the earlier Egyptian doctrine. The earth remained at the centre, but the planets revolved around the sun. The recognition that the sun's apparent annual motion is not a perfect circle was a severe blow to idealistic dogmas which had reigned unchallenged for centuries. Ten years after the publication of his work on Mars, Kepler broke boldly away from the geocentric view of the universe and restated the doctrine of Aristarchus and Copernicus in the three laws which usually bear his name. These are:

1. The earth and the planets move in ellipses with the sun at one focus.
2. The radius vector of a planet's motion describes equal areas in equal times.
3. The square of the sidereal period (T) of any planet bears a constant ratio to the cube of its mean distance (*d*) from the sun, i.e.

$$\frac{T^2}{d^3} = K$$

If the year is the unit of time and the mean distance of the earth from the sun is taken as the unit of distance, the periodic times and mean distances of the planets at Kepler's time are given approximately in the following table, from which you will see that their ratio is constant to about the same degree of accuracy as the figures themselves.

Planet	T	d	$T^3 \div d^3$
Mercury	0·24	0·39	0·971
Venus	0·61	0·72	0·997
Earth	1·00	1·00	1·000
Mars	1·88	1·52	1·006
Jupiter	11·86	5·20	1·000
Saturn	29·46	9·54	1·000

Kepler's account of the movements of the planets was not more satisfactory than the hypothesis of Ptolemy because the case was stated with greater logical subtlety, because it placed greater reliance on mathematical ingenuity, or even because it was simpler to grasp. It was more satisfactory because it *could help people to do things.* If we want to know when and where to put a telescope to see a planet in the sky, Kepler's recipe helps us in situations when Ptolemy's recipe would lead us astray. If we want to know when and where to look for an occultation of Mars, Kepler's hypothesis shows us how to make an almanac which will be serviceable for a long while ahead. Ptolemy's hypothesis could not. *A scientific hypothesis is not a passive prediction of future events. It is an active prescription for human conduct.* For a long while to come the Copernican doctrine in its new form was still open to the objection that no annual parallax of the fixed stars could be detected by the instruments then available. Its universal acceptance by the scientific world was ensured by the fact that the earth's diurnal rotation and the laws of Kepler received independent confirmation from new knowledge about laws of motion to be explained in the next chapter. The recognition that the apparent paths of the sun and planets are not perfect circles was a far more drastic step than we might suppose. In the age of Kepler, science was only beginning to shake off the Platonic teaching which seeks to arrive at truth by logical argument based on self-evident principles and verbal definitions. Plato taught that the heavenly bodies must move in circles because the circle is the most perfect figure. Ptolemy had founded his system on the self-evident principle that the whole celestial sphere rotates around the earth. Arguing from these premisses his logic was flawless. The success of Kepler's calculations started a steady decline in the belief that logic is a sufficient guide to truth.

To recapture the atmosphere of the time we may recall a type specimen of Aristotle's astronomy: " The shape of the heavens is of necessity spherical, for that is the shape most appropriate to its substance and also by nature primary. . . . Every plane figure must be either rectilinear or curvilinear. Now the rectilinear is bounded by more than one line, the curvilinear by one only. . . . If then the complete is prior to the incomplete, it follows on this ground also that the circle is primary among figures, and the sphere holds the same position among solids. . . . Now the first figure belongs to the first body, and the first body is that of the farthest circumference." Contrast these words with those of Francis Bacon: "It cannot be that axioms discovered by argumentations should avail for the discovery of new works; since the subtlety of nature is greater many times over than the subtlety of arguments. . . . Radical errors in the first concoction of the mind are not to be cured by the excellence of functions and remedies subsequent. . . . We must lead men to the particulars themselves, while men on their side must force themselves for a while to lay their notions by and begin to familiarize themselves with the facts."

The supremacy of fact over logic, the use of logic as an instrument to be calibrated continually by recourse to fact, is a lesson which every branch of science has had to master. If we may gain profit from the record of man's growing knowledge of nature, we may be sure that scientific study of social institutions will be possible when our economists "lay their notions by and begin to familiarize themselves with the facts." One by one the natural sciences have abandoned the self-evident principles of Aristotle. Logical deductions from the self-evident truth that nature abhors a vacuum have proved unable to suggest the proper way of pumping water out of a mine, and the self-evident truth that bodies fall where they belong is not particularly useful when we come to calculate the path of a projectile. The past history of human culture shows us that a high level of scientific attainment in isolated fields has flourished when men have been forced to bring their beliefs to the bar of fact and use them as recipes of social conduct. That the social sciences have not passed out of the stage from which the natural sciences were emerging in the time of Kepler is sufficiently evident from the following exposition of *The Nature and Significance of Economic Science* by Professor Robbins:

We have not yet discussed the nature and derivation of Economic Laws. . . . It will be convenient, therefore, at the outset of our investigations, if, instead of attempting to derive the nature of Economic Generalizations from the pure categories of our subject-matter, we commence by examining a typical specimen. . . . It is a well-known generalization of elementary Price Theory that, in a free market, intervention by some outside body to fix a price below the market price will lead to an excess of demand over supply. . . . Upon what foundations does it rest?

It should not be necessary to spend much time showing that it cannot rest upon any appeal to History. The frequent concomitance of certain phenomena in time may suggest a problem to be solved. It cannot by itself be taken to imply a definite causal relationship. . . . It is one of the great merits of the modern Philosophy of History that it has repudiated all claims of this sort, and indeed makes it the *fundamentum divisionis* between History and Natural Science that history does not proceed by way of generalizing abstraction. . . . It is equally clear that our belief does not rest upon the results of controlled experiment . . . our belief in this particular generalization and many others is more complete than belief based upon any number of controlled experiments. . . . But on what, then, does it depend? . . . In the last analysis, therefore, our proposition rests upon deductions which are implicit in our initial definition of the subject-matter of Economic Science as a whole.

This passage briefly summarizes every attitude to knowledge discarded by the natural sciences in reaching the prestige they now enjoy. The natural sciences owe their prestige to the fact that they provide man with the means of regulating his social conduct. They are able to do this because science rests on a wholesome distrust of logic, except in so far as the results of a logical process are tested continually by return to the real world. Sprat, Bishop of Rochester, in the first history of the Royal Society, which he speaks of as an "enterprise for the Benefit of Human Life by the *Advancement of Real Knowledge*," devoted the beginning of his narrative to the way in which real knowledge is gained. His résumé of the scholastic tradition is worth quoting side by side with the preceding extracts from a contemporary economist.

They began with some general definitions of the Things themselves, according to their universal Natures, then divided them into their Parts, and then out into several propositions, which they laid down as Problems: These they controverted on both sides and by many niceties of Arguments, and Citations of Authorities, confuted their Adversaries and strengthened their own Dictates. But though this notional War had been carry'd on with far more care and calmness amongst them than it was. Yet it was never able to do any great Good towards the Enlargement of Knowledge, because it rely'd on *general Terms* which had not much Foundation in *Nature* and also because they took no other Course but that of *Disputing*.

Some folk seem to think that the human imagination is impoverished by accepting the supremacy of fact over mere logic. So it is healthy to recall the eloquent fervour with which Kepler began the announcement of his doctrine:

What I prophesied two-and-twenty years ago, as soon as I discovered the five solids among the heavenly orbits—what I firmly believed long before I had seen Ptolemy's Harmonies—what I had promised my friends in the title of this book, which I named before I was sure of my discovery—what sixteen years ago I urged as a thing to be sought—that for which I joined Tycho Brahe, for which I settled in Prague, for which I have devoted the best part of my life to astronomical contemplations, at length I have brought to light, and recognized its truth beyond my most sanguine expectations. It is not eighteen months since I got the first glimpse of light, three months since the dawn, very few days since the unveiled sun, most admirable to gaze upon, burst upon me. Nothing holds me; I will indulge my sacred fury; I will triumph over mankind by the honest confession that I have stolen the golden vases of the Egyptians to build up a tabernacle for my God far away from the confines of Egypt. If you forgive me, I rejoice; if you are angry, I can bear it; the die is cast, the book is written, to be read either now or by posterity, I care not which; it may well wait a century for a reader, as God has waited six thousand years for an observer!

PRECESSION AND THE DATE OF ANCIENT MONUMENTS

In Chapter I reference has been made to the work of Sir Norman Lockyer and others on early calendrical monuments. With the aid of the methods dealt with in this chapter the principles of orientation can now be made more explicit. The possibility of dating archaeological remains of this type is based on alignment to greet the rising or setting or—in the case of the Great Pyramid—transit of stars. The azimuths and transit elevation of stars depend on their declination which changes in the course of centuries owing to precession. While the positions of the stars with reference to the plane of the ecliptic do not change, the axis of the celestial equator rotates about the ecliptic axis (Fig. 138) at an angle (the obliquity (*e*) of the ecliptic) which varies only very slightly in the course of millennia between the limits 22° 35′ and 24° 13′ during the whole period of historic time. According to the

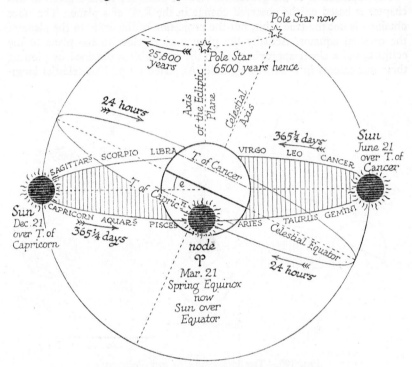

FIG. 138.—THE PRECESSION OF THE EQUINOXES

The position of the stars with reference to the plane of the celestial equator slowly changes, but remains constant with reference to the plane of the ecliptic. From the standpoint of an earth-observer (i.e. according to the geocentric view) this slow change is equivalent to a rotation of the plane of the celestial equator about the pole of the ecliptic at approximately constant inclination (23½°) to the ecliptic. Consequently the celestial pole revolves around the pole of the ecliptic at the same angle, and any bright star on the circle of its revolution will be a Pole Star at some time during the course of a complete cycle of about 26,000 years. The point of intersection of the equator and ecliptic shifts along the ecliptic in the same direction as the diurnal motion of the celestial sphere. Hence the vernal equinox which in the time of Hipparchus occurred when the sun occupied the same relative position as Aries now occurs when the sun is in Pisces, though the node ♈ is still called "The First Point of Aries." The two "Pole Stars" shown are, of course, different ones—not two positions of the same one.

Ptolemaic view (Fig. 138), the nodes or points of intersection of the sun's apparent path with the celestial equator shift in the course of a year about 50¼ seconds of an arc along the ecliptic circle in the direction opposite to the sun's annual retreat. According to the Copernican view (Fig. 139), the precession of the equinoxes results from the slow rotation of the earth's polar axis about the axis of the ecliptic at approximately constant inclination (*e*) to the latter. The result is that the sun's position among the fixed stars on the vernal equinox has shifted from the constellation of Aries to Pisces since the time of Hipparchus, though the node is still called "the first point of Aries" denoted by the zodiacal sign for the ram (♈).

The explanation of the geocentric view of planetary motion given in this chapter is based on the observed change in the R.A. of a planet. The trace obtained is not the true orbit, but the projection of the orbit on the plane of the celestial equator. Actually the planets move close to the plane of the ecliptic, and a closer approximation to the true orbit is obtained by plotting their movements in celestial longitude. As stated on p. 105, celestial longi-

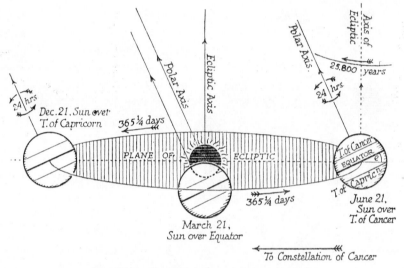

FIG. 139.—THE PRECESSION OF THE EQUINOXES

From the standpoint of a sun observer (heliocentric or Copernican view) the Precession can be regarded as analogous to the wobble of a spinning top. The earth's polar axis rotates slowly about the pole of the ecliptic and the earth's equator revolves at the approximately fixed inclination of 23½° to the plane of the earth's orbit. This rotation means that the north pole, which is tilted sunward when the sun is "in Cancer," will be tilted away from the sun in Cancer a half-cycle (½.26000 = 13,000 years) later.

tude and latitude have the same relation to the axis and plane of the ecliptic as R.A. and declination to the polar axis and the celestial equator. Great circles of longitude intersect at the pole of the ecliptic just as great circles of R.A. (Fig. 141) intersect at the celestial pole, and longitude is measured like R.A. eastwards from ♈. Latitude is measured by elevation above the plane of the ecliptic just as declination is measured by elevation from the celestial equator, and colatitude (90° − Lat.) is analogous to polar distance. Though this system is less useful for ready calculations for geographical use, it has special advantages for observations carried on over long periods, because the position of the stars with reference to the plane of the ecliptic is fixed. So the latitude of a star, i.e. its elevation above the ecliptic plane, is not affected by precession and its longitude increases 50¼ seconds of an arc per year. The sun's celestial latitude is always zero, and its motion in longitude is more nearly uniform than its motion in R.A. If we know the latitude and longitude of a star at one date we can therefore find it easily at another, and we can calculate the change in R.A. and declination due to the rotation of the nodes if we know how to convert observations from one system of co-ordinates to the other. We can then calculate the azimuth and times of rising

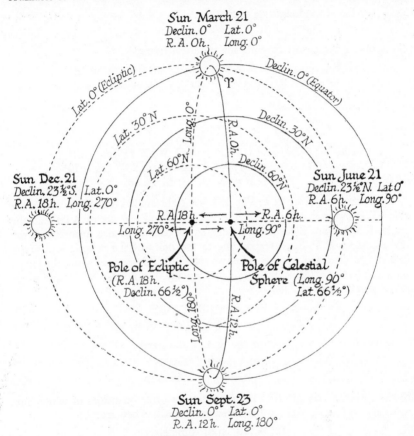

FIG. 140.—ECLIPTIC AND EQUATORIAL CO-ORDINATES OF THE HEAVENS SUPERIMPOSED IN A PLANE

By representing both the latitude and declination parallels as circles in conformity with Fig. 51 a distortion of the great circles of longitude and Right Ascension is produced.

or setting of stars at different periods in the history of the earth. The solution of the problem also illustrates the method for determining the true orbit of a planet.

Since longitude and R.A. are both reckoned from the intersection (♈) of the plane of the ecliptic and equator, i.e. the sun's position on the vernal equinox, ♈ is 90° from the pole (E) of the ecliptic along the great circle of longitude 0° and 90° from the celestial pole (P) along the great circle R.A. 0h.

(see Fig. 141). The pole of the ecliptic, the celestial pole, and ♈, form three corners of a spherical triangle of which

EP is the colatitude of the celestial pole or the polar distance of the ecliptic pole and is equal to the obliquity of the ecliptic (approximately $23\frac{1}{2}°$).

$E♈ = 90° = P♈$

$\angle ♈EP =$ the longitude of P

$\angle ♈PE = 360° -$ R.A. of E.

So applying the cosine formula for spherical triangles:

$$\cos E♈ = \cos EP \cos P♈ + \sin EP \sin P♈ \cos ♈PE$$
$$\therefore \quad \cos 90° = \cos 23\frac{1}{2}° \cos 90° + \sin 23\frac{1}{2}° \sin 90° \cos ♈PE$$
$$\therefore \quad \cos ♈PE = 0$$
$$\therefore \quad ♈PE = 90°$$

Similarly

$$\cos P♈ = \cos E♈ \cos EP + \sin E♈ \sin EP \cos ♈EP$$
$$\therefore \cos 90° = \cos 90° \cos 23\frac{1}{2}° + \sin 90° \sin 23\frac{1}{2}° \cos ♈EP$$
$$\therefore \quad \cos ♈EP = 0 \quad \therefore \quad ♈EP = 90°$$

Thus the triangle EP♈ in Fig. 141 is a right-angled triangle in which the side EP is (approximately) $23\frac{1}{2}°$, the sides E♈ and P♈ are each 90° and the angles E and P are also each 90°. A spherical triangle is also formed with the three corners E, P, S, corresponding to the poles of the ecliptic and of the celestial equator and a star S. The two sides ES, PS, are arcs along the longitude and R.A. meridians of the star respectively. Since ♈EP = 90° and ♈ES is the longitude of the star,

$$PES = ♈EP - ♈ES$$
$$= 90° - \text{Long. of S}$$

Since ♈PE = 90° and ♈PS is the R.A. of the star,

$$EPS = ♈PE + ♈PS$$
$$= 90° + \text{R.A. of S.}$$

In the spherical triangle EPS therefore we have five quantities of which any two may be found, if the other three are known. They are:

$$EP = 23\frac{1}{2}° \text{ approximately}$$
$$ES = 90° - \text{Lat.} (=\text{colatitude})$$
$$PS = 90° - \text{declin.} (=\text{polar distance})$$
$$PES = 90° - \text{Long.}$$
$$EPS = 90° + \text{R.A.}$$

Applying the cosine formulae:

(i) $\cos PS = \cos EP \cos ES + \sin EP \sin ES \cos PES$

$\therefore \quad \sin (\text{declin.}) = \cos 23\frac{1}{2}° \sin (\text{lat.}) + \sin 23\frac{1}{2}° \cos (\text{lat.}) \sin (\text{long.})$

(ii) $\cos ES = \cos EP \cos PS + \sin EP \sin PS \cos EPS$

$\therefore \quad \sin (\text{lat.}) = \cos 23\frac{1}{2}° \sin (\text{declin.}) - \sin 23\frac{1}{2}° \cos (\text{declin.}) \sin (\text{R.A.})*$

---

* Since $\cos (90° + A) = -\sin A$.

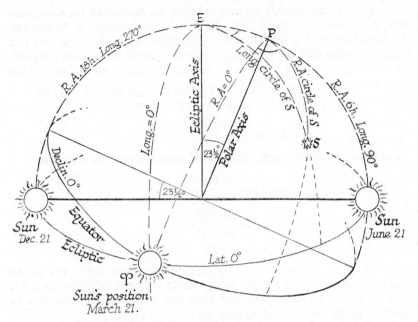

FIG. 141.—THE TWO SYSTEMS OF CELESTIAL CO-ORDINATES

Celestial latitude and longitude give the direction of a star as seen from the earth's centre with reference to the plane of the ecliptic (or earth's orbit about the sun). Declination and R.A. give its direction as seen from the earth centre with reference to the plane of the celestial equator (at right angles to the earth's polar axis). Since the position of the stars with reference to the ecliptic plane is fixed the latitude of a star is not affected by precession. Longitude is reckoned like R.A. from the meridian which passes through the node ♈. Since this slowly retreats at 50¼ seconds of an arc per year the longitude of any star increases by 50¼″ per year. Compare this figure carefully with Fig. 48 in Chapter 2 by tilting either through 23½°.

So if we know the R.A. and declination of a star we can calculate its celestial latitude, and if we know the celestial longitude and latitude of a star we can get its declination by the cosine formula. Similarly, applying the sine formula:

$$\frac{\sin EPS}{\sin ES} = \frac{\sin PES}{\sin PS}$$

$$\therefore \frac{\sin (90° + \text{R.A.})}{\sin (90° - \text{lat.})} = \frac{\sin (90° - \text{long.})}{\sin (90° - \text{declin.})}$$

$$\therefore \frac{\cos (\text{R.A.})}{\cos (\text{lat.})} = \frac{\cos (\text{long.})}{\cos (\text{declin.})}$$

$$\therefore \text{(iii)} \quad \cos (\text{R.A.}) = \frac{\cos (\text{long.}) \cos (\text{lat.})}{\cos (\text{declin.})}$$

and

$$\therefore \text{(iv)} \quad \cos (\text{long.}) = \frac{\cos (\text{R.A.}) \cos (\text{declin.})}{\cos (\text{lat.})}$$

For a check to the formula we may calculate the azimuth of the rising May year (p. 69) sun at the terrestrial latitude (51° approximately) of Stonehenge. To do this we need to know the sun's declination on May 6th. The May year begins at a date half-way between the vernal equinox and summer solstice. So the longitude is 45°. The sun's celestial latitude is always zero. Thus

$$\sin (\text{declin.}) = \cos 23\tfrac{1}{2}° \sin 0 + \sin 23\tfrac{1}{2}° \cos 0 \sin 45°$$
$$= 0 + 0\cdot3987 \times 0\cdot7071$$
$$= + 0\cdot2819$$
$$\text{declin.} = + 16\tfrac{1}{4}°$$

At 51° (terrestrial) latitude the azimuth of rising is given by the formula:

$$\cos (\text{azim.}) = \frac{\sin (\text{declin.})}{\cos (\text{lat.})}$$
$$= \frac{\sin 16\tfrac{1}{4}°}{\cos 51°}$$
$$= 0\cdot448$$

$\therefore$ azimuth $= 63\tfrac{1}{2}°$ (approximately), or $26\tfrac{1}{2}°$ north of the east point. Allowing for a slight change in the obliquity of the ecliptic, this corresponds to the older May year alignment which Lockyer describes in addition to the solstitial setting (Fig. 1).

As a problem in assigning a date to archaeological remains the Great Pyramid will serve for illustration. According to one theory the tunnel sloped to greet the transit of *Soth*, or Sirius as we now call it. To simplify the issue we may calculate the declination of Sirius 4,100 years ago, i.e. in 2164 B.C. The present declination of Sirius is (approximately) $16\tfrac{1}{2}°$ South, and its R.A. is 6 hours 42 minutes (approximately), or 101°. To get its co-ordinates at the date mentioned we may first refer its position to the plane of the ecliptic, thus:

(i) $\quad \sin (\text{lat.}) = \cos 23\tfrac{1}{2}° \sin (- 16\tfrac{1}{2}°) - \sin 23\tfrac{1}{2}° \cos (-16\tfrac{1}{2}°) \sin 101°$
$$= - \cos 23\tfrac{1}{2}° \sin 16\tfrac{1}{2}° - \sin 23\tfrac{1}{2}° \cos 16\tfrac{1}{2}° \cos 11° \star$$
$$= - 0\cdot6358$$
$\therefore \quad \text{lat.} = - 39\cdot5°$

(ii) $\quad \cos (\text{long.}) = + \dfrac{\cos (- 16\tfrac{1}{2}°) \cos 101°}{\cos (- 39\cdot5)}$
$$= - \frac{\cos 16\tfrac{1}{2}° \sin 11°}{\cos 39\cdot5°}$$
$$= - 0\cdot2371$$

Since $\quad \cos 76\cdot3° = 0\cdot2371$ (approx.)
$$\cos (180° - 76\cdot3°) = - 0\cdot2371$$
$$\therefore \quad \text{longitude} = 103\cdot7°$$

The precessional shift is $50\tfrac{1}{4}$ seconds of an arc in the longitude of all stars per year. Hence the increase since 2164 B.C. is $(50\tfrac{1}{4} \times 4100)''$ or

★ Since $\sin (90 + A) = \cos A$.

$50\frac{1}{4} \times 4100 \div 3600$ degrees, i.e. $57 \cdot 2°$. Thus the longitude of Sirius at that date was $103 \cdot 7° - 57 \cdot 2° = 46 \cdot 5°$. So that the declination of Sirius at that time is given by:

$$\begin{aligned}
\sin(\text{declin.}) &= \cos 23\frac{1}{2}° \sin(-39 \cdot 5°) + \sin 23\frac{1}{2}° \cos(-39 \cdot 5°) \sin(46 \cdot 5°) \\
&= -\cos 23\frac{1}{2}° \sin 39 \cdot 5° + \sin 23\frac{1}{2}° \cos 39 \cdot 5° \sin 46 \cdot 5° \\
&= -0 \cdot 5833 + 0 \cdot 2232 \\
&= -0 \cdot 3601
\end{aligned}$$

$\therefore$ declination $= 21 \cdot 1°$ S.

The accompanying figure (Fig. 142), which should be compared with Fig. 2, shows that if the angle of the Pyramid is approximately $52°$, the beam of

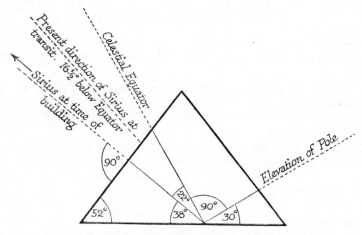

FIG. 142.—The Geometrical Relations of the Transit of Sirius to the Great Pyramid

Sirius striking its face at right angles when crossing the meridian is elevated $38°$ from the horizon. The terrestrial latitude of the Pyramid is $30°$, so that the angle which the star made with the celestial equator (i.e. its declination at the time when it was built) was approximately $-22°$, which differs by less than a degree from the figure calculated, for the date assigned, with the aid of four-figure tables and approximate values for the obliquity of the ecliptic and the angle of the Pyramid. Proceeding in this way we get $-20 \cdot 8°$ in 2064 and $-23 \cdot 6°$ in 2864 B.C. for the declination of Sirius. If, then, the tunnel was in line with the transit of Sirius, the Pyramid must have been completed about 2400 B.C. To assign a more precise date a graph of more accurate values of declinations at different dates, as given in Lockyer's book on *Stonehenge*, can be prepared, and the date when the declination of the star agreed most closely with the architectural data can be read off from it.

The possibility of dating a solar monument like Stonehenge depends on a different principle. What we call the summer solstice is the day on which the positive declination of the sun is equivalent to the angle of obliquity, and since the inclination of the equator to the ecliptic is not involved in the precession of the equinoxes, the precessional rotation does not affect the sun's declination and therefore its azimuth of rising and setting on the solstice. Actually, the observations which have accumulated from the time of the Alexandrian Hipparchus and his Babylonian predecessors show that the obliquity of the ecliptic has changed very slightly—less than a degree—since the beginning of recorded history. Hence the sun's declination, which is now about $23\frac{1}{2}°$ on the solstice, was about $24°$ at the time when Stonehenge was erected, and this makes a perceptible azimuth difference which can be detected by the alignment of an avenue placed to meet the rising midsummer sun.

EXAMPLES ON CHAPTER IV

For these the reader will need *Whitaker's Almanack* and a planisphere, which can be obtained from an educational bookseller for about 2s. 6d. or half a dollar.

1. With the aid of a map on which ocean distances are given, work out the distances by great-circle sailing from ports connected by direct routes. What are the distances between London and New York, London and Moscow, London and Liverpool?

2. On April 26th, the sun's R.A. being 2 hours 13 minutes, the bearings of three stars were found to be as follows, by a home-made instrument:

	Azimuth	Zenith Distance	Local Time
Pollux	W. 80° from S.	45°	9.28 p.m.
Regulus	W. 28° from S.	41°	9.39 p.m.
Arcturus	W 7° from N.	31°	12.50 p.m.

Find the declination and R.A. of each star and compare these rough estimates made at Lat. $50\frac{3}{4}°$ N. with the accurate determinations given in *Whitaker's Almanack*.

3. To get the exact position of the meridian a line was drawn between two posts in line with the setting sun on July 4th at a place Lat. 43° N. At what angle to this line did the meridian lie? (*Whitaker* gives the sun's declination on July 4th as 23° N.) What was the approximate time of sunset?

4. If the R.A. of Sirius is 6 hours 42 minutes and its declination is $16\frac{3}{5}°$ S., find its local times of rising and setting on January 1st at

Gizeh	Lat. 30° N.
New York	Lat. 41° N.
London	Lat. $51\frac{1}{2}°$ N.

Check with planisphere.

5. Find the times of rising and setting of the sun on February 9th, also the azimuth of rising and setting on the same date at the latitudes of London, New York, and Cape Town.

6. Find the times of rising and setting of Vega, a week before and a week after the vernal equinox at Lat. 51° N. Compare them with the times of sunrise or sunset. Give the azimuths of rising and setting at the same latitude. (R.A. of Vega 18 hours 35 minutes, Declination 38° 43'.)

7. From the tables of R.A. and Declination in *Whitaker*, make a graph of the times of rising and setting of any star and of the sun throughout the year at your own latitude. Hence find the date on which the star is seen rising and setting in morning twilight (one hour before sunrise) or evening twilight (one hour after sunset). Check with a planisphere.

8. Find the declination of Polaris and γ Draconis in the time of Hipparchus (150 B.C.).

9. According to Fotheringham, the Chaldean astronomer Cidenas taught that Mercury was never more than 22° distant from the sun. If its orbit were circular what would be the relative distances of Mercury and the earth from the sun?

10. With the aid of three consecutive issues of *Whitaker* tabulate the R.A. of Venus and Mars for a sufficient period to determine the sidereal period of each planet, and determine the relative breadth of their heliocentric orbits, assuming that they are the circular form.

11. Use the sidereal periods of the moon and one of the planets Venus, Mars or Jupiter, the R.A. of the moon and the R.A. of the planet chosen as given for the first day of the month in *Whitaker*, to calculate approximate times of lunar conjunction and opposition during the ensuing lunar cycle. Check from the same source.

THINGS TO MEMORIZE

1 Solution of spherical triangles:
$$\cos a = \cos b \cos c + \sin b \sin c \cos A$$
$$\sin A = \pm \frac{\sin a \sin C}{\sin c}.$$

2. If Azim. is reckoned from the south point:
$$\sin \text{Decl.} = \sin \text{Lat.} \cos \text{Z.D.} - \cos \text{Lat.} \sin \text{Z.D.} \cos \text{Azim.}$$

When a heavenly body is rising or setting
$$\sin \text{Decl.} = - \cos \text{Lat.} \cos \text{Azim.}$$

3.
$$\sin \text{Hour Angle} = \frac{\sin \text{Azim.} \sin \text{Z.D.}}{\cos \text{Decl.}}$$

4. If Azimuth is reckoned from the south point, cos Azim. is positive for stars with southerly, and negative for stars of northerly, bearing. Sin Azim. is reckoned negative when a star is east of the meridian.

5. Eccentricity of ellipse $= \dfrac{\text{distance between foci}}{\text{major axis}}$

$$= \sqrt{1 - \left(\frac{\text{minor axis}}{\text{major axis}}\right)^2}$$

6. Kepler's Third Law. If T is the sidereal period of a planet and d its distance from the sun, $T^2 \div d^3$ is the same for all the planets.

7. See also the four formulae on pp. 222–3 relating celestial latitude and longitude to declination and R.A.

CHAPTER V

WHEEL, WEIGHT, AND WATCHSPRING

The Laws of Motion

THE determination of longitude in modern navigation and exploration depends upon comparing local time as determined by the sun or stars with time at Greenwich, as explained on p. 79. This method has only been in use a hundred and fifty years. Before then, it was not possible to construct clocks with sufficient reliability to keep in step with standard time during a sea

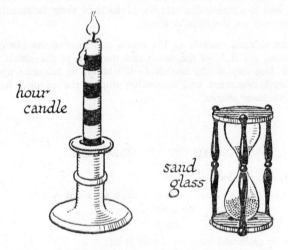

hour candle

sand glass

FIG. 143.—PRIMITIVE TIMEPIECES

Before the introduction of clocks the early monasteries of northern Europe regulated the routine of daily ritual by the use of hour candles. The word clock is derived from *cloche*, a bell. The bell which tolled matins and vespers was once the village clock. Hour-glasses of great antiquity were comparable to the device still used to time the boiling of an egg.

voyage. The laborious method of lunar distances or the use of eclipses and occultations, when they happened to be visible, were the only methods available when long-distance westerly courses were first undertaken in the closing years of the fifteenth century. For practical purposes the use of the moon as a celestial signpost had two immense disadvantages. One is that clear-cut moon signals suitable for observation with rough-and-ready instruments at sea are comparatively rare events. The other is that methods of finding longitude by relying on the moon's position (as illustrated in Fig. 37 and Fig. 110) are liable to involve a large error unless correction is made for parallax. Thus the method of Amerigo cited on p. 180 gives a very poor result, and its use in the Spanish and Portuguese fleets would have been

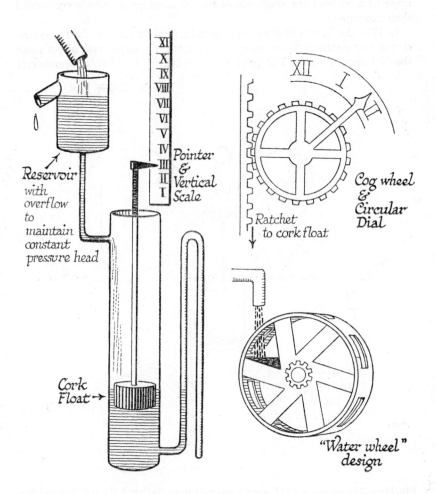

FIG. 144.—WATER CLOCKS

The clepsydras of the early Mediterranean civilizations were simply graduated vessels of conical shape to ensure a steady rate of flow as they emptied. They were filled daily. The mechanics of Alexandria made more elaborate devices which, so far as we can be sure from the descriptions available, seem to have employed two principles. One was the float with an upright rod. This might bear a simple pointer which recorded the hours on a vertical scale. It might have a ratchet which worked a cog wheel carrying a pointer for a circular dial. Alternatively a revolving mechanism something like a water wheel in design was used. Water clocks of this type were still used in seventeenth-century Europe. The float clock shown in this figure is provided with a reservoir designed to maintain a fixed rate of flow. Hence it could be used to record hours of equal length. Alexandrian clocks were not so made. Before the invention of the Arab sundial with its style pointing to the celestial pole the interval from sunrise to sunset was taken as a unit of time, and the hours were not equivalent in different seasons. In ancient clepsydras, an adjustment was made by a plunger which varied the capacity of the vessel, and hence the rate of flow from it. The bent tube on the right side of the float clock acts as a siphon which automatically empties the vessel, and thus makes possible the continuous record of time without personal attention.

impossible without the assistance of trained astronomers who accompanied their expeditions.

In 1714 the British Government offered a prize of £20,000 for the invention of any means of determining longitude at sea with an error of not more than 30 nautical miles. The prize was awarded for Harrison's chronometer

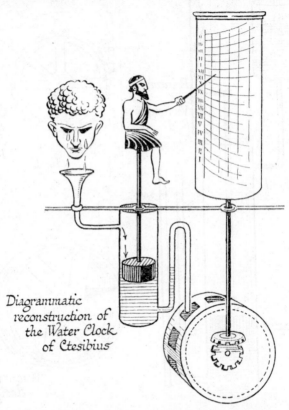

Diagrammatic reconstruction of the Water Clock of Ctesibius

FIG. 145.—The water clock of Ctesibius invented about 250 B.C. had water dropping like tears into a funnel from the eyes of a statue. A float mechanism raised another human figure with a pointer which indicated the hours on a vertical cylinder. Once in twenty-four hours the figure descended to the bottom of the column by a siphon mechanism as shown in the previous illustration. The siphon outflow worked a water wheel which very slowly rotated the cylinder dial, making a complete rotation in a year. The graduation of the cylinder was adapted to the varying lengths of the hours throughout the seasons. The gearing is not shown. The curious feature of this device is the application of so much ingenuity to conserve the seasonal hours which preceded the invention of the Arab sundial. It is said to have been installed in a temple.

in 1765. Simultaneously, Le Roy of Paris invented a better device which is in principle like the modern chronometer. These patents were the crowning achievement of sustained effort over a long period. As early as 1530, Gemma Frisius, a Dutch mathematician and cosmographer, had pointed out the great advantage of a chronometric method (p. 79) for finding longitude at sea. Thereafter the improvement of the clock constantly engaged the attention of

the leaders of physical science. Galileo, Hooke, and Huyghens, who laid the
foundations of the dynamical principles systematized by Newton in the
Principia, were actively concerned with the betterment of the timepiece; and
some of the most fruitful theoretical work was a by-product of their interest
in doing so. One of the last acts of Galileo, who discovered the principle of
the pendulum, was to dictate a project for the construction of a pendulum
clock. Hooke, who is said to have first introduced the hair spring, also invented the "anchor escapement" and a device for cutting watch wheels
accurately. In a very real sense, his Law of the Spring was a by-product
of the technology of time-keeping. Huyghens, who first developed the theory
of centrifugal motion, published it in his *Horologium Oscillatorium* which

FIG. 146

The design of these two clocks illustrates vividly the dual social context in which
the technology of mechanical timekeeping progressed in the middle ages.

describes his invention of the pendulum clock. He also made several attempts
to make a seaworthy clock suitable for finding longitude by the method of
Frisius and subjected his models to tests at sea.

The first clocks in the modern sense, i.e. clocks geared with toothed
wheels, were driven by the falling of a weight, and checked daily by the noon
sun. They were large clumsy affairs, scarcely as accurate as the magnificent
but quite immovable water clock or *clepsydra* which was constructed by
Ctesibius at Alexandria (see Fig. 145) in the third century B.C. Although
designs were put forward at an earlier date, weight-driven clocks did not
come into use before about A.D. 1000, when they were first put up in churches
and monasteries. For two centuries their use was confined to the official
timekeepers of Christendom. Till about A.D. 1450 they were not sold for
secular use except for installation in public buildings. In England the first
public clock was erected in A.D. 1288. Meanwhile Arabic astronomy was

beginning to filter into northern Europe. In the generation which preceded Copernicus, Walther of Nuremburg (1430–1504) equipped what appears to have been the first observatory with mechanical clocks. Spring-driven portable watches—the so-called "Nuremburg eggs"—were marketed at the beginning of the sixteenth century.

In previous chapters enough has been said to emphasize the importance of an accurate and portable device for registering time as a basis for astronomical measurements which underlie calendrical practice and navigation. Mechanical clocks made no mean contribution to the great progress of astronomy during the epoch of the great navigations. Aside from its usefulness as an instrument of observation, the wheel-driven clock created a new problem in mechanics. Finding the laws which describe the motion of the clock also disclosed new laws which describe the motions of the solar system. Though the telescope did much to encourage a favourable reception for the doctrine which Copernicus had revived, the invention of the pendulum clock was the incident which gave the death-blow to the geocentric principle.

The Copernican doctrine, and still more the laws of Kepler, equipped navigational astronomy with more reliable and manageable rules for calculating conjunctions of planets. Apart from the convenience of doing so, there is nothing to explain the popularity of the Copernican teaching. A century after the death of Copernicus no known facts of terrestrial experience could be brought forward to justify the major premises on which his doctrine rests. The supposed orbital motion of the earth was difficult to reconcile with failure to measure the annual parallax of a star, a feat which was not accomplished till about 1830, when improvements in optical instruments made it first possible. Telescopic observations like Galileo's descriptions of sunspots suggested the diurnal rotation of other heavenly bodies before it was possible to point out a single occurrence due to the earth's axial motion. Even when Kepler published his final treatise on planetary orbits, scepticism was common among his contemporaries; and Bacon, whose *Novum Organum* was written as a challenge to the Aristotelian tradition, obstinately rejected the heliocentric view. From a landsman's point of view, the earth remained at rest till it was discovered that pendulum clocks lose time if taken to a place nearer the equator (see p. 288). After the invention of Huyghens the earth's axial motion was a socially necessary foundation for the colonial export of pendulum clocks.

The mechanical principles discovered by Newton's immediate predecessors, Stevinus, Galileo, Hooke, and Huyghens, bring us face to face with one of the great dichotomies in the history of human achievement. While science in the ancient world was chiefly concerned with heavenly motions, that of our own time is largely occupied with earthly ones. This neglect of terrestrial motion by men of science in antiquity is not surprising. Neither their technical equipment nor their social environment was propitious to studying it. Antiquity was ill supplied with mechanical devices for registering small intervals of time, and so long as civilized life was restricted to sunny climates there was no pressing need to invent them. While slave labour was abundant there was no social pressure to bother about how things get moved. Merchandise was carried by slave-driven galleys equipped with sails for use

(a)

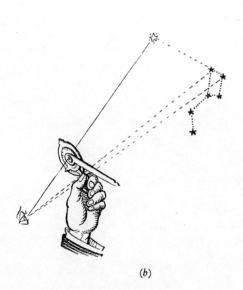

(b)

FIG. 147

(a) Nocturnal or Night Dial (about 1700).   (b) A Nocturnal in Use.
Reproduced by permission of H.M. Stationery Office from "Time Measurement,"
Part I, by Dr. F. A. B. Ward.

H*

FIG. 148

(a) Harrison's First Marine Timekeeper (1735).   (b) Harrison's Fourth Marine Timekeeper (1759).
Reproduced by permission of H.M. Stationery Office from "Time Measurement," Part I, by Dr. F. A. B. Ward.

when winds were favourable. It was the business of the overseer to control the slave and of the priests to propitiate the winds. Science was equally irrelevant to both methods of persuasion.

Northern civilization, where knowledge was rapidly advancing in the sixteenth and seventeenth centuries of the Christian era, presents a different picture. Mechanical timekeeping is a social necessity for a highly developed culture in the grey northern climate. During the decline of chattel slavery,

FIG. 149.—ASTRONOMICAL CLOCK OF THE SIXTEENTH CENTURY

from the time of Constantine onwards, mechanism had penetrated everyday life in other ways. The water mill was replacing irksome toil. Gunpowder had entered the theatre of war. Marksmanship required a close-up view of motion, and metallurgical development (p. 363) received a new impetus, making new demands on water power. The circumstances of artillery practice, of clock manufacture, of navigation, and of water power, belong to a social context in which men of capacity could find wealthy patrons to encourage mechanical enquiries. The new power with which gunpowder equipped imperialist designs on the New World, the increasing importance of astronomy in westerly navigation, and the introduction of the clock into secular use, were the

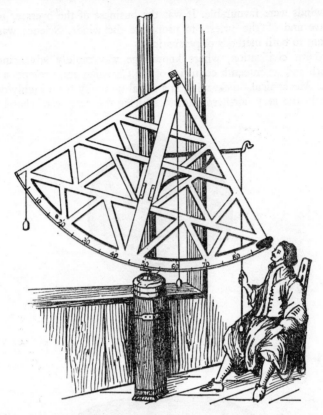

FIG. 150.—EARLY SEVENTEENTH-CENTURY OBSERVATORY WITH SIMPLE QUADRANT
(NON-TELESCOPIC) AND MECHANICAL CLOCKS

The introduction of clocks into astronomical practice during the latter end of the
fifteenth century increased the facility of determining the time of transit, and hence
R.A. of stars. With more accurate clocks at their disposal in the middle of the seventeenth century astronomers undertook extensive revision of the star catalogues.
Prominent among them was Hevel of Danzig. His observatory is here seen. The
catalogue of Hevel formed the basis of more refined observations with telescopic sights
in the Paris and Greenwich observatories during the latter end of the seventeenth
century.

(Note that the accuracy achieved by medieval astronomers who worked like Tycho
Brahe without telescopic instruments was due to the large scale of their instruments.
Thus Tycho Brahe used a quadrant 19 feet across. A circle of radius 19 feet has a
circumference (360 degrees) of $19 \times 2 \times 3 \cdot 14$ feet, i.e. roughly 120 feet or 4 inches
per degree. Since it is quite easy to distinguish half a millimetre (one-fiftieth of an
inch), an accuracy of from one hundredth to one two-hundredth of a degree could be
obtained, if the scale was accurately calibrated.)

principal circumstances which conspired to create the adventurous hopefulness of seventeenth-century capitalism, when Bacon penned his eloquent
plea, "the true and lawful goal of science is that human life be endowed with
new powers and inventions."

The military manuals published from 1500 onwards (see Fig. 151) bear
eloquent testimony to a new impetus in the social background of Galileo's

"Two New Sciences." For the first time in the history of mankind precise
measurement of rapid long-range motion became a social necessity. In its
turn this demanded instruments for measuring time in short intervals. In

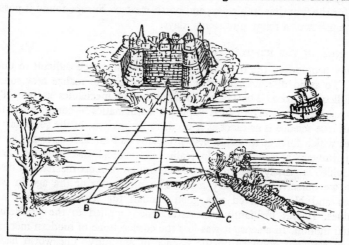

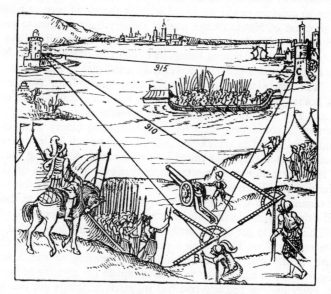

FIG. 151.—MILITARY MATHEMATICS

These two prints taken from old books show one way in which solving the problem
of motion had become a technical necessity in the period of Stevinus and Galileo.
The upper one is from Bettino's *Apiaria* (Bologna, 1645). The lower from Zubler's
work on geometric instruments (1607).

the sixteenth and seventeenth centuries the improvement of clock design
was a matter of as much importance as the improvement of motor cars today.
Exploration and navigation demanded a seaworthy timepiece, while marks-

manship called for a new unit of time reckoning. The problem of longitude in westerly courses and the problem of range-finding in mechanized warfare converged to a common focus, when the *second* became a unit of time measurement for the first time in history, and north-western Europe found it possible to dispense with a religion of saints' days.

MECHANICS IN THE NEWTONIAN AGE

Many people find the mechanics of the Newtonian age difficult to understand. To avoid discouragement it is therefore best to realize how some of the difficulties arise. The custom of speaking of mechanics as one of the exact sciences—it is even called "applied mathematics"—conceals the truth that all true science is as exact as it needs to be in virtue of the social circumstances which force it to tackle new problems and as exact as it can be with the instruments at its disposal. In reality the textbook mechanics of Newton and Galileo is grossly inaccurate as a description of most mechanical devices which we ourselves commonly meet. The mechanics of the age in which Galileo and Newton lived was good enough for what were then called machines. It was brilliantly successful when applied to the problems of celestial motion. In a sense it was less the corner-stone of modern mechanics than an eloquent obituary on the science of antiquity. The world had not yet begun to measure power produced without the aid of man or beasts.

The problem of Newton's age was to connect the new motive power of the cannon ball with the behaviour of devices like levers and pulleys which distribute the power of human beings or of animals. Machines like dynamos and gas engines which generate power from inanimate sources were not yet known. The water wheel or windmill took power from Nature at no cost to human effort. Newtonian science had no balance-sheet for heat and work. You will not understand the mechanical principles of Galileo and Newton if you expect them to apply to the machinery of rapid large-scale industrialization in the Soviet Union, and you will be less worried by the words in which they were stated if you remember something else. Views which are now commonplace were entirely novel in the age of the first pendulum clocks. Because they were novel and because they were still in violent opposition to traditional belief it was pardonable to state them in a cut-and-dried way, neglecting qualifications which seem imperative to us.

It will help you to get the atmosphere of the time, and to see what the last sentence means, if we begin with a principle which is implicit in Galileo's treatment of the path of the cannon ball. According to the Aristotelian teaching, which was adapted by St. Paul to explain the mystery of the Resurrection, everything in the universe had its place. If things got out of place they returned sooner or later to the place where they belonged—earthly bodies to earth, celestial bodies (including the "spirits" of the retort) to heaven. Like other self-evident principles on which economists rely, this had very little relevance to the conduct of secular life, unless taken to signify that smoking is a celestial occupation. In particular it does not help you to decide where a bullet belongs. So long as Aristotle's physics enjoyed as much authority as the Bible, it was a novel and exciting discovery to find that things just go on moving till something stops them. It was just as novel as Darwin's doctrine when most Englishmen still believed the Biblical account of creation. The words in which Newton's generation announced the discovery are no more surprising than the fact that Huxley's views about man's nearest Simian ancestors are not universally held at the present time.

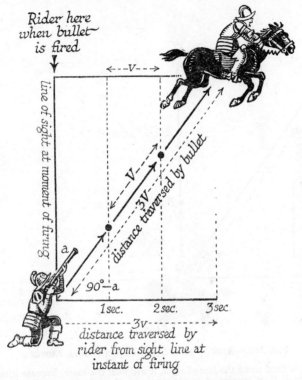

FIG. 152.—HITTING A MOVING OBJECT

If the bullet is fired along the line of sight, it will miss. The rider will have moved on beyond where he was along the line of sight at the instant when the bullet left the muzzle. To hit the mark the gun must be tilted away from the line of sight in the direction of the rider's motion. If the rider moves at a velocity v feet per second, he covers vt feet (here $3v$, since the time is 3 seconds) in t seconds. In the same time the bullet travelling with velocity V feet per second covers a distance of Vt (here 3V) feet along its own path. If bullet and rider reach the same point, as when the bullet hits its mark, their paths make two sides of a right-angled triangle with the sight line at the moment of firing, enclosing the angle a which measures the tilt of the gun to the direct line of sight, when the aim is correct. The rider's path (vt) and the bullet's path (Vt) are respectively the perpendicular and hypotenuse to a, i.e. $\sin a = vt \div Vt$ or

$$\sin a = v \div V = \cos (90° - a)$$

The proper angle depends only on the speeds of the bullet and rider, and it is not necessary to know the distances.

How the principle of inertia emerges from the social context of the time is shown in Figs. 152 and 153, which illustrate two of the most elementary problems of marksmanship. If you are standing still (Fig. 152) you have to shoot ahead of it to hit an object moving at right angles to your direct line of vision at the instant when the charge explodes. Conversely, if you are moving at right angles to the direction in which you are sighting a still object, you have to tilt the gun to the rear (Fig. 153). If you aim straight at the object the bullet will be ahead of it by the time it is level with its mark. The bullet

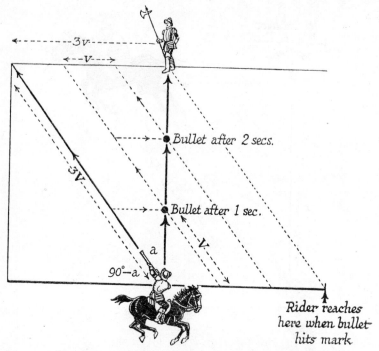

FIG. 153.—AIMING AT A STILL OBJECT WHILE MOVING

If the bullet is fired along the line of sight, it will miss the mark, because it moves as if in each second: (i) it continued to progress with the velocity v of the rider along its course (i.e. the motion it had while it was still in the muzzle), (ii) it had also the same velocity, V, along the direction in which the gun points, as it would have if the rider were at rest. To hit the mark it must be tilted away from the direct line of sight in the direction opposite to the rider's motion. Travelling at V feet per second in line with the axis of the gun, it moves simultaneously v feet per second parallel to the rider. If the angle of tilt (a) from the sight line is correct, its velocity v along the rider's course must keep it in the direct line of sight at the moment of firing. Hence, if a is the right angle of aim, the distance (vt) the rider would travel in time t, the distance (Vt) the bullet would travel if the marksman were at rest and the direct line of sight, together form a right-angled triangle, in which $\sin a = vt \div Vt$, or

$$\sin a = v \div V = \cos (90° - a)$$

Thus the same rule describes the correct angle of tilt whether the marksman is moving at a particular velocity or the object at which he aims is moving at the same velocity, one or the other being still. In other words the tilt of the gun is only concerned with their relative velocities.

therefore behaves as if it *kept* its motion sideways at the moment of leaving the muzzle and gained at the same time a new motion along the line of aim, just as a boat drifting in a current (Fig. 154) keeps the motion it gets from the oars and gains a simultaneous drift down stream.

The fact that it does so was quite unexpected when the science of marksmanship was in its infancy. This you can judge from the opening sentence of the second chapter in the *Leviathan*:

That when a thing is still, unless something else stir it, it will lie forever still, is a truth that no man doubts of. But that when a thing is in motion, it will eternally be in motion unless something else stay it, though the reason be the same, that nothing can change of itself, is not so easily assented to.

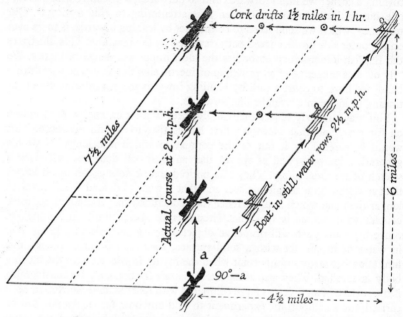

FIG. 154.—COMPOSITE MOTION OF BOAT IN CURRENT

As the moving marksman must tilt his gun from the sight line, so an oarsman must keep the keel turned away from the direction in which the boat must progress to reach its destination in a straight line. The same construction for finding the correct angle fits either case. If the boat is to be rowed along a course at right angles to the current, the keel must be inclined at a to this correct course, and at $(90° - a)$ to the current. To make a scale diagram, lay off equivalent distances traversed by a cork drifting in the current and by the boat, rowing at its ordinary straight line velocity in still water. These must be the sides of a right-angled triangle, or of a parallelogram whose diagonal is at right angles to the current. The figure is drawn for a three-hour course, during which the boat would row $7\frac{1}{2}$ miles in still water, and a cork would drift $4\frac{1}{2}$ miles. Only one right-angled triangle can be made with these two sides, if one is the hypotenuse. In this case, $\sin a = 4\frac{1}{2} \div 7\frac{1}{2} = 0·6$, which is the same as the ratio of the current velocity (v), and the velocity (V) of the boat in still water. In general, $\sin a = v \div V = \cos (90° - a)$, so that a can be got from tables of sines. The resultant velocity is $\sqrt{V^2 - v^2}$.

These words, written by the materialist philosopher Hobbes when Newton was still a boy, are almost identical with those in which Newton himself stated his *First Law of Motion*. As they stand they are somewhat metaphysical. We have no experience of bodies moving with absolutely constant speed or of things being permanently at rest or of any process going on for ever. Still, the essential fact of the sluggishness of matter or *inertia* is a very tangible one, and directly contrary to Aristotle's teaching. We all know that when a train or bus stops or starts our bodies continue to move in the direction of the previous movement, or remain at rest, as the case may be. Our feet, firmly set on the floor, follow the movement of the vehicle. Consequently we lurch backwards when the train or bus starts, or forwards when it stops. In this instance the movement of the vehicle is usually straight at the time. In turning a corner we lurch forwards and so outwards, a difficulty which everyone has to learn to forestall when first attempting to ride a bicycle. Our tendency, which we soon learn to counteract by leaning inwards, is to go over on the outer side of the curved path traversed by the machine. This illustrates the English idiom which embodies the most important aspect of inertia. We "fly off at a tangent." The principle of inertia signifies that when we turn a bend, we have to exert a pull by bending inwards to prevent ourselves continuing to move in a straight line forwards.

You may properly object that the flywheel of a steam engine does not go on for ever, and that Newton's first law is therefore plain nonsense. This would be wrenching it out of the context to which it belongs. Newton's generation knew as well as we do that an iron ball does not roll along a stretch of ice indefinitely. They also noticed that it does go on much longer than it would on a rough surface, and that a well-lubricated wheel revolves longer than one which is dry. Hence they concluded that friction or adhesive contact with matter is the chief circumstance which limits the principle. Since the same push will propel an object over a longer distance in air than in water or in contact with a solid surface, they argued correctly that this limitation is usually unimportant when the matter in contact with the moving body is rarefied. They also recognized that air friction may be considerable if the surface of an object is large compared with its bulk, and Newton himself carried out an important experiment to find out how far air friction can be neglected (see p. 376). For calculating the range and height of the slow-moving short-range projectiles of Galileo's time, the error due to air friction is very small.

It was thus natural to go a step farther. If there were no air, and no contact with matter, there would be nothing to stop a cannon ball from going on in a straight line at the speed with which it left the muzzle, except the fact that like all other solid bodies it is being pulled earthwards during its range. If so, why should not the planets move in a straight line through the vastness of empty space with no friction to stop them? Might not the answer be that they were pulled sunwards as the cannon ball in *its* curved path (Fig. 171) is pulled earthwards? This was the problem to which Newton's first "law" was preliminary. The words in which he propounded the principle of inertia, though seemingly speculative in circumstances with which Newton was not concerned, are easily intelligible in their own setting.

MECHANICS IN THE ANCIENT WORLD

To trace the steps which led to Newton's mechanical view of the solar system we must start with *machines* as the word was still used in Newton's time. With the exception of the sailing ship, the windmill, and the water wheel, machines were still devices for spending human effort in a more convenient way. A machine was not something that did work for you like a dynamo. It was something which gave you *mechanical advantage*, another term for adapting a task to the normal rate at which a human being works efficiently or, more simply, allowing you to take time over your job. In effect they gave you the choice of carrying a light load over a long stretch instead of straining yourself with a heavy load over a short distance. It is sometimes essential to choose the first alternative, because there is a limit to the load against which the human muscles will contract at all. It is also a social limitation imposed by the circumstances of slave labour. An overseer can

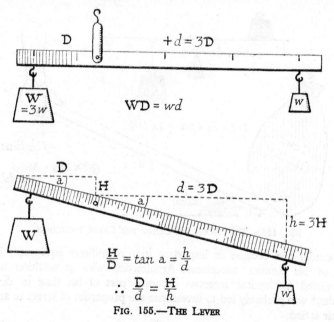

FIG. 155.—THE LEVER

keep slaves on the move. Only freemen are capable of sustained maximum effort. While slaves were abundant the mechanical ingenuity of the ancient world was mainly focused on devices of this sort, and what mechanical principles were recognized as such were chiefly concerned with them.

The two broad generalizations of mechanics in the ancient world arose respectively on the one hand from the practice of architecture, navigation, and mining (stresses, lifting stone blocks, cargoes, and ore), and on the other from irrigation (water level) and assay. The principle of the lever and the principle of buoyancy are both set forth in the works of Archimedes, and circumscribe the theoretical basis of mechanics in Alexandrian civilization. The bearing of the latter on other problems which arose in artillery warfare will be touched on in Chapter VIII. The principle of the lever, which can be used to measure the mechanical advantage of the "simple machines" referred to in the last paragraph, in all probability emerged directly from the practice of warfare. Powerful catapults were first used in the campaigns

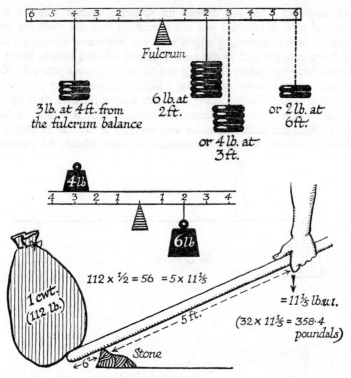

FIG. 156.—TWO WAYS OF USING THE LEVER PRINCIPLE

of Alexander and became an important item of military equipment in the hands of his Roman successors. Archimedes, who in addition to his other varied mechanical interests occupied part of his time in devising catapults,* was probably led to investigate the properties of levers to account for their action.

* Archimedes' part in the defence of Syracuse in 215–214 B.C. is described by Polybius in the following passage from his *Histories*:

"The city was strong. . . . Taking advantage of this, Archimedes had constructed such defence . . . that the garrison would have everything at hand which they might require at any moment. . . . The attack was begun by Appius bringing his pent houses, and scaling ladders, and attempting to fix the latter against that part of the wall which abuts on Hexapylus towards the east. At the same time Marcus Claudius Marcellus with sixty quinqueremes was making a descent upon Achradina. Each of these vessels was full of men with bows and slings and javelins. . . . On these double vessels, rowed by the outer oars of each of the pair, they brought up under the walls some engines called 'Sambucae' [large scaling ladders for use from ships]. . . . But Archimedes had constructed catapults to suit every range; and as the ships sailing up were still at a considerable distance, he wounded the enemy with stones and darts, from the tighter wound and longer engines, as to harass and perplex them to the last degree; and when these began to carry over their heads, he used smaller engines graduated according to the range required from time to time. . . . As often too as they tried to work their Sambucae, he had engines ready all along the walls, not visible at other times, but which suddenly reared themselves above the wall from inside, when the moment for their use had come, and stretched their beams far over the battlements, some of them carrying stones weighing as much as ten talents, and others great masses of lead. So whenever the Sambucae were approaching these beams swung round on their pivot the required distance, and by means of a rope running through a pulley dropped the stone upon the Sambucae, with the result that it not only smashed the

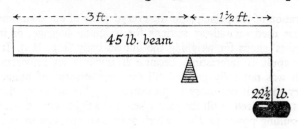

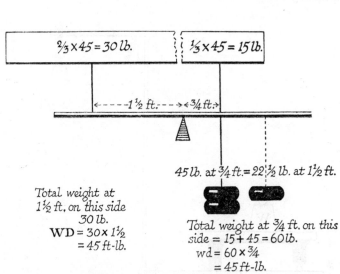

FIG. 157.—THE LEVER—AVERAGING OUT THE WEIGHT OF THE BEAM

The Law of the Lever states the distances from the fulcrum at which different weights must be attached if they are to balance. The rule given by Archimedes is that the load is inversely proportional to the distance. That is to say, two weights, W at a distance D, and w at a distance d from the fulcrum balance when*: $WD = wd$.

machine itself to pieces, but put the ship and all on board into the most serious danger. Other machines which he invented were directed against storming parties. . . . Against these he either shot stones big enough to drive the marines from the prow; or let down an iron hand swung on a chain, by which the man who guided the crane, having fastened on some part of the prow where he could get a hold, pressed down the lever of the machine inside the wall; and when he had thus lifted the prow and made the vessel rest upright on its stern, he fastened the lever of his machine so that it could not be moved; and then suddenly slackened the hand and chain by means of a rope and pulley. . . . Such was the end of the attempt at storming Syracuse by sea. . . . So true it is that one man and one intellect, properly qualified for the particular undertaking, is a host in itself. . . ."

* In this equation all the quantities are positive. It is, however, sometimes convenient to represent co-ordinates (i.e. distances with a sign attached) to the left of the pivot as negative, whilst those to the right are still considered positive (or *vice versa*). If this is done, D will be a negative quantity, so that we must write the equation as $-WD = wd$. Though the left-hand side of this equation has a negative sign attached, it is really positive. The quantity *wd* measures the turning-power of the weight *w*, called its *moment*, about the pivot. In our example the moment is positive if it tends to turn the beam clockwise about the pivot and negative if it tends to turn it anti-clockwise, so it is evident that WD should be a negative quantity.

A familiar application of the principle in the everyday life of our own time is the type of scales used on railway stations for weighing luggage, or in hospitals and chemists' shops for weighing the human body (Fig. 156). Its bearing on the catapult is interesting, because it involves an important consequence which was not fully grasped till the displacement of human effort by machinery made it necessary to measure *work*. We all know that practically no effort is required to tilt the pans when two weights are balanced on a scale. If the pulling power or *Force* which your own arm can exert is capable of raising a hundredweight, it can also balance a ton at the end of a

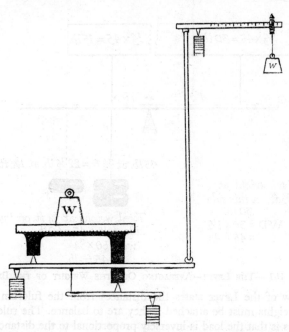

FIG. 158.—WEIGHING MACHINE BASED ON THE PRINCIPLE OF THE LEVER

lever, when the hand is applied to the opposite end at twenty times the distance of the load from the fulcrum. A negligible additional effort is then required to jerk the load upwards.

Not being concerned with machines which are driven without human effort, Archimedes did not recognize that his principle gives us a clue to the right way of measuring work, so that we know when we are working economically. If you think of one of the earliest mechanisms devised to facilitate human labour, you will see that the modern way of measuring work is a matter of common sense. The first Magdalenian man who drew a sledge, must have been fully aware that a day's work could be reckoned by the pull exerted and the distance covered. Using E for work, *p* for pull and *h* for distance, we should say:

$$E \propto p \times h$$

If we call a unit of work, work done in traversing a unit of distance with a unit of pull

$$E = ph$$

The Law of the Lever tells us that this way of measuring work in so many lb. wt. and so many feet (foot pounds weight) is in general a satisfactory way of measuring work. When two weights are balanced

$$WD = wd$$

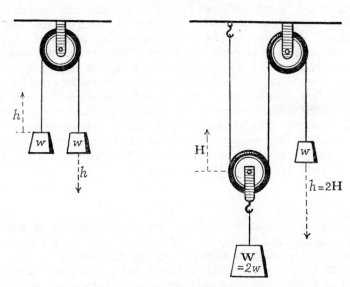

FIG. 159.—THE PULLEY

It we now tilt the beam a little, so that the small weight descends through h, and the large ascends through H, Fig. 155 shows that

$$\frac{d}{D} = \frac{h}{H}$$

It follows, therefore, that

$$WH = wh$$

i.e. one load gains in power to do work to the same extent as the other loses power to do work.

So if we measure work by the product of the weight lifted and the distance covered, no work is done in tilting a lever when it is just balanced. That we know this to be true shows that this is a satisfactory way of measuring the work of a machine as well as the day's work of Magdalenian man.

The same principle can be applied to another ancient device, balancing weights by means of a pulley. If a cord is suspended over a simple pulley shown in the left of Fig. 159, two equivalent weights attached to its ends balance. If a weight is attached to the free end of the cord in a compound pulley like that shown on the right, experiment shows that it will balance two equivalent weights attached to the second pulley. The principle of the lever leads to the same conclusion as experiment. If the smaller one (w) falls through a small distance $+ h$, the pulley is *raised* through a distance $+ \frac{1}{2}h$. With the usual convention of signs, it therefore *falls* through $- \frac{1}{2}h$. If no work is required, the total work done in a small shift is:

$$wh - \tfrac{1}{2}Wh = 0$$
$$w = \tfrac{1}{2}W$$

Yet a third "simple machine" for getting the same task done in a more leisurely way without reducing the total effort expended was the "screw and cogwheel," the name of which is self-explanatory. In a work which has come down to us in an Arabic translation, Hero, who was the most voluminous writer on mechanics in the Alexandrian age, describes a hypothetical combination of lever and multiple pulley with screw and cogwheel for raising weights. How scant was the encouragement for mechanical ingenuity in the modern sense is illustrated by another remarkable device which is described in his *Pneumatica*. The expansion of air in a hollow altar during the sacrificial fire is made to force water out of a closed vessel into buckets. The descent of the latter, when full, is used to pull open the doors of the temple where profane labour was precluded.

WEIGHT AND MASS

During the fifteenth century the elementary principles of balancing weights as they had been expounded in the Alexandrian schools became known in Italy, especially through a treatise of Leonardo da Vinci, who described his own experiments on gliders and a hypothetical man-driven aeroplane. What proved to be an important bridge between the mechanics of the old world and modern science was the extension of the Archimedean principle to one of the oldest devices for producing mechanical advantage. Stevinus of Bruges, a quartermaster in the army of William of Orange, carried out experiments on the equilibrium of a load hanging vertically with a load resting on a smooth slope. Like Archimedes, Stevinus attempted unsuccessfully to improve the numeral system of his time, and like Archimedes he was specially interested in the mechanics of warfare and navigation. He designed "machines" for lifting the Dutch fishing boats above high-water mark, and was an expert in the art of fortification.

In applying the principle of the lever to other situations, it is necessary to add a very important qualification, which has not been clearly stated so far. In all the cases we have so far considered, the body has moved in the direction in which the force applied acts, either forwards, giving *positive* work which we do ourselves, or backwards, giving *negative* work which is done for us. For the sledge, the direction was horizontal, and for the lever and compound pulley, vertical. If we roll a truck up several hills, we soon find out that more work is needed to push it up a steep hill than is needed to push it through the same distance up an easier slope. If we forget about frictional resistance, the amount of work needed depends only on the total gain in *height* above the original level.

This suggests the law of balancing weights when one (w) hangs vertically, and the other (W) rests on a smooth slope inclined at a fixed angle (B) to the horizontal. If the weight w descends through a vertical distance D in Fig. 160, the weight W ascends through the same distance D along the inclined surface. Since $\sin B = h \div D$, its vertical displacement $h = D \sin B$. If we measure the work done *on* W in rising through the vertical distance h and the work done *by* w in falling through the vertical distance D as we have done in the treatment of the lever and pulley (i.e. by the products of the

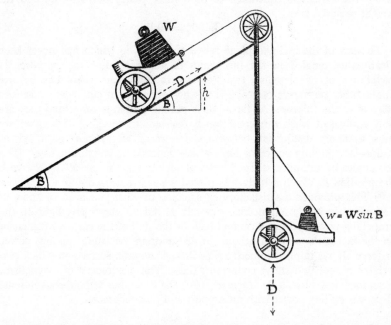

Fig. 160.—Rest (Balance of Two Opposed Motions) on the Inclined Plane

The Law of the Inclined Plane is that if a weight found to be w times some standard weight by the balance when hanging vertically just supports a weight W times the same standard lying on an inclined surface of elevation B,

$$w = W \sin B$$

or

$$\frac{\text{Weight hanging vertically}}{\text{Balanced weight on slope}} = \sin B$$

weights and their corresponding vertical displacements) the total work done by both weights is $- Wh + wD$. So if no work is done in shifting them when the weights are balanced

$$- Wh + wD = 0$$
$$\therefore \qquad Wh = wD$$
$$\therefore \quad WD \sin B = wD$$
$$\therefore \qquad w = W \sin B$$

According to this the weight required to balance a 10 lb. load resting on an inclined plane of 30°, when it hangs vertically is

$$10 \times \sin 30° = 10 \times 0 \cdot 5 \text{ lb.}$$

i.e. 5 lb. If the angle of the sloping surface is 45° the weight required is

$$10 \times \sin 45° = 10 \times 0 \cdot 707 \text{ lb.}$$

i.e. just over 7 lb. The hypothesis is evidently true at the limits. If the slope is 90° the system is equivalent to the simple pulley of Fig. 159, and the weight required is

$$10 \times \sin 90° = 10 \text{ lb.}$$

The law of the inclined plane raised a distinction which had never been clearly disentangled in the mechanics of antiquity. For the purposes of metallurgy or merchandise, two weights are equivalent when they balance one another on a pair of scales, i.e. when they are in equivalent positions relative to the fulcrum. As far as their pulling power is concerned they are only equivalent when this condition is realized. In speaking of weights, we must therefore distinguish between *mass*—which we "weigh" on a pair of scales—and pulling power or *force* which depends on something else.* The mechanics of antiquity stopped short at identifying this *something else* with the position in which a body was placed when it balanced another body *at rest*. This provided a satisfactory explanation of what you need to know in designing the best Archimedean catapult. It did not throw any light on the propelling power behind a cannon ball, or the pull of the earth's magnetism on the mariner's compass needle. In Alexandrian mechanics pulling power or force always implied some tangible link, a common surface on which two weights rested, or a string connecting them. The phenomena of magnetism, as set forth in Gilbert's *De Magnete* (1600), defied all the accepted conventions. Here was pulling power with no support and no attachment.

FORCE AND MOTION

The experiments of Stevinus suggested the clue to a new technique of measurement. Besides being able to balance another weight at rest in virtue of its mass and position, a weight can also generate motion, as when a load attached to a cord wound about the axle of a wheel is allowed to descend. We all know that we slide down a slope more quickly if it is steep; that is, the weight of our bodies can generate more motion if the angle of descent is increased. So, too, the balancing power of a weight also increases if the elevation of the slope on which it rests is increased. Hence the principle of the inclined plane suggests two new possibilities. One is that the pulling power of a load in different positions simply depends on the fact that its power to generate motion also depends on its position. The other is that two weights balance when their power to generate motion is equally great and is exercised in opposite directions. The obstacle to pursuing this plausible clue in the sixteenth century was the fact that no one had yet attempted to measure the way in which things fall. According to the Aristotelian world

* See also p. 292.

outlook, rest was the rule and motion an exceptional state of affairs. The alternative view that rest is only motion at a deadlock had little to commend it in the ancient world. Before the introduction of gunpowder there was no pressing social necessity to compel anyone to make exact measurements of the rates at which bodies fall.

Indeed, it is not likely that Aristotle's doctrine would have been contested, if range-finding had not come to the aid of curiosity in an age when the fate of a new civilization depended on a new technique of war. Aristotle had taught that a "body is heavier than another which in an equal bulk moves downward more quickly." The belief that the vertical motion of a body is proportional to its density (mass per unit volume) is not intrinsically unlikely. Our common experience of falling objects seems to confirm it. We can see leaves falling from a tree, or a cup falling when it leaves our hand, but we cannot see a cannon ball in its course. We have blown up paper bags or toy balloons as children, and bladders inflated with air were part of the medieval jester's equipment. The behaviour of all these familiar objects seems to agree with Aristotle's teaching, and the simple discovery which enabled Galileo to lay the foundations of scientific artillery therefore ranks as one of the most daring achievements in science.

Apart from the last passage cited, Aristotle had not committed himself to any very definite statement about the way in which things fall. His discussion of physical problems, like his political philosophy, is mainly concerned with justifying, defending, and making a lawyer's case in favour of, the world as it is. In his doctrine of the state every individual had a fixed social class which was right and proper in the nature of things. In his natural philosophy every material object also had its proper place; and if it got out of its proper place, nature personified as the strong arm of the law put it back sooner or later. Unhappily for his influence as a philosopher Aristotle committed himself to one assertion which is easy to test by dropping a cannon ball and a croquet ball of the same size from the top of a building. Although it is obviously true that some very light things like toy balloons and some objects with a large surface relative to bulk, like feathers, leaves, or wood cut in fine shavings, do fall more slowly than cannon balls, it is also true that most compact objects fall from the same height in approximately the same time. That this is so within wide limits of relative heaviness was the surprising new truth which Galileo established.

Mach says that Galileo's outlook was essentially modern, because he asked *how* things fall instead of *why* they fall. There is nothing specifically modern in this except in so far as the ceremonial and priestly outlook is losing ground, while the attitude of the artisan exercises an increasing influence on our social culture. Galileo was modern only because he was workmanlike. The history of science has been a long struggle between the same two conflicting inclinations. Priestly and ceremonial speculation is content to reflect on the world, or attempts to propitiate an unseen supposititious purpose in things personified explicitly as deities or implicitly in the "explanations" of the unofficial theologians who teach philosophy. If you follow to its logical conclusion Aristotle's doctrine that everything has a place to which it belongs you end in an act of special creation. Any question which begins with *why* leads you back to an assumed design by an individual who cannot be identified but may possibly be bribed. The artisan or technician looks at things as they are, and finds out how they can be changed in accordance with human needs. The influence of their world view expands as the satisfaction of man's common needs becomes the common business of mankind. A workmanlike or truly scientific *explanation* gives you a recipe for doing something. The distinction between a real or scientific explanation and a philosophical one is easier to see nowadays because few people believe that prayer can control meteorological events. So long as they did, teleological "explanations" were intelligible.

A cannon ball or a croquet ball dropped from the top of a three-story building, say 36 feet high, reaches the ground in about a second and a half. Even from the top of the highest New York skyscraper the drop would be over inside nine seconds. It goes without saying that direct measurement of how bodies fall vertically cannot be precise, unless there are very good recording instruments to use. Stop-watches, electric signals, metronomes, kymographs (Fig. 196), had not been invented in Galileo's day. He had to tackle the problem by an indirect method which involved two kinds of measurement. He first established a simple rule connecting the distance (d) traversed and the time (t) of the descent of a ball (see Figs. 161 and 162) on a smooth gentle-sloping surface. Then he sought for a rule connecting the time taken to traverse a given distance with the angle at which the surface is tilted. The limiting angle is 90°, when the ball falls vertically.

The time taken for a ball to descend from different levels on a gently inclined surface is not difficult to measure. Having no stop-watch, Galileo let water drip steadily into a vessel during the interval occupied by the descent, and weighed the water to get an estimate of the time. A table of results obtained in an experiment of this kind discloses a simple numerical rule which is at once recognized when a graph of the distances traversed and time taken is plotted. The graph answers to the textbook parabola $y = px^2$, and an examination of the figures shows that the ratio of the distance traversed to the square of the time taken is fixed, i.e.

$$\frac{d}{t^2} = k \quad \text{or} \quad d = kt^2.$$

If we now look at the motion of the ball from a different point of view, there is more in this than meets the eye at a first glance. Galileo did so. He introduced what is now a familiar but was then an entirely novel criterion of motion. Crude estimates of speed (or *velocity* as we shall now say when speaking of motion in a particular direction along a *straight* course) had probably been made from the first experience of travel, route marches, and public games. Hitherto there had been no occasion to measure how motion *grows*. Galileo adopted the modern measure of *acceleration*, or *velocity gained in unit time*. There is no longer an unusual flavour in the word, though we shall see later that it is used loosely in everyday speech and that the terms speed and velocity, used interchangeably when we are describing motion in a straight path, have to be restricted when we are describing motion round a bend. For the present we need only concern ourselves with the ordinary use of the term. If the speedometer reading of a car increases steadily during 10 seconds of a *straight* course from 30 miles per hour

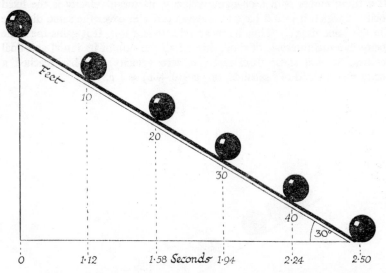

FIG. 161.—A SMOOTH BALL RUNNING DOWN A VERY SMOOTH SLOPE AT 30°
UNDER GRAVITY

If acceleration is constant, the acceleration calculated from the formula $d = \frac{1}{2}at^2$ will be the same whether the distance (d) fallen is large or small. The figures in the horizontal row give the total interval of time from the start at each 10-foot stage in a 50-foot journey. The results tabulated as follows give a numerical illustration of the reasoning in the text. The velocity gained per second, i.e. *the acceleration*, at different stages in the descent is given to the nearest unit, and does not vary consistently in either direction from an approximately constant figure of 16.

Distance in Feet	Time in secs.	Velocity	at time	Velocity gained	in time	Velocity gained per second
0	0					
		$\dfrac{10}{1\cdot12-0}=8\cdot93$	$\frac{1}{2}(1\cdot12+0)$ $=0\cdot56$			
				$(21\cdot74-8\cdot93)$ $=12\cdot81$	$(1\cdot35-0\cdot56)$ $=0\cdot79$	$12\cdot81\div0\cdot79$ $=16$
10	1·12					
		$\dfrac{10}{1\cdot58-1\cdot12}=21\cdot74$	$\frac{1}{2}(1\cdot58+1\cdot12)$ $=1\cdot35$			
				$(27\cdot78-21\cdot74)$ $=6\cdot04$	$(1\cdot76-1\cdot35)$ $=0\cdot41$	$6\cdot04\div0\cdot41$ $=15$
20	1·58					
		$\dfrac{10}{1\cdot94-1\cdot58}=27\cdot78$	$\frac{1}{2}(1\cdot94+1\cdot58)$ $=1\cdot76$			
				$(33\cdot33-27\cdot78)$ $=5\cdot55$	$(2\cdot09-1\cdot76)$ $=0\cdot33$	$5\cdot55\div0\cdot33$ $=17$
30	1·94					
		$\dfrac{10}{2\cdot24-1\cdot94}=33\cdot33$	$\frac{1}{2}(2\cdot24+1\cdot94)$ $=2\cdot09$			
				$(38\cdot46-33\cdot33)$ $=5\cdot13$	$(2\cdot37-2\cdot09)$ $=0\cdot28$	$5\cdot13\div0\cdot28$ $=18$
40	2·24					
		$\dfrac{10}{2\cdot50-2\cdot24}=38\cdot46$	$\frac{1}{2}(2\cdot50+2\cdot24)$ $=2\cdot37$			
50	2·50					

(or 44 feet per second) to 45 miles per hour (or 66 feet per second) it has *gained* in velocity 22 feet per second in 10 seconds or 2·2 feet per second in 1 second. Its mean acceleration is + 2·2 feet per second per second.

If the reading falls from 45 to 30 miles per hour, it has *lost* 2·2 feet per second in one second. Its mean acceleration is − 2·2 feet per second per second.*

If a thing moves with a changing velocity, its mean velocity is the fixed velocity at which it would have to move in order to cover the same distance (*d*) in the same time (*t*). Thus its mean velocity is $d \div t$. If it gains the same velocity in equal intervals of time, this is half the sum of its initial and final velocities. So if it starts from rest (i.e. zero velocity) and has reached a velocity *v* at the end of *t* seconds, this is $\frac{1}{2}(0 + v) = \frac{1}{2}v$.

$$\therefore \frac{d}{t} = \tfrac{1}{2}v$$

$$\therefore v = \frac{2a}{t}$$

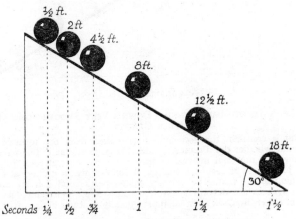

FIG. 162.—MOTION ON THE INCLINED PLANE

The final velocity *v* is then the velocity it has gained in the time *t*. Since its acceleration (*a*) is the velocity gained in one second,

$$a = \frac{v}{t} = \frac{2d}{t^2}$$

$$\therefore \frac{d}{t^2} = \tfrac{1}{2}a$$

If it moves from rest with a *constant acceleration*, the ratio of the distance to the square of the time taken is therefore fixed. Galileo's experiments showed that when a ball rolls down a smooth slope, the distance traversed bears a fixed ratio to the square of the time occupied by the descent. They therefore showed that the ball rolls down the slope with a *constant* acceleration.

So long as the slope is the same, this is true within wide limits for the acceleration of balls of different weights and densities. The next thing is to

* "Per second per second" is often written "per sec.²."

find how the slope, i.e. the angle *b* which the surface makes with the horizontal, affects the acceleration. This is done by varying the slope and measuring the time taken to traverse a fixed distance. We get a clue to the kind of relation which exists from the fact that a body moves most quickly when it falls straight down (i.e. $b = 90°$), and remains still when the surface is quite flat (i.e. $b = 0°$). So the acceleration depends on something about an angle which is greatest when the angle is 90°, and is zero when the angle itself is zero. This is true of the sine of an angle, and experiment shows that the acceleration is directly proportional to the sine of the angle of slope, i.e.

$$a \propto \sin b$$

or putting it in the form of an equation, in which *g* is a constant

$$a = g \sin b$$

Experiment shows that if the slope is 30° the acceleration is approximately 16 feet per second per second, i.e. the velocity along the slope increases every second by 16 feet per second. So

$$16 = g \sin 30°$$
$$\therefore 16 = g \times \tfrac{1}{2}$$
$$\therefore g = 32 \text{ (approximately)}$$

Since $\sin 45° = 0·707$, if the slope were 45° the acceleration would be

$$32 \times 0·707 = 22·6 \text{ feet per second per second.}$$

If the angle *b* is 90° the body falls vertically (Fig. 163), and since $\sin 90° = 1$

$$a = g$$

i.e. *g* is the acceleration with which a heavy body falls vertically. Galileo showed this was so by finding the time taken by heavy objects to fall from the top of a tower to test the rule in the limiting case. The acceleration can be found as before by using the rule

$$a = \frac{2d}{t^2}$$

So if the rule holds good, when *d* is the vertical height of the tower, and *t* the time between dropping the body and seeing it strike the ground,

$$\frac{2d}{t^2} = g$$
$$\therefore d = \tfrac{1}{2}gt^2$$
$$= 16t^2 \text{ (approximately)}$$

Thus a pebble dropped from the top of a lighthouse 100 feet high would strike the water $\sqrt{100 \div 16} = 2\tfrac{1}{2}$ seconds later.

In this way Galileo established two conclusions which Newton used in his theory of universal gravitation. The first, called the law of *terrestrial gravitation*, is that when bodies fall vertically (i.e. along the plumb line which points towards the centre of the earth) they move with a constant acceleration. Near

the earth's surface this is approximately 32 feet per sec.². In air it is independent of mass or density within wide limits. The second conclusion is that

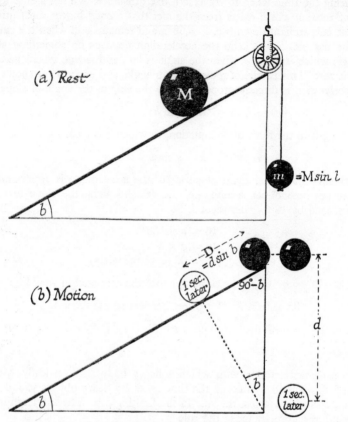

FIG. 163.—MOTION DOWN AN INCLINED PLANE

The law of Motion is:

$$\frac{\text{Acceleration (A) along slope}}{\text{Acceleration (}a\text{) of free vertical fall}} = \sin b$$

The law of rest (Fig. 160) is:

$$\frac{\text{Vertically suspended mass (}m\text{)}}{\text{Balanced mass on slope (M)}} = \sin b$$

Hence

$$A \div a = m \div M$$
$$\therefore MA = ma$$

or, in this case, MA = mg.

Thus the pulling powers exerted by two masses in different situations are equal when
the product of one mass and the acceleration with which it would move if not constrained by the second is the same as the product of the second mass and the acceleration with which it would move if it were not posed against the first.

the law of equilibrium of solid bodies at rest is only another way of stating
the same law of motion. The mechanics of antiquity had shown that equilibrium of solid bodies at rest involves (p. 250) position as well as mass. The

inclined plane suggested that this might be due to the fact that in different positions heavy bodies do not always have the same power to generate motion. Galileo's experiments show us how the position of a body affects its motion, when it is displaced. The law which describes how weights balance one another when one of mass M rests on a smooth slope at an inclination b to the ground level, and the other of mass m hangs vertically, may be written

$$\frac{m}{M} = \sin b$$

The law of motion down a smooth slope is

$$\frac{a}{g} = \sin b$$

Comparing both, we see that

$$\frac{m}{M} = \frac{a}{g}$$
$$mg = Ma$$

Thus our first suspicion is correct. Two loads balance on a smooth flat slope when the product of the mass of one and the motion it would generate if released is the same as the product of the mass of the other and the motion *it* would generate if released. In other words, they remain at rest *because their power to generate motion is equal and opposite*. Hence the mass-acceleration product is a way of measuring the pulling power (F) of a load, i.e. $F = m \cdot a$. If one body is falling with a smaller acceleration than another it has less effective pulling power, unless its mass is proportionately larger. To hold a greater mass of one demands a greater mobility of the other. Thus a force has two aspects, one *acceleration* which measures the *mobility* of an object, the other *mass* which measures its sluggishness or *inertia*.

To measure forces by the mass-acceleration product we have now to agree about the measurement of mass and of acceleration. When the unit of mass is 1 lb, the unit of distance 1 foot, and the unit of time 1 second, the unit of force is called the *poundal*, i.e. one poundal is the force required to impart an acceleration of 1 foot per second per second to a mass of 1 lb. The force exerted by a 1 lb. "weight" falling under gravity or the force required to prevent a pound "weight" from falling under gravity near the earth's surface is approximately 32 *poundals*. Since $g = 32$ (approximately), $m = \frac{1}{32}$ lb. when $mg = 1$. Hence one poundal is the pulling power of a half ounce weight when suspended in a vertical position. It is therefore the pulling power of a spring balance when the scale reading is $\frac{1}{2}$ oz.

In the international metric system based on the reports originally drawn up by the French Academy for the National Assembly of the French Revolution, the units of mass and length are respectively the gram and the metre. The former is conveniently chosen as the mass of 1 cubic centimetre of water at 4° C. (i.e. the density of water in grams per c.c. is 1 at this temperature, when its density is greatest). The unit of force, the dyne, is the pulling power which can make 1 gram move with an acceleration of 1 cm. per second per second. Since 1 British foot $= 30 \cdot 48$ cm., and 1 British pound

= 453·6 grams, 1 poundal is equivalent to 30·48 × 453·6 = 13,826 dynes. Since 32 feet = 975 cm., 1 gram hanging vertically exerts a pull of 975 dynes, and 1 lb. exerts a pull of 975 × 453·6 = 442,260 dynes at a place where the value of g is exactly 32 feet per second per second. We shall see later that the value of g is generally a little larger than 32 feet per second per second, and also varies a little with latitude and altitude, being at sea-level 32·09 feet or 978 cm. per second per second on the equator and 32·26 feet or 983 cm. per second per second at the North Pole. Fifteen miles above sea-level at the equator, it is about 30·9 feet or 941 cm. per second per second.

Before we go on, four simple rules which connect time, distance in a straight path, velocity, and acceleration when the acceleration is constant, should be committed to memory, so that you recognize them at once, when you come across them in what follows. They are as follows:

(1) If an object moves through a distance d in a time t with a velocity v, since $v = d \div t$,

$$d = vt$$

(2) If an object is moving with a velocity v_a at the beginning of an interval of time t and is moving with a velocity v_b at the end of it, its mean velocity, which is the velocity with which it is moving half-way through the time interval, is $\frac{1}{2}(v_a + v_b)$, and the distance traversed in the interval t is the same as if it moved at its mean velocity throughout the whole of it, i.e.

$$d = \frac{1}{2}(v_a + v_b)t$$

(3) If an object gains a velocity a feet per second in each second, a is its acceleration; and it will have increased its velocity by at in t seconds. If its velocity was v_a at the beginning of the interval t its velocity at the end of it will be $v_a + at$, so that its mean velocity is $\frac{1}{2}[v_a + (v_a + at)] = v_a + \frac{1}{2}at$, and the distance moved during the interval by rule (2) is $(v_a + \frac{1}{2}at)t$. If the object starts from rest, so that $v_a = 0$,

$$d = \frac{1}{2}at^2 \quad (\text{or } a = 2d \div t^2)$$

(4) The fourth rule which has not been used so far is illustrated in Fig. 164 and explained in the legend. If an object moves with a velocity v and an acceleration a along a line (AC in the figure) inclined at an angle b to a second line (AB), an observer, who keeps his eye at right angles to the second line, watching its progress along the latter will see it move with a velocity $v \cos b$ and an acceleration $a \cos b$. If a_x is the acceleration referred to a line inclined at b to the path along which an object moves with acceleration a,

$$a_x = a \cos b$$

The first, third, and fourth should be memorized and tested with the aid of numerical illustrations and scale diagrams like Fig. 164. The velocity formulae should be tested from the numerical data in the boat diagram of Fig. 167.

The last rule throws a new light on the measurement of force if we put it in a more active form. The same source of motive power which propels a body with an acceleration a in one line gives it an acceleration $a \cos b$ along

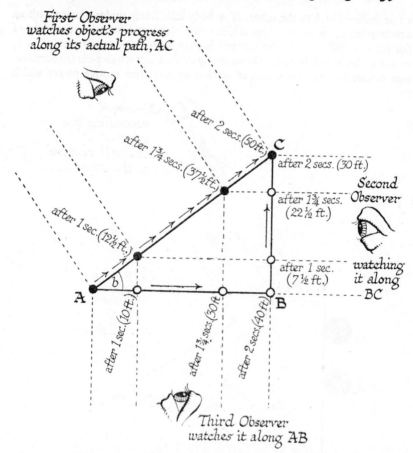

First Observer watches object's progress along its actual path, AC

after 2 secs. (50 ft.)

after 1¾ secs. (37½ ft.)

after 1 sec. (12½ ft.)

after 2 secs. (30 ft.)

Second Observer

after 1¾ secs. (22½ ft.)

after 1 sec. (7½ ft.)

watching it along BC

after 1 sec. (10 ft.)

after 1½ secs. (30 ft.)

after 2 secs. (40 ft.)

Third Observer watches it along AB

FIG. 164.—TRIANGLE OF VELOCITIES AND ACCELERATIONS

This illustrates the rule that if a body moves with a velocity v or an acceleration a along a straight path, its velocity v_x and its acceleration a_x along a line of reference inclined at an angle b to the path can be found by using the formulae:

$$v_x = v \cos b$$
$$a_x = a \cos b$$

The object shown moves from rest at A with an acceleration a (here 25) feet per second per second for t (here 2) seconds along AC. Its motion referred to the line AB is its motion as it would be seen by an observer looking along a line at right angles to AB at each stage in its course. This would be equivalent to watching its shadow projected on a ground glass screen at AB with a beam at right angles to the screen. Thus AB, AC, and the observer's sight line form a succession of right-angled triangles in which $\cos b = AB \div AC$. Its acceleration along AC is $2AC \div t^2$, and its acceleration (a_x) along AB is $2AB \div t^2$. Hence $a_x \div a = (2AB \div t^2) \div (2AC \div t^2) = AB \div AC$ $= \cos b$. At the end of t seconds its velocity (v) along AC is at and its velocity (v_x) along AB is $a_x t$. Hence $v_x \div v = a_x \div a = \cos b$. Along the line at right angles to AB, i.e. BC, inclined at $90^\circ - b$ to AC the acceleration (a_y) is $a \cos (90^\circ - b) = a \sin b$, and similarly $v_y = v \sin b$. In the figure the ratio of the sides of the triangle is $5 : 4 : 3$, so that $\cos b = 0 \cdot 8$ and $\sin b = 0 \cdot 6$. The figure $1\frac{3}{4}$ is approximate in the diagram. More exactly it is $\sqrt{3}$.

a line inclined at b to the other. If a body falls freely under gravity with an acceleration a, its acceleration relative to a slope at b to its vertical line of fall (or $c = (90° - b)$ to the ground) is $g \cos b$ or $g \sin c$ (since $\sin (90° - b)$ $= \cos b$). So its acceleration when moving down a smooth slope is the acceleration referred to the same line of motion by the same motive power which

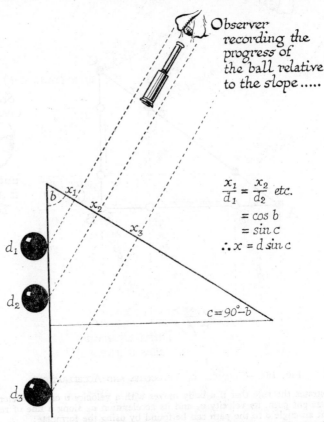

FIG. 165.—MOTION DOWN THE INCLINED PLANE AS FREE VERTICAL MOTION RESOLVED ALONG THE PLANE

When a body falls vertically through a distance d ($= \frac{1}{2}gt^2$) its acceleration (g) under gravity is $2d \div t^2$. An observer (O) watching its progress along a line inclined at b to the vertical (or $c = 90° - b$ to the ground) would see it move through $x = d \cos b$ with an acceleration $2x \div t^2 = g \cos b$ or $g \sin c$. This is the value to which actual acceleration down the slope approximates when friction is negligible, and hence its acceleration down the slope is equivalent to its acceleration when falling vertically resolved along its path.

imparts an acceleration g in the vertical direction. The law of terrestrial gravitation may therefore be put in another way by saying that the mobility of falling bodies can be attributed to the same motive power which pulls them in the same line of action with a force proportional to their masses. Thus the force of gravity acting on a weight of M lb. is 32M poundals, and a force of 1 lb. weight, i.e. the force with which a pound weight is pulled earthward, when it hangs from a spring balance, is 32 poundals.

The view to which Galileo's experiments led therefore reduced Aristotle's logic to an absurdity. If the same motive power pulls all material bodies near the earth's surface in the direction of the plumb line, i.e. *towards the earth's centre*, the place to which all bodies "belong" is the centre of the earth. It is difficult to see how there can be enough room for them. Consequently there is no intelligible meaning in the question, where does a body "belong"? The only question for which we can hope to find an answer is: how do bodies actually behave? This we can only discover by observing them, making theories about how one observation is connected with another, and then testing them to see whether they are right.

THE PATH OF THE CANNON BALL

Artillery was at first used more to destroy the enemy's morale than for the material destruction it produced. To be effective in the latter sense it was necessary to know how to hit the objective. Accuracy of aim demanded a theoretical basis. Galileo's law of falling bodies provided it with one. A cannon ball when fired into the air has two movements. One results from the explosion, giving it an initial velocity in a certain direction depending on the angle which the muzzle makes with the horizon. The other movement is due to the fact that gravitation is pulling the projectile vertically downwards, so that it tends to gather velocity towards the earth. The result is that it travels along a curved path. The theory of the pendulum clock, and with it that of the earth's orbital motion, depends upon understanding how movement in one direction can be represented as the result of movement in two other directions.

It is so natural to split a complicated form of movement into simpler components that you may not have realized that we have done so already. The description of the sun's *apparent* course in the heavens as a diurnal rotation in a plane parallel to the equinoctial and an annual retreat in the ecliptic is a purely arbitrary trick to assist us (Fig. 166) in following its continuous apparent track through a closely wound closed spiral. The same trick was suggested by the practice of navigation in another way. To reach a destination when rowing or sailing in a steady current, you have to keep the boat's prow tilted away from the direct line of approach in the direction opposite to the current (Fig. 154). The velocity of currents is easy to measure by the progress of corks floating away from a vessel at anchor, and experience gives you a fairly good estimate of your average working velocity when rowing in still water.

To find your progress along the actual line of approach you have only to lay off the distance (AB) a cork would drift with the current, and the distance (BC) you would move in still water during the same interval of time along the direction of the boat's axis. These two lines form the sides of a triangle of which the third (AC) is the distance covered in the same time along the actual path of motion, or, what comes to the same thing, the two adjacent sides of a parallelogram whose diagonal through A gives the distance of the actual path. If the interval of time is one unit, and the velocity is fixed, the component and resultant distances are numerically the same as the corresponding velocities. The same construction holds for accelerations. Since $d = \frac{1}{2}at^2 = \frac{1}{2}a$ when $t = 1$, i.e. one unit of time after the motion starts, accelerations are directly proportional to distances traversed in equivalent time intervals from rest.

In dealing with several simultaneous movements it is much better to

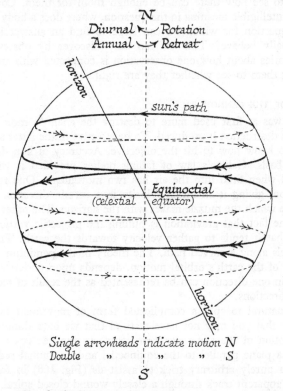

FIG. 166.—SUN'S APPARENT MOTION IN THE CELESTIAL SPHERE

The sun's apparent motion in the celestial sphere is continuous. Though we find it convenient to think of it as two separate motions, a diurnal rotation westwards over the horizon, and an annual retreat eastwards, a quick motion picture would reveal it as movement in a closed spiral with 365 turns. A closed spiral of five turns is here shown to simplify the issue. The figure would represent a continuous tableau of the sun's apparent motion through a year, if the earth took 73 of our days to complete a single revolution about its axis.

follow the nautical plan by keeping a separate balance sheet of eastward (positive), westward (negative), or northward (positive), southward (negative), bearings, as explained in Figs. 168 and 169. The map method is really, as it is historically, the same thing as the graphical method of representing a movement, i.e. so many *x*-measurements and so many simultaneous *y*-measurements. All you have to do is to add up all the east-west bearings or *x*-measurements and all the north-south bearings or *y*-measurements to

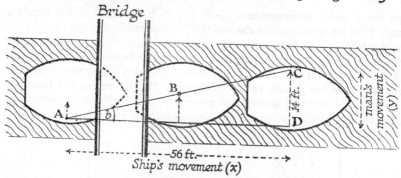

FIG. 167.—DISSECTION OF COMPLEX MOVEMENT

During an interval t (here $3\frac{3}{16}$ seconds) the boat moves with a fixed velocity 12 miles per hour ($17\frac{3}{5}$ feet per second) through a distance 56 feet along a straight canal, while the man moves straight across the deck 14 feet wide with a fixed velocity of 3 miles per hour ($4\frac{2}{5}$ feet per second). Relative to an observer at right angles to the line AC the man appears to pursue a steady path with a velocity $v = AC \div t$. Since $AC^2 = CD^2 + AD^2$

$$\left(\frac{AC}{t}\right)^2 = \left(\frac{CD}{t}\right)^2 + \left(\frac{AD}{t}\right)^2$$

So if we call the man's velocity relative to the bridge $v_y = CD \div t$, and his velocity relative to the bank $v_x = AD \div t$

$$v^2 = v_y^2 + v_x^2$$

His *resultant* velocity along the actual path which he pursues in space (shown in an air photograph with the boat blacked out) is therefore $\sqrt{9 + 144}$, or approximately $12\frac{1}{3}$ miles per hour. Since $\tan b = CD \div AD = 3 \div 12$ or $0 \cdot 25$, the inclination of his path to the bank is the angle whose tangent is $0 \cdot 25$, approximately $14°$ from tables of tangents. Knowing the angle we could deduce his velocity relative to the bank (boat's motion) and to the bridge (his own) from the cinema record taken from the air, from the fact that he moves through CD relative to the bridge and AD relative to the bank during the time taken to move AC with his resultant velocity v. Since $\cos b = AD \div AC = (AD \div t) \div (AC \div t)$, $\cos b = v_x \div v$ and $v_x = v \cos b$. Similarly $v_y = v \sin b$.

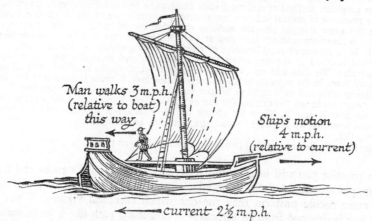

Man walks 3 m.p.h. (relative to boat) this way

Ship's motion 4 m.p.h. (relative to current)

current 2½ m.p.h.

FIG. 168.—RELATIVE MOTION IN THE SAME STRAIGHT LINE

Distances traversed in the same time and hence velocities or accelerations can be added or subtracted according to direction. In the figure the resultant motion of the man relative to the bank is $4 - 2\frac{1}{2} - 3 = -1\frac{1}{2}$ miles per hour, using the positive sign for motion left to right.

get the x and y measurements (E-W and N-S bearings) of the resulting path. If all the distances in a chart of this kind correspond to the same unit of time, the final result does equally for velocity or acceleration, since the velocity of a moving object after moving for t units of time from rest is proportional to the distance through which it has moved, and this is also proportional to the velocity it has gained, i.e. its acceleration. If the time interval from rest is 1 unit, velocity and acceleration are represented by the same number of units and the number of units of distance covered is half as great.

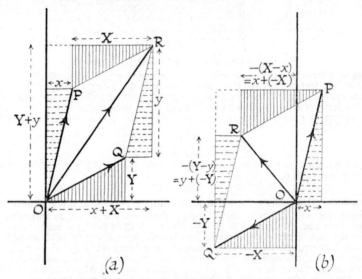

FIG. 169.—GRAPHICAL REPRESENTATION OF COMPOSITE MOTION

In the graphical method of making a scale diagram to find the direction or magnitude of the resultant of several independent motions, we make use of the fact that motions along the same straight line are additive with due regard to sign. Each component motion is therefore split up into two at right angles like the N-S (y measurements) and E-W (x measurements) bearings of a ship's moving course (which suggested the graphical method in the age when maps in latitude and longitude were first used extensively). We then add up (with due regard to sign) all the northerly and all the westerly items in the separate balance sheets of bearings, keeping the positive sign for the direction from S to N or from W to E and the negative sign for the converse.

For example in (a), the motion OP can be split up into x and y; and the motion OQ split up into X and Y. Then by adding the E-W bearings together and the N-S bearings together we are able to find the direction and magnitude of the resultant velocity OR.

Case (b) is similar, except that two of the bearings happen to be negative.

In practice you will usually find it simpler to work in distances and use the graphical method of dissection which we shall first apply to an analogous but more pacific problem than the one which exercised Galileo. When a mail bag is dropped from an aeroplane it executes a path like a jet of water projected horizontally from a hose, the reason being the same. Its own inertia in virtue of the motion of the plane, which we shall assume to be moving parallel to the ground, gives it a drift forwards as it falls. So in order to know where to let go if it is to reach its proper destination it is necessary to drop it before the aeroplane is directly over its destination, and to be able to calculate the distance between the position of the aeroplane at the correct time of dropping the mail bag and a point directly above the place where the bag is supposed to land.

The graphical representation of the descent of a mail bag dropped from an aeroplane moving horizontally with a velocity v at a height h in Fig. 170 is made by combining the principle of inertia with what we know about the way in which bodies fall. If the aeroplane moves through x feet in t seconds, $x = vt$. The mail bag would continue to move in this way if its motion were

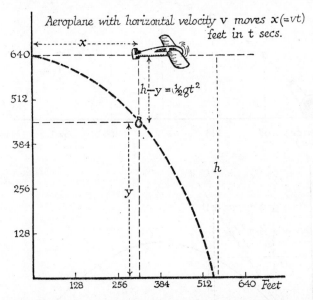

FIG. 170.—Descent of a Mail Bag from an Aeroplane Cruising at 60 Miles
Per Hour at a Height of 640 Feet Above Ground

Air resistance is neglected, if the speed of the 'plane is not very great

not also affected by gravity. While it is moving through vt feet in the horizontal direction in virtue of its inertia, it is also dropping through a vertical height $d = \frac{1}{2}gt^2$ under gravity. If it sinks to a height y, while it moves forwards through a distance x, you will see from the figure that

$$y = h - d$$
$$= h - \tfrac{1}{2}gt^2$$

And since $x = vt$,

$$t^2 = \frac{x^2}{v^2}$$

and

$$y = h - \frac{gx^2}{2v^2}$$

I*

When the mail bag reaches the ground $y = 0$ and so

$$h = \frac{gx^2}{2v^2}$$

$$\therefore \quad x = v\sqrt{2h \div g}$$

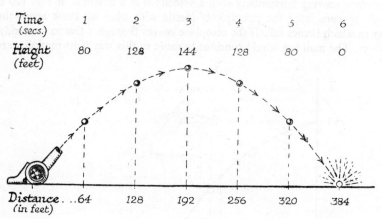

Time (secs.)	1	2	3	4	5	6
Height (feet)	80	128	144	128	80	0

| Distance (in feet) | 64 | 128 | 192 | 256 | 320 | 384 |

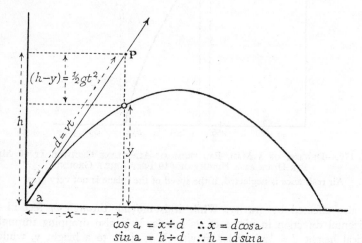

$$\cos a = x \div d \quad \therefore x = d\cos a$$
$$\sin a = h \div d \quad \therefore h = d\sin a$$

FIG. 171.—GALILEO'S CANNON BALL PROBLEM

This is calculated for a muzzle velocity of 116 feet per second at an elevation of $56\frac{1}{4}°$.

The numerical dimensions of the figure correspond to the course of a mail bag dropped from an aeroplane cruising 640 feet above ground at 60 miles per hour (88 feet per second). Hence the horizontal distance which it travels before it reaches the ground is

$$88\sqrt{1,280 \div 32} = 556 \text{ feet (approximately).}$$

That is to say, the bag must be dropped when the aeroplane has still to travel

556 feet before it is directly above the place of delivery. The points on the curve are plotted from the equation, which corresponds to part of a parabola.

The cannon ball problem which Galileo tackled is identical with that in which the aeroplane is rising steadily as it drops the bag. If the ball leaves the gun with a velocity v at an angle a, it would move through a distance $d = vt$ reaching P in t seconds, if gravity did not pull it earthward. It would then be h feet above ground, instead of y the height to which it has fallen meanwhile. The height through which it falls in t seconds is therefore $h - y$, and

$$h - y = \tfrac{1}{2}gt^2$$

The figure shows that

$$h = d \sin a$$
$$= vt \sin a$$
$$\therefore \quad y = vt \sin a - \tfrac{1}{2}gt^2$$

The horizontal displacement along the x axis during the first t seconds is $x = vt \cos a$, so that $t = x \div v \cos a$. If we put this for t in the last expression for y,

$$y = \frac{x \sin a}{\cos a} - \frac{gx^2}{2v^2 \cos^2 a}$$

When the ball reaches the ground $y = 0$, so that

$$\frac{gx}{2v^2 \sin a \cos a} = 1$$

Since $\sin 2a = 2 \sin a \cos a$:

$$x = \frac{v^2 \sin 2a}{g}$$

This gives the range of the cannon ball. To get the maximum height, substitute half this value of x in the original formula for y.

In applying the law of terrestrial gravitation to the range of the cannon ball, Galileo was the first to use the principle of inertia. The obvious limitations of this law did not escape his attention and his confidence in applying it was based on simple considerations. Since wood shavings fall slowly, while a wooden ball falls from the same height in approximately the same time as a cannon ball, we can conclude that air resistance does not make much difference to the movement of compact solid bodies. Newton showed that a coin and a feather keep pace in a long cylinder from which all the air has been pumped out, when the cylinder is turned upside down. He thus concluded that the presence of air is the only circumstance which limits the rule that all bodies fall to earth with the same acceleration. That air itself is pulled earthward is shown by the very existence of the atmosphere, and we see later (Chapter VIII) that the behaviour of balloons is no exception to the more general law that all matter falls earthward with the same acceleration at the same place in a vacuum. We now know that air friction increases enormously at very high speeds. So it cannot be neglected in the practice of modern artillery. Calculations which gave a tolerable precision when applied to the slow-moving short-range projectiles of Galileo's time would lead to grossly inaccurate conclusions about the shells used in warfare today. When the Germans in World War I shelled Paris at a distance of 76 miles with shells rising to a height of 24 miles and a muzzle velocity of 1 mile a second, the actual range and the height of projection were just less than half the figures calculated by the method shown in Fig. 171.

Apart from the big resistance of the air when modern projectiles are fired at very high speeds, the method Galileo used would not be correct for another

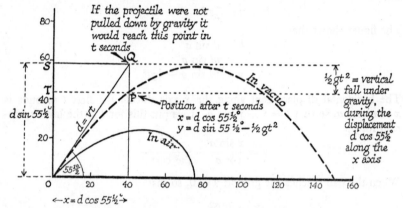

FIG. 172.—AIR FRICTION AND RANGE OF PROJECTILE

Neglecting air resistance and gravity the projectile would reach Q in *t* seconds travelling with velocity *v* at $55\frac{1}{2}°$ to the ground.

Neglecting air resistance only the distance travelled before hitting the ground is given by

$$x = \frac{v^2 \sin 2d}{g} \quad \text{(see p. 267)}$$

This calculation would be strictly true in a vacuum, where there is no *air resistance*. In real life there is considerable friction in the passage of the projectile through the air. Experiment shows that the frictional resistance of the air increases with the velocity of projection, and is small at low speeds. Hence the formula gives a fairly good rough estimate for a slow cannon ball like those used in the time of Galileo. It is grossly inaccurate for modern artillery which can project shells like those of Big Bertha at 1 mile a second. Big Bertha shelled Paris 76 miles away at an angle of $55\frac{1}{2}°$. Neglecting air resistance the shells would have fallen at twice this distance, i.e. (since 1 mile = 5,280 feet).

$$\frac{(5,280)^2 \sin 111°}{32} \text{feet} = 5,280 \times 165 \times \sin 69° \text{ feet} = 165 \times 0·934 \text{ miles} = 154 \text{ miles.}$$

Its maximal height of 24 miles was less than half the height 56 miles given by the graph of *x* and *y*.

reason. Over a short range we can regard the earth as flat, the direction of the plumb line as everywhere parallel, and the value of *g* as fixed. We shall see later that *g* falls off quite appreciably at a high altitude, and the angle of the plumb line rotates through a degree in a 70-mile range. So it would be more correct to reckon the acceleration of the shell at each stage of a long course as if it were directed towards the centre of the earth, and we should have to make allowance for the fact that its numerical value as well as its direction changes during the shell's journey.

When anything moves in a curved path, like a cannon ball, we can often look on its motion as if it were made up of a fixed velocity along one line and an acceleration directed to some fixed point. If it moves with a fixed speed in a complete circle, it has an acceleration towards the centre. When we make a stone swing in a circle at the end of a string, the latter exerts a pull on the fingers, or, to put it in another way, the fingers exert a pull on the stone to keep it from flying off at a tangent. Since pulling power implies acceleration, there is a continuous acceleration of the stone to the centre. At first sight this may seem to be a paradox because the stone keeps the same distance from the centre throughout its journey. The paradox disappears when you recollect what it would do, if the string were cut. It would fly off at a tangent. The very fact that it keeps a fixed distance from the centre implies that at each stage in its journey it is falling in towards the centre from the path it would follow if no string were pulling on it. Like the long-range projectile fired horizontally from a high mountain it has two motions, its own inertia which drives it along the tangent to the circle, and an acceleration towards a centre. When its implications were fully understood, this novel aspect of motion in a circle revolutionized the technology of clock-making, and the theory of planetary orbits.

CENTRIFUGAL MOTION

Before any substantial progress could be made in the theoretical design of seaworthy clocks it was necessary to understand rotary motion. The problem of range-finding is to reconstruct the curved path of the cannon ball from the circumstances of its motion. Rotary motion sets us the converse problem of reconstructing the central acceleration of a moving body whose path is known. If we could make a film of the path of a mail bag dropped from an aeroplane flying at a known horizontal speed we could calculate *g* from the graph. When we rotate a stone in a circle at fixed speed we know the path, and the calculation is comparatively simple.

The chief thing which is likely to cause difficulty is that the word acceleration is now used in everyday speech for increasing (or decreasing) the speedometer reading without regard to the course itself. As long as the course is a *straight* one the car driver's *acceleration* is the same as Galileo's. This is not so when the car is turning a bend. If Galileo's acceleration merely meant change in the reading of a speedometer, no pull would be needed to change the direction of a car which kept a fixed speedometer reading while turning a bend. Acceleration as a measure of pulling power is not necessarily the same as change in speedometer reading. It is based on stop-watch readings like those of speed-cops watching the car as it passes two fixed points at the ends of a surveyor's chain. This comes to the same thing if the car's course is a straight one parallel to the chain.

When we have to deal with motion in a curved path, the ordinary meanings of the words speed, velocity, and acceleration, as they are used loosely in everyday life, have to be modified to take account of the principle of inertia. A weight can be applied to affect the motion of an object in either (or both) of two ways. One is to change its speed along its own straight path. When this is so, the *velocity* of the moving object is numerically the same thing as its speed, and the acceleration imparted to it merely signifies increase or decrease of speed in one direction or its opposite, as in the everyday use of the words. A weight can also deflect the straight line motion of an object from the direction in which it is moving. So, if pulling power depends on the acceleration it can impart, acceleration must be measured so that it implies *change of direction* as well as change of speed. This can be done without sacrificing its ordinary meaning as applied to motion in a straight line, like motion down a flat slope or vertical motion under gravity. To make it measure change in direction as well as change in speed (actual distance traversed in one second), is not difficult if we recall how we measure direction when we have to be precise about it.

To measure the direction in which a body is moving we have to select some fixed line or plane of reference. Commonly we choose the N–S meridian or the line joining the east and west points on the horizon, when we are speaking of terrestrial motion like that of a ship. We use the meridian and the plumb line when we are talking of celestial motions like that of the sun. We measure the direction of a movement by the angle which the fixed line or plane of reference makes with the path of the moving body at any instant if its path is straight, or with the tangent to it if it is turning a corner. The distance which a moving object traverses in a given time depends on the direction *from which we are looking at it.* If we call its progress measured along a line at right angles to the direction in which a person is looking at it, its *motion relative to the observer*, its movement relative to observers looking at it from different aspects will generally be different. In what follows, we shall assume that the observer is a long way off. The "lines of sight" are then parallel for the same person.

The observer who watches the progress of the car in Fig. 173 by the telegraph poles along the road AC, which is its actual path of motion, sees it pass five gaps. During the same time an observer watching it pass the telegraph poles on the road BC sees it pass only three of the gaps between the poles at the side of the latter. A third observer counting the telegraph poles along the road AB as it passes them, sees it pass four gaps. Relative to the three observers the distances covered during the same time are in the ratio 5 : 3 : 4. If one gap is the unit of distance, the first of these is the speedometer reading, i.e. its *speed* in the ordinary sense, which signifies *the actual distance traversed by the car in unit time.* Speed, then, is distance covered in unit time relative to an observer looking along the line at right angles to the actual path. If the path itself is curved, the observer can only do so by changing his point of view. So speed, as the term is ordinarily used, does not imply motion relative to a *fixed observer*, i.e. to an observer watching it with reference to the same fixed line.

In everyday speech we draw no distinction between speed and *velocity*. If we limit the use of the word velocity to the measurement of motion relative to a *fixed* observer, there is no difficulty in adapting our definition of acceleration as increase (positive sign) or decrease (negative sign) of velocity in unit time to the measurement of a pull when it only affects the *direction* without changing the speed with which an object is moving. As long as a body moves in a straight line the actual speed or *distance* traversed in unit time is numerically the same as its velocity relative to an observer looking along a line at right angles to its path, i.e. its *displacement* in unit time along the line of reference. Its acceleration is therefore numerically the same as the rate at which its speed is changing. On the other hand, an object moving with a fixed speed round a corner cannot move through equal distances, measured parallel to the same straight line, in equivalent intervals of time. So it cannot have

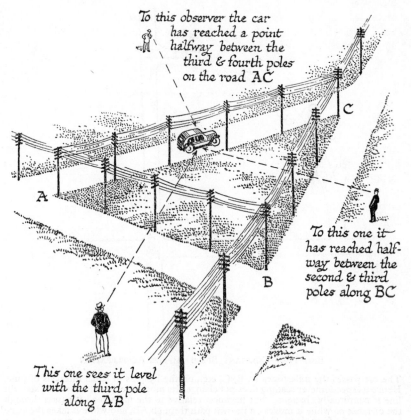

To this observer the car has reached a point halfway between the third & fourth poles on the road AC

To this one it has reached half-way between the second & third poles along BC

This one sees it level with the third pole along AB

FIG. 173.—MOTION RELATIVE TO DIFFERENT FIXED OBSERVERS

For reasons stated in the text, the observers stand at a distance much greater than can be shown in a diagram.

a constant *velocity* relative to any fixed observer. A car (Fig. 174) which passes the milestones on a circular by-pass in equal intervals of time would give a constant speedometer reading, while its progress relative to the milestones on the main road would exhibit a continual decrease. So if a body moves in a curve at fixed speed, or in other words if it is changing its direction without changing its speed, it will have an acceleration relative to any fixed observer. The driver of the car in Fig. 174 might regulate his speed so that he always appeared to pass the milestones along the main road in the same interval of time. Although he would then have no acceleration with reference to the main road, he would still have an acceleration (cf. Fig. 175) with reference to a road at right angles to it. Thus change of speed or change of direction always involves acceleration of motion (positive or negative) relative to some fixed observer.

At every point in its course a weight moving at fixed *speed* in a circle

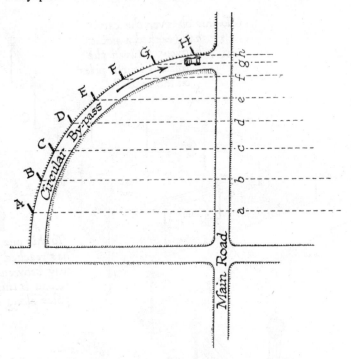

FIG. 174.—CONSTANT SPEED IMPLIES ACCELERATION

The car passes the milestones A, B, C, etc., on the by-pass in equal intervals of time. Hence its speedometer reading does not change. Its motion relative to any fixed straight line is continually changing. For instance, relative to the main road it passes through the distance *ab* while it moves on its own path through AB, and while it takes the same time to move from F to G it only traverses *fg* relative to the main road. Thus its velocity decreases as it appears to move away from the cross road which forms the centre of the arc. If it moved in the opposite direction, its velocity would appear to increase. It has a negative acceleration along the diameter to its path as it moves away from the centre.

has an acceleration along the line joining it to the centre. This acceleration measures the rate at which it must be pulled in to counteract its own sluggishness which would carry it forwards along the tangent. If it makes one revolution in a circle of radius r feet during T seconds (called its periodic time), it actually moves through $2\pi r$ feet with a speedometer reading of $(2\pi r) \div T$ feet per second. Having reached some stage represented by P in Fig. 176, it would continue to move in the straight line along the tangent to its circular course if there were no force pulling it to the centre. At P it is actually moving

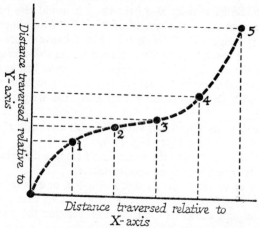

FIG. 175.—CHANGING DIRECTION ALWAYS IMPLIES ACCELERATION RELATIVE TO SOME OBSERVER

The figure shows successive positions at the end of each second during a 5-second movement of an object in a curved path. Its speed as well as its direction is changing, being obviously greater in the last than in the middle second interval. Relative to the **X-axis** the change in speed makes up for the change in direction, and the distance traversed in unit time is the same and is always to the right. Relative to the **Y-axis** its velocity changes proportionately more than its speed along its actual path.

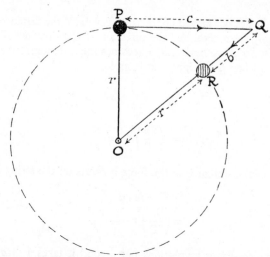

FIG. 176.—WEIGHT REVOLVING IN A CIRCLE AT FIXED SPEED *s* FEET PER SECOND AT THE END OF A CORD *r* FEET LONG

If there were no pull exerted by the cord, i.e. if the cord were cut at the instant when the weight reaches P, it would fly off at a tangent, reaching Q during the time in which it would otherwise get to R. At the instant when it is at P its direction of movement is along PQ. Hence its speed *s* is numerically the velocity with which it would continue to move of its own inertia through the distance $c = $ PQ in time *t*, i.e. $c = st$. To bring it to R during the same time, we have to supplement its motion in virtue of its own inertia, like that of the mail bag in Fig. 170 with a motion parallel with RO at each stage in its course. This must make it fall a distance *b* along RP while it would otherwise reach Q. If its acceleration along RO is *a*, $b = \frac{1}{2}at^2$.

in this direction. So its velocity along the tangent would also be $(2\pi r) \div$ T if the cord were cut when the weight reaches P. In a short interval of time t seconds it would then traverse a certain distance c feet reaching Q. Actually it does not reach Q. The force exerted by the string keeps it moving inwards, so that it is at a fixed distance r from the centre. Just as the mail bag continues to move with the horizontal velocity of the aeroplane, while falling simultaneously with an acceleration g earthward, the weight would travel from P to R if:

(a) it continued to move forwards along PQ with a velocity s ($= 2\pi r \div$ T) through a distance c in time t (see Fig. 176),

(b) it also fell inwards during the same time t along a direction parallel to RO through a distance b with fixed acceleration a.

The definition of velocity tells us that $s = c \div t$, or $c = st = 2\pi rt \div$ T. The rule connecting acceleration and distance tells us that $b = \frac{1}{2}at^2$. The theorem of Pythagoras shows us the connexion between the distances b and c, i.e.

$$(r + b)^2 = c^2 + r^2$$
$$\therefore 2br + b^2 = c^2$$
$$\therefore 2b(r + \tfrac{1}{2}b) = c^2$$
$$\therefore at^2(r + \tfrac{1}{2}b) = 4\pi^2 r^2 t^2 \div T^2$$
$$\therefore a(r + \tfrac{1}{2}b) = \frac{4\pi^2}{T^2} . r^2$$

When the weight has not moved appreciably beyond P the distance b does not differ appreciably from zero, and the direction of QO does not differ appreciably from PO. So, if we neglect b, a becomes the instantaneous acceleration along the radius when the weight is at P, and

$$ar = \frac{4\pi^2}{T^2} . r^2$$

$$\therefore a = \left(\frac{2\pi}{T}\right)^2 r \ = \frac{s^2}{r}$$

If the mass of the weight is m the force it exerts on the string is therefore

$$F = m . a$$
$$= m\left(\frac{2\pi}{T}\right)^2 r \ = \frac{ms^2}{r}$$

If the circular speed is n revolutions per second it takes $1 \div n$ seconds to rotate once and

$$T = \frac{1}{n}$$

Hence we can also write for the force exerted on a mass of m rotating at a distance r from the centre of a wheel making n revolutions per second

$$F = (2\pi n)^2 mr$$

If m is measured in pounds, n in revolutions per second, and r in feet, this gives the force in poundals. If m is measured in grams, n in revolutions per second, and r in centimetres, it gives the force in dynes.

There are two ways of representing the motion of an object revolving at fixed speed in a circle. Each is useful, and the two are complementary. In a tug of war, when each side is keeping the same distance from the line, the two teams are pulling with equal strength in opposite directions. The forces exerted are numerically equal, and we represent them with opposite signs to signify that their sum in either direction is zero. Hence there is no motion. In the preceding paragraphs we started with the principle of inertia, that is to say with the known fact that the weight would fly off at a tangent if the cord were cut. We then asked what acceleration towards the centre is necessary to keep the weight at the same distance from it. We are equally entitled to put the question in the converse form. If a weight revolving in this way has an acceleration towards the centre, we must also say that it has an equal acceleration away from the centre to keep it at the same distance from it. The first or *centripetal* acceleration $-(2\pi n)^2 r$ depends on the cohesive power of the cord which resists any attempt to stretch it. The second or *centrifugal* acceleration $+(2\pi n)^2 r$ is a mathematical trick put in to signify that there is no actual motion towards the centre. Because of the power of the cord or support to resist stretching, a revolving weight is pulled towards the centre of motion. As in a tug of war, the two pulls, away from and towards the centre, are balanced. If we use the positive sign for the outward direction, it comes to the same thing whether we say that the *centripetal force* exerted on the weight by the cord is $-(2\pi n)^2 mr$ or that the *centrifugal force* exerted by the weight on the cord is $+(2\pi n)^2 mr$.

The practical importance of the distinction is easier to see, if a piece of elastic is used instead of an ordinary cord which does not appear to stretch appreciably. It is a matter of common experience that a large weight stretches a piece of elastic more than a small one. When a weight hangs vertically from a piece of elastic, the power of the latter to *resist further stretching* cancels out the action of gravity and must therefore be represented as a force of equal strength and opposite sign. The resisting force of a piece of elastic therefore increases with the load. It is easy to satisfy yourself that a weight swung in a circle at the end of a piece of elastic stretches the elastic more when the speed is increased. As we increase the speed, the centrifugal force outwards from the centre is also increased. The weight moves farther away from the centre, thereby increasing its centrifugal force, while at the same time increasing the power of the elastic to resist any further stretching. When the latter just balances the former, the weight continues to revolve at a fixed distance from the centre. If the speed is reduced, the centrifugal force is weakened. The elastic resistance being now the greater draws the weight inwards. Since diminishing the length diminishes the power of the elastic to resist stretching (see p. 291), there comes a point when the elastic pull is no longer in excess, and the weight continues to revolve at fixed distance from the centre, though nearer to it than it was when the speed was greater.

To test the law of motion in a circle we have only to attach a weight to a spring balance fixed by a ring to the axle of a turntable, on which the weight can slide without appreciable friction (Fig. 177). When the table is made to rotate the weight will move outwards and stop at a certain distance from the centre. This distance r depends on the speed. The spring balance records the pull of a weight hanging vertically. So an extension marked M lb. corre-

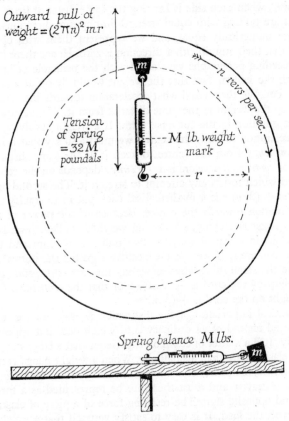

Outward pull of weight $= (2\pi n)^2 mr$

n revs per sec.

Tension of spring $= 32M$ poundals

M lb. weight mark

r

Spring balance M lbs.

FIG. 177.—MEASURING CENTRIFUGAL FORCE

sponds to 32M poundals. If the mass m is rotating at n revolutions per second r feet from the centre,

$$32M = (2\pi n)^2 mr$$

If the mass attached to the spring balance is 2 lb., and it remains steady 2 feet from the centre when the wheel rotates at 20 revolutions per second,

$$32M = \left(\frac{44}{7} \times 20\right)^2 \times 2 \times 2$$

Taking $4\pi^2$ as approximately 40

$$M = 2,000 \text{ lb.}$$

That is to say, the scale reading of the spring balance would correspond to a hanging weight of 2,000 lb.

The construction of a variety of devices based on this principle provides

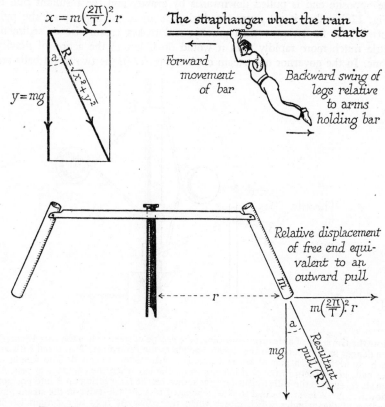

FIG. 178.—PRINCIPLE OF THE CREAM SEPARATOR OR CENTRIFUGE

To calculate the angle of tilt of the two tubes rotating on a bar of radius r at a given speed

$$\tan a = m\left(\frac{2\pi}{T}\right)^2 r \div mg = \frac{4\pi^2 r}{T^2 g}$$

Thus if the distance of the fixed end from the centre is 1 foot and the axle makes 6,000 revolutions per minute the time of a revolution is $60 \div 6,000 = 0\cdot01$ second. Taking $4\pi^2 = 40$ and $g = 32$ feet per sec².

$$\tan a = \frac{40 \times 1}{32 \times 0\cdot01^2} = 12,500$$

Since $\tan 89° = 57\cdot29$, the tubes are inclined at over 89° to the vertical, and would hence be practically horizontal at this speed.

tangible evidence of this pull. Examples from the everyday life of our own time are the cream separator, the governor of a steam engine, and the analogous device with air vanes used as a brake to ensure the constant speed of a gramophone record. The cream separator is essentially like the laboratory centrifuge, which consists of a rotating bar or flywheel, from the rim of which a series of tubes are suspended so that the lower end is free to tilt upwards and outwards (Fig. 178). During rotation the centrifugal acceleration $(2\pi n)^2 r$ at the top of the tube is balanced by the rigidity of the support, while the opposite end is pulled downwards by gravity and the resultant pull R (Fig. 178) makes it tilt outwards during rotation. At high speed the pull outwards is far stronger than gravity, and makes cream rise or sediment settle much more rapidly than it would do if left to the action of gravity alone. In the governor of a steam engine (Fig. 179), the two metal balls are

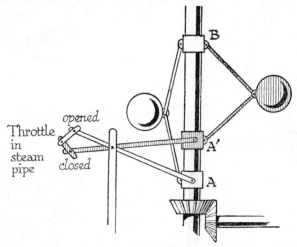

FIG. 179

How the *Governor* of a steam engine allows the escape of steam when the speed exceeds the danger limit depends on the same principle as the centrifuge. Two metal balls are each connected by a pair of levers with two collars A or A' and B. The weight of the balls keeps them in the position shown on the left when the engine is at rest. As the shaft revolves the balls fly outwards as shown on the right lifting up A into position shown as A'. A lever attached to A is connected to a throttle-valve in the steam pipe leading to the cylinder which closes when the collar A' rises to a certain height depending on the speed of rotation. Only one ball is shown in each position.

connected with a lever device. At a certain speed the balls fly apart so far that the lever closes a throttle controlling the supply of steam to the cylinder, so the speed cannot exceed the limits of safety. A common type of speed regulator for gramophones has a lever attachment like that of the steam engine governor, working a brake when the speed reaches the limit required. In the analogous device which is used to regulate gramophone speed, the air-resisting surface of the vanes increases and thereby opposes further increase of speed.

The calculation of centrifugal force is also necessary for laying rails at appropriate heights to allow for the tilt of trains in turning a bend. In its own social context it arose from the technology of the pendulum clock, and the formula was first actually published in Huyghens' *Horologium Oscillatorium*. The first clocks were purely empirical devices, in which a descending weight was the motive power. Later the weight was replaced by a spring.

The problem of clock construction is to regulate the fall of a weight, or the contraction of a stretched spring, so as to drive a wheel at a constant speed. This is done by a device called the *escapement* (Fig. 181), which consists of two arms cut so that one is free when the other engages the obliquely toothed rim of the driving wheel, and vice versa. As the driving wheel revolves, the pressure of a tooth swings one arm up. As it clears the tooth, the other comes down between a pair of teeth, engaging them till its fellow swings down. The motive force is thus regulated to impart constant speed by the regular swinging of the escapement to and fro. So accuracy of timekeeping depends on making the interval of the escapement swing constant.

In the first clocks this was done by what was called the "verge escapement" (Fig. 181). The escapement was fixed to a bar with a heavy weight at each end. First it was turned one way by one tooth of the driving wheel. Then another tooth on the opposite side swung it the other way. If the teeth of the rim were of the same size and cut at the same angle, the bar

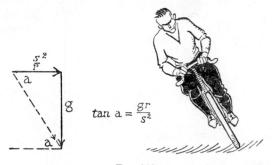

$$\tan a = \frac{g\,r}{s^2}$$

Fig. 180

Inclination (*a*) of rider on a circular speed track as the resultant of two accelerations at right angles.

and weights turned through the same angle in opposite directions taking the same interval of time for each swing. To make this arrangement work with great accuracy therefore required very great precision in the construction of the wheel and the escapement; and since the heaviness of the weights generated considerable friction, calculation of the dimensions was beset with formidable difficulties. Accuracy in clock construction was not achieved until it was possible to devise an escapement which has a fixed period, independent of the size of the teeth on the driving wheel. This can be done by means of a pendulum or a spring.

THE PRINCIPLE OF THE FIXED PERIOD

The rule for rotational motion leads directly to another rule about the circumstances of to-and-fro motion with a fixed period. In the steam engine the to-and-fro stroke of the piston is converted into the rotary motion of the wheel. Conversely if we rotate the wheel when there is no steam in the piston we can convert the *rotary* into a *periodic* motion. It is not difficult to see that a wheel rotating at fixed speed can be made to produce a pendulum-like movement with a fixed periodic time. The complete period, i.e. the time taken to move forwards and backwards to the same position, is the time taken for the wheel to make a complete revolution, i.e. its periodic time T. Fig. 182 shows a type of piston rod attachment by which the *horizontal*

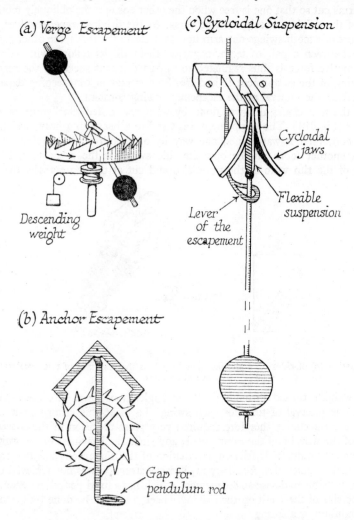

(a) *Verge Escapement*

(c) *Cycloidal Suspension*

Cycloidal jaws

Flexible suspension

Lever of the escapement

Descending weight

(b) *Anchor Escapement*

Gap for pendulum rod

FIG. 181.—EVOLUTION OF THE PENDULUM CLOCK

A pendulum swinging in a small arc of a circle is almost but not quite *isochronous* (i.e. with a period independent of the distance through which it swings). It is completely so, if the path of the bob is a cycloid, which is a curve like a semi-circle but steeper at the extremities. By having a flexible support which bends round the curved jaws shown in the figure, the pendulum performs a cycloidal motion for wide angles of swing.

displacement of a peg projecting from a circular wheel drives a pendulum to and fro. The horizontal displacement of the centre of the pendulum bob from its midway position exactly corresponds to the horizontal displacement of the pin along the diameter of the wheel, and hence the acceleration of the pendulum bob is also equivalent to the acceleration of the peg along the diameter of the wheel.

Suppose now that at some instant during the rotation of the wheel in Fig. 182 the radius r drawn from the centre to the peg makes an angle b with the axis of the piston. The peg is moving in a circle at fixed speed. Inwards along r (see Fig. 176) it has an acceleration whose numerical value may be represented by a_r. According to rule 4, p. 258, this is equivalent to an acceleration $a_r \cos b$ along the piston axis (see also Fig. 174). If the numerical value of this horizontal acceleration is a_x,

$$a_x = a_r \cos b$$

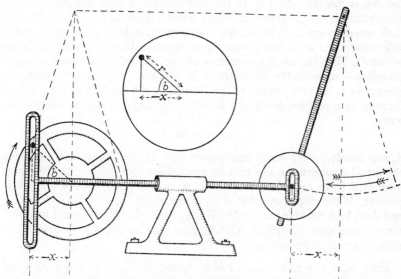

FIG. 182.—REGULAR PENDULUM-LIKE MOTION OF A PIN ATTACHED TO THE RIM OF A WHEEL ROTATING AT A FIXED SPEED, AS SEEN IN THE HORIZONTAL PLANE

If x is the horizontal distance of the peg from the centre (regardless of whether it is right or left of it) $\cos b = x \div r$,

$$\therefore \ a_x = a_r x \div r$$
$$\therefore \ a_x \div x = a \div r$$

And since a_r and r are both fixed

$$\frac{a_x}{x} = \text{const}$$

The pendulum of Fig. 182 swings with a fixed period corresponding to one rotation of the wheel at fixed speed. We now know that when it does so, the ratio of the *numerical* values of its acceleration and displacement along the line of swing is fixed. This clue is not enough to define a periodic motion of fixed period. As it stands, the last formula takes no account of the direction of motion, and would also describe that of an object moving continuously with increasing speed in the same straight line. The motion of the pendulum involves reversal of direction in each revolution with slowing down and speeding up in each half turn. To define its direction we must use appropriate signs.

If x is the horizontal distance of the peg from the centre, its displacement may be $- x$ (x ft. to the left) or $+ x$ (x ft. to the right of it). With the same convention an acceleration $+ a_x$ means *gaining* a_x ft. per sec. in each second while moving to the *right* or losing a_x ft. per sec.^{2} while moving *leftwards*, and $- a_x$ means *gaining* a_x ft. per sec.^{2} moving *leftwards* or losing a_x ft. per sec.^{2} moving rightwards. In a complete clockwise rotation the horizontal displacement is $+ x$, when the peg is moving downwards, and $- x$, when the peg is moving upwards. In the downward half turn (see Fig. 174) its acceleration is $- a_x$, because it is first slowing down as it moves right, and then speeding up as it moves left. Conversely, it is $+ a_x$ in the upward half turn, when it is first slowing down rightwards and then speeding up leftwards. With the usual conventions of sign the horizontal acceleration is therefore $- a_x$ when the displacement is $+ x$, and $+ a_x$ when the displacement is $- x$. To take account of this we replace the constant in the previous formula by a positive quantity k to which the negative sign is fixed. If we write,

$$a_x = - kx$$

a_x now stands for the actual acceleration *with its appropriate sign*, and x for the actual displacement also with its appropriate sign. Thus if the displacement is d ft. to the left, $x = - d$ and $a_x = - k (- d) = + kd$, which is positive. If the displacement is d ft. to the right, $a_x = - kd$, and since k and d are both positive the acceleration is represented by a number to which the negative sign is attached. This signifies slowing down in motion to the right or speeding up leftwards.

Since $a_r \div r = a_x \div x, a_r \div r = - k$, and we know that the *numerical value* of a_r, the *centripetal* acceleration, (p. 275) is $(2\pi \div \mathrm{T})^2 r$.

$$\therefore a_r \div r = (2\pi \div \mathrm{T})^2$$
$$\therefore \mathrm{T} = 2\pi \div \sqrt{k}$$

So we have now two clues to the perfect clock escapement. We have to find something which moves so that it has an acceleration of opposite sign and with a constant ratio (k) to its displacement along a fixed line. When we have done so its periodic time will be $2\pi \div \sqrt{k}$.

To visualize a periodic motion with correct use of signs, complete the following table showing the mean horizontal acceleration of the pendulum device in Fig. 182 in successive seconds. The wheel rotates once in 36 seconds, i.e. 10° per second. Starting when the pin is at the extreme right-hand position, its horizontal displacement x is also r, the distance of the pin from the centre, so if $r = 1$, $x = 1$. At the end of a second the pin has rotated through 10° and $x = r \cos 10° = \cos 10°$. At the end of two seconds $x = \cos 20°$ and so on. Tables of cosines tell us that $\cos 10° = 0 \cdot 9848$ and $\cos 20° = 0 \cdot 9397$. During the first second the displacement changes from $x = 1$ to $x = 0 \cdot 9848$, i.e. $- 0 \cdot 0152$ ft. to the right. In the next second it moves $- 0 \cdot 0451$ ft. Thus its mean velocity in the first second is $- 0.0152$ ft. per sec. and its mean velocity in the next second is $- 0.0451$ ft. per sec. and the mean velocity gained in one second (mean acceleration) is $- 0.0451 - (- 0.0152) = - 0.0299$ ft. per sec.[2] This is its approximate acceleration midway between the middle of the first and the middle of the next second, i.e. at the end of the first when its distance is 0.9848 ft. The ratio of its acceleration to its distance is $- 0.0299 \div 0.9848 = - 0.0304$. The table below calculated in this way shows that the ratio $- a_x \div x$ is approximately constant, and closely agrees with the value of $4\pi^2 \div T^2 = 4 \times 9.87 \div (36)^2 = 0.0305$.

Time	Angle (o)	Displacement $= x$	Mean Velocity (Displacement gained per sec.)	Mean Acceleration (Velocity gained per sec.) $= a_x$	$- a_x \div x$
0	0	1.0000			
0.5			$- 0.0152$		
1.0	10	0.9848		$- 0.0299$	0.0304
1.5			$- 0.0451$		
2.0	20	0.9397		$- 0.0286$	0.0304
2.5			$- 0.0737$		
3.0	30	0.8660		$- 0.0263$	0.0304
3.5			$- 0.1000$		
4.0	40	0.7660		$- 0.0232$	0.0303
4.5			$- 0.1232$		
5.0	50	0.6428			

THE LAW OF THE PENDULUM

So long as the escapement was unreliable, it was neither possible to make a clock with sufficient accuracy for finding longitude at sea nor to fix a convenient unit for measuring short intervals of time. Galileo seems to have been the first person who recognized that a pendulum device might be used to make an escapement whose period does not depend on the angle of swing, and is therefore independent of the precision of the teeth on the wheel. The principle of the pendulum is that when a small weight swings through a small angle, at a fixed distance from a fixed point, its time of swing is constant. It is said that Galileo noticed this phenomenon, as a student, when he timed the swing of a lamp suspended from the roof of a church by counting his pulse beats. It is more probable that the practice already existed among physicians, and that when he subsequently made accurate clinical observations on pulse rate by using a pendulum to count the heart beats of patients in high fever, he merely adopted the practice of contemporary medicine. Be that as it may, his important contribution was to show that the period of the swing is approximately constant by mechanical standards, which had been used from time immemorial to measure astronomical time. He determined the number of swings of a pendulum during the time occupied by the emptying of a vessel; found that it did not vary appreciably for larger and smaller swings; suggested its use in observatories for measuring short intervals between the transits of neighbouring stars, and designed, without completing, a clock with a pendulum escapement.

Having discovered the first simple and reliable means of measuring short intervals of time, the next problem was how to construct a pendulum of which the swing occupies some convenient fraction of a standard long interval of time, e.g. a sixtieth of a minute, or, as we now call this new unit, a second. By counting the number of swings corresponding to the flow of a fixed quantity of water from a vessel, he established the following conclusions: (*a*) within wide limits the time occupied by a complete swing ("period" of the pendulum) is not affected by the size or material of the weight, provided that the length of the cord or rod is the same; (*b*) if the length of the pendulum is varied, the square of the period (T) is directly proportional to the length, i.e.

$$T^2 = KL$$

To see what this means, suppose a bob hanging at the end of a cord 3 feet 3 inches long makes 30 complete swings (i.e. from one position back to the same position) in a minute. The period is then 2 seconds, i.e.

$$2^2 = K \times 3\tfrac{1}{4}$$
$$\therefore \ K = 16/13 = 1 \cdot 23$$

So to make a pendulum which gives a half swing in 2 seconds (i.e. one with a period of 4 seconds), the length is given by the equation

$$4^2 = \tfrac{16}{13} \times L$$
$$\therefore \ L = 13 \text{ feet}$$

In a clock the escapement engages the teeth every half period. So what is called a *seconds* pendulum is a pendulum whose *half* period is one second (i.e. T = 2 secs.). Shortly after Galileo's death his French pupil Mersenne (1644) determined the length of a seconds pendulum with great care, and a little later Huyghens made the first successful pendulum clock (Fig. 183). He also modified the form of the escapement ordinarily used so that the motion would withstand the rocking of a ship, and at last it seemed as if Huyghens' marine clock had achieved what his fellow countryman, Gemma Frisius, had dreamed of more than a century since.

This was not to be. A pendulum clock loses time, if taken from Paris to Cayenne in French Guiana. This is because the swing of the pendulum depends on the pull of gravity, and the latter is not exactly the same in all parts of the world. It weakens as we get away from the earth's centre in climbing a mountain (p. 300). It is also different at sea-level in different latitudes, and this would still be so if the earth were perfectly spherical. The latitude variation provided a new means of testing the Copernican doctrine. Long before Copernicus adopted it as part of his system for calculating planetary motions, the Pythagorean brotherhoods, the Athenian Archytas, and Aristarchus of Samos, had in turn toyed with the earth's axial motion as a speculative possibility. In Kepler's time it still seemed to contradict everyday experience, and was justified only by arithmetical convenience. The practical failure of the first marine clock brought it to earth. What was a serious setback to practical achievement set the stage for the new theories associated with Newton's name.

Discovery was now becoming an organized social institution. One of the cultural offshoots of "Colbertism" in France was the foundation of the Paris Academy of Sciences in 1666, four years after the Royal Society received its charter in England. As the latter grew out of the meetings of the Invisible College (see p. 556), the Paris Academy arose from an association of a group which used to meet at the cell of Mersenne. Mersenne was active in spreading Galileo's teaching. The original members included Descartes, Pascal, the mathematician Fermat, and Gassendi, whose commentaries on Epicurus revived the atomistic speculations of the early Greek materialists. In con-

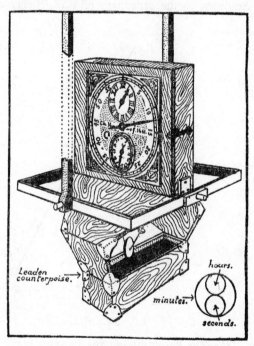

Leaden counterpoise.

hours.

minutes.

seconds.

FIG. 183.—HUYGHENS' MARINE CLOCK

formity with Colbert's policy the Paris Academy, like the English Royal Society, was actively interested in all problems related to navigation, then the touchstone of mercantile supremacy. Under its auspices the Paris Observatory was inaugurated and completed three years before the one at Greenwich was established as a national undertaking. A rich harvest of discoveries followed immediately. To Paris came Cassini from Italy and Römer from Denmark. Cassini undertook the calculation of tables forecasting eclipses of Jupiter's satellites for use in determining longitude at sea. The project was undertaken in accordance, Professor Wolf tells us, with a suggestion made by Galileo himself. A remarkable discovery to which Römer was led in the course of a similar enquiry will emerge in the next chapter. The Academy sponsored several expeditions, notably one to French Guiana with a view to simultaneous observations on the parallax of Mars from the

Paris Observatory and Cayenne (Lat. 5° N.). This expedition, which gave the first relatively satisfactory scale of measurement for the planetary system, signalizes an epoch in clock technology.

The technology of the clock, like other problems of navigation, was a prominent feature in the researches encouraged by the Paris Academy and undertaken by Mersenne himself. Twelve years after the invention of Huyghens' pendulum clock (1657), Picard, one of the foremost astronomers of the Academy, made careful measurements to determine the length of a sidereal seconds pendulum by star observations at Paris and Lyons. At the request of the Academy, in the expedition of 1672, Richer observed the

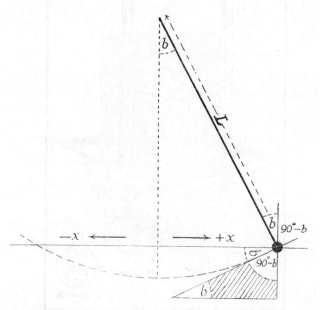

FIG. 184.—THE PENDULUM AND THE INCLINED PLANE

length of the seconds pendulum at Cayenne. On returning to Paris he found that the same pendulum must there be lengthened by $1\frac{1}{4}$ Paris lines (12 to the inch). A year later Huyghens published the theory of the pendulum clock (*Horologium Oscillatorium*). In this he explained the retardation of the clock by the earth's axial motion, established the mechanical principle involved in rotation at constant speed, and arrived at the correct conclusion that the earth must be slightly flattened at the poles.

We can see why a pendulum clock cannot be used as a reliable chronometer at sea by applying our two clues to the perfect clock (p. 282) and the law of the inclined plane. Turn first to Fig. 184, which illustrates a small weight swinging like the bob of a pendulum, in an arc of a circle of radius r. At any point in its course, we may consider it to be sliding down an inclined surface represented by the tangent to the curve at the point where it is, with downward acceleration $g \sin b$. From the geometry of the figure, $\sin b = x \div L$; and its acceleration (a) to the *right* along the tangent is, therefore,

$$-\left(\frac{g}{L}\right)x$$

Thus the acceleration is actually to the *left*. Along the line at right angles to the resting position of the axis of the pendulum, the equivalent acceleration a_x of the bob is $a \cos b$ (see Fig. 164). Now $\cos b$ does not differ much from 1 when b is small (e.g. $\cos 5° = 0 \cdot 9962$ differs by only 4 parts in a thousand from $\cos 0° = 1 \cdot 0000$) at any part of its journey. For a 4-inch swing (2 inches each way) of a 36-inch pendulum the maximum angle is $3 \cdot 2°$ from the vertical and $\cos 3 \cdot 2° = 0 \cdot 9984$. So $\cos b$ differs from 1 by only 16 parts in 10,000 over the extreme limits of the swing. Even for a three times greater swing of 12 inches or 6 inches each way when the maximum value of b is $9 \cdot 5°$, $\cos b$ only varies between $\cos 0° = 1 \cdot 0000$ and $\cos 9 \cdot 5° = 0 \cdot 986$, differing from the mean of $0 \cdot 993$ by 7 parts in a thousand. It also differs from the mean value $0 \cdot 9992$ for a swing a third as great by less than 13 parts in a thousand. So a very small difference in the angle of swing due to irregularities of tooth cutting in a clock wheel can make only a negligible difference to the extreme values between which $\cos b$ varies. We may therefore draw this conclusion. To a high degree of precision for relatively small angles of swing the horizontal acceleration a_x

$$= -\frac{g}{L}x \cos b = -\frac{g}{L}x$$

The horizontal acceleration towards the resting position is therefore proportional to x, the horizontal displacement, and the constant ratio k is $g \div L$. The rule given on p. 282 shows:

(*a*) that the pendulum swings with a constant periodic movement as we should expect if Galileo's principles are right;

(*b*) that the constant ratio k must be $(2\pi \div T)^2$ so that

$$T = 2\pi \div \sqrt{k} = 2\pi\sqrt{\frac{L}{g}}$$

This you can test easily for yourself by hanging a button on the end of a piece of thread and counting the swings with a watch. On measuring the length L of the thread you should get a value for g within 2 per cent of the best values with little trouble. You can also see that it gives the length of the seconds pendulum (period 2 seconds) given already. Taking $(2\pi)^2$ as approximately 40, $L = g \div 10 = 3 \cdot 2$ feet or 3 feet 2 inches.

The important thing about the calculation we have just made is that the period of the pendulum depends on g. So if g varies at different places the pendulum clock can only be relied on to work properly while it is kept at the place where it was regulated. The Cayenne expedition showed that g does vary, and Huyghens found the answer.

The earth like a great wheel makes a complete rotation about its axis with a periodic time (T) of 24 hours. A man who could work miracles might suspend the pull of gravitation as in the story by Mr. Wells. Any object would then fly off immediately at a tangent to its circle of latitude L (radius *r*). To keep an object from doing so, it would be necessary to impart an acceleration $(2\pi \div T)^2 r$ towards the earth's axis parallel to the plane of the equator, or $(2\pi \div T)^2 r \cos L$ in the direction of the earth's centre. If the man who could work miracles decided to stop the earth's rotation instead of suspending the earth's gravitational pull, the effective acceleration which the latter could impart to a body would be greater. Objects would fall to earth a little faster, because gravitation would no longer be opposed by "centrifugal force." Although we cannot stop the earth's rotation we can get to the poles, where *r* is zero, and the value of *g* is not affected by the earth's spin. At any other latitude the pull of gravity has to do two things: (*a*) keep a body from flying off at a tangent to the earth's surface, (*b*) keep it moving towards the earth's centre if free to do so. When we measure its acceleration towards the latter, we are therefore measuring the difference between its acceleration at the poles where the pull of gravitation has only to do (*b*) and the acceleration which would keep it at a fixed distance from the earth's centre, if it kept to a circular path. The observed value of *g* at latitude L should therefore be:

$$g - \left(\frac{2\pi}{T}\right)^2 r \cos L$$

and if R is the radius of the equator (see Fig. 185), this is

$$g - \left(\frac{2\pi}{T}\right)^2 R \cos^2 L$$

At the equator L = 0 and cos L = 1, R is 4,000 miles or 4,000 × 5,280 feet, and the time of a revolution is 24 hours or 24 × 3,600 seconds. Taking $4\pi^2$ as 40, the observed acceleration is diminished by:

$$\frac{4,000 \times 40 \times 5,280}{24 \times 3,600 \times 24 \times 3,600} = 0 \cdot 114 \text{ foot per second per second}$$

The earth's spin therefore should reduce the value of *g* by 1·4 inches per second per second at the equator. How to make a corresponding calculation for any other latitude is shown in Fig. 185. The value of *g* thus diminishes at sea-level from the poles to the equator, and since the pendulum period varies inversely with *g*, T increases. That is to say, there are fewer swings in the same period of astronomical time, and the clock will be "slower" if taken to a latitude nearer the equator. A "marine" pendulum clock would only work during a course along the same parallel of latitude. It would also be useless for exploration, because the value of *g* is measurably smaller at the top of a high mountain and greater at the bottom of a deep mine than it is at sea-level.

The explanation given refers to a simple pendulum, i.e. small weight suspended from a light axis such as a thread, *at sea-level* (see p. 300). We can then regard all the effective movement as the movement of the weight. To calculate the movement of an ordinary pendulum is a little more complicated, because we have to average out along the axis the effective weight involved in the descent by the methods explained on pp. 614-615 in Chapter XII. Huyghens calculated the motion of the compound, i.e. ordinary, pendulum in his great treatise on the theory of clock motion, and also made another important discovery. There is—as we have seen—a small error in the principle of the simple pendulum moving in a circle. The period is almost but not quite independent of the excursion. This error does not exist if the suspension (Fig. 181) is modified so that the weight describes an

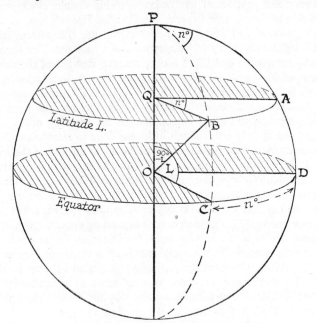

FIG. 185.—THE VARIATION OF *g* WITH LATITUDE

$$\frac{QB}{OB} = \sin QOB = \sin (90° - L) = \cos L$$

So if r = radius of Latitude L (QB) and R the radius of the terrestrial sphere (OB),

$$r = R \cos L = \cos L \times 4{,}000 \text{ miles,}$$

e.g. at Lat. 45°, since cos 45° = 0·707, r = 2,828 miles. The central acceleration as Lat. 45°, when the units of distance and time are the foot and second, is

$$\frac{(2\pi)^2 r}{T^2} = \frac{40 \times 2{,}828 \times 5{,}280}{24^2 \times 60^2 \times 60^2} = 0·08 \text{ ft. per sec.}^2 \text{ (approx.)}$$

So $(2\pi \div T)^2 r \cos L$ is 0·08 × 0·707 = 0·06. Thus, if the value of *g* at the North Pole is 32·26, it is 32·20 (feet per sec.²) at Lat. 45°.

arc of the curve called a *cycloid*. The cycloidal pendulum is isochronous. The quest for a perfect clock stimulated mathematical researches into the characteristics of new families of curves such as the cycloids and epicycloids.

THE LAW OF THE SPRING

The struggle for mercantile supremacy during the period which intervened between the two English revolutions of the seventeenth century was accompanied by a lively interest in all scientific problems bearing on navigation. Foremost among this English group of scientific men in the early days of the Royal Society and its parent body the Invisible College were Robert Hooke, Newton, Halley of comet fame, and Flamsteed, the first director of the newly founded observatory at Greenwich. Newton's studies on telescopy have been mentioned. Hooke's contributions to weather forecasting will come later (pp. 561–3). Not the least important of his researches in the theory and practice of navigation were his various clock inventions. The principle of the stretched spring is still called Hooke's law.

Hooke's position and personal characteristics are the portent of a new epoch in scientific discovery and the symbol of a past age. The socialization of scientific knowledge had taken a decisive step forward at the foundation of the new academies for the free distribution of new discoveries by regular publication in journals printed in the *vernacular*. Prominent among these was the *Philosophical Transactions* of the Royal Society. The need for new organs of education to replace or supplement the teaching of the medieval universities was already felt, though little was done to establish colleges and technical institutions free from ecclesiastical control until after the industrial revolution. In Britain, London, the hub of British mercantilism, was exceptional. At Gresham College, the earliest forerunner of the London University, Hooke professed mathematics and mechanics. In the older universities astronomy had retained its traditional prestige, and medicine had gained a foothold (see pp. 561–3). There were now expanding opportunities of regular employment, and men of scientific capabilities were no longer wholly dependent on wealthy patrons if their social antecedents vouchsafed the necessary training. Regular employment for scientific pursuits and regular publication of discoveries went hand in hand. A new sense of common endeavour usurped the atmosphere of secrecy sustained by the insecurity of patronage and the dread of the Inquisition.

Hooke's practice combined the generosity of the new age and the parsimony of the past. He was active in promoting schemes for co-operative endeavour, like his weather records, and lavish with fruitful suggestions (see p. 558). No doubt Newton reaped the benefit of some of them. He was never profuse in acknowledgments to Flamsteed, who supplied so many of his astronomical data, or to Huyghens or to Leibnitz with whom he corresponded. In contradistinction to this liberality, Hooke had a forgivable if childish anxiety to wear the laurels of priority, and was one of the last scientific authors to use the time-honoured device of securing it by preliminary announcement as an anagram. He gave the law of the spring as the anagram *ceiiinosssttuv* two years before he disclosed the solution *ut tensio sic vis* in a published description of the experimental evidence for the law.

Translated into the vernacular it means that the pulling power of a stretched spring is proportional to the displacement, a rule equally true for small displacements whether it is applied to elongation or lateral bending. It is easy to remember the rule when you know what it means, because the uniform graduation of a spring balance scale is an everyday illustration of its truth. Thus a weight of 3 lb. stretches a spring $1\frac{1}{2}$ inches if a weight of 2 lb. stretches it 1 inch from its "natural" length, when no weight is attached to it. The stretch is therefore 0·5 inches per pound weight hanging from the spring, and the pound marks on the scale would be 0·5 inches apart.

At first sight we might therefore draw the conclusion that the *mass* bears a constant ratio to the *stretch*. This is not necessarily true. The pulling power of the spring is what prevents a weight at rest from falling. The string is stretched till the upward pull of the spring exactly balances the downward pull of the weight. If its mass is m, this pull is mg, and we already know that g is not exactly the same in all parts of the world. Provided the spring is not stretched too far, the ratio $(m \div x)$ of mass (m) to distance

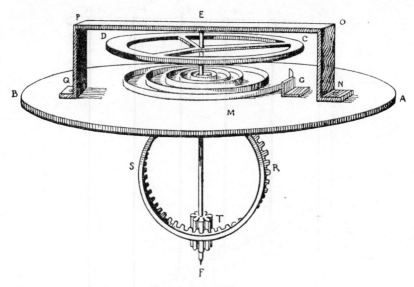

Fig. 185A.—A Seventeenth-Century Balance Spring (by permission of Prof. Wolf)

stretched (x) is fixed at any one place. It is not fixed for all places. What we should expect to find, and what we do find, is that the ratio $mg \div x$ is fixed, i.e.

$$mg = kx$$

The practical importance of this may be illustrated by the behaviour of a spring balance with a scale recording 2 lb. per inch, at a place where $g = 32$ feet per second per second. The extension (x) is $\frac{1}{12}$ foot for a mass of 2 lb., i.e.

$$2 \times 32 = k \div 12$$
$$\therefore \quad k = 768 \text{ (poundals per foot)}$$

If we took the same spring and the same weights to the top of a high mountain where acceleration under gravity is somewhat less, let us say 31 feet per second per second, the extension would be less for each weight and the scale readings would not agree with the previous estimate.

The spring tension sufficient to balance a 2 lb. weight would then be 2×31 $= 62$ poundals, and since $mg = kx$,

$$x = 62 \div 768 \text{ (feet)}$$
$$= 0 \cdot 96875 \text{ inch}$$

When we weigh with ordinary *scales*, we compare a body of unknown mass with a *standard* at the same place under the same pull of gravity. This is not

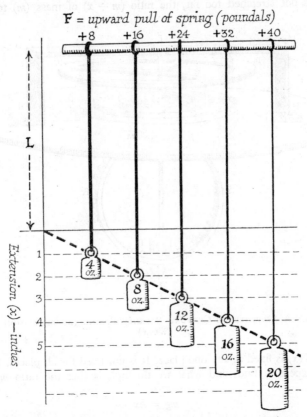

FIG. 186.—TESTING HOOKE'S LAW FOR A PIECE OF ELASTIC

Up to 50 per cent extension an ordinary piece of rubber tubing gives a good result. The graph extension (x) plotted against the tension (F) is a straight line of which the slope is k, in this case $40 \div \frac{5}{12}$ or 96 poundals per foot.

true of a spring balance. A 2-lb. weight which produced an extension of 1 inch at the bottom of the mountain would produce an extension of $0 \cdot 96875$ $(= 31 \div 32)$ inch at the top. If the scale were marked at the bottom, a standard 2-lb. weight would register $1\frac{15}{16}$ lb. at the top. So a spring balance like a pendulum clock is only reliable at the place where it was made, and the two devices provide independent methods for finding how g varies in different places.

In certain circumstances, as we all know, a spring balance can be made to behave like a pendulum, as when a sudden jerk makes the load bob up and down. The fact that it does this illustrates in a new way the fruitfulness of measuring force by the acceleration imparted to a mass. If a mass of m hangs at rest on a spring (Fig. 187) stretched *downward* through a distance x beyond its natural length, Hooke's law tells us that its *downward* pull (mg) is balanced by the *upward* tension of the spring kx. If it is pulled through a further distance y and held, so that the total extension is now $(x + y)$, the total force exerted by hand and weight must be balanced by an upward

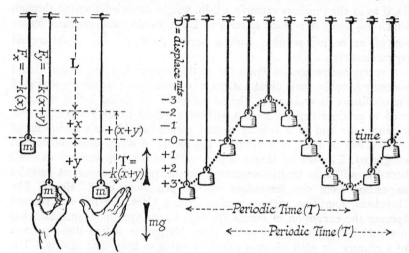

FIG. 187.—PERIODIC MOTION OF A WEIGHT AT THE END OF A SPRING

The time graph is shown as it would be given by snaps at successive intervals of equivalent length. The equation can be built up from the mechanical model of Figs. 182 and 195, which show that it has the general form (in circular measure):

$$y_t = r \sin (2\pi t \div T)$$

The constant r is the "amplitude" of the excursion, i.e. y, and the periodic time T is given in the text as $2\pi \sqrt{x} \div g$. Hence the equation of the time trace is

$$D = y \sin \left(\sqrt{\frac{g}{x}}\right) t$$

The initial extension y does not affect the period. It only affects the excursion.

tension of $k(x + y)$. When the hand is released, this upward pull is only offset by its own weight ($mg = kx$) pulling it downwards. The latter is not sufficient to neutralize it. The difference between them is $k(x + y) - kx = ky$. Hence there is still an *upward* tension numerically equal to ky, and the load begins to move upwards with an acceleration $-a$. The force required to impart this acceleration to a mass m is $-ma$, since the direction of motion (upward) is opposite to the direction (downward) along which y is measured. Hence

$$- ma = ky$$

$$\therefore \quad a = -\frac{k}{m} y$$

The acceleration is therefore in fixed proportion to the displacement y from the resting position of the weight, and of opposite sign to this displacement. In other words, the acceleration is always towards the resting position. Hence (p. 282) the motion is to and fro, and its period is

$$2\pi\sqrt{m \div k}$$

Since $k = mg \div x$, this is the same as

$$2\pi\sqrt{x \div g}$$

So, if as in the previous example a 2-lb. weight extended a spring through 1 inch ($\frac{1}{12}$ foot) at a place where $g = 32$, it would oscillate when jerked out of its resting position with a period $2\pi\sqrt{\frac{1}{12} \div 32} = 0\cdot32$ second (approximately).

A spring escapement of which the teeth engage a hanging weight would naturally have the same disadvantages as a pendulum, because the period of the oscillation depends on g. The advantage of the spring is that it can be used to produce periodic motion without a weight hanging vertically. For instance, the end of a spirally wound spring like Hooke's hairspring of watches can be fixed to a flywheel, the inertia of which does not depend on gravity. The law of Hooke applies with remarkable accuracy to small lateral as well as to lengthwise strains. So this type of escapement provides an escape from the limitations of the pendulum clock. Hooke, like Huyghens, hoped to make a perfect marine clock. He did not succeed because the expansion of metals (p. 581) by changes in temperature was not sufficiently understood at the time. Navigation waited three-quarters of a century for what Newton called "a watch to keep time exactly." The social importance of the issue is shown by the Act of 1714, when the British Government offered a reward of £20,000 for any method to enable a ship to get its longitude with an error not exceeding 30 miles at the end of a voyage to the West Indies. Twenty years after the *Board of Longitude* was appointed to act as umpire, Newton's words were still true: "by reason of the Motion of a Ship, the Variation of Heat and Cold, Wet and Dry, and the Difference of Gravity in different Latitudes, such a Watch hath not yet been made."

In 1736 a Yorkshire carpenter made a clock with a grid of brass and steel bars (see Fig. 292, p.580) to compensate for variations in the tension of the balance springs at different temperatures. Harrison's first clock was tested in May of that year on a six weeks' voyage to Lisbon and back, making the outward journey on the *Centurion*, later Anson's flagship. The official certificate reproduced by Commander Gould in a centenary article discloses that Harrison located the Lizard correctly when the official navigator, Roger Willes, believed that the ship had reached Start Point "one degree and twenty-six miles" east of it. The invention was not offered for the prize. With small subsidies from the Board of Longitude Harrison persevered for more than twenty years. His fourth model in a test voyage to Jamaica in 1761 led to an error of only one mile. The error was under ten miles in a second voyage to Barbados three years later. He was paid half the reward in

1765 and only received the other half after a long legal quibble settled by a private Act in 1773. An exact duplicate of the fourth was made for the Admiralty at a cost of £450, and used by Captain Cook. A few years later Earnshaw, the inventor of the modern type, produced chronometers at less than a tenth of this price.

UNIVERSAL GRAVITATION

Artillery warfare first began to present new problems for research in the age of the great navigations, when astronomy was still the queen of the sciences. In one way or another *inertia*, the fundamental principle of range-finding, impressed itself on speculations about planetary motion before Galileo actually applied it to physical measurements. If a pull is necessary to keep a stone revolving at the end of a cord in its circular path, and if a bullet keeps its own motion in a straight line when the marksman is riding, how does it happen that the planets move in closed orbits round the sun? In an earlier age the question would have been meaningless. In the generation of Galileo there was a special reason for asking it. The mariner's compass was one of the new wonders of the age of the great navigations. Here for the first time was something which pulled without cords and pulleys. Here for the first time was "action at a distance." At the Court of Elizabeth the theory of the mariner's compass had as much news value as the Peking Skull in post-war England. The queen herself and her naval commanders gathered to watch experiments by Gilbert, the queen's physician, who had likened the influence of the sun on the planets to the earth's magnetism.

Kepler had endorsed the analogy before Galileo showed how to measure pulling power by the motion it produces. The law of circular motion, which seems to have been discovered independently by Hooke and Newton as well as by Huyghens who first published it, made it possible to bring these speculations to earth. If a body moves with constant speed in a circle its acceleration along the radius is also constant and is equal to $(2\pi)^2 r \div T^2$. Kepler had shown that the ratio of the square of the time of revolution of a planet (or satellite) to the cube of the radius of its approximately circular path is the same for all planets (or for all satellites of the same planet), i.e.

$$r^3 = KT^2 \quad \text{or} \quad \frac{1}{T^2} = \frac{K}{r^3}$$

If we combine both rules,

$$a = \frac{(2\pi)^2 K}{r^2}$$

That is to say, the acceleration along the radius of a planet's orbit is inversely proportional to the square of its distance from the sun round which it moves.

Although this conclusion occurred to several people at the same time, Newton was apparently the first to test it. He argued that if the same pulling power draws a stone to the centre of the earth and keeps continually deflecting the moon from a straight path in its frictionless motion through empty space, the acceleration of the stone and the acceleration of the moon along the line joining it to earth must be in an inverse ratio to the square of their distances from the earth's centre. So he calculated the vertical acceleration of a body at the earth's surface from the moon's motion on the assumption that the same pull acts on both. The moon's distance r from the earth is 60 times the earth's radius. So the acceleration of a body towards the earth's centre, if moving round the earth in the moon's course, should be $\frac{1}{60^2}$ times the vertical acceleration of a body on the earth's surface. Since the latter is 32 feet per second per second, it should require an acceleration of $32 \div 60^2$ feet per second per second to keep the moon bent in a circular course. A simple calculation is sufficient to show that this is correct. The mean distance (r) of the moon from the earth is approximately 240,000 miles or (240,000 × 5,280) feet. The time (T) of a complete revolution is approximately $27\frac{1}{3}$ days or ($27\frac{1}{3}$ × 24 × 60 × 60) seconds. According to the principle of inertia, the acceleration required to keep the moon in its course is

$$\frac{4\pi^2}{T^2} \cdot r = \frac{4\pi^2 \times 240,000 \times 5,280}{27\frac{1}{3}^2 \times 24^2 \times 60^2 \times 60^2} = 32 \div 60^2 \text{ (approximately)}$$

The result obtained agrees with the assumptions that the rules which describe the regular motion of the clock wheels can also be used to calculate the motion of the heavenly bodies. When Newton first thought of making this calculation at the age of 23, the estimated distance of the moon was not very accurate, and the value he obtained was only seven-eighths of what he expected. Recognizing that reasoning by impeccable logic from self-evident principles is no substitute for solid fact in science, he locked away his calculations for over ten years. Meanwhile much discussion about the meaning of Kepler's laws had taken place among men of science. Hooke had arrived at the same conclusion as Newton, but was unable to solve the mathematical difficulties which arise when the orbit is elliptical, and the acceleration directed to the focus. A prize was offered for the solution of the problem by Sir Christopher Wren. Under pressure of his friends, Newton repeated his calculations with a new and more accurate estimate of the moon's distance based on the Cayenne expedition. The result was now satisfactory. So he was able to show that if the principle of inertia is true, a body can only move in an ellipse if the acceleration directed to its focus is inversely proportional to the square of the distance. He also showed that a body which moves in an ellipse with an acceleration directed to the focus must describe equal areas in equal times.

Thus Kepler's three laws, which contradict our first impressions of the way in which the celestial objects appear to move, were brought into harmony with the experience of motion in everyday life. As with Hipparchus, so with Newton, experience of nature demanded new rules of reasoning. To solve all the problems which arose, Newton was compelled to improvise a new mathematical technique, the differential calculus. Contemporary idealist philosophers, notably Berkeley, poured the utmost contempt upon the new logical instrument. Today stubborn fact has triumphed over Berkeley's logic. The hostility of the metaphysicians has been long forgotten by a world which prefers the comforts of science to the consolations of philosophy; and the belief that the rules of theory are exempt from the test of practice has been transferred from real science to political economy.

Up to this point, Newton's contribution did little more than bring together the conclusions of his own contemporaries with more mathematical ingenuity than they had shown, and it is a falsification of history to look on Newton's theory as the production of isolated genius. His genius worked on problems which were set by the social circumstances of his time. In Galileo's treatment of the path of the cannon ball and in Huyghens' treatise on the clock the problem of motion in curved tracks had emerged from imperative social needs of the time. Again and again Newton's speculations turn to one or the other. In the elementary treatment of the mail bag given on p. 265 and the analogous problem of a cannon ball (Figs. 171 and 172) fired in a horizontal direction, we assume that the height and range of projection are relatively small. We take the earth as approximately flat for our purpose and the acceleration of gravity as approximately constant, and directed towards the earth's surface. In an age of progress in artillery warfare it was natural to speculate further about what would happen if a projectile were fired at a great height with an enormous velocity. We then have to reckon with a variable acceleration directed to the earth's centre instead of an approximately constant g directed to an approximately flat surface. In the following passage Newton pictures the planets shot off from the sun at some time remotely past:

That by means of centripetal forces the planets may be retained in certain orbits we may easily understand, if we consider the motions of projectiles. . . . The greater the velocity by which it is projected the farther it goes before it falls to the earth. We may thus suppose the velocity to be so increased that it would describe an arc of 1, 2, 5, 10, 100, 1,000 miles before it arrived at the earth, till at last exceeding the limits of the earth, it should pass quite by without touching it. . . . If we now imagine bodies to be projected in the directions of lines parallel to the horizon at greater heights . . . those bodies, according to their different velocity and the different force of gravity in different heights, will describe arcs either concentric with the earth or variously eccentric and go on revolving through the heavens in those trajectories; just as the planets do in their orbs (see Fig. 188).

Newton's special contribution was the next step. He had satisfied himself that the earth's attraction on bodies at its surface extends as far away as the moon. What was the nature of this pull which Kepler had likened to the action of a magnet? The sun pulled on the planets which are smaller than it is; the earth pulled the moon which is smaller than itself; and the earth's pull or terrestrial gravity is proportional to the mass on which it acts. So the pulling power of the sun on the planets might be connected with the fact that their masses are different. If so, it seems that every piece of matter exerts on every other piece of matter a pull directed to its centre and proportional to its mass. The *mutual* attraction between any two pieces of matter of mass m and M separated by a distance r would therefore be proportional to

$$m \times M \div r^4$$

Putting this in the form of an equation, in which G is a universal constant

$$F = G \cdot \frac{Mm}{r^2}$$

If this is true, it is possible to calculate both the absolute mass of the earth itself, and the relative masses of the earth and other heavenly bodies. The first can be done in a variety of ways, one of which is shown diagrammatically in Fig. 189. How to find the ratio of the mass of the earth to that of another heavenly body may be illustrated by comparing its mass with that of the sun.

In Newton's calculation of the falling stone and the moon, E is the earth's mass and the force on unit mass of either is $GE \div r^2$.

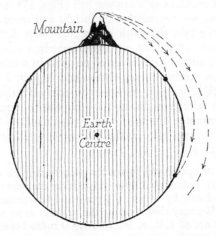

FIG. 188.—NEWTON'S PARABLE OF PROJECTILES FIRED WITH INCREASINGLY HIGH VELOCITY FROM THE TOP OF A VERY HIGH PEAK

Note.—The higher the initial velocity (see Figs. 171 and 172) the smaller the deflection towards the earth's centre in a given distance traversed. By increasing the velocity of projection the motion therefore approaches a closed *elliptical* orbit, such as a rocket projected beyond the stratosphere would pursue in empty space. Air resistance is neglected.

Since $F = ma$, the acceleration g_e of the stone at the earth's surface, and the earthward acceleration, g_m, of the moon, are in the ratio $r_m^2 : r_e^2$, and the earth's mass cancels out. The problem is different when we compare the size of the earth's orbit about the sun with the size of the moon's orbit about the earth. We then have two different masses: S, the sun's pulling on the earth at a distance R; and E, the earth's pulling on the moon's M at a distance r. The attraction of the earth to the sun is

$$G \cdot SE \div R^2$$

The attraction of the moon to the earth is

$$G \cdot EM \div r^2$$

So the ratio of the two attractions (earth to sun) : (moon to earth) is

$$Sr^2 \div MR^2$$

If A is the acceleration of the earth sunward along the radius of its orbit,

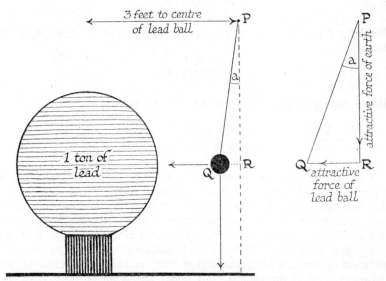

FIG. 189.—WEIGHING THE EARTH

The principle of weighing the earth by the deflection of the plumb line towards the mountain is the same as that used in the direct determination of the mass of the earth by Cavendish and later workers who have used a sort of microscope to measure the deflection of a suspended pellet Q towards a large mass. Gravity acts towards the centre of a spherical mass. If a pellet is deflected through *a* from the vertical when placed near a large mass, like a ton weight of lead, the ratio of the attractive forces of the lead and the earth itself is tan *a* (see legend to Fig. 167). According to Newton's hypothesis of universal gravitation, the attractive power of a body is directly proportional to its mass and inversely proportional to the square of the distance between its centre of mass and the body attracted by it. Hence if *m* is the mass of a body whose centre is *r* feet from the pellet, and M is the mass of the earth whose radius is R,

$$\tan a = \frac{mR^2}{Mr^2}$$

Suppose in such an experiment (crudely diagrammatized in this figure) $a = 0\cdot00000045°$ (i.e. tan $a = 8 \times 10^{-9}$) when $m = 1$ ton and $r = 1$ yard or $\frac{1}{1760}$ miles.

$$8 \times 10^{-9} = \frac{1 \times (4,000)^2}{M \times (1 \div 1,760)^2} = \frac{4,000^2 \times 1,760^2}{M}$$

$$M = \frac{16 \times 176^2 \times 10^6}{8 \times 10^{-9}}$$

$$= 6\cdot5 \times 10^{21} \text{ tons approximately.}$$

the force pulling the earth to the sun is EA. And if Y is the time of a complete revolution of the earth round the sun,

$$EA = E \cdot \frac{4\pi^2}{Y^2} \cdot R$$

$$\therefore \frac{GSE}{R^2} = E \, \frac{4\pi^2}{Y^2} \cdot R$$

$$\therefore S = \frac{4\pi^2}{GY^2} \cdot R^3$$

Similarly if L is the time of a complete revolution of the moon round the earth

$$E = \frac{4\pi^2}{GL^2} \cdot r^3$$

Hence the ratio of the sun's mass to the earth's mass or

$$\frac{S}{E} = \frac{R^3 L^2}{r^3 Y^2} = \frac{(93,000,000)^3 \times (27\frac{1}{3})^2}{(240,000)^3 \times (365)^2} = 340,000 \text{ (approximately).}$$

The best determinations give 333,434. The large mass of the sun, compared with that of any of the planets, is the reason for the fact that they all appear to describe orbits around the sun as focus. However, their orbits do not absolutely correspond to Kepler's laws, because they exert attractions on one another. The great triumph of Newton's theory of universal gravitation was the fact that such irregularities can be calculated, when the masses have been estimated in some such way as the example given illustrates. Just as the planets exert minor effects on the motion of their neighbours, the sun, which is too far from the moon to affect the more obvious characteristics of its motion, produces various irregularities which had been quite unintelligible. From the ratio of the mass of the moon and the sun, and their distances from the earth, Newton was able to account for the variations of the tides with the phases of the moon (Fig. 190), for the inclination of the moon's orbit and the regression of its nodes.

It is natural and proper for you to ask at this point whether Newton's theory provides any guidance for social practice. One, directly related to the focal problem of technology in the social context of Newton's time, is the increase in the period of a pendulum or the apparent decrease of a mass weighed in a spring balance when we ascend a mountain. If the law of inverse squares is right the value of the earth's pulling power on unit mass (i.e. *g*) must increase as we get nearer the earth's centre and decrease as we get farther away from it by a calculable amount. Taking the earth's radius as 4,000 miles at the surface, the ratio of *g* at the surface to *g* one mile above it at the top of the mountain should be $(4001)^2 : (4000)^2$, and if *g* were 32 at the bottom it would be $31 \cdot 984$ at the top. Hence at the bottom the period of a pendulum would be $2\pi\sqrt{L \div 32}$ and at the top $2\pi\sqrt{L \div 31 \cdot 984}$, and the periods at the bottom and top would be in the ratio $\sqrt{31 \cdot 984} \div \sqrt{32}$. The clock would lose time in this ratio per second.*

* Huyghens rightly assumed that differences of *sea-level* measurements of *g* in different latitudes are not due to irregularities of this kind. The perfect sphericity of the earth was an accepted dogma, sufficiently justified by later measurements in low latitudes.

The application of Newton's theory was first made by Bouguer in one of the great scientific explorations of the eighteenth century. Bouguer compared the lengths of the seconds pendulum at sea-level and at the top of Pinchincha, a high mountain above Quito in Ecuador. The necessary reduction for the ascent calculated by the inverse square law was $\frac{1}{1118}$, and

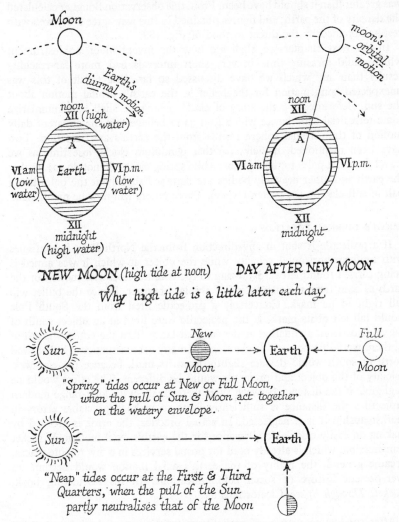

Moon

noon
XII (high water)

VI a.m. (low water)   Earth   VI p.m. (low water)

XII midnight (high water)

Earth's diurnal motion

A

moon's orbital motion

noon
XII

VI a.m.   A   VI p.m.

XII midnight

NEW MOON *(high tide at noon)*   DAY AFTER NEW MOON

Why high tide is a little later each day

Sun   New ⊖ Moon   →   Earth   ←   Full ◯ Moon

"Spring" tides occur at New or Full Moon,
when the pull of Sun & Moon act together
on the watery envelope.

Sun   — — — — — — — — →   Earth

"Neap" tides occur at the First & Third
Quarters, when the pull of the Sun
partly neutralises that of the Moon

FIG. 190.—THE TIDES

this proved to be larger than the observed value $\frac{1}{1331}$. What seemed to be a disappointing result led to a new vindication of the Newtonian theory. Bouguer argued that a *large mass* such as a mountain must exert an appreciable sideways attraction. This was triumphantly confirmed by a simple device. He selected two stations on the same parallel of latitude, one close to

Chimborazo, a mountain 20,000 feet high, and one some distance due west-ward, away from the influence. The inclination of a telescope to the plumbline, i.e. the zenith distance, should have been the same at meridian transit since the latitudes were identical. Owing to the attraction exerted by the mountain on the weight of the plumbline the zenith distance of the star at the near station was greater than it should have been. From this observation Bouguer calculated the density of the earth, and figures obtained in this way agree fairly well with results obtained by the direct method of Fig. 189.

In the next chapter we shall see how the invention of an instrument which could measure time in very short intervals had more far-reaching results than any which we have discussed so far. One result of this was unexpected confirmation for the belief in the earth's orbital motion about the sun. Before leaving the story of clock-making we shall now summarize some terrestrial experiences which lead us to believe that the apparent daily motion of the celestial sphere results from the earth's axial rotation. Two have been mentioned, namely: (a) that pendulum clocks lose time as we travel from the poles to the equator, while spring clocks do not do so; (b) that the earth and other heavenly bodies are flattened slightly at the poles like a ball of soft clay on the potter's wheel. Three others will now be mentioned.

EARTH'S DIURNAL ROTATION

If a projectile is shot in any direction from the North Pole, it continues with uniform horizontal velocity while the object at which it was aimed is being carried round leftwards, owing to the counter-clockwise motion of the earth as seen from the standpoint of a polar observer. Hence the bullet will fall right of its mark. Conversely a projectile fired from the South Pole would fall left of its mark. If the projectile were fired at an object south of the equator from a situation at the same distance from the equator north of it, there would be no such displacement. In any other situation a bullet fired north or south would deviate slightly from its mark because the east-west velocity of the object and projectile would be different. The effect would be negligible if the distance between them were small. With long-range modern projectiles the distance is sufficiently large to make appreciable errors in marksmanship if it is neglected. In actual practice, the error is avoided by making an easily calculable allowance for the earth's axial motion. If rocket transmission, which is already used for postal services in a few remote places, became general, the reality of the earth's axial motion would become an ever-present feature of social communications. In his fascinating book, *Rockets Through Space*, Cleator tells us:

After conducting a series of preliminary experiments, Schmiedl succeeded in establishing, in 1931, an officially recognized rocket postal service. He operated his service between the small towns of Schockel and Radegund, near Graz, Austria. Although the distance covered was only about two miles, the mountainous nature of the district enabled him to transmit letters from one town to the other in as many minutes as the ordinary postman required hours. The success of the Schmiedl service inspired Gerhard Zucker to perform a like experiment in Germany. And in 1933 he successfully transported letters by rocket over the Harz mountains. A year later, as is well known, he brought one of his rockets to England—where his experiments were a fiasco. . . . Experimenters visualize the time when mail rockets will carry their cargo between London and New York, a distance which even the liquid fuels of today will enable the vessel to cover in less than an hour.

Another consideration is not so obvious. If a pendulum bob is suspended from a very long cord (e.g. 100 feet), free to rotate in any direction and set in motion, it should continue to swing in the same direction. If the direction of

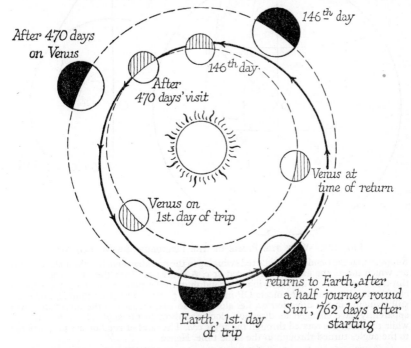

FIG. 191.—WILL THEORIES OF GRAVITATION BECOME NECESSARY FOR TRAVEL?
The figure shows Dr. Walter Hohmann's project for a space trip by rocket transmission out of the first 50 miles of the earth's atmosphere. Beyond this distance air resistance becomes negligible and the space ship behaves like a planet moving in a curved path. The trip would take 762 days, including a stay on Venus of 470 days, or more than two Venus (225-day) years. The present cost would be about £20,000,000. Considering that we have not yet liquidated the social inconveniences resulting from the African slave trade which followed the discovery of America, this is not necessarily a discouraging fact.

the swing is marked by a line on the ground, the pendulum swing will appear to twist slowly around it in a clockwise direction (in the northern hemisphere). No force has been applied to the pendulum to change its direction, and we ought therefore to say that the line has twisted in an anti-clockwise direction beneath the pendulum. You will have no difficulty in seeing that this is a necessary consequence of the earth's axial rotation if you suppose the pendulum to be suspended at the North Pole, in which case the line will perform a complete anti-clockwise rotation in 24 hours. At the equator the line will

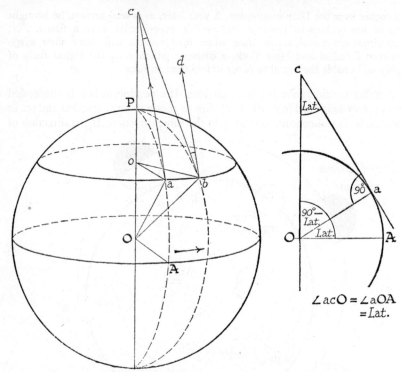

FIG. 192.—WHY THE PLANE OF THE PENDULUM SWING ROTATES

Suppose that the pendulum is started swinging in the meridian at *a*, i.e. along the tangent *ac*, which meets the axis OP produced at *c*. A short time later the earth has rotated through a small angle *aob*, carrying the pendulum to the point *b* on the same parallel of latitude. The tangent *bc* meets OP in the same point *c*. The pendulum is, however, still swinging in the direction *ac*, i.e. along *bd*, so that relative to the meridian it will apparently have changed its direction clockwise through the angle *cbd* = *bca*. Meanwhile the earth has rotated through the angle *boa*. The rates of rotation are proportional to the angles turned through in the same time. Hence

$$\frac{\text{rate of rotation of pendulum}}{\text{rate of rotation of earth}} = \frac{\angle bca}{\angle boa} = \frac{\text{arc } ab}{ac} \div \frac{\text{arc } ab}{ao}$$

$$= \frac{ao}{ac} = \sin aco = \sin aOA = \sin \text{Lat.}$$

So the *time* of rotation of pendulum $= \dfrac{1}{\sin \text{Lat.}}$ days.

Thus in Foucault's experiment the pendulum swing rotated through 360° in 32 hours or $1\frac{1}{3}$ days. Since the latitude of Paris is 48° 50′, $\dfrac{1}{\sin \text{Lat.}} = \dfrac{1}{0 \cdot 75 \text{ (approx.)}} = 1\frac{1}{3}$.

not rotate. At the South Pole the line will rotate completely in a clockwise direction in 24 hours. At intermediate latitudes, the time of rotation of the line is $\dfrac{1}{\sin \text{Lat.}}$ days, as shown in Fig. 192. A large pendulum suspended from a high roof above a dial was exhibited at the Paris Exhibition by Foucault to show this phenomenon to the public. Foucault's pendulum is now shown in one of the great museums of the U.S.S.R.

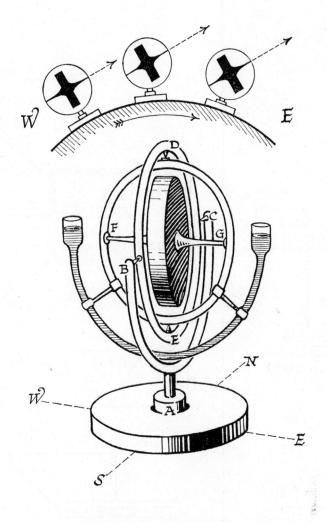

FIG. 193.—THE GYROCOMPASS

The framework of a gyrostat turns freely at A, and round the axes BC and DE, so that the axle FG can point in any direction in space. If no force is applied to the framework, the axle FG will continue to point in the direction in which it was set when the flywheel was started. If, however, a turning force is applied to the framework, the axle turns, not in the plane of the force, but in a plane at right angles to it and continues to do so, until the plane of rotation coincides with the plane of the turning force. This is why the gyrocompass turns to the north. If, for example, the axle FG is at first pointing eastwards, it will tip upwards as the earth rotates. If the framework is provided with some kind of ballast (like the mercury tube in the figure) this will now exert a turning force on the framework. The axle will therefore turn at right angles to the plane of the force, until it points to the north. The axle will then return to the horizontal, and the turning force will cease to act.

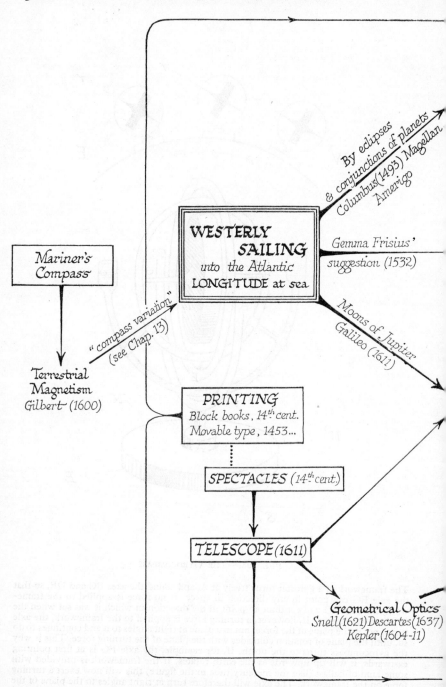

By eclipses
& conjunctions of planets
Columbus (1493) Magellan
Amerigo

WESTERLY SAILING *unto the Atlantic* **LONGITUDE** *at sea*

Gemma Frisius' *suggestion (1532)*

Mariner's Compass

Moons of Jupiter Galileo (1611)

" *compass variation* " *(see Chap. 13)*

Terrestrial Magnetism Gilbert (1600)

PRINTING *Block books, 14th cent.* *Movable type, 1453...*

SPECTACLES (14th cent.)

TELESCOPE (1611)

Geometrical Optics *Snell (1621) Descartes (1637) Kepler (1604-11)*

TIME

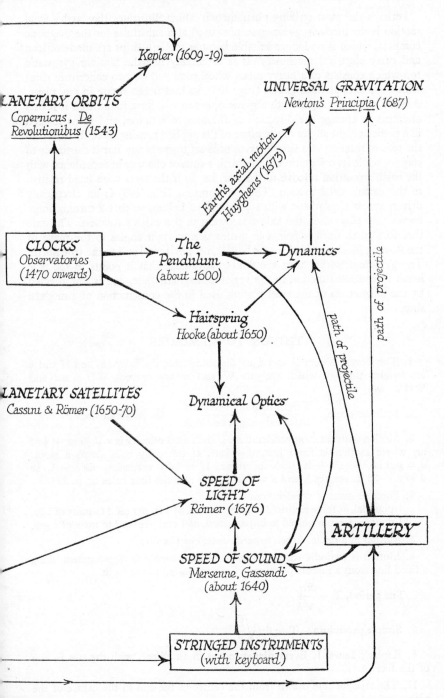

Kepler (1609-19)

UNIVERSAL GRAVITATION
Newton's *Principia* (1687)

PLANETARY ORBITS
Copernicus, *De Revolutionibus* (1543)

Earth's axial motion
Huyghens (1673)

CLOCKS
Observatories
(1470 onwards)

The Pendulum
(about 1600)

Dynamics

Hairspring
Hooke (about 1650)

PLANETARY SATELLITES
Cassini & Römer (1650-70)

Dynamical Optics

SPEED OF LIGHT
Römer (1676)

path of projectile

path of projectile

ARTILLERY

SPEED OF SOUND
Mersenne, Gassendi
(about 1640)

STRINGED INSTRUMENTS
(with keyboard)

CHART II

Perhaps the most striking phenomenon which illustrates the earth's axial motion is the modern *gyrocompass* now used as a substitute for the magnetic compass, which is no longer suitable because modern ships are made of iron and carry electrical machinery. It is essentially like the familiar gyrostatic top which consists of a heavy metal wheel mounted on two concentric rings with their axes at right angles (Fig. 193), so that it can rotate in any plane. Anyone who has played with a gyroscopic top will have found that it resists attempts to change the direction of the axis of rotation, and turns instead in a plane at right angles to the plane of the applied turning force. If therefore the axis of rotation of a simple gyrostat is set towards any star it continues to stay so, while its orientation to the earth's surface changes in accordance with the earth's position relative to the star, i.e. as if the stars were fixed relative to the earth's axial motion. The gyrocompass (Fig. 193) is an electrically driven gyrostat, provided with some form of ballast, so that a turning force comes into play when the axle tips owing to the earth's rotation. The axle therefore turns until it points in a direction at right angles to the plane of the turning force provided by the ballast, i.e. horizontal and to the true north. The gyrocompass has thus the double advantage that it points to the true north in contradistinction to the variable magnetic pole, and is not affected by the magnetism of the steel plating used in the construction of a modern ship.

THINGS TO MEMORIZE

1. The Lever. Where D and d are distances from the fulcrum, and H and h are heights through which weights W and w are moved, $WD = wd$ and $WH = wh$.

2. Inclined plane. $\dfrac{\text{Weight hanging vertically}}{\text{Balanced weight on slope}} = \sin$ (angle of slope).

3. Motion with constant acceleration. If the initial velocity is u, $d = ut + \frac{1}{2}at^2$ or, where motion is from rest, $d = \frac{1}{2}at^2$. If the body rolls down a slope, $a = g \sin b$, where b is angle of slope. If it falls vertically, $\sin b = 1$, so $a = g = 32$ ft. per sec.^{2}, and $d = 16t^2$ ft. See also the four rules on p. 258.

4. Force = mass × acceleration.
   1 poundal = force required to impart accel. of 1 ft. per sec.^{2} to mass of 1 lb.
   1 dyne = force required to impart accel. of 1 cm. per sec.^{2} to mass of 1 gm.

5. Motion in a circle. Accel. towards centre = $(2\pi n)^2 r$.

6. Motion is periodic when: Accel = $- kx$, where x is displacement along a fixed line from a middle position. Both measured to the right.

   The period, $T = \dfrac{2\pi}{\sqrt{k}}$

7. Simple pendulum. $T = 2\pi \sqrt{\dfrac{L}{g}}$

8. Kepler's Laws. I. Every planet moves in an ellipse, with the sun in one of the foci.

   II. The straight line drawn from the centre of the sun to the centre of the planet sweeps out equal areas in equal times.

III. The squares of the periodic times of the several planets are proportional to the cubes of their mean distances from the sun, i.e. $r^3 = KT^2$. Hence accel. along the radius of the orbit $= \dfrac{(2\pi)^2 K}{r^2}$

9. Law of gravitation. $F = G \cdot \dfrac{Mm}{r^2}$, where G is a universal constant.

EXAMPLES ON CHAPTER V
Take g as 32 ft. per sec.², unless another value is given

1. Find the velocity at which a man must swim across a river 140 yards wide, if the current velocity is 2 miles an hour, and if he does not wish to be carried farther down the river than 40 yards.

2. A marksman in an express train moving at 60 miles an hour sees a stationary object 100 yards away on a line at right angles to his line of motion. How far to one side of the object must he aim if he wants to hit it, the bullet moving with a velocity of 440 ft. per sec.?

3. What is the resultant velocity of a ship heading in a northerly direction at 5 miles per hour, but drifting westward with the tide at 3 miles per hour?

4. A trawler is steaming due north with a velocity of 15 miles an hour and a north-east wind is blowing with a velocity of 10 miles an hour. Show by a diagram the direction of the smoke track.

5. At a certain time one ship is 10 miles west of another. If the first sails north-east at 20 miles an hour, and the second north-west at 16 miles an hour, how near do they approach?

6. A stick 100 cm. long weighs 92 gm., and balances on a knife-edge at 50·2 cm. along it. Where will the stick balance if a 50 gm. weight is slung on it by a piece of thread at the 10 cm. mark?

7. At what distances from the fulcrum can weights of 20, 40, 80, and 150 lb. balance a 60-lb. weight attached 1 foot 8 inches from it on the opposite side?

8. What is the force exerted by a spring balance attached by a piece of thread to a metre stick, weighing 92 gm., at 90 cm., when the stick is resting on a wedge at 10 cm. and carries a 50 gm. weight at 60 cm.?

9. Making no allowance for the weight of a 4-ft. crowbar, what force (poundals) must the arm apply to one end of it to lift a weight of 1 cwt. (112 lb.) when a stone is placed under the crowbar 6 inches away from the end on which the load rests? If the load is 100 kilos give the force in dynes.

10. A pole of 5 yards and of negligible weight has weights of 7, 5, 3 and 1 cwt., at 1, 2, 3 and 4 yards respectively from the end where it is hinged. What pulling power in hundredweights must be exerted upwards at the free end to sustain the weights? What is the upward pull exerted by the hinge?

11. If a 4-ft. crowbar weighing 20 lb. is suspended by a cord 2½ feet from one end, find what weight placed 1 foot from one end will balance a 5-lb. weight at 9 inches from the other, taking into consideration the weight of the crowbar itself.

12. A pole, whose weight can be neglected, rests on the shoulders of two men. If the maximum weight one man can carry is 120 lb. and the maximum weight the other man can carry is 90 lb., how heavy a man can they carry between them, and where must he balance on the pole from the stronger man?

13. A weight of 50 lb. rests on a smooth surface. What weight suspended vertically will balance it, if the surface is tilted through 10°, 30°, 45°, 60°, and 90°?

14. The ends of a cord are stretched over two pulleys with weights of 3 and 4 lb. respectively. If a weight of 5 lb. is attached to the cord between the pulleys what will be the angle at the point of suspension?

15. Making no allowance for friction, tabulate the acceleration of a billiard ball down a smooth slope tilted successively from 0° to 90° in intervals of 10°.

16. What are the distances traversed in 1 second, and the velocities acquired in that time, by smooth balls rolling down smooth slopes of inclinations 30°, 45°, 60°?

17. Making no allowance for friction, find (with scale diagram or tables of sines):

(*a*) How long it will take a billiard ball to traverse 1 yard along a slippery slope at 60° to the ground.

(*b*) How far the ball will move along a slope tilted at 15° in 5 seconds.

(*c*) The speed of a ball which has traversed 2 feet on a slope tilted at 10° upwards.

(*d*) The speed of a ball after moving for 3 seconds on an inclined surface at 5° to the ground.

In each case the ball starts from rest.

18. A billiard ball starting from rest on an inclined glass surface describes 40 feet in the third second. What is the inclination of the plane?

19. If *g* is 32 ft. per sec. per sec. at a certain place, what is the value of *g* in cm. per sec. per sec.? If the metrical unit of force called the *dyne* is exerted on 1 gram to produce an acceleration of 1 cm. per sec. per sec., how many dynes correspond to (*a*) one poundal, (*b*) one pound weight suspended vertically? (1 kilogram = 2·2 lb.)

20. What is the mass in pounds of a body, if an 8-lb. weight, hanging vertically from a pulley, acts on it for 3 seconds, raising it with a final velocity of 6 ft. per sec.?

21. What force in tons weight dragging horizontally from a train of 200 tons mass going at 30 miles per hour will stop it (*a*) in one minute, (*b*) at a distance of 400 yards?

22. What is the stretching force in the cable if a lift weighing one ton descends with an acceleration of 16 ft. per sec.²? With what force does a mass of 8 lb., lying on the bottom of the lift, press on the latter?

23. Draw the speed time diagram of the motion of a train starting from rest, having uniform acceleration for the first 15 seconds of its run, running ½ minute at a constant speed, and then coming to rest in 7½ seconds with uniform retardation. What is its maximum speed if the distance traversed is 2,420 feet?

24. If a train is brought to rest in 1⅔ minutes, with uniform retardation, when it is moving at ½ mile per minute, how far has it travelled in this time and what is the retardation in feet per sec. per sec.?

25. If the initial velocity of a body moving in a straight line is v_0 and its velocity after moving *d* feet in *t* seconds with a constant acceleration *a* is v_t, show that the distance moved can be determined from the formulae:

(i) $d = v_0 t + \frac{1}{2}at^2$

(ii) $d = (v_t^2 - v_0^2) \div 2a$

(iii) and when the initial velocity is zero $v_t = \sqrt{2ad}$

26. How high will a ball rise, and how long will it take to reach the highest point, if it is thrown vertically upwards with a velocity of 2,760 yards per minute?

27. A bullet moving in a straight line has a velocity of 5 yards per second, and an acceleration of 10 feet per second per second. How long will it be before the velocity is tripled and how far will the bullet travel in this time?

28. A ball is thrown vertically upwards and rises to a height of 10 yards. Find the velocity the ball must have been given and the time it takes to reach this height.

29. How far must a ball fall from rest to gain a velocity of 20 feet per second? How much farther must it fall so that the velocity is increased to 30 feet per second?

30. At what speed does a train moving with uniform acceleration run at the end of 4 minutes from starting up, if it traverses exactly one mile in the interval? Find also its acceleration in feet per sec. per sec.

31. A cannon ball is fired horizontally from a 49-foot tower, with a muzzle velocity of 2,000 feet per second. Neglecting friction, calculate the distance from the tower at which the cannon ball will hit the ground.

32. A bomb is dropped on a gasometer by an aeroplane flying horizontally 1,000 feet above it. If the aeroplane is travelling at 60 miles per hour, what is the angle between the vertical and the line joining the bomb and gasometer when the bomb is released?

33. If the muzzle velocity of a cannon ball is 420 feet per second and the range is 1,800 yards, find the angle at which the cannon is tilted.

34. A cannon ball is projected at an angle of 30°, with a velocity of 192 feet per second. When will it reach a height of 80 feet above the ground, and how far from the cannon will it be at that instant?

35. (*a*) If a cyclist takes a corner at 10 miles per hour in a curve of 5 yards radius, what is his acceleration towards the centre of curvature? (*b*) Find the central acceleration of a point on the equator in feet per sec. per sec. Take the earth's equatorial radius as 3,962 miles and the sidereal day as 23 hours 56 minutes 4 seconds.

36. A motor cyclist goes round a circular racecourse at 120 miles per hour. Find how far from the vertical he must lean inwards to keep his balance (*a*) if the track is 1 mile long, (*b*) if it is 880 yards long (see Fig. 180).

37. A locomotive goes round a curve, whose radius of curvature is $\frac{1}{5}$ of a mile, at 30 miles per hour. If the rails are 4 feet apart horizontally, how much higher must the outer rail be, so that the engine wheels exert no pressure outwards on it?

38. By counting the beats over two minutes, test the formula for the period (p. 287) of a pendulum by attaching a button to a piece of cotton 1 foot, 2 feet, 3 feet, 4 feet long, suspended by a loop from a drawing pin.

39. What are the lengths of simple pendulums which make complete beats (forwards and backwards) in (*a*) $1\frac{1}{2}$ seconds and (*b*) in $2\frac{1}{4}$ seconds? (Take *g* as 32 feet per sec. per sec.)

40. What is the acceleration due to gravity at a place where a simple pendulum, of length 37·8 inches, makes 183 beats (half periods) in 3 minutes?

41. Show that a pendulum, 450 feet long, makes a complete beat in about $23\frac{4}{7}$ seconds.

42. What is the length of a simple pendulum, if on shortening it by 1 inch the period is diminished by $\frac{1}{80}$ of its value?

43. A seconds pendulum at a place where *g* is 981·4 cm. per sec.² is taken to a place where *g* is 981·0 cm. per sec.². Find how much it gains or loses in a day.

44. A simple pendulum, which should beat seconds (i.e. one whose half period is one second) loses 20 minutes in a week. How much per cent must its length be shortened to make it keep time?

45. A pound weight is attached to the end of a piece of string 1 yard long. What stretching force would be registered by a spring balance, when the weight is swung in a horizontal circle so that it takes $\frac{2}{3}$ second to make one complete circle?

46. A wire of 497 cm. is stretched $0 \cdot 35$ cm. by a weight of $6\frac{1}{4}$ kg. How much would it be stretched by $\frac{1}{2}$ cwt. and by 1 lb. if Hooke's law applies over the whole range? (1 kg. $= 2 \cdot 2$ lb.)

47. If a weight of 1 lb. oscillating at the end of a spring executes a complete movement up and down in half a second, find the extension per lb.

48. If a weight of 250 grams executes a periodic motion with a complete period of $1\frac{1}{2}$ seconds at the end of a metal spring, what would be the period of oscillation of a 160-gram weight attached to the same spring?

49. If F_L is the sea-level centrifugal acceleration at latitude L due to the earth's motion and g_{90} is the acceleration of a body under gravity at the pole, show that the corresponding acceleration under gravity at latitude L on a spherical earth is

$$g_{90} - F_L \cdot \cos L$$

With a similar figure show that if R is the radius of the equator plane, the radius of the latitude circle L is R cos L. Hence, taking R $= 4,000$ miles, calculate the values of g at latitudes $50°$, $45°$, and $30°$ in ft. per sec. per sec. and cm. per sec. per sec.

50. At one place A the value of g is $983 \cdot 0$ cm. per sec. per sec. At a second place B it is $981 \cdot 0$ cm. per sec. per sec. One spring balance is calibrated at A and another at B. What will be the weight of a standard 10 lb. mass indicated on the scale of each balance at each place? (g at London $= 981 \cdot 17$).

51. If the force of terrestrial gravity varies inversely as the square of the distance from the earth's centre, what would be the difference between the value of g at sea-level and at the top of a peak 5 miles high? How would a spring clock and a pendulum clock which synchronize at sea-level behave in the two situations?

52. A pendulum clock with a seconds pendulum* is carried in a balloon, which is ascending with a constant acceleration, to a height of 900 feet in 1 minute. Show that the clock gains at the rate of roughly 28 seconds in an hour.

53. A seconds pendulum beats $60\frac{1}{2}$ times in 1 minute in a train, which is moving uniformly round a curve at 60 miles per hour. Show that the radius of the circular curve must be roughly 1,317 feet.

54. At the top of a mountain a seconds pendulum loses 10 seconds in a day. How high is the mountain, and how many seconds would the pendulum lose when only halfway up the mountain?

55. How high is a mountain if a clock, which gains 10 seconds a day, is taken up it and is found to lose 10 seconds a day? What is the difference in the accelerations due to gravity at the top and bottom of the mountain?

56. With the aid of Fig. 185, tabulate the radius of the latitude circle and the speed of rotation in miles per hour at Aberdeen $57°$ N., Edinburgh $56°$ N., London $51\frac{1}{2}°$ N., Falmouth $50°$ N., Paris $49°$ N., Philadelphia $40°$ N., New Orleans $30°$ N., and Cayenne $5°$ N., taking the equator radius as 4,000 miles.

* A seconds pendulum has a *half period* of one second.

57. Taking the value of g as $32 \cdot 26$ (ft./sec.^{2}) at the North Pole, use these measurements to calculate for each place at sea-level.

    (*a*) the value of g;
    (*b*) the length of the seconds pendulum in inches.

58. Use the same data to calculate the daily retardation of a pendulum clock

    (*a*) set at Aberdeen and sent to Falmouth;
    (*b*) set at Paris and sent to Cayenne;
    (*c*) set at Philadelphia and sent to New Orleans;
    (*d*) set at Edinburgh and sent to London.

59. Using the same data calculate how slow or fast a London pendulum clock would be if taken to the top of Mt. Everest ($5\frac{1}{4}$ miles high, Lat. 28° N.).

60. If a man standing at the North Pole fired a bullet with a range of 3 miles and a mean horizontal speed of 400 feet per second at an object 3 miles away, how far wide of the mark would it fall and on which side?

61. If a cyclist is riding at 14 miles an hour with a wind blowing at right angles to his path with a velocity of 10 miles an hour, show by a diagram or otherwise the direction of the wind relative to the cyclist.

62. A man is walking due west with a velocity of 5 miles an hour. If another man rides in a direction 30° west of north, what is his velocity if he always keeps due north of the first man?

63. A north wind is blowing at 10 miles an hour. If to a cyclist it appears to be an east wind of 10 miles an hour, find the direction and the rate at which he is riding?

CHAPTER VI

THE SAILOR'S WORLD VIEW

The Wave Metaphor of Modern Science

WE can only find our way about in space when we have learned to find our way about in time, and the accuracy with which we can ascertain where we are depends on the accuracy with which we determine the time when we happen to be there. Our own generation has witnessed a revolution which may prove to have more far-reaching results than the invention of the clock. A ship's captain is no longer dependent on a chronometer set by Greenwich time at the beginning of a voyage. Standard time is transmitted from ocean to ocean by wireless signals, and the very word *wave* has come to have a new meaning in the everyday life of mankind. Today the complete narrative of man's conquest of time and space would have to tell how it has become possible to put any single being in instantaneous communication with anyone else on the planet which we now inhabit. At some future date it may even record how human beings learned to find their way across interplanetary space. We must leave the way in which man has established the means of world communication till we come to the story of man's conquest of power.

Before we do so, we shall have to come to grips with one of the most difficult concepts of contemporary science. The invention of wireless transmission was made possible by the theory of wave motion, which developed as a by-product of Newtonian science. In man's earliest attempts to find his bearings in time and space the nature of light had already forced itself on his attention. The discovery of the telescope gave a new impetus to the study of optical phenomena. One result of this was Newton's discovery that white light is complex. Very soon after the invention of the telescope a Danish contemporary of Newton made the first telescopic maps of the moon's mountains. Römer also took up the study of Jupiter's satellites. Having determined their period of revolution when Jupiter and the earth are on the same side of the sun, he calculated their position when Jupiter is on the side opposite to the earth. An eclipse of one of Jupiter's moons occurred later than he expected. Being satisfied that this was not due to faulty instruments he concluded that light does not travel instantaneously. To put it less metaphorically, we do not see an event when it happens. A measurable interval of time elapses between a flash of light and the instant when we see it. This interval depends, like sending a message, on the distance between the sender and the receiver.

At first sight it seems a far cry from the moons of Jupiter to the everyday life of mankind in seventeenth-century Europe. In its own context Römer's work was not so remote from practical application as it would have been if it had been undertaken a century later, when clock technology had reached a higher level. The determination of longitude still remained a thorny problem. Judging from the prize they offered (p. 294), the method of lunar distances which Newton advocated with appropriate corrections for parallax and atmospheric refraction required laborious calculations which did not commend themselves to the Admiralty. Others among Newton's contemporaries proposed to discard astronomy and use a co-ordinate based on the dip of the magnetic needle (see Chapter XIII). Failing a reliable chronometer, which was not available till 1760, the astronomer could only retain his privileged position as doyen of nautical science by devising a method as simple as the observations of eclipses or occultations. The only serious objection to this method is that celestial signals known before Galileo's observations on the moons of Jupiter did not occur very often. The objection could be met if other more frequent signals could be added. *Whitaker's Almanack* shows that fifty-six appearances or disappearances of Jupiter's satellites could be seen at Greenwich after dark in 1936. There were only two visible eclipses and no planetary occultations in the same year.

Galileo himself seems (see p. 134) to have realized the practical importance of the discovery which brought him into conflict with the Inquisition. At the new Paris observatory where Römer worked with Picard, Richer, and others among the leading astronomers of the day, the Italian Cassini undertook the preparation of tables for calculating longitude by observations on the satellites of Jupiter, and his tables were used in the French Navy during the first half of the eighteenth century. In his book *Histoire de la Longitude de la Mer au XVIIIe siècle en France*, Marguet tells us:

After 1690 the *Connaissance des Temps* gave the time of eclipses of the first satellite, calculated according to the tables of Cassini, and forty years later, from 1730 onwards, there were added to the ephemerides three other small moons of Jupiter known at this period.

The determination of longitude by eclipses of Jupiter's satellites merely depends on the known fact that the same event (Fig. 37) does not occur at the same solar time in two places on different meridians of longitude. Römer's observations showed that one event seen before a second event at one and the same place may really have happened later. The full consequences of this startling conclusion which has since (p. 330) been established by direct experimental proof in the laboratory is only beginning to be grasped. When we look at the moon we are really seeing what it looked like one and a half seconds before. Some nebulae are so far away that if our telescopes could bring them as near to us as the moon, we should only know what they looked like 140 million years ago. One result of Römer's discovery was to show how we can calculate the earth's distance from the sun by observations on the stars. The calculation based on the assumption that the earth moves round the sun like the other planets, agrees with the distance calculated from the parallax of a planet, as explained on p. 342, and thus established Kepler's doctrine more firmly than ever.

During the latter half of the seventeenth century the Paris Observatory undertook extensive enquiries to adapt and improve the telescope for astronomical observations. In the latter half of the eighteenth century extensive improvements in the technology of glass renewed interest in the study of light. Some of the discoveries which resulted have been dealt with in a previous chapter. Others which we shall now examine introduce a new feature of progress in scientific knowledge.

So research into the nature of light received a renewed impetus from the star lore of the two centuries which witnessed a hitherto unparalleled growth of maritime communications and colonization. The way in which enquiry progressed was also influenced by the growth of another branch of knowledge. Side by side with the study of light, a different class of physical phenomena, in which some progress had been achieved in very remote times, began to arouse interest. The origins of music are buried in a very remote past. For some reason, doubtless inherent in the structure of our organs of hearing, a certain sequence of sounds, the octave scale, came into widespread use at a very early date. Aside from Ptolemy's experiments on refraction and the mechanics of Archimedes, the construction of musical instruments provides one of the rare illustrations of exact measurement applied to terrestrial phenomena in classical antiquity. Pythagoras (see p. 77, Chapter II) is reputed to have discovered the relation between the length of a vibrating string and the note emitted, when stretched at constant tension. If the length of the vibrating portion is halved the string gives out a note an octave higher. If diminished to two-thirds, it gives a note higher by an interval which musicians call a *fifth*.* If diminished to three-quarters a note called a *fourth* higher, and so on.

The series of numbers called harmonical progressions in textbooks of algebra are a survival from the somewhat mystical significance which the Pythagorean brotherhoods attached to this early discovery in experimental science. Though there are few extant data concerning the way in which the production of sound was studied in ancient civilizations, there is no doubt that a keen interest in the improvement of musical instruments had prompted a clear understanding of the nature of the stimulus which excites our auditory organs. Thus Aristotle, whose views on other departments of physical knowledge are usually worthless, knew that sound is communicated from the vibration of the string to our ears by movements of the intervening air, and was also familiar with the fact that a vibration occupies double the time when the length of a pipe is doubled. From the everyday experience of the interval between lightning and thunder-clap, or the influence of winds and echoes in an age when people lived more in the open air and buildings were not designed for acoustical perfection, there was ample evidence for the fact that sounds are reflected from solid surfaces, that they are transmitted through the motion of the atmosphere, and that they travel with a finite speed.

It is not difficult to recognize how a variety of features in the everyday life of the middle ages conspired to revive interest in sound. In particular, three may be mentioned. The first was a noteworthy improvement in musical instruments. The Alexandrian mechanicians Ctesibius and Hero are known to have designed a hydraulic organ. A similar model has been recovered from Carthage dating about A.D. 200. The daily ritual of the Christian Church encouraged the use of instruments suitable for choral accompaniment. From the church organ the device of the keyboard was extended to stringed instru-

* Thus in the scale of C (CDEFGABC), the interval CC, i.e. eight notes including both Cs, is an *octave*. CG is a *fifth*, CF a *fourth*.

ments in the fifteenth century. Thenceforth the modern piano evolved from the clavichord, the virginal, and the spinet. During the sixteenth century the manufacture of musical instruments for secular use was developing into an important craft. In this milieu Galileo devoted himself to experiments on the vibrations of strings. The publication (1636) of *Harmonie Universelle*, a treatise on the mechanical basis of pitch and timbre in stringed instruments, composed by his ecclesiastical disciple Mersenne, was the signal of renewed interest in acoustical phenomena.

Two other innovations made a new instrument available for investigation into the theoretical issues arising out of the technology of stringed instruments. Hitherto no attempts had been made to find the speed with which

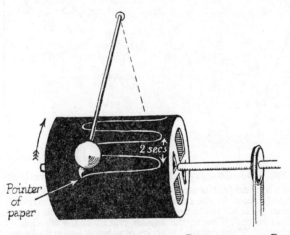

FIG. 194.—WAVE-LIKE MOTION TRACED BY A PENDULUM ON A REVOLVING LAMP BLACK SURFACE

Just as the horizontal or vertical trace of a circular motion is a periodic motion of the pendulum type, the trace of the pendulum motion represented as a graph of displacements and time intervals is a simple wave-like motion such as can be propelled along a skipping-rope. The periodic time of the wave motion is the interval between two crests or two troughs next to one another. In this case it is 2, i.e. the pendulum is a "seconds" pendulum (period 2 seconds).

a sound travels. The introduction of gunpowder into warfare made the experience of lightning and thunder claps more tangible. By using the new seconds pendulum to time the lag between the flash and the explosion at a measured distance from a cannon, Mersenne and Gassendi found the speed of sound to be about 1,400 feet per second. More accurate modern determinations give approximately 1,120 feet at 15° C. Boyle, Flamsteed of the Greenwich Observatory, and Halley in England repeated the observations of Mersenne and Gassendi, obtaining results in closer agreement with the correct figure, as did also Cassini, Huyghens, Picard, and Römer of the Paris Observatory. Progress was made possible by the fact that the eighteenth century was equipped with what the ancients lacked. Musical technology could make use of a convenient device for measuring time in short intervals.

Closely connected with this was another circumstance. Being without the means of measuring short intervals of time, mechanics made little headway in antiquity. The dynamical principles which developed in the design of the pendulum clock were specially concerned with periodic, that is to say wave-like, motions (Figs. 194, 195). A new logical technique drawn from

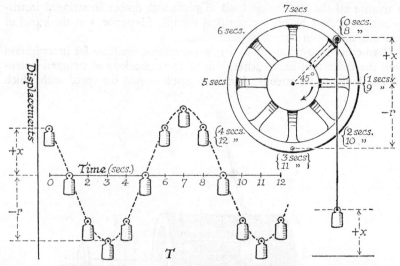

FIG. 195.—CONNEXION BETWEEN ROTARY AND WAVE MOTION

We can find a formula for the wave-like trace of the pendulum by a model. The wheel rotates at fixed speed. At the start the radius of the wheel from which a weight is hung makes an angle 45° to the peg with the horizontal and this angle decreases at the rate of 45° per second. That is, the *angular velocity* of the wheel is — 45° or — $\pi/4$ radians per second, if the positive direction of rotation is anticlockwise. After a time t (measured in seconds) this radius thus makes an angle 45° $(1 - t)$ with the horizontal and the weight is a height x_t above its mean position (horizontal radius), where

$$x_t = r \sin 45°(1 - t)$$

More generally, if the radius starts at an initial angle a with angular velocity b, then

$$x_t = r \sin (a + bt)$$

a and b are constants which can be measured in degrees or radians. We can make things simpler if we use a stop-watch and start it at the moment the radius is horizontal, i.e. measure t from the time when $a = 0$. Then

$$x_t = r \sin bt$$

If the wheel revolves through 360° in T secs., T is the periodic time (i.e. the time between two consecutive crests or two consecutive troughs) and b, the angle through which the wheel revolves in one second, is 360°/T, so

$$x_t = r \sin 360°t/T$$

or measured in radians, 2π to a revolution

$$x_t = r \sin 2\pi t/T$$

If the wheel makes n revolutions a second, T = $1/n$ and

$$x_t = r \sin 2\pi nt$$

contact with the mechanical amenities of everyday life supplied the guidance which unaided intellectual ingenuity had failed to devise, and successful application of the new mechanics to the elastic vibration of strings furnished the clue to new discoveries about the nature of light.

THE NATURE OF SOUND

Nineteenth-century science inherited from the two preceding centuries a framework of metaphors drawn from a pre-existing technology. Navigation and water power have now ceased to play a prominent part in the daily experience of most of us. For that reason the analogy of "wave" or "current" is liable to mystify us unless we firmly grasp the significance they had for an earlier generation of scientific workers. To understand the wave theory of light it is first essential to understand how sounds are produced and communicated to our ears.

Sounds may be produced by the vibration of a string as with the violin and piano; by the vibration of a diaphragm, membrane, or metal plate, as

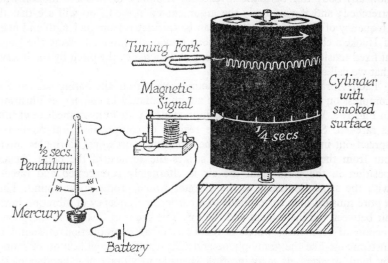

FIG. 196

Simple apparatus for measuring frequency of a tuning fork accurately. The tip of a pendulum with a complete period of one half second just dips into the mercury making contact in the signal circuit every half period when it reaches the vertical position.

with the drum, the gramophone, the bell or the telephone; by the vibration of a column of air as in a tin whistle or organ; or by concussion between solids or liquids as when an explosion or splash is heard. Common to all these sources of sounds is the fact that air is set in motion to and fro. If air is exhausted from a vessel in which an electric bell is suspended no sound is heard when the current is turned on.

That different qualities of sound are produced by different rates of vibration is easily shown in various ways, of which the simplest is to fix a hair or thin pointer of tissue paper to one prong of a tuning fork, and trace a wave-like image of its movements, when struck, on the smoked surface of a revolving cylinder (Fig. 196). If the speed of the cylinder is constant, two tuning forks which emit the same musical note will trace out the same number of crests on the same length of smoked surface, and tuning forks which emit different musical notes will trace out different numbers. The number of wave crests (or troughs) traced out in a second is called the frequency of the tuning fork or the frequency corresponding to the note. It can be conveniently determined if a signal of essentially the same construction as an electric bell, designed to tick out seconds, is made to write on the revolving surface below or above the trace of the vibrations which the tuning fork executes. What are called pure musical notes correspond to a fixed frequency of some vibrating object like the prongs of a tuning fork, the air column of an organ pipe, the string of a harp, or the diaphragm of a gramophone. The frequency of middle C is 261 vibrations per second.* Few bodies when struck vibrate as a whole. So most sounds are combinations of notes of different frequency, harmonizing or otherwise with our aesthetic preferences. Hooke's law of the spring shows how any body can be made to execute vibratory or periodic motion when stretched; and if you apply the argument on p. 293, you will see that the frequency of vibration of a string can be calculated from its length and mass, if Hooke's elastic constant k has been previously found. Halving the length at fixed tension doubles the frequency and increases the pitch by the interval that we call an octave.

Each vibration of a source of sound sets up an alternating sequence of compression and rarefaction in the air immediately in contact, as illustrated in Fig. 199. Whenever the air is compressed, the air in its immediate vicinity is rarefied. So a train of alternate regions of compression and rarefaction spread out in all directions from the vibrating source, just as ripples spread out from the spot where a stone strikes the surface of the pond. At any position in the wave train the air is alternately compressed and rarefied with the same frequency as the vibrator which produces the sound. Thus a pure musical note corresponds to a particular frequency of vibration in the air between the instrument and the ear. The proof of this lies in the phenomenon of resonance, which is the basis of all reproduction of sound by instruments like the gramophone and telephone, or magnification of sounds by loud speakers. If a tuning fork is made to vibrate near another of the same frequency the latter takes up the note and is itself audible, when held close to the ear. This only happens if both tuning forks have the same frequency. The only way in which we can easily imagine how this could happen is that the air vibrates in unison with the two forks.

A flat membrane or plate when struck emits a great variety of vibrations, and will consequently resonate to a great variety. This fact underlies the construction of the gramophone. The instrument used for making the record is essentially like the one used for playing it. A flat diaphragm transmits vibrations in unison with the frequency emitted by a neighbouring source of sound to the holder of a hard steel needle, which makes minute indentations on the blank record. When a needle similarly attached to a diaphragm moves over these minute notches, it forces the diaphragm to execute similar vibrations which communicate motion to the surrounding air precisely similar to the air vibrations which were impressed on the blank record. The drum of the human ear is a resonator of a similar type to the diaphragm of the gramophone. It only responds to vibrations between a lower frequency of 18 per second and an upper frequency in the neighbourhood of 30,000 per

* New Philharmonic pitch. The old value 256 is used in our numerical illustrations.

second. The limits are not quite the same for all people. Some individuals can hear the shrill squeak of a bat. Others cannot hear notes of such high frequency. The limits also vary very greatly in different species of animals. Some animals can guide their movements in the dark, because their ears pick up vibrations which our own ears cannot detect.

The vibration of the air between one tuning fork and another vibrating in resonance with it might be imagined to happen in one of two ways. First we might suppose a column of air surging to and fro like a piston rod fixed between the two prongs, or a column of water forced backwards and forwards through a tube. There are several reasons why this cannot be true, one being, that sounds do not travel instantaneously. The only alternative is that

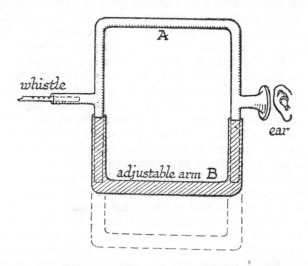

FIG. 197.—SIMPLE APPARATUS FOR SHOWING INTERFERENCE OF SOUND

the vibrations are transmitted through the air in the way described, just as ripples on a pond spread out from a region where a stone is thrown or a stick is stirred in it. This alternative is supported by two other phenomena connected with the production of sound. One is *interference*. The other is the "Doppler effect."

Generally speaking, the effect of hearing two identical notes played together is an increase in the volume of sound. In certain circumstances simultaneous notes of the same frequency from two different sources interfere. That is to say, neither is heard. One way in which the phenomenon can be demonstrated is to strike a tuning fork, hold it near the ear, and rotate it by the handle. It will then be noticed that in certain positions, at the same distance from the ear, the sound is intensified, and in other positions no sound is heard. A better demonstration which shows the nature of the phenomenon is to blow a whistle in the end of a tube with two arms (Fig. 197) leading to the ear. If the length of one arm can be altered by a sliding tube like that of the trombone, the sound of the whistle alternately increases to a maximum and is silenced as the length of the adjustable tube is gradually diminished or made greater. In this device there is only one vibrator. So if the air surges to and fro as a single column in each of the two arms leading to the ear, altering the length of one of them would not prevent the air column in it from keeping in step with that in the other. The alternative theory that sound travels in alternating regions of compression and rarefaction makes it easy to understand what happens. If the lengths of the two arms are not the same, a region of compression at the end of one arm may coincide with a region of rarefaction at the end of the other, and vice versa alternately (Figs. 199 and 200).

To form a clearer picture of the nature of interference, it is necessary to recall that sound travels with a definite speed in a given medium. In air at 15° C. this is about 1,120 feet per second. The time which elapses between seeing the flash and hearing the noise of an explosion is directly proportional to the distance. For practical purposes we assume that the transmission of light from the source to the eye is instantaneous, that is to say, the interval is negligible as compared with the time which elapses between the emission of the sound and the moment when we hear it. To say that sound travels in air at about 1,100 feet per second, therefore, means that if we are a mile away from a gun, approximately $4\frac{3}{4}$ seconds will intervene between seeing the flash and hearing the sound, or $9\frac{1}{2}$ seconds if we are 2 miles away. With modern apparatus, the speed of sound in water (about 4,700 ft. per sec.) can be found by connecting a microphone with an electric signal recording on a revolving cylinder, while some delicate time-signal, like a vibrating tuning fork, gives a simultaneous time tracing. The microphone picks up an echo as well as the original detonation. The wave trace of the time marker gives the interval which elapses between the detonation and the echo. Thus if the time marker is a tuning fork emitting middle C, and 16 wave crests intervene between the two microphone signals, the interval is $16 \div 256$, or one-sixteenth of a second. In this time (t) the sound has reached the sea floor and returned, traversing twice the depth (d). So if the depth is known, the speed is easily calculated, being $2d \div t$.

Once this speed (s) is known the depth of any ocean can be found, by the same method, since $d = \frac{1}{2}st$. This is how "soundings" of ocean depths are made in modern oceanography. Another application of the speed of sound is made in warfare to determine the position of a concealed field battery, at an unknown situation X. Three microphones are placed at measured distances from one another, and the intervals between the time when the sound reaches the first and the time when it reaches the other two is recorded at headquarters with electric signals. The reconstruction is shown in Fig. 198.

The fact that sound travels with a definite speed implies that the path along which the disturbance set up by the vibrator proceeds must be divided up at any instant in a regular way, as shown in Fig. 199. The string of a violin or diaphragm of a telephone vibrates to and fro, like a piston, pressing on the neighbouring layers of air and sucking back. Matter does not change its state of motion instantaneously. The force with which a stretched string or diaphragm presses or pulls on the air in contact with it is measured by the *acceleration* it imparts. This means that it takes time for a column of air to move forward with the same speed as something pressing on it or pulling it. So the string or diaphragm can only move by forcing the air in front of it to occupy a smaller or larger space. A vibrator such as the string of a violin when stretched towards the hearer compresses the layers of air immediately in front of it, and this region of high density moves forward with a speed S (Fig. 199). If we call the time of a complete vibration T, we may divide the

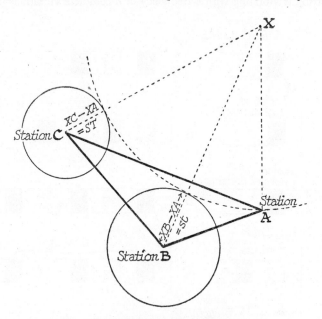

FIG. 198.—SOUND RANGING IN ARTILLERY

A, B, C are stations with microphones at known distances apart. The microphones record simultaneously with an electric signal and timekeepers (on the same general principle suggested by Fig. 196) at Headquarters. X is the hidden field battery. The sound is heard first at A. At B it is heard t seconds, at C, T seconds after A. If S is the speed of sound, it travels St feet during t and ST feet during T seconds. Hence

$$XB - XA = St$$
$$XC - XA = ST$$

Describe circles about B and C of radii $XB - XA$ and $XC - XA$ respectively. The location of X is now the trigonometrical problem of finding the centre of a circle which just grazes the circumference of the first two circles and also passes through A.

period between a forward swing (1) and the next forward swing (5) into three phases. In (2) the string has swung back to its unstretched position, and is neither pressing on the neighbouring layers of air nor sucking them back. A quarter of a period later (in 3) it has swung backwards as far as it will go, sucking on the neighbouring layers of air, and creating a region of low density. At the end of the next quarter of a period the string is again unstretched and the surrounding air is at normal pressure. At the end of another quarter period it has swung forwards as far as it will go, creating a region of high pressure in the layers of air just in front of it. During the complete period T the first compression has moved over a certain distance from the string, where the neighbouring air layers are also in a state of compression. So the distance W between two adjacent regions of compression (or two regions of rarefaction) in the track of the sound is the product of the time T and the speed S, or

$$W = ST$$

If the string is vibrating with a frequency of n complete vibrations (forward

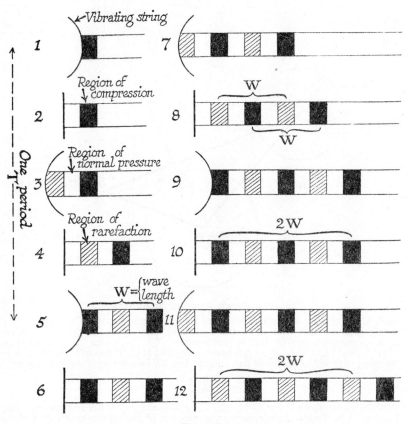

Fig. 199

Diagrammatic representation of successive changes of pressure in a sound track, starting from a vibrating string, showing how the speed of sound (S) is connected with the "wave length" (W) and period (T) of time occupied by one complete vibration

$$\text{Speed} = \text{Distance} \div \text{Time}$$
$$= W \div T$$

If one vibration takes T seconds, $\frac{1}{T}$ vibrations occur in one second. If the frequency is n per second

$$n = \frac{1}{T}$$

Hence

$$S = Wn$$

back to the forward stroke) per second, it makes one vibration in $1/n$ seconds,

i.e.

$$T = \frac{1}{n}$$

Hence, according to the hypothesis we are going to test, the speed of sound, the frequency of the vibrator, and the "wave-length" W, are connected by the simple formula:

$$S = Wn$$

The reason for calling the distance W a *wave-length* is that every layer of air in the track of a sound suffers compression and rarefaction in alternate half periods of the vibrator, just as every particle of water in the path of an advancing wave alternately moves above and below the normal level of the water when at rest. If we could make a graph (Fig. 203) by plotting time along the x axis and the pressure of any thin slice of air in the sound track above (+) or below (−) the normal pressure of the air, it would be exactly like a graph of the upward and downward movements of a cork, floating on water as a wave progressed along the surface, made by plotting time along the x axis and the displacement of the cork above (+) or below (−) the resting level of the water along the y axis. It would also be mathematically equivalent to the horizontal or vertical displacement of a body moving in a circle, as seen in Fig. 195.

We have seen that the phenomenon of interference is very difficult to explain by any hypothesis other than the one which is illustrated in Fig. 199, and we can now put it to a more severe test. To be useful it must do more than explain how interference *might* occur. Since a scientific hypothesis is first and foremost a guide to conduct, it must tell us how to establish the conditions in which interference will occur. For simplicity we will take as the source of sound in an experiment like the one in Fig. 197, a tuning fork giving 280 complete vibrations per second (just below middle D and above C sharp). To make the calculation simple let us also suppose both arms A and B in Fig. 197 are 10 feet long. The wave-length of the note in air is given by

$$1,120 = 280 \, W \text{ (feet)}$$
$$\therefore W = 4 \text{ feet}$$

So, to begin with, the sound track in each arm is $2\frac{1}{2}$ wave-lengths (Fig. 200). Imagine an instant of time when the air in the neighbourhood of a prong of the tuning fork may be rarefied. At the point where both arms lead into the earpiece a region of compression will then exist. Half a period later the air at the beginning of the sound track will be compressed, and at the earpiece it will be rarefied. Suppose that we now extend the arm B to 12 feet, making it half a wave-length longer. The disturbance at its end will be a compression when the disturbance at the end of A is a rarefaction, and vice versa. In the earpiece compressions and rarefactions arrive together, each neutralizing the effect of the other. So the air in the earpiece will remain at rest and no sound will be heard. If B is now extended to 14 feet ($3\frac{1}{2}$ W) so that it exceeds the length of A by a complete wave-length, the air at the ends of both tubes will be in a state of low, normal, or high pressure simultaneously. The sound will be loud again. On extending B by another $\frac{1}{2}$W to 16 feet silence will result, and so on. In practice the apparatus shown in Fig. 197 is not the best type for putting the hypothesis to the test of actual measurement, since the sound track does not follow a straight line. However, it is easy to devise apparatus with which we can show with great accuracy that silence occurs at any point where the disturbance, arriving along one sound track, differs by a half a period, or an odd number of half periods, from the disturbance, arriving along another sound track, from the same vibrator.

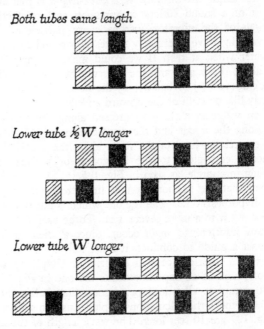

Both tubes same length

Lower tube ½ W longer

Lower tube W longer

Fig. 200.—Interference in Two Sound Tracks Differing by Half a Wave-Length

There are several other ways in which this view of the nature of sound can be tested. In the last chapter we found that Hooke's law allows us to calculate the frequency with which a weight bobs up and down if we know the density, physical dimensions, and elastic constant K, of the spring. Air also has the characteristics of a spring, and Hooke himself established an analogous law for the "spring of the air" as he called it. If we have found the elastic constant for air, we can also calculate the frequency with which a column of particular length will vibrate. Hence the frequency of the note given out by an organ pipe can be calculated, and so also, as Newton first showed, the velocity of sound in air.* As a check on the hypothesis both these quantities can be found by other means.

* The frequency of a vibrating string is given by $n = \frac{1}{2l}\sqrt{\frac{F}{m}}$ where n is the number of vibrations per second, l is the length in cm., F is the force or tension in dynes and m the mass of the string in gm. per cm. length.

We can also infer the existence of a phenomenon which we now encounter in everyday life, though the circumstances for verifying it did not exist when our present belief about the nature of sound was first tested out. If you have been standing by a railway track when an express is blowing its whistle as it passes you, you may have noticed a sudden change of pitch at the moment of passing. This is an example of what is known as the Doppler effect, after the physicist who pointed out its existence, as a necessary consequence of the theory, before it had been noticed. Its chief interest lies in its bearing on the nature of light. To understand it, we must draw a distinction which is not necessary so long as we suppose that the person who hears a sound

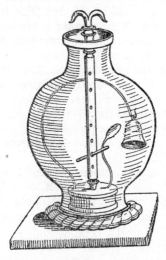

FIG. 201.—SEVENTEENTH-CENTURY ILLUSTRATION OF GLASS JAR CONNECTED WITH A VACUUM PUMP TO SHOW THAT THE SOUND OF THE BELL IS ONLY HEARD WHEN AIR IS PRESENT IN THE JAR

is at rest relative to the source of sound, or moving at a slow speed compared with the speed of sound in air. To begin with we distinguished musical notes by the frequency or period of the vibrator. Thus middle C is the note which we hear when a violin string vibrates as a whole, with a frequency of 256 vibrations per second or a period of $\frac{1}{256}$th of a second. If we are, comparatively speaking, at rest this is transmitted to us along a track in which at any given instant successive layers of compression or rarefaction are separated by a distance $1{,}120 \div 256 = 4$ feet $4\frac{1}{2}$ inches. We might therefore equally well say that the note we are describing is one which reaches us by a sound track of wave-length 4 feet $4\frac{1}{2}$ inches. Suppose, on the other hand, that we are moving rapidly in the direction of a source of sound. The time taken for a disturbance, starting at the vibrator, to reach our ears will be less or greater, according as we are moving towards or away from it. Relatively to ourselves the speed of sound is greater or less than it would be if we were at rest. The speed of a sound relative to anybody who hears it is Wn. So if the relative speed of sound changes, either W or n must be different from its previous value. We might therefore say that the wave-length remains the same, and the vibrator appears to have a different frequency. Since the frequency of the vibrator is directly measurable, we may equally well prefer to say that the wave-length has changed. Whichever we choose, the fact remains that the vibrator no longer appears to have the physical characteristic which defines the particular note which we hear when we are at rest.

The argument is more easy to grasp if you consider the person hearing the sound to be at rest, and the source like the engine whistle moving towards or away from him. If the vibrator in Fig. 199 is at rest along the sound track, a compression starting as in (1) covers a distance W during one complete period of vibration, by which time another has been generated. In the period T the distance covered would be ST feet. This is then the actual wavelength of the sound track. If the vibrator is moving in the direction of the sound track travelling towards the observer with a speed v, it will move forward through vT feet in a time T and the next compression begins $ST - vT$ feet behind the preceding one. Thus the wave-length will not be ST but $(S - v)T$. If the source moves away from the person listening to the sound, it will be $ST + vT$ feet from the wave front when the next compression is generated, and the wave-length will be $(S + v)T$. So at the moment when a train passes by a person listening to the whistle, the sound experiences a sudden increase of wave-length from $(S - v)T$ to $(S + v)T$, i.e. by an amount $2vT$.

To make this more definite, imagine an aeroplane flying at 191 miles per hour or approximately 280 feet per second, close to a high building from which a steam whistle is blowing, the pitch of the whistle being two octaves above middle C, i.e. a frequency of 1,024. As it approaches, the wave-length of the sound is $\dfrac{(1,120 - 280)}{1,024}$ ft. = 10 in. (approx.). If the aeroplane were at rest a wave-length of 10 inches or 5/6 foot would correspond to a frequency of approximately 1,344 vibrations per second. A vibrator of this frequency would emit a note nearly a third of an octave higher than one with frequency 1,024 on the natural scale. So the aviator hears a much higher note than the man in the street. On passing the building the wave-length of the sound which reaches him is $\dfrac{(1,120 + 280)}{1,024}$ = 1 foot 4 inches (approximately). A sound of this wave-length would correspond to the note given out by a vibrator of frequency 840. So the aviator hears a note about two-fifths of an octave lower than the man in the street. The total change which the aviator experiences as he passes over the building is a sudden increase of wavelength $2vT$, i.e. $560 \div 1,024$ feet or approximately 6 inches.

THE NATURE OF LIGHT

Although the hypotheses which have been advanced in the study of sound involve difficult reasoning, they do not come into violent conflict with our first-hand impressions of nature. Similar hypotheses, which have been very fruitful in leading to the discovery of new knowledge about the nature of light, introduce us into a realm of bewildering paradoxes if we start with wrong ideas about the nature of scientific enquiry. Science is not a photographic picture of the real world which exists independently of our views about it, and will continue to exist when we are no longer part of it. It is an ordnance map which guides us in finding our way in it. The mountain peaks are not painted brown because they really are of that colour. The brown is put there to show us where it would be waste of time to build a railway track or appropriate to erect a sanatorium. The enduring fact about the real world is that there is (at the time of speaking) a mountain peak in such and such a place. The colour is the hypothesis which is useless without the key provided by the colour scale at the foot of the map. If you grasp this firmly you will find no paradox in the statements that light travels in waves, and that there is nothing in which the waves travel.

Much that is written about science for people who want to know more about it merely consists of a scaffolding of metaphors of this kind. To say that light travels in waves is a metaphor which means as much as the brown colour of the mountain peak. Everything depends on whether you know the colour scale which tells you the height. Useful and fruitful facts are the permanent contribution of scientific enquiry to the edifice of human knowledge, and hypotheses are the scaffolding of metaphors. This may be illustrated by taking a useful and fruitful fact of great antiquity. To say that the obliquity of the ecliptic is approximately $23\frac{1}{2}°$ makes it possible for anyone to calculate his latitude, knowing the day of the year, or to find the day of the year if he knows his latitude. Its usefulness as a guide of conduct is not diminished in the slightest degree, even if we no longer accept the hypothesis which led the Babylonian priesthood or the Chinese astronomers to discover it about three thousand years ago.

Römer's hypothesis, that light travels with a finite speed, followed about thirty years after the first determination of the speed of sound by Mersenne, who perfected the seconds pendulum. Four of the satellites of Jupiter revolve very nearly within the plane of its orbit, and are hidden in its shadow once in nearly every revolution. Römer had determined their periods and orbits accurately enough to know how much error could arise in calculating at what intervals eclipses will recur, and the calculation can be verified whenever the Earth and Jupiter are in the same position relative to the sun. On calculating the time of an eclipse when Jupiter was near conjunction from the time at which a particular eclipse occurred when it was in opposition, he found that the observed time was retarded by $16\frac{2}{3}$ minutes.

There are several conceivable ways in which he might have modified his original hypothesis. For instance, propinquity to the earth might exert some specific influence on the motion of the satellites. Alternatively the explanation does not lie in their motion, but in the conditions for observing them. The second possibility is suggested by our experience of sound. Suppose at one place we observe that a gun fires at exactly noon every day. If we set a watch accordingly, and move ten miles farther away from the gun, we shall not hear it when the dial points to 12 on the following day. The sound will reach us about 47 seconds after noon. This retardation is not the only physical fact conveyed by saying that sound travels with a certain finite speed. By itself it might be due to the fact that the time of firing changes every time we happen to move. This can be rejected for two reasons. One is that the same experience also happens to other people. The other is the measurable time which elapses between hearing a sound and its echo.

According to Römer's observation, an event which was timed for, let us say, midnight occurred at $16\frac{2}{3}$ minutes after. This retardation, which occurs when the distance of Jupiter is increased by the width of the earth's orbit ($2 \times 93,000,000$ miles), is one of the physical facts implied by saying that light travels at a speed of

$$\frac{2 \times 93,000,000}{16\frac{2}{3} \times 60} = 186,000 \text{ miles per second}$$

However, there is more than this implied in the statement that light "travels" at 186,000 miles per second. We can make various calculations analogous to those which we have made in connexion with measurements of sounds, if we pursue the metaphor suggested by the track of bullets, as Newton did, or by a succession of ocean waves, as Huyghens preferred to do. Thus astronomical retardation agrees with measurements that can be made in the laboratory corresponding to measuring the retardation of an echo. It is possible to measure the interval which occurs between the time a beam of light leaves its source and is reflected back again. This interval depends, like the retardation of a sound echo, on the total path which the beam of light traverses.

A simplified apparatus showing the essential features for measuring the ratio of the distance to the retardation, i.e. the speed with which light "travels," is seen in Fig. 202. Light falls from the source S on a semi-transparent mirror at A. Some of it passes through the latter, and some of it is reflected towards another mirror C, situated at some considerable distance (e.g. about 10 miles). Near A at B there is a toothed wheel between the notches of which the light has to pass on its way to C and on its return journey to the semi-transparent mirror A, where some of it passes through to be seen by the eye. If the wheel is rotated at a low speed the brightness of the beam which reaches the eye is first reduced until it eventually disappears when a certain speed is reached. Then it reappears and on doubling the speed it becomes bright again. A further increase results in dimming and so on. If we compare the incident and reflected light to a shower of bullets bouncing back from a target along their original path, there must be a speed of rotation at which the light passing through the middle of a notch has only just enough time to reach the mirror C, and get back to the wheel before the middle of the next tooth obstructs its path, so that all the light reflected from the first mirror is intercepted at its return journey. If n is the speed at which disappearance first occurs, the time taken for this to happen, when the wheel has x teeth, as shown in the legend of Fig. 202, is

$$\frac{1}{2nx} \text{ secs.}$$

During this time the light traverses *twice* the distance D between B and C, so the speed of light is

$$2D \div \frac{1}{2nx} = 4nxD$$

If the speed is further increased to m revolutions, the wheel rotates from the middle of a notch to the middle of the next tooth but one. This is the speed at which disappearance next occurs, the speed of light being

$$2D \div \frac{3}{2mx} = \tfrac{4}{3}mxD$$

Of course, m must be approximately three times n, if the reasoning applies to the facts, and the two determinations should lead to the same result.

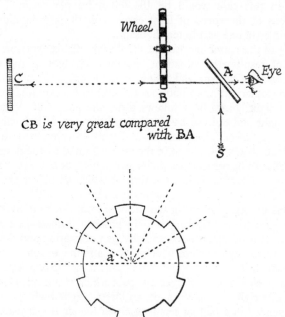

FIG. 202.—SIMPLIFIED APPARATUS FOR FINDING THE SPEED OF LIGHT

If there are x equally spaced teeth and notches (6 in the figure for simplicity) and a is the angle between the middle of a notch and the middle of the next tooth.

$$a = \frac{360°}{2x}$$

i.e. $a = 30°$ if there are 6 teeth and 6 notches. A wheel turns through 360° in one revolution. If it rotates at n revolutions per second, it goes through $(360 \times n)°$ in a second, and through one degree in

$$\frac{1}{360 \times n} \text{ seconds}$$

and through a in $\qquad \dfrac{360°}{2x} \times \dfrac{1}{360 \times n} = \dfrac{1}{2nx} \text{ seconds}$

This is the time taken to rotate between the middle of a notch and the middle of the next tooth. To rotate between the middle of a notch and the middle of the next tooth but one, it must go through an angle $3a$, i.e.

$$\frac{3}{2} \times \frac{360}{x} \text{ degrees}$$

If the speed of revolution is then m per second, the time taken to do this is

$$\frac{3}{2mx} \text{ secs.}$$

Actually it is best to take the average of the two. For instance, suppose the wheel B and the mirror C are 5 miles apart, the number of teeth 720 and the speeds of rotation at which disappearance occurs first and next are 13 and 38 per second. We have now two values for the speed of light

$$4 \times 13 \times 720 \times 5 = 187{,}200 \text{ miles per second}$$
$$\tfrac{4}{3} \times 38 \times 720 \times 5 = 182{,}400 \text{ miles per second}$$

The mean in this case would be 184,800 miles per second. Terrestrial determinations of the speed of light agree with the astronomical estimate with an accuracy of one part in ten thousand.

According to the reasoning used in the design of this experiment and the calculation of results, the situations in which changes in the real world excite our organs of hearing and vision resemble one another in three ways. Using the customary abstract noun as a convenient metaphor, we say three things about light. First, light follows a definite path. The space between a source of light and the eye has local characteristics. If it is charged with dust particles a "beam" is visible to a second observer, and shadows are only cast where objects are placed in the region limited by the beam. Second, a beam of light can be turned back on its own course, or as we say "reflected," like the echo of a sound. Third, the time at which an object appears to be visible depends on how far it is separated from the observer's eye.

But for one unfortunate circumstance there would be nothing remarkable about these similarities. Hearing is only possible if there is a substantial connexion, e.g. air or water, between the organ of hearing and the source of sound, or between any resonator which acts as a source of sound and another vibrator to which it responds (Fig. 201). This is not true of light. We can see objects separated from our eyes by space which is not filled by anything which we can weigh. If, for instance, an electric light bulb and an electric bell are suspended in a bell jar from which all the air is exhausted, the bell becomes inaudible till air is readmitted, while the light is just as visible throughout the experiment. This is a formidable objection to pursuing the analogy further. When we say that sound travels in waves, we mean two things. One is that at any region in the sound track, the air or other medium becomes successively more and less dense than it would otherwise be. The other is that at any instant of time a measurable distance separates successive places where the medium is more or less dense. The first is what we mean by frequency. The second is what we mean by wave-length, and the two are connected with the speed of sound in a definite way. Since light can pass where there is nothing weighable, its path cannot be mapped out in regions of varying density in a literal sense. Consequently the similarity seems to break down.

In spite of this there are a variety of facts about light which encourage us to look for further similarities, and we may be less surprised to find this is so if we bear in mind the real nature of the similarity between a sound wave and a wave of the sea. The fundamental similarity is that the displacement of a particle of water in the track of a sea wave and the density of a thin layer of air in the sound track can be represented *graphically* in the same form (Fig. 203). Measurements which involve the way these quantities vary from time to time can, therefore, be expressed *algebraically* in the same form. The resemblance between two patches coloured dark brown on an ordnance map does not lie in the physical property of colour. Mountain peaks are

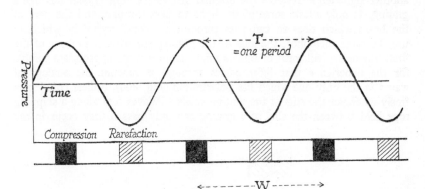

FIG. 203

The graphical representation on the variations of density in a sound track is a wave form.

generally white. The key to the resemblance, implied in saying that sound is a form of wave motion, lies in the sort of mathematics which is used in connexion with sound measurements.

A phenomenon which encourages us to search for similarity between the

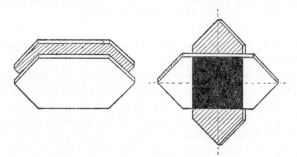

FIG. 204

Obstruction of light by two crystals of Tourmaline placed with their long axes at right angles.

kind of measurements which we can make in studying light on the one hand and sea waves on the other, is a change which sometimes occurs when a beam of light passes through a mineral crystal. This phenomenon called *polarization* was first studied by Huyghens. It is very well seen when a beam passes through a crystal of tourmaline cut into two slices parallel to its long axis. If the slices are placed in line so that the long axes are parallel (Fig. 204) a source of light can be seen through them, though not

as brightly as when the crystals are taken away. There is no visible change
if both halves are rotated simultaneously. If one is rotated slightly while the
other is held in position, the source becomes dim. When the long axes of
the two crystals are at right angles *complete* darkness results. Rotation through
another right angle restores the original brightness. The crystal acts like a
grating. It only allows some of the light to pass through, and the part of
the beam which does so can pass through a second crystal in which, to
use the same metaphor, the slits of the grating are parallel to those of the
first. Though a hailstorm of bullets might seem a more appropriate parable
for the experience that light passes through a vacuum, the analogy of
waves is the only one which fits polarization (Fig. 205). Bullets could pass
freely wherever the slits of the grating crossed. Waves sent along a skipping
rope held between the slits of a grating can only pass if they occur in the

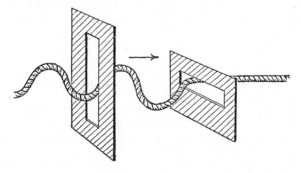

Fig. 205.—Waves Like Displacements Along a Skipping Rope Obstructed by
Two Slits at Right Angles

plane of the slits, and are completely obstructed by a second grating with
slits at right angles to those of the first.

The wave analogy was suggested by Huyghens, the bullet analogy by
Newton. Newton's reputation was in the ascendant, and further theoretical
interest in optical theory declined after Newton's work on the spectrum, till
practical scientific instrument makers solved the problem of making achromatic lenses. The issue of Dollond's patent in the latter half of the eighteenth
century prompted a commercial demand for large telescope lenses of high-
grade glass, and the renewal of interest in the theory of light followed the
invention of a process for making optical glass in thick homogeneous slabs
during the closing years of the same century. There was steady progress
during the first three decades of the nineteenth century, an enormous improvement in optical instruments, and with it a new drive to theoretical
research. For example, the Committee of the Royal Astronomical Society
commissioned Faraday in 1824 to investigate the chemistry of optical glass
production; and Foucault, the French physicist, invented new methods for
polishing large discs of flint glass. In England Young, and in France, where
Laplace was the centre of an influential school of astronomers, Foucault and
Fresnel, returned to the problem which had been neglected for more than a

century, and elucidated the phenomena of interference and diffraction which had emerged already in Newton's work on colour fringes.

You may say that Huyghens' hypothesis was merely reasoning from analogy. In our childhood and adolescence we are continually warned against the fallacies that beset this method of argument. The truth is that analogy is a very powerful instrument of scientific reasoning, and most of the really fruitful known facts about nature have been discovered by reasoning from analogy, often analogy of a very crude kind. Analogy like any other instrument in the technique of reasoning is helpful or harmful according as it is used to suggest further enquiry or to close the door to it. If, like a man of science or a craftsman, you want to get something done, you cannot afford to run the risks of inexperience. So analogy will point the road to new discoveries. If, like an economist, you want excuses for leaving things as they are, analogy will provide you with as many as you want.

Among the class of fruitful facts which the wave analogy has stimulated people to discover, the phenomenon called *interference* provides the simplest

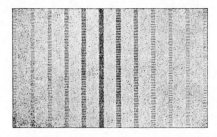

FIG. 206.—INTERFERENCE BANDS FORMED BY TWO MIRRORS ON A SCREEN

illustration of the way in which the same kind of mathematics can be used in calculating measurements of light or waves. We have seen in what circumstances two sounds can combine to produce no audible effect. In analogous circumstances two beams of light can produce darkness. To demonstrate interference of sound directly we have to use sound tracks of the same wave-length, and this is generally done by forcing sound to reach the ear by paths of different length from the same vibrator. The white light by which we usually see things is not pure. It is a mixture (p. 169) of several kinds of coloured lights, just as most of the sounds we hear are the result of simultaneous vibrations of different frequency. If two notes of a chord were sounded together in a tube like the one shown in Fig. 197 we should not get complete silence as the result of changing the length of one arm. An extension of the adjustable tube sufficient to produce interference of one note would not lead to extinction of the other. Increasing its length would result in hearing first one note alone, next the other note alone, then the complete chord, and so on. Many situations occur in which we see a region of brightness split up into bands corresponding to the complete chord of the spectrum alternating with coloured fringes like the spectra produced by prisms. You have probably seen this effect when the moon is surrounded by clouds, and you can always observe it by looking at the sun between the gap of two fingers pressed close together. In the laboratory it can be produced in various ways, such as focusing light on a screen from a narrow slit through two edges of a prism simultaneously, or by reflection from two mirrors inclined at a very small angle. Another way is to make light pass through a very fine grating of parallel slits, like the fine slits between the hairs of your fingers. When pure spectral light, like the yellow glow produced when a pinch of common salt is thrown in the non-luminous flame of an oil cooker or blow pipe flame, is used instead of white light, bands of pure coloured light alternate with streaks of complete darkness.

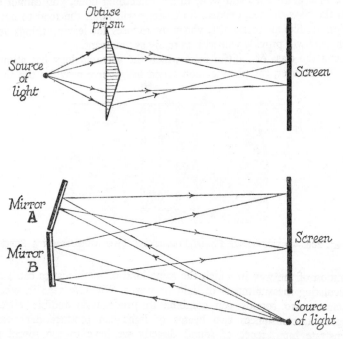

FIG 207.—TWO ARRANGEMENTS FOR SHOWING INTERFERENCE BANDS

The distance which separates these interference bands has a definite relation to the conditions of the experiment. It varies according to the distance of the source and screen from the prism, etching, or mirrors, the angle of inclination of the mirrors or prism faces, and the distance apart of the etchings in a "diffraction" grating. If the same conditions are reproduced the bands are the same distance apart so long as the same kind of pure light is used. So we can associate a particular measurement with light of a particular colour, just as Pythagoras found that a particular length of a string is characteristic of a particular musical note. By itself, the discovery of Pythagoras could not tell Ctesibius how long to make the pipes of his organ. So likewise, by themselves, the measurements which tell us how to get interference bands for a certain kind of light with two mirrors do not tell us how to get the same result with a prism. Before it was possible to calculate the dimensions of an organ pipe, which will give a note equivalent to one produced by a string of known length, thickness, tension, and elasticity, it was necessary to find a number, which defines it independently of the nature of the instrument used to produce it. This number is its *wave-length*.

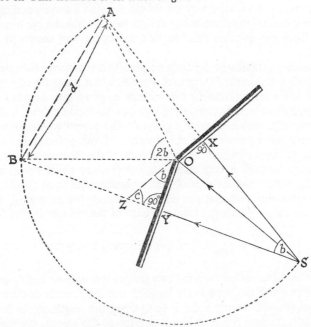

FIG. 208.—CALCULATING THE DISTANCE APART OF THE TWO IMAGES FROM THE SAME SOURCE WHEN TWO MIRRORS ARE INCLINED TO ONE ANOTHER AT AN ANGLE 180°–b, b BEING SMALL

The image of the slit S in the upper mirror appears to be at A, the same perpendicular distance (AX) behind the mirror as separates the mirror from the slit. The ray so striking the mirror at its edge O also appears to come from A at the same distance from O as S, i.e. OA = OS. The image of S in the lower mirror appears to be at B, and for the same reasons SY = BY and OB = OS. Hence OB = OA and the two images A and B, together with S the slit, lie on the same circle of radius OS = r.

The triangles ZOY and ZXS are both right-angled with a common angle c. So the third angles b are equivalent. The angle ASB (= b) stands on the same arc as AOB, and since the angle which an arc subtends at the centre (O) is twice the angle it subtends at any point (S) on the circumference, AOB = 2b. If b is measured in degrees, the length of the arc AB is

$$\frac{2\pi r \times 2b}{360} \text{ or } \frac{4\pi r b}{360}$$

If b is very small the arc AB differs by a negligible quantity from the chord AB which is the actual distance of one image from the other.

So although a wave is merely a metaphor, a wave-length, if we care to use the same expression, is not. The number which enables us to make measurements on the interference of light embodies a physical truth about the way in which we succeed in making correct measurements of changes which occur in the real world. By pressing the analogy of wave motion farther we obtain a set of numbers which have a relation to different regions of the spectrum similar to the relation between the wave-lengths of notes in a musical chord. A wave-length in sound is a number applied to a distance. One of its characteristics is that if the distance traversed by two sound tracks simultaneously reaching the ear from the same vibrator differs by half the distance called the wave-length of the note it gives out, no sound is heard. Clearly, there is no reason why we should not find a corresponding distance connecting the length of two beams of light which reach the eye from the same source. With two mirrors this can be done in the way shown in Figs. 207 and 208.

The mirror experiment depends on placing the source of single-coloured light, which is a thin slit (S), in such a position that the paths of any two rays reflected on the screen from the two mirrors are of unequal length. Light from a plane mirror appears to come from a point equidistant behind it. The paths of any two rays which meet at a point on the screen where they reinforce or interfere are equivalent to the distance of the point from the images (A and B) of the slit behind the two mirrors. If the mirrors are tilted towards one another through a very small angle b (i.e. the angle between them is $180° - b$), so that the distance of their common edge from the slit is r, you will see from Fig. 208 that the distance between the images (d) is related to their distance (r) from the common edge of the mirrors by the formula

$$d = \frac{4\pi r b}{360} \text{ (when } b \text{ is measured in degrees)}$$

So to get the distance between the two images it is only necessary to measure the angle at which the mirrors are inclined and the distance of their common edge from the slit. At any point P or Q along the length of the illuminated patch where the two reflected beams overlap on the screen, the paths of the two reflected rays differ by a small distance which is calculable. If the difference at P is p and the difference at Q, separated from P by the distance PQ, is q, Fig. 209 shows that if the mid-point between the two images is separated from the screen by a distance D

$$p - q = \pm \frac{d}{D}PQ$$

If the screen is separated from the common edges of the two mirrors by a distance s, and is perpendicular, or nearly so, to the plane bisecting the angle between the mirrors, $D = s + r$. According to what we have agreed to mean by a wave-length, if P is a point in the middle of a dark interference band, the difference in the length of the paths traversed by the interfering rays is either $\frac{1}{2}$ a wave-length, or $1\frac{1}{2}$ wave-lengths, or $2\frac{1}{2}$ wave-lengths and so on. For simplicity suppose it is $3\frac{1}{2}$W. Interference will next occur if the difference of the paths is $2\frac{1}{2}$ or $4\frac{1}{2}$W. So if Q is the middle of the nearest interference band separated from P by the distance PQ, q is either $2\frac{1}{2}$W or $4\frac{1}{2}$W. Whatever p is, the difference between p and q is always W, i.e.

$$W = \frac{d}{D}PQ$$

or

$$W = \frac{4\pi r b}{360(s + r)} \cdot PQ$$

The distance (PQ) between the middle of adjacent streaks of darkness can be measured accurately with a microscope. It is then found that the value of W for yellow sodium light (from common salt) is 0·0005893 millimetre (0·0000232 inch).

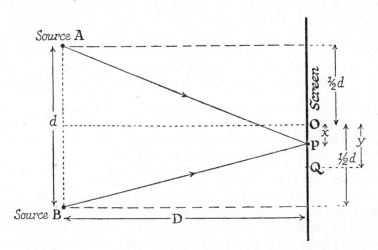

FIG. 209.—DIFFERENCE BETWEEN THE LENGTH OF TWO RAYS IMPINGING ON THE SAME POINT (P OR Q) OF A SCREEN EQUIDISTANT FROM TWO SOURCES OF LIGHT A AND B

The point P is separated by a distance x from O, the point vertically opposite the midpoint of the line joining A to B. The distance of the sources from the screen is D and from one another d. By Pythagoras' theorem

$$AP^2 = (\tfrac{1}{2}d + x)^2 + D^2$$
$$= \tfrac{1}{4}d^2 + dx + x^2 + D^2$$
$$BP^2 = (\tfrac{1}{2}d - x)^2 + D^2$$
$$= \tfrac{1}{4}d^2 - dx + x^2 + D^2$$
$$\therefore AP^2 - BP^2 = 2dx$$
$$\therefore (AP - BP)(AP + BP) = 2dx$$

If P is near O, and D is great compared with d, AP + BP does not differ appreciably from 2D.

$$\therefore AP - BP = \frac{2dx}{2D} = \frac{dx}{D}$$

If Q is another point and OQ $= y$

$$AQ - BQ = \frac{dy}{D}$$

If p is the difference in length of the rays meeting at P (i.e. AP — BP), and q is the difference in length of the rays meeting at Q (i.e. AQ — BQ)

$$q - p = \frac{d}{D}(y - x)$$
$$= \frac{d}{D}PQ$$

This measurement, like the wave-length of a musical note, is independent of the instrument. By applying the law of refraction in the same way as we have here applied the law of reflection we can calculate the position (d and D) of the two images when yellow sodium light (from common salt) is passed simultaneously through two faces of a prism. The same result is obtained from the measurement of the interference bands, i.e. $W = PQ(d \div D)$. With pure lights of different colour different values of W are found. For describing wave-lengths in whole numbers it is now usual to express them in 10-millionths of a millimetre (called an *ångström*). Each colour which the eye recognizes as distinct corresponds to a certain range of wave-lengths, extending between roughly 4,000 and 8,000 angstroms. The middle of the violet region of the spectrum corresponds to about 4,200 A.; the middle of the blue to about 4,500 A.; the middle of the green to about 5,200 A.; the middle of the yellow to about 5,800 A.; and the middle of the red to about 7,000 A.

Any method of demonstrating interference or of measuring the wave-length of light depends on making rays from one and the same source traverse different paths to reach the same goal. Two methods other than those already described are of special importance in connexion with the determination of the wave-length of X-rays and the use of X-rays to explore the structure of crystals (pp. 490–6). One of these is the *diffraction grating* referred to (p. 336) above. The diffraction grating is simply an arrangement of very fine equidistant lines ruled on glass (or other transparent material). A beam of white light transmitted through such a grating resolves itself into a sequence of spectra and a beam of monochromatic light into alternate light and dark bands. The distance between the grating and the image, the distance between the lines of the grid and the distance between consecutive dark or light bands have a simple relation to the wave-length of the radiation incident on the grating itself. The geometry of the arrangement is complicated, but irrelevant for our purpose, because we have now acquainted ourselves with the theory of two simpler, though less convenient, methods, which yield the same result in practice. We are therefore entitled to use either or both as a yardstick to calibrate a diffraction grating set-up, i.e. to find at what distance from a particular grating, and at what distance apart, alternate light bands occur for radiation of a particular wave-length. Having done this, we can use the grating as a wave-length detector without invoking any theory about how it works.

As stated above, this possibility suggests itself to the experimentalist because we sometimes see spectra when we look through a fine grid, e.g. the lashes of our half-closed eyes. We may also see spectra as the result of simultaneous reflection of light from two closely applied liquid surfaces, e.g. paraffin on water. This invites us to explore a fourth method of determining the wave-length of a radiation. It has a special interest, because the principle involved is the basis of all the fundamental discoveries about crystal structure dealt with in Chapter IX (p. 490). The principle itself relies on the fact that a ray reflected from a thin film of oil spread out on water may suffer reflection along the same path as a parallel ray striking the upper surface of the water below it, after passing through the oil itself. The waves of the first will necessarily traverse a shorter distance than those of the second before their final paths coincide; and the path difference may then tally exactly with an odd number of half wave-lengths. There will therefore be interference, if the incident light is monochromatic. This will result in a black-out; and if the source is white light the production of a spectrum will be the visible outcome.

The path difference of the two rays will depend on the angle at which the beam strikes the liquid reflecting surfaces, and on the thickness of the oil film. The angle of total reflection (p. 147) limits the possibility that a ray will penetrate the oil film. So the film has to be very thin.

If it were possible to roll out or blow out into laminae as thin as oil films, it would also be possible to make a pile of glass plates with optical properties comparable to those of a crystal reflecting a beam of X-rays. Though it is not practicable to construct a pile of this sort, we can discuss the theoretical possibility with a clear conscience, because it involves no principle other than the principle of interference at liquid faces, as stated above; and it is profitable

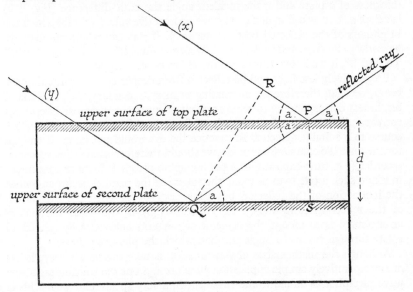

FIG. 210.—THE CRYSTAL MODEL

Interference by simultaneous Reflection at Parallel Surfaces of a Pile of thin laminae. Two incident rays (x) and (y) from the same source respectively impinge on parallel surfaces d cm. apart at P and Q. If reflected along a common track, the path difference is $PQ-RP$.

From the geometry of the figure we see:

$$RP \div PQ = \cos 2a = 1 - 2 \sin^2 a$$
$$\therefore \ RP = PQ \cos 2a = PQ - 2\,PQ \sin^2 a$$
$$\therefore \ PQ-RP = 2\,PQ \sin^2 a \ . \ . \ . \ . \ \text{(i)}$$

$$PS \div PQ = d \div PQ = \sin a$$
$$\therefore \ PQ = d \div \sin a$$
$$\therefore \ 2\,PQ \sin^2 a = 2d \sin a \ \ . \ . \ . \ . \ \text{(ii)}$$

By combining (i) and (ii) we get the path difference formula:

$$PQ-RP = 2d \sin a$$

to do so, because it serves as a model, albeit a *fictitious* model, for the pioneer work of Bragg on crystal analysis. A beam of parallel rays impinging obliquely on such a pile may be reflected or transmitted at the surface of any one of the constituent plates. Some of the rays reflected by one surface will coincide (Fig. 210) with rays reflected by a surface below. The result is that coincident rays from the same source emerge from the pile after traversing different distances. If the path difference is half a wave-length or any odd multiple of a half wave-length, they will interfere. If the path difference is a whole wave-length or any *even* multiple of a half wave-length they will reinforce. Fig. 210 shows that there is a simple relation between the path difference between rays reflected from adjacent surfaces and the incident angle of the beam of light. Whether interference or reinforcement occurs therefore depends on the angle at which the incident beam strikes the pile. This means that the reflected beam will become successively brighter and darker as we make the incident beam impinge more (or less) steeply on its upper surface. If d is the thickness of a plate and a the incident angle the path difference (Fig. 210) is $2d \sin a$. Let us call a_1 and a_2 any two consecutive values of a for which the brightness of the reflected beam is maximal. If n is any whole number, we have $nW = 2d \sin a_1$ and $(n+1) W = 2d \sin a_2$. Thus, $W = 2d (\sin a_2 - \sin a_1)$. To find W, if we know d, we have merely to observe a_1 and a_2.

Progressively less light will be reflected from deeper layers. In rotating the beam, we shall therefore get alternating primary, secondary, etc., maxima of brightness corresponding to reinforcement at successively deeper layers; but corresponding maxima for any pair of faces would be recognizable by recourse to a suitable detector. In practice the eye would not be good enough for the task. To complete our model we should therefore need an instrumental recorder (e.g. time-exposure of a photographic plate). It is more convenient to rotate such a pile than to rotate the source of the parallel beam; and since the inclination of the reflected beam increases by $2a$ when the inclination of the reflecting surface (Fig. 211) increases by a, the most satisfactory arrangement is to mount the detector on an arm automatically geared to rotate through twice the angle through which the pile itself turns.

Although the mathematics of wave motion is not particularly easy, it has one comparatively simple application which brings out the fruitfulness of the wave metaphor as an aid to measurement in a very spectacular way. This is the fact that we can calculate from measurements based on a phenomenon comparable to the Doppler effect, a value for the earth's distance from the sun in close agreement with the value obtained from the parallax of a near planet (p. 210). The spectrum of sunlight is crossed by fine dark lines. In the spectra of light from some of the stars similar lines appear. Measurement of where these lie by photographing their spectra side by side with that of a terrestrial source of light (like sodium light or the iron arc) shows that they undergo a slight shift in the course of the year, according as the earth is moving in its orbit towards or away from the particular star whose spectrum is studied. The pitch of sound is different when we are moving towards or away from the source. The shift in the wave-length of the dark lines in starlight is analogous. If the speed of the observer (v) is known, the shift can be calculated from the speed of light (S) by the Doppler formula $2vT$, in which T is the period of the vibrator (p. 328). If the wave-length is W when the observer is at rest, $T = W \div S$. So that the shift from a wave-length W_1 when the observer is moving towards the source to W_2 when he is moving away from it is $2vW \div S$. The wave-length of the sound heard by an observer at rest may be taken as the mean of the wave-lengths (W_1 and W_2) of the sound when the observer is in motion. An analogous calculation may be made for the annual shift in the spectra of the stars.

For a star suitably chosen the observer's speed (v) can thus be the rate at which the earth rotates in its orbit. If r miles is the mean distance of the earth from the sun, the circumference of the orbit is $2\pi r$ miles, which it traverses in 365 days, or $365 \times 24 \times 3,600$ seconds. Twice in the course of a year, at intervals of six months, a physicist examining the spectrum of such a star can

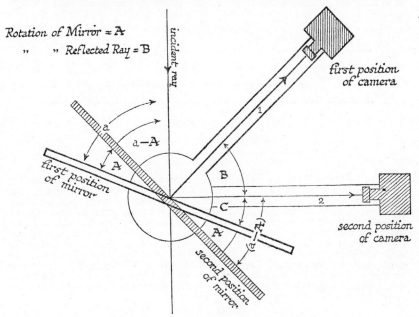

FIG. 211.—TRAVELLING DETECTOR FOR BEAM FROM A REFLECTOR WHICH CAN ROTATE

In the first position:

$$\text{Glancing angle of the incident ray} = a$$
$$\text{ditto} \qquad \text{reflected ray} = B + C$$
$$\therefore \quad C = a - B \tag{i}$$

In the second position:

$$\text{Glancing angle of the incident ray} = a - A$$
$$\text{ditto} \qquad \text{reflected ray} = C + A$$
$$\therefore \quad C = a - 2A \tag{ii}$$

From (i) and (ii)

$$a - B = a - 2A$$
$$\therefore \quad B = 2A$$

Hence it is necessary to rotate the detector through twice the angle of rotation of the reflector.

do so when it is moving directly in the line of sight either towards or away from the source, with a speed

$$v = 2\pi r \div (365 \times 24 \times 3,600) \text{ miles per second}$$

Having found the wave-lengths of various sources of pure light, it is possible to graduate the whole spectrum in wave-lengths. Hence the shift of a line (or the middle of a broad one) can be expressed as a wave-length. If we sub-

stitute the value of the shift, the speed of light (S), and the wave-length corresponding to the mean position of the band in Doppler's formula for sound,
we can get a value for v; and from this r is found to be approximately $92\frac{1}{2}$
million miles, which agrees to less than one part in two hundred with the
parallax value. The Doppler effect can also be used to calculate the rate at
which the fixed stars appear to be moving away from us. A readable account
of recent speculations on the expanding universe is given in the 1935 edition
of *Whitaker's Almanack* and in J. G. Crowther's *Progress of Science*.

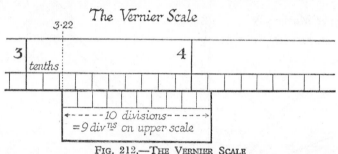

The Vernier Scale

FIG. 212.—THE VERNIER SCALE

Invented by Pierre Vernier, a French mathematician, early in the sixteenth century,
the vernier scale is an auxiliary movable ruler device, which permits great accuracy.
On the lower ruler a distance equivalent to 9 divisions on the upper scale is divided
into 10 parts. To measure an object the end of which is marked by the thin line between
$3 \cdot 2$ and $3 \cdot 3$ in the figure, set the beginning of the vernier scale at this level and look
for the first division on the vernier which exactly coincides with a division on the
upper scale. In the figure this is the second division and the correct measurement is
$3 \cdot 22$. The theory of the device is as follows. If x is some fraction of a division on the
upper scale to be ascertained, the correct measurement is $3 \cdot 2 + x$. The first whole
number a of the smaller divisions on the lower scale which coincides with the upper
differs from a divisions on the upper scale by the distance x. Now 1 division on the
lower scale is $\frac{9}{10}$ of a division on the upper. Hence

$$(\tfrac{9}{10}a) + x = a$$
$$\therefore \quad x = \tfrac{1}{10}a$$

If a is 2, $x = 2$ tenths of a scale division on the upper scale. If a division on the upper
scale is $0 \cdot 1$, $x = 0 \cdot 02$.

Researches of this kind may seem to be very remote from the everyday
life of mankind. This is far from true. The initial stimulus which spectroscopic
research received from the progress of glass technology, after the long period
of inertia subsequent to Newton's work, was reinforced by the discovery
of chemical regularities in spectra at a time when chemical manufacture
was actively encouraging exploration into new fields of enquiry. How spectroscopy has helped us to build dirigibles and make the coloured lights of advertising signs will be explained later to be one of the crowning victories of man's
conquest of materials. How the extension of the wave metaphor led to the
discovery of wireless transmission which has broken down so many social
barriers of space and time will appear in the story of man's conquest of
Power. The distinction between fruitful and useful facts which was made
elsewhere is more superficial than real. Information that is fruitful in acting
as a check on methods of discovery and a correct hypothesis leads in the
long run to the kind of knowledge which can be used to provide more of
the means of life and leisure.

THE "ABERRATION" OF LIGHT

During the period which immediately followed Newton's work on colour fringes the only important advance in the study of light had been independent confirmation of Römer's view from an unexpected source by Bradley, the Astronomer Royal, in 1728. The confidence which Newton's theory conferred on the Copernican doctrine stimulated renewed attempts to obtain decisive evidence of the earth's orbital motion from the detection of a measurable displacement of the position of a fixed star at times when the earth is at opposite ends of a diameter of its orbit. In the early part of the seventeenth century accuracy of measurement had been greatly advanced by two inventions, the telescope and the *vernier* device shown in Fig. 212. If the earth revolves around the sun, there should be detectable differences in the R.A. and declination of any star at different seasons. The maximum displacement of R.A. (see Fig. 213) occurs when the star's R.A. differs from that of the sun by 6 hours or 18 hours. There is then no difference in declination. The maximum difference of declination should occur (Fig. 214) when the sun's R.A. differs from that of the star by 0 hours or 12 hours. There should then be no parallax in R.A. From these seasonal differences we can calculate the star's *heliocentric parallax*, which is approximately the ratio of the sun's distance to the star's distance from the earth.

These parallaxes are very small. For the nearest star (Fig. 215) of great brightness visible from the latitude of London—Sirius—the angle of parallax is only about one-third of a second of arc (0·371″), i.e. one ten thousandth of a degree; and there were no instruments sufficiently delicate to measure such small differences until the beginning of the nineteenth century, when the new patent of Dollond, improved manufacture of optical glass, Foucault's method for polishing lenses, and the theoretical researches into achromatism

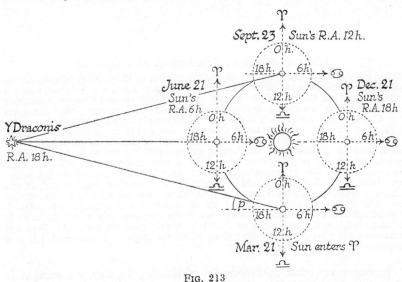

FIG. 213

When the sun's R.A. differs from the star's by 6 hours or 18 hours, the parallax is in R.A. only, and there is no parallax in declination. If the star's distance from the solar system is d, and the radius of the earth's orbit r, $\tan p = r \div d$ or $d = r \div \tan p$. The star chosen is γ Draconis with R.A. 18 hours. It is not actually in the plane of the earth's orbit, but considerably north of it.

which accompanied the progress of scientific glass technology, bore fruit in great improvements of telescope construction and in the invention of the compound microscope.

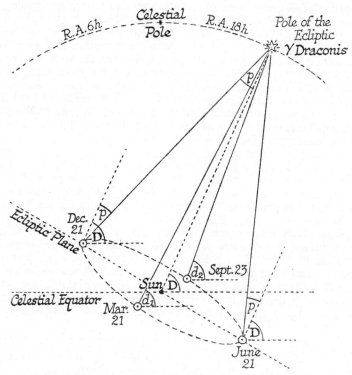

FIG. 214.—BRADLEY'S OBSERVATIONS ON γ DRACONIS

When the sun's R.A. is the same as the star's (or differs by 12 hours), there is maximum parallax in declination and no parallax in R.A. The star drawn is γ Draconis, which is taken to be near the pole of the ecliptic: it is actually about 15° away. Remember (see Fig. 127) in reading this figure that the earth is "in Capricorn" when the sun is "in Cancer" and vice versa. The R.A. of γ Draconis is approximately 18 hours, i.e. its lower transit is at midnight about December 21st, and its upper transit at midnight June 21st. On these dates its declination should exceed its mean value D (the declination of the star from the celestial equator with the *sun* as its centre) by the minute parallactic angle $-p$ or $+p$. This is now known to be $0 \cdot 17$, an angle too small for Bradley to measure. On the contrary he found that the declination, d_1 on March 21st, when there should be no parallax in declination, was less than D, and that the declination d_2 on September 23rd, when there should also be no parallax in declination, was greater than D by one-third of a minute of arc ($20 \cdot 5''$). On March 21st the earth is travelling *towards* the direction from which the angle D is measured, i.e. it is moving *away* from the celestial pole. On September 23rd it is travelling away from the direction from which the angle D is measured, i.e. it is moving *towards* the celestial pole.

Among many other contemporaries of Newton, Bradley was engaged in the search for a detectable star parallax. He chose a star in the constellation of Draco. The star γ Draconis lies about 15° from the pole of the ecliptic. For simplicity it is drawn as if it were at the pole of the ecliptic in Figs. 214 and 218,, which more nearly describe the position of ω Draconis, only 3° from the ecliptic pole. The R.A. of γ Draconis is very nearly 18 hours. So it should show maximum displacement of declination about June 21st and December 21st. Bradley could detect none with his instruments. On the contrary he found a displacement which was greatest about March 21st and September 23rd, the dates on which the declination should not be affected by parallax at all. Bradley confined his observations to the measurement of declination. The difference in declination of two stars is simply the difference of the two

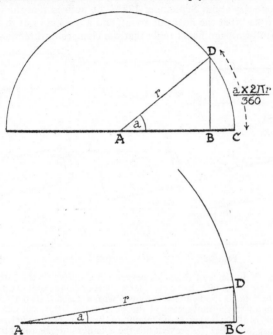

FIG. 215.—SINES AND TANGENTS OF VERY SMALL ANGLES

The sine of the angle a is BD $\div$ AD and the tangent is BD $\div$ AB. When a is very small, the arc CD does not differ appreciably from the perpendicular BD, and the base AB does not differ appreciably from the radius of the circle AD $= r$. So sin a = CD $\div r$ and tan a = CD $\div r$. If the angle a is measured in degrees the arc CD is $a(2\pi r) \div 360$. If it is measured in seconds of arc, it is $2\pi r a \div (360 \times 60 \times 60)$. Hence sin a'' and tan a'' are each

$$\frac{2\pi a}{360 \times 60 \times 60} = \frac{44a}{7 \times 36^2 \times 10^3}$$

So if p'' is the parallax of a star

$$\tan p'' = \frac{44p}{7 \times 36^2 \times 10^3}$$

$\therefore$ star's distance = sun's distance $\div \dfrac{44p}{7 \times 36^2 \times 10^3}$

$$= \frac{93,000,000 \times 36^2 \times 10^3 \times 7}{44p}$$

$$= \frac{192 \times 10^{11}}{p}$$

The parallax of Sirius is $0 \cdot 371''$. Hence the distance of Sirius is

$$192 \times 10^{14} \div 371 = 52 \times 10^{12} \text{ or } 52 \text{ billion miles}$$

zenith distances at transit (D = z.d. + lat.) if measured at the same latitude. An equivalent difference in R.A. is also found when the star's R.A. is the same as the sun's or differs from it by 12 hours, i.e. when there should be no difference due to parallax.

According to Cajori the clue to this anomalous behaviour came to him from a class of everyday experiences which greatly helped to elucidate the laws of the combination of motions in different directions, when navigation was at the mercy of wind and current. "Accompanying a pleasure party on a sail on the Thames one day about September 1728," he noticed that the wind seemed to shift each time "that the boat put about, and a question put to the boatman brought the (to him) significant reply that the changes in direction of the vane

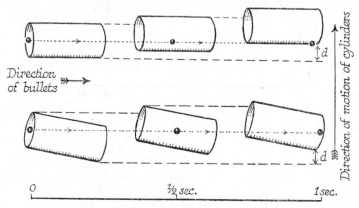

FIG. 216.—THE TILT OF THE TELESCOPE

To envisage the significance of Bradley's observations, imagine a train of bullets from a machine gun fired at the mouth of a cylinder with its opening pointed directly towards the oncoming bullets. If the cylinder is moved with a speed *d* ft. per sec. in a direction at right angles to the movement of the bullets, the latter will not pass straight down the middle of the cylinder. If the motion of the cylinder is sufficiently swift they will strike against the sides. To prevent this the cylinder must be tilted in its direction of motion. At a suitable tilt the bullets will pass straight along the middle of the cylinder. The propagation of a wave front of light along Bradley's telescope was analogous. That is to say, the object glass of the telescope has to be tilted slightly towards the direction of the observer's motion.

at the top of the mast were merely due to change in the boat's course, the wind remaining steady throughout. . . ." The significant fact about the shift called "aberration" which Bradley first observed was that the greatest displacement of the star's position is found at times when the earth is moving in its orbit either towards or away from the direction from which the angle is measured (Fig. 214). This fact receives a simple explanation from the fact that light travels with a finite speed. Hence the direction from which light reaches an observer is the resultant of his motion and that of the light. If the light is to pass down the centre of the telescope and be seen by the eye, the object-glass of the telescope must be tilted slightly in the direction of the observer's motion (Fig. 216). If the telescope is used to measure the angle between the star's direction and some direction of reference (e.g. a direction along the celestial equator in Fig. 214, or along the ecliptic plane in Fig. 217), then the angle is increased if the observer's motion is away from the direction of reference and decreased if his motion is towards this direction. For example, in Fig. 214, declination is measured from a line on the celestial equator plane, joining the

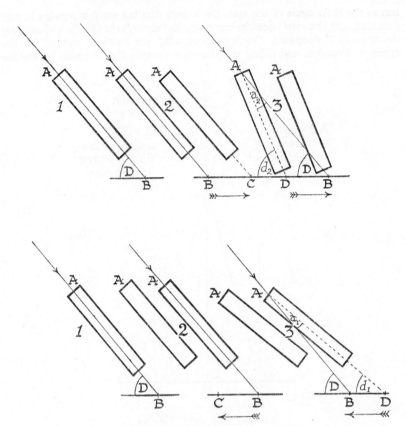

FIG. 217.—ABERRATION OF LIGHT

If the observer is at rest with his eye at B, light strikes the objective of his telescope at A, and traverses the distance AB in x seconds. The angle D is the elevation of the star above the plane of the ecliptic in which the earth is moving, i.e. the celestial latitude of the star. This is the true direction of the star. The observer is moving away from the source of light in the upper figure and towards it in the lower figure, in the line BC, and traverses the distance BC in x seconds. If he is moving away from the source and holds his telescope at the angle D, his eye reaches C when the light has traversed the distance AB. So he does not see the source. To see it, the telescope must be tilted *upwards*, i.e. in the direction of his motion, at an angle d_2 so that the light strikes the objective at A when he is at D before he gets to B, and does not reach B till he and his telescope have traversed the distance DB, x seconds later. Hence DB = BC. If he is moving towards the source of light as in the lower figure the telescope must be tilted *downward*, i.e. in the direction of his motions, making an angle d_1. Since light passes over a distance AB in x seconds, and the speed of light is AB ÷ x, the observer's speed is BC ÷ x

$$\therefore \frac{AB}{BC} = \frac{\text{Speed of light}}{\text{Speed of observer}}$$

In the upper figure the exterior angle $d_2 = D + a_2$. In the lower figure the exterior angle $D = d_1 + a_1$, i.e. $d_1 = D - a_1$.

sun to the R.A. circle of the star. On March 21st the earth is moving in this direction, and since the telescope must be tilted towards the direction of motion, the angle D is decreased. On September 23rd the earth is moving in the opposite direction, and tilting the telescope towards the direction of motion

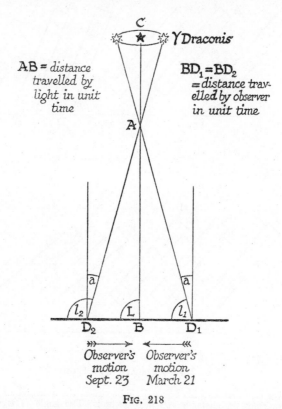

AB = *distance travelled by light in unit time*

$BD_1 = BD_2$ = *distance travelled by observer in unit time*

γ *Draconis*

Observer's motion Sept. 23 *Observer's motion March 21*

FIG. 218

Since γ Draconis is fairly near the pole of the ecliptic, its celestial latitude, L, may be taken as about 90°. But on March 21st, tilting the telescope in the direction of the observer's motion decreases the observed latitude by a small angle, a, to l_1. Similarly on September 23rd, the angle is increased by a to l_2.

Now $\tan a = \dfrac{BD}{AB}$, and since a is a very small angle (see Fig. 215)

$$a = \frac{BD}{AB}$$

$$= \frac{\text{earth's orbital speed}}{\text{speed of light}}$$

increases the angle. The plane of the earth's orbital motion is not the celestial equator, but that of the ecliptic. So the elevation of the star from the ecliptic, i.e. its celestial latitude (see p. 220), measures the inclination of the star-beam to the observer's motion. This can be calculated from its declination and R.A. by an application of the formulae in the appendix to Chapter IV. When the celestial latitude is 90°, i.e. when the star is at the pole of the ecliptic, the correct set of the telescope simply depends on the speed of the earth in its orbit and the speed of light, just as the correct angle for aiming at a pheasant flying directly overhead (p. 239) simply depends on the speed of the bird and the speed of the bullet. If r is the distance of the sun from the earth, the observer is moving through $2\pi r = \frac{44}{7}r$ miles in 365 days. His speed is therefore

$$\frac{44r}{7 \times 365 \times 24 \times 60 \times 60} = \frac{11r}{42 \times 365 \times 36 \times 10^2} \text{ miles per second}$$

If the star is at the pole of the ecliptic, the angle a is $20 \cdot 5''$, i.e. $20 \cdot 5 \div (60 \times 60)$ degrees, and:

$$\tan a = \frac{\text{speed of earth's orbital motion}}{\text{speed of light}}$$

If the speed of light is 186,000 miles per second,

$$\tan a = \frac{11r}{42 \times 365 \times 36 \times 10^5 \times 186}$$

The tangent of this angle can be found without recourse to tables (Fig. 215), being

$$\frac{20 \cdot 5}{60 \times 60} \times \frac{\pi}{180} = \frac{41 \times 22}{72 \times 18 \times 7 \times 10^3}$$

So we may put:

$$\frac{11r}{186 \times 42 \times 365 \times 36 \times 10^5} = \frac{41 \times 22}{72 \times 18 \times 7 \times 10^3}$$

$$\therefore r = \frac{41 \times 22 \times 42 \times 186 \times 365 \times 36 \times 10^2}{11 \times 72 \times 18 \times 7} = \frac{9259 \times 10^9}{998 \times 10^2} \text{ approx.}$$

To three significant figures this is 92,800,000 miles, in close agreement with the sun's distance calculated from parallax or from the annual shift of the spectra of the fixed stars.

THE SURVIVAL OF WORD MAGIC

During the nineteenth century, when the phenomena of interference were first fully investigated, the wave metaphor became firmly entrenched in scientific discussion. It was the fashion to speak of a supposititious all-pervading ether, which remained when all weighable matter had been removed from a space. The plain truth is that this *ether* was less a description of what we encounter when investigating the world than a description of the kind of mathematics with which we calculate what happens in certain circumstances. In the study of how chemical qualities of substances (like a pinch of common salt) are related to the spectra which they yield when made to glow in a non-luminous flame, recent discoveries have received less help from the wave metaphor and more from the analogy of the bullet. Consequently the *ether* is receding into the realm of word magic along with phlogiston (p. 422), the life force and the Real Presence.

Science has nothing to lose from the decease of a metaphor. In a different social context from the one in which we live, the change might be regarded as a welcome release from reliance on the existence of something beyond the range of our senses. If we wish to understand why the new outlook in physics is interpreted as a reason for rejecting the materialistic temper of the century which began with Diderot and ended with Darwin, we must not expect to find an answer in the progress of scientific knowledge. The story of man's conquest of Substance and of Power will make it clear that we have reached a situation in which social machinery can no longer accommodate rapid advance in discovering the material amenities which science confers. We are thus faced with two alternatives. One is to devise the social machinery which will ensure the further progress of science by finding social uses for new discoveries. The other is to discredit confidence in the fact-loving method of science. This can be done most effectively by surrounding the work of the scientific investigator with an air of mystery, so that he fulfils the rôle of the first men of science in human history. The ancient calendar priests were the first scientists and the first civil servants. They ceased to be scientists as they aspired to become masters. The world tires of its masters and finds a growing need for efficient civil servants. So we may hope that the adventure of human knowledge will survive all the efforts to reinstate mysticism in the present period of cultural decay.

The phase of discovery which has been dealt with in this chapter draws attention to aspects of scientific method often overlooked, especially in the study of social institutions. There are two errors commonly held among people who study human society. The one to which the economist is prone is the use of facts to illustrate hypotheses based on seemingly self-evident principles, instead of the use of facts to test whether seemingly self-evident principles are a safe guide to conduct. At the opposite extreme is the school of historians who eschew all hypothesis and discourage "rash" generalization, apparently content to collect facts as an end in themselves. The truth is that scientific knowledge is not a mere collection of facts. It is an organized repository of useful and fruitful facts. Some of the most useful and fruitful facts have been found by using theories which seem utterly absurd in retrospect. What specially distinguishes the method of genuine science is that theory and practice, hypothesis and fact, work hand in hand. In a scientific experiment the investigator sets out to collect the facts that he expects to get. If they do not exist he fails to get them. If he fails to get them there must be something wrong with his expectations. So if he is a good investigator he will either discard his hypothesis or modify it and submit it to further test in its modified form. A scientific hypothesis must live dangerously or die of inanition. Science thrives on daring generalizations. There is nothing particularly scientific about excessive caution. Cautious explorers do not cross the Atlantic of truth.

THINGS TO MEMORIZE

1. Wave-length × frequency = speed of sound = 1,120 feet per second at 15° C.

2. Frequency of vibrating string $n = \dfrac{1}{2l}\sqrt{\dfrac{F}{m}}$

3. The change in wave-length observed when someone moving with a velocity v passes a source of period T is $2v$T.

EXAMPLES ON CHAPTER VI

Take the speed of sound as 1,120 feet per second.

1. What is the wave-length of a note if the velocity of the waves is 1,100 feet per second and the frequency is 440?

2. If the shortest wave-length a man can hear is about 18 cm. and the longest about 900 cm. calculate the frequency in both cases. Take the velocity of sound to be 33,000 cm. per second.

3. What is the wave-length of a pure note if the speed of propagation is 340 metres per second and its frequency is 256 per second?

4. A steamer nearing the coast blows a whistle and after 10 seconds an echo is heard. When the whistle is blown five minutes later the echo is heard after 8 seconds. Calculate how far from the coast the steamer was when the second whistle was sounded, and her speed.

5. How far away is a thunderstorm, if a flash of lightning is seen 4 seconds before a clap of thunder is heard?

6. A man standing in a ravine with parallel sides fires a rifle. He hears an echo after $1\frac{1}{2}$ seconds and another 1 second later. After another $1\frac{1}{2}$ seconds he hears a third echo. How do you account for these echoes, and how wide is the ravine?

7. The echo of the blast of a ship's siren is heard in $1\frac{1}{4}$ seconds. If the reflection is caused by an iceberg, how many seconds after hearing the echo will it be before the ship, steaming at $13\frac{9}{11}$ miles per hour, hits it?

8. An engine, blowing a whistle whose frequency is 500, passes a man in a signal box at a mile a minute. What does the frequency of the whistle appear to be to the man, before and after the engine passes?

9. When half a mile away from a tunnel through a hill, an engine blows its whistle, and an echo is heard by the driver $4\frac{1}{2}$ seconds later. Taking the velocity of sound as 1,100 feet per second, how fast is the engine going?

10. A train rushes past a stationary engine, which is blowing a whistle of frequency 600, at 60 miles per hour. What value would the passengers in the train give to the frequency of the whistle before and after passing?

11. A bullet is heard to strike a target $2\frac{1}{2}$ seconds after it has been fired with a velocity of 2,000 feet per second. How far away is the target from the marksman?

12. A tuning fork has a bristle attached to one of its prongs which just touches a vertical smoked glass plate. When the tuning fork is sounded and the plate allowed to fall under the action of gravity a wavy line is traced on the plate. If a distance d marks off N waves show that the frequency is $N\sqrt{2d/g}$.

13. Using the same apparatus as in Example 12, the plate is dropped from rest through a distance of $1 \cdot 8$ cm. In the next $10 \cdot 2$ cm. fall the fork makes 35 waves. What is the frequency of the fork?

14. What is the depth of a well, if a stone is heard to strike the water 2 seconds after it is dropped? (Take $g = 32$ ft. sec.²)

15. When two vibrating bodies have not exactly the same frequency, there are times when the compressions or rarefactions from both sources pass a given spot simultaneously, and times when a compression from one neutralizes a rarefaction from the other. These alternate periods of much disturbance and then comparatively little disturbance produce a pulsating effect called beats. If two strings of frequencies 300 and 302 per second are bowed, how many beats are produced in a second?

16. Two tuning forks, one of frequency 256 per second, are sounded simultaneously and produce 4 beats per second. When the other fork of unknown

frequency is loaded with a small piece of wax the beats stop. Determine the frequency of this fork.

17. Two tuning forks of frequency 512 are taken. One of the forks has its prongs filed, so that when sounded with the other 5 beats per second are produced. Find the frequency of the filed fork.

18. A noise is heard at three stations A, B and C. A hears the noise 13·14 seconds before B and 8·89 seconds before C. If the rectangular co-ordinates of A, B, and C, are respectively (4,0), (0,0) and (0,2) on a map, a mile being the unit, by means of a geometrical construction find the co-ordinates of the source of the noise. Take the speed of sound as 1,100 ft. sec.

19. From Fig. 197 we see that sound waves from *a* can reach the ear by two separate paths. When one path is 16 cm. longer than the other no sound is heard. When it is 32 cm. longer a sound can be heard, and when 48 cm. longer no sound, and so on. Taking the velocity of sound to be 33,200 cm. per second, what is the frequency of the whistle?

20. As an engine, blowing its whistle, passes a station, the pitch of the whistle appears to a man on the platform to drop a minor third, i.e. to $\frac{5}{6}$ths of its apparent frequency before passing. How fast is the train going? Take the speed of sound as 1,100 ft. sec.

21. If the greatest interval between successive eclipses of Jupiter's second moon is 42 hours 28 minutes 56 seconds, and the least interval is 42 hours 28 minutes 28 seconds, determine the speed of light (miles per second), given that the radius of the earth's orbit is $92 \cdot 7 \times 10^6$ miles.

22. Using Fig. 202 to determine the velocity of light, find the angular velocity in radians per second of the wheel for the third and fourth disappearance of the image, when the distance from C to B is 10 km. and the wheel has 720 teeth.

23. Using the same figure, let the distance from C to B be 15 km. and the wheel have 600 teeth. Given the speed of light $= 3 \cdot 0 \times 10^{10}$ cm. per second, how many revolutions in a second must the toothed wheel make so that light passing through a gap on one journey is stopped by the next tooth on the return journey?

24. A beam of light on a revolving mirror is reflected by it and travels a distance of 750 metres to a mirror, which reflects the beam back along its path. The beam is then reflected again by the revolving mirror, and is found to make an angle of one minute with its original path. What is the angular velocity of the revolving mirror in revolutions per second?

SELECTED REFERENCES FOR PART I

ANTHIAUME, L'ABBÉ: *L'Evolution et l'Enseignement de la Science Nautique en France*. (Paris: Dumont.) 1920.

ANTHIAUME, L'ABBÉ: *L'histoire de la Science Nautique antérieurement à la Découverte du Nouveau Monde*. (Le Havre.) 1913.

BENSAUDE, JOAQUIM: *L'Astronomie Nautique au Portugal à l'Epoque des Grandes Découvertes*. (Bern, Akademische Buchhandlung von Max Drechsel.) 1912.

BRUNET, P.: *Histoire des Sciences, Antiquité*. (Paris: Payot.) 1935.

BURGEL, BRUNO H.: *Aus Fernen Welten*. (Berlin: Verlag Ullstein.) 1920.

DOBELL, CLIFFORD: *Antony van Leeuwenhoek and His Little Animals*. (Bale.) 1932.

FERRAND, GABRIEL: *Introduction à l'Astronomie Nautique Arabe*. (Paris: Paul Geuthner.) 1928.

GALILEO, GALILEI: *Dialogues Concerning Two New Sciences*. (New York: The Macmillan Co.) 1914.

HAKLUYT, RICHARD: *The Principal Navigations, Voyages, Traffiques and Discoveries of the English Nation.* (Text of 1589.) (Dent.) 1928.

HART, IVOR B.: *The Mechanical Investigations of Leonardo da Vinci.* (Chapman and Hall.) 1925.

HEATH, SIR T.: *Aristarchus of Samos.* (S.P.C.K.) 1921.

HOOKE, ROBERT: *The Diary of Robert Hooke.* Editd. by H. W. Robinson and W. Adams. (Taylor and Francis.) 1935.

HOOKE, S. H.: *New Year's Day.* (Gerald Howe.) 1927.

LOCKYER, SIR J. NORMAN: *The Dawn of Astronomy.* (Cassell.) 1894.

MARGUET, F.: *Histoire de la longitude à la mer au XVIIIe siècle en France.* (Paris, Chalomell.) 1917.

MEYER, E.: *Geschichte des Altertums.* (Stuttgart and Berlin: J. G. Cotta.) 1928.

MEYER, E.: *Die ältere Chronologie Babyloniens, Assyriens und Aegyptiens.* (Stuttgart and Berlin: J. G. Cotta.) 1925.

MORLEY, S. G.: *Introduction to the Study of Maya Hieroglyphs.* (Bureau of Am. Ethnol. Bull. 57.) 1915.

NEUBURGER, ALBERT: *The Technical Arts and Sciences of the Ancients.* (Methuen.) 1930.

NILSSON, MARTIN P.: *Primitive Time Reckoning.* (Lund: Sweden: C. W. K. Gleerup.) 1920.

PARSONS, L. M.: *Everyday Science.* (Macmillan.) 1929.

PETRIE, SIR FLINDERS: *History of Egypt,* vol. i. (Methuen.) 1923.

REINHARDT, K.: *Poseidonius.* (Munich: Beck.) 1921.

REINHARDT, K.: *Kosmos und Sympathie.* (Munich: Beck.) 1925.

REY, ABEL: *La Science Oriental Avant les Grecs.* (Paris: La Renaissance du Livre.) 1930.

RUSSELL, DUGAN, AND STEWART: *Astronomy* (2 vols). (Ginn).

SCHMIDT, W. (edit.): *Hero Alexandrinus.* Bibliothec. script. Graec. Rom. (Teubner.) 1899.

SMITH, DAVID EUGENE: *History of Mathematics* (2 vols.) (Boston: Ginn.) 1923.

SNYDER, CARL: *The World Machine.* (Longmans.) 1907.

SPRAT, THOMAS: *The History of the Royal Society of London, for the Improving of Natural Knowledge.* (London.) 1722.

TAYLOR, E. G. R.: "Jean Rotz: His Neglected Treatise on Nautical Science," *The Geographical Journal,* May 1929.

TAYLOR, E. G. R.: "A Sixteenth-Century MS. Navigating Manual in the Society's Library," *The Geographical Journal,* October 1931.

TAYLOR, E. G. R.: *Tudor Geography, 1485–1583.* (Methuen.) 1930.

THOMPSON, J. E.: *The Civilisation of the Mayas.* (Field Museum, Chicago, Anthrop. Handbook 25.) 1927.

THOMPSON, J. E.: *A Correlation of Maya and European Calendars.* (Field Museum, Chicago, Anthrop. Series vol. 17, 1.) 1927.

THORNDIKE, LYNN: *History of Magic and Experimental Science.* (2 vols.) (Macmillan.) 1934.

THULIN, C.: *Corpus Agrim. Rom.* vol. i, 1911.

WARD, F. A. B.: *Time Measurement.* Part I. Historical Review Handbooks of the Science Museum. (Stat. Office.) 1936.

WILDE, E.: *Geschichte der Optik.* Berlin. 1843.

WOLF, A.: *A History of Science, Philosophy and Technology in the Sixteenth and Seventeenth Centuries.* (George Allen & Unwin.) 1935.

WRIGHT, J. K.: *Notes on the Knowledge of Latitude and Longitude in the Middle Ages.* (Isis. vol. v, pt. i, Brussels.) 1923.

WRIGHT, J. K.: *The Geographical Lore of the Time of the Crusades.* (American Geog. Soc.) 1925.

PART II

The Conquest of Substitutes

But the mortallest enemy unto knowledge, and that which hath done the greatest execution upon truth, hath been a peremptory adhesion unto authority; and more especially, the establishing of our belief upon the dictates of antiquity. For (as every capacity may observe) most men, of ages present, so superstitiously do look upon ages past, that the authorities of the one exceed the reasons of the other. Whose persons indeed far removed from our times, their works, which seldom with us pass uncontrolled, either by contemporaries, or immediate successors, are now become out of the distance of envies; and, the farther removed from present times, are conceived to approach the nearer unto truth itself. Now hereby methinks we manifestly delude ourselves, and widely walk out of the track of truth.—SIR THOMAS BROWNE'S *Pseudodoxia Epidemica*.

CHAPTER VII

THE THIRD STATE OF MATTER

The Freeborn Miner

ONE characteristic which specially distinguishes human beings from other animals is their power to change the nature of their environment. By selecting other organisms for their associates and collecting different sorts of lifeless matter from their surroundings, they provide themselves with the means of food, of shelter, of locomotion, and of adornment. Mankind has thus risen superior to the barriers of climate and situation limiting the distribution of other living creatures. In establishing himself as a species with a world-wide distribution, man's power to change his environment is circumscribed by two facts. A comparatively small number of plants and animals are suitable for cultivation or domestication, and a comparatively small number of substances which are found in nature are directly suitable for fabricating articles of use or amusement. Organisms and their products suitable to human requirements of one or the other sort—myrrh and cedarwood, silk and pearls—had a very limited distribution in the ancient world. So likewise had the metals which man learned to treasure first, and later to work. In the ages of scarcity, when the trade routes were of fundamental importance to the diffusion of culture, man had to discover how to find his way about a world in which the basic means of human satisfaction were sparse. Until the end of the eighteenth century of our era man's greatest intellectual achievements were associated with the survey of a world in which the good things of life were very unequally distributed.

The story of how man learned to find his way about the world has been told in the preceding chapters. This stage in the growth of man's understanding of the universe reached a climax in the three centuries which witnessed the opening up of the resources of two new continents to European civilization. By the end of the eighteenth century the habitable world had been explored with the aid of the sextant and telescope, the theodolite and chronometer. An inventory of man's resources for continuing a mode of living which had changed very little since the construction of the Pyramids had been accomplished. So at this point we may fittingly take leave of the story of man's conquest of time reckoning and earth measurement. When the nineteenth century dawned progress in the knowledge of nature had assumed a different aspect. The ages of scarcity were drawing to a close. Space and Time were making way for the study of Matter, Power, and Health.

If we consider the variety of substances available for human use and the resources of power which can now replace human effort, the gap separating us from the seventeenth century of our own era is far greater than that which separates the seventeenth century of the present era from the Mediterranean world of 1700 B.C. In the long period which intervened there had been no radical additions to knowledge of the use of materials, nor any radical improvement in mechanical substitutes for human labour. The knowledge of metals, of glass making, of pottery, of weaving, of dyeing, of brewing, of irrigation, of enamels, and of cosmetics, had scarcely surpassed the achievements of the early civilizations in the Mediterranean. The plough, the wind sail, and the water-wheel, were older than the hanging gardens of Babylon. The best silks were still the silks of Old Cathay. What material progress had occurred in the world as a whole was little more than a process of give and take. There had been no important new inventions, nor new industries, other than those to which reference has been made already. That is to say, gunpowder, printing, spectacles, and mechanical clocks.

Our task will now be to trace the story of man's conquest of materials, and to indicate the social prospect which it unfolds. What we call the science of chemistry today is made up of rules for making and recognizing the presence of substances which have very definite physical properties, such as density, colour, crystalline form, melting and boiling points, odour, texture, and so forth. So in textbooks of chemistry it is customary to begin with the definition of a pure substance. Perhaps it is better not to do so. There is no way of capturing the meaning of a pure substance in a simple sentence. Any definition which we attempt to frame registers the stage we have reached in discovering reliable recipes for making things. Primitive man collected materials from rocks and springs, from animal tissues and plant juices, and used them to make metals, pigments and fabrics, perfumes, dyes, and medicines. His success and the quality of his products depended on local peculiarities of the minerals, or on local species of plants and animals. All the early industries of civilization had the same *local* character. Sand was mixed with lime or potashes and various minerals found here and there. The quality of the glass of a particular locality became famous. The secretion of a Mediterranean sea-slug furnished the Tyrian purple of Phoenician trade. It was nobody's business to know why the glass of a particular place was better, or to make the dye which the sea-slug excreted. Man took the fruits of nature as they came. What science he had was mainly used to get to the places where they were to be found.

In the new phase on which we are now entering the reverse is true. Every advance of science makes man less dependent on local materials. We know the nature of the dyes and drugs which were once obtained exclusively from animals and plants, and we manufacture them from substances like coal, which are more widely distributed. If we cared to do so, we could make them from substances which are universally distributed. We no longer depend on the manure dumps of India for the nitrates used for making gunpowder in medieval times, nor on the natural deposits of Chile for the nitrates which were introduced for use as fertilizers in the nineteenth century. Nitrates can be made from the nitrogen of the air and the common salt of the ocean. For metals of great hardness and strength we are no longer dependent on local ores. We know innumerable ways of making alloys. Aluminium, which is the most abundant and universally distributed of all the metals in the superficial layers of the earth's crust, is already beginning to displace the use of the heavier metals which nations have struggled to monopolize in the past.

Aside from structural materials, among which wood, clay, stone, and sand still predominate, the basic ingredients of modern industry are of a totally different kind from those used in the time of Newton. Modern chemistry recognizes more than a quarter of a million distinct substances. Hundreds are being discovered yearly, and an enormous number are already employed in making articles of everyday use. Three hundred years ago chemical industry as we now know it did not exist. Crude lime, made by cooking chalk and limestone in kilns, was sold for making cement and glass, or for curing leather. Incinerated charcoal or "potashes" rich in alkaline potassium carbonate from the forests of central and eastern Europe was imported into Britain for cleaning wool fibres and making soap, prepared by boiling the solution with lard or mutton fat. Crude alum from the Isle of Wight was employed in preparing cloth for dyeing. At most a dozen vegetable juices in place of the many hundreds of modern synthetic pigments were in everyday use. Salt sold for preserving meat owed its chief commercial use to its principal impurity—the hygroscopic magnesium chloride, which is removed from the best table salt of today. All the pure metals then known—gold, silver, copper, tin, iron, lead, zinc, mercury, and antimony—had been worked in the ancient world, and were prepared from their ores by the same processes. Mineral pigments like the vermilion cinnabar (mercury sulphide) and green malachite (copper carbonate), or cosmetics like galena (lead sulphide), were probably used less in sixteenth-century England than in ancient Egypt. More medicinal chemicals were recognized, but these had not become important articles of commerce. Jewels, which owe their special characteristics to crystal form, one of the fundamental criteria of a pure substance in the modern sense, represented almost the only articles of commerce which the chemist of today would recognize as such.

To be sure, it would be an exaggeration to say that there was no science of chemistry before the nineteenth century, or that no progress was made in its study between the age of Archimedes and the age of Newton. No sharp line can be drawn between organized scientific knowledge and mere rule-of-thumb methods of recognizing the characteristics of nature. The latter must always precede the former, and the former grows out of the latter. What can be truthfully said is that there was no substantial improvement in the actual technique of preparing materials of reliable quality, that is to say making "pure" substances, between the fall of the Alexandrian civilization and the middle of the seventeenth century of our era. No substantial improvements in processes of preparing, detecting, and assaying metals were made in the first sixteen centuries of the present era, and if Arab medicine had added a number of new substances to the list of those previously known, it had done little to clarify any general rules for making them.

The search for pure substances was mainly prompted by three principal requirements of everyday life in civilized communities—metals, munitions (pp. 406-8), and medicines. The enormous influence of the latter may seem strange when we reflect upon the scope of reliable medical knowledge as late as the time of Jenner. Still, it would be a mistake to regard primitive medicine as mere superstition. One of the commonest complaints of everyday life is constipation, and the possibility of relieving it by the use of various reagents was a discovery of great antiquity. The purgative calomel (a chloride of mercury) was known to the Egyptians; and if the achievements of the physician were less conspicuous in other fields, the gratitude of their fellows for the use of aperients and purgatives is amply illustrated by the lyrical flourish with which discoveries of new ones were announced. As late as A.D. 1648 Glauber could proclaim the addition of sodium sulphate to the pharmacopoeia with a tract entitled *Miraculo Mundi*, and Glauber's salt enjoyed the sobriquet *sal mirabile*. A little later Nehemiah Grew described the uses of Epsom salts (magnesium sulphate) with the evangelical fervour of an all too familiar advertisement.

From the practice of mining, ancient chemistry had learned the processes now called *oxidation* and *reduction*. The history of man's earliest attempts to extract metals from their ores is still largely speculative. Both gold and silver occur as metals in nature, and both could be shaped with the stone hammers which primitive man possessed. Native gold and native silver were treasured before the dawn of city life, and were first used for making simple ornaments. Metallic copper also exists in the regions where civilization began, and native copper seems to have been the source of the first hammered copper instruments. These are found along with chisels and adzes of gold, silver, and electrum (a silver-gold alloy), in the recent excavations at Ur. Little progress in the use of metals could be made when only gold and silver were known. Though native copper is soft, it is hardened by hammering. Rickard (*Man and Metals*, Vol. I) says:

> As soon as primitive man began to shape his finds of copper he must have observed this important fact, which was decisive in making the metal more serviceable for the fabrication of instruments. At once the red stone became more useful than the yellow. . . . The use of native copper marks the beginnings of every ancient metal culture. . . . Perhaps two millennia separated the first use of hammered copper from the beginning of true metal culture, when copper was smelted from its ores and cast in a mould.

Elliott Smith has put forward reasons to support a plausible hypothesis to account for this momentous discovery. The green copper carbonate called *malachite* is readily converted by a dull red heat into copper oxide, which is reduced to the metal itself when roasted with charcoal. Over a long period of pre-history there is ample evidence that mankind used powdered malachite as a pigment. In pre-dynastic Egypt it was used for facial adornment. Whenever debris containing malachite was dropped among the embers of a charcoal fire, spangles of metallic copper would be formed. We may well suppose that this was not a very rare occurrence. The use of bronze (a copper-tin alloy) came much later—about 1500 B.C., and its discovery was probably due to the fact that ores of copper and tin often occur side by side. Though iron occurs with great rarity as a truly indigenous metal apart from its ores, the Jovian thunderbolt had familiarized man with it from early times. Fragments of meteoric iron are found with human remains long before the age of iron instruments began—about 1200 B.C., and modern Esquimaux have been observed to make knives by inserting flakes of meteoric iron in grooved strips of walrus bone. Several common pigments, the ochres such as haematite, are rich in iron. So the discovery of smelting iron from its ores may have been made by analogy with the pre-existing technique for extracting copper.

Primitive metallurgy began with the *reduction* of the class of ores now called metallic carbonates or oxides, i.e. by heating them *with charcoal in a closed space*. This was all that was necessary for preparing the tin used in making bronze from its common ores. Many of the common ores are what we now know to be *sulphides*, i.e. combinations of a metal with the element sulphur. The next step in the progress of metallurgy was probably the discovery that some of the "sulphureous" ores, like those of lead, copper, iron, zinc, silver, and mercury, can be reduced *if previously heated in air*, or as we now say, if they are first "*oxidized*." The discovery that the process is facilitated by keeping the air in motion probably led to the invention of the bellows and the first crude blast furnaces for oxidizing the more recalcitrant sulphureous ores like pyrites (iron sulphide). Natural ores are always mixed with fragments of sand, which is mainly composed of the same substance (silica or silicon oxide) as quartz. The trick of heating the ore with some "flux" such as lime, to make it readily form a molten mass, may have been gleaned from the discovery of glass, or it may have led to it.

These processes were practised more than three thousand years ago, and their nature remained an enigma till the end of the eighteenth century. The craft of the goldsmith and the silversmith offered great opportunities for chicanery, as a familiar legend about Archimedes reminds us. The artificers of Alexandria were apparently familiar with various devices for detecting and manufacturing fraudulent articles by dissolving metals in acids and reprecipitating them from their salts. According to a legend current in the alchemical works of the Middle Ages, Diocletian ordered the suppression of all the Alexandrian books on the art of chemistry for fear that the artificers would enrich themselves exorbitantly. An unduly sanguine interpretation of their achievements led to a futile search for the supposedly lost secret of transmuting lead into gold. Slowly Europe recovered the real secrets of Alexandrian chemistry, without recognizing them as such.

The technique of preparing pure chemicals for medicinal use owes much to the very ancient industry of brewing. The formation of tartaric acid crystals in wine vats was already known to the Egyptians. This was possibly the origin of the preparation of pure substances by allowing them to crystallize out by cooling, and also of the practice of recognizing them by their crystalline form. Most important of all devices for separating substances with individual characteristics was the process of *distillation*, which is used in the preparation of alcoholic liquors. The retort had already become an important instrument of medical research in Alexandria. In the hands of the Arabs, to whom we owe the word *alcohol*, it became the means of adding many new members to the known list of chemical species. The Moorish physicians made some advance towards classifying the nature of substances. They recognized solutions of acids, alkalis, or of salts, according to their effect on vegetable dyes, used in the preparation of fabrics. One of the dyes which was formerly used in this way is the familiar "litmus," which turns red when dipped in a mineral acid, or blue if dipped in the solution of an alkali (i.e. "*bases*" like sodium hydroxide and quicklime, or "carbonates" of sodium and potassium). The Arab chemists gave recipes for making the three chief mineral acids (nitric, sulphuric, and hydrochloric) of modern commerce by distilling off the vapours formed when various salts are heated.

M*

The nature of distillation, like the nature of reduction and oxidation, remained an enigma. In the processes of the laboratory substances seemingly disappeared on heating. They became "spirits," and the art of chemistry was to make these *spirits* materialize. The spirits of the retort, which still remain in our vocabulary as *spirits of wine*, *spirits of salt*, and the like, are now recognized to be a third state of matter. In the ancient world what we now call gases and vapours were not recognized as a form of matter, and it was utterly impossible to see any common thread running through the familiar processes of distillation in medicine and reduction or oxidation in metallurgy. Although Greek materialism had proclaimed the robust doctrine on which modern chemistry rests, neither the experience of the physician nor the art of the metalworker seemed to support the belief that matter is indestructible. The ancient world recognized two classes of things which could be weighed

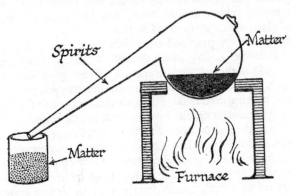

FIG. 219

According to the ancient conception of chemical processes the fire of the furnace dissolved the matter contained in the retort into its earthy constituent and the "spirits" which escaped. That the spirits, or as we now say *gases*, had weight was not recognized.

with scales—solids and liquids. Aristotle's physics had rejected the possibility that air could have weight.

Before the middle of the sixteenth century there was no clear evidence that air is a form of matter in this sense, nor was there the least apprehension of the fact that innumerable forms of matter exist like air in the gaseous state. So the distinction which we now draw between the two classes of pure substances called elements and compounds completely eluded the science of antiquity. What was neither liquid nor solid was spirit. The discovery that air has weight, separating the theory of chemistry today from the practice of chemistry till the time of Galileo, Hooke, and Boyle, is one of the great dichotomies in the history of human knowledge. Circumstances of everyday life contributed in various ways to this discovery, which revolutionized man's command over the use of materials. In the great age of the sailing ship men of science were beginning to measure forces as matter in motion. This raised the question, Is the force of the wind also a manifestation of matter in motion? Galileo's experiments on the way in which heavy bodies fall prompted enquiry into the material nature of air for another and far more important reason, related to the immediate social context of his researches in a different way. Laboratory experience showed that heavy bodies gain speed at the same fixed rate when falling through air. This seems (see p. 366) to be in flat contradiction to experience of everyday life. We shall now see how Galileo resolved the paradox, and how his pupils and successors proved the truth of his solution.

The source from which Galileo got his clue made the study of air and its characteristics an issue of momentous importance about the same time, and it was of special significance in Britain, where the revival of the teachings of the Greek atomists was received by men of science with enthusiasm. Extensive development of deep-shaft mining took place in the sixteenth and seventeenth centuries owing, among other things, to the wastage of iron in warfare after the introduction of artillery. Speaking of the change in Britain (*Econ. Hist. Rev.*, 1934), Nef remarks:

Though the output of tin, unlike other metallic ores, was not increasing, even in tin mines technical problems assumed an entirely new importance, because the more easily accessible supplies of ore had been largely exhausted in the Middle Ages. During the reigns of Elizabeth and her two Stuart successors money was poured out lavishly in the construction of hundreds of adits and ventilation shafts and of hundreds of drainage engines driven by water. . . . The high cost of fuel began to check the expansion of the output of iron before the end of Elizabeth's reign. . . . During the reigns of Elizabeth, Charles I, and James I, coal was successfully substituted for wood fuel in calcining ores . . and in nearly all finishing processes.

The mere technique of deep-shaft mining was not a new development in human industry. Neuberger's book *The Technical Art and Sciences of the Ancients* tells us:

Mining was at different stages of advancement among the various ancient peoples. It was particularly developed among the Egyptians, who probably opened up copper mines on the peninsula of Sinai as early as the third millennium B.C. Besides these the vast quarries of Turra near Cairo have also been preserved; they prove to us that at that very early date open working had been given up in favour of shafts. The ancient Egyptians were thus not satisfied with merely removing the stones in the hill from the outside, but penetrated far into the interior. Wells of the same period, for example, Joseph's well at Cairo, descend up to 300 feet vertically into the earth. In view of the fact that these shafts were constructed about 2500 B.C., it can hardly be doubted that similar ones were also dug out for mining purposes in some cases. The high standard of mining construction attained by the Egyptians is rivalled by the Indians and the Chinese, who likewise sank pits about five thousand years ago.

Though the technique was not essentially new, there was an important difference between the conditions of deep-shaft mining in the seventeenth century and the practice of more ancient times. Mining in antiquity was made possible by abundant supplies of slave labour, which was used with what now seems to be almost an incredibly reckless disregard for human life. Neuberger goes on to state:*

* See also A. Zimmern, *The Greek Commonwealth*, and B. Farrington, *Diodorus Siculus* (Univ. Wales Press).

There were no precautions against accidents. The galleries were not propped up, and therefore often collapsed, burying workmen beneath them. In ancient mines many skeletons have been found of slaves who had lost their lives in this way while at work. Nor were attempts made to replenish the supply of air or to take other steps for preserving health. When the air in the mines became so hot and foul that breathing was rendered impossible the place was abandoned and an attack was made at some other point. These conditions must have become still more trying wherever, in addition to the mallet and chisel, the only other means of detaching the stone was applied, namely fire. The mineral-bearing stone was heated and water was then poured over it. There was no outlet for the resulting smoke and vapours. This method of constructing tunnels and galleries is described by Pliny somewhat as follows: "Tunnels are bored into the mountains and carefully explored. These tunnels are called 'arrugiae,' little ways or little streets. They often collapse and bury many workers. When hard minerals occur one seeks to blast them with fire and vinegar. As the resulting steam and smoke often fill the tunnels, the workmen prefer to split the rock into pieces of 150 lb. or more, and for this purpose they use iron wedges and hammers. These pieces are removed from the galleries that have been hewn out, so that an open cavern is formed. So many of these caverns or hollows are made adjacent to each other in the mountain that finally they collapse with a loud noise, and so the mineral in the interior becomes exposed. Often the eagerly sought gold vein fails to appear, and the long-sustained and arduous work which had often cost many human lives has been in vain." . . . The miner of ancient times was nearly always either a slave or a criminal. This explains why the means used remained unchanged for thousands of years. The purpose of machines is to economize labour or time. It was not considered necessary to make the work easier for the slave, whose hard lot inspired no sympathy, although it kept him to the end of his days buried in the gloomy depths of the earth, suffering all sorts of torments and privations. There was mostly a superabundance of slaves. After campaigns there were usually so many that great numbers of them were massacred. So there was no dearth of labour. Time was as yet but little valued. And so it happened that in almost all the mines of the ancients only the simplest means were adopted. In the copper mines of Rio Tinto and Tharsis in the Spanish province of Huelva, which were worked by the Romans and the Carthaginians, the method of working was so simple that the slaves in the mines had to scratch off with their fingers the clay which covered the ore. The clay which is found nowadays in ancient mines still bears the impress of thousands of fingers.

Quite otherwise were the social foundations of the mining industry when civilization spread to northern Europe. Surface work on tin in Cornwall and Devon probably continued from the Bronze Age to early medieval times on an essentially tribal basis. According to Lewis (*The Stannaries*) the tin workers of twelfth-century England were associations of free men. In time these profit-sharing syndicates became transformed into share-owning companies, employing wage earners. Even so, labour was still scarce, and penetration to deeper levels in a humid climate was accompanied by constant flooding. Coal-mining, which encountered further difficulties on its own account, was a new industrial enterprise. Concerning the condition of the medieval coal miner, Nef (*The Rise of the British Coal Industry*) says:

The modern organization of the coal industry, involving as it does the employment of a large industrial proletariat by absentee capitalists, makes it easy to assume that the miner has always been a wage earner. When a labour leader in our day refers to the miners as the aristocrats of the labour movement . . . what he almost certainly has not in mind, though it might well appeal to his audiences, is the position of the miners in the Middle Ages. In medieval England labourers in the metal mines were often granted special privileges and immunities of a kind rarely enjoyed by other manual workers. . . . Feudal lords in some cases turned over their minerals in return for a share of the output, to small autonomous associations of working miners. In coal mining "many pits were worked by '*associations charbonières.*'"

Nef hints that coal, like gunpowder, paper, and (probably) the magnet, is possibly part of our cultural debt to Chinese civilization. The Chinese apparently knew its use before the Christian era, and Marco Polo mentions the strange practice of the natives who burned for fuel "black stone . . . dug out of mountains where it runs in veins." In western civilization its use does not seem to have been known before about 1200, at which date a Liège chronicler refers to a "black earth very similar to charcoal" used by smiths and metal workers. Though export from Newcastle is recorded in the fourteenth century, coal was little used before the beginning of the sixteenth century, and then mainly from outcrops. By 1597 it was "one principall commoditie of this realme." By 1661 we are told that a "hellish and dismall cloud of Sea-Coale hangs perpetually over London." Mine-owners could no longer afford to throw away life with the recklessness of the Mediterranean slave-owning civilizations. How air becomes unfit for human beings to breathe, why some air is inflammable and why explosions occur, were questions which demanded an answer, and engaged the attention of the best brains. Francis Bacon, generally more ready with advice than with remedy, proposed a scheme for raising water from "drown'd mineral works." Pumps were being introduced to drive fresh air into the tunnels as well as to draw water out of them. The wind was no longer blowing whither it listeth. When we know how to control anything, we cease to regard it as spiritual.

This aspect of the social background of scientific discoveries which led to the rise of modern chemistry is discussed by Nef (*The Rise of the British Coal Industry*) in the following citation:

Boyle's interest in experiments of this nature, and the constant discussion of the Royal Society concerning the means of increasing the output of various commodities, or of heightening the efficiency of different technical processes, show a trend of the utmost importance. These "natural philosophers" of the English Restoration were economists as well as scientists; and, beside their old religion, which they resolved should not stand in the way of their achievements, they had begun to erect a new religion—the religion of production. It was one of Boyle's principal propositions, to which he reverted again and again, "that the Goods of Mankind may be much increased by the Naturalist's Insight into Trades." . . . There is a clear relation between the appearance of the extremely influential British school of "natural philosophers," and the growth of the British coal industry. The proceedings of the Royal Society for the first thirty or forty years following the grant of its charter in 1660, are full of discussions which have a bearing, often direct and perhaps even more frequently indirect, upon problems connected with mineralogy, with the mining and the use of coal. Colliery owners like Lowther, who was a member, or

Sir Roger Mostyn, who was not, send in accounts of explosions or of new methods of finding coal. Local naturalists send in samples of mineral fuel, or of strata resembling it, to be analysed and examined. Sir Robert Southwell reads a paper on the advantages of digging canals to supply London with cheaper coal. Boyle conducts experiments in order to determine the difference between coal and wood. The members meet to consider the projects on foot for smelting with coal. They puzzle over the causes for the strange fires which occur in the coal seams. . . . Soon after the incorporation of the Royal Society the King signified his pleasure that no patent should be granted for any "philosophical or mechanical invention," until it had been approved by the Society. And the problem of invention in the seventeenth century was to a considerable degree directly related to coal. "Through necessitie, which is the mother of all artes," wrote Howe, in 1631, "they have of very late yeeres devised the making of iron, the making of all sorts of glasse, and the burning of bricke, with sea coal or pitcoale." In this case the necessity was the substitution of coal for wood; in other cases it was the more adequate drainage of the mines, or the cheaper carriage of fuel over ground (pp. 253–4).

THE MECHANICS OF FLUIDS

Galileo's experiments on the way in which bodies fall overturned Aristotle's doctrine without providing any alternative explanation of the familiar experiences which seem to support it. Our everyday experience of falling bodies —of leaves blown from a tree, or tiles falling from a roof—suggests that the rate at which bodies fall depends chiefly on their density or relative "heaviness." Galileo's experiments showed that this is not true about comparatively heavy bodies of compact shape falling through air. To resolve the paradox experience of everyday life suggests that we have to reckon with other circumstances affecting the motion of falling bodies. Bodies fall under their own weight through liquids. We all know that a penny falls faster in water than in treacle, just as it falls faster in air than in water. We all know, too, that some bodies fall upwards, i.e. *float*, while others fall downwards, i.e. *sink*, in a liquid, and that bodies like a piece of tin which will sink in water may float on a *heavier* fluid like mercury. In other words, we have to take into account two facts which Aristotle rejected. One is that air has *weight*. The other is that like other weighty things it has *inertia*, i.e. it objects to being pushed to make way for falling bodies (p. 375). Galileo's solution of the paradox was that if solid bodies are immensely heavy compared with air, the effect of the air on the rate at which they fall must be negligible. So a croquet ball as large as a cannon ball gathers speed at nearly the same rate. On the other hand, a toy balloon as large as a cannon ball is mostly air. Its density is not very much greater than air itself. So it falls more slowly.

Alexandrian science had already supplied the clue, without recognizing its worth. One good reason why Alexandrian science failed to take the step which would have made chemistry an exact science is suggested by the fact which led Galileo to conclude that the weight of air raises water in the same way as the weight of mercury (Fig. 231) does. Galileo knew what the miners of his time knew to their cost, since it compelled them to raise water by relays of pumps and cisterns (Fig. 220). The Greek word for vulgarity was βαναυσία, which also meant handicraft, especially smithy work. It came from βαυνός, a

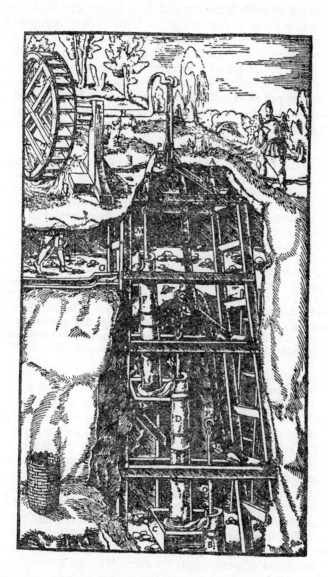

FIG. 220

(From Professor Wolf's *History of Science, Technology and Philosophy in the XVIth and XVIIth Centuries*)

This illustration from the Agricola Treatise shows pumps used in relays because the weight of the air is only sufficient to raise water about 33 feet. In Galileo's time it was respectable to know what every miner knew. The Greek materialists who taught that air has weight probably based their conclusion on the same experience of everyday life in mining areas. Aristotle, who despised manual work and advocated slavery for getting it done, devoted himself to refuting the materialist doctrine. His predilection for slavery helped to stop chemistry from further advance for about two thousand years.

forge. Perhaps Aristotle himself would have known that water cannot be lifted more than about 30 feet by a pump, if his intellectual powers had not been hampered by contempt for work which could be carried out by slaves. Those who accepted the Aristotelian teaching relied on the self-evident principle that "nature abhors a vacuum" to account for the way a pump works. As Galileo sceptically remarked, they could offer no reason why this abhorrence stopped short suddenly at a height of 30 feet from the ground.

In Galileo's *Dialogues concerning Two New Sciences* the following passage explicitly refers to the way in which everyday experience of the world's work compelled attention to the weight of the air:

Thanks to this discussion, I have learned the cause of a certain effect which I have long wondered at and despaired of understanding. I once saw a cistern which had been provided with a pump under the mistaken impression that the water might thus be drawn with less effort or in greater quantity than by means of the ordinary bucket. The stock of the pump carried its sucker and valve in the upper part so that the water was lifted by attraction and not by a push as is the case with pumps in which the sucker is placed lower down. This pump worked perfectly so long as the water in the cistern stood above a certain level; but below this level the pump failed to work. When I first noticed this phenomenon I thought the machine was out of order; but the workman whom I called in to repair it told me the defect was not in the pump but in the water which had fallen too low to be raised through such a height; and he added that it was not possible, either by a pump or by any other machine working on the principle of attraction, to lift water a hair's breadth above eighteen cubits; whether the pump be large or small, this is the extreme limit of the lift.

We have seen (p. 243) that Alexandrian science had established what we call the fundamental laws of static equilibrium for solids, that is to say, the conditions which must be satisfied when two or more weights are perfectly balanced. The advanced development of irrigation in ancient times had also borne fruit in the discovery of general principles about the equilibrium of liquids. The basic principle of equilibrium for liquids depends on a fact of everyday observation. If two columns of the same liquid are in direct connexion and both open to the outside air, they are at rest only when the height of each is the same. For practical purposes height in this context usually means vertical distance above the ground, but if we consider the water of the oceans, it is evident that vertical height implies distance from the centre of the earth. The very old device called the siphon (Fig. 221) for emptying cisterns depends on the same elementary principle of fluid equilibrium, which is the basis of any rational system of water supply for a city. Why the Romans built aqueducts across valleys is still an enigma. It may have been through inability to make strong pipes, or it may have been because much of the available knowledge in ancient civilization was wasted through the absence of a system of public instruction to diffuse knowledge from one field of human activity to another. The principles of irrigation were fully understood by Archimedes in 200 B.C., and the feats of hydraulic engineering achieved in dynastic Egypt were far superior to those of the Romans.

If we apply Galileo's way of measuring forces to the force which pulls one column up and another down till the water "finds its own level," we can state the principle in a way which points to a number of other truths about fluids. Fig. 222 shows two columns of a fluid contained in two tubes connected by a cross-piece, hence the height (h) of fluid in each is the same. The bore of each tube is uniform. The areas of cross-section (A and a) are different. The height (h) of fluid above any horizontal level in either column is the volume per unit area of cross section ($h = v \div a$), and the volume is propor-

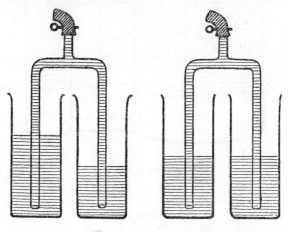

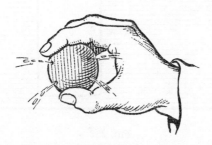

FIG. 221

The principle that a liquid "finds its own level" implies that a difference of pressure between two columns of liquid, free to move vertically upwards, is communicated equally in all directions. Thus a tube used to connect two fluid columns of different vertical height siphons off the fluid in the higher column till both levels are the same. Likewise the pressure of the fingers on a punctured rubber ball filled with water forces water out of the pores at all angles to the plane of compression.

tional to the mass, if the density of both columns is the same. So if the height is the same in both columns, the mass per unit area ($m \div a$) is the same, and the force of gravity acting on unit area ($mg \div a$) is also the same in each column at the same level. Force per unit area is called *pressure*. So two columns are balanced when the pressure at one and the same horizontal level is the same in both. The siphon shows that the connexion between the columns may take any path upwards or downwards. Hence the law of equilibrium for fluids also implies that pressure is communicated equally in all directions.

This is the principle of the hydraulic press which has long been used in

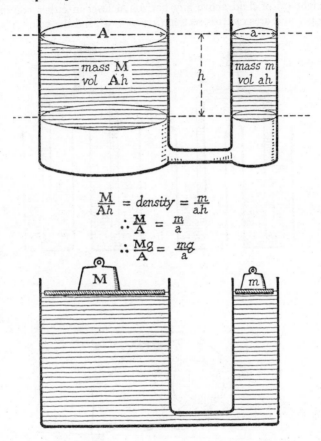

$$\frac{M}{Ah} = density = \frac{m}{ah}$$
$$\therefore \frac{M}{A} = \frac{m}{a}$$
$$\therefore \frac{Mg}{A} = \frac{mg}{a}$$

Fig. 222

Equilibrium between two connected columns of the same fluid, if both are free to move vertically upwards, is attained when both are the same vertical height. This implies that the force on unit area is the same at any level in each; hence a column of large sectional area will support a proportionately larger weight than a column of smaller area. Thus a small force acting on a column of small sectional area will cause a connected column of large sectional area to exert a proportionately larger force in the opposite direction.

You will notice also that a large downward displacement of *m* would be necessary to produce a small upward displacement of M. As in the lever, the pulley, and other machines, work is the product of the *weight* and the *distance* through which it moves.

the textile industry. If a mass M rests on a float in one limb of area A, the pressure of the column below is increased by an amount M ÷ A. Equilibrium is restored when a mass *m* is placed on the float in the other limb of sectional area *a*, provided that Mg ÷ A = *mg* ÷ *a*. So a small weight applied to a small area will keep up a very large weight resting on a wider area in an arrangement like the one shown in Fig. 223.

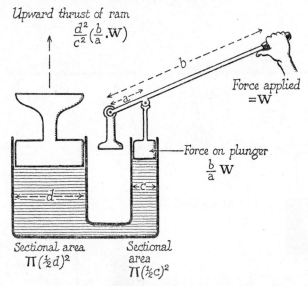

Upward thrust of ram

$$\frac{d^2}{c^2}\left(\frac{b}{a}.W\right)$$

$-b$

Force applied $=W$

Force on plunger $\frac{b}{a}W$

$-a-$

$-c-$

$-d-$

Sectional area $\pi\left(\tfrac{1}{2}d\right)^2$

Sectional area $\pi\left(\tfrac{1}{2}c\right)^2$

FIG. 223.—THE HYDRAULIC PRESS

A second principle of equilibrium for fluids known in ancient times is sometimes called the Archimedian principle. If you have ever tried to raise yourself while taking a bath you will have noticed that your body seems to be lighter when immersed in water than it is ordinarily. The downward pulling power on a body immersed in a liquid is therefore less than it would be in air. If a weight is immersed in water a smaller weight hanging freely in air will balance it.

The difference is equivalent to the weight of the water displaced. A mass M in descending through a fluid is not immersed till it has raised an equivalent volume of the liquid (Fig. 224). It has to raise a mass w of liquid equivalent to its own volume, as well as the mass m in the scale pan, i.e. a total mass $(m + w)$. If the mass in the scale pan balances it,

$$M = m + w$$

or

$$w = M - m$$

A body therefore loses weight in a liquid by an amount (wg) equivalent to that of the same volume of liquid.

According to the Galilean method of measuring it, the pull on the descending weight is the product of its acceleration and its mass. It weighs less in a liquid because, as we know, it falls more slowly than in air. If we call its acceleration when it *starts** to fall in water a, its pulling power is Ma. This pulling power is balanced by a mass m ($= M - w$) suspended in air. If the

* Remarks on the parachute in a later paragraph (p. 375) will explain the need for this qualification.

acceleration of a body falling in air is g, we have a pulling power Ma balanced by a pulling power mg, i.e.

$$Ma = (M - w)g$$
$$\therefore a = \left(1 - \frac{w}{M}\right)g$$

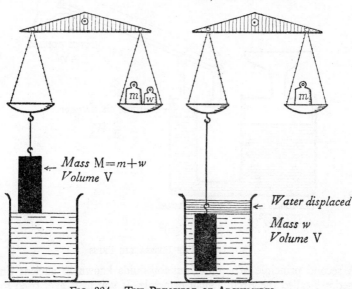

Mass $M = m + w$
Volume V

← *Water displaced*
Mass w
Volume V

FIG. 224.—THE PRINCIPLE OF ARCHIMEDES

If M is the mass of the body when weighed in air, m its apparent mass when weighed in water, and w the mass of the water displaced, i.e. of the equivalent *volume* of liquid,

$$M = m + w$$
or
$$w = M - m$$

If V is the volume of the body (and hence of the water it displaces), its density is $M \div V$. The density of the fluid is $w \div V$. Hence the ratio of the density of the body to the density of fluid is

$$M \div V : w \div V = M \div w$$

The ratio of the density of a body to that of water (its "specific gravity") is therefore
Weight in air $\div$ (Weight in air — weight in water)

Since w and M are masses corresponding to the same volume, they are in the same ratio as the densities (d and D) of the fluid and the descending weight.

$$\therefore a = \left(1 - \frac{d}{D}\right)g$$

Galileo's way of measuring forces therefore shows us correctly when a body floats or sinks. If the body is very much denser than the fluid, d is very small compared with D, and $d \div D$ is a very small fraction. Hence $1 - \dfrac{d}{D}$ will not differ very much from unity, and the acceleration a of the body descending through the fluid will be nearly as great as it would be if it were falling through air. If the density of the fluid is nearly as great as that of the body itself, $\dfrac{d}{D}$ will be a fraction just less than unity, $1 - \dfrac{d}{D}$ will therefore be small, and a will be small compared with g. That is to say, the body will fall very slowly. If the body is less dense than the fluid, $\frac{d}{D}$ is greater than unity, and $1 - \frac{d}{D}$ is a negative quantity. That is to say, the body immersed in the fluid will have an acceleration upwards instead of downwards. In other words, it will float. If d is exactly equal to D, $\left(1 - \frac{d}{D}\right)$ is zero, and the acceleration is therefore zero. The body neither sinks nor floats. It rises or falls with the application of a very small force. The modern submarine is equipped with tanks which can be filled with water or emptied by means of a store of compressed air. When the tanks are quite full the total density of the submarine is slightly greater than water. The expulsion of a small quantity of water is then sufficient to make the submarine rise to the surface.

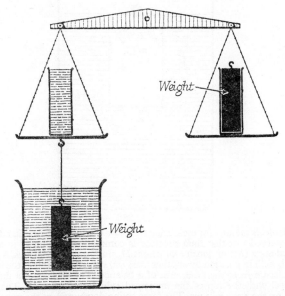

FIG. 225.—EXPERIMENTAL PROOF OF THE PRINCIPLE OF ARCHIMEDES

Two identical weights fit exactly into two cylindrical vessels. When one weight is suspended in water from a scale pan, the weight and its vessel in the opposite scale pan may be made to balance it by filling the other vessel with water to the brim.

The same reasoning leads to another conclusion which can be verified, namely, the fact that a very small part of an iceberg is visible above the water-line. At freezing-point water is $1 \cdot 083$ times as dense as ice. So the mass M of ice below the water has an acceleration $(1 - 1 \cdot 083)g$, and exerts a push on the ice above equivalent to $(1 - 1 \cdot 083)Mg = - 0 \cdot 083 \, Mg$. The negative sign indicates that the acceleration and push are directed upwards. If downwards, acceleration is denoted by the positive sign. The mass (m) of ice above pushes downwards with a force equivalent to mg. And since these forces balance one another, they are equal. Hence $m = 0\cdot083\,\mathrm{M}$, i.e. M the mass of submerged ice is about twelve times m, the mass of ice exposed.

This gives us a clue for which we are seeking. Aristotle rejected the possibility that air has weight because a bladder weighs as much when it is blown up as when it is collapsed. We might just as well argue that water has no weight because a tin can weighs just as much in water after a steam hammer has flattened it out. A bladder inflated with air could only weigh more than one which was not inflated if both were weighed in something lighter than air, or in an empty space. If air has weight, its weight must be

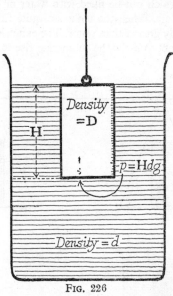

FIG. 226

If we use Galileo's method for measuring force, we can infer the Archimedean principle from the observed fact that fluid pressure is communicated equally in all directions. A cylindrical mass (M) of density D, height H, uniform sectional area A, and volume $V(= \mathrm{AH})$, is held in position by another mass (m) suspended in air at the same distance from the fulcrum from the other arm of a balance. The surface of a fluid of density d is just level with the top of the immersed cylinder of mass M. The force acting downwards on the mass m is mg. The force acting downward on the mass M would be $\mathrm{M}g(= \mathrm{VD}g)$, if it were not opposed by the upward push of the fluid acting on the base with a force per unit area $\mathrm{H}dg$. Hence the total upward force on the base is $\mathrm{AH}dg = \mathrm{V}dg$, and the weight mg is therefore balanced by a net downward pull $\mathrm{VD}g - \mathrm{V}dg$, i.e.

$$mg = \mathrm{VD}g - \mathrm{V}dg$$
$$m = \mathrm{VD} - \mathrm{V}d = \mathrm{VD}\left(1 - \frac{d}{\mathrm{D}}\right)$$

Since density is mass per unit volume (i.e. $\mathrm{M} = \mathrm{VD}$)

$$m = \mathrm{M}\left(1 - \frac{d}{\mathrm{D}}\right)$$

extremely small compared with that of most solid bodies and liquids, and we can accommodate Galileo's experiments with the slow initial descent of a toy balloon without difficulty by a very small modification in the original form of Galileo's principle. Suppose that bodies fall through empty space near the earth's surface with constant acceleration g. If a is the acceleration with which a solid body falls in air, it will rarely differ appreciably from g, because the density D of most solid bodies is very large compared with d the density of air. This is obviously not true of a toy balloon. It is largely composed of air when it is blown up. Its density D considered as a whole is not very much

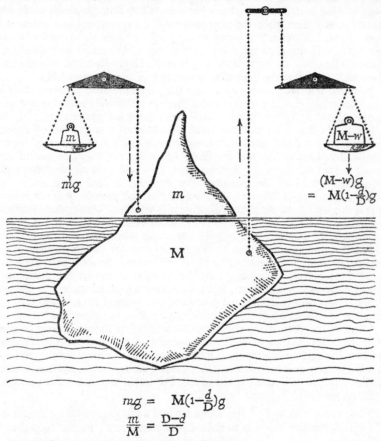

$$mg = M(1-\tfrac{d}{D})g$$
$$\frac{m}{M} = \frac{D-d}{D}$$

FIG. 227.—THE ICEBERG

The balances indicate the forces necessary to balance the downward pull and upward push of the two parts. For convenience of drawing the attachments are at the sides. Of course tilting will occur unless the attachment is vertically in line with the centre of gravity.

greater than d, and $\left(1 - \dfrac{d}{D}\right)$ is a small fraction. Hence it falls slowly. A gas

less dense than the surrounding air (e.g. hotter air or coal gas) must have a negative acceleration for analogous reasons, and will therefore rise upwards.

The behaviour of a parachute illustrates the fact that air has another characteristic of weighty matter. It is sluggish, and this sluggishness or *inertia* gives us a clue to the propagation of sound (p. 321) and to certain peculiarities of falling bodies. On account of its inertia air resists any attempt to push it out of the way. This resistance to displacement naturally depends to some extent on the shape of an object. It is relatively great if a moving object presents a large surface relative to its bulk, and this fact is the basis of *streamline* designs for fast cars. What is not easily recognized from our everyday experience of motion is that air resistance and that of any fluid medium is greater *at greater speeds*. Roughly speaking, air resistance is proportional to the square of the speed of a body moving in it. So when a body has been falling through air for some time, there comes a time when the resistance which it encounters just balances its own weight. Thereafter it gains no more speed. It continues to move at a fixed speed. On account of its shape a parachute has a high initial resistance. Since it traps a lot of air, its effective density is small. Hence its initial acceleration is also small. It reaches the limit of its power to gain speed very quickly.

If he did not cut the cord to release the parachute after jumping from his plane, an aviator would continue to fall through a relatively long distance while gaining speed at a rate differing little from the fixed acceleration of bodies falling in a vacuum. At a certain limit his acceleration would fall off rapidly, reaching a "terminal" fixed speed many times greater than that of a parachutist. By the time he was travelling 170 miles per hour, he would have ceased to gain speed. In the Galilean sense, he would have no effective weight. Why then would he be mangled? An everyday experience provides the answer. If an egg is dropped from a height of half an inch, it is not broken. If it is dropped from a height of six feet it is smashed. Within these limits its Galilean weight does not differ sensibly. So its Galilean weight is not directly responsible for disaster. The egg shell has internal inertia, and extensibility. It cannot communicate motion throughout all its parts instantaneously. When the bottom touches the ground, the top is still moving. So some parts are losing speed more quickly than others. At the moment of impact the distribution of accelerations is not uniform, and these accelerations correspond to Galilean forces. Thus there is an unequal distribution of internal stresses which in one direction or another exceed the breaking point. How big these internal stresses are depends on whether the speed immediately before impact is great or small compared with the rate at which the material of the shell can communicate motion. The surface of a mouse is much greater relative to its weight than that of a horse. Hence it encounters much greater air resistance and has a much smaller terminal or limiting speed of fall. For this reason it can fall through a much greater height without being killed.

When von Guericke and Boyle had devised a pump for sucking the air out of a vessel, Newton was able to show that a guinea and a feather keep pace in falling through a vacuum. Proof that air has weight first came from another source. Before explaining how the discovery was made, two empirical applications of the Archimedean principle in everyday life may be noted. The density of some saleable fluids (e.g. milk and spirits) is controlled by legislation, and the density of the fluid in storage batteries is a useful indicator for testing when they are fully charged. For routine determinations of this kind, accurate weighing of an accurately ascertained volume of fluid would be much too laborious, and is replaced by the device known as the hydrometer (Fig. 228). This is essentially a metal tube or a glass tube with some mercury at the bottom to make it sink till the weight of fluid displaced is equivalent to the weight of the instrument. The volume of fluid whose weight is equivalent to weight of the instrument depends on its density. So the hydrometer sinks more if the density is lower. A graduated scale records the length of the submerged part. The divisions marked off correspond to the levels which fluids of particular densities reach. Only relative measurement of densities is made in this way, water being taken as the standard. Density referred to water as the standard ($d = 1$) is called specific gravity.*

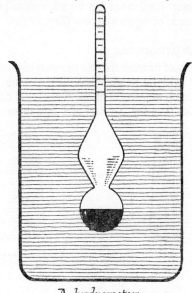

A hydrometer

FIG. 228

The scale marks show how deeply it sinks in fluids of different density

A second application of the principle of buoyancy is the "*Plimsoll*" line. An iron ship floats because the weight of the shell is far less than the weight of the total volume of water displaced. Every addition of cargo makes it sink

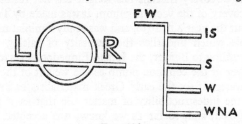

FIG. 229

The Plimsoll line on all ships in Lloyd's register, L.R. The several marks are the loading limits for fresh water, Indian summer seas, temperate seas in summer and winter, and winter in the north Atlantic.

further till an equivalent weight of water is displaced. It is not safe to load a ship so heavily that the addition of a small amount of extra ballast will sink it. The limit of safety depends on the density of the water, which varies

* If volume is measured in c.c. and weight in grams, the density and the specific gravity of the same substance have the same numerical value at 4° C., since 1 c.c. of water at this temperature weighs 1 gm.

appreciably according to its salt content and temperature. Sea water is denser than fresh water, as we know if we are swimmers, and the warm tropical waters are less dense than Arctic seas. The law now enacts that all vessels carry a scale like the scale of a hydrometer, showing the different levels beyond which the water level must not be allowed to pass when loading in fresh or sea water, arctic or equatorial seas (Fig. 229).

THE PRESSURE OF THE ATMOSPHERE

The most direct way of proving that air has weight is to compare the weight of an exhausted vessel with its weight when filled with air. When the temperature is 60° F. at sea-level, the weight of one litre (1,000 c.c.) of air is approximately 1¼ grams. That is to say, a vessel of 1 litre capacity (roughly one-fifth

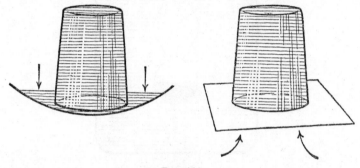

FIG. 230

Two simple experiments illustrating the weight of the atmosphere. In the right-hand one, the pressure of the air, communicated like the pressure of the water in the siphon in all directions, keeps a full tumbler sealed by a piece of paper placed across the open end.

of a gallon) weighs 1¼ grams (about a twentieth of an ounce) less when exhausted. The discovery that air has weight did not result from, but preceded, the discovery of the vacuum pump. It was made by Torricelli, a pupil of Galileo, about the year A.D. 1643, and was really a miniature demonstration of the principle which underlies the necessity of raising water in relays (Fig. 220). According to Burnet, the Ionian Empedocles correctly interpreted the raising power of the common pump as the weight of the air pressing on the source of water. If so, the early Greek materialists had solid ground for their faith in the indestructibility of matter. Be that as it may, Aristotle's teaching triumphed, and, so far as we know, was accepted by the Alexandrians, whose knowledge of the mechanics of fluids should have sufficed to exhibit the flaw in his reasoning.

An old trick which is easy to repeat with a tumbler of water and a wash basin may have suggested the experiments of Torricelli. If we turn a tumbler upside down under water and draw it upwards, the water does not descend inside it, so long as the rim is just below the surface of the water. If we place a piece of paper on a tumbler brimming over with water, we can turn it upside down in air without emptying it. The paper remains apparently glued to the edge. In performing similar experiments, in which a cylinder filled with mercury was inverted over a trough containing mercury, Torricelli found that the fluid descends a certain distance if the cylinder is sufficiently long, leaving a space above it without any sign that bubbles of air have passed up. The vertical height of the mercury column with the empty space (Torricellian vacuum) above it was not affected by tilting the cylinder sideways, or by using tubes of different sectional area. At sea-level the height of the mercury column above the level of mercury in the trough is 760 mm., or roughly 30 inches. A variation of the original form of the experiment is to fill with mercury a U-tube of which one limb is closed, holding it in a nearly horizontal position, taking care to let in no air bubbles. If the other limb is sufficiently long the mercury sinks in the closed one when the U-tube is held upright till the vertical difference between the two columns is 760 mm. (at sea-level). Either arrangement is what we now call a mercury barometer (Fig. 231).

We have seen that pressure at any horizontal level in a fluid is the force exerted by the weight of the overlying fluid on unit area ($mg \div a$). Since mass is the product of volume (v) and density (d),

$$\text{pressure} = vdg \div a,$$

and since volume per unit area ($v \div a$) is the height (h) of the overlying column, the pressure or force per unit area of a column of fluid on its base is hdg. To put it in another way, a pressure hdg is required to raise a column of fluid to a height h. For measuring what supplies this pressure, the equilibrium of two liquids of different density (Fig. 231) furnishes a precise parallel. Two connected columns of fluid are only in equilibrium when the vertical height of both is the same, providing that their densities are the same. If a straight open tube dips into a trough of mercury, the mercury in it rises above the level of mercury in the trough when water is poured on to the latter. Similarly, if water is poured into one limb of a U-tube containing mercury, the mercury in the other rises a little. In either case the more general form of the law of equilibrium is true. At any level in the mercury the pressure of both columns above it is the same, e.g. at the level where the mercury (density D) is in contact with water (density d), the heights of the overlying columns of water (h) and mercury (H) are such that

$$HDg = hdg$$

or

$$\therefore \quad H \div h = d \div D$$

This means that if mercury is $13\frac{1}{2}$ times as dense as water, a column of mercury could just be supported in a vertical position by the pressure of a column of water $13\frac{1}{2}$ times as long, in the same way as the water in the tumbler is supported in a vertical position by something pressing on the paper and communicating its pressure upwards and downwards in all directions equally.

In these experiments we have water on one side of a mercury column, and no water on the other. The pressure exerted by the weight of the water maintains the difference in level between the two columns of mercury. In the barometer we have air on one side and apparently none on the other. Is the pressure supplied by the fact that the air has weight? A simple experiment completes the analogy. If we withdraw some of the water in the last experiment (Fig. 231), the height of the water column is less, and the difference between the two levels of mercury is diminished. We can make the height of the air column pressing on a mercury barometer less by taking the barometer to the top of a mountain. This test was devised by Pascal

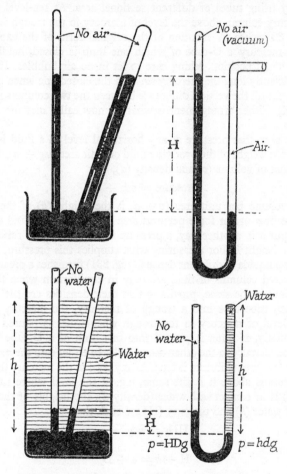

FIG. 231

Above, two forms of the barometer. Below, the weight of a column of water, pressing on mercury (density D) with a force HDg = hdg per unit area, lifts a column of mercury to a height H in the same way as the weight of the atmosphere maintains the mercury level of the barometer.

(about 1648) soon after Torricelli's experiments, and is now used as a means of calculating altitude. At the top of Mount Everest (5½ miles up) the weight of the atmosphere will only support a column of mercury 11 inches high. At the height of 9·6 miles, reached by Professor Picard in 1931 (Fig. 243), the mercury barometer only registers 5 inches. That the same force acts on any liquid is easily proved. Since mercury is 13½ times as dense as water, the pressure which supports a column of mercury 30 inches long at sea-level would support a column of water $13\frac{1}{2}$ times as high, i.e. about 34 feet. This is easily shown to be true, and provides a good enough reason for preferring the use of mercury to water in constructing a barometer. There are several others.

The most familiar use of the barometer in everyday life depends on the fact that water vapour is less dense than air. So a mixture of water vapour and dry air is less dense than pure air. Since the height of the atmosphere may be taken to be nearly constant, changes in the atmospheric pressure at any particular place chiefly depend on moisture and temperature. A fall of pressure means that the air is less dense, and this generally means that it is more moist. Hence rain is to be expected. This rule is not highly reliable, because changes in pressure also result from unequal heating of the earth's surface. Warm air is less dense than cold air, and the atmospheric pressure, therefore, depends partly on the temperature. It is constantly changing because of the winds so produced. A further complication arises from the fact that more water vapour is required to saturate warm than to saturate cold air. In an island climate, the direction of the wind is specially important. In England rain may be anticipated when cold winds are blowing over the sea from the north-east, even if the barometer is rising. In the weather forecasts now published, most importance is attached to the relative distribution of pressure based on wireless signals which make it possible to record how zones of high and low pressure are shifting from day to day. A chart constructed on the basis of simultaneous records of pressure at different stations will frequently show closed areas of high pressure (anti-cyclones) from which dry winds are blowing spirally outwards, or closed areas of low pressure (cyclones) where wet winds are blowing spirally inwards. Their position changes from hour to hour, so that it is possible to foretell within short limits where they will next be. The approach of a cyclone betokens wet weather, that of an anti-cyclone dry weather.

At sea-level in our climate the height of the mercury column varies between 29 and 31 inches. Since the force acting on unit area at the base of a column of fluid (hdg) only depends on its height, density, and the value of g which varies only very slightly with latitude and altitude, it can be calculated at once from the height of a column of fluid of known density. The mass of 1 cub. ft. of mercury is 848 lb. The weight of a column 1 sq. ft. in cross-sectional area and 30 inches high is $848 \times 30 \div 12 = 2,120$ lb. So the pressure of air which supports it is equivalent to a weight of 2,120 lb. on every square foot, or approximately $14\frac{3}{4}$ lb. per square inch. A barometer can also be adapted as a pressure gauge (Fig. 232) in measuring low or high air pressure when exhausting a space, compressing a gas, or recording the pressure of a water supply. Pressure is often measured in "atmospheres," the standard or unit (one atmosphere) being the mean pressure at freezing temperature in latitude 45°. This is 760 mm., or $29 \cdot 92$ inches of mercury, or $33\frac{1}{2}$ feet of water. Thus the pressure of a town water supply that will raise water in an upright tube 100 feet high is almost exactly 3 atmospheres. That is to say, the force exerted on every square inch is equivalent to a weight of $3 \times 14\frac{3}{4}$ or 44 lb. to the nearest pound.

THE SPRING OF THE AIR

To be useful, a recipe for making substances must include the quantities of the ingredients and the yield. The importance of chemistry in modern life depends on the fact that it can give us rules for finding recipes of this sort. Modern chemistry rests on the doctrine of the Greek materialists. In chemical processes no matter is lost. Increase in the weight of one ingredient of a

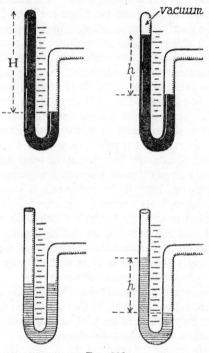

FIG. 232

Two types of pressure gauge. The upper one is for measuring small pressures in the neighbourhood of a vacuum. The fluid does not begin to fall until the pressure in the chamber to which the open end is attached falls below that of a column of fluid of length H; i.e. the gauge only measures pressures less than H. When the fluid begins to drop the difference *h* measures the actual pressure in the chamber. The lower one is for measuring small pressures in excess of that of the atmosphere (e.g. that of the gas supply). The difference *h* is the *excess* of pressure over that of the atmosphere; i.e. *h* must be added to the height of the barometer reading to get the pressure in the chamber. Either type of gauge may be made more sensitive by using a light fluid like water instead of mercury. Of course, pressure measured in lengths of a column of fluid means nothing unless the fluid is stated. If water is used for the lower type the barometer reading which must be added to *h* must be given in water units, i.e. 13·6 times the reading of the mercury barometer.

mixture is accompanied by loss of weight of others which go to its making. The science of antiquity knew no *general* rules for obtaining a good yield. In the ancient chemical arts of metallurgy, medicine, and fermentation, substances appeared to gain weight and lose it according to no detectable rules. The Arab chemists knew that the oxide ore or calx produced when a metal is heated in air is heavier than the metal from which it is formed. When the ore was reduced in the absence of air by heating with charcoal, the latter disappeared, leaving only metal lighter than the original calx. Why this should happen they could not see, because they did not realize that air is ponderable matter. From the beginnings of the Iron Age, no substantial progress in the understanding of chemical processes was made, or was possible till air had ceased to be a spirit. When first carried out the experiments

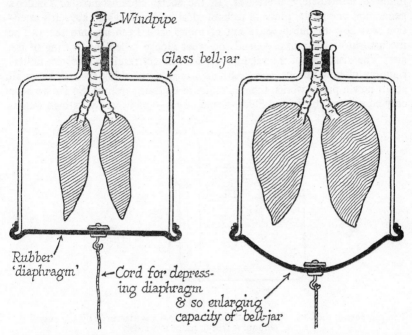

FIG. 233.—MEDICAL ADVANCES IN THE SOCIAL CONTEXT OF THE COMMON PUMP

When the mechanism of the common pump was fully understood, the old belief that respiration allows the vital spirits to escape from the body made way for the recognition that the chest movements are simply a mechanical device to ensure that the spongy cavities of the lungs whose thin walls are abundantly supplied with blood vessels receive a constant supply of fresh air. The fundamental peculiarity of the third state of matter is that it spreads out in all directions to occupy all the empty space available. Among his many experiments on the mechanics of the pump, von Guericke showed that a balloon can be expanded till it burst, if enclosed in a large air space from which the air is pumped out. The experiment can be varied by using the lungs of a freshly killed sheep. If the windpipe is made airtight by a ligature the lungs can be inflated to bursting point. In other words, the space which a gas occupies depends on the external pressure to which it is subjected. An alternative modification of von Guericke's experiment shown in this figure illustrates what happens in normal breathing. The windpipe is open to the air. The cavity of the glass bell jar in which the lungs are suspended is airtight, and the floor of the bell jar is closed by a rubber sheet which can be depressed by a cord, thereby increasing the capacity of the overlying space containing the lungs. When this is done the lungs can be rhythmically inflated and deflated by the up and down movements of the cord. This corresponds to the action of the muscular diaphragm or midriff which separates the chest cavity or thorax from the abdomen. During inspiration the midriff is depressed so that fresh air rushes through the windpipe into the lungs. When it is elevated during expiration, some of the foul air is expelled. The internal capacity of the chest cavity is also increased during inspiration by the expansion resulting from the contraction of muscles which lie between the ribs and force the latter to bulge outwards.

of Torricelli and Pascal, now almost commonplace in their simplicity, were the focus of one of the greatest revolutions in human knowledge. They made air a weighty matter.

By themselves, all these experiments showed was that air has weight. They tell us what the weight of the whole atmosphere is, but not the weight of a given quantity of air. This was made possible by a discovery which followed immediately afterwards. In the social circumstances of Galileo's generation one of the pressing technological problems which attracted attention was how to pump water out of mines, and fresh air into them. The mechanism of the pump depends on what Hooke called the "spring of the air." The discovery of the vacuum was a necessary result of a correct understanding of how pumps work. Although most of us think that we know all about how a pump works, there is much to be learnt from it. So far we have only considered the force a fluid—liquid or gas—can exert by its own weight

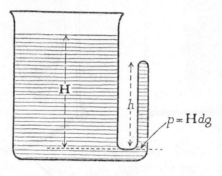

FIG. 234

The pressure at the base of a column of fluid of height h is measured by hdg only if the column is free to move upwards.

downwards. The measurement of pressure by the product hdg implies that the fluid is only prevented from moving upward by its own weight. In a vessel closed at the top this is not so. Since a fluid communicates pressure in all directions the pressure of fluid at the base of the projecting arm in Fig. 234 is the same as the pressure at the same level in the main body of the fluid, and this does not depend on the height of the fluid in the closed limb. Similarly, solid bodies do not merely exert pressure in virtue of their weight. They also exert pressure against any attempt to change their shape or volume, and hence *density*. If we stretch a piece of spring it returns to its normal position when we let go. If we press on the handle of a bicycle pump when the orifice is closed, it springs back when we release our grip. The pressure of the air within it is greater than that of the outside air when its volume is diminished. Conversely, it is less than that of the atmosphere when its volume is increased. The action of the once "common pump" depends on the same fact (Fig. 235). Raising the piston increases the volume of air in the cylinder, and the water rises because the pressure of the atmosphere in the well is greater than the pressure of the air in the pump itself.

A difficulty which prevented people from looking on air as a material sub-

stance may have been partly due to the characteristic which specially distinguishes the third state of matter from solids or liquids. In the gaseous state
matter is highly compressible. Liquids and solids only suffer minute changes
of volume under tremendous pressure. In ordinary conditions each has its
own characteristic density which is fixed. So, when we speak of a quantity
of something in everyday life we do not need to draw a sharp distinction
between mass and volume. We measure groceries in pounds or pints
according to convenience. A pint of bran or meal or beer represents as
definite a quantity of matter as a pound to us. Nothing we do to a pint of
beer by ordinary methods at our disposal makes it less than a pint, and two

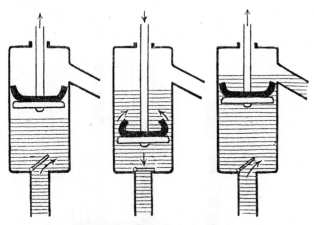

FIG. 235.—THE COMMON PUMP

Any pump which continuously forces or sucks up a fluid must have two valves. In
the figure one valve is the leather washer of the piston. The lips of this are kept closed
by the pressure of the air in the upstroke. The other is a metal trapdoor kept tightly
shut by the pressure of the water in the downstroke.

pints weigh twice as much as one. Unless we know the state of compression
of a gas nothing of the sort is true. Two pints may weigh less than one pint.
   When we stretch a spring its mass remains constant, but its mass per unit
length diminishes. So to deduce its mass from its length we need to be told
what is the stretching force, and how its length varies with it. To deduce
anything about the mass of a gas from its volume we have to know how the
density of a unit of mass, i.e. its volume, depends on the pressure. There are
two very good reasons why it is important to know this connexion. We usually
measure liquids and powdery solids by volume, because it is generally
easier to measure volume than to measure mass. This is specially true of
gases, because they are so light in ordinary circumstances. So no advance
towards an understanding of how the weights of gases and solids are connected, when they enter into combination, could be rapid, until it was possible
to calculate the weight of a gas from the volume it occupies at a particular
pressure. To get an idea of how much the progress of chemistry depends on
knowing the spring of the air, you have only to imagine how many people
would get served before closing-up time if all beer were weighed out on

scales before being sold. Another fact which made it important to determine
the spring of the air was that we cannot calculate how the barometer is
affected by altitude unless we know it. The atmosphere gets more rare as
we ascend. If the density of the air were the same at all levels we could
calculate pressure at any altitude from the product hdg. Since the lower
layers of air are pressed under the weight of all the air lying above them,
they are more dense.

Discoveries, like misfortunes, rarely (if ever) come singly. They have
their roots in the social experience of the time. The law of the spring of
the air was independently discovered by Boyle and Hooke in England,

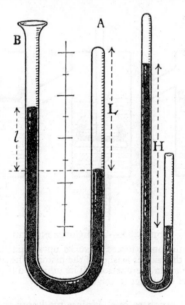

FIG. 236.—BOYLE'S EXPERIMENT

The outside pressure is H, the difference of pressure between the air in the closed and
open columns is l. So the pressure in the closed column is $l + $ H.

and by Mariotte in France, within a few years of Pascal's experiment. In
England it is called Boyle's law, though the credit is probably due to Hooke.
To discover it, he used a U-tube containing mercury, one limb being
closed (Fig. 236). If the bore of the tube is uniform, the volume (v) of air
in the closed limb is directly proportional to the length of the air column L.
When the level of mercury in both limbs is the same, the air in the closed
one (A) is not compressed. Its pressure is therefore equal to that of the
atmosphere (H), (i.e. that on the base of a column of mercury roughly
30 inches high). If the limb A were in communication with the air the
mercury would rise to the same level in both limbs when more was added
to limb B. If it is closed, the mercury does not rise so far in limb A, and
the difference of pressure is proportional to the difference (l) between the
heights of the two columns. So the total pressure (p) of the gas in the closed

limb is measured by the $(l + H)$. Since pressure increases when volume diminishes, the simplest rule to explore is that the pressure varies inversely as the volume, i.e.

$$p = \frac{k}{v}$$

or

$$pv = k$$

Since L is proportional to v and $(l + H)$ to p, this is true if

$$L(l + H) = \text{constant}$$

Some data from one of Boyle's experiments (1662), when the barometer reading was $29\frac{1}{8}$ inches, show how closely this rule was found to be true.

L	l	$L(l + 29\frac{1}{8})$
12	0	349·5
11	$2\frac{13}{16}$	351·3
10	$6\frac{3}{16}$	353·1
9	$10\frac{2}{16}$	353·3
8	$15\frac{5}{16}$	355·5
7	$21\frac{3}{16}$	352·2
6	$29\frac{11}{16}$	352·9
5	$41\frac{9}{16}$	353·4
4	$58\frac{2}{16}$	349·0
3	$88\frac{7}{16}$	352·7

Taking the mean value of the product as 352·3, you will find it instructive to test the limits of accuracy by calculating l from observed values of L, thus

$$L(l + 29 \tfrac{2}{16}) = 352\cdot3$$
$$\therefore \ l = (352\cdot3 \div L) - 29\tfrac{2}{16}$$

The largest discrepancy, when $L = 4$, gives $l = 88\cdot075 - 29\cdot125 = 58\cdot95$ as compared with 58·125, an error of less than $1\frac{1}{2}$ per cent. Over a wide range the experimental error is very much smaller when the best modern glass and a more finely graduated scale is used. For most practical purposes the connexion between the pressure and volume of gas is therefore given by the formula

$$pv = k$$

Since volume is inversely proportional to density, this is equivalent to saying that pressure is directly proportional to the density of air (or other gas), i.e.

$$p = Kd$$

or that density is directly proportional to pressure, i.e.

$$d = K'p$$

Assuming that the temperature at which all experiments are carried out is the same, Boyle's law tells us how to calculate the density of a gas at any given pressure. Hence we can calculate the mass of a given volume at a particular pressure, once its density has been found at some standard pressure. The densities of gases are usually given at the standard pressure of 760 mm. of mercury. If a gas occupies a vessel whose capacity is 38 c.c. at 750 mm., and at the temperature of freezing water (0° C.), $750 \times 38 = k$. If its volume at 0° C. and standard pressure is V, $760 \, V = k$. Hence

$$V = \frac{750 \times 38}{760} = 37 \cdot 5 \text{ c.c.}$$

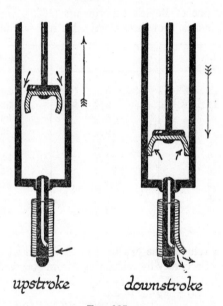

upstroke   *downstroke*

FIG. 237

The bicycle pump and tyre, like the common pump for raising water, have two valves. The leather washer valve of the piston is kept closed by the greater pressure in the cylinder during the downstroke, and the rubber tube valve of the tyre is kept closed by the greater pressure of the air in the tyre during the upstroke.

So if its density at standard pressure and 0° C. is 1·3 grams per litre, (1,000 c.c.), the mass of 38 c.c. at 750 mm. and 0° C. is

$$(1 \cdot 3 \times 37 \cdot 5) \div 1,000 = 0 \cdot 04875 \text{ grams.}$$

As we all know, hot air rises. The density of air or any gas diminishes considerably as the temperature is changed, if the pressure is kept the same. So Boyle's law by itself is a safe guide for measuring gases only if all experiments are done *at the same temperature*. Mariotte used it to calculate (see Fig. 243) the pressure of the atmosphere at any height above sea-level, by allowing for the changes in density due to the compression of the lower layers of air by the ones lying above.

THE VACUUM

To measure gases by means of Boyle's law in the way illustrated by the example, we need to know their densities at some standard pressure and temperature. This can be done once for all by weighing a vessel of known capacity when filled with the gas, if its weight has been found when it contains no gas at all, like the empty space above the mercury in a barometer. A great advance was made when the common pump was adapted for creating a vacuum. The invention, for which von Guericke seems to have priority over Boyle, was made about the same time as the discovery of the spring of the air, and like it happened independently in England and on the Continent

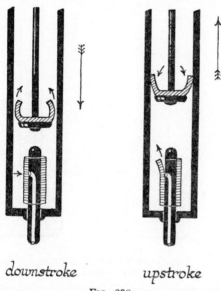

downstroke   *upstroke*

FIG. 238

A vacuum pump may be made from a bicycle pump by reversing the position of the valves.

about the same time. If Boyle is justly called the father of modern chemistry, von Guericke might with equal justice be called the father of steam power. A device with which he used the suction of air in filling a vacuum to raise weights was without doubt the parent of the mechanisms which led to the construction of the Newcomen engine.

The invention of the vacuum pump also made it possible to submit Galileo's doctrine of terrestrial gravitation in the modified form, which has been stated earlier in this chapter, to the decisive test which Newton applied. By showing that a feather and a guinea fall through a long glass cylinder at the same rate when all the air is drawn out of it, Newton furnished direct proof that bodies fall with constant acceleration *in vacuo*. The constancy with which compact heavy solids fall, as in Galileo's experiment, through air is not remarkable when we remember how bodies gain speed in falling through a fluid. The vacuum pump made it possible to show then that the weight of air at room temperature is only about 75 lb. per 1,000 cub. ft. An equal quantity of glycerine weighs about 1,000 times, and of water about 800 times, as much as air at atmospheric pressure. Neglecting air resistance, this means (see p. 372) that a substance with the density of glycerine would fall through air at an acceleration $(1 - \frac{1}{1000})$ times its acceleration in a vacuum. So the value of g calculated from observations in air would only differ by one part in a thousand from g measured *in vacuo*. A solid piece of indiarubber has about the same density as glycerine, and if it happens to be a golf ball, falls

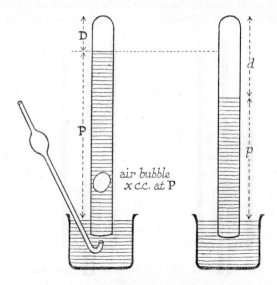

FIG. 239.—DEPRESSION OF THE BAROMETER COLUMN BY
AN AIR BUBBLE

In making a barometer or pressure gauge, it is important to exclude small air bubbles between the mercury and the glass. The presence of bubbles exerts a pressure in the dead space, depressing the mercury column below the level to which it would rise if the vacuum were perfect. The height of the column measures the difference in pressure between the atmosphere (pressure P) and that of the dead space. If the latter is a vacuum the pressure in the dead space is 0, and the difference $P - 0 = P$. If the dead space is not a perfect vacuum:

difference in pressure (p) = pressure of atmosphere (P) — pressure in dead space.

∴ pressure of air in dead space = $P - p$.

Suppose e.g. that an air bubble of x c.c. at pressure P is introduced into the dead space of a tube of uniform sectional area a sq. cm. By the law for the spring of the air, $Px = k$. If the dead space is increased from D cm. to d cm. and the pressure drops from P to p cm., $d - D = P - p$.

$$\therefore d = P - p + D$$

The volume occupied by the air bubble at the new pressure $(P - p)$ is ad

$$\therefore (P - p)ad = k = Px$$
$$\therefore a(P - p)(P - p + D) = Px$$

The only unknown quantity in this equation is p, if the dimensions of the tube, size of the air bubble, and the external pressure, have been measured. Hence the new height of the column can be calculated.

like the balls in Galileo's experiments. If it is made in the form of a football bladder, which can be blown up till the volume of air it displaces is several hundred times as great as the rubber itself, $\frac{d}{D}$ may be very nearly equal to unity, and $\left(1 - \frac{d}{D}\right)$ very nearly equal to zero. So it will fall very slowly.

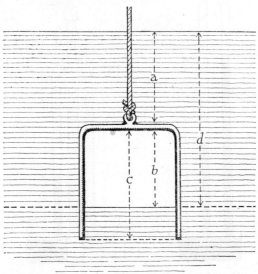

FIG. 240.—RELATION OF THE AIR SPACE IN A DIVING BELL TO THE DEPTH OF IMMERSION

If the sectional area of the bell is A, the dead space is Ab, and the total capacity is Ac. Hence the relative volume of the air space is $b \div c$. The pressure of water at the depth d is equivalent to atmospheric pressure P (cm. of mercury), together with the weight per unit area of d cm. of water. Since mercury is 13·6 times as dense as water d cm. of water is equivalent to $d \div 13·6$ cm. of mercury, and since water transmits pressure equally in all directions the pressure in the dead space in equilibrium with water at the same depth in cm. of mercury is

$$P + \frac{d}{13·6} \text{ cm.}$$

Hence according to Boyle's Law,

$$Ac \times P = Ab\left(P + \frac{d}{13·6}\right)$$

$$\therefore \frac{b}{c} = \frac{13·6\,P}{13·6\,P + d}$$

If the depth is very great we can put a instead of d.

THE REVIVAL OF ATOMISM

Whatever credit may be due to Aristotle as a student of animal life, his treatise on physics was neither original nor in advance of his time. His Attic partiality for disputation triumphed over the robust common sense of his Ionian predecessors in an attempt to accommodate Plato's idealism with the claims of natural enquiry to rank as a gentlemanly pastime. In the end the supremacy of Plato's mysticism was the death-blow to Greek natural science. Cyril Bailey's collection of the remnants of Ionian knowledge show that the earlier Greeks had an uncanny gift for drawing correct conclusions from careful observation of nature without elaborate equip-

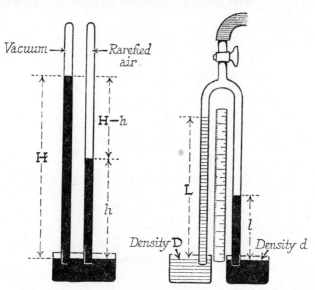

FIG. 241.—MEASUREMENT OF DENSITY BY FLUID LEVEL

On the left are two tubes immersed in the same fluid of density D. The dead space of one, in which the mercury level is H cm., is a vacuum; and HDg is the difference of pressure between the atmosphere and a vacuum, i.e. the atmospheric pressure in units of force. The dead space of the other, in which the mercury level is h, contains some air. The difference in pressure between the dead space and the outside air is hDg. Hence if P is the pressure inside the dead space, HDg − P = hDg and P = HDg − hDg = Dg(H − h). Since D is the same if the same fluid is used and g is the same at the same locality we can express the pressure difference between two lots of gas by the difference of height (H − h) of two pressure gauge readings. If some air is sucked out of a U-tube dipping into two different liquids, one of density D rising to level L, the other of density d rising to level l, the difference between the pressure of air P in the closed space and that of the outside air (A) is A − LDg as measured by the rise of fluid in the left-hand limb, or A − ldg measured by the rise of fluid in the right-hand limb. Hence

$$A - LDg = A - ldg$$
$$LDg = ldg$$
$$\frac{L}{l} = \frac{d}{D}$$

.e. the densities are inversely proportional to the heights of the columns.

ment such as we possess. The doctrine of Atomism which Aristotle applied all his ingenuity to overthrow was more than a lucky guess. It was the fruit of close observation by men in close contact with the world's work.

Although dominated by Plato's teaching, which treated the shadow world of everyday experience with contumely, the revival of classical learning had one salutary effect on scientific enquiry. It led to the study of Plato's antagonist, Epicurus, who had adopted the Atomic doctrine of Leucippus and Democritus. Prominent among the translators and commentators of Epicurus was Gassendi, who was one of the founders of the Paris Academy. Gassendi was the irreverent ecclesiastic who first determined the speed of sound in air. He also carried out an experimental demonstration which led to the abolition of witch-burning in Catholic France more than half a century in advance of Protestant Scotland. The incident is recounted in Robertson's *A Short History of Freethought Ancient and Modern* (Vol. II), as follows:

Among his other practical services to rationalism was a curious experiment, made in a village of the Lower Alps, by way of investigating the doctrine of witchcraft. A drug prepared by one sorcerer was administered to others of the craft in presence of witnesses. It threw them into a deep sleep, on awakening from which they declared that they had been at a witches' Sabbath. As they had never left their beds, the experiment went far to discredit the superstition. One significant result of the experiment was seen in the course later taken by Colbert in overriding a decision of the Parlement of Rouen as to witchcraft (1670). That Parlement proposed to burn fourteen sorcerers. Colbert, who had doubtless read Montaigne as well as Gassendi, gave Montaigne's prescription that the culprits should be dosed with hellebore—a medicine for brain disturbance. In 1672, finally, the king issued a declaration forbidding the tribunals to admit charges of mere sorcery; and any future condemnations were on the score of blasphemy and poisoning.

Epicurus was not himself a scientific investigator. He was interested in man's social life. Like Karl Marx (who wrote his doctorate dissertation on the Greek atomists), he regarded the teachings of natural philosophy as the proper basis for social conduct. Seeing how stupidity and cruelty like witch-burning results from terror of the gods, he believed that human relations would become more wholesome as men learned to recognize the orderly routine of a world in which no divine dispensation gives them a natural right to keep slaves. So Aristotle's hatred of materialism receives a sufficient explanation from his partiality for slavery.

The materialism of Democritus had two fundamental tenets. The first is what we now call the conservation of matter. It is expressed at the conclusion of an eloquent passage by the Epicurean poet Lucretius in the memorable words:

When human life to view lay foully prostrate upon earth crushed down under the weight of religion, who shewed her head from the quarters of heaven with hideous aspect lowering upon mortals, a man of Greece ventured first to lift up his mortal eyes to her face and first to withstand her to her face. Him neither story of the gods nor thunderbolts nor heaven with threatening roar could quell, but only stirred up the more the eager courage of his soul, filling him with desire to be the first to burst the fast base of nature's portals. . . . On he passed far beyond the flaming walls of the world and traversed in mind and spirit the immeasurable universe; whence he returns a conqueror to tell us what can, what cannot come into being, in short on what principle each thing has its powers defined, its deep-set boundary marked. Therefore religion is put under foot and trampled upon in its turn. Us his victory brings level with heaven. This is what I fear herein, lest haply you should fancy that you are entering on unholy grounds of reason and treading the path of sin, whereas on the contrary heinous religion has given birth to sinful and unholy deeds. . . . You yourself some time or other overcome by the terror-seeking tales of the seers will seek to fall away from us. Ay, indeed, for how many dreams may they now imagine for you, sufficient to upset the calculations of life and trouble all fortunes with fear. And with good cause, for if men saw that there was a fixed limit to their woes, they would be able in some way to withstand the religious scruples and threatenings of the seers. . . . This terror then and darkness of mind must be dispelled not by the rays of the sun and glittering shafts of day, but by the aspect and the law of nature, whose first principle we shall begin by thus stating, *nothing is ever gotten out of nothing by divine power*. Fear in sooth takes such a hold of all mortals, because they see many operations go on in earth and heaven, the causes of which they can in no way understand, believing them therefore to be done by divine power. For these reasons when we shall have seen that nothing can be produced from nothing, we shall then more correctly ascertain that which we are pursuing, both the elements out of which everything can be produced and the manner in which all things are done without the hand of the gods.

The vacuum pump destroyed this terror and darkness of mind. It established a new realm of matter, and removed the air we breathe from the domain of "spirits." Lest we be accused of emphasizing the "material" benefits of scientific progress unduly, we may recall the fact that witch-burning died out in England during the three decades which followed the revival of materialism. In Scotland, where belief in the authority of the seers was more firmly rooted, the amiable practice persisted longer. As late as 1664 one traveller records the spectacle of nine old women dying at the stake on the same day in Leith for dispensing herbs—contrary to Scripture. When at length correct information about the way in which chemical changes can be brought about had become more generally available, the execution and torture* of people supposed to be capable of suspending the laws of nature came to an end.

* The following citation from R. D. Melville in the *Scottish Historical Review*, vol. 2 (1905), tells of the ingenious sources of entertainment of which we have been robbed by the decline of Calvinism.
"The barbarity of the tortures wreaked upon persons . . . suspected of witchcraft or sorcery is sufficiently instanced by the well-known case of . . . Dr. Fian, alias Cunningham, schoolmaster at Saltpans, in Lothian. . . . In the first place, his head or neck was 'thrawn' or twisted with a rope; he was then 'put to the most Severe and Cruell paine in the world called the bootes'; shortly afterwards the nails of all his fingers were torn out with pincers, two needles having previously been thrust under every nail 'over even up to the heads'; this proving unavailing to extort a confession, he was again subjected to the boot, 'wherein he did continue a long time, and did abide so many blows in them that his legges were crusht and beaten together as small as might bee; and the bones and the flesh so brused that the blood and marrow spouted forth in great abundance, whereby they were made unserviceable for ever.' But, continues the report, 'all these grievous paines and cruel torments' failed to extort a confession, 'so deeply had the Devil entered into his heart.' Thereafter, by way of a terror and example to all others 'that shall attempt to deall in the lyke wicked and ungodlye actions as witchcraft, sorcerie, conspiration, and such like,' Fian was condemned to die in the special manner provided by the law of the land 'on that behalfe'; and he was accordingly conveyed in a cart to the Castle Hill of Edinburgh, and having first been strangled at a stake, his body was thrown into a fire, 'ready provided, and there burned . . . on a Saterdaie in the end of Januarie last past, 1591.' The narrative then quaintly but significantly proceeds to observe 'The rest of the witches which are not yet executed, remayne in prison till farther triall and knowledge of his Majestie's pleasure.'"

In Scotland the last cases occurred about 1727. Lecky tells us that nine years later the ministers of the associated presbytery met to record with grief their inability to stem the tide of modern doubt before turning their attention to new expedients for satisfying the deeper needs of mankind.

In 1643, Sir Thomas Browne, who was more enlightened than most of his contemporaries, wrote of witches: "they that doubt of these . . . are obliquely and upon consequence a sort not of Infidels but Atheists . . . the Devil hath them already in a Heresie as Capital as Witchcraft." His views on Lucretius were appropriate. "I do not much recommend the reading or studying of it, there being divers Impieties in it, and 'tis no credit to be punctually versed in it." Nevertheless the new naturalistic temper which Browne did much to sponsor was gaining ascendancy over what Browne himself called "the mortallest enemy unto knowledge and that which has done the greatest execution upon truth." The testimony of the surgeon was becoming as influential as the counsels of the Church. Needham relates a significant episode:

On May 16, 1634, Sir William Pelham wrote to Lord Conway as follows: "The greatest news from the country is of a huge pack of witches which are lately discovered in Lancashire, wherof it is said 19 are condemned and at least 60 already discovered; there are divers of them of good ability, and they have done much harm. 'Tis suspected that they had a hand in raising the great storm wherein his Majesty was in so great danger at sea in Scotland." The women examined by Harvey and his colleagues were the survivors of a batch of seven, three of whom had died in prison, and they had already been examined by Bishop Bridgeman of Chester, who had made a hair-raising report on their spiritual condition. In due course Mr. Alexander Baker and Mr. William Clowes, both Surgeons to the King, Dr. William Harvey, his physician, with six other medical men and ten midwives co-opted by them, proceeded to the Ship Tavern at Greenwich, where the prisoners lay, in order to make their examination. On the report which was subsequently made Harvey's signature does not appear, but instead of it that of Alexander Reid, M.D., the Anatomy Lecturer at Surgeons' Hall. The upshot of the affair was that no physical sign of diabolical intercourse could be found on the bodies of any of the women, no abnormal teats, cutaneous discolorations, or satanic brandings. And the report was sent in to that effect, stating that the examination had been under the direction and in the presence of Dr. William Harvey.

A second tenet of the Greek materialists was that matter is not continuous. Before there were good thermometers little was known about the expansion of solids or liquids. Compressibility was especially the characteristic of matter in the airy state. The recognition that air is material had to take account of this fact. The Greek materialists drew the bold conclusion that matter must be made up of weighty particles separated by a variable expanse of empty space. English physicists of the seventeenth century, engaged in studying the rules of gas compression, naturally welcomed the revival of the atomistic doctrine. A century later it furnished the clue to the fixed proportions in which elements combine to form new compounds. Seemingly the stage was now set for a great theoretical development of chemistry. This did not come till a much later date. Like those who now tell us that economics in one subject and psychology is another, the professional chemists of the day were still following the trail of self-evident principles.

ELASTICITY, COHESION, AND ADHESION

How the existence of pulling power exerted by the particles of which matter is supposed to be made up may affect the behaviour of matter in bulk is illustrated by the phenomenon of elasticity or the resistance of solids to

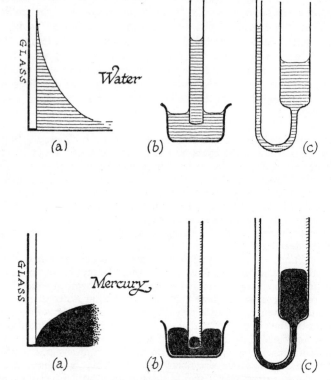

FIG. 242.—ADHESION AND COHESION

The cohesive power of water is less than its adhesive power to glass. Hence water (a) clings to glass and wets it, (b) exhibits a concave meniscus, and (c) creeps up a *fine* tube. The cohesive power of mercury is greater than its adhesive power for glass. Hence mercury (a) does not cling to glass or wet it, (b) exhibits a convex meniscus and (c) sinks below the gross equilibrium level in a *fine* glass tube. The height of a convex meniscus is easier to read than that of a column which wets glass. Hence mercury is better for thermometers or barometers. (It is also better for thermometers because it expands regularly over a wide range, and has a high boiling point. It is also better for barometers because it is very dense and has a very low vapour pressure—see p. 570.)

change of shape. A large quantity of a liquid exhibits no analogous phenomenon. It takes the shape of the vessel in which it lies, and presents a flat level surface where it is free to move except in so far as the pull of terrestrial gravity holds it in position. When the behaviour of liquids in fine drops, thin films, and very narrow tubes is examined new characteristics manifest themselves. They were first studied in the same social context as the air pump and the water-wheel by an English clergyman, Stephen Hales, who published an account of experiments on the ascent of sap in 1727.

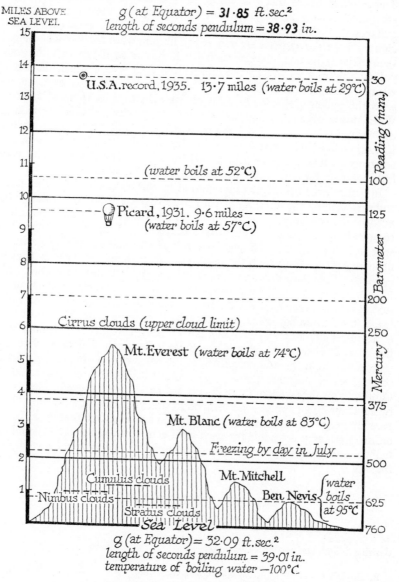

g (at Equator) = **31·85** ft. sec.^{2}
length of seconds pendulum = **38·93** in.

MILES ABOVE SEA LEVEL.

U.S.A. record, 1935. 13·7 miles (*water boils at 29°C*)

(*water boils at 52°C*)

Picard, 1931. 9·6 miles
(*water boils at 57°C*)

Cirrus clouds (*upper cloud limit*)

Mt. Everest (*water boils at 74°C*)

Mt. Blanc (*water boils at 83°C*)

Freezing by day in July

Mt. Mitchell

Ben Nevis { *water boils at 95°C* }

Cumulus clouds

Nimbus clouds

Stratus clouds

Sea Level

Barometer Reading (mm.) Mercury: 30, 100, 125, 200, 250, 375, 500, 625, 760

g (at Equator) = 32·09 ft. sec.^{2}
length of seconds pendulum = 39·01 in.
temperature of boiling water = 100°C.

FIG. 243.—THE EARTH'S ATMOSPHERE

One of these characteristics, called *cohesion*, is seen when a soap film is stretched, or drops of oil are allowed to trickle on to a large surface of water. The other, called *adhesion*, is seen when a film of water clings to the finger after it is withdrawn from water in which it was previously immersed. According to the Newtonian view of matter, cohesion is interpreted as the result of the pull which particles of the same substance exert on one another. The result of this is that whereas all the particles in the centre of a liquid are pulled equally in all directions, the particles at the surface can only pull on one another and those below them, and behave like a stretched sheath. Hence the surface particles are only in equilibrium when they are all arranged symmetrically around the central bulk. If this is small, so that the total pulling power of gravity on the bulk of the fluid is also small, the liquid assumes the spherical form of a drop. Adhesion, on the other hand, represents the pulling power of particles of one substance on those of another. When this is large compared with the force of gravity, as when the bulk of the water has trickled off the finger, it may be sufficient to resist further separation beyond a certain point. A film of fluid therefore clings to the surface with which it is in contact and "wets" it. Some fluids exhibit very little adhesion for particular surfaces, and do not "wet" them.

In general, the behaviour of a liquid at its surface of contact with a solid is determined by the interplay of both these characteristics. If the fluid does not wet the solid, i.e. if the power of adhesion is relatively insignificant as compared with cohesion, the surface of the liquid tends to assume the spherical shape so that the edge of the liquid in contact with the solid is depressed (Fig. 242), and the meniscus or air-liquid surface is convex upwards. If the fluid does wet the solid the edge of the fluid in contact with it is drawn upwards, and the meniscus is concave upwards. The result is that in tubes of very fine bore the rule that liquids find their own level is no longer true. If the liquid (e.g. mercury) does not wet a glass tube, its surface is depressed appreciably below the gravity level. If (e.g. water) it does wet the glass, it rises appreciably above it. In exceedingly fine tubes, like the minute vessels in the wood of plants, or the narrow spaces between particles of soil, water may rise to a very considerable height on this account. Capillarity, as the ascent of fluids in very fine tubes is called, can be illustrated by substituting a piece of dead bamboo for the wick of a paraffin lamp. The paraffin creeps up the bores, and the bamboo acts as an efficient wick. In an ordinary oil-lamp or candle the wick itself acts in the same way. The oil or molten wax creeps up to the flame through the fine spaces between the threads.

THINGS TO MEMORIZE

1. The initial downward acceleration of a body of density D in a fluid of density d is given by $a = \left(1 - \dfrac{d}{D}\right)g$.

2. Boyle's Law. $pv = k$, or, where d is the density $p = Kd$ and $d = K'p$.

EXAMPLES ON CHAPTER VII

1. In the following table the sign — indicates that the substance sinks, + indicates that it floats and 0 that it does not decidedly do either. Find the approximate density of each of the solids.

Liquid	Density (gm. per c.c.)	Larch-wood	Butter	Beeswax	Resin	Glue	Celluloid
Gasolene ..	0·69	+	—	—	—	—	—
Ether.. ..	0·74	+	—	—	—	—	—
Ethyl alcohol	0·79	+	—	—	—	—	—
Wood spirit ..	0·81	+	—	—	—	—	—
Turpentine ..	0·87	+	0	—	—	—	—
Olive oil ..	0·92	+	+	—	—	—	—
Castor oil ..	0·97	+	+	0	—	—	—
Water	1·00	+	+	+	—	—	—
Creosote ..	1·10	+	+	+	0	—	—
Glycerine ..	1·26	+	+	+	+	0	—
Chloroform ..	1·48	+	+	+	+	+	+

2. Taking the density of mercury as 13·5 gm. per c.c., iron 7·8, gold 19·3, lead 11·35, silver 10·5, aluminium 2·7, and magnesium 1·74, calculate the acceleration with which each of these metals will begin to rise or fall under gravity when placed in (a) mercury, (b) chloroform, (c) water, (d) gasolene.

3. If the density of sea water is 1·025 gm. per c.c., what will be the pressure in kg. per sq. cm. at a depth of 1 km. below the surface of the sea, neglecting atmospheric pressure?

4. A U-tube of uniform bore of diameter 1 cm. is about half filled with water. If the density of oil is 0·85 gm. per c.c., how many c.c. of oil must be poured into one limb to make the level of the water rise 6 cm. in the other?

5. At what angle to the vertical must a glass tube open at the top and containing water be gradually tilted until the pressure at the foot of it due to the water is diminished by half?

6. What is the ratio of the pressure on the upper half of one side of a cistern full of water to the pressure on its lower half?

7. The lock gate of a canal is 14 feet wide and 9 feet deep. How great is the pressure in tons weight on one side of it, if the water is level with the top and the density of water is 62·4 lb. per cub. ft.?

8. In a hydraulic press the cross-sectional areas of the small and large plungers are respectively 1 sq. in. and 100 sq. in. If the mechanical advantage of the lever handle is 5, what is the upward force of the ram when the lever handle exerts a force of 1 cwt.?

9. If the densities of glycerine, water, and ethyl alcohol, are respectively 1·26, 1·0, 0·79 gm. per c.c., find the initial acceleration of a piece of iron of density 7·86 gm. per c.c. falling in each.

10. The diameter of a small plunger in a hydraulic press is 1 inch and that of the large plunger 1 foot. What is the upward force exerted by the ram when a downward force of 56 lb. is applied to the smaller plunger? If the smaller piston moves through 1¼ inches in one stroke, find how far the ram has moved after 10 strokes.

11. Find the height of a barometer in which oil is used of density 0·845 gm.

per c.c., knowing that the height of a mercury barometer is 752 mm. and the density of mercury is 13·6 gm. per c.c.

12. A closed vertical tube has its open end inserted in a bowl of water. It is noticed that the surface of the water is 10 feet below the closed end of the tube. Knowing that the height of the water barometer is 33 feet, what is the pressure in the enclosed space due to the column of water?

13. Observation shows that the barometer falls an inch for every 900 feet above sea-level. A man takes a pocket aneroid barometer, which is used to determine the heights of mountains, up a mountain, ascending in 3 hours and descending in 1½ hours. The barometer registers 29·0 inches at the foot, 26·8 inches at the top, and 28·7 inches at the foot of the mountain after descending. Estimate the height of the mountain.

14. What is the atmospheric pressure in lb. weight on a circular disc 3 inches in diameter?

15. A man blowing into one limb of a U-tube half filled with mercury causes a difference of level of 4 cm. in the two limbs. What pressure does he exert in dynes per sq. cm.?

16. What is the volume of a quantity of gas at standard pressure, i.e. 76 cm., if, when the barometer reads 72 cm., the volume of the gas is 159 c.c.? Find the pressure at which it would have a volume of 200 c.c.

17. A cylinder 12 inches long has a piston halfway down so that there are equal quantities of air on each side of it. Find the ratio of the pressures on the two sides if the piston is pushed down so that it is only 1 inch from one end.

18. A closed tube 150 cm. long is half filled with mercury, and its open end inserted in a bath of mercury, making sure no air escapes from the tube. If the barometer reads 75 cm., what is the length of the mercury column in the tube?

19. A depression of the mercury column in a barometer is caused by a little air in the space at the top of the column, so that the barometer reads 28 inches instead of 29 inches, and 29 inches instead of 30·2 inches. Determine the correct value of the atmospheric pressure when the erroneous reading is 29·4 inches.

20. A thin tube of soft glass is taken and a thread of mercury 8 cm. long is drawn into it. One end of the tube is sealed off in a bunsen flame entrapping a quantity of air between the mercury and the end. When the tube is suspended with its closed end down, the length of the air column is 16·1 cm., but when it is suspended with its closed end up, the length of the column of air is 20·0 cm. What is the pressure of the atmosphere?

21. If the mercury barometer reads 45 inches inside a cylindrical diving bell 8 feet high, of which the top is submerged 12 feet below the surface of the water, how high has the water risen in the bell?

22. If a litre (1,000 c.c.) of dry air at 76 cm. is found to weigh 1·3 gm., how much space does 2 gm. of dry air occupy at the same temperature when the pressure is 70 cm.?

23. A closed cylinder of sectional area 10 sq. cm. stands 25 cm. above the level of water in a wide dish. The level of water in the cylinder is 20 cm. above the level of water in the dish. Find (a) the pressure of the air in the cylinder in terms of the mercury barometer, taking the specific gravity of mercury as 13; (b) how high the cylinder will stand above the level of water in the dish, if it is depressed till the level of fluid inside and outside is the same.

24. A rubber balloon weighs 0·5 gm. With what acceleration will it begin to fall if it is blown up till its cubic capacity is (a) 750 c.c., (b) 1 litre, (c) 2·5 litres?

Assume the pressure inside the balloon to be $1\frac{1}{4}$ atmospheres in each case, and that the density of air is $0 \cdot 0013$ gm. per c.c.

25. When a U-tube hydrometer as shown in Fig. 241 is inverted with one limb in mercury and the other in water, the fluids rise respectively to $0 \cdot 75$ cm. and $9 \cdot 75$ cm. when some air is sucked out. A little air is readmitted, and the mercury drops to $0 \cdot 4$ cm. What is the water level?

26. One limb of the same apparatus dips in mercury, the other in turpentine. The level of the turpentine is $8 \cdot 9$ cm. and that of the mercury is $0 \cdot 6$ cm. Use the data of the last example to find the height of the water column if one limb dipped in water and the level of turpentine in the other was 10 cm.

27. The glass tube of a mercury barometer of sectional area $0 \cdot 75$ sq. in. stands 38 inches above the level of mercury in a large deep dish. The level of fluid in the latter does not vary appreciably when all the fluid in the tube is removed. If the atmospheric pressure is 30 inches, how much will the mercury be depressed by introducing a bubble of air (a) $0 \cdot 001$, (b) $0 \cdot 01$, (c) $0 \cdot 1$ cub. in.?

28. If at a certain temperature 1 gm. of air occupies 1 litre, at 76 cm. pressure on the mercury barometer, we can put instead of $pv = k$

$$76 \times 1,000 = k.$$

At that temperature k has the value 76,000 when the unit of pressure is 1 cm. of mercury and the unit of volume is 1 c.c. Similarly calculate for the same temperature the numerical value of k (a) when the unit of volume is the litre and the unit of pressure the "atmo," i.e. the pressure exerted by a column of mercury 76 cm. in length; (b) when the unit of volume is the cubic centimetre and the unit of pressure is 1 dyne per sq. cm. (Density of mercury $= 13 \cdot 6$ gm. per c.c., and $g = 981$ cm. per second per second.)

29. At $0°$ C. 1 gm. of hydrogen was found to occupy $11 \cdot 2$ litres at 760 mm. on the mercury barometer. At the same temperature 1 gm. of oxygen occupied $0 \cdot 710$ litres when the pressure was 750 mm., and 1 gm. of nitrogen occupied $0 \cdot 789$ litres at 770 mm. Give the density in gm. per c.c. of the three gases, and express to the nearest whole number the *relative densities* of oxygen and nitrogen taking hydrogen (RD $= 1$) as standard.

30. The density of hydrogen at $0°$ C. and 760 mm. pressure is $0 \cdot 00009$ gm. per c.c. The relative densities of ammonia, carbon dioxide, and sulphur dioxide, are respectively $8 \cdot 5$, 22, and 32. Find how much space at $0°$ C. 1 gm. of ammonia would occupy at 750 mm., 1 gm. of carbon dioxide at 740 mm. and 1 gm. of sulphur dioxide at 770 mm.

31. The density of petrol is about $0 \cdot 7$ gm. per c.c. and of cork $0 \cdot 25$. If air at $0°$ C. and 760 mm. pressure is $14\frac{1}{2}$ times and sulphur trioxide is 40 times as dense as hydrogen, compare the initial acceleration under gravity of a drop of mercury, a rain drop, a drop of petrol, and a piece of cork, falling in each of these three gases at a place where g in vacuo is 32 ft. sec.² Use any relevant data in the foregoing examples.

32. At a place where the value of g is 32 ft. sec.², compare the period of a platinum pendulum which beats seconds in vacuo, if made to swing in an atmosphere of (a) air, (b) hydrogen, (c) sulphur trioxide. Neglect atmospheric resistance.

CHAPTER VIII

THE REBIRTH OF MATERIALISM

The Exhaustion of the Neolithic Economy

PHARMACEUTICAL establishments are sometimes called chemist's shops. Until the Industrial Revolution what chemistry was taught in the official seats of learning was a branch of medicine. According to a statement of Voltaire in the *Dictionnaire Philosophique*, the Parliament of Paris in 1624 passed a law which compelled the chemists of the Sorbonne to conform to the teaching of Aristotle on pain of death and confiscation of goods. The great intellectual progress which occurred in the nascent Protestant democracies during the ensuing half century is illustrated by the words of Joseph Glanvill, who is notable for his tract on witch-burning. In his book *Modern Improvements of Useful Knowledge* published in 1675, Glanvill wrote:

> Among the Egyptians and Arabians, the Paracelsians and some other moderns chymistry was very phantastic, unintelligible and elusive. . . . But its later cultivators, and particularly the Royal Society, have refined it from its dross and made it honest and sober, and intelligible, an excellent interpreter to philosophy and help to common life. For they have laid aside the delusory designs and vain transmutations, the Rosicrucian vapours, magical charms and superstitions, and formed it into an instrument to know the depths and efficacies of nature. And this is no small advantage that we have above the old philosophers of the *Notional* way.

The *Notional* way was the phrase which Sprat (p. 556) and the founders of the Royal Society referred to the Aristotelian attempt to found a science on self-evident principles. Events proved that chemists, like the economists of our own time, were reluctant to abandon it. In this chapter we shall see how new social needs which accompanied the industrial expansion of the seventeenth and eighteenth centuries refined chemistry from the dross of Aristotelian philosophy and the Rosicrucian vapours to which Joseph Glanvill alludes.

Mercury combines with the yellow gas *chlorine* to form two different substances. One is the highly poisonous corrosive sublimate (mercuric chloride), now used as an antiseptic for washing wounds. The other, which contains twice the ratio of mercury to chlorine by weight, is the purgative *calomel* (mercurous chloride). In an old chemical work, written before the recognition that air has weight, the formation of the calomel by grinding crystals of corrosive sublimate with the liquid metal itself was described by the statement, "the fierce serpent is tamed, and the dragon so reduced to subjection as to oblige him to devour his own tail." The words will not appear to be pure rhetoric, if we recall the expedients employed to make the supposedly imponderable spirits pass out of the air into the ingredients of the retort. Ancient number magic had associated the seven best-known metals with the seven bodies classified as planets in the pre-Copernican astronomy: the Sun with gold, the Moon with silver, Mercury with mercury, Venus with copper, Mars with iron, Jupiter with tin, and Saturn with lead. Success in conjuring the spirits which presided over chemical processes in which these metals formed compounds, or were extracted from their compounds, was not to be expected unless the experiment was carried out when the appropriate celestial body was making its transit above the meridian. The various conjunctions of the several planets offered specially propitious circumstances for carrying out reactions in which different metals participated.

Only three centuries have passed since these beliefs were widely accepted.

FIG. 244.—AN OLD SYMBOL REPRESENTING THE DISSOLUTION OF GOLD IN AQUA REGIA

We are apt to dismiss them as magic, and to forget that the distinction between the world of matter and the world of spirit was a very tangible one when theology upheld witch-burning. In the sixteenth century its professors had not conveniently fixed the boundary where the realm of possible proof and disproof ends. Medieval Europe accepted the authority of Aristotle and of the Apostle Paul. According to the Pauline view stated in the First Epistle to the Corinthians (1 Cor. xv. 40–52), anything which did not obey the Aristotelian law of gravitation was *ipso facto* spirit. The resurrected body was not invisible. It was merely imponderable, as the vapours of the alchemical retort were then supposed to be. A literal belief in the resurrection offered no difficulties in an age when the basic processes of medicine and metallurgy were believed to be modelled on the same plan.

The discovery that air has weight, and that air is, in short, a form of ponderable matter, carried with it the recognition that there is a third state of matter in contradistinction to the liquid and the solid state. Since there are many different sorts of matter called solids or liquids, it was natural to suppose that other substances may share with air the characteristics which distinguish air from matter in the liquid or the solid state. A new word *gas* now replaced "spirits," derived from an equivalent Teutonic word which did not carry into international usage the mystical content of its original meaning. It was first used by van Helmont in 1648, about the time when Torricelli's experiments gave new and conclusive evidence for the weight of the air. During the century and a half which elapsed between the death of van Helmont and the beginning of the nineteenth century the arts of manufacture received a new impetus from discoveries which made it possible to distinguish different forms of air, or, as we now say, different gases. These discoveries led to new rules about how substances combine or can be broken down to form new ones. What we call modern chemistry, in contradistinction to the chemistry of antiquity or the Middle Ages, is the theory of manufacture based on the knowledge that different gaseous elements enter into the composition of different objects of use.

The recognition of the gaseous elements bears a very close relation to the growth of mining and its problems in the sixteenth century. Agricola's *De Re Metallica* (1566) gives us a comprehensive picture of the class of technical problems which stimulated research into the physical properties of air. The story it tells is very different from the description of mining given by such classical historians as Diodorus Siculus. The miner is no longer a slave in a chain gang working under the overseer's lash. "A miner, since we think he ought to be a good and serious man," writes Agricola, "should not make use of an enchanted twig, because if he is prudent and skilled in the nature of signs, he understands that a forked stick is of no use to him." The sixth book of Agricola's treatise, dealing especially with the problems of pumping and ventilation (Fig. 245), ends with a section on "the ailments and accidents of miners, and the methods by which they can guard against these." It is not an exaggeration to say that these represent the two principal themes which underlie the recognition of the individuality of gases.

With the growth of deep-shaft mining for metals and the introduction of coal as fuel in the latter part of the sixteenth century two new problems had emerged in the everyday life of mankind. One was: What makes air foul to breathe or capable of sustaining life? The other was: What makes air inflammable and explosive like gunpowder, or incapable of supporting combustion? The phenomenon of combustion itself took on a new complexion through the introduction of gunpowder and the use of coal for fuel. Previous sources of fuel had been exclusively animal (e.g. tallow) or vegetable (wood and charcoal). That a seemingly mineral substance of "earthy" origin should produce fire was contrary to the prevailing belief that all substances were built up by combinations of earth, air, fire, and water, or of sulphur, salt, and mercury. The introduction of steam power, beginning with such inventions as the Marquis of Worcester's patent at the end of the seventeenth century, made the nature of combustion a topic of increasing interest. Meanwhile, the rapid industrial development which accompanied the successive introduction of water power and steam power was leading to the gradual exhaustion of the sources from which the crude chemicals employed by the traditional methods of the cloth, mining, glass, and soap-making industries were derived.

FIG. 245

Two prints from Agricola's Treatise, showing the importance of ventilation in deep-shaft mining. The lower displays a pivoted barrel over the flue. The upper shows a ventilating fan placed above the flue and driven by a windmill.

One important facet of the social background of the growth of chemical science in the seventeenth century is that warfare was making an increasing demand on gunpowder, and the success of the rising Protestant democracies depended on exploiting the new technique of self-defence and imperialist expansion. Of the three most usual constituents of "gunpowder"—charcoal, sulphur, and saltpetre, i.e. nitrates—the supply of the first from wood and the second from volcanic sources, offered comparatively little difficulty. The detection of sources of natural *nitrates* involved more analytical sophistication. Concerning the discovery of gunpowder, various dates are cited. The truth is that no precise date can be given. The various recipes which are called by that name emerged gradually from the practice of incendiary warfare before the means of purifying the constituents as yet existed. The use of burning pitch and oil, camphor and resins, to discomfit a besieging force is of great antiquity, and the certainty that explosive mixtures were known to the Chinese and in India before the use of artillery in Europe helps us to understand how the knowledge grew by easy stages. In these countries natural deposits of nitrates are formed where there are manure heaps. The accidental recognition that pitch contaminated with this natural "salt" would burn more vigorously cannot have been a specially remarkable discovery.

The natural salt was first known as "Chinese Snow," later as saltpetre. Crackers and rockets made of bamboo packed with saltpetre and combustible material were used as incendiary devices before the construction of a metal cannon to propel a dart or ball was accomplished in the thirteenth century. The earliest recipes of explosive or incendiary mixtures include, in addition to saltpetre, resin and brimstone (sulphur), sulphur and charcoal, or sulphur, charcoal and camphor as the combustible constituents. Once the metal case was introduced, the destructive possibilities of gunpowder became a dominant feature of military technique, and a new industry which promoted the search for materials of dependable purity came into being. Marshall (*Explosives*, Vol. 1) tells us that:

In the fourteenth century gunpowder was only used on a small scale, and was made in ordinary houses with pestle and mortar. We hear, for instance, that the Rathaus at Lübeck was destroyed by fire in 1360 through the carelessness of powder makers. Berthelot has stated that there were powder mills at Augsburg in 1340, at Spandau in 1344, and Liegnitz in 1348, but Feldhaus could find no confirmation of these statements in the archives of these towns. There is no mention of gunpowder or fire-arms in Augsburg before 1372 to 1373, and the first powder mill was erected at Spandau in 1578. The scale of operations gradually increased, and in 1461 we find the first mention of a "powder-house" in the Tower of London; powder was made there for many years, as also in Porchester Castle. In the sixteenth century mills of considerable size were in existence: the Liebfrauenkirche in Liegnitz suffered at this time from the effects of explosions in a mill near by. In 1554 to 1555 a gunpowder mill is said to have been erected at Rotherhithe, and about 1561 George Evelyn, the grandfather of John Evelyn, the diarist, had mills at Long Ditton and Godstone, having learned the methods of manufacture in Flanders. A few years later he obtained from Queen Elizabeth a monopoly of the manufacture of gunpowder, which he and his sons were able to maintain more or less until 1636, when Samuel Cordewell obtained the monopoly, which was abolished by Parliament in 1641, the year before the outbreak of the Civil War. George Evelyn made a fortune out of gunpowder.

Among the first papers communicated to the English Royal Society we find an account of the "History of the Making of Salt-Peter," in which the author, Mr. Henshaw, declares: ". . . the only place therefore where saltpeter is to be found in these northern countries is in stables, pigeon houses. . . ." Henshaw gave a recipe for making "salt-peter" from the natural nitrate content of fertile earth. About 1650 the German chemist Glauber showed that saltpetre can replace manure as a means of restoring the fertility of exhausted soils. He called his book *The Prosperity of Germany*. The discovery of new sources of materials had now become a necessary prerequisite of prosperity. How Glauber's discovery that saltpetre can be used as a substitute for manure arose from the social practice of his times is illustrated well enough by the following passage from Marshall's treatise on the history of *Explosives*:

In Europe there are very few localities where nitrate can accumulate in the soil to such an extent that a profit could be made by extracting it. There is no prolonged dry season during which deposits can form without being washed away again. Consequently saltpetre could only accumulate in sheltered places, such as cellars and stables, especially those in which there was much nitrogenous matter undergoing decomposition. As it was of the utmost importance in every country to have a sufficient supply of saltpetre, especially in time of war, its production formed the subject of royal decrees and orders at an early date. In France, officers (salpêtriers commissionés) were appointed in 1540 to search for and extract saltpetre, and no doubt the industry was in existence some time before. This edict was confirmed and renewed in 1572, and again whenever France was waging a serious war. The saltpetre workers operated on the earth of stables, sheep-pens, cattle-sheds, cellars and pigeon-houses, and on the plaster and rubbish removed when houses were pulled down. They had the right to gather material everywhere, with scrapers and brushes in the houses, with picks and shovels in places not inhabited. No building or wall could be pulled down until notice had been given to the saltpetre workers, who stated which parts they wanted reserved. . . . In the reign of Louis XIII (1610 to 1643) the annual crop of saltpetre amounted to 3,500,000 lb., but it gradually diminished in the eighteenth century largely on account of the strong objection the people naturally had to the presence of saltpetre workers in their houses and domains. . . . Until the sixteenth century saltpetre seems mostly to have been imported into England, much of it coming from Spain, but in 1515 Hans Wolf, a foreigner, was appointed to be one of the King's gunpowder makers in the Tower of London and elsewhere. He was to go from shire to shire to find a place where there is stuff to make saltpetre of, and "where he and his labourers shall labour, dig or break in any ground." He is to make compensation to its owners. And in 1531 Thomas à Lee, one of the King's gunners, was appointed principal searcher and maker of gunpowder . . . gunpowder was only manufactured in England on a small scale until the second half of the sixteenth century when George Evelyn started mills on a comparatively large scale. Consequently there was little difficulty before that time in obtaining sufficient saltpetre, but then it became necessary to grant the saltpetre men special privileges for digging up the floors of stables, dovecots and even private dwellings, and the kingdom was divided into a number of areas in which the collection and working of the saltpetre was assigned to various people. In 1561 Queen Elizabeth granted Gerard Honrick, a Dutchman, £500 (or £300) for teaching two of her subjects how to make saltpetre. In 1588 she granted a monopoly for gathering and working saltpetre to George Evelyn, Richard Hills, and John Evelyn. The monopoly extended over the whole of the south of England and the Midlands, except the City of London and two miles outside it. In 1596 Robert Evelyn acquired the rights in London and Westminster from the licensees there. As a rule, however, the Evelyns did not work saltpetre themselves, but bought it from the saltpetre men. In the reign of Charles I there was considerable friction between the saltpetre men and the public, but it was probably due more to the weakness of the Crown than to any real difficulty in obtaining in England the quantity of saltpetre required, viz. 240 lasts per annum. There was also competition between the saltpetre men and the soap-boilers for wood ashes, which were then practically the only source of potash and were required for the conversion of sodium nitrate into the potassium compound. . . . The East India Company, then in its infancy, imported Indian saltpetre into England as early as 1625, and set up a powder mill in Windsor Forest, which, however, was stopped on the ground that it interfered with the King's deer. Next year the Company received a license to erect mills in Surrey, Kent, and Sussex. At this time its importations were on a small scale, but when its charter was renewed in 1693 it was stipulated that 500 tons of saltpetre should be supplied every year to the Ordnance. Ever since then, Indian saltpetre has been used very largely in England for the manufacture of gunpowder.

The need for saltpetre affected chemical enquiry in two ways. It provided a direct incentive to studying the natural history of salts, and indirectly encouraged research into the way in which the green plant gets its food. Glauber's work, which showed that the saltpetre, i.e. nitrate content, of manure is mainly responsible for its effect on the fertility of the soil, stimulated parallel enquiries in England. Such experiments on soil fertility are among the first examples of chemical analysis, in which the weight of all the constituents of a reaction is tested. The same care in measuring the weight of substances taking part in a reaction is also shown in experiments suggested by the use of metallic alloys in making coins of the realm. An account of such experiments by Lord Brouncker is given in Sprat's *History of the Royal Society*. The paper entitled "Experiments on the Weight of Bodies increased in the Fire, Made at the Tower," gives examples of metals which gain weight when heated in air.

Sprat's *History* also mentions that the Royal Society had encouraged "the chymical examination of *French* and *English* wines." The "Proposal for Making Wine" put forward by Dr. Goddard, and included in Sprat's collection of communications made to the Society in the first few years of its work, contains a passage worth quoting:

It is recommended to the Care of some skilful Planters in Barbadoes, to try whether good Wine may not be made out of the Juice of Sugar-canes. That which may induce them to believe this Work to be possible, is this Observation, that the Juice of Wine, when it is dried, does always granulate into Sugar, as appears in Raisins, or dried Grapes: and also that in these Vessels wherein a cute, or unfermented Wine is put, the Sides are wont to be cover'd over with a Crust of Sugar. Hence it may be gather'd, that there is so great a Likeness of the Liquor of the Cane, to that of the Vine, that it may probably be brought to serve for the same Uses. If this Attempt shall succeed, the Advantages of it will be very considerable. For the English being the chief Masters of the Sugar Trade, and that falling very much in its Price of late Years, while all other outlandish Productions are risen in their Value; it would be a great Benefit to this Kingdom, as well as to our Western Plantations, if Part of our Sugar, which is now in a manner a meer Drug, might be turn'd into Wine, which is a foreign Commodity, and grows every Day dearer; especially seeing this might be done, by only bruising and pressing the Canes, which would be a far less Labour and Charge, than the Way by which Sugar is now made.

The subsequent history of enquiries on these lines justified itself by the promotion of one of the earliest industries based on direct application of chemical knowledge. The beet-sugar industry was destined to play a most important part in the beginnings of what we now call "organic chemistry." Cohen tells us that

the presence of sugar in beetroot was observed in 1747 by the German chemist Marggraf who suggested the cultivation of beet as a source of sugar, but the early attempts to utilize it commercially proved unprofitable. The success of the industry dates from about the year 1830 when important improvements began to be introduced. Careful selection of seed and improved cultivation nearly doubled the quantity of sugar in the beet. The use of steam-heated vacuum pans gave a larger yield of crystallizable sugar and new mechanical appliances for saving labour lowered the cost of production.

Another industry which played an important part in creating the demand for chemical knowledge was the manufacture of earthenware and china. In England it did so indirectly by stimulating the demand for coal, as well as by its immediate need for information about the nature of impurities in local clays and marls (brickearths), the art of colouring the finished product, and glazing. Dr. Plot, one of the earliest secretaries of the Royal Society and a Professor of Chemistry at Oxford, in his book *The Natural History of Staffordshire* (1686) tells us "for making the severall sorts of pots they have as many different sorts of clay . . . the best being found near the coale." Thus the juxtaposition of coal and boulder clay seams on the site of an industry which made heavy demands on fuel for baking, made the Potteries a focal centre of industrial development in the eighteenth century. Even in the seventeenth century it called for chemical skill. The colours, says Plot, were obtained by using different varieties of "slip" clays—"except the motley colour which is procured by blending lead with manganese, by the workmen called *magnus*." In a book on the history of the same county, published in 1798, Shaw tells us that in the eighteenth century the natural clays of the neighbourhood were little used, because they were metalliferous:

each having a portion of oxide of iron . . . the clays from Dorset or Devon have all their impurities extracted before they are vended to the purchasers . . . being extremely white when fired owing to being scarcely impregnated with oxide of iron, which would make the ware yellow or red in proportion to the quantity of clay.

Wedgwood, the "Prince of Potters," was in the forefront of the cultural renaissance in the latter half of the eighteenth century. As an industrial leader, he founded the first chamber of commerce in England. As an experimenter, he was elected a Fellow of the Royal Society on his own merits. His attitude to the relations of industry and science comes out in a letter to Bentley (1767).

I am going on with my experiments upon various earths . . . many of my experiments turn out to my wishes and convince me more and more of the extensive capability of our manufactures for further improvement . . . such a revolution is at hand and you must assist in and profit by it.

As with coal mining, the human problem of the Potteries had repercussions in the domain of chemistry. At the end of the eighteenth century interest in occupational diseases (see Chapter XVII) had materialized in a lively public health agitation, of which one of the most notable figures was Dr. Percival, of Manchester. Percival and Dr. Gouldsdon, of Liverpool, vigorously exposed the dangers of lead poisoning in the glazing of Pottery products. Wedgwood was much embarrassed by their pamphlets. We find him writing to Bentley (about 1775), "I will try in earnest to make a glaze without lead, and if I succeed will certainly advertise it." Leadless glazes, of which the ingredients were either lime, alkaline carbonates ("potashes"), or borates (imported from Tuscany), were introduced in the latter end of the eighteenth century under the impact of the public feeling aroused.

The new sense of social responsibility which emerged in the medical profession in the latter half of the eighteenth century also revived interest in the problem of ventilation which had arisen earlier in connection with deep-shaft mining for coal and tin. Davy, who seems to have acquired his interest in theoretical chemistry from an early friendship with the younger son of James Watt, the engineer, obtained his first scientific employment in the "Medical Pneumatic Institution" at Clifton, Bristol. This was founded by Beddoes, who—partly on account of his strong Jacobin views—had left the chair in chemistry at Oxford to take up medical practice. Davy's first important chemical researches were concerned with laughing gas (nitrous oxide), and one of his great inventions was the miner's safety lamp.

RESPIRATION

Among the "information they have given to others to provoke them to enquire," Sprat mentions that the founders of the Royal Society included in their programme "the fatal Effects of *Damps* on *Miners* and the Ways of recovering them." The human aspect of ventilation in mines was not the only practical issue which provoked enquiry into respiration. In the same context as "Relations . . . of deep *Mines* and deep *Wells*," Sprat also mentions

Relations . . . of *Divers* and *Diving*, their Habit, their long holding of breath and of other notable Things observed by them.

In the social context of early coal mining the discovery that air is a form of matter was highly propitious to a systematic attack on the subject-matter of Agricola's book dealing with "health and accidents of miners." The importance of this theme is borne out by the fact that "pneumatic" chemistry was a recognized major branch of the subject during the eighteenth century. During the Middle Ages breathing had been a spiritual accomplishment. The identification of "spirits" with the gaseous state of matter is implied by the synonymous use of the Latin word *anima* for soul and breath. So,

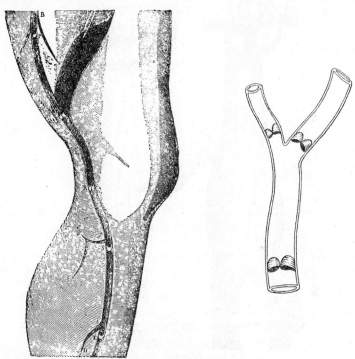

FIG. 246.—THE VALVES IN THE VEINS

On the left the figure shown by Fabricius. On the right diagrammatic view of three sets of valves.

too, the Hebrew scriptures declare that man became a living spirit when the Deity breathed into his nostrils the breath of life. Such assertions offered no difficulties to the literate classes of Europe while they continued to share Aristotle's contempt for slave labour. Modern doubt begins with the study of the common pump.

Precise information about what breathing really involves came through the recognition that the heart performs the part of a pump maintaining a continuous circulation of blood from the lungs to the tissues, and the tissues to the lungs. In the latter half of the sixteenth century Servetus had concluded that all the blood from the right side of the heart is pumped through the minute vessels of the lungs and returns thence to the left. Owing to a difference in celestial arithmetic between himself and Calvin, who had lately established the kingdom of God in Geneva, Servetus was burned at the stake before he had time to complete his researches. Half a century elapsed before the English physician Harvey convinced his contemporaries that the blood from the left side of the heart is pumped through the minute vessels of the rest of the body before its return to the right side, where it is dispatched to the lungs. As a result of Galileo's experiments, the pump had become an object of scientific interest. Fabricius, under whom Harvey studied at Padua, had discovered that the veins have watchpocket valves which can

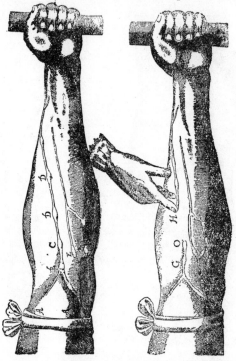

FIG. 247.—HARVEY'S FIGURE TO ILLUSTRATE HIS EXPERIMENT
(From Singer.)

only let blood pass one way, as the valves of a common pump only let water pass one way (Fig. 246). Fabricius was a colleague of Galileo. Harvey was a fellow-student with Torricelli.

A conclusion which rests on so few and such simple experiments might have been made by the physicians of antiquity, if an understanding of the way in which a pump-valve acts had been part of their social culture. With the discovery of the continuous circulation of the blood a long familiar fact about the body was endowed with new interest. The "venous" blood which returns to the right side of the heart from the tissues and passes thence to the lungs is dark purple. The "arterial" blood which issues from the lungs, and is pumped by the heart into the main arteries, is bright scarlet. The blood undergoes a definite and very obvious change through coming into contact with the air taken into the lungs.

One of the first experiments which Boyle demonstrated to the Fellows of the Royal Society was the fact that an animal dies at once when all the air is exhausted from a vessel in which it is placed. He also showed that a lighted candle is extinguished by the same treatment, and that sulphur and charcoal refuse to burn if heated in a vacuum, though they burst into flames when air is admitted. Gunpowder, which is a mixture of nitre (saltpetre), sulphur, and charcoal, did not behave in the same way. In a vacuum it was found to burn readily. Hooke proved that animals can be kept alive, when their normal respiratory movements are prevented, if air is blown through the lungs with bellows. He also showed that the respiration of an animal or the burning of a flame lasts longer in a large than in a small closed space containing air. Lower, another member of the same coterie of English men of science, showed that dark "venous" blood obtained by cutting a vein becomes bright scarlet when shaken with air. Thus the change of colour was due to "the particles of air insinuating themselves into the blood." In an early publication of the Royal Society, Slare (1693) develops the conclusion a little further by analogy with experiments in which solutions of copper compounds changed colour in a vacuum. Curiously enough he did not carry out the simple experiment to show that arterial blood acquires the purple hue of venous blood when shaken in an exhausted vessel connected with an air-pump. This was done by Priestley a century later.

The power of gunpowder to ignite when heated in a vacuum suggested to Hooke that combustion depends on the combination of substances with a constituent common to air and nitre. Proof was provided by Mayow, a contemporary English physician (*circa* 1670). Mayow adapted an experiment which had been carried out centuries before his time. In classical antiquity it was known that a candle burning in a space closed by inverting a glass vessel over water makes the latter rise in the vessel (Fig. 248). Mayow repeated this experiment, substituting a mouse for a candle, with the same result, i.e. the water level rose. The mouse eventually died, just as the candle-flame is eventually extinguished. Thereafter the residual air will no longer support life or combustion.

Adopting the atomistic views of Hooke, Mayow drew the radical conclusion that air consists of two sorts of particles. One sort is taken up by the lungs, or used by the candle-flame, and another is incapable of taking part in combustion or respiration. Having shown that the residual or foul air could be made suitable for breathing, or combustion by heating the nitre (or saltpetre) used in making gunpowder, he concluded rightly that respiration and combustion both result in removing the same "nitro-aerial particles." These *nitro-aerial particles*, or as we now say atoms of oxygen, make it possible for gunpowder to explode in a closed space. Thus air is not a simple substance, or element incapable of further dissolution. It contains at least two gaseous constituents, one being present in saltpetre. If Mayow's fundamental experiment had been carried out with an air-trap of mercury instead of water, no rise of level would have happened as the air lost its power to support life and flame. Mayow showed that air was deprived of one of its constituents without realizing that this constituent was replaced by another gas, the characteristics of which were first studied by Black (1754) in the middle of the eighteenth century.

Van Helmont was led to invent the word gas by discovering that the bubbles produced in fermentation and the "air" in which charcoal had been burned to ashes, are both unable to support combustion. Hence they are not identical with ordinary air. The "gas sylvestre" which van Helmont collected from the wine vat was found to turn a solution of lime milky. Black found that the bubbles of gas given off when acids are poured on chalk, and the air we breathe out, both have the same characteristic. He thus showed that the oxygen which is taken from the air by breathing or by the combustion of charcoal is replaced by another gas, which he called *fixed air*. This fixed

FIG. 248.—BURNING A CANDLE IN A CLOSED SPACE

To measure the volume of air at the end of the experiment the glass jar must be depressed till the level of the water inside it and outside it is the same. The residual gas in the vessel is then at the same pressure (atmospheric) as at the beginning of the experiment.

air, which we now call carbon dioxide or carbonic acid gas, is unlike the air we breathe into our lungs in many ways. For instance, it dissolves readily in water, with which it forms a slightly acid solution. Hence it disappeared in Mayow's experiment, leaving the air less dense. The water therefore rose to equalize the pressure.

Black was a professor in Glasgow, and later in Edinburgh University. His many fundamental discoveries in chemistry and physics will be referred to again and again. He was the central figure of a brilliant coterie of Scotsmen about whom more will be said. The activities of this circle show how theoretical science continually renews its youth by the infusion of new problems derived from the common experience of mankind and from contemporary social needs. The immediate problem which prompted Black's researches on lime is indicated in the biographical sketch accompanying Kay's *Original Portraits*:

We are informed by himself that he was led to the examination of the absorbent earths partly by the hope of discovering a new sort of lime and lime-water which might possibly be a more powerful solvent of the stone than that commonly used. The attention of the public had been directed to this subject for some years. Sir Robert, as well as his brother Horace, afterwards Lord Walpole, were troubled with the stone. They imagined they had received benefit from a medicine invented by Mrs. Stephens, and, through their interest principally, she received five thousand pounds for revealing the secret. It was accordingly published in the *London Gazette* on June 19, 1739. This had directed the attention of medical men to the employment of lime-water in cure of the stone.

The eminence of the Walpoles would not have ensured immortality to Black if other and more important circumstances had not drawn attention to his work. Shyness and ill-health prevented Black from publishing his important discoveries on heat. They were communicated verbally to the Newtonian Society of Edinburgh, and they would have passed unnoticed, if they had not inspired the invention of Watt's steam engine (see pp. 588–93). His friendship with Dr. Roebuck, who started large-scale commercial manufacture of sulphuric acid, brought Black into contact with social forces which could find a use for new knowledge. But for that his discovery of fixed air would have been buried in the medical thesis in which it was announced.

Dr. Roebuck, a physician from Birmingham, established a sulphuric acid factory at Prestonpans in 1749, started the famous ironworks at Carron in Stirlingshire in 1760, and leased the Duke of Hamilton's coalfield to use pit coal for reducing iron ores. Scotland, which had lagged behind England in the exploitation of its mineral resources, had begun to develop rapidly in this direction after the Act of Union and the Stuart rebellions. Coal mining was extended in Fifeshire and in the Lothians, where the Newcomen engine was introduced for pumping. In 1755, when an Edinburgh Society was established to promote the arts and manufactures, social conditions in Scotland were comparable to those in England when the Royal Society was founded. Industry was primarily concerned with the search for materials, and chemistry was therefore in demand.

Mechanization had begun in the coalfields, where Newcomen's atmospheric engine was in use, when Black and Roebuck provided financial backing for a young technical assistant in Glasgow University to improve its design. In 1765 Watt is carrying out experiments on their behalf to test a process for making alkali by the decomposition of lime and sea salt. Hamilton (*The Industrial Revolution in Scotland*) tells us that the middle of the eighteenth century was also a period of rapid agrarian development in Scotland. Francis Home, Professor of Materia Medica and a prominent figure in the Edinburgh circle, is busy finding out "how far chymistry will go in settling the principles of agriculture." His treatise was published (1775) a year after the presentation of Black's thesis. Interest in capitalist farming had been an outstanding feature of the programme which the English Royal Society had undertaken in the first decade of its existence, when Glauber had lately shown that saltpetre is the "active principle" of manure. These early researches on soil chemistry led Francis Home to important discoveries which laid the foundations of commercial soil chemistry. A year after the publication of his *Principles of Agriculture* he received a gold medal from the "Honourable Board of Trustees for the Improvement of Manufactures in North Britain" in recognition of his "Experiments on Bleaching." We are told in Kay's *Portraits* that "he received many testimonies of eminent manufacturers whose art it had much improved." He was instrumental in introducing sulphuric acid for use in bleaching linen, and thus created a new commercial demand for the parent substance of modern chemical industry.

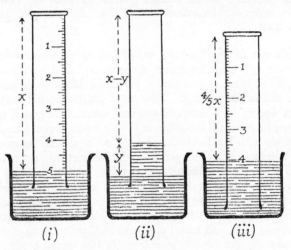

FIG. 249.—MEASURING THE VOLUME OF A GAS

In measuring the volume of a gas in a graduated glass vessel over a fluid, it is important to depress the latter till the level of the fluid inside and outside it is the same. If not, there will be a pressure difference between the gas and the outside air depending on the height to which the water rises. Suppose in the first cylinder (i), of sectional area a sq. cm., the length of the empty column is x cm., then its volume is ax c.c. If the oxygen is used up, e.g. by burning magnesium in it, the residual volume is $\frac{4}{5}ax$, and the height of the dead space $\frac{4}{5}x$ when the pressure is the same as before (i.e. in equilibrium with the atmosphere). To make it equal (iii) the cylinder must be pushed down a little. Otherwise, the fluid will rise as it has risen y cm. in (ii). The volume of the dead space in (ii) is therefore $a(x - y)$. If the fluid is mercury and the atmospheric pressure is P cm. of mercury, the difference in pressure between the outside air and air in (ii) is y cm. of mercury, and the pressure of air in (ii) is therefore P $- y$ cm. of mercury. So

$$P(\tfrac{4}{5}ax) = k = (P - y)a(x - y)$$

The only unknown quantity here is y, if the barometric pressure is known, and the height to which the fluid will rise is calculable. If the fluid is water the numerical value of P is 13·6 times the figure for the mercury barometer.

In Black's researches on lime the Aristotelian belief that chemical changes result from combinations of the "volatile" and imponderable elements air and fire with weighable matter in its elemental forms of water and earth, is making way for the modern view. Black found that fixed air is given off when chalk is heated to form quicklime, and estimated the quantity of fixed air which is combined with lime (calcium oxide) to form chalk by weighing the quicklime produced when a weighed quantity of chalk was heated. He determined how much chalk and how much quicklime are required to neutralize an acid, i.e. to make the acid no longer able to change the colour of a dye like litmus, and found that the weight of lime which neutralizes an acid without producing effervescence is equivalent to the weight of lime produced by heating the amount of chalk required to neutralize the same amount of acid. Hence the gaseous constituent combined with lime in chalk, and liberated as bubbles when acid is poured on the latter, does not affect its power to neutralize an acid.

The interest which Black's researches aroused in men of Roebuck's type was partly due to the fact that commercial production of alkali was becoming an imperative need of textile industry. The older chemists had used the word alkali for any substance which neutralizes an acid. Quicklime, potashes, and caustic potash, obtained by boiling a solution of potashes with lime, were all "alkalis." Black showed that the potashes of industry (potassium carbonate), like chalk, liberate fixed air when acted on by acids. His experiments proved that the way in which chalk and potashes are built up has more in common than the way in which quicklime and potashes are built up. We express this today when we say that both belong to the class of compounds called *carbonates*.

Two new methods of enquiry were emerging. Each had tremendous consequences for the future of man's command over the materials at his disposal. Hitherto chemists had classified the qualities of substances by their *uses*, and had neglected the *observed* quantities in which they combine. About this time they begin to classify them by their *constituents*, and to study the proportions in which their constituents are combined by weight. The former makes it possible to make a comprehensive survey of the sources of materials for social use. The second tells us whether the yield we can expect from a particular source justifies the effort expended. One difference between the chemistry of today and the chemical art of the Middle Ages lies in the fact that it can tell us all the possible *sources* from which we can get material substitutes and the *yield* we can get by using them.

Medical men and pharmacists like Black, Francis Home, and Scheele were prominent among the theoretical leaders who prepared the way for the rise of chemical industry, and Roebuck and Keir, two of the leading entrepreneurs of the period (*vide infra*), were medically qualified. Since chemistry was not as yet separated from the practice of medicine it inevitably benefited from the contemporary revolution in biological classification. The classification of plants arose out of the social practice of ancient medicine. Commercial horticulture, seed production for agriculture, and the systematic policy of surveying the unexploited wealth of new countries during the period of colonial expansion which intervened between the discovery of the New World and Cook's Australian voyage, conspired to give a new and powerful impetus to biological classification. This reached its zenith in the *Systema Naturae* of Linnaeus published in the middle of the eighteenth century. Linnaeus set forth a classification of the "mineral kingdom" along with that of animals and plants. In this he followed a practice which grew out of the instructions which Elizabeth issued to her sea captains. The proceedings of learned academies from 1650 to 1670 contain innumerable miscellanies of local information about plants, animals, or minerals, communicated from colonies, like Ceylon or Malabar. Such accounts were often based on collections made with direct encouragement from colonial governors. Although Linnaeus himself did not embody the results of new knowledge about chemical composition in his classification of the mineral kingdom, it was important because it focused attention on a new theoretical need.

EXPLOSIONS

Let us now see how researches suggested by the properties of gunpowder and by explosions in coal-mines conspired to stimulate other discoveries about the individuality of gases. The former encouraged the study of the gas called *sulphur dioxide*. Sulphur and charcoal both burn in air. If they are impure there is a small solid residue of salts. If sufficiently pure they leave no solid residue. The burning of sulphur is accompanied by the formation of very pungent fumes, which dissolve in water to form a solution which affects vegetable dyes, such as litmus, in the same way as the mineral acids. Similar fumes are produced in the absence of air when sulphur is heated with another constituent of gunpowder—saltpetre or nitre. The explanation of this lies in another fact. When heated alone, nitre gives off a "gas"—oxygen—which sustains combustion more readily than air itself, and makes foul air shaken with water suitable for breathing. When nitre is mixed with sulphur and charcoal, this gas is taken up by the sulphur and charcoal with the formation of two gases, fixed air (carbon dioxide), and fumes of burnt sulphur (sulphur dioxide). An explosion is nothing more than the sudden change of volume which occurs when these gases are liberated in a closed space. Put in modern phraseology, these were essentially the conclusions to which Boyle's experiments with his air pump led him. In his famous book, the *Sceptical Chymist*, he roundly attacked the doctrine accepted by nearly all his predecessors who interpreted the use of heat to facilitate chemical changes as proof that fire dissolves complex substances into simpler ones. He rejected the belief that there were only a few elementary substances which participate in chemical processes.

A clue to the nature of explosions in coal-mines was found when Clayton (1691) prepared an "inflammable air" by heating coal in a retort. A few years later the physician Stephen Hales, who first made experiments on the pressure of the blood, recorded the observation that 158 grains of Newcastle coal yield 180 cub. in. of the new gas. Coal gas is not a single chemical substance of constant composition. Though its discovery did not, therefore, intrinsically add to the existing stock of knowledge about how substances combine, it presented two arresting features which quickened the growing recognition that a great variety of different substances exist in the gaseous state. It was inflammable and lighter than air. The search for other gases received a powerful impetus from its novelty, and was also reinforced by the fact that acids were now being manufactured on a commercial scale. In the middle of the eighteenth century Cavendish made a thorough examination of the bubbles given off from the action of strong acids on metals. He introduced a simple device (Fig. 250) for collecting them, and thus discovered a new inflammable gas which proved to be much lighter than air or coal gas.

Coal gas burns in a closed space with a sooty flame. In abundant air, water vapour is produced, and the residual gas turns lime water milky. The gas that we now call *hydrogen*, which Cavendish (1766) obtained from the action of sulphuric acid on zinc or of hydrochloric acid on tin, burns without the production of soot or fixed air (carbon dioxide). The only product of its combustion is steam, i.e. water in the gaseous state.

The discovery that water is a compound substance was made by Priestley two years after he joined the circle of James Watt the inventor, in Birmingham (see page 431). The Aristotelian catalogue of elements, from which air had been removed, therefore sustained a second rude shock from the discovery of hydrogen. Elemental water could now be made by

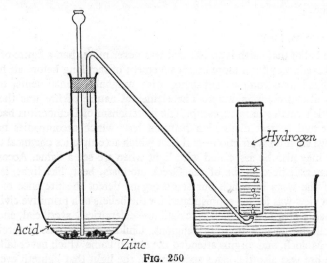

Acid
Zinc

Hydrogen

FIG. 250

Apparatus for collecting hydrogen gas by the action of hot, strong hydrochloric acid (introduced through the thistle funnel) on tin, or of sulphuric acid on zinc. The cylinder in which the gas is collected over water is at first completely full of water. To collect a water-soluble gas such as carbon dioxide or ammonia, mercury or paraffin should be used instead.

combining hydrogen, a constituent of acids, with oxygen, a constituent of elemental air.

The temper of the times had moved far from witch burning when a new secular miracle added to the prestige of chemical science. Black had demonstrated the ascent of toy balloons filled with coal gas, and subsequent events soon brought its novelty into the arena of everyday life. In the year 1782 two Frenchmen, the brothers Montgolfier, devised a startling demonstration that hot air is less dense than cold. A large silk bag with an opening at the bottom was held by ropes over a bonfire. When it was deemed to be sufficiently full of hot air, the ropes were released, and the first balloon made its ascent. A year later a similar attempt was made, this time with a carrier in which a duck, a hen, and a sheep were sent up. Owing to the carelessness of the sheep, the results were fatal to the hen. Otherwise the experiment was a triumph. In the same year Rozier made an ascent, traversing a distance of over five miles, in a hot-air balloon. Meanwhile Charles had constructed a large hydrogen balloon in Paris. A great concourse collected at the Champs-Élysées to witness the spectacle. His success made it possible to remain in the air without fear of being forced to descend owing to cooling. In 1784 crowds collected in the Strand to see the first ascent in a hydrogen balloon by Lunardi, and a year later Blanchard crossed the channel. The Soho group, to which we shall refer later on, took an active interest in the possibilities of the invention. Prosser tells us that John Southern, a Fellow of the Royal Society, employed by Boulton and Watt,

was the author of a tract on balloons, published at Birmingham in 1783 at the time when the ascents by the French aeronauts were exciting much attention.

HEAT AND WEIGHT

The belief that earth is an element was never more than a figure of speech. It had made way for a more literal statement of fact long before air had been recognized as a complex substance with weighable constituents, of which one is also present in water. The elemental nature of fire was the last of Aristotle's catalogue to succumb. The materialism of Democritus had drawn a clear and correct distinction between heat which accompanies motion— or, as we should say, friction—and heat which accompanies chemical changes, which may also be associated with light when we see a flame. According to the materialistic doctrine of the Greek atomists, heat, like light, is merely one of the ways in which our sense organs detect the presence of matter. Such a view was far too sophisticated for the beliefs of a primitive civilization. Fire had a host of hallowed associations—calendrical, sacrificial, and sexual —in all the ancient mystery religions. Children were passed through the fire to Moloch, and virgins attended the sacred flame which never failed. The divine fire was also the logos spermatikos, the light that lighteth every man. In Platonism, Stoicism, Gnosticism, and Mithraism, from which Christian theological ritual severally derived so many of its ingredients, fire was an object of veneration, and a symbol of unspeakable mysteries. It is little matter for surprise that Fire was the last of Aristotle's elements to go.

It retained its hold most tenaciously in the oldest branch of chemical technology. Two basic processes of metallurgy had persisted unchanged from the dawn of the Iron Age till the introduction of pitcoal to replace charcoal. For extraction of some metals, it was sufficient to roast the ore or *calx* with charcoal in a closed space. Chalk was also added as a "flux" to combine the quartz and clay present in the ore into a fusible glass which could be easily separated from the metallic mass. Another source of metal, the sulphureous ores, could only be extracted by previous roasting in a current of air. This was accompanied by the evolution of sulphureous fumes (sulphur dioxide). On subsequent reduction with charcoal the calx formed from the sulphureous ore yielded the metal. Alchemical experiments with metals had added three important items of additional information:

(a) Some metals, especially tin and mercury, could be converted into *calces* (oxides) by heating strongly in air.

(*b*) The formation of the calx is accompanied by increase of weight.

(*c*) Some metals, e.g. iron, yield sulphureous ores (sulphides) when strongly heated with sulphur in a closed space.

In addition to the seven metals associated with the seven pre-Copernican "planets" two others, antimony and zinc, had been worked as early as 1000 B.C. Thereafter practically no progress was made in practical metallurgy, and no new facts of theoretical importance, other than the three stated above, had been ascertained till towards the end of the eighteenth century. In ancient metallurgy the use of charcoal to reduce the oxide ores, and the preliminary treatment of sulphureous ores in the blast furnace, were empirical facts. Their significance resided in the mysterious properties of fire. Failure to form correct conclusions about the way ores are built up made it impossible to lay down rules for seeking new sources and sorts of metal.

In the light of what we have now learned about combustion and explosion, it is easy to see what happens in the extraction of metals. The sulphureous ore is a compound (sulphide) of metal and sulphur. The sulphureous fumes (sulphur dioxide) and calx (metallic oxide) formed in the roasting furnace are compounds of oxygen with sulphur and metal respectively. The air of the blast furnace supplies the oxygen (or nitro-aerial particles) which converts the sulphur of the ore into sulphur dioxide, and the metal of the ore into metallic oxide. The charcoal or coke used in reducing the calx is consumed when it burns, forming fixed air (carbon dioxide) by combining with oxygen. In a closed space it cannot take this oxygen quickly from the air. It takes it slowly from the ore, as it takes it rapidly from the nitre when gunpowder ignites in a vacuum. The formation of a calx from a metal when heated in air is essentially like the combustion of charcoal to form fixed air. The only difference is that charcoal ignites at comparatively low temperatures, whereas, with a few exceptions like the magnesium of flash-light photography, metals only combine rapidly with oxygen at very high temperatures. The entire sequence of changes when metals are extracted will be made clear if we now separate the known facts from what we now know to be the correct explanation.

The known facts were:

(1) sulphur (solid) + metal (solid) = sulphureous ore (solid)
                  (e.g. iron)   (e.g. pyrites)

(2) sulphur (solid) + oxygen (gas) = sulphureous fumes (gas)
                  (of the air)   (sulphur dioxide)

(3) metal (solid) + oxygen (gas) = calx (solid)
                  (of the air)

(4) charcoal (solid) + oxygen (gas) = fixed air (gas)
                  (of the air)   (carbon dioxide)

The likely explanation of the industrial processes was therefore—

(5) In the roasting furnace,
    sulphureous ore + oxygen = calx + sulphur dioxide.

(6) In the closed furnace,
    calx + charcoal = metal + carbon dioxide.

For complete proof of this it was necessary to show:

(a) that the increase of weight when the calx is formed from its metal is due to the disappearance of an equivalent weight of oxygen;

(b) that the gases formed in the roasting and closed furnaces were respectively identical with those formed when sulphur and charcoal burn in air;

(c) that the difference between the weight of calx used and metal formed is equal to the difference between the weight of fixed air produced and the weight of carbon used up.

The first step (a) had already been surmised by a French chemist Rey (1630), who had absorbed Galileo's doctrine, before Boyle, "with the help of our engine," had shown how he could "weigh the aire as we weigh other bodies in its natural or ordinary consistence." "Let all the greatest minds in the world," said Rey, "be fused into one mind, and let him seek diligently on the earth and in the heavens; let him search into every cranny of nature: he will only find the cause of this augmentation in the air." The last step (c) was made possible by Black's discovery. Carbon dioxide turns a solution of lime milky because it precipitates the insoluble compound calcium carbonate (chalk). Black had found the weight of carbon dioxide in a given quantity of chalk. So the quantity of carbon dioxide in a given quantity of air can be ascertained by shaking it with lime water, filtering off the precipitate, drying the latter and weighing it.

Even the English physicists, whose "nitro-aerial particles" offered the necessary clue to the nature of combustion, were readier to recognize its kinship to the breath of life than to probe into the Promethean secrets of metallurgy. Boyle himself stuck to the belief that metals like tin and lead, which readily form oxides when heated in air, increase in weight by absorbing the fiery particles with power to penetrate the walls of the furnace. Meanwhile a school of continental chemists preserved the purity of their studies from contamination with the growing knowledge of the nature of heat by fabricating a doctrine which may well commend itself to those economists who believe in the possibility of erecting science on a foundation of self-evident principles. The doctrine of phlogiston, which was the last attempt to sustain the elemental nature of fire, was concocted towards the end of the seventeenth century. It provides an instructive example of the way in which facts may be used to *illustrate* instead of to *test* the truth of a theory. The argument runs as follows. It is self-evident that if things burn, they must contain the fire principle. A combustible substance is, therefore, a combination of a calx or non-combustible material with the fire principle phlogiston. The escape of phlogiston when a combustible substance burns is accompanied by production of incombustible material which actually weighs more than its predecessor. It is therefore self-evident that phlogiston must be endowed with the opposite of weight, *levity*, or the power to make a body weigh less. Much valuable time was wasted in disproving a theory with nothing to commend it but the elegance of flawless reasoning from premises which have no foundation in fact.

What contributed most to discredit phlogiston in the long run was growing interest in the nature of heat. Heat, as a source of mechanical power, was beginning to effect a veritable revolution in human life. The problem of measuring heat and of classifying the different sources and means of transmitting it was beginning to eclipse the physical problems which had arisen from the practice of time reckoning and of earth survey. As we all know, the production of heat alone or of heat and light together can be brought about without any other change in the properties of a body. A poker which is heated till it glows is in other respects just a piece of iron weighing as much as it did before. The heat which is accompanied by incan-

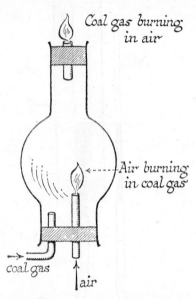

FIG. 251.—APPARATUS SHOWING AIR BURNING IN COAL GAS

descence when a body is said to burn away only differs in intensity from the heat given out or taken in in any change from one substance to another. It is the same physical phenomenon as the heat produced by friction when a wheel is not lubricated, or the heat acquired by contact when the poker is put in the fire.

All chemical changes are associated with difference of temperature. When washing soda (sodium carbonate) is dissolved in water the solution is cooler than the surrounding air. When sulphuric acid is added to water the mixture is hotter. If we let sulphuric acid trickle through a narrow tube immersed in a large bath of water, the fluid round the orifice will get hot. If we let water trickle through a narrow tube into a bath of sulphuric acid, the fluid near the orifice becomes exceedingly hot. Similarly air will burn in coal gas just as coal gas will burn in air (see Fig. 251). When we speak of a combustible substance, or a substance which supports combustion, we are using relative terms, assuming that we are carrying out an experiment in particular conditions.

CHARLES' LAW

The hot air which makes the Montgolfier balloon go up is not less dense because it absorbs "fiery" particles endowed with the peculiar gift of levity from the matter burned to inflate it. Hot air is less dense, because the same number of particles occupy more space. The volume occupied by a given weight of a gas *whose other characteristics remain unchanged* increases

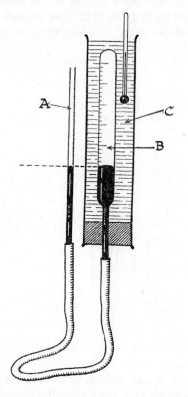

FIG. 252

Apparatus for finding effect of temperature on the volume of a gas at constant pressure. The tube A can be raised and lowered so that the level of mercury in the tubes A and B is always the same. Thus the volume of gas, shown by the scale of the graduated limb B, is always at atmospheric pressure when the measurements are made. The temperature is changed by putting warm water into the glass jacket C.

according to a definite rule as the temperature is raised. This rule was first discovered by the inventor of the hydrogen balloon.

Boyle's Law is not a satisfactory guide for calculating the weight of a gas from its volume, unless the temperature remains the same. So in Boyle's time accurate weighing was hampered because a satisfactory thermometric scale had not been fixed (see Chapter XI). The rule, which is called *Charles' Law*, provides us with an opportunity of illustrating how *graphical* methods are used in science to detect the rule which connects a set of observations. The changes in volume which a fixed weight of gas undergoes when the temperature is raised and the same pressure is maintained, can be recorded by the simple apparatus shown in Fig. 252. The results of such an experiment are plotted in the next figure. The distance of each point measured along the y-axis corresponds to the volume of a gas at a particular temperature. The latter is represented by a distance measured along the x-axis. Thus the line BC represents the difference between the volume of gas v measured at $t°$ on the centigrade scale and the volume V (= AO) of the same sample of gas measured at 0° C., i.e. BC = v — V. The line AB is the corresponding temperature difference $t — 0 = t$.

Since all the observations fall approximately on a straight line, the ratio BC ÷ AB or $(v — V) ÷ t$ is approximately the same for corresponding values of v and t included in the observations made on the same sample at the same pressure. Since V is fixed in any such experiment the ratio $[(v — V) ÷ t] ÷ V$ is also fixed in any particular experiment. This ratio is found to have the same numerical value, approximately $\frac{1}{273}$, in different experiments with different cases, i.e.

$$\frac{v — V}{Vt} = \frac{1}{273}$$

$$\therefore \frac{v — V}{V} = \frac{t}{273}$$

$$\therefore \frac{v}{V} — 1 = \frac{t}{273}$$

$$\therefore \frac{v}{V} = 1 + \frac{t}{273} = \frac{273 + t}{273}$$

$$\therefore v = \left(\frac{273 + t}{273}\right) V$$

If we put T instead of $(t + 273)$, the volume v of a gas at any temperature t is directly proportional to T.

$$v = \frac{V}{273} \cdot T$$

The ratio V ÷ 273 involves two fixed numbers, since V is the volume of gas at 0° C. in any particular experiment. Throughout a single experiment it may thus be replaced by one constant thus—

$$v = CT$$

The number T obtained by adding 273 to the temperature registered by a centigrade thermometer is called the *absolute temperature* of the gas. At constant pressure, the ratio of the volume of a given weight of gas to its absolute temperature is fixed, just as at a fixed temperature the product of the pressure and volume of a given weight of gas is constant. The volume of a gas at constant pressure is increased by $\frac{1}{273}$ of its volume at 0° C. for each degree rise in absolute temperature.

By applying Boyle's law and that of Charles, the weight of gases participating in chemical processes can be measured with the greatest ease. Their densities at a standard temperature and pressure must first be tabulated once and for all for reference. The densities of gases determined directly by weighing an evacuated vessel, filling it with gas at standard pressure and reweighing it, are usually recorded for the standard temperature 0° C. (273° on the absolute scale), and a standard pressure of 760 mm. on the mercury barometer (called 1 *atmosphere*). The weight of any gas can then be calculated from its volume recorded in a graduated glass vessel (Fig. 249) at a known temperature and atmospheric pressure. The following problem illustrates how the gas laws are applied to save the trouble of weighing a gas.

Suppose the chemist who wants to know the proportions in which magne-

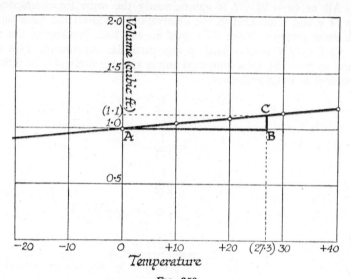

FIG. 253

Graphical representation of change of volume which a quantity of gas occupying 1 cub. ft. at 0° C. undergoes as the temperature is raised, the pressure at which the gas is measured being constant (atmospheric) throughout.

sium combines with oxygen to form its "calx," has found that 1·123 grams of magnesium combine with 560 c.c. of oxygen measured in a graduated vessel when the mercury barometer reads 75 cm. and the temperature is 15° C. His tables of density tell him that 1 litre of oxygen weighs 1·43 grams at S.T.P. (0° and 760 mm.). By applying Boyle's law (page 387), which tells us that volume is inversely proportional to pressure, he can find how much space the gas would occupy at standard pressure. This is

$$\frac{560 \times 75}{76} = 552 \cdot 6 \text{ c.c}$$

To apply Charles' law he converts the centigrade temperature 15° C. to the absolute scale, 273°+ 15°= 288°. Since 0° C. on the absolute scale is 273°, the volume of gas measured at standard temperature is

$$552 \cdot 6 \times \tfrac{273}{288} = 523 \cdot 8 \text{ c.c.}$$

Hence the measured volume of 560 c.c. at 15° C. and 750 mm. would occupy 523·8 c.c. at S.T.P., and therefore weighed $(523·8 \times 1·43) \div 1,000 = 0·749$ grams. Thus 0·749 grams of oxygen combine with 1·123 grams of magnesium, and the combining ratio is approximately $2:3$.

Graphs which are superficially like the one shown in Fig. 253 are exhibited in textbooks of economics to illustrate theories about supply and demand, or wages and profits. This makes readers who lack self-confidence infer that economics is an "exact" science. Two characteristics of the graph in Fig. 253 should therefore be recognized. One is that it tells you *how to do something*, i.e. to find the weight of a given volume of gas by reference to tables of density. The other is that each point on it corresponds to two actual measurements. The draughtsmanship exhibited in textbooks to illustrate marginal utility has neither of these characteristics. Neither of his co-ordinates corresponds to a measured—or, in the present state of knowledge measurable—entity when Dr. Hicks (*Theory of Wages*) states:

> If now the employer's concession curve cuts the resistance curve on the horizontal part, the Union will generally succeed in maintaining its claim; but if it cuts it at a lower point, compromise will be necessary and it is over such compromises that misunderstandings and strikes most easily arise.

THE CALCINATION OF METALS

The recognition that the roasting of a sulphureous ore in the furnace, the formation of a calx or oxide when a metal is heated in air, or the slower rusting of iron in moist air, each involve processes akin to the explosion of gunpowder, to the burning of charcoal, or to the respiration of a mouse, followed quickly after the work of Black and Cavendish. Shortly after the discovery of hydrogen, a clearer insight into the process of oxidation, that is to say, chemical change in which oxygen enters into a new combination with an element, was gained through the complete separation of both the principal constituents of air. Rutherford (1772) used up all the oxygen (roughly one-fifth of the total volume) by burning in air substances like charcoal, sulphur, and phosphorus, recently prepared by the Swedish chemist Scheele from bone ash. When this is done, the acid products (oxides of carbon, sulphur, and phosphorus), being soluble, are easily removed by shaking the residual gas with a mildly alkaline solution. What remains forms four-fifths of the air by volume. It can be most readily prepared by burning magnesium in air till no more magnesium will burn. The oxide of magnesium, being a solid powder, settles on the sides of the vessel, leaving a residual gas which is 99 per cent nitrogen. Nitrogen neither burns like hydrogen, nor allows substances to burn in it as oxygen does. Like oxygen and hydrogen it is colourless, odourless, and only sparsely soluble in water. It is but little less dense than air itself.

The separation of this relatively inert portion of the atmosphere was followed by a careful study of the characteristics of its active partner. As early as 1489 the alchemist de Sultzbach had noticed a "spirit" given off when red oxide of mercury is heated, leaving the metal behind. Shortly after Hooke's work several chemists had collected "fire air" liberated by heating saltpetre. Apart from noting that combustible substances burn more fiercely and brightly in it, none of these pioneer claimants to the "discovery" of oxygen made a careful study of the characteristic properties which distinguish the gas from the rest of the atmosphere. Simultaneously in the year after the separation of nitrogen, three chemists, Scheele, a Swedish apothecary, Priestley in England, and Lavoisier in France, showed the identical character-istics of a gas produced from several different sources. They also established its identity with the "nitro-aerial particles" of common air by recognizing the same products of combustion, such as (*a*) carbon dioxide which turns lime water milky, (*b*) sulphur dioxide and phosphorus pentoxide, each with its characteristic odour, and (*c*) the solid reducible metallic calces like iron rust.

Although the elementary nature of air had been tacitly abandoned by Boyle and Hooke, chemists had found it hard to realize how many kinds of matter exist in the gaseous state. For long it was the fashion to speak of the new gases which had been successively discovered as different kinds of air. The elementary gas hydrogen, having great levity and inflammability, was *inflammable* air. The compound gas carbon dioxide formed by burning charcoal, heating chalk, or pouring acids on potashes, was *fixed* air. The pungent, highly soluble, and powerfully acid "spirits of salt" exhaled by distilling vitriol (sulphuric acid) with sea salt (sodium chloride) to make Glauber's salts was not yet called by its modern name. What we now call hydrochloric acid gas or hydrogen chloride was "marine acid air." The pungent highly soluble and strongly alkaline spirit prepared by heating lime with smelling-salts (ammonium carbonate) or sal ammoniac (ammonium chloride) and collecting the gas over mercury was "alkaline air." The resolution of the air into two distinct constituents, each with its own characteristic properties, finally put a stop to this confusion. Henceforth each gas had a name of its own.

Every obstacle to an intelligible account of the metallurgical processes was now removed. After a century of futile sophistication, deductive chemistry succumbed to Lavoisier's experiments on calcination, and the phlogiston theory was abandoned. Lavoisier's experiments on the formation of the calx when tin is heated in air showed three things:

(*a*) A fixed quantity of tin could be converted into calx by a fixed quantity of air, yet some air remained however much tin was used. The calx was, therefore, a combination of metal and one of the constituents of air in definite proportions.

(*b*) A sealed retort containing the metal from which no air was allowed to escape weighed exactly the same before or after conversion of the metal and its calx. Therefore, the greater weight of the calx was not due to the penetration of "fiery particles" through the walls of the vessel.

(*c*) The increased weight of the calx was exactly offset by the diminished weight of the air. The diminished weight of the air is not due to an increase of "levity." At fixed pressure it is accompanied by an actual decrease of volume. This was shown by the fact that air rushed in when the sealed retort was opened. The inrush of air was accompanied by an increase of weight, equivalent to the increase of weight when the same quantity of metal was converted into calx in an open vessel.

Similar results were obtained by heating mercury to its boiling point, when it forms the red oxide which can easily be converted back to its constituents as a source of oxygen. These experiments combined the essential features of Mayow's experiments with the mouse and the candle, with the additional information gained from weighing all the ingredients and products.

THE RISE OF CHEMICAL INDUSTRY

The death-blow to phlogiston was the need for precise guidance to meet the new social needs of chemical manufacture. The work of Priestley, Scheele, and Lavoisier, was undertaken when chemical manufacture in the modern sense was just beginning. In France, Lavoisier was one of a group of chemists which included Berthollet, who discovered the bleaching power of chlorine, and Leblanc, whose alkali process solved an acute technological problem of the revolutionary wars during the last decade of the eighteenth century. The encouragement which Lavoisier's work received from a growing demand for chemical knowledge in his time is sufficiently illustrated by the fact that he was appointed to direct the manufacture of gunpowder by Turgot two years after (1776) the completion of his researches on metallic oxides. He succeeded in making the saltpetre output of France fivefold greater, abolished the irksome regulations for collecting refuse and manure from private cellars, etc. (see page 407), and increased the explosive power of the mixture. He was later (1791) commissioned by the National Assembly to draw up a conspectus of the mineralogical resources of France.

Priestley's parallel enquiries into metallic oxides are intimately related to the metallurgical problems of the Industrial Revolution which began in Birmingham. In 1760 Matthew Boulton set up a hardware factory employing over six hundred skilled workmen. The machinery was run by a waterwheel, for which the supply of water was insufficient in dry summers. Boulton conceived the plan of using a pump to return water from the outflow to the conduit. He had a keen interest in the nascent physical science of his time, fostered to some extent by a Scots physician named Small, to whom he had been introduced by Benjamin Franklin. Small was responsible for bringing Boulton into touch with James Watt, the young Scots engineer who had been working to improve the Newcomen design. From the partnership between Boulton and Watt in 1775 the new era of machine manufacture came into being. Boulton was a close friend of Roebuck, whose first attempt to manufacture sulphuric acid on a commercial scale had been made during his residence in Birmingham three years before he set up his factory with Garbett in Prestonpans. His keen interest in the chemical problems of metallurgy arose partly from the use of alloys in his factories. He was also a contractor for the Royal Mint. For a short time he was in partnership with Keir, who afterwards set up an alkali factory in Britain.

The device which led to the partnership of Boulton and Watt may have been directly inspired by the propinquity of the Birmingham factory to the Potteries which provided an early market for the Boulton-Watt products. At that time the Potteries were importing their best clays from Cornwall. Between 1750 and 1760 two master potters of Staffordshire, John Turner and Josiah Spode, had also employed a Cornish steam pump to work a waterwheel in their industry, which relied for fuel on the North Staffordshire coalfields. Like Boulton, Wedgwood, the leading figure in the expansion of the Potteries, was an intrepid experimentalist. Like Boulton, he maintained a correspondence with Priestley, encouraged him to come to Birmingham, supplied him with free apparatus, and, in particular, took great pains to construct for him the best retorts and stoves. Wedgwood was elected a Fellow of the Royal Society in the same year as Priestley. After Priestley moved to Birmingham, Wedgwood co-operated with Boulton in providing financial resources to support him in his researches.

The ensuing passage from Smiles' biography of Boulton and Watt gives us a vivid picture of the cultural renaissance which accompanied their partnership in England:

Towards the close of last century, there were many little clubs or coteries of scientific and literary men established in the provinces, the like of which do not now exist. . . . At Liverpool, Roscoe and Currie were the centres of some such group; at Warrington, Aikin, Enfield, and Priestley of another; at Bristol, Dr. Beddoes and Humphry Davy of a third; and at Norwich, the Taylors and Martineaus of a fourth. But perhaps the most distinguished of these provincial societies was that at Birmingham, of which Boulton and Watt were among the most prominent members. . . . The meetings were appointed to be held monthly at the full of the moon, to enable distant members to drive home by moonlight; and this was the more necessary as some of them—such as Darwin and Wedgwood—lived at a considerable distance from Birmingham. . . . Dr. Darwin was regarded as the patriarch of the Society. His fame as a doctor, philosopher, and poet was great throughout the Midland Counties. He was extremely speculative in all directions, even in such matters as driving wheel-carriages by steam. . . . Dr. Priestley, the discoverer of oxygen and other gases, was one of the youngest. We find Boulton corresponding with him in 1775, principally on chemical subjects, and supplying him with fluor spar for purposes of experiment. Five years later, in 1780, he was appointed minister of the Presbyterian Congregation assembling in the New Meeting-house, Birmingham; and from that time forward he was one of the most active members of the Lunar Society. . . . At the time when he settled at Birmingham, Priestley was actively engaged in prosecuting inquiries into the constitution of bodies. He had been occupied for several years before in making investigations as to the gases. The discovery of carbonic acid gas by Dr. Black of Edinburgh had attracted his attention; and, living conveniently near to a brewery at Leeds, where he then was, he proceeded to make experiments on the fixed air or carbonic acid gas evolved during fermentation. From these he went on to other experiments, making use of the rudest apparatus—phials, tobacco pipes, kitchen utensils, a few glass tubes, and an old gun-barrel. The pursuit was a source of constant pleasure to him. . . . Such was Priestley, and such were his pursuits, when he settled at Birmingham in 1780. There can be little doubt that his enthusiasm as an experimenter in chemistry exercised a powerful influence on the minds of both Boulton and Watt, who, though both full of work, anxiety and financial troubles, were nevertheless found taking an active interest from this time forward in the progress of chemical science. Chemistry became the chief subject of discussion at the meetings of the Lunar Society, and chemical experiments the principal recreation of their leisure hours. "I dined yesterday at the Lunar Society (Keir's house)," wrote Boulton to Watt; "there was Blair, Priestley, Withering, Galton, and an American 'rebel,' Mr. Collins. Nothing new except that some of my white Spathos Iron ore was found to contain more air than any ore Priestley had ever tried, and, what is singular, it contains no common air, but is part fixable and part inflammable." To Henderson, in Cornwall, Boulton wrote, two months later, "Chemistry has for some time been my hobby-horse, but I am prevented from riding it by cursed business, except now and then of a Sunday. However, I have made great progress since I saw you, and am almost an adept in metallurgical moist chemistry. I have got all that part of Bergmann's last volume translated, and have learnt from it many new facts. I have annihilated Wm. Murdock's bedchamber, having taken away the floor, and made the chicken kitchen into one high room covered over with shelves, and these I have filled with chemical apparatus. I have likewise set up a Priestleyan water-tub, and likewise a mercurial tub for experiments on gases, vapours, etc., and next year I shall annex to these a laboratory with furnaces of all sorts, and all other utensils for dry chemistry." The "Priestleyan water-tub" and "mercurial tub," here alluded to, were invented by Priestley in the course of his investigations for the purpose of collecting and handling gases; and the pneumatic trough, with glass retorts and receivers, shortly became part of the furniture of every chemical laboratory.

Another passage from Smiles refers to the tangible support which Priestley received from Boulton and Wedgwood:

Josiah Wedgwood was another member of the Lunar Society, who was infected by Dr. Priestley's enthusiasm for chemistry; and knowing that the Doctor's income from his congregation was small, he and Boulton took private counsel together as to the best means of providing him with funds, so as to place him in a position of comparative ease, and enable him freely to pursue his investigations. . . . Wedgwood had undertaken to sound Dr. Priestley, and he thus communicated the result to Boulton: "The Doctor says he never did intend or think of making any pecuniary advantage from any of his experiments, but gave them to the public with their results, just as they happened, and so he should continue to do, without ever attempting to make any private emolument from them to himself. I mentioned this business to our good friend, Dr. Darwin, who agrees with us in sentiment, that it would be a pity that Dr. Priestley should have any cares or cramps to interrupt him in the fine vein of experiments he is in the midst of, and is willing to devote his time to the pursuit of, for the public good. . . . Dr. Darwin will be very cautious whom he mentions this affair to, for reasons of delicacy which will have equal weight with us all. I mentioned your generous intention to Dr. P., and that we thought of £20 each; but that, you will perceive, cannot be, and the Doctor says much less will suffice, as he can go on very well with £100 per annum.

The Darwin referred to in this passage was Erasmus, the grandfather of Charles, and author of the first book (*Zoonomica*) setting forth the evolutionary doctrine in Britain. The description of the Lunar Society given by Smiles emphasizes in a very forcible way the cultural decadence of the older seats of British learning in the period that extended from the generation of Newton and Bradley to the repeal of the Test Acts, which followed the foundation of new institutions such as those in which Davy, Dalton, and Faraday carried out their work. It is instructive to note that some of the leaders of science like Priestley and Benjamin Franklin were intensely alive to the political struggles which anticipated and accompanied the next stage of industrial expansion. Thus Smiles tells us:

The impressionable mind of Dr. Priestley was moved in an extraordinary degree by the startling events which followed each other in quick succession at Paris; and he entered with zeal into the advocacy of the doctrines of liberty, equality, and fraternity, so vehemently promulgated by the French "friends of man." His chemical pursuits were for a time forgotten, and he wrote and preached of human brotherhood, and of the downfall of tyranny and priest-craft. He hailed with delight the successive acts of the National Assembly—abolishing monarchy, nobility, church, corporations, and other long-established institutions. He had already been long and hotly engaged in polemical dis-cussions with the local clergy on disputed points of faith; and now he addressed a larger audience in a work which he published in answer to Mr. Burke's famous attack on the "French Revolution." Burke, in consequence, attacked him in the House of Commons; while the French Revolutionists, on the other hand, hailed him as a brother, and admitted him to the rights of French citizen-ship. These proceedings concentrated on Dr. Priestley an amount of local exasperation that shortly after burst forth in open outrage. On July 14, 1791, a public dinner was held at the principal hotel to celebrate the second anni-versary of the French Revolution. About eighty gentlemen were present but Priestley was not of the number. A mob collected outside, and after shouting "Church and King!" they proceeded to demolish the inn windows. The magistrates shut their eyes to the riotous proceedings, if they did not actually connive at them. A cry was raised, "To the New Meeting-house," the chapel in which Priestley ministered; and thither the mob surged. The door was at once burst open, and the place set on fire. . . . They made at once for Dr. Priestley's house at Fairhill, about a mile and a half distant. The Doctor and his family had escaped about half an hour before their arrival; and the house was at their mercy. They broke in at once, emptied the cellars, smashed the furniture, tore up the books in the library, destroyed the philosophical and chemical apparatus in the laboratory, and ended by setting fire to the house. The roads for miles around were afterwards found strewed with shreds of the valuable manuscripts in which were recorded the results of twenty years' labour and study—a loss which Priestley continued bitterly to lament until the close of his life. . . . The members of the Lunar Society, or "the Lunatics," as they were popularly called, were especially marked for attack during the riots. . . . Boulton and Watt were not without apprehensions that an attack would be made upon them, as being the head and front of the "Philosophers" of Birmingham. They accordingly prepared for the worst; called their workmen together, pointed out to them the criminality of the rioters' proceedings, and placed arms in their hands on their promising to do their utmost to defend the premises if attacked. . . . As for Dr. Priestley, he shook the dust of Birmingham from his feet, and fled to London; from thence emigrating to America, where he died in 1804. While such was the blind fury of the populace of Birmingham, the principles of the French Revolution found adherents in all parts of England. Clubs were formed in London and the principal pro-vincial towns, and a brisk correspondence was carried on between them and the Revolutionary leaders of France. Among those invested with the rights of French citizenship were Dr. Priestley, Mr. Wilberforce, Thomas Tooke, and Mr. (afterwards Sir) James Mackintosh. Thomas Paine and Dr. Priestley were chosen members of the National Convention; and though the former took his seat for Calais, the latter declined, on the ground of his inability to speak the language sufficiently. Among those carried away by the political epidemic of the time were young James Watt and his friend Mr. Cooper of Manchester. In 1792 they were deputed, by the "Constitutional Society" of that town, to proceed to Paris and present an address of congratulation to the Jacobin Club, then known as the "Société des Amis de la Constitution." While at Paris, young Watt seems to have taken an active part in the fiery agitation of the time. He was on intimate terms with the Jacobin leaders. Southey says that he was even the means of preventing a duel between Danton and Robespierre, to the former of whom he acted as second. Robespierre afterwards took occasion to denounce both Cooper and Watt as secret emissaries of Pitt, on which young Watt sprang into the tribune, pushing Robespierre aside, and defended himself in a strain of vehement eloquence which completely carried the assembly with him.

Alger asserts that Watt junior was the anonymous Whig mentioned in Carlyle's narrative. The account of Priestley's career given in *The Dictionary of National Biography* says that Priestley himself was also

elected a member for the Department of Orne in the National Convention. Other Departments followed suit, but while he accepted citizenship, he declined election. The majority of members of the Royal Society fought shy of him. Finding that they *were rejecting candidates on political grounds*, he withdrew attendance (1793).

The mechanical innovations associated with what is usually called the Industrial Revolution have overshadowed an important feature of the change which manufacturing underwent during the latter half of the eighteenth century. It is mentioned in the concluding remarks of the following extract from Nef's *Rise of the British Coal Industry*:

The expansion of industry and particularly the expansion of the woollen industry, diminished the space available for planting new trees. . . . In all countries near the sea, writes an anonymous authority towards the end of Elizabeth's reign, "most of the woods are consumed and the ground converted to corn and pasture." . . . If the growth of the woollen industry in particular discouraged the planting of trees, the demands of industry quickly drained the existing forests of their timber. For in that age wood was the raw material of all industry to an extent which it is difficult for us now to conceive. Charcoal had to be mixed with saltpetre in preparing gunpowder. From the bark of trees workmen extracted a sap then indispensable in making pitch and tar, with which to caulk the hulls of ships, and from wood ashes came potash, an essential constituent for the production of soap, glass and saltpetre. The principal drain caused by the expansion of industry arose . . . from the demands for it as building material and as fuel. Ours has often been called an age of coal and iron, and it is perhaps no less appropriate to call the sixteenth and seventeenth centuries an age of timber. . . . It is unnecessary to dwell at length on the many thousand uses for firewood in early industry. It is sufficient to point out that no change could be wrought in ore or metal without the aid of fuel, that substantial quantities of wood and charcoal were being consumed in making starch, refining sugar, baking bread, firing pottery, tiles, bricks, and tobacco pipes, drying malt and hops, and boiling soap. . . . Every increase in the quantity of bricks, or saltpetre, lime or salt manufactured with wood fuel involved serious new encroachments upon native timber resources. But the chief wastage was caused by glass makers and smelters. . . . The smelting of iron was only a part of the larger problem of smelting and refining all metals, and that again was only a part of the still larger problem of making coal a suitable substitute for wood in industry generally, and of reducing the total consumption of fuel of all kinds in a given process. . . . In 1623 a certain Lewyn van Hack had undertaken to extract silver from lead in Cardiganshire, using sea-coal in the smelting and charcoal "only in the refyning." We know nothing about his methods or his success, but in an article written 1678, and devoted to the methods of separating silver and other bodies from lead ore, Dr. Christopher Merret remarks that the "latest invention is a new furnace. The convenience . . . is, that a little fire, and that of New Castle coals, will do the work." . . . In 1620 the Crown granted a patent for "charking earth fuel" to be used in smelting, and this is the first unmistakable reference to such an attempt that has been found. . . . With coke made in much the same way, Abraham Darby solved the problem of iron smelting, which, unlike the smelting of lead and tin, could not be accomplished with raw coal, even after the invention of the reverberatory furnace. . . . The ultimate discovery by the elder Darby at the beginning of the eighteenth century of a successful process depended on innumerable experiments . . . often directed towards the smelting of metals other than iron, and even more often *not directed towards a solution of the smelting problem at all.*

The activities of Roebuck, whose Carron Works at Stirling took a prominent part in the introduction of coal for reducing metal ores, illustrate the words italicized in the foregoing citation. While "the furnaces and forges had eaten up the woodlands of Sussex," and, as the Hammonds tell us, "were beginning to strip less promising districts bare," *all the manufactures which depended on wood were forced into the search for material substitutes.* One of the more important by-products was the alkaline potashes prepared by incinerating charcoal. Potashes were used for the making of glass and of soap, and for the cleaning of wool. Keir, whose house is mentioned by Smiles in a previous quotation, was one of the first to set up a factory for making alkali from sea salt. By the end of the century the commercial production of alkali was well established.

The foundation of the synthetic alkali industry was made possible by the commercial production of sulphuric acid. Sulphuric acid was indeed the parent substance of modern chemical manufacture. Its composition will be dealt with more fully in the next chapter. Brimstone burns in air to form sulphur dioxide, a pungent gas which dissolves in water to form sulphurous acid. Sulphurous acid dissolves metallic oxides and alkalis forming salts called "sulphites." When heated with air in the presence of spongy platinum, sulphur dioxide is partially converted into sulphur trioxide, which contains more oxygen. Sulphur trioxide combines with water to form a heavy oily liquid, "vitriol" or sulphuric acid, which dissolves metals, alkalis, etc., thereby forming metallic "sulphates." The present world output of sulphuric acid is about 16,000,000 tons per year. Writing about 1840, a century after Ward's patent was first put into operation, Liebig said:

We may judge with great accuracy the commercial prosperity of a country from the amount of sulphuric acid it consumes.*

* Liebig's *Letters on Chemistry.*

The preceding remarks describe how sulphuric acid is made nowadays. The early history of sulphuric acid is briefly recounted by Lunge* as follows:

Gerhard Dornaeus (1570) described its properties accurately; Libavius (1595) recognized the identity of the acids from different processes of preparation; the same was done by Angelus Sata (1613), who pointed out the fact, which had sunk into oblivion since Basilius, that sulphuric acid can be obtained by burning sulphur in moist vessels (of course with access of air); after that time it was prepared by the apothecaries in this way. An essential improvement, viz. the addition of a little saltpetre, was introduced in 1666 by Nicolas le Fèvre and Nicolas Lémery. . . . A quack doctor of the name of Ward first carried on sulphuric-acid making on a large scale at Richmond near London, probably a little before 1740. Ward employed large glass vessels up to 66 gallons capacity, which stood in two rows in a sand-bath, and which were provided with horizontally projecting necks; at the bottom they contained a little water. In each neck there was an earthenware pot, and on this a small red-hot iron dish, into which a mixture of one part saltpetre and eight parts of brimstone were put; then the neck of the bottle was closed with a wooden plug; on the combustion being finished, fresh air was allowed to enter the vessel, and the operation was repeated till the acid had become strong enough to pay for concentrating in glass retorts. . . . Ward's process, troublesome as it is, reduced the price of the acid from 2s. 6d. per ounce (the price of the acid from copperas or from burning brimstone under a moist glass jar) to 2s. per lb.

Roebuck improved on the Ward process by introducing lead chambers which reduced the expense incurred by the use of large glass vessels. Prosser (*Birmingham Inventors and Inventions*) says that he set up a manufactory at Steelhouse Lane, *Birmingham*, with his partner, Mr. Samuel Garbett, in 1746, and that the works, afterwards sold to Alston and Sons, continued to make the acid till 1825. Lunge tells us that soon after he set up his factory at Prestonpans several others were started in England:

Soon other works followed at Bridgenorth, and at Dowles in Worcestershire where the chambers were already made 10 feet square; in 1772 there was a factory erected in London with 71 cylindrical lead chambers, each 6 feet diameter and 6 feet high. In 1797 there were already six or eight works in Glasgow alone. According to the statements given in Mactear's *Report of the Alkali and Bleaching-Powder Manufacture in the Glasgow District* (p. 8), the acid at that time cost the Glasgow manufacturers £32 per ton, and was sold at £54. At Radcliffe, near Manchester, it cost, in 1799, £21 10s. per ton, without interest on capital.

According to Lunge the acid was first sold for the bleaching of linen. Since Home did not receive his medal till six years after the factory at Prestonpans began production, it seems unlikely that this was the original intention. Before making experiments on the lead-chamber process Roebuck had been engaged in work on refining precious metals, and it is possible that vitriol was used for dissolving traces of copper in the latter, or for making

* Since this was written H. W. Dickinson, the biographer of Boulton, has published an account of the early history of sulphuric acid in the Journal of the Newcomen Society.

nitric acid from saltpetre to dissolve out lead. We also learn* that Achard, a pioneer in the commercialization of beet sugar, used sulphuric acid (1792) for purification of beet juice. In England, Ward's product may have been wanted for the purification of clay used in the Potteries. The invention of the hydrogen balloon was an incidental consequence of its preparation in large quantities.

In a small way it had been used by apothecaries for making the aperient called Glauber's salt. Glauber's salt, or sodium sulphate, was made by heating brine (the solid content of which is mainly sodium chloride) with vitriol. In the reaction which ensues a highly soluble pungent gas (now called hydrochloric acid) is evolved. The two products of this reaction were the parent substances for two other chemical industries established before the century ended. New methods for bleaching linen stimulated industrialists to seek for new expedients, and led to the introduction of chlorine gas, and bleaching powder prepared from it. The former is prepared by heating hydrochloric acid with black manganese dioxide, the latter by passing chlorine over dry lime. The antecedents of this new chemical industry are described by Smiles:

Among Watt's numerous scientific correspondents was M. Berthollet, the eminent French chemist, who communicated to him the process he had discovered of bleaching by chlorine. Watt proceeded to test the value of the discovery by experiment, after which he recommended his father-in-law, Mr. Macgregor, of Glasgow, to make trial of it on a larger scale. This, however, was postponed until Watt himself could find time to superintend it in person. At the end of 1787 we find him on a visit to Glasgow for the purpose, and writing to Boulton that he is making ready for the trial. "I mean," he writes, "to try it tomorrow, though I am somewhat afraid to attack so fierce and strong a beast. There is almost no bearing the fumes of it. After all, it does not appear that it will prove a cheap way of bleaching and it weakens the goods more than could be wished, whatever good it may do in the way of expedition." The experiment succeeded, and we find Mr. Macgregor, in the following February, "engaged in whitening 1,500 yards of linen by the process." The discovery, not being protected by a patent, was immediately made use of by other firms; but the offensive odour of the chlorine was found exceedingly objectionable, until it was discovered that chlorine could be absorbed by slaked lime, the solution of which possessed great bleaching power, and this process in course of time superseded all the old methods of bleaching by chlorine.

The commercialization of bleaching powder was successfully accomplished by Tennant of Glasgow in 1799. Meanwhile Glauber's salt had been put to a new use. The ashes left by incinerating charcoal (mostly potassium carbonate) or sea weeds (mostly sodium carbonate) had been used as the chief source of alkali in the glass, soap, and wool industries from time immemorial. In medieval times the forests of eastern Europe were responsible for a considerable export trade of "potashes" for the English wool industry. During the revolutionary wars the available supplies had run so short in France that the Academy was forced to offer a large prize for a suitable method of making alkalis from other sources. The prize was won by Leblanc in 1791. The

* Private communication from Mr. J. L. Mackie.

Leblanc process for making sodium carbonate consists of three stages.
First sodium chloride is obtained from sea water, of which it forms about
75 per cent of the solid matter, by evaporation to the stage when the crystals

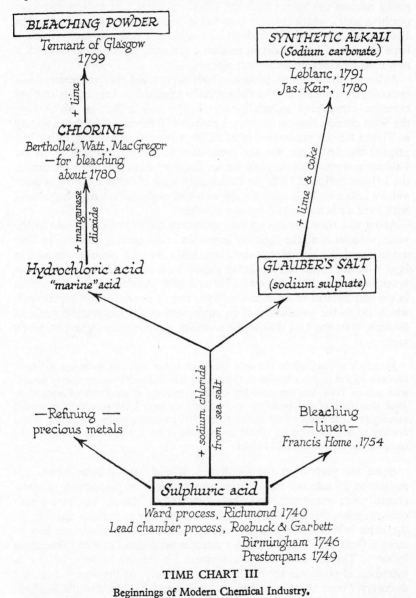

TIME CHART III

Beginnings of Modern Chemical Industry.

of sodium chloride separate out. The sodium chloride is next heated with
sulphuric acid. Hydrochloric acid gas escapes, and can be collected by passing
it into water. Sodium sulphate or Glauber's salt remains behind. In the

final stage this is dried and cooked in a furnace with coke (carbon). The oxygen is thus removed from it. Carbon dioxide escapes, and sodium sulphide remains behind. The latter is heated with chalk (calcium carbonate) giving calcium sulphide, which is insoluble in water, and sodium carbonate (washing soda), which is easily removed because of its great solubility. The Leblanc process produces hydrochloric acid as a main by-product and a large number of less important products, including carbon dioxide which is now used for charging soda-water siphons.

Although the Leblanc process which superseded its predecessors was undoubtedly more efficient, it did not differ in principle from earlier and less extensive commercial undertakings in France and in Britain. About 1780 the Scots chemist Keir, at one time a partner of Boulton, established a factory at Tipton for the production of alkali from sea salt. According to his biographer the first stage was the production of sodium sulphate, as in the Leblanc process. Collison took out an English patent essentially similar to the Leblanc recipe in 1782. An earlier suggestion of Scheele (1776) to make sodium carbonate by heating sea salt with lead oxide and treating the solution with fixed air is not known to have been used.

About this time Boulton's works sponsored the beginnings of one of the most powerful of all the chemical industries in the ensuing century. In 1785 a continental chemist, Maestrichte, had shown that coal gas could be used to light a lecture room. A Frenchman named Le Loss used it to light his own house in Paris in 1786. Between 1792 and 1802 Murdock, a Scots workman in the employment of Boulton and Watt, carried out successful experiments which led to the installation of an equipment in the engineering works of Boulton, Watt and Co., at Soho, Birmingham. Prosser (*Birmingham Inventors*) says:

> Murdock is entitled to the sole credit of being the first to bring gas-light into the region of practice. Part of the Soho establishment was regularly lighted with gas in 1798. On the occasion of the rejoicings at the Peace of Amiens in 1802 the front of the building was lighted by gas. After that time it spread rapidly to other parts of the country. In 1808 he read a paper before the Royal Society giving an account of his investigations on the subject, for which he received the Rumford Gold Medal.

Some ten years after the installation of coal gas in Soho commercial production of matches from phosphorus began. The preparation of phosphorus from excrement had been undertaken during the seventeenth century, when Boyle had toyed with the possibility of making matches. In the latter half of the eighteenth century Scheele (1771) discovered how to make it from bone ash, for which a commercial demand existed in the china industry. Thomas Frye took out a patent for the use of bone ash as an ingredient of pottery in the mid-eighteenth century. At the time of Scheele's discovery, "bone china" was being manufactured by Spode of the Staffordshire Potteries. When the nineteenth century began, the trained chemist had become essential to industry, and the encouragement of chemical research to make the fullest use of every by-product was a matter of the utmost importance to the new manufacturing class.

THE STRUCTURE AND CLASSIFICATION OF MATERIALS

Before it is possible to find laws which embody correct rules of conduct it is necessary to observe relevant facts with accuracy and classify them intelligently. Although comprehensive principles underlying the manufacture of new substances and the discovery of new sources of materials did not emerge during the century and a half which followed the issue of Glauber's *Prosperity of Germany*, the accumulative results of the recognition of a third realm of matter, including a variety of substances with totally distinct characteristics, had provided the only foundation on which a useful body of theory could be built. Through the realization that the new gases were not various forms of "air," but individual substances with characteristics as distinct and constant as those of pure solids and liquids, a classification of substances based on the way in which they are built up, and hence on the sources from which they can be obtained, was gradually replacing that of the alchemists.

Black's work (1754) on carbon dioxide and that of Cavendish (1766) on hydrogen had been followed by a plethora of discoveries. Compounds which had been dismissed as fumes and smells were systematically investigated. Besides those of the four elementary gases (oxygen, nitrogen, hydrogen, and chlorine) the characteristics of about a dozen other gaseous substances had been studied by the end of the eighties. Priestley described the properties of sulphur dioxide (1770), hydrochloric acid gas, nitrous and nitric oxide (1772), ammonia (1774), and sulphuretted hydrogen (1777). Scheele and Priestley discovered silicon tetrafluoride in 1776. Scheele, who had first made chlorine in 1774, also made sulphur trioxide. Carbon monoxide was first studied by de Lassone in 1776. Methane and ethylene (two other constituents of the mixture that is called coal gas) were respectively investigated by Berthollet (1785) and by a group of Dutch chemists.

By the end of the eighteenth century it was possible to distinguish between a group of simple substances or *elements*—solids like sulphur, carbon (charcoal), phosphorus, and the metals, gases like oxygen, hydrogen, and nitrogen—which combine to form *compound* substances with equally definite characteristics such as density, solubility, colour, odour, texture, power to conduct heat, and so forth. The class called compounds included first and foremost the oxides formed by combination with oxygen. One large class of oxides were all *acidic*, i.e. dissolving like the oxides of sulphur, carbon, nitrogen, and phosphorus, in water to form "acids." The definition of an acid retains to this day its early association with the dyeing of textiles. Acid solutions were recognized by their power to turn the blue litmus dye red. In contradistinction another class, the oxides of the metals, are distinguished as *basic*, being capable of combining with acids to form more complex bodies called *salts*. Some of these basic oxides, like quicklime, unite with water to form more complex substances called caustic alkalis containing hydrogen as well as oxygen and metal (e.g. slaked lime). Salts, which can also be formed by dissolving a metal in a strong acid like nitric acid, sulphuric acid, and hydrochloric acid, were being classified according to the acid or acidic oxide from which they were derived. Thus gypsum (calcium sulphate), blue vitriol (copper sulphate), green vitriol (iron sulphate), and Epsom salt (magnesium sulphate) are all now recognized as members of the class of sulphates (salts formed by dissolving a metal or its oxide in sulphuric acid); potashes (potassium carbonate), malachite (copper carbonate), and chalk (calcium carbonate) as carbonates (salts formed by the union of a metal oxide and carbon dioxide); and common salt (sodium chloride), calomel (mercury chloride), and horn silver (silver chloride) as chlorides.

Substances of another class were known to be compounds because they could be broken down into two or more other distinct substances. Not all substances recognized as elements or compounds a century and a half ago are regarded as such today. Some substances which we can now build up from their elements were still believed to be elements. The yellow gas *chlorine*, which is an element given off when manganese dioxide is heated with a solution of hydrochloric acid, was then believed to be an oxide. Chlorine unites with hydrogen in sunlight to form the colourless hydrochloric acid gas. Since it was thought that all acids are formed from oxides, like carbon dioxide, sulphur dioxide, or phosphorus pentoxide, chlorine was at first supposed to be the oxide of an undiscovered element, and the use of manganese dioxide in its preparation seemed to support this conclusion. Repeated attempts to break it down eventually discouraged this belief.

The new method of classification was not merely a question of what names we give to substances. It meant far more. Calling three substances litharge, galena, and sugar of lead, communicates nothing about the way they are built up. When we call them by their new names, lead oxide, lead sulphide, and lead acetate, we convey new information about the way in which they may be obtained, or the use to which they may be put. For instance, each is a source of *lead*. Most sulphides can be converted into oxides by heating with an oxidizing agent—something that gives up oxygen readily. Thus the malodorous gas sulphuretted hydrogen or hydrogen sulphide, liberated by strong acids from metallic sulphides like pyrites, will burn in air to form water (hydrogen oxide) and sulphur dioxide. Most oxides of metals can be converted into metal by heating them with a "*reducing*" agent, such as hydrogen gas, which combines with the oxygen to form water vapour, or charcoal, which combines with the oxygen to form carbon dioxide. Among the best oxidizing agents for soluble substances are hydrogen peroxide and potassium permanganate. Among the best reducing agents are the bubbles of hydrogen given off when tin or zinc dust are dissolved in a strong acid like hydrochloric acid. Metallic acetates in general are converted into oxides by heat, and made by dissolving a metallic oxide or carbonate in acetic acid, which gives vinegar its sour taste. From such general knowledge of the characteristics of acetates, oxides, and sulphides, and general knowledge of the characteristics of lead compounds, we can condense a mass of useful information in the statement that a substance is the acetate, oxide, or sulphide of lead.

Hence the new label for *galena* tells us something about how we should set about looking for the substance. Metallic sulphides give off sulphuretted hydrogen when treated with a strong mineral acid like hydrochloric. Lead salts are identified by the fact that nearly all chlorides are soluble in cold water, the notable exceptions being lead, silver, and mercury, of which the last two are not soluble in hot water. So if a lead compound is dissolved in nitric acid, all the salts of which (*nitrates*) are soluble, a precipitate which redissolves in hot water is formed on adding hydrochloric acid.

In short, the new method of classification based on the way things are built up is an inventory of man's resources of materials, known and as yet unknown. The discovery of the metal chromium which is now used as an ingredient of rustless steel in the middle of the eighteenth century illustrates how the new method helps to discover new kinds of materials, as well as directing our attention to new sources of known materials. In the middle of the eighteenth century a Siberian mineral (now known to be lead chromate) was found to be the representative of a class of salts which did not correspond to those formed from the oxides of any known element. Subsequent search led to the discovery of a new metallic element.

At the end of the eighteenth century the four elements of Aristotle had been replaced by about fifteen. Today we recognize about ninety. More than half of those known at the time of Lavoisier had been objects of use for several millennia. Those known to the ancients in a comparatively pure form included carbon, sulphur, and the metals gold, silver, iron, copper, tin, lead, antimony, mercury, and zinc. During the seventeenth and eighteenth centuries the list of solid elements was extended by the addition of phosphorus and several new metals, notably platinum, chromium, arsenic, and manganese. Three gaseous elements, oxygen, nitrogen, and hydrogen, which were discovered in the eighteenth century, had not been previously known as separate substances. Chlorine had been isolated, though not as yet known to be an element.

The list of elements then known excluded many names which are familiar to any civilized person today. The commonest metallic elements were only known in their compounds. Sodium, whose chloride is the chief solid constituent of the sea—common salt; potassium, whose nitrate is the essential constituent of gunpowder; calcium, whose carbonate (chalk) forms the cliffs of our shores, and whose oxide (lime) had been used from time immemorial for curing leather and making cement, were not known in the pure state. Boron, whose compounds were already used in medicine, had not been separated. Beryllium, a metal like magnesium, forming three crystalline salts which are the familiar jewels beryl, aquamarine, and emerald, was not known.

To this list of common elements, unknown in Lavoisier's time, we must also add the two elements aluminium and silicon. With oxygen they form the overwhelming bulk of the superficial layers of the earth's crust. Aluminium, a metal, is now used in paint, kitchen utensils, piston heads, and aeroplane engines. Its oxide, tinted with various impurities, is the main constituent of the gems sapphire, ruby, and amethyst. In combination with silica (aluminium silicate) it is the chief constituent of common clay. It is ubiquitous, and vastly more abundant than any other metal to a depth of half a mile of the earth's crust; and even to a depth of 25 miles approaching the iron core of the earth it is at least actually more abundant than iron. Silicon is not a metal. Its oxide (*silica*) is rock crystal or quartz. Sand is mainly silica with various impurities. Glass, which was originally made by heating sand with an alkali (lime or potashes) or basic oxide (e.g. litharge), is a mixture of various metallic silicates (commonly calcium, sodium, potassium, and lead). Window and table glass is a sodium calcium silicate mixture, flint glass and cut glass a lead potassium silicate mixture. Jena glass is a potassium calcium silicate mixture.

The elements known in the eighteenth century did not include the comparatively rare element radium, nor selenium, whose great sensitivity to light is used in television. The three elements (bromine, iodine, and fluorine) whose compounds closely resemble those of chlorine were not yet isolated. A silver compound of one of these (silver bromide), which is very sensitive to light, is the basis of the photographic industry. The solution of iodine (generally dissolved in a solution of potassium iodide) is a familiar antiseptic. Fluorine in combination with silica forms complex salts (fluosilicates) which occur as minerals. It is also a constituent of the acid called hydrofluoric acid which attacks glass and for this reason is used for etching.

QUANTITATIVE ANALYSIS

It is a common delusion to think that the introduction of a little mathematics into a subject necessarily makes it more scientific. Mathematics is useful when we wish to recognize the significance of *measurements*. In the early stages of a science the important thing is to know very thoroughly the *characteristics* of the things which we are studying. We can only make useful measurements when we are clear *about what we are measuring*. This was the task of chemistry in the eighteenth century. Till the beginning of the nineteenth century, only one important rule of measurement in chemical reactions had been discovered. This is usually called the *Law of Constant Proportions*. It would be foolish to put a date to its discovery, because it represents a conclusion which gained increasing confidence as chemists acquired the habit of weighing all the ingredients and products of a process.

The Law of Constant Proportions is that the ratio of the weights of the ingredients *used up* in making the same substance is always the same. If the ingredients are themselves elements this is the same as saying that the proportions by weight of the constituent elements in any compound is fixed. To prove this rule it is necessary to weigh separately each constituent, as Lavoisier did in his experiments on calcination. Once we are satisfied that it is true much labour may be saved. We can use it to calculate some quantities if we have recorded others. This may be illustrated by the way in which we can find the proportion by weight of magnesium and oxygen in the oxide of the metal (Fig. 254). A tube with a wire to hold it in place on the balance and a plug of glass wool are first weighed. A strip of magnesium is then put in the tube and the glass wool is inserted. The glass wool and tube with magnesium in it are now weighed, and the difference between the two weighings is the weight of magnesium added. If the tube is now held in a flame, the magnesium ignites with the blinding brilliancy now familiar in flashlight photography, and a dense cloud of white powder (magnesium oxide) is formed. The glass wool prevents explosion by admitting air freely, while at the same time stopping the particles of oxide from getting out. A third weighing when the tube has cooled now shows an increase in weight. If we call the weight of the tube and glass wool before adding magnesium a, the glass wool and tube with magnesium b, and the same after ignition c, the weight of magnesium is $(b - a)$, the weight of magnesium oxide formed is $(c - a)$, and the weight of oxygen with which $(b - a)$ grams of magnesium combines is $(c - a) - (b - a) = (c - b)$. Providing the magnesium is as pure as we can get it, the ratio of $(b - a)$ magnesium to $(c - b)$ oxygen is always the same.

How we might determine the proportion by weight of silver and chlorine in silver chloride provides a second illustration of what chemists call *gravimetric analysis*. A clean dry centrifuge tube is weighed. A small quantity of pure silver is placed in it, and it is weighed again to get the amount of silver $(b - a)$. A solution of moderately strong nitric acid is added to dissolve the silver. From the solution of silver nitrate so formed the insoluble chloride

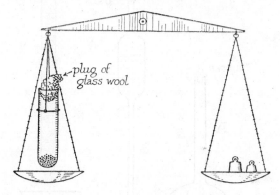

plug of glass wool

FIG. 254.—GRAVIMETRIC ANALYSIS OF MAGNESIUM OXIDE

is precipitated, if a strong solution of pure sodium chloride is added. This white powder (which darkens in sunlight) is thrown to the bottom of the tube in a hard cake, after rotation in a high-speed centrifuge. The fluid can now be poured off, the tube with the cake of silver chloride rinsed with pure water and placed in a warm oven till it is dry, i.e. when repeated weighing gives constant results. The difference between the final weighing (c) of the tube plus silver chloride and the second weighing (b) of the tube plus silver is the weight of chlorine which unites with the weight $(b - a)$ of silver.

In both these examples the irksome necessity of weighing a gas is avoided by using the Law of Conservation (p. 393) to get the result indirectly. In all analysis one or other of the constituents is obtained by inference. One useful method of analysis avoids repeated weighing and drying by measuring volumes of solutions of known strength. Standard solutions for "volumetric" analysis are made in large quantities by weighing out accurately a suitable amount of a reagent and dissolving it in a "volumetric" flask (Fig. 255). This bears a mark corresponding to the level of water which exactly occupies a stated volume, e.g. 1,000 cubic centimetres (1 litre) at a stated temperature. Let us suppose that we wish to know in what proportions by weight sodium and chlorine unite to form sodium chloride (common salt), and that we already know how much silver chloride is formed from a given quantity of silver nitrate. We have to start with a solution of silver nitrate formed by dissolving exactly x grams in a litre, so that 1 c.c. of the solution contains $0.001x$ grams. If y grams of silver chloride are formed from x grams of silver nitrate, 1 c.c. of the solution is equivalent to $0.001y$ grams of silver chloride, and if y grams of silver chloride contains z grams of chlorine, 1 c.c. of the solution is capable of

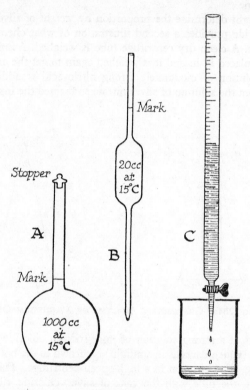

FIG. 255

One litre volumetric flask (A), 20 c.c. pipette (B), and burette (C), used in volumetric analysis.

throwing down $0.001z$ grams of chlorine as silver chloride precipitate. Silver nitrate is a common laboratory reagent for estimating chlorides, so a standard solution of it is usually kept in a laboratory. To find the proportions of sodium and chlorine in a solution of sodium chloride without going to the trouble of preparing and keeping the metal pure, we might make up a standard solution of sodium chloride by dissolving n grams of sodium chloride in a litre, so that 1 c.c. of the solution contained $0.001n$ grams. We now measure out a fixed quantity, e.g. 10 c.c., of this into a glass vessel with a marked tube ("pipette"). This is done by sucking up the fluid with the mouth and keeping the level exactly at the mark by applying a finger to the orifice. Finally, we drop into this vessel the standard solution of silver nitrate from a graduated tube (burette) with a tap which can be turned off when all the sodium chloride has been used up to form insoluble silver chloride. The graduation marks of the burette tell us how much standard silver nitrate has been run in, when this point is reached.

To gauge the end of the reaction exactly a few drops of potassium chromate are added to the solution of sodium chloride. A drop of silver solution in a solution of potassium chromate produces a brick red colour, which may, therefore, be used to detect when silver nitrate is present. As long as there is any sodium chloride in the solution the silver nitrate is converted into silver chloride. When it is all used up a further drop of silver nitrate will reveal its presence in the solution by the appearance of the brick-red colour. If the quantity of sodium chloride taken is 10 c.c. the weight of sodium chloride is $0 \cdot 01n$ grams. If $8 \cdot 5$ c.c. of standard silver nitrate solution are run in before the brick-red colour appears, $8 \cdot 5 \times 0 \cdot 001z$ grams of chlorine have been thrown out of the solution. So $0 \cdot 01n$ grams of sodium chloride contain $8 \cdot 5 \times 0 \cdot 001z$ grams of chlorine and $0 \cdot 01n - (8 \cdot 5 \times 0 \cdot 001z)$ grams of sodium.

THINGS TO MEMORIZE

Charles' Law. $v = \dfrac{V}{273} \cdot T$, where V is the volume at $0°$ C. and T is the absolute temperature.

EXAMPLES ON CHAPTER VIII

1. A closed glass graduated cylinder of 10 sq. cm. sectional area, containing a mixture at atmospheric pressure of ammonia and air in equal parts by volume, stands in a dish of mercury with the top 25 cm. above the level of the latter. A few drops of fairly strong nitric acid are introduced by a bent tube into the cylinder till all the ammonia has been absorbed. To what level will the mercury rise?

2. If two parts of hydrogen combine with one part of oxygen by volume to form water vapour, how high will the mercury rise when an electric spark is passed through a mixture of 200 c.c. of hydrogen and 50 c.c. of oxygen at atmospheric pressure in a glass cylinder of 10 sq. cm. sectional area? If the fluid were water (13 times less dense than mercury) how high would it rise?

3. A quantity of oxygen in a cylinder inverted over water measures 200 c.c. at $20°$ C. and 740 mm. pressure. What is the volume of the oxygen dry and when measured at $0°$ and 76 cm. pressure?

4. A vessel of 2,000 litres capacity holds a quantity of gas at $0°$ C. and 740 mm. pressure. If the temperature rises to $24°$ C., what does the pressure become?

5. If at $0°$ C. and 76 cm. pressure a litre of air weighs $1 \cdot 293$ gm., what will be the temperature at which a litre of air at 74 cm. pressure weighs 1 gm.?

6. The temperature and pressure of the air at the top of a mine are $10°$ C. and 30 inches of mercury respectively, at the bottom of the mine are $14°$ C.

and 30·5 inches. Compare the density of the air at the bottom with that of the top.

7. A globe of diameter 8 inches has 10 cub. ft. of dry air at 32° F. and at 28 inches pressure pumped into it. What is the pressure when the globe is heated to 200° F.? 0° C. = 32° F., 100° C. = 212° F.

8. Pure sulphuric acid of density 1·84 gm. per c.c. is diluted with water until its final volume is one hundred times as great. Then 5 c.c. are measured and a drop of bromthymol blue gives it a bright yellow tint. From a stock solution caustic soda is added drop by drop till the mixture suddenly turns a faint blue. The burette shows that 7·5 c.c. have been used up. If 10 c.c. of another solution of sulphuric acid requires 9 c.c. of the same stock solution to neutralize it, how many grams of pure sulphuric acid per litre does it contain?

9. What volume would 100 c.c. of oxygen measured at 0° and 755 mm. pressure occupy if the temperature were raised to 20° C. and the pressure lowered to 750 mm.?

10. If 32 gm. of oxygen at 76 cm. pressure and 0° C. occupy 22·4 litres, how much oxygen would occupy 20 litres at 100° C. and 80 cm. pressure?

11. To compare the densities of gases the weight of 1 litre is usually calculated from observed data for the standard temperature of 0° C. and pressure of 760 mm. (called briefly S.T.P.). Tabulate the densities of the following gases and their relative densities to the nearest half integer, taking hydrogen (= 1) as the standard, from the following data.

Gas			Weight (g.)	Volume (c.c.)	Temperature (C.)	Pressure (mm.)
Oxygen	..	..	3·4234	2,500	10°	755
Ammonia	..	..	2·1606	3,000	15°	749
Nitrogen	..	..	1·7529	1,500	20°	762
Chlorine	..	..	7·7446	2,500	10°	758
Hydrogen	..	..	0·1027	1,200	15°	763

12. A graduated glass vessel inverted over sulphuric acid to absorb water vapour contains 500 c.c. of hydrogen at atmospheric pressure. 100 c.c. of oxygen are admitted and an electric spark is introduced by insulated wires. When the vessel is depressed till the level of fluid is the same inside and outside, the volume of gas contracts to 300 c.c. Again 100 c.c. of oxygen are admitted. The volume now contracts to 100 c.c. when the mixture is sparked. When the same procedure is repeated the total volume is reduced to 50 c.c. A fourth repetition results in no contraction after sparking. From this deduce the relative proportions in which hydrogen combines with oxygen to form water. If the densities of hydrogen and oxygen at S.T.P. are 0·0899 and 1·429 gm. per litre respectively, find the combining ratio of hydrogen and oxygen by weight.

13. Using the conclusion established in the preceding experiment, deduce the proportion of oxygen in atmospheric air from the following data of an experiment in which all the water vapour formed is absorbed as before with sulphuric acid:

Hydrogen (c.c.)	Air (c.c.)	Total Volume after Sparking
500	500	700
500	750	800
500	1,500	1,250
500	2,000	1,750

14. 1·958 gm. of sulphur burns in air with the production of 1,500 c.c. of sulphur dioxide when the atmospheric pressure is 740 mm. and the temperature at which the gas is collected is 20° C. If the density of sulphur dioxide at S.T.P. is 2·877 gm. per litre, find the combining ratios of oxygen and sulphur by weight.

15. If 1·605 gm. of carbon burn in air with the production of 3,500 c.c. of carbon dioxide (density 1·978 gm. per litre at S.T.P.) collected at 0·9 atmos. pressure and 16° C., find the combining ratios of oxygen and carbon by weight.

16. If 1 gm. of hydrogen at 0° C. and 76 cm. pressure on the mercury barometer occupies 11·2 litres, find the weight of 1 litre at 20° C. and 75 cm. pressure.

17. If 16 gm. of oxygen at 0° C. and 76 cm. pressure occupies 11·2 litres, find the density of oxygen at 25° C. and 765 mm. pressure referred to hydrogen at S.T.P. as standard.

CHAPTER IX

THE ATOMS OF DEMOCRITUS

Intimations of the Age of Plenty

IT is an error to draw a sharp distinction between the debt which science owes to the contributions of specially gifted individuals on the one hand and to social demand on the other. The social background of science includes the material use of the fruits of scientific knowledge, the material environment which directs individual interest to specific problems, the social tradition which checks or stimulates enquiry in one direction or another, and the way in which society makes use of its own personnel. The exhaustion of former fuel supplies and the substitution of new ones towards the latter end of the eighteenth century culminated in the foundation of new chemical industries for the manufacture of sulphuric acid, bleaching powder, coal gas, beet sugar, synthetic alkalis, and phosphorus matches. Chemistry was in demand. New benefactions and endowments provided it with new problems and new resources. Consequently it could now command the services of a greater number of gifted individuals and select them from a more ample reservoir of talent.

The experimental chemist of the eighteenth century was, generally speaking, a man of means. Boyle, Cavendish and Lavoisier belonged to the prosperous classes. The great figures of the nineteenth century like Davy and Faraday did not. The new demand for talent was too great to be supplied by the social personnel from which the great chemists in the old tradition had been recruited. When we have acknowledged to the full the debt which chemistry owes to men like Davy or Faraday, we are forced to recognize that a decisive aspect of the rapid progress with which their names are associated was expansion of educational opportunities. As far as we can be certain of anything about individual human lives we can be tolerably sure that the great Faraday, a bookbinder's errand boy, would never have been a chemist if he had lived a century before the Royal Institution was founded.

The new social demand for chemical knowledge in the decade which immediately preceded the great theoretical advances of the nineteenth century is well illustrated by a remark in one of Boulton's letters. Referring to his son, he says: "Matt is a tolerable good chemist. . . . I shall be glad when the time arrives for him to assist me in the business." A good account of the circumstances which led to the foundation of the Royal Institution is given in J. G. Crowther's illuminating essay on Davy. Equally notable among the new organs of education adapted to the cultural needs of the manufacturing class in England was Owens College at Manchester. Just as Birmingham, the centre of the new machine industry which created a new demand for metallurgical knowledge, was also the focus of an important school of chemical discovery in the latter part of the eighteenth century, Manchester, then rising to prominence as a centre of the textile industry, was the home of an active school of chemical research in the opening years of the nineteenth.

Priestley himself had been a tutor at the Warrington Academy, which was founded in the latter half of the eighteenth century to provide instruction for the sons of prosperous industrialists and business men with dissenting views. Chiefly from among the pupils of the Warrington Academy came the group of men who started the Manchester Philosophical and Literary Society with much the same character as the Lunar Society of Birmingham. Its corresponding members included Benjamin Franklin, Erasmus Darwin, and Josiah Wedgwood. Thomas Henry, who was one of the original members, was an active chemist, his son, a later member, being better known as such. In an address to an early meeting (1781) Henry (*père*) emphasized the pre-eminence of chemical science in connexion with the needs of Manchester industrialism:

Nor is the utility of chemistry more confined, or less connected with manufactures than mechanics. Indeed chemistry may be, not improperly, called the corner-stone of the arts. . . . To show the advantages arising from this science in all the arts through which they might be traced, would carry me far beyond the limits of my present design. It may be sufficient to point out the connection which subsists between chemistry and those manufactures which are the pride and glory of this respectable commercial town. Bleaching is a chemical operation. The end of it is to abstract the oily and phlogistic parts from the yarn or cloth, whereby it is rendered more fit for acquiring a greater degree of whiteness, and absorbing the particles of any colouring materials to which it may be exposed. The materials for this process are also the creatures of chemistry, and some degree of chemical knowledge is requisite to enable the operator to judge of their goodness. Quicklime is prepared by a chemical process. Potash is a product of the same art, to which also vitriolic and all the acids owe their existence. The manufacture of soap is also a branch of this science. All the operations of the whitster, the steeping, washing, and boiling in alkaline lixiviums, exposing to the sun's light, scouring, rubbing and blueing, are chemical operations, or founded on chemical principles.

James Watt, junior, representing his father's interests in Manchester, became the Secretary of the Society in 1790. Among the original members were several who, like Priestley, showed an active sympathy with the French Jacobins. Walker and Jackson, the secretary and president, promoted a correspondence with the Club of the Jacobins. James Watt and Cooper, another member, were delegated to present an address to the Society of the Friends of the Constitution at Paris in 1792. In his *Reflections*, Burke alludes to this event obliquely with characteristic violence.

The most important figures associated with the early history of the society were William Henry and John Dalton. The name of Henry, who published a system of chemistry which had passed through eleven editions by 1809, is associated with the rule governing the relation of the pressure to the solubility of a gas. Henry's law states that the mass of gas dissolved in a liquid at fixed temperature is directly proportional to the external pressure of the gas. If the gas in contact with the fluid is a mixture each constituent exercises its own "partial" pressure (Fig. 287). For instance, water in contact with air at a pressure of five atmospheres dissolves the same mass of oxygen as water in contact with pure oxygen at atmospheric pressure, since air is a mixture of four-fifths nitrogen and one-fifth oxygen by volume.

Dalton's *New System of Chemical Philosophy* (1808) is a landmark in the history of science. The editor of the Manchester memoirs rightly remarks that it placed him among "that great race of thinkers which includes many of the finest names from Leucippus and Epicurus to Lucretius and onwards to Newton and Modern Science." He it was who first saw a significant connexion between the known laws of chemical combination and a particular theory of matter. Thereafter the progress of chemical science is largely associated with the Atomic view.

The atomic theory of Dalton and his successors was fundamentally distinct from the speculations of the Greek materialists and the chemists of Newton's generation. It was primarily concerned with the *quantity* of the ingredients used in chemical combination. During the period of incubation which intervened between the recognition of a third state of matter in manifold distinct forms and the rapid progress of chemistry in the nineteenth century, gentlemen of leisure, apothecaries, and others, had added much to facts already known about what kinds of substances combine to form others. There were as yet no general rules of qualitative combination to direct chemical industry. Still less could chemical science provide it with guidance of another kind. In chemical manufacture it is not enough to know what ingredients to use. It is equally important to know in what quantities to use them and in what circumstances the best yield is obtained.

LAW OF COMBINATION BY WEIGHT

Two new classes of discoveries made during the last decade of the eighteenth and the first decade of the nineteenth century paved the way for the new doctrine. One is embodied in the law of combination by weight, and the other in the law of combination by volume. The law of combination by weight embodies several distinct contributions, of which the earliest has already been mentioned. The researches of Black and Lavoisier had made the balance an essential part of the chemist's equipment, and had foreshadowed the principle that the same substances combine in constant numerical proportions by weight to form a particular compound. The discovery of *constant proportion* in chemical combination was followed by the recognition of definite regularities in, and resemblances between, the proportions of ingredients in related compounds. The two most important of these are concerned with the proportions in which the same elements combine to form more than one different substance and the proportions in which different elements combine with the same element to form compounds.

What is called the principle of *multiple proportions* is the statement that when one substance unites with another to form more than one compound, the proportions in the different compounds which may be formed from the union of the same substances exhibit a *simple* numerical relation. This may be illustrated by the composition of the oxides of carbon and nitrogen.

Carbon may unite with oxygen to form two different compounds. One which is formed by burning carbon *in excess of air* is the *carbon dioxide* present in the air we breathe out. If carbon dioxide is passed over heated carbon a colourless inflammable gas is formed. This gas is not absorbed appreciably by lime. So it can be easily separated from unchanged carbon dioxide to compare its weight with that of the carbon which is used up in the process. *Carbon monoxide* has the peculiarity of expelling oxygen from combination with the red pigment (haemoglobin) of our blood, making it useless as an oxygen carrier to the tissues. On this account it is highly poisonous, and its presence in coal gas makes the latter dangerous in quantities too small of themselves to produce mere suffocation. It is thus quite distinct from carbon dioxide in its properties; and the proportion of carbon and oxygen contained in it is easily found by comparing the weight of carbon dioxide used up with the weight of carbon required to convert a fixed amount of it into carbon monoxide. One way of doing this is to heat a known weight of carbon dioxide in a closed tube with a known weight of carbon. At the end of the experiment the gas is blown into lime. The amount of chalk produced tells us how much carbon dioxide is left (see p. 417), and therefore how much has disappeared. The final weight of the carbon tells us how much carbon has disappeared in combining with the carbon dioxide which has also disappeared. A simpler method is to burn a known weight of carbon monoxide in air. The only new substance produced is carbon dioxide, the weight of which can be got by absorbing it with lime water (or other alkali). The difference between the weight of carbon dioxide formed and the weight of carbon monoxide tells us how much more oxygen a given weight of carbon dioxide contains. We thus find that 11 grams of carbon dioxide contain 3 of carbon, while 7 grams of carbon monoxide contain 3 of carbon. Thus 3 grams of carbon are combined with 8 grams of oxygen in carbon dioxide and with 4 grams of oxygen in carbon monoxide. For an equal quantity of carbon in each there is twice as much oxygen in carbon dioxide as in carbon monoxide.

Nitrogen forms several different compounds with oxygen in different proportions. One of these which comes off when ammonium nitrate is heated was called by Priestley "laughing gas," and is now a familiar dental anaesthetic. Its composition was discovered by Davy. It is quite colourless and has the peculiarity of supporting combustion, like oxygen itself: i.e. things which burn easily in air will also burn in laughing gas. Another oxide of nitrogen (nitric oxide) is formed when *dilute* nitric acid is poured on to copper. It also is colourless, but produces brown fumes when mixed with air, is poisonous, and does not support combustion. The oxides of nitrogen are decomposed when passed over red-hot copper, which takes up the oxygen contained in the gas with formation of copper oxide and nitrogen. By weighing the quantities of nitrogen and copper oxide formed we can ascertain the proportions of oxygen and nitrogen in the oxide. In 11 grams of nitrous oxide or laughing gas there are 4 grams of oxygen. Hence 7 grams of nitrogen are combined with 4 grams of oxygen. In 15 grams of nitric oxide there are 8 grams of oxygen. Hence 7 grams of nitrogen are combined with 8 grams. Thus the amount of oxygen combined with 7 grams of nitrogen in nitric oxide is twice as great as in nitrous oxide.

The significance of this rule is easy to visualize, when we picture pure substances as if they were made up of discrete particles, each with a definite weight characteristic of the substance itself. The simple ratios that we find when we compare the *proportions* of different ingredients which make up different substances containing the same constituents, are simply explained if we reject the self-evident conclusion that matter is homogeneous, and choose the hypothesis that each particle of a pure substance is made up of one and the same whole number of elementary particles. We can then picture each particle of a compound substance as the union of a fixed number of each of the elementary particles from which it is made (Fig. 256).

Such models also suggest the truth of another rule called the principle of *reciprocal proportions*. It was experimentally established about the same time as the principle of multiple proportions. Suppose A and B combine to form a compound AB, that B and C combine to form a compound BC, and that A and C combine to form a compound AC. If the particular proportions in which A, B, and C combine are due to the fixed weight of the particles of which they are made up, we should also expect to find a simple numerical connexion between the combining ratios of A and B, B and C, C and A.

It is easier to see clearly what this means by examining an actual example such as the composition of three compounds of the elements hydrogen, carbon, and oxygen. Hydrogen forms with carbon a gaseous compound which is the principal combustible constituent, other than hydrogen itself, in coal gas. It is called marsh gas or methane. Methane is exuded from decomposition of organic material in stagnant water, sometimes igniting to form marsh fire or will o' the wisp. In 4 grams of marsh gas 3 grams of carbon are combined with 1 gram of hydrogen. In water, which is an oxide of hydrogen, 8 grams of oxygen are combined with 1 gram of hydrogen. In carbon dioxide 8 grams of oxygen are combined with 3 grams of carbon.

All the facts which are illustrated by the examples given may be combined in a single rule of combination by weight. If we take some element as our standard, e.g. hydrogen, and compare the weights of other elements which combine with one another, we find that they are generally simple multiples or submultiples of the ratios of the weights,* in which they respectively combine with 1 gram of hydrogen. The table which follows illustrates the regularity of these combining ratios by reference to the compounds already mentioned and certain others which are all articles of commerce.

LAW OF COMBINATION BY VOLUME

If each particle of a compound is made up of a fixed number of elementary particles each with a fixed weight, the simple numerical ratios of chemical combination by weight find a simple explanation. Still the facts which establish the law of combination by weight do not tell us the relative weights of the particles involved in chemical reactions. This is illustrated in Fig. 256. We might equally well explain the combining proportions of oxygen and carbon by saying either (a) the weights of a particle of oxygen and a particle of carbon are in the ratio 8 : 3, one particle of each being present in carbon dioxide and two particles of carbon combined with one of oxygen in carbon monoxide, or (b) the weights of a particle of oxygen and carbon are in the ratio 16 : 12 (or 4 : 3), one particle of each being present in a particle of

---

* The weight of an element which will combine with, or take the place of, one gram of hydrogen is called its *combining weight* or *equivalent weight*.

THE LAW OF COMBINING WEIGHTS

	(a) Percentage Composition					(b) Crude Ratios					(c) Combining Ratios				
	Hydrogen	Oxygen	Carbon	Sulphur	Nitrogen	H_2	O_2	C	S	N_2	H_2	O_2	C	S	N_2
Water ..	11·1	88·9	—	—	—	1	8	—	—	—	1	8	—	—	—
Marsh gas ..	25	—	75	—	—	1	—	3	—	—	1	—	3	—	—
Carbon dioxide ..	—	72·7	27·3	—	—	—	8	3	—	—	—	8	3	—	—
Carbon monoxide ..	—	57·2	42·8	—	—	—	4	3	—	—	—	8	2(3)	—	—
Sulphur dioxide ..	—	50	—	50	—	—	1	—	1	—	—	2(8)	—	16	—
Sulphuretted hydrogen ..	5·9	—	—	94·1	—	1	—	—	16	—	1	—	—	16	—
Carbon bisulphide ..	—	—	15·8	84·2	—	—	—	3	16	—	—	—	3	16	—
Ammonia ..	17·7	—	—	—	82·3	3	—	—	—	14	3(1)	—	—	—	14
Laughing gas ..	—	36·4	—	—	63·6	—	8	—	—	14	—	8	—	—	14
Prussic acid ..	3·7	—	44·4	—	51·9	1	—	12	—	14	1	—	4(3)	—	14
Sulphuric acid ..	2	65·3	—	32·7	—	1	32	—	16	—	1	4(8)	—	16	—

carbon monoxide and two particles of oxygen combined with one of carbon in carbon dioxide.

A clearer picture of the structure of compounds is got by studying the way in which gases combine by volume. The law of combination by volume is that when gases combine to form other gases the volume of each of the products is a *simple* fraction or multiple of the volumes which react to produce them. This rule, discovered by Gay-Lussac in 1808, is only true if all the volumes are measured at the same temperature and pressure or so calculated by using the gas laws of Boyle and Charles. If we mix 100 c.c. of hydrogen with 150 c.c. of chlorine in sunlight, the two gases combine to form hydrochloric acid gas. The total volume of gas after combination is 250 c.c. On

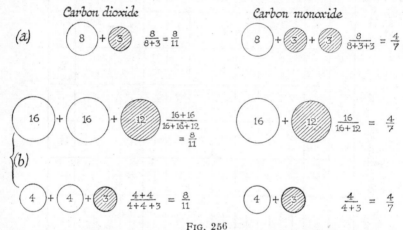

FIG. 256
Atomic models to illustrate same percentage composition by Weight.

removing the hydrochloric acid gas (which is much more soluble than pure chlorine) the volume shrinks to 50 c.c. This remainder is pure chlorine. Thus 100 c.c. of hydrogen have combined with 100 c.c. of chlorine to produce 200 c.c. of hydrochloric acid gas. If an electric spark is passed through a mixture of hydrogen and oxygen at a temperature above the boiling point of water, water vapour (steam) is produced. If 100 c.c. of hydrogen are mixed with 100 c.c. of oxygen the final volume of gas is 150 c.c. If the water vapour is absorbed by some "dehydrating agent" 50 c.c. of gas (oxygen) are left. Thus 100 c.c. of hydrogen combine with 50 c.c. of oxygen to make 100 c.c. of steam.

The meaning of this simple relation was at first puzzling, because it was taken for granted that the individual particles of each element present in the particles of a compound were quite separate in an element. This is not intrinsically likely for a simple reason. When we say that charcoal and diamond are different forms of the element carbon, we mean that both burn in air to form, weight for weight, the same quantity of the same substance, carbon dioxide, and nothing else. Both charcoal and diamond (also soot and the graphite of our pencils) are therefore built up of the same elementary particles. The fact remains that they are not identical. An elementary gas can also exist in two forms. When electric sparks are passed through oxygen, its volume shrinks somewhat. It becomes more dense. If the denser mixture is shaken with turpentine, it shrinks further, and what is left has the same density as ordinary oxygen. The original volume of oxygen present before sparking and extraction with turpentine combines with more carbon, and with more magnesium, than does the residual gas which has the same density as ordinary oxygen. Sparked oxygen is thus a mixture of two things, ordinary oxygen and turpentine-soluble oxygen, which is called *ozone*. If the ozone is expelled from turpentine, it combines with magnesium or with carbon to form the ordinary oxides of these elements. Thus oxygen and ozone are made up of the same elementary particles. If the atomic view is correct there is only one way in which they can differ. The particles of an element must be compounds of several elementary particles like those of a compound.

The particles of a compound are built up of elementary particles which are not all alike. Likewise the particles of an element are built of smaller particles which are all the same. Since the number (and arrangement) of these smaller particles may conceivably be different, we need not be surprised if we meet a chemical element in more than one disguise. Once we have drawn a distinction between complex particles or *molecules* and elementary particles or *atoms* into which molecules break up during a chemical reaction to combine in some new way, the law of combination by volume fits into the atomic scheme. According to our hypothesis the weight of a molecule of a given kind is fixed. The volume occupied by a given weight of gas therefore depends on the number of molecules of which it is composed. If there is a simple relation between the volumes of combining gases, there must therefore be a simple relation between the number of molecules in the same volume of different gases. A relation which fits all the facts is the most straightforward one, first put forward by Avogadro in 1811. Avogadro's explanation was that *equal volumes of all gases measured at the same temperature and pressure contain the same number of molecules*. Its acceptability does *not* depend upon being the *only* conceivable interpretation of the observed facts about the combination of gases. We accept it for two reasons; one is that after long trial, during which many chemists remained judiciously sceptical, it has been found *to weld all the known facts of chemical combination into a very simple scheme*. The usefulness of this scheme will appear when we see how it is applied. Another reason for accepting it depends on the physical properties of gases. This will be explained later (p. 479).

According to Avogadro's hypothesis, equal volumes of hydrogen, oxygen, and water vapour, at the same temperature, have the same number (x) of molecules. Hence if 100 c.c. of steam is made up of 100 c.c. of hydrogen and 50 c.c. of oxygen, x molecules of oxygen combine with $2x$ molecules of hydrogen to make $2x$ molecules of steam. So 2 molecules of steam must be made from the reaction of two molecules of hydrogen with one molecule of oxygen. This means that one molecule of oxygen goes to the making of two molecules of steam, each containing at least one atom of oxygen. One molecule of oxygen must therefore contain at least two atoms. Again, since 100 c.c. of hydrogen and 100 c.c. of chlorine combine to 200 c.c. of hydrochloric acid gas, one molecule of hydrogen and one molecule of chlorine react to form two molecules of hydrochloric acid gas. Hence a molecule of hydrogen or of chlorine must contain two (or some other even number of) atoms. Oxygen is sixteen times as dense as hydrogen, and steam is nine times as dense. If we take the simplest view, which is only justified by the fact that it works, a molecule of hydrogen consists of two atoms. So if a molecule of steam is nine times as heavy as a molecule of hydrogen it is eighteen times as heavy as an atom of hydrogen. This ratio, the weight of a molecule compared with the

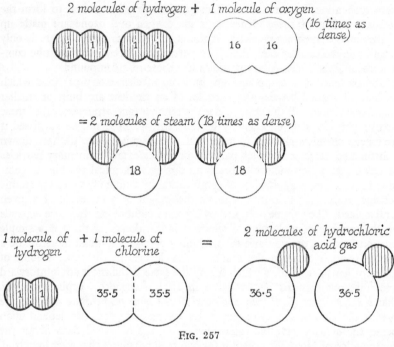

FIG. 257

Atomic models to illustrate Law of Combination of Gases by Volume.

weight of an atom of hydrogen, is called the *molecular weight* of the substance. So the molecular weight of steam is said to be 18.

The relation between molecular weight and relative density, when hydrogen is the standard, can also be stated in a symbolic form which will be useful later. If a single molecule of a gaseous compound weighs M times as much as a hydrogen atom, M is called its molecular weight. As a working hypothesis we assume that hydrogen has two atoms in each of its molecules. So, if an atom of hydrogen weighs m grams, a molecule of hydrogen weighs $2m$ grams, and a molecule of the gaseous compound weighs Mm grams. According to Avogadro 1 litre of hydrogen contains the same number (x) of molecules as 1 litre of the gaseous compound at the same temperature and pressure. So the weight (w) of 1 litre of hydrogen is $2mx$, i.e. $mx = \frac{1}{2}w$, and the weight (W) of 1 litre of the gaseous compound is Mmx. Hence W $= \frac{1}{2}$Mw, that is to say M $= 2$ (W $\div$ w). The ratio W $\div$ w is the relative density of the gaseous compound when the standard is hydrogen. It is usually called its *vapour density*. The molecular weight of a gaseous compound is thus the same as *twice its vapour density*. The vapour density of marsh gas or methane is 8. So its molecular weight is sixteen,

Similarly the molecular weight of oxygen is 32. Taking once more the simplest view, we may say that the weight of an atom of oxygen is 16 times the weight of an atom of hydrogen. This number is called the *atomic weight* of oxygen. Chlorine is 35·5 times as dense as hydrogen. So its molecular weight is 70, and if its molecule contains 2 atoms, its atomic weight is 35·5.

In the last.paragraph we assumed that the molecule of oxygen and the molecule of chlorine are both built up of two atoms. All we know is that if the atomic view is correct each must be built up of some even number of atoms. The only initial assumption we really need to make is that the hydrogen molecule is diatomic. The molecular weight of any gaseous compound is then twice the ratio of its density to that of hydrogen. The weight of the molecule of a substance of molecular weight W is the weight of W atoms of hydrogen. Likewise the weight of an atom of an element whose atomic weight is A is the weight of A atoms of hydrogen. So if there are x atoms of this element in a compound of molecular weight W, it contributes a weight equivalent to xA atoms of hydrogen to the total weight corresponding to W atoms of hydrogen. That is to say, the proportion (p) by weight in every molecule is xA $\div$ W, whence pW $= x$A. The smallest number (x) of atoms of an element which could occur in the molecule of any of its compounds is 1, in which case pW $=$ A. This means that the atomic weight is the smallest value of the product of the molecular weight and the proportion of an element in the same compound. So we can check the provisional value of 16 assigned to oxygen by an independent method, which involves making a table like the following, in which the proportions of oxygen are determined by analysis:

Oxide	Density compared with Hydrogen $\frac{1}{2}$W	Molecular Weight W	Proportion of Oxygen by Weight p	Weight of Oxygen in one Mol xA ($= p$W)
Carbon monoxide ..	14	28	$\frac{4}{7}$	16
Carbon dioxide ..	22	44	$\frac{8}{11}$	32
Sulphur dioxide ..	32	64	$\frac{1}{2}$	32
Water	9	18	$\frac{8}{9}$	16
Nitrous oxide ..	22	44	$\frac{4}{11}$	16
Nitric acid	31·5	63	$\frac{16}{21}$	48
Sulphuric acid ..	49	98	$\frac{32}{49}$	64

We always find that if W is the molecular weight of any one of the thousands of oxygen compounds known, the number of grams of oxygen in W grams is either 16 or some multiple of 16 (i.e. x times 16), never less. We therefore conclude that A $=$ 16. Thus if the molecule of hydrogen contains two atoms, the atom of oxygen weighs 16 times as much as the hydrogen atom. This method can be used for finding the atomic weight of any element.

To make sure that this is clear we may retrace our steps, using the symbolism already applied to the relation between molecular weight and vapour density. If a single atom of an element weighs A times as much as an atom of hydrogen, A is called its atomic weight. So if one hydrogen atom weighs m grams, one atom of the element weighs Am grams. If there are n atoms of the element in one of its compounds, the total weight of the element in one molecule of the same compound is Amn, and if the molecular weight of the compound is M, the mass of a single molecule is Mm. Hence the proportion (p) by mass of the element in a single molecule of its compound is A$mn \div$ Mm, and p M $= n$ A. If all the molecules of a gaseous compound are alike, the mass proportion of an element in one molecule of its compound is the same as the mass proportion of the element in any quantity which can be measured and analysed. If we take M grams (called one *mol*) of the compound, the mass of the element present in it must be pM, which is nA. So nA is the *number of grams of the element in one mol of one of its compounds.* Among the compounds of an element some will have molecules with 1, some with 2, some with 3, and some with more, atoms of the element. The smallest value of n is therefore 1. If one molecule of a compound contains one atom of an element whose atomic weight is A, one mol of the compound will contain A grams of the element. Unless the element never forms compounds in which only one atom of it is present in each molecule, A is the *least number* of grams of the element *contained in one mol of any of its compounds.* Even if none of the known compounds of an element is made up of molecules which only contain one of its atoms, the correct atomic weight can usually be inferred. Suppose the only known oxygen compounds were sulphuric acid, nitric acid, and carbon dioxide. We should then get the following values for nA: 64, 48, and 32. Since 48 is one and a half times 32, we cannot give oxygen an atomic weight of 32. If we did, we should have to make $n = 1\frac{1}{2}$ in nitric oxide. Since we have constructed our molecular model on the assumption that it must contain a *whole* number of atoms, the atomic weight of oxygen cannot be greater than 16.

What we commonly call the chemical *formula* of a pure substance is a concise statement of the build-up of its molecule in the *gaseous state*, embodying both the relative contributions of its elementary constituents to its mass and its relative density. To assign such a formula as H_2O for water vapour or H_2SO_4 for the vapour of sulphuric acid, the first prerequisite is to know the density of the compound relative to hydrogen. A given volume of steam is 9 times as heavy as the same volume of hydrogen at the same temperature and pressure. In accordance with Avogadro's principle, the molecular weight of steam is therefore 9 times that of hydrogen itself. If 2 atoms of hydrogen make up a molecule of the gas, the M.W. of hydrogen is 2, and that of water vapour is therefore 18. The atomic weight of hydrogen being our standard is 1. That of oxygen is 16. So the molecule of water is built up of two atoms of hydrogen and one of oxygen. This fits the facts of combination by weight and volume. By weight 9 grams of steam contain 8 of oxygen and 1 of hydrogen. By volume 2 of hydrogen unite with one of oxygen to make one of steam.

The density of sulphuric acid vapour is 49 times as great as that of hydrogen. Its molecular weight is therefore taken to be 98. It contains only the elements hydrogen, sulphur, and oxygen. Hence we may say a molecule of sulphuric acid is built up from n atoms of hydrogen, m atoms of sulphur and l atoms of oxygen, meaning:

(a) *n* times the atomic weight of hydrogen = number of grams of hydrogen in 98 grams of sulphuric acid.

(b) *m* times the atomic weight of sulphur = number of grams of sulphur in 98 grams of sulphuric acid.

(c) *l* times the atomic weight of oxygen = number of grams of oxygen in 98 grams of sulphuric acid.

Analysis shows that the hydrogen content is approximately 2 per cent or 2 grams in every 98 grams. Since *n* times the atomic weight of hydrogen is 2, and the atomic weight of hydrogen is 1, *n* itself is 2. The sulphur content is 32·7 per cent or 32 grams in every 98 grams. Since the atomic weight of sulphur is 32, *m* times 32 is 32, whence *m* = 1. The oxygen content is 65·3 per cent or 64 grams in every 98. Since the atomic weight of oxygen is 16, *l* times 16 is 64, i.e. *l* = 4. Thus the molecule of sulphuric acid is said to be made up of 2 atoms of hydrogen, one of sulphur and 4 of oxygen. This is briefly indicated by the formula H_2SO_4.

In such formulae some of the commoner elements are represented by the initial letters of the English names, and others, to avoid duplication, by Latin or Arabic names. Thus carbon dioxide is CO_2, carbon monoxide CO, nitrous oxide N_2O. Sodium is represented by the symbol Na (short for Natrium) and Potassium by the symbol K (short for Kalium from kali *ashes*), caustic soda (sodium hydroxide) and caustic potash (potassium hydroxide) being NaOH and KOH respectively. Here is a table of the atomic weights of the elements already mentioned and of a few additional ones*:

Hydrogen	H	1·01	Iron	Fe	55·8
Helium	He	4	Nickel	Ni	58·7
Lithium	Li	6·94	Cobalt	Co	58·9
Beryllium	Be	9·02	Copper	Cu	63·6
Boron	B	10·8	Zinc	Zn	65·4
Carbon	C	12	Arsenic	As	74·9
Nitrogen	N	14	Bromine	Br	79·9
Oxygen	O	16	Strontium	Sr	87·6
Fluorine	F	19	Silver	Ag	108
Neon	Ne	20·2	Cadmium	Cd	112
Sodium	Na	23	Tin	Sn	119
Magnesium	Mg	24·3	Antimony	Sb	122
Aluminium	Al	27	Iodine	I	127
Silicon	Si	28·1	Barium	Ba	137
Phosphorus	P	31	Tantalum	Ta	181
Sulphur	S	32·1	Tungsten	W	184
Chlorine	Cl	35·5	Platinum	Pt	195
Potassium	K	39·1	Gold	Au	197
Argon	A	39·9	Lead	Pb	207
Calcium	Ca	40·1	Bismuth	Bi	209
Chromium	Cr	52	Radium	Ra	226
Manganese	Mn	54·9	Uranium	U	238

* The values given are correct to three significant figures. The weight of an atom of oxygen is not exactly 16 times the weight of an atom of hydrogen. Since hydrogen compounds of the elements are less common or suitable than oxides for determination of atomic weights, oxygen is now given the standard value of 16. The atomic weight of hydrogen (correct to four figures) is then 1·008.

USEFULNESS OF THE ATOMIC VIEW

We shall have plenty of opportunities at a later stage to show why the atomic view is useful. Here we may examine only three of its uses. The first raises an issue which has not emerged in any of our previous discussions of the nature of scientific method. Scientific method cannot be kept in the strait-jacket of any simple definition. One way of defining science is to say that it is an inventory of the furniture of nature. The essence of a good inventory is that you should be able to turn up the information which you want quickly. So one aspect of scientific knowledge is classification. It is a very important aspect of those branches of scientific knowledge which deal with a great variety of objects, as, for instance, chemistry, biology, and sociology.

Scientific classification involves making new words or symbols for objects. These new words have two uses. The first is to convey as much relevant information as possible, and the second is to avoid confusing different things or introducing *irrelevant* associations. Students of social questions would do well to ponder on the immense debt which chemistry and biology owe to the deliberate invention of new symbols which have this characteristic. They are often referred to contemptuously as jargon, especially by the sort of people who think it is tremendously important to be able to place Francesca da Rimini or repeat the correct tags for *objets d'art*.

Compare with its atomic label H_2SO_4 the medieval name for sulphuric acid, oil of vitriol. If you are a classical scholar the latter suggests that it has some connexion with or similarity to glass. This is not true. The only other thing you are likely to recall when the word is used is that ladies sometimes throw vitriol at one another. Contrast this with the information which is conveyed by the formula H_2SO_4. To begin with, it tells you from what elements sulphuric acid is built up. If you have a table of atomic weights, it also tells you in what proportion by weight they are present in it. Since the atomic weights of the common elements are easy to remember, a table is rarely necessary. When you know a little more about other compounds it tells you much about the way in which their properties and preparation are interconnected. The words alabaster and Epsom salts suggest no connexion with vitriol. The formula $CaSO_4$ and $MgSO_4$ at once direct your attention to the fact that the first (which in combination with water is alabaster) and the second (which in combination with water is Epsom salts) both have the same cluster of atoms or *radicle*, as chemists say, i.e. SO_4, present in oil of vitriol.

In one this radicle is combined with the metal calcium and in the other with the metal magnesium. When hydrogen takes the place of a metal in association with such a cluster of atoms the compound is an acid. The metallic derivatives of an acid or *salts* can sometimes be formed, as in this example, by direct action of the acid on the metal. They can also be formed by dissolving a metallic oxide, the hydroxide of a metal, or a metallic carbonate in the acid. If we know that chalk is $CaCO_3$, i.e. it has the CO_3 radicle of all carbonates, or that quicklime is CaO, i.e. it is the oxide of calcium, or that slaked lime is $Ca(OH)_2$, i.e. it is the hydroxide (alkali) of calcium, we know that any one of these substances will combine with sulphuric acid to produce calcium sulphate. This is not merely an economy of effort. *It also stands for a social achievement.* Chalk, lime, oil of vitriol, alabaster, and Epsom salts, are just names of objects which occur in nature or can be made by some rule of thumb method from some special constituents which exist in some particular place. Write their names in the new symbols, and you exhibit all sorts of ways of making them from all sorts of materials. It may be that some of them will be found available almost anywhere. They have ceased to be mere articles of consumption and have become instruments of production.

There are several other interesting items of information contained in the formula H_2SO_4. As already explained, analysis of salts formed when acids attack metals or dissolve their oxides, etc., shows that a salt is a compound in which an atom of metal takes the place of one, two, or more, atoms of hydrogen. Sulphuric acid has two atoms of hydrogen in each molecule. One or both can be replaced. Thus we can have two salts formed by the combination of sulphuric acid and caustic soda (NaOH): sodium hydrogen sulphate $NaHSO_4$, and disodium sulphate Na_2SO_4. Similarly carbonic acid (H_2CO_3) formed by dissolving carbon dioxide in water forms two sodium salts, sodium bicarbonate (sodium hydrogen carbonate) or baking powder ($NaHCO_3$), and sodium carbonate (di-sodium carbonate) or Na_2CO_3 which is anhydrous washing soda. On heating it, baking powder gives up carbon dioxide and water vapour becoming washing soda. The bubbles of gas (carbon dioxide), also produced by the respiration of the yeast organism, can be used to "raise" bread, etc. They get imprisoned in the dough and thus give it the spongy texture required for culinary purposes. The way in which this happens may be represented in symbolic form by what is called a chemical equation thus:

$$2NaHCO_3 \rightarrow Na_2CO_3 + H_2O + CO_2$$

This means that when sodium bicarbonate breaks up, one molecule of water and one molecule of carbon dioxide gas are formed with each new molecule of sodium carbonate. In pastry the taste of the washing soda is disguised by sugar and other ingredients. For bread which is not specially flavoured yeast is preferred as a gas generator.

If we have found the atomic weight of calcium, as explained on p. 457, analysis shows that a possible formula for calcium sulphate is $CaSO_4$, and a corresponding one for sodium sulphate (disodium sulphate) is Na_2SO_4. So likewise chalk or calcium carbonate may be written as $CaCO_3$, and washing soda as Na_2CO_3. Corresponding to a bisulphate (or hydrogen sulphate) and a bicarbonate (or hydrogen carbonate) of sodium there are salts of calcium. Calcium bicarbonate is represented by the formula $Ca(HCO_3)_2$. One atom of sodium takes the place of one atom of hydrogen, and one atom of calcium takes the place of two atoms of hydrogen. On this account sodium is said to have a *valency* of 1 and calcium of 2.

Unlike calcium carbonate (chalk), calcium bicarbonate is fairly soluble. It is present in very appreciable quantities in the natural waters of chalky soils. When boiled it behaves like baking soda, as represented by the chemical "equation":

$$Ca(HCO_3)_2 \rightarrow CaCO_3 + H_2O + CO_2$$

Thus it is turned into chalk which is not soluble. Soluble calcium salts unite with soaps which are sodium (hard) or potassium (soft) salts of certain acids derived from fats and oils. Calcium replaces sodium (or potassium) to form an insoluble salt "curds." If the calcium is present in the form of bicarbonate it may be removed by simply boiling the water. This is one reason for boiling water before shaving. "Hard" water is sometimes hard because it contains calcium sulphate which is not precipitated, i.e. thrown out of solution, by boiling. Calcium sulphate will react with any soluble carbonate to form the insoluble calcium carbonate and the sulphate of the other metal. That is why we use washing soda. The reaction proceeds according to the chemical equation

$$Na_2CO_3 + CaSO_4 \rightarrow CaCO_3 + Na_2SO_4$$

We have not nearly exhausted the information contained in an atomic formula. If you tell me that something is common salt (which is mostly sodium chloride), I may recall the biblical assertion that a virtuous woman without discretion is like an egg without salt, or maybe one or two other things. None of them tells me how to go out and look for it, or to recognize it except by a taste which is by no means peculiar to it. When you say that a substance is NaCl, I infer that it is built up of the two elements sodium and chlorine; that it is a salt of hydrochloric acid and could therefore be made by dissolving washing soda in "spirits of salt." Because nearly all sodium salts are soluble and nearly all chlorides are soluble, I can conclude that it almost certainly dissolves readily in water.

I can also infer that its presence can be detected by applying the tests for identifying the element sodium, and the tests for identifying any soluble chloride. All sodium compounds colour a flame bright yellow. Among the few insoluble chlorides is silver chloride, which is light-sensitive, darkening on exposure to sunlight. If a soluble silver salt (e.g. silver nitrate) is added to a soluble chloride in solution the insoluble silver chloride is precipitated as a flocculent mass which darkens in sunlight. So I know that a drop of silver nitrate solution added to a solution of sodium chloride will produce this result. Consider another salt. Call it potash fertilizer, and I only know that it is used for soils deficient in the element potassium which is essential to plant life. Call it K_2SO_4 and I know how to detect it. Like all potassium compounds, it will tint a non-luminous flame with a violet hue. The element barium, which is closely related to calcium, and like it has a valency of 2, forms an extremely insoluble sulphate which is precipitated from any solution of a soluble sulphate as a very heavy white powder when a soluble compound of barium like barium chloride is added. Potassium sulphate is recognized as a potassium salt by the flame test and as a sulphate by adding a soluble barium compound in solution. The ensuing reaction may then be written:

$$K_2SO_4 + BaCl_2 \rightarrow 2KCl + BaSO_4$$

Our formula thus enables us to make a rapid conspectus of a very large number of otherwise unrelated facts about how to prepare and how to recognize or search for a substance. Much more than this is involved. The atomic formula is a recipe for the *assay* of a substance. Once chemical manufacture began to develop, the purity of the material sold required a guarantee. Under the old economy of natural products the guarantee of purity was the source from which the material was obtained. Thus Castille soap was soap of special excellence. The atomic theory reduced the whole technique of estimating the purity of compounds to a system so simple that you need to know very few facts to find out how much you have got, if you also know the formula of a substance.

To make this clear we will suppose that we have a mixture of washing soda and potash fertilizer and want to know how much of each a weighed quantity of the mixture contains. We might then proceed in one of two ways, or combine both to check one another. We first dissolve a weighed quantity in a known volume of water, and hence know the weight of mixture in 1 c.c. of the solution. Should we decide to estimate the washing soda, one simple way depends on the fact that carbonates will neutralize nearly all acids. Nearly all acids decompose them, making them effervesce, owing to the liberation of carbon dioxide. For instance, the effervescence of sherbet is due to the admixture of tartaric acid crystals with baking soda and sugar. When the acid dissolves, it sets free CO_2 forming sodium tartrate.

If, therefore, we add a measured quantity of hydrochloric acid solution of known strength to a measured quantity of the mixture we shall break up the washing soda (sodium carbonate), using up a corresponding quantity of hydrochloric acid to form sodium chloride. The atomic formula tells us what the corresponding quantity is, i.e. what weight of washing soda neutralizes what weight of dissolved hydrochloric acid gas.

What weight of hydrochloric acid is neutralized is easily determined in the following way. From a burette (p. 444) we add a solution of caustic soda which turns litmus dye blue to a known quantity of acid solution, made red by addition of a little litmus solution. If we add the soda drop by drop we reach a point where one drop just turns the colour from red to blue. At this point all the hydrochloric acid is used up to form sodium chloride. If it takes 12 c.c. of caustic soda to neutralize 10 c.c. of our standard acid solution, 1 c.c. of the soda corresponds to five-sixths of a c.c. of the acid standard. We may now add the same quantity (10 c.c.) of acid to a measured quantity of mixture containing sodium carbonate and find that on adding dye when all effervescence has ceased only 8 c.c. of soda are required to change the tint. Before adding the soda there must have been five-sixths of 8 c.c., i.e. 6·7 c.c., of hydrochloric acid left, and 3·3 c.c. had been used up to decompose the sodium carbonate. The acid solution is of known strength, i.e. a known weight of hydrochloric acid gas has been dissolved in a measured volume of water. So we know how much of the former is contained in 3·3 c.c. The corresponding amount of carbonate is contained in the formula. Since sodium chloride has the formula NaCl and sodium carbonate has the formula Na_2CO_3 the reaction proceeds in this way

$$2HCl + Na_2CO_3 \rightarrow 2NaCl + H_2O + CO_2$$

This means that for every molecule of sodium carbonate present two molecules of hydrochloric acid are used up. The molecular weight of the latter is 36·5 (see p. 457). The atomic weights of carbon and sodium are given in tables prepared by the method explained on pp. 457–9 as 23 and 12 respectively. Thus the molecular weight which corresponds to the formula adopted for sodium carbonate is $2(23) + 12 + 3(16) = 106$. The ratio of the weights of two molecules of hydrochloric acid and one molecule of sodium carbonate are $2(36·5) : 106$. Hence, 106 grams of sodium carbonate corresponds to 73 grams of hydrochloric acid, and if x grams of the latter are used up the amount of sodium carbonate present was $106x \div 73$ grams.

COOL CLEAN CHEMISTRY

You must not imagine that all the wealth of information which is carried in a single atomic formula came into being suddenly. Avogadro's hypothesis put forward in 1811 was the master clue to a vast jigsaw puzzle. Till the end of the nineteenth century many of the pieces remained out of place. The atomic weights ascribed to some of the elements were twice as large as they ought to have been, because compounds with the minimum number (i.e. 1) of atoms per molecule had not been studied. The formulae ascribed to substances which were not known in the gaseous state were largely conjectural; and indeed it does not make any difference for calculation of corresponding quantities in an analysis whether we represent the reaction between caustic soda and hydrochloric acid, the molecular weight of which can be determined by direct application of Avogadro's principle, as:

$$NaOH + HCl = NaCl + H_2O$$

or (wrongly) as:

$$Na_2(OH)_2 + 2HCl = Na_2Cl_2 + 2H_2O$$

The formulae which we now use depend to a large extent on the discovery of new theoretical principles which we shall come to later. Before order finally emerged out of chaos, the study of chemistry was acquiring a new impetus from the application of new technique and instruments, just as astronomy had benefited in the seventeenth century from the discovery of the pendulum clock, the telescope, and the vernier.

One of the most striking things about the progress of chemical technique in the nineteenth century is the wide horizon of human possibilities which it disclosed. Instead of superseding, it merely enriched the theoretical knowledge required to carry on with the old technique of chemical manufacture. In a large measure this is the technique still used. Consequently we have at our disposal for producing wealth vast stores of knowledge which have never been fully exploited. Few of our legislators or social theorists even yet realize that the pattern of social life fashioned by the rise of chemical manufacture was in no sense a necessary result of applying science to human life. The use of chemistry was determined by the same blind economic forces which encouraged its early growth with no prescience of the social outcome. Meanwhile growing knowledge was pointing to the possibility of a different pattern of social life. Only a few visionaries could see it. Politicians do not study science and scientists are not encouraged to meddle in politics.

The multiplicity of commodities which resulted from the rise of chemical manufacture was accompanied by the multiplication of congested urban populations living in sooty squalor. People became accustomed to regard one as contingent on the other. From earliest antiquity towns had been the focus of any scientific culture. The hypertrophied urban squalor which is now bearing fruit in universal sterility and the prospect of racial extinction was therefore accepted as the price we pay for what is called a high standard of life. The social outlook of people who were hostile to innovation identified the dark satanic mills of Blake's poem with the application of science and England's green and pleasant land with the lack of it. The social outlook of people who welcomed the prosperity which the new knowledge brought in its train identified the social use of science with the production of an ever-increasing multiplicity of commodities, and accepted urban congestion as a necessary evil. These two alternatives still represent the attitude of the majority of people educated in a culture which has no place for studying the social background of science.

We shall be able to find our way through the jungle of silliness which lies behind this false antithesis when we come to the conquest of power. The England which Blake loved was a land in which there were windmills and watermills in picturesque and healthy surroundings. Virile people who did not as yet think it shameful to bear children were learning to replace the slave labour of antiquity by non-human sources of power.

The use of coal as a source of power coincided with its introduction as a basic necessity for continuing the oldest of all the chemical industries—the one which ministered especially to the needs of the production of new machinery. From antiquity we associate metallurgical operations with Vulcan's anvil and Etna's fires. Till the final death of the phlogiston doctrine, fire reigned supreme as the universal solvent, the touchstone of chemical processes. When coal replaced charcoal as the reducing agent of the furnace, power production and metallurgy coalesced in the areas where iron and coal were found together. The new chemical industries, like synthetic alkalis, following the traditional technique of the furnace, equally relied on coal as their source of the universal solvent.

Till the beginning of the nineteenth century mankind depended on two methods of inducing chemical combination and decomposition. One was *precipitation* in solution. Concerning this more will be said later. The other was *heat*. The introduction of coal made dirt a necessary accompaniment of heat in chemical industry. The rapid progress of theoretical chemistry which followed the rise of chemical manufacture was largely due to the introduction of methods which do not demand heat or dirt. Chemistry was becoming cleaner and cooler while society was getting hotter and dirtier.

Three features of the new technique of chemical research will now be mentioned. The first will help us to see that science is not merely an instrument for multiplying commodities to distract neurotic urban populations. If rationally used and socially directed it could be the means of redesigning social life in accordance with fundamental and universal human needs, as for instance the need to bear children if the race is to continue, and the need for a little privacy as a safeguard against universal insanity.

(a) *Electrolytic Decomposition.*—Electrical phenomena might have remained almost completely unknown, as they had been for centuries, if they had not suddenly become important for a simple reason. The toys or electrical machines which had previously been mere curiosities, now became an essential part of the chemist's equipment. The early frictional machines made it

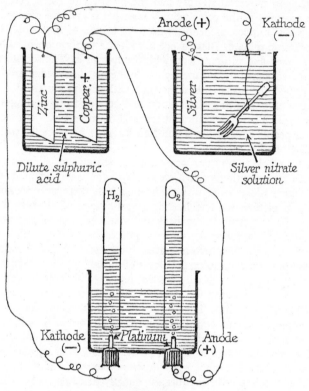

FIG. 258

Electroplating and the decomposition of water by a simple voltaic cell of copper (+) and zinc (−) electrodes. Note, hydrogen and metals are deposited on the electrode connected with the negative terminal of the cell. In silver-plating a mixture of silver cyanide and potassium cyanide is often used instead of silver nitrate as it gives a more uniform deposit.

possible to bring into a closed vessel the spark which induces hydrogen to combine with oxygen. One of the first tricks which was carried out with the electric battery was the converse operation of decomposing slightly acidified water. If the two free ends of pieces of wire connected with a battery are dipped into water containing a trace of acid, salt, or alkali, there is a brisk evolution of bubbles. Analysis shows that the bubbles from the free end connected with the positive pole (anode) of the battery are oxygen. Bubbles of hydrogen come off from the free end connected with the negative pole (kathode). It is easy to collect these bubbles (Fig. 258) and thus to show that when water decomposes the volume of hydrogen produced is twice as large as the volume of oxygen. Thus electricity makes it possible to establish the composition of water both by compelling its constituent elements to combine (*synthesis*) and by decomposing it into its constituent elements (*analysis*).

Further study revealed a very important division of chemical compounds. If the free ends of two pieces of wire are placed at the ends of a tube containing pure water a current does not pass along it. If some common salt is dissolved in the water, the tube conducts a current just as if it were a wire. This is not true of all soluble substances. Alcohol or sugar, for instance, do not make water conduct electricity. There is, however, a very large class of substances (called on that account *electrolytes*) which make water conduct. Acids, soluble salts, and alkalis, are electrolytes. When a current passes through a solution of an electrolyte, the latter always undergoes decomposition. The so-called decomposition of water by electricity is rather a complicated process resulting from the break up of the acid, etc., added to make the water conduct, and the reaction of the products of decomposition on the water itself.

Generally speaking, with weak solutions this is all that is obvious. Thus a very weak solution of table salt will electrolyse with the production of hydrogen and oxygen. On the other hand electrolysis of a very strong solution with a strong current will be accompanied by vigorous evolution of chlorine gas, which was first discovered in this way to be an element. The year 1807 may well rank as one of far greater importance to mankind than the year 1815 which we all remember. Davy then discovered that if a strong current is applied to a moist electrolyte it first melts, conducts electricity well, and decomposes in the process. He used solid caustic soda and caustic potash and found that in each case a new metal collected around the negative pole.

These two new metals—sodium and potassium—are essential elements of two of the oldest ingredients—salt and pot ashes—of a chemical economy, which had persisted from the Neolithic. The discovery of calcium from the electrolysis of its compounds which had been used in the manufacture of glass, the curing of leather, and the preparation of cement from remote antiquity, followed shortly after. All three metals had stubbornly refused to yield to the universal solvent of the Iron and Copper Age metallurgies. Their discovery announced the existence of a new agency in man's social life—the light metals, which cannot be separated by the traditional method of the blast furnace. Two things about these new light metals are specially important. One is that although they remained undiscovered so long, they include all the most abundant metals in the earth's *superficial* crust as far down as we can penetrate it. Living as we do in the twilight of the Iron Age, most of us think of iron as a very common metal, perhaps as the most common of the metals. This is wrong, as you will see at once when you stop to think about how much salt there is in the sea, or how much chalk in the cliffs.

Neither sodium nor calcium could replace iron for social use. Both metals oxidize rapidly in air, and combine with water to form their hydroxides, liberating hydrogen which catches fire. The reaction proceeds as represented in the equations:

$$2Na + 2H_2O \rightarrow 2NaOH + H_2$$
$$Ca + 2H_2O \rightarrow Ca(OH)_2 + H_2$$

Although the use of sodium, potassium, and calcium in the elementary state is confined to a limited number of processes, the light metals include elements which are just as durable as iron. With a small admixture of other metals they yield alloys which are as hard. The two most important are *magnesium* and *aluminium*. Both are extremely abundant, and are distributed universally. About 10 per cent of sea salt is the chloride of magnesium, a very deliquescent* compound which confers on common cooking salt its drying properties. So brine is a sufficient source, and the ocean contains a well-nigh inexhaustible store of it. Down to a depth of about twenty-five miles aluminium is estimated to be about twice as abundant as iron. In the more superficial layers of the earth's crust accessible to mining operations it is immensely more abundant than any other metal. Nations do not need to go to war to get aluminium and magnesium compounds. Aluminium is present in every scrap of ground we stand or build on. Common clay is mainly an aluminium salt—aluminium silicate. The Soviet Union have now mastered the technical difficulties of producing aluminium from clay on an industrial scale.

The last two decades have witnessed a veritable revolution in metallurgy through the electrochemical production of the two light metals As one American chemist puts it, we are passing out of the Iron Age which has lasted since about 1000 B.C., and are now on the threshold of the *Mag-Al Age*. A very good account of this development which was made possible by Davy's discovery is epitomized in the following citations from Mantell's book *Sparks from the Electrode* (pp. 64–78), written in 1931:

Aluminum is truly a metal of the modern age, for its development on a commercial scale has taken place within the memory of many now living. The Danish chemist Oersted in 1825 announced in a paper before the Royal Danish Academy of Sciences that he had produced aluminum "the metal of clay" . . . In 1845 at Göttingen, Wöhler made some of the metallic particles as large as big pinheads. In 1854 Sainte-Claire Deville, a Frenchman, announced a substitution of sodium metal for potassium in Wöhler's method and with the addition of common salt, or sodium chloride, to the aluminum chloride made a readily melted material which acted as a flux and caused the aluminum globules to run together. . . . Napoleon III, because he saw the possibilities of using the light metal aluminum for helmets and armour, aided Deville's work. Bars of aluminum were exhibited at the Paris Exposition in 1855. In 1856 the metal cost $100 a pound, and the year afterwards about $27 a pound. Two years later, because of improvements in the process, it was down to $17. . . . The Aluminium Company Ltd. at Oldbury near Birmingham, England, erected a works in 1888 using the Castner sodium process and the Deville aluminum method. Production reached 500 pounds a day and the metal was sold for about $4 a pound. . . . Charles Martin Hall, while still a student at Oberlin College, became interested in the problem of finding a cheaper method for producing aluminum. His imagination had been fired when he read of Deville's work and found the statement that every clay bank was a mine of aluminum, and that the metal was as costly as silver. He reasoned that aluminum oxide could be obtained cheaply and in the pure condition, but its melting point (2050° C.) was too high for it to be electrolyzed while in the

---

* I.e. capable of removing water vapour from the air and of dissolving in the moisture so formed.

molten condition. If he could but find a salt or material which would melt at a lower temperature and dissolve the alumina, or aluminum oxide, as sugar dissolves in water, he could electrolyze it in solution. This viewpoint was different from that of previous experimenters. He discovered that the mineral cryolite, found in large quantities in Greenland, when melted would dissolve alumina. The alumina in solution could be decomposed by the current to produce aluminum metal. . . . Ultimately he became acquainted with the men who organized the Pittsburg Reduction Company to operate his process. This organization eventually became the Aluminum Company of America. The hot molten cryolite and aluminum are quite destructive of material used for the furnace. Hall solved the problem by the use of an iron crucible or box lined with carbon. . . . The pot, as the workmen call the furnace, is thus a strong steel box, usually rectangular in shape and provided with a carbon lining 6 to 10 inches in thickness. Blocks of carbon dip into the molten bath. This consists of cryolite in which aluminum oxide is dissolved. The carbon lining and the pot itself constitute the cathode or negative pole. The alumina is broken up into aluminum metal which sinks to the bottom of the cell, and oxygen which rises to the top. . . . When enough aluminum forms, the tap hole is forced open and the aluminum drained from the cell into a ladle from which it is cast into its pig or ingot form. An aluminum plant consists of row upon row of these pots, each with its little indicator lamp to show the workman how the pot is functioning. The pots operate continuously through the bright hours of the day and the long hours of the night, the men working in shifts of eight hours. . . . The world production of aluminum had grown from 16 metric tons in 1886 to 19,800 tons in 1907. More than half of the growth had taken place from 1904 to 1907. By 1929 there had been an increase of 1300 per cent to an annual total of over 270,000 tons. In the same period, the production of iron had increased 60 per cent, that of lead less than 75 per cent, and zinc 100 per cent, while copper, the metal most largely used in electrical machinery and as such the principal competitor of aluminum, made a gain of 170 per cent. The possible growth of aluminum can be judged from the fact that the world produces about one-fifth as much aluminum as zinc, and 1/350 as much aluminum as iron. . . . Aluminum is an international metal, yet it has only become so within the last twenty-five years, for we find that five of the present Norwegian plants, all the Italian and Russian plants, all of those of Germany except one small one, two of those of Great Britain, five in France including the largest one there, and half the plants in the United States and Canada, came into existence in that period, while most of the previously existing works were made larger.

The same author gives the following account of the recent growth of the magnesium industry. Aluminium and magnesium are usually alloyed together and aid one another in their industrial activities, especially in connexion with aviation:

Although Bunsen, as far back as 1852, produced magnesium metal by electrolysis of its chloride, the first commercial plant using this method began operation only in 1886, in Germany. In America, the magnesium industry was not established until 1915, some thirty years later. Magnesium is one of the lightest metals and as such, or alloyed with other materials, it is becoming more widely used in industries such as aviation, automobile, railroad, structural, etc. From a pound of magnesium we can make a bar of the metal a

half inch square and 64 inches long, while such a bar from a pound of aluminum would be 42 inches long, and from steel only 14 inches long. A beam of magnesium, light enough in itself to be carried by one man, can yet support an automobile! A steel piece of similar size probably could not be lifted by even four men. The advantage of magnesium in the matter of weight alone, especially in aviation and building, makes its production worth the effort. . . . Only one American company has outlived the difficulties. That company entered the field because of an abundance of magnesium chloride which it desired to convert into useful and profitable material, and because of an increasing demand for magnesium in military pyrotechnics. It spent seven discouraging years in experimentation and development. . . . The low period of 1920 and 1921 slowed industry to the extent of again stopping production in order to dispose of stocks on hand. Meanwhile German manufacture of magnesium had flourished. The metal was imported into the United States in quantities, trebling the purchase of domestic magnesium during 1922, threatening to wipe out its manufacture here. Late 1921 saw a new start and the 1922 tariff protected the new industry. The last commercial plant now in operation can produce tons of metal per day, of the very high purity of $99 \cdot 9$ per cent. An improved process goes on smoothly and economically. Appreciation of the many possibilities for this very light metal and its alloys has increased demand. In recent years the total American consumption was over 500,000 pounds. Aviation, automobile, railroad, structural, and metallurgical industries are increasing their use of magnesium. . . . Magnesium furnaces consist of large rectangular cast steel pots holding several tons of melted magnesium chloride. The pot serves as a cathode; inserted in the top of the molten contents and suspended vertically are the graphite anodes. The magnesium deposits at the cathode. Being lighter than the bath, it rises to the top and, while protected from oxidation by a top crust on the cell, flows to a collecting chamber outside the cell proper. The metal is removed daily. . .
With development of processes and markets, magnesium prices have tumbled from $5.00 per pound in 1915 when some 80,000 pounds were produced, to $1.00 a pound in 1924, 48 cents in 1930 when over a million pounds were made, and 30 cents a pound in 1931. It will be remembered that the magnesium is made from magnesium chloride obtained from salt brines.

The countries which export aluminium are countries with abundant hydroelectric power. If you turn the leaves of any good chemistry book, like Mellor's *Inorganic Chemistry*, you will find that dozens of electrolytic processes have been patented for the chemical industry. In the Castner process, for instance, brine is decomposed to produce caustic soda by reaction between the water and the sodium liberated at the kathode, while pure chlorine gas is collected at the anode. This is a straightforward application of the discovery Davy himself made. Yet the furnaces of the Leblanc process (p. 436) for making alkalis continued to pollute the landscape till our own generation. Although there is an electrolytic method available for a vast number of mineral products, it is still true to say the only substances exclusively produced by electrical methods are those which like aluminium and magnesium cannot be produced in any other way. The reason for this is that existing chemical industry has its historic roots in a coal economy of private enterprise which had no social plan for the co-ordinated use of scientific knowledge. It was lack of science which took people away from the watermills of England's green and pleasant land, and forced them to where coal and iron were found together. Science can do more with the power that drives the watermill than with a blast furnace. We shall be making the fullest use of it when we pass out of the age of coal and iron into the age of hydroelectricity and light metals.

Within the framework of private enterprise the chief effect of new theoretical knowledge on metallurgical practice of the nineteenth century was to conserve the pre-existing economy of the heavy metals. The history of steel production is told in *Our Mineral Civilization* by Thomas T. Read.

Iron is found all over the earth in the form of iron oxide and the metal can be made from the oxide by heating it with carbon. . . . That will produce soft iron, with the impurities that were in the ore embedded in the iron. By hammering it while it is hot they can be gotten rid of fairly well, and a skilful person can hammer the iron into almost any desired shape. The difficulty is that it remains soft, too soft to be of much practical use. Nor can it be melted down and cast, for the melting point of pure iron, around 2700° F., was far above the reach of the early metallurgists. The early workers were clever, however, and they eventually found out how to harden iron. They made the soft metal, worked it by hammering into the shape desired, heated it for a while buried in carbon, and then took it out and plunged it into water or oil. If they did it just right they could made it as hard as a modern razor blade. Of course they did not know why it happened. . . . Now we understand that the carbon of the fuel bed slowly soaks into the hot iron, much as moisture soaks into wood. Iron with carbon dissolved in it has the property of becoming hard when chilled from a red heat. . . . Since the carbon soaked in from the outside a skilful smith could make a sword with a hard edge and a tough body that was an excellent weapon. They could make good steel, but they could not make it in large quantities and it was quite expensive. Meanwhile the early metallurgists had learned how to melt iron. If they used a blast and increased the depth of the fuel bed they could produce melted metal, though it hardly seemed like iron, for when it was cold it was as brittle as glass. They could cast it, however, and much of the iron used before 1750 was cast iron. We know now that when made in this way the iron takes up as much as 3·5 per cent of carbon and its melting point is lowered some 500°F., though still far above that of bronze. At the beginning of our century of progress this kind of iron was still universally made in furnaces that had a capacity of six tons per day. . . . Steel was still made from the soft iron and only on a small scale. What Bessemer learned to do, in 1856, was to produce steel from the melted hard iron by blowing air through it; in 20 minutes he could convert 15 tons of the hard, brittle metal into steel soft enough to be rolled, yet much stronger than the pure soft iron. Now it was possible to produce the kind of metal needed for building railroads, in large quantities and at a low price. The process was introduced in this country in 1865. The total iron production of the country in 1864 was about a million tons; ten years later it was more than 2½ million tons and twenty years later about 5 million tons. Sixty years later it was about 40 million tons. For many years after its introduction the Bessemer process was the principal way of making steel. Contemporaneous with it was another process, known as the open-hearth, that at first seemed less advantageous, since it required more fuel and had less capacity. . . . This other process could not only handle metal made from any kind of ore, but the steel was of better quality. By 1907 more steel was made by the open-hearth process than by the Bessemer, and by 1929 seven times as much.

The production of steel on a large scale intensified research into the influence which elements other than carbon exercise on the physical properties of iron. Read tells us:

One of the things thus learned was that nickel, chromium, tungsten, and some other metals, if added to steel, make it stronger without making it brittle, as carbon does. Long, careful, and painstaking work was needed, because the effects produced by different amounts are surprisingly different. . . . With nickel . . . by using between 2 and 4 per cent the tensile strength of the steel is increased about 6,000 pounds per square inch for each per cent of nickel added, it is also more resistant to rusting and abrasion. . . . Above 10 per cent nickel the steel, instead of getting harder when heated and chilled, gets softer. Steel containing 13 per cent nickel is tremendously strong, but so hard it cannot be cut or drilled. At 24 per cent nickel the alloy becomes non-magnetic, and from that up to 32 per cent it has a high resistance to the passage of the electric current. . . . At 36 per cent nickel the alloy develops another curious property; it does not expand and contract with changes in the temperature, fitting it for special uses, such as measuring tapes. The wires that lead in through the glass of an electric light bulb are made from a 38 per cent nickel iron alloy plated with copper. They expand and contract at the same rate as the glass and consequently do not crack away from it. At 78 per cent nickel its magnetic permeability becomes exceedingly high. . . . The practical importance of such special qualities is seen in a recent estimate that the electrical transformers now in use in the United States waste about ten billion kilowatt-hours of energy annually in useless heat. Half of this could be saved if the nickel-iron alloy (50 per cent) which has the combination of highest permeability and lowest hysteresis loss were used in their construction. Chromium makes steel hard. Files contain about 0·5 per cent of it, axes and hammers and chains up to nearly 1 per cent. Balls and rollers for bearings are probably the most important use for chromium steel. . . . Armour plate for battleships, which typically has about 4 per cent nickel and 2 per cent chromium, is an important use, but the nickel-chromium steels that enter most directly into the lives of ordinary people are those employed in motor-car building. . . The front axle must be strong and tough, and so will usually contain nickel; the hardness necessary in the bearings will be provided by chromium, and so on. Formerly motor cars were trimmed with nickel-plated iron. . . . Some of the cheaper cars have substituted an iron-nickel-chromium alloy that is highly resistant to tarnish and almost silver-white in colour. This belongs to the group of alloys, of recent devising, that are popularly known by the somewhat ungrammatical name of stainless steel. The various companies that produce this material apply different trade names to it; but the material always contains about 18 per cent chromium and 8 per cent nickel. . . . For many uses steel can be protected by dipping it in melted tin or zinc, and for others it is plated with nickel or chromium. These recent developments have not only produced a metal that is truly resistant to corrosion (there are also rustless cast irons) but have led to the production of special alloys having a remarkable resistance to the attack of almost any reagent, including strong acids. An important alloy that has not yet been mentioned is that with tungsten. That metal when mixed with iron not only makes a hard steel but one that stays hard even when red hot, when all other varieties of steel soften. Modern boring and cutting machines were previously limited in speed by ability to keep the tool cool, as it gets hot when working and as soon as it heats up loses its edge. A great deal of work, done over a long period of years, has disclosed that about

18 per cent tungsten with 3·5 per cent chromium gives the best results. . . . Vanadium and molybdenum are two other metals that improve steel quality. Vanadium produces much the same effect as nickel, but a much smaller amount is required. Chrome-vanadium steels are used in an important way in the driving axles and other forgings of locomotives, automobile springs and axles, gun forgings and many other purposes. Molybdenum-vanadium steels have proved valuable for making centrifugally cast guns.

To this it may be added that 13 per cent manganese makes a steel which is highly non-magnetic, and as such suitable for the manufacture of bulkheads for ships. It does not acquire the feeble magnetism induced by the vertical (dip) component of the earth's field (see p. 637), and hence forestalls the compass-bias which may arise therefrom. Notable progress has been made recently in the discovery of new lead alloys. The addition of less than 1 per cent of cadmium and tin makes lead as hard as copper. Lead itself may now be removed from the category of "heavy" metals, since it is quite easy to prepare it from its ores by electrolytic decomposition. We are only at the threshold of discovering what remarkable new physical properties are conferred by the introduction of relatively small quantities of different metals in alloys. Progress already accomplished points the way to a new potential ·of local self-sufficiency.

(*b*) *Catalysis.*—A second technique which chemistry developed during the nineteenth century has touched industry still less, though it may hold even more spectacular possibilities for a rationally planned future of human existence. Some reactions which otherwise require the expenditure of considerable energy can be induced to proceed rapidly by adding small quantities of substances which do not participate appreciably in the final products. They act as it were as *lubricants*. This lubricating action is called in a general way *catalysis*, and the lubricant is called a *catalyst*. The physical nature of the process is not necessarily the same in all reactions described by the term. Its use lies in directing attention to the social importance of encouraging reactions with the minimum expenditure of effort. Thus, if starch is boiled continuously with dilute acids it is gradually broken down into grape sugar (dextrose). The same result can be brought about by simply adding a small quantity of malt extract and leaving it in a warm place. What the acid accomplishes with the expenditure of relatively much fuel to supply heat, the extract can do at a much lower level of energy consumption.

An example of the production of an inorganic reaction by catalysis is the union of hydrogen and oxygen in presence of finely divided platinum (gas lighters may be so made) without sparking. In industry the *contact* process for making sulphuric acid is to pass the gas SO_2, formed by burning sulphur in air, with air over vanadium oxide—this helps to oxidize it to SO_3, which dissolves in water forming H_2SO_4. In the *Deacon* process for making chlorine the union of HCl and oxygen is promoted by passing HCl and air over pumice soaked in copper chloride at a comparatively low temperature.

There are vast untapped resources for further industrial development by developing the natural catalysts called ferments or *enzymes*. The decomposition of starch in the presence of malt illustrates one step in two very ancient industrial processes which were not understood fully until comparatively recent times. Beer and Spirits provide an example of a chemical industry which is largely empirical, like photography. Probably the earliest liquors were prepared from fruit juices which ferment spontaneously, being nearly always infected with wild strains of the micro-organism *yeast*. This breaks down sugar into alcohol with liberation of CO_2. The production of the former is the reason for adding yeast to malted grain. The production of the latter is the reason for using yeast to raise bread. In the making of beer, grain is soaked and kept warm till it begins to germinate. This allows a catalyst or enzyme called *diastase* (like one present in our own saliva) to convert the starchy content of the grain to sugar. The germinating grain is dried and the extract of the dried matter (malt) may be used as a source of diastase to convert potato starch into sugar as mentioned. In the nineties of the last century it was shown that crushed yeast in which there are no living organisms yields an extract which will catalyse the breakdown of sugar into alcohol just as well as the living organism.

(c) *Spectroscopy*.—A third technique has proved to be of great theoretical and practical importance in so far as it has led to the discovery of new elements, which now play a part in familiar features of our daily life. It will be mentioned briefly, because the discoveries which resulted from its use will be dealt with elsewhere. In Chapter III it was stated that a pinch of salt tints the non-luminous flame of a gas fire yellow. This you can easily see for yourself. Similarly, as you can also see for yourself, a copper salt will tint it bluish green. Compounds of the few elements which intensely colour a flame are used in making fireworks. Potassium salts give a violet flame. Calcium salts give a brick-red flame. The closely allied element strontium gives a brilliant crimson flame. Barium gives a beautiful apple green.

When we examine spectroscopically a flame which has been made luminous by particles of a pure chemical we find that it shows no continuous gradation from red to blue. It is composed of a few isolated bright lines. They are in the yellow region if a sodium salt is used. Although few elements, like the foregoing, give a highly characteristic luminosity to a non-luminous flame, they all exhibit bright line spectra. During the fifties it was noted that the position of the bright lines in the spectrum of an element is characteristic of the element, and the spectrum of a compound is simply a collection of all the lines characteristic of its constituent elements. Another interesting fact about the spectra of elements is that when a luminous flame with a continuous spectrum (white-hot body) is screened by a cold elementary gas, the continuous spectrum is interrupted by black lines in the same position as the bright lines which would make up the spectrum of the gas if it were incandescent. It had long been noticed that the spectrum of sunlight is crossed by dark lines. It was now possible to recognize that many of these lines correspond to the dark lines of "absorption" spectra of familiar earthly elements, as if the incandescent mass of the sun were screened by an envelope of relatively colder matter in the gaseous state. There were also other lines, and one particularly prominent one, called the *helium* line (from the Greek word for the sun). These did not correspond to any element then known.

The helium which is now used in dirigibles and the neon of neon lamps were both known to exist and named before they had been found in our own world. We shall return to them later. The horizon of theoretical knowledge about the structure of the universe, the age and composition of the stars, and so forth, unfolded by the spectroscope is one of the most fascinating romances of modern science. If you are inclined to overlook the social considerations which have encouraged research with the spectroscope, remember your sky-signs. Several terrestrial metals were first discovered with the spectroscope, e.g. rubidium, caesium, thallium, indium, scandium. Aside from leading to the discovery of new elements, the spectroscope has a more immediate utility. It provides the most sensitive gauge of the purity of chemical products. It will detect the presence of about a hundred millionth of a gram of sodium chloride.

LATER DEVELOPMENTS OF ATOMIC THEORY

The prestige and usefulness of the atomic theory was reinforced during the latter half of the nineteenth century by the recognition of three important principles: the Law of Pressure in Solution (or *osmosis*), the Law of Chemical Equilibrium (or Mass Action), and the construction of the Periodic Table of Elements.

(a) *The Law of Pressure in Solution* (or *Osmosis*).—While Avogadro's principle provided the means of setting a standard of atomic weight, it was limited in its application to substances which are gaseous or volatilize with comparative ease. One of the most important theoretical developments in the next half century, emerging incidentally through study of the ascent of sap in plants, led to the discovery of an analogous principle which applies to all substances in aqueous solution. In everyday life we are familiar with many examples of a common feature which matter displays when dispersed in the gaseous state or in a solvent. We all know with what rapidity an odour "diffuses" in a closed space, and most of us have observed the colour diffusing of its own accord through a perfectly still tumbler of water, when a crystal of potassium permanganate is dropped in it. In certain circumstances the phenomenon of diffusion can result in the production of differences in pressure. The laws of solution pressure which describe such phenomena are precisely analogous to the laws of gas pressure discovered by Boyle, Marriotte, and Charles.

Pressure differences arising from diffusion can be studied by obstructing the process with porous membranes (Fig. 259). Lighter gases pass more rapidly than heavy ones through a porous membrane, e.g. unglazed porcelain (like the porous pot of an old-fashioned electric bell battery). If, therefore, two gases of different density are separated by a porous partition, the more rapid passage of the lighter one through the partition results in an excess of molecules on one side. Since equal volumes of different gases at the same temperature and pressure contain an equal number of molecules, the result prescribed by Avogadro's principle is that the volume of gas on one side should be greater than on the other. This cannot happen if the walls are closed. So, as we should expect, a difference in pressure is produced. The difference is easily demonstrated by connecting the open end of a porous pot with a U-tube of mercury. If the porous pot is surrounded by hydrogen which is less dense than air there is a gradual increase of pressure in the pot. If it is surrounded by carbon dioxide, which is more dense, there is a gradual fall of pressure. One of the methods by which the separation of gaseous substances can be brought about is repeated diffusion by use of this principle.

An essentially similar apparatus will serve to demonstrate the somewhat analogous phenomenon of pressure in solution or *osmosis*. The porous pot and the limb of the U-tube connected with it are filled with water, and the gas chamber with a solution of table sugar, or conversely the solution is used to fill the porous pot, etc., and the outer chamber is filled with water. Iu the

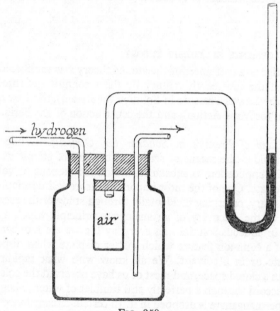

FIG. 259

Positive pressure resulting from the more rapid diffusion of hydrogen into the porous pot than of air passing out of it.

first case, there is a gradual decrease of pressure, in the second a slow rise. In experiments such as these the pressure registered by the pressure gauge reaches a maximum or minimum, and the mercury returns to its previous level when the gases or dissolved substances are equally distributed on both sides of the partition.

Experiment shows that some membranes easily allow light gases or dissolved substances with small molecules to pass through them, but almost completely exclude larger and heavier ones. So it is possible to maintain a steady pressure by using a membrane which allows the passage of only one constituent (Fig. 260). If a porous pot is filled with copper sulphate solution and plunged into a solution of potassium ferrocyanide, the pores are coated with copper ferrocyanide. Water can still diffuse freely through its walls, but alcohol cannot appreciably traverse the film of copper ferrocyanide. If the temperature is kept constant the pressure inside a porous pot filled with a watery solution of alcohol and surrounded by pure water rises to a definite level, and remains fairly steady.

The steady level varies in a definite way with the strength of the solution. The pressure attained is directly proportional to the concentration. If the temperature is varied and the concentration of the dissolved substance is kept the same, the pressure is directly proportional to the *absolute* temperature. The rule for osmotic pressure thus corresponds to the law of gases

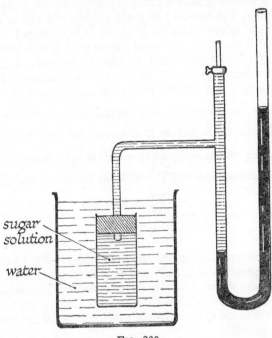

FIG. 260

Measurement of osmotic pressure of a sugar solution surrounded by water only.

discovered by Charles (p. 425). Boyle's law (p. 387) states that the volume of a gas is inversely proportional to its pressure. When the same mass of gaseous material is compressed into a small volume, the mass per unit volume or concentration of the gas increases proportionately. That is to say the volume of a given mass is inversely proportional to the concentration. Hence the concentration is directly proportional to the pressure. Thus the law of osmotic pressure for soluble organic compounds like alcohol or sugar is precisely analogous to Boyle's law of gas pressure.

The chemical importance of this depends on a connexion between Avogadro's theory and the physical properties of gases. The two laws of Boyle and Charles can be combined in a single statement with one constant K:

$$pv = KT$$

The constant K depends on the quantity of gas used. If the temperature is constant throughout an experiment KT is constant, and the equation is the same as Boyle's law. If v is kept constant $p \div T$ is constant; or if p is constant, $v \div T$ is constant, and the equation is equivalent to Charles' law. Avogadro's hypothesis asserts that when the pressure and temperature is the same, equal volumes of all gases contain the same number of molecules. This leads us to suspect that the constant K will be the same for all gases, if a suitable quantity of gas is chosen.

As it stands, the formula $pv = KT$ is only useful for calculation when we are dealing with some fixed quantity of gas subjected to different pressures and temperatures. The suitable unit is the product of 1 unit of mass and the molecular weight of the substance. If the mass is measured in grams, it is called the mol. Thus one mol of water vapour is 18 grams, one mol of ethyl alcohol (C_2H_5OH) is 46 grams, and one mol of hydrogen is 2 grams. If W is the weight of a litre of gas at 273° on the absolute scale (p. 425), i.e. at 0° C. and at 1 atmosphere pressure (760 mm. of mercury), the volume occupied by 1 gram at the same temperature and pressure is $\dfrac{1}{W}$ litres. Since 1 mol of a substance of molecular weight M is M grams, the volume occupied by one mol is $\dfrac{M}{W}$. So the volume occupied by n mols is $\dfrac{nM}{W}$, when $p = 1$ if pressure is measured in *atmospheres*, and T = 273. We can then put for $pv = KT$

$$1 \times \frac{nM}{W} = K \times 273$$

$$\therefore \ K = \frac{nM}{273W} \qquad \cdots \qquad \text{(i)}$$

Avogadro's hypothesis tells us that any fixed volume—e.g. 1 litre, of any gas at a fixed temperature—e.g. 273°, and at a fixed pressure—e.g. 1 "*atmo*" pressure—contains the same number (N) of molecules. The weight (W) of one litre of which every molecule weighs m grams is Nm, and since the molecular weight (M) is the ratio of the weight of a molecule (m) of the gas to that of an atom of hydrogen (h),

$$m = Mh$$

$$\therefore \ W = NMh \qquad \cdots \qquad \text{(ii)}$$

Combining both results—(i) and (ii)

$$K = n\left(\frac{1}{273Nh}\right) \qquad \cdots \qquad \text{(iii)}$$

In the last expression h, the weight of a hydrogen atom, is a fixed quantity. N, the number of molecules in 1 litre of any gas at 273° and one atmosphere pressure, is always the same, if Avogadro is right. So

$$\frac{1}{273Nh} = \text{constant}$$

This constant is usually written R, and hence (iii) can be written

$$K = nR$$

$$\therefore \ pv = nRT \qquad \cdots \qquad \text{(iv)}$$

If N, the number of molecules in a litre of different gases at the same temperature and pressure, were not the same, the constant R would be different for different gases. According to Avogadro's hypothesis the constant R is therefore the same for all gases, and the formula $pv = nRT$ applies to all gases. Experiment shows that this is true in agreement with theory. So, if we know the weight (W) of one litre of the gas and hence how many (n) mols (i.e. $W \div M$) of gas we are using, we can calculate (a) the volume it will occupy at a given temperature or pressure; (b) the pressure which a given volume will exert at a given temperature; or (c) the temperature a given volume must have to exert a given pressure. To do this we need to know the numerical value of R, for which we only need to know the volume occupied by one mol of a gas at a fixed pressure and temperature. One mol (32 grams) of oxygen at one atmo and $273°$ T occupies $22 \cdot 4$ litres.

$$1 \times 22 \cdot 4 = R \times 273$$
$$R = \frac{22 \cdot 4}{273} = 0 \cdot 082$$

For a solution of fixed concentration the number of mols (n) per unit volume is a fixed quantity. So the law of osmotic pressure can also be expressed in the form:

$$pv = n \times \text{constant} \times T \quad . \quad . \quad . \quad . \quad . \quad \text{(v)}$$

Since alcohol volatilizes readily we can find its density and hence its molecular weight (M). Hence we know how many mols $\left(n = \dfrac{W}{M} \right)$ correspond to a given weight (W) in a given volume (v) of solution of known concentration. Experiment shows that the constant in the formula (iv) for solutions *has the same numerical value as the gas constant* (R). This means that if we know the strength of a solution of known molecular weight we can calculate the osmotic pressure it exerts at a fixed temperature. Thus to find the osmotic pressure of 5 per cent (grams per 100 c.c.) alcohol (molecular weight = 46) at $10°$ C. ($283°$ T) we first calculate n. The weight of alcohol in 1 litre (1,000 c.c.) of a 5 per cent solution is 50 grams. Hence $n = 50 \div 46 = 1 \cdot 09$. Thus we may write for

$$pv = nRT$$
$$p \times 1 = 1 \cdot 09 \times 0 \cdot 082 \times 283$$
$$\therefore \quad p = 25 \cdot 2 \text{ atmospheres}$$

This tremendous pressure which a 5 per cent solution of alcohol can exert will help you to see how the roots of trees are able to split rocks.

Once this principle has been established by experiment we can use it to calculate the molecular weight of a substance by the pressure it exerts in solution. For instance, suppose we find that a $0 \cdot 1$ per cent solution of the nitrogenous substance *urea* found in urine exerts an osmotic pressure of $0 \cdot 42$ atmospheres at $27°$ C. (or $300°$ abs.). If there are n mols of urea in 1 litre we can put for

$$pv = nRT$$
$$0 \cdot 42 \times 1 = n \times 0 \cdot 082 \times 300$$
$$\therefore \quad n = \frac{7}{410} \text{ or approximately } \frac{1}{60}$$

The actual weight of urea in one litre of 0·1 per cent (grams per 100 c.c.) solution is 1 gram. The number of mols in one litre is the actual weight divided by the molecular weight (W ÷ M). Hence

$$\frac{1}{M} = \frac{7}{410}$$

$$\therefore \quad M = \text{(approx.)} \; 60$$

Although the molecular weight of volatile water-soluble organic substances like alcohol, determined by the method of osmotic pressure, agrees with the result obtained by measuring the density of its vapour, the same is not true of volatile water-soluble mineral products like hydrochloric acid gas. In comparatively dilute solutions the values calculated from the osmotic pressure of substances of the latter class are almost an exact multiple of the true molecular weight based on the measurement of their density. Seemingly the new law lets us down.

Experience shows that some of the most fruitful advances of science have occurred when mere logic does let us down. When a hypothesis fits some facts and fails to fit others, careful study of the exceptions often leads to important discoveries. The broad distinction between two classes of substances, some which obey the gas laws in solution and others which do not appear to do so, corresponds to another broad distinction which we can make between the general characteristics of the common reactions of typical organic and inorganic substances (excluding the metallic salts of the organic acids) in solution. The solutions of substances like alcohol or sugar do not conduct an electric current and their reactions take place slowly and usually require some "catalyst" to help them. The solutions of substances like caustic soda, hydrochloric acid, or Epsom salts, readily conduct an electric current, and react almost instantaneously if at all. Furthermore, the passage of an electric current through a conducting solution is always accompanied by chemical decomposition, which also occurs if a current is passed through the molten inorganic compounds in the dry state. The decomposition of a salt always results in concentrating the acidic constituent where the current flows from the positive pole of the battery, and the basic or metallic constituent where the current flows out of the solution by the electrode connected to the negative pole.

We shall see more clearly when we study electricity that the power of solutions to conduct the electric current can receive a satisfactory explanation, if we assume that the molecules of substances like sodium chloride break down, when dissolved in water, into two or more electrically conducting sub-molecules or *ions*. According to this view a solution of such substances is an equilibrium between the number of parent molecules and the number of submolecules. A substance like potassium carboante in solution is thus a mixture of non-conducting molecules of K_2CO_3 and conducting submolecules or *ions* K and CO_3. In very dilute solution all the K_2CO_3 breaks down, so that there are three submolecules for each parent molecule, and the osmotic pressure of one *mol* of K_2CO_3 per litre is the total pressure exerted by one mol per litre of each of the three submolecules, i.e.

it is three times what it would be if the parent molecule did not "*dissociate*." At any particular concentration the discrepancy between the observed osmotic pressure and that calculated on the assumption that the molecule is stable, tells us at once how much of the molecule is broken up in this way.

Thus the osmotic pressure of a substance like sodium chloride can be used to determine its molecular weight although it does not obey the gas laws so simply as does alcohol. The percentage composition of sodium chloride shows that it contains approximately 61 per cent of chlorine and therefore 39 per cent of sodium. The ratio of the weights of sodium and chlorine 39 : 61 is thus the same as the ratio of their atomic weights 23 : 35·5. Therefore the molecule of sodium chloride must contain the same number of atoms of sodium and chlorine. If the number is 1 the molecular weight would be 58·5, and since it must break up into an even number of ions the molecular weight calculated from its osmotic pressure in *very dilute* solution will be 2, 4, 6 or some even multiple of 58·5. Actually the value obtained is about 117. The true molecular weight of the undissociated molecule is some even submultiple of 117. Since the first submultiple is the lowest value (58·5) it can have, this must be its molecular weight.

(b) *The Law of Equilibrium* (or Mass Action).—The classical philosophers spoke of the principles of love and hate when we should refer to attraction and repulsion in mechanical occurrences. Remains of this anthropomorphic conception lingered in the ideas of chemical affinity which nineteenth-century chemists inherited from the alchemists. A reaction occurred because the reacting substances had affinity for one another, and decomposition was an American divorce. Like the Aristotelian doctrine of gravitation this is nothing more than an obituary notice on the fact after it has occurred. The business of science is to tell us *how* to make a reaction occur.

Early experiments on respiration put the issues in a more tangible form, though it was long before they were clearly understood. In Priestley's experiments the bright red oxyhaemoglobin assumed the dull purple of venous blood when oxygen was pumped off. Venous blood reassumed its bright arterial colour when shaken up with oxygen. If he had noted the change more carefully he would have observed that the change in colour is gradual. After the pressure in the vessel has been reduced to a certain point there is a corresponding shade of colour for each further reduction or increase. Hence the direction of the reaction depends on the quantity of reacting substances.

Other early enquiries point to this. Black showed that when chalk is heated it becomes lime through loss of carbon dioxide. The lime is water-soluble, and lime water itself deposits chalk when CO_2 is passed into it. We can put for the reaction in the lime kiln,

$$chalk \rightarrow fixed\ air + lime$$

The reaction in a beaker of lime water is:

$$fixed\ air + lime \rightarrow chalk$$

What is it that decides whether we make the arrow point from right to left, as it occurs in the lime kiln, or from left to right as in the beaker of lime water? There is clearly nothing absolute about the affinity of the reacting substances.

Take again an analogous change. If steam is passed over heated iron, the iron oxidizes and hydrogen is carried off in the steam, i.e.

$$3Fe + 4H_2O \rightarrow Fe_3O_4 + 4H_2$$

iron + steam → iron oxide + hydrogen

On the other hand a stream of hydrogen passed over the oxide reduces it to the metal with the formation of water vapour which is carried off in the stream of hydrogen, i.e.

$$Fe_3O_4 + 4H_2 \rightarrow 4H_2O + 3Fe$$

iron oxide + hydrogen → steam + iron

One significant feature is common to both examples. From the lime kiln the carbon dioxide escapes into the air. In the beaker the chalk, being insoluble, escapes from the water. When iron oxidizes in a stream of water vapour, the hydrogen escapes as it is formed. When the reverse reaction occurs the water vapour is carried off as soon as it appears. This means that to make the reaction go in the way prescribed one of the reagents has to be *in excess*.

How much in excess is a very practical problem for chemical manufacture, because the yield depends upon it. A chemical reaction is like a see-saw or lever, which can swing up or down. The problem of economical chemistry is to find *where* we have to put the weight to make it go down or up. Like the problem of constructing a weighing machine, it is a matter of discovering the law of equilibrium, and the simple rule that *nothing succeeds like excess* suggests a more precise principle which underlies chemical reaction. Suppose that you heat n molecules of iron oxide with y molecules of hydrogen till x molecules of iron oxide have been converted into iron. Since

$$Fe_3O_4 + 4H_2 \rightarrow 3Fe + 4H_2O$$
$$\therefore \quad xFe_3O_4 + 4xH_2 \rightarrow 3xFe + 4xH_2O$$

So if no further change occurs when x molecules of iron oxide have been changed, we have complete equilibrium when there are $(y - 4x)$ molecules of hydrogen left, i.e. when the actual number of molecules of each kind is represented by

$$[(n - x)Fe_3O_4 + (y - 4x)H_2] + [3xFe + 4xH_2O]$$

Any more hydrogen added will be in excess, and excess means that more iron oxide can be broken down, i.e. there will now be *less* than $(n - x)$ molecules of iron oxide if there are *more* than $(y - 4x)$ molecules of hydrogen. So the quantities of iron oxide and hydrogen in equilibrium with one another are inversely proportional. Similarly, more steam added in excess means that more iron will be oxidized. If there are more than $4x$ molecules of steam there will have to be less than $3x$ molecules of iron. Hence the quantities of steam and iron are inversely proportional.

If a molecules of iron oxide, b molecules of hydrogen, c molecules of steam, and d molecules of iron, are in equilibrium, the principle of excess suggests

$$ab = \text{constant}$$
$$cd = \text{constant}$$
$$\therefore \quad \frac{ab}{cd} = \text{constant}$$

To test this rule it is not necessary to be able to measure the actual number of molecules with which we are dealing. Suppose we have x mols of a substance A of molecular weight M, since 1 mol is M grams, x mols = xM grams. Similarly, y mols of a substance B whose molecular weight is N weigh yN grams. Hence

$$\frac{\text{wt of A}}{\text{wt of B}} = \frac{xM}{yN}$$

If there are m molecules of A the weight of A is mM times the weight of an atom of hydrogen, and that of B is nN times the weight of an atom of hydrogen. Hence

$$\frac{\text{wt of A}}{\text{wt of B}} = \frac{mM}{nN}$$

Thus $x \div y = m \div n$. In other words, the numbers of molecules are in the same ratio as the weights of the reacting substances, when the unit of weight for each substance is the *mol*. One example will show you how the principle is tested and applied.

If ethyl alcohol is boiled with acetic acid, the two substances combine to form a fragrant volatile compound, called ethyl acetate, and water. Conversely if ethyl acetate and water are boiled, decomposition to form alcohol and acid occurs. In either case the reaction is partial. The chemical equation which describes it is

$$\underset{\text{(ethyl alcohol)}}{C_2H_5OH} + \underset{\text{(acetic acid)}}{CH_3COOH} \leftrightarrows \underset{\text{(ethyl acetate)}}{CH_3COO \cdot C_2H_5} + \underset{\text{(water)}}{H_2O}$$

The molecular weights of the substances reading rom left to right are therefore 46, 60, 88, 18. Experiment shows that when 46 grams of alcohol (1 mol) are heated with 60 grams of acetic acid (1 mol), combination continues till $15\frac{1}{3}$ grams of alcohol ($\frac{1}{3}$ mol) and 20 grams of acetic acid ($\frac{1}{3}$ mol) are left. Conversely if 88 grams of ethyl acetate and 18 grams of water are heated, decomposition occurs until $58\frac{2}{3}$ grams ($\frac{2}{3}$ mol) of acetate and 12 grams ($\frac{2}{3}$ mol) of water are left. The end result is the same, i.e. we are left with

$\frac{1}{3}$ mol alcohol + $\frac{1}{3}$ mol acetic acid $\rightleftarrows$ $\frac{2}{3}$ mol ethyl acetate + $\frac{2}{3}$ mol water

Applying the principle of equilibrium

$$\frac{\frac{1}{3} \times \frac{1}{3}}{\frac{2}{3} \times \frac{2}{3}} = \text{constant}$$
$$\therefore \quad \text{constant} = \frac{1}{4}$$

If the rule is true, as experiment proves, we can now deduce what yield we shall get if we boil 120 grams or 2 mols of acetic acid with 1 mol of alcohol. If x mols of each combine, we have $(2 - x)$ mols of acetic acid, $(1 - x)$ mols of alcohol, x of acetate and x of water at the end. This will be the end of the reaction if

$$\frac{(2 - x)(1 - x)}{x \cdot x} = \frac{1}{4}$$

i.e. $x = \frac{5}{6} = 0\cdot 845$

Hence equilibrium occurs when $0\cdot 845$ mols of alcohol and acetic acid have combined. Thus the yield of acetate for the same quantity of alcohol is two and a half times as great as when an equal amount of acetic acid is used. The rule therefore tells you how much acetic acid is required to make the best use of a fixed quantity of alcohol or how much alcohol must be used if we have a limited quantity of acetic acid from which to manufacture ethyl acetate. To apply it to any reaction, it is only necessary to make one exact analysis of the quantities of all the ingredients, when the reaction has gone on till no further change occurs. From the figures obtained, we can then deduce the value of the constant which is characteristic of the particular process.

It is often possible to tell how a reaction will proceed without determining the actual value of the equilibrium constant. If one of the constituents of a reaction is removed as the reaction proceeds, more of another must be formed to keep all the products in proper proportion. Hence combination or decomposition continues till one of the essential ingredients is used up. This at once explains why in the early commercial preparation of alkalis the reaction between sulphuric acid and common salt proceeds as follows:

$$2NaCl + H_2SO_4 \rightarrow Na_2SO_4 + 2HCl\uparrow$$

Whereas the reaction between barium chloride and sodium sulphate proceeds

$$BaCl_2 + Na_2SO_4 \rightarrow BaSO_4\downarrow + 2NaCl$$

In the first reaction HCl removes itself, because it is *volatile*, i.e. a gas. More sodium sulphate has to be formed to take its place till all the sulphuric acid is used up. In the second reaction, barium sulphate removes itself, because it is *insoluble*. So more sodium chloride is continually formed to take its place till all the sodium sulphate is used up.

Even if none of the constituents is precipitated, or gaseous at ordinary temperatures, it is still possible to carry the reaction to completion if the end product desired has a much lower boiling point than the other liquid reagent. For example, in Glauber's reaction for the preparation of nitric acid:

$$NaNO_3 + H_2SO_4 \rightarrow NaHSO_4 + HNO_3\uparrow$$

the mixture is heated gently to drive off the nitric acid (b.p. 86° C.), but the sulphuric acid (b.p. 330° C.) remains till the process is completed.

(c) *The Periodic Law.*—About the time when Mendel and Darwin were directing their attention to the problem of evolution in living organisms, a generalization which has an important bearing on the evolution of inorganic matter was put forward by Newlands in England, by Lothar Meyer in Germany, and by Mendeljeff in Russia. It is called the Periodic Law.

Before evolutionary ideas in chemistry or biology could take root, a thorough reclassification of the differences and similarities of the various species of inorganic and living matter had to be accomplished. In comparing the properties of the elements and their compounds, certain similarities were recognized very early. For instance, the metals sodium and potassium attack water liberating hydrogen with the formation of a soluble hydroxide. Unlike most others, the three metals calcium, strontium, and barium form strongly alkaline oxides which dissolve to form soluble hydroxides like those of sodium and potassium. Unlike sodium and potassium, and like most other metals, their carbonates are insoluble. The non-metallic elements chlorine, bromine, and iodine unite with hydrogen to form strong acids, the salts of which are with few exceptions very soluble in water.

Thus there are clearly recognizable families of elements. One feature characteristic of some such families is that their members have the same *valency*. Most elements have a specially characteristic combining weight, of which the atomic weight is some simple multiple. This multiple is called the *valency* of the element. It has been defined as the number of atoms of hydrogen which can be replaced by one atom of the element, and, broadly speaking, corresponds with the number of atoms of oxygen with which *two* atoms of the element combine in its oxides. Thus sodium and potassium (oxides Na_2O and K_2O) have a valency of one; calcium, strontium, barium (oxides CaO, SrO, BaO) have a valency of two. Nitrogen and phosphorus form oxides N_2O_5 and P_2O_5 corresponding to the nitric and phosphoric acids. They have the valency five in these. In ammonia and phosphine NH_3, PH_3, they have a valency of three. When an element forms two series of stable compounds in which its valency is different, the two valencies usually add up to eight, as in this example.

When the atomic weights of a large number of the elements had been determined with comparative accuracy, it began to be seen that the properties of individual members of a family vary with the size of the atom. If we compare compounds of calcium (A.W. 40·1), strontium (A.W. 87·6), and barium (A.W. 137·4), we find that the sulphates decrease in solubility as the atomic weight increases. Barium sulphate is highly insoluble. That of strontium is very slightly soluble, and that of calcium is relatively easy to dissolve. We see a corresponding regularity in the solubility of the silver salts of hydrochloric, hydrobromic, and hydriodic acid. Chlorine is the lightest of the three elements chlorine, bromine, iodine. Its silver salt is the least soluble in water. Iodine is the heaviest and its silver salt is the most soluble. Again chlorine (A.W. 35·5) is a gas, bromine (A.W. 79·9) a liquid, and iodine (A.W. 127) a solid at ordinary temperatures.

A preliminary survey of the elements therefore suggests a regular gradation in their physical properties and the properties of these compounds when elements of the same family are arranged in order of their atomic weights. It was a short step to place the families in parallel columns, so spaced that the atomic weights increase uniformly along the rows from left to right as well as down the columns from top to bottom. For instance, if we take the first fourteen elements known in the middle of the nineteenth century, excluding hydrogen, we can arrange those with the same valency in parallel columns, as follows:

1. Lithium	6·9	Sodium	23·0	(Potassium	39·1)
2. Beryllium	9·1	Magnesium	24·3	(Calcium	40·0)
3. Boron	10·8	Aluminium	27·1		
4. Carbon	12·0	Silicon	28·3		
5. Nitrogen	14·0	Phosphorus	31·0		
6. Oxygen	16·0	Sulphur	32·0		
7. Fluorine	19·0	Chlorine	35·5		

The resemblance of any element in this first set of sixteen is much greater towards its twin with the same valency than towards any of the others. Thus lithium, a metal which is present in a few rather rare minerals (e.g. petalite), decomposes water like sodium to form a soluble hydroxide. Silicon, whose oxide SiO_2 or silica is the chief constituent of quartz and sand, is unique in forming a large number of compounds corresponding to the organic carbon compounds dealt with in the next chapter. Fluorine, like chlorine, forms a very strong acid with hydrogen. Boron is not a metal, but aluminium has characteristics which are not typically those of the common metals; its oxide is both feebly *basic* and feebly *acidic*, forming salts like aluminium silicate (the chief constituent of clay and felspar) and sodium aluminate (on account of which it is corroded by alkalis). In order of atomic weight the fifteenth element would be potassium which rightly falls next to sodium, and then comes calcium which has more in common with magnesium than with the others.

Proceeding in this way we can arrange the elements known at the time of Mendeljeff in columns headed by lithium, beryllium, etc., arranging the columns in order of atomic weight with the heaviest at the bottom, and leaving gaps so that the atomic weights increase regularly from left to right as well as from top to bottom. This is what Mendeljeff did, making an eighth column for a group of metals including iron with no representatives in the higher rows. The importance of the arrangement (p. 487) was shown by two things. The first was that in several cases of rare elements, e.g. indium, which were little known at the time, the assigned values of the atomic weights were wrong. To fit them into the table they had to be given atomic weights which were different multiples of their combining weights, as afterwards confirmed by more thorough investigation. The second is that the gaps began to be filled up with elements previously unknown, and the table assisted in their discovery by directing attention to their outstanding properties in advance.

The discovery of the heavier "inert gases" illustrates this use of Mendeljeff's rule. During an eclipse in 1868 a new element was detected by a prominent orange line in the spectrum of the sun's atmosphere. Since it did not correspond to that of any known element it was called *Helium*. In 1882 it was again recognized in the flame spectrum of Vesuvius—this time on our own earth. About 1894 Ramsay took up a problem which had been raised a century earlier by Cavendish. When O_2, CO_2, etc., have been

PERIODIC TABLE OF ELEMENTS

Group 0	Group I	Group II	Group III	Group IV	Group V	Group VI	Group VII	Group VIII
Helium He, 4								
Neon Ne, 20·2	Lithium Li, 6·94	Beryllium Be, 9·02	Boron B, 10·8	Carbon C, 12	Nitrogen N, 14	Oxygen O, 16	Fluorine F, 19	
Argon A, 39·9	Sodium Na, 23	Magnesium Mg, 24·3	Aluminium Al, 27	Silicon Si, 28·1	Phosphorus P, 31	Sulphur S, 32·1	Chlorine Cl, 35·5	
	Potassium K, 39·1	Calcium Ca, 40·1	Scandium Sc, 45·1	Titanium Ti, 47·9	Vanadium V, 51	Chromium Cr, 52	Manganese Mn, 54·9	Iron Fe, 55·8; Cobalt Co, 58·9; Nickel Ni, 58·7
Krypton Kr, 82·9	Copper Cu, 63·6	Zinc Zn, 65·4	Gallium Ga, 69·7	Germanium Ge, 72·6	Arsenic As, 74·9	Selenium Se, 79·2	Bromine Br, 79·9	
	Rubidium Rb, 85·4	Strontium Sr, 87·6	Yttrium Y, 88·9	Zirconium Zr, 91·2	Columbium* Cb, 93·3	Molybdenum Mo, 96	Masurium Ma, ?	Ruthenium Ru, 101·7; Rhodium Rh, 103; Palladium Pd, 107
Xenon Xe, 130	Silver Ag, 108	Cadmium Cd, 112	Indium In, 115	Tin Sn, 119	Antimony Sb, 122	Tellurium Te, 128	Iodine I, 127	
	Caesium Cs, 133	Barium Ba, 137	Lanthanum La, 139	Hafnium Hf, 179	Tantalum Ta, 181	Tungsten W, 184	Rhenium Re, 186	Osmium Os, 191; Iridium Ir, 193; Platinum Pt, 195
Niton Nt, 222	Gold Au, 197	Mercury Hg, 201	Thallium Tl, 204	Lead Pb, 207	Bismuth Bi, 209	Polonium Po, ?		
	Radium Ra, 226		Actinium Ac, ?	Thorium Th, 232	Protoactinium Pa, ?	Uranium U, 238		

Atomic weights are given correct to three significant figures. Hydrogen and the rare earth elements between Lanthanum and Hafnium are omitted. * Columbium is also called Niobium (Nb).

removed from air the residual nitrogen is somewhat heavier than nitrogen prepared from nitrates (about $\frac{1}{2}$ per cent). If this residual nitrogen is removed by means of heated magnesium and quicklime (or sparking with O_2 to convert it into oxides which are easily absorbed) there is a residue (about 1 per cent) of a heavier inert gas which Ramsay called *argon*. On examining the "occluded nitrogen" of radioactive minerals, Ramsay found it was mainly composed of another inert gas whose spectrum proved that it was the sun-element helium. These two elements did not fit into the existing Periodic Table. They required a *new column* in which, presumably, other as yet undiscovered elements would fit. A search for them was made, and it was thought that traces of them might be present, like argon, in air. Subsequent liquefaction of air led to the filling of the gaps in the new column by a class of five gases, helium, neon, argon, krypton, and xenon. All of these gases can be prepared from liquid air. Helium is also obtainable in the gas from certain springs (e.g. 8 to 10 per cent at Sautenay), or by pulverizing certain minerals, e.g. monazite sand.

Helium is the second lightest element, being only twice as heavy as hydrogen—less than a sixth as dense as air. Being neither inflammable nor corrosive it is specially suitable for dirigibles. Several recent disasters have resulted from the criminal irresponsibility of using hydrogen. Argon being inert is specially useful for filling electric bulbs, since it does not wear away the hot filament. The other inert gases have recently assumed a prominent rôle in everyday life as advertising signs. If a minute quantity of an inert gas is put in a vacuum bulb a characteristic coloured glow is obtained when an electric current is passed through it (p. 782). Argon and helium give white and gold, and neon a brilliant orange red. With the addition of a trace of mercury vapour a bright blue results. If this is filtered through uranium glass, a green light is obtained.

When the Periodic Law was put forward there were several conspicuous gaps in the middle of the table such as those now occupied by scandium and gallium in the boron-aluminium family, and by germanium in the same family as carbon and silicon. Thus in 1870 it was possible to prescribe the following properties of an unknown element (then called "eka-silicon") with A.W. about 72; specific gravity about 5·5; of greyish colour; forming a white, slightly basic oxide XO_2 decomposed by sodium and having a specific gravity 4·7; forming a chloride XCl_4 with boiling point just below that of water and twice the specific gravity, a solid fluoride XF_4, and an alkyl derivative $X(C_2H_5)_4$ boiling at 160° and very slightly below the specific gravity of water. All of these were precisely realized by the discovery of Germanium (A.W. 72·6) in 1887.

The law which Mendeljeff announced is only the germ of a more precise generalization. As stated by him it asserts that the properties of the elements and their compounds are a periodic function of their *atomic weights*. When due allowance has been made for inaccuracies, which were current in his time, there are still three pairs of elements which do not fit perfectly. According to the best modern determinations argon has the atomic weight 39·9, and potassium, which ought to be the next element after argon reading the table from left to right, has the atomic weight 39·1. With the exception of these three pairs (argon-potassium, tellurium-iodine, cobalt-nickel) the 90 odd known terrestrial elements form a coherent series in conformity with Mendeljeff's original declaration. The present position is that the properties of the elements and their compounds are clearly a periodic function of some aspect of the size or complexity of the atom. This complexity is in some way very closely related to atomic weight. To discuss it in greater detail would carry us beyond the allotted task of this book.

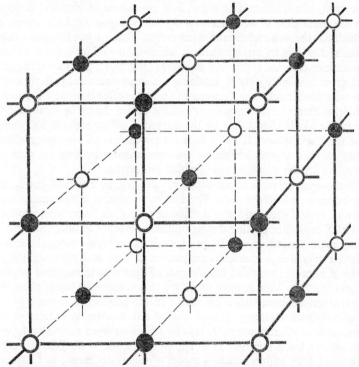

FIG. 261.—THE POTASSIUM CHLORIDE CRYSTAL.—POTASSIUM ATOMS BLACK, CHLORINE ATOMS WHITE. THE LINES ARE MERELY TO INDICATE THE ARRANGEMENT OF THE ATOM-LAYERS

THE CRYSTALLINE STATE

In common parlance, a crystal is a solid body with a characteristic shape definable by the geometric relations of its edges and faces. The characteristics of crystalline form as a means of identifying substances of value for manufacture or ornament—ores and jewels—have prompted chemists from earliest times to study them and to speculate about their nature. Thus the modern attack on crystal structure does not start with a clean slate. The mineralogists and crystallographers of the eighteenth and nineteenth centuries had created a considerable corpus of knowledge embodying meticulous classification of the geometrical relations of crystalline bodies; and to those who made such a special study of crystals, the existence of matter in the crystalline state presented an enigma for which nineteenth-century theories of molecular structure offered no clue.

A pivotal fact about the crystalline state is that a crystal preserves its characteristic geometrical properties, as it grows from indefinitely small dimensions to a body of relatively enormous bulk. Thus a crystal has a geometrical identity which is not affected by its size, however small; and this visible geometrical identity goes with other peculiarities. Its elasticity, electrical conductivity and other physical properties are not identical with respect to *different axes*. Neither of these peculiarities is easily intelligible if a crystal, like a solution or a gas, is a population of identical molecules. Both are intelligible if we conceive a crystal as a *space lattice* of atoms each of which has the same relation to other atoms. Thus we can imagine a cubical crystal of NaCl as an arrangement in which each sodium atom is united to 6 equidistant chlorine atoms and *vice versa* (Fig. 261). Such an arrangement could grow uniformly only by retaining the same structural pattern, and the same quantitative relations between the number of sodium and the number of chlorine atoms in the smallest cell of the lattice. Large or small, a crystal so conceived is held together by the attraction of the sodium and chlorine *atoms* for one another. If so, it is *not* a population of separate molecules. In one sense, a crystal visible to the eyes shares the title to rank as a molecule with the smallest crystal which can exist.

Till the opening years of our century, there was no means of putting such speculations to a decisive test. The first step towards a new attack on the nature of crystal structure was a discovery by Laue, who photographed a beam of X-rays after passing through different crystals in different axes. The photographic impression of a beam transmitted through a particular axis of a particular crystal is a characteristic pattern of dark and light regions, suggestive of reinforcement and interference of light rays transmitted through a fine grid (p. 336). This at once suggested that equidistant layers of atoms in the hypothetical space-lattice postulated in the previous paragraph play the part of a *diffraction grating*. If so, it should also be—and is in fact—possible to demonstrate interference of X-rays by reflection from successive layers of atoms when a beam impinges at an appropriate angle on the face of a crystal.

We have dealt with a fictitious model of such interference in Chapter VI (p. 341). The essential parts are a source of radiation, a *laminated* reflector and a detector geared to rotate through twice the angle through which the reflector itself turns. The source of X-rays in experiments of this kind is the type of discharge bulb shown in Fig. 393 with a special metallic *anti-kathode* on which the stream of electrified particles released by the current impinges and excites to emit them. In practice the most convenient detector for X-rays is an electroscope (p. 645) kept at a high potential (e.g. 10,000 volts). Owing to the fact that X-rays make gases conduct electricity the leaves of the electroscope will diverge most when interference is maximal. Experiment shows that the divergence of the leaves increases and diminishes periodically, as the crystal turns about the selected axis. The results plotted as a graph display recognisably distinguishable primary, secondary, etc., maxima (p. 342), and minima corresponding to interference and reinforcement at the first and second, first and third, etc., layers of atoms. Fig. 263 shows the experimental set-up for which Fig. 210 is the model. Our glass pile (p. 341) to serve as an elementary model of crystal structure exhibited the principle of one method of determining the wave-length of monochromatic light. If we know the absolute value of d the thickness of the laminae we can calculate the absolute wave-length of a particular region of the visible spectrum from observations on the relation between the intensity of the reflected and the angle of the incident beam. The only two quantities involved are d and the angle (a) at which interference or brightness is maximal. Provided we use the same pile, or piles with laminae of the same thickness, for observations on light of different wave-lengths W_1, W_2, etc., the relevant relation is $nW_1 : nW_2 = {}_2d \sin a_1 : {}_2d \sin a_2$, so that $W_1 : W_2 = \sin a_1 : \sin a_2$. This means that we could adapt such a set-up to determine the *relative* wavelengths of different regions in the spectrum even if we do not know the numerical value of the thickness d. Conversely, we could use it to find the thickness d of a lamina, if we knew the absolute wave-length of the incident beam, or the relative thickness of the laminae of different piles otherwise constructed to the same plan by observing the angular interval between primary, secondary, etc., maxima of interference by reflection of one and the same beam of monochromatic light from their surfaces.

This is also the underlying principle of crystal analysis by means of X-rays; but our model crystal is in one respect over-simple for the end in view. The glass laminae of the pile constitute only one set of parallel planes. If a crystal is a space lattice of atoms, there are in fact many sets of parallel equidistant planes in which the constituent atoms lie; and if our hypothesis is correct, the distances between different sets of planes will not all be the same. A crystal so conceived is indeed a different pile, if X-rays which impinge on its surface are coincident with *different axes*; and we can use the angle of maximal interference referable to different sets of planes as a yardstick of the relative distances which separate them. For a particular set of planes, we know (p. 342) that $nW = 2d \sin a$. If a_1, a_2, a_3 are the angles at which we get the first maxima in three different planes, with atoms respectively spaced at distances d_1, d_2, d_3, we therefore have:

$$d_1 \sin a_1 = d_2 \sin a_2 = d_3 \sin a_3.$$

To make use of this information, we have two clues to go on: (a) the geometrical characteristics of the crystal itself; (b) the numerical ratio of the constituent atoms as assigned by chemical analyses. The most simple type of crystalline compound will serve to illustrate how the parts of the puzzle fit together. Sodium chloride and potassium chloride both form cubical crystals, suggesting that the spacing of the atoms is equidistant in three planes at right angles to each other and coincident with the three edges of the crystal. Since every sodium atom of NaCl and every potassium atom of KCl is associated with the one atom of chlorine and *vice versa*, such an arrangement (Fig. 261) is possible if each sodium (or potassium) atom lies at the origin of three rectangular axes connecting equidistant pairs of chlorine atoms and each chlorine atom lies at the origin of three rectangular axes connecting three equally spaced pairs of sodium (or potassium) atoms. If this is indeed the relation between the constituent atoms of the crystal of NaCl, or of KCl, geometry prescribes (Fig. 262) what must be the distances d_1, d_2, d_3 between the laminae of atoms respectively in the axes:

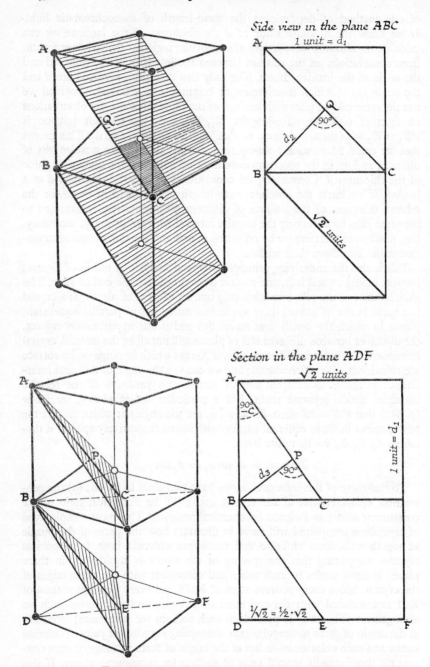

Side view in the plane ABC

1 unit = d_1

d_2

90°

√2 units

Section in the plane ADF

√2 units

1 unit = d_1

d_3

90°

90°

$1/\sqrt{2} = 1/2 \cdot \sqrt{2}$

FIG. 262.—THE GEOMETRY OF A CUBIC LATTICE

These figures show the relation between the distances d_1, d_2, d_3, between the three principal planes referred to on page 491, the unit of length being d_1. From the upper figure we see that:

(i) at right angles to the face of the crystal;
(ii) at right angles to the plane intersecting diagonally opposite edges;
(iii) at right angles to the plane passing through one vertex and the edge diagonally opposite to it.

The relation which geometry prescribes for this set-up is:

$$d_1 : d_2 : d_3 = 1 : \frac{1}{\sqrt{2}} : \frac{1}{\sqrt{3}}.$$

If our hypothesis is correct d_1, d_2, d_3 are inversely proportional to $\sin a_1$, $\sin a_2$, $\sin a_3$. Hence

$$\sin a_1 : \sin a_2 : \sin a_3 = 1 : \sqrt{2} : \sqrt{3}.$$

Results of experiments on crystals of KCl tally with this calculation; but experiments on crystals of NaCl do not, and the discrepancy brings into focus a consideration we have so far neglected and one which provides a powerful clue to the analysis of more complex types of crystalline compounds. In our preview of the consequences of our hypothesis, we have taken no account of an important difference between the three planes concerned, i.e. the *face* planes d_1 apart, the *oblique* planes d_2 apart and the *cross-diagonal* planes d_3 apart. Each of the face planes and each of the diagonal planes consists of *both* chlorine and potassium or sodium atoms. Alternate cross diagonal planes of KCl consist wholly of chlorine or wholly of potassium atoms. Alternate cross-diagonal planes of NaCl consist wholly of chlorine or wholly of sodium atoms. The atom of chlorine (Atomic Weight 35·5) is not much smaller than that of potassium (A.W. 39·1), but it is half as big again as the atom of sodium (A.W. 23). In the NaCl crystal, the cross-diagonal planes composed exclusively of chlorine atoms must therefore be more

---

Continued from previous page

$$AC = \sqrt{2} \qquad AQ = \tfrac{1}{2}.\sqrt{2} = \frac{1}{\sqrt{2}}$$

$$d_2{}^2 = BQ^2 = AB^2 - AQ^2 = 1^2 - \left(\frac{1}{\sqrt{2}}\right)^2 = \tfrac{1}{2}$$

$$\therefore \ d_2 = \frac{1}{\sqrt{2}}$$

From the lower figure, we see that:

$$\cos C = \sin(90°-C) = BP \div BA = BP = d_3$$
$$\therefore \ \cos^2 C = d_3{}^2$$
$$\text{Sin } C = BP \div BC = \sqrt{2}.d_3$$
$$\therefore \ \sin^2 C = 2\,d_3{}^2$$
$$\therefore \ 1 - 2d_3{}^2 = 1 - \sin^2 C = \cos^2 C = d_3{}^2$$
$$\therefore \ 1 - 2d_3{}^2 = d_3{}^2$$
$$\therefore \ d_3{}^2 = \tfrac{1}{3} \text{ and } d_3 = \frac{1}{\sqrt{3}}$$

Hence we have:

$$d_1 : d_2 : d_3 = 1 : \frac{1}{\sqrt{2}} : \frac{1}{\sqrt{3}}$$

packed with appreciably less intervening space than the alternating cross-diagonal planes of sodium atoms only. Presumably then, they will reflect X-rays more efficiently. If so, we should expect maximum brightness by reflection at the chlorine planes separated by a distance $2d_3$. Our brightness maxima should thus arise from reflection at planes separated by distances in the ratio:

$$d_1 : d_2 : 2d_3 = 1 : \frac{1}{\sqrt{2}} : \frac{2}{\sqrt{3}}$$

Accordingly the *sines* of the corresponding angles of reflection with maximum reinforcement should be in the ratio:

$$1 : \sqrt{2} : \frac{\sqrt{3}}{2}$$

Bragg found this to be so; and in finding it disclosed how the identity, as well as the arrangement, of the atoms in a crystal lattice can influence its power to reflect X-rays. When first undertaken, the task of elucidating the structure of a crystal of less simple geometrical form and composed like $CaCl_2 \cdot 10\,H_2O$ (crystalline calcium chloride with its component *water of crystallisation*) of more than two sorts of atoms not equal in number was, of course, much more difficult than that of elucidating the structure of crystalline sodium chloride. It was a process of painstaking trial and error based on construction of models which satisfied the requirements of a particular case, and deduction of the geometrical relations between the principal planes of atoms at which appreciable reflection could occur. If the experiment along the lines indicated confirmed the relative distances prescribed by the model, the model justified itself; and in course of time accumulated knowledge of the space-lattice type of different families of crystals and their characteristic X-ray diffraction patterns, made the task of elucidating the structure of others less exacting. Indeed, it is now possible to form a picture of the structure of extremely complex solids, such as the protein *Keratin* which makes up the bulk of hair.

We do not need exact knowledge about the wave-lengths of X-rays to explore the space lattice of a crystal. Experiments yield the same results, if we use one and the same source, i.e. a discharge tube with an *anti-kathode* of one and the same material, e.g. *cobalt*; and results obtained by substituting an anti-kathode of a different metal, e.g. *nickel*, are consistent in so far as they lead to identical relative values for the spacing of corresponding planes in which the atoms lie. By using this knowledge to evaluate *relative* values for the characteristic wave-lengths emitted by the impact of the kathode stream (p. 784) on different metals, Moseley (1912) elucidated the fact that the wave-length characteristic of a metal of high atomic weight is less than that of a metal of low atomic weight. By comparing the X-ray wave-lengths characteristic of a sequence of metals which succeed one another in the order of their atomic weights, he thus hit on a simple rule. In the following table W_r stands for the wave-length of the characteristic ray of an element *relative* to that of *Titanium*, here taken as the yardstick, because the lightest one of the set. Its reciprocal (f_r) is the relative *frequency* (p. 325) of the ray.

		Atomic Weight	f_r	$\sqrt{f_r}$	Difference
Titanium	..	48·1	1·000	1·000	
					0·046
Vanadium	..	51·1	1·094	1·046	
					0·049
Chromium	..	52·0	1·199	1·095	
					0·048
Manganese	..	54·9	1·306	1·143	
					0·048
Iron	..	55·8	1·418	1·191	

The table shows that the differences between the square roots of the reciprocals of the characteristic X-ray wave-lengths of the elements arranged

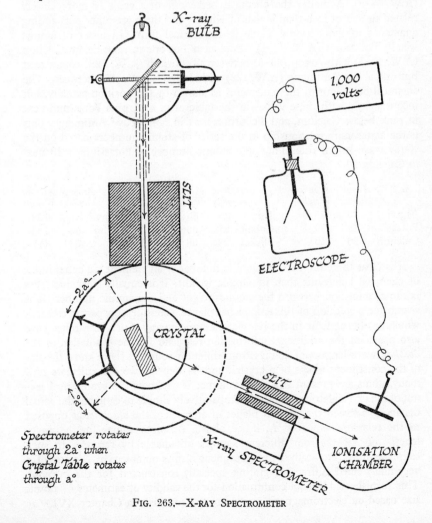

FIG. 263.—X-RAY SPECTROMETER

in this sequence go up by equal steps, as nearly as one can expect. This is another way of saying that we can arrange the elements in a sequence of which the wave-length of any one of them is inversely proportional to the square of its *rank*, which is, of course, an *integer*. The name for its rank in such a sequence is its *Atomic Number*. In the set shown above the atomic weights of the elements go up consistently in order of rank based on this principle. The next two elements are Cobalt (A.W. 58·97) and Nickel (A.W. 58·68) which fall out of step with the Periodic Table (p. 487) devised to show a relation between the chemical behaviour of the elements and their atomic *weights*. In the sequence starting with Hydrogen (Atomic Number 1), Cobalt (A.N. 27) comes immediately after Iron (A.N. 26) and before Nickel (A.N. 28). In the order of their atomic weights the corresponding sequence is Iron (A.W. 55·8), Nickel (A.W. 58·7) and Cobalt (A.W. 58·9). Actually, the chemical behaviour of Cobalt is more closely related to that of Iron than is that of Nickel; and there are other outstanding anomalies in the Periodic Table in its original form. In order of atomic weight Potassium (A.W. 39·1) comes next but one in rank below Calcium (A.W. 40·1) with Argon (39·9) between. Tellurium (A.W. 128) comes next but one above Antimony (A.W. 122) with Iodine (A.W. 127) between. The chemical behaviour of these elements as shown by the position actually, but inconsistently with these values in the table of p. 487, puts Potassium next in rank below Calcium, and Tellurium next in rank above Antimony. This is the actual rank relationship in the series of atomic numbers based on the X-ray wave-length rule. Thus, the atomic number of Potassium is 19 next to Calcium 20.

	Atomic Number	Atomic Weight		Atomic Number	Atomic Weight		Atomic Number	Atomic Weight
Argon	18	39·9	Iron	26	55·8	Antimony	51	122
Potassium	19	39·1	Cobalt	27	58·9	Tellurium	52	128
Calcium	20	40·1	Nickel	28	58·7	Iodine	53	127

It is clear therefore that the atomic number of an element is a better index of chemical behaviour than its atomic weight. It is equally clear that there is some connexion between the atomic weight and the atomic number. The search for a solution of this enigma has played a considerable part in research which has borne fruit in the release of atomic energy. Such researches have also provided the additional information requisite for the evaluation of the *absolute* wave-lengths of X-rays from different sources. If we know the size of the constituent atoms of a crystal, and its density, we can calculate how many atoms are present in a given volume. If we know the geometrical layout of the crystal lattice, it is then comparatively simple to estimate the actual distances between the various planes of atoms, i.e. the *absolute*, as opposed to the relative, values of d_1, d_2, d_3 above. Absolute values for the wavelengths of X-rays from different sources obtainable by recourse to such estimates of d_1, etc., tally with subsequent results obtained by the use of a very finely ruled diffraction grating specially constructed for the purpose. This furnishes additional confirmation for the validity of estimates of atomic size based on electromagnetic measurements set forth in Chapter XVI.

EXAMPLES ON CHAPTER IX

1. If 100 c.c. of carbon monoxide measured at standard pressure and temperature are burned in 600 c.c. of air, what will be the volume of the residual gas measured (*a*) over mercury, (*b*) over a solution of caustic soda or lime at S.T.P.?

2. If 500 c.c. of chlorine and 200 c.c. of hydrogen (both measured at S.T.P.) are left to combine in sunlight, what will be the final volume of residual gas measured over paraffin at S.T.P.?

3. If 500 c.c. of ammonia (NH_3) are mixed with 600 c.c. of hydrochloric acid gas (HCl), what will be the volume of residual gas measured first over paraffin and subsequently over caustic soda? To what do you attribute the presence of a cloud of white particles in the gas?

4. What will be the residual volume of gas measured over a drying agent at S.T.P., if 400 c.c. of hydrogen are exploded with 500 c.c., 750 c.c., 1,500 c.c. of air (21 per cent oxygen) at S.T.P.?

5. In a graduated cylindrical vessel of 10 sq. cm. sectional area 200 c.c. of hydrogen are sparked with 125 c.c. of air over sulphuric acid (specific gravity $1 \cdot 8$) at atmospheric pressure (76 cm. mercury barometer). The residual gas after absorption of water vapour by the acid measures 250 c.c. when the cylinder is depressed till the fluid is at the same level inside and outside. How high did the sulphuric acid rise in the cylinder after sparking?

6. Given that 1 mol. of any gas occupies $22 \cdot 4$ litres at S.T.P., compare the values of R in the equation $pv = nRT$,
    (*a*) when the units are atmos and litres.
    (*b*) when the units are dynes per sq. cm. and c.c.
    (*c*) when the units are cm. mercury and c.c.

7. The relative densities of prussic acid, which is a compound containing hydrogen, carbon, and nitrogen only, and of carbon monoxide (formed by burning excess of carbon in oxygen) are respectively $13 \cdot 5$ and 14. What are the only molecular formulae consistent with these figures and those for the atomic weights of the elements in these compounds?

8. Two oxides, one of carbon and the other of nitrogen, both have the same relative density of 22. Give their formulae and calculate their percentage composition by weight.

9. The relative density of sulphuretted hydrogen is 17. It is twice as dense as ammonia. What are the only formulae for these two substances consistent with the knowledge that one is a compound of sulphur and hydrogen, and the other of nitrogen and hydrogen?

10. If 100 c.c. of carbon monoxide (CO) is burned in a closed space containing a litre (1,000 c.c.) of air and quicklime, what is the final volume of gas, and its percentage composition by volume? The air may be taken to contain 21 per cent oxygen by volume.

11. At 140° C. an oxide of nitrogen which has a deep brown hue is found to have a relative density of 23. When it is cooled below 30° C. it becomes nearly colourless and progressively more dense. Its relative density approaches a value of 46, as it is cooled further. Analysis shows that no free nitrogen or oxygen are present. What conclusions do you draw? If the relative density at 28° C. (referred to hydrogen at the same temperature) is 39, what is the composition of the nearly colourless gas at that temperature?

12. Find the formulae of the following substances from the vapour density (V.D.) and percentage composition by weight as given below:

(a) Nitric Acid V.D. 31·5   Hydrogen 1·6, Nitrogen 22·2, Oxygen 76·2

(b) Ammonia V.D. 8·5   Hydrogen 17·65, Nitrogen 82·35

(c) Chloroform V.D. 59·75   Hydrogen 0·8, Carbon 10, Chlorine 89·2

(d) Acetic Acid V.D. 30   Hydrogen 6·7, Carbon 40, Oxygen 53·3

(e) Glycerine V.D. 46   Carbon 39, Hydrogen 9, Oxygen 52

(f) Formaldehyde V.D. 15   Hydrogen 6·7, Carbon 40, Oxygen 53·3

(g) Acetone V.D. 29   Hydrogen 10·3, Carbon 62·1, Oxygen 27·6

(h) Methyl Cyanide V.D. 20·5   Hydrogen 7·3, Carbon 58·5, Nitrogen 34·2

(i) Carbolic Acid V.D. 47   Hydrogen 6·4, Carbon 76·6, Oxygen 17

13. After continuous sparking through 100 c.c. of pure oxygen, the smell of ozone is detected and the volume is found to have contracted to 98 c.c. Ozone, unlike oxygen, is absorbed by turpentine. When shaken with turpentine the gas occupies only 94 c.c. and the smell of ozone is no longer detected. How is this explained? Use your explanation to calculate the percentage ozone content of a mixture of which 100 c.c. expand to 101 c.c. when exposed to platinum black which decomposes ozone.

14. If 1 gram of hydrogen at 0° C. and 760 mm. pressure occupies 11·2 litres, how many grams of sulphur must be burned in 50 litres of air to absorb all the oxygen in it?

15. Illustrate the laws of reciprocal and multiple proportion by the following analyses giving percentage composition of chlorides, oxides, sulphides, and hydrides. Give the combining weight of each element taking hydrogen as unity:

Substance	Hydrogen	Oxygen	Chlorine	Sulphur	Metal
Copper oxide	—	20·1	—	—	79·9
Water	11·2	88·8	—	—	—
Magnesium oxide	—	39·7	—	—	60·3
Iron (ferrous) oxide	—	22·2	—	—	77·8
Mercury oxide	—	7·4	—	—	92·6
Hydrochloric acid	2·7	—	97·3	—	—
Sulphuretted hydrogen	5·9	—	—	94·1	—
Magnesium chloride	—	—	74·5	—	25·5
Copper chloride	—	—	52·7	—	47·3
Silver chloride	—	—	24·7	—	75·3
Mercury sulphide	—	—	—	13·8	86·2
Silver sulphide	—	—	—	22·9	77·1

16. The density of a substance is found to be 38 times that of hydrogen at the same temperature and pressure. Its percentage composition is 84·25 per cent sulphur and 15·75 per cent carbon. What is its formula?

17. One mol. of any gas at S.T.P. occupies 22·4 litres. If the formula of potassium chlorate is $KClO_3$, what weight and what volume of oxygen at 10° C. and 750 mm. pressure may be obtained from the decomposition of 20 grams of it?

18. The molecular weight of ammonia is 17·03. Taking the atomic weights of hydrogen, nitrogen and oxygen as 1, 14, and 16, assuming that the molecule of each of them contains two atoms, and taking the percentage of oxygen in air as 21, what is the density of ammonia referred to air?

19. The percentage composition of an organic compound is hydrogen 6·3, carbon 40, oxygen 53·3. Half a gram gave 327·6 c.c. of vapour at 200° C. and 750 mm. pressure. What was its molecular formula?

20. If 80 grams of gas given off from the electrolysis of water occupied 60 litres at 17° C., what were the partial pressures of oxygen and hydrogen?

21. What volume would 40 grams of oxygen occupy at 2 atmospheres pressure and 27° C.?

22. What pressure would 40 grams of cane sugar dissolved in 1 litre exert at 27° C.?

23. The formula of urea is CON_2H_4. At 10° C. the osmotic pressure of a water solution of urea is 500 mm. of mercury. If the solution is diluted to 10 times its former volume, what would be its osmotic pressure at 15° C.?

24. The osmotic pressure of a solution of 0·184 gram of urea in 100 c.c. of water at 30° C. was found to be 56 cm. of mercury. Calculate from this its approximate molecular weight.

25. A solution of 1 mol of potassium bromide (KBr) in 8 litres of water at 25° C. is 82 per cent dissociated into ions. What is its osmotic pressure?

26. A solution containing 1·9 mols of calcium chloride ($CaCl_2$) is in osmotic equilibrium with a solution containing 4·05 mols of glucose. If the formula of glucose is $C_6H_{12}O_6$, what is the percentage ionic dissociation of the salt?

27. If 1 mol of acetic acid ($C_2H_4O_2$) and 1 mol of ethyl alcohol (C_2H_6O) are heated in the presence of a catalyst the reaction proceeds till 1/3 mols acetic and 1/3 mols alcohol remain. If we start with (a) 60 g. of acid and 92 g. of alcohol, (b) 60 g. of acid, 46 g. of alcohol and 18 g. of water, (c) 88 g. of ethyl acetate and 54 g. of water; how much ethyl acetate will be formed after long boiling?

28. Iron and steam react according to the "equation"

$$3Fe + 4H_2O = Fe_3O_4 + 4H_2$$

In an experiment the partial pressure of steam and hydrogen in equilibrium at 200° C. were 4·6 cm. and 95·9 cm. (mercury) respectively. What is the pressure of hydrogen in equilibrium with it, when the partial pressure of the steam is 9·7 cm.?

29. If iron is heated at 200° in a closed vessel with steam at a pressure of 1 atmos., use the data of the last example to find the partial pressures of steam and hydrogen, when no further reaction occurs.

30. Amyl alcohol and trichloracetic acid react to form amyl trichloracetate as follows:

$$CCl_3 . COOH + C_5H_{11}OH = CCl_3COOC_5H_{11}$$

At 100° C. a mixture in equilibrium contains 3·846 mols amyl alcohol, 0·6594 mols acid and 2·111 mols of ester per litre. If it had started with 1 mol of acid and 4·48 mols of alcohol in 638 c.c. at 100°, what would be its composition at equilibrium?

31. At 2000° C. under atmospheric pressure 1·8 per cent of carbon dioxide is broken down into oxygen and carbon monoxide as follows:

$$2CO_2 = 2CO + O_2$$

What is the equilibrium constant of the reaction at that temperature expressed in pressures (atmos.)?

CHAPTER X

THE LAST RESTING PLACE OF SPIRITS

A Planned Economy of Carbon Compounds

THE rise of one great chemical industry—gas manufacture—followed immediately upon the introduction of coal as a source of power and the utilization of coal for metallurgical operations. Coal gas itself is a mixture, mainly of four inflammable constituents in varying proportions of which the following figures may be taken as typical: hydrogen 50 per cent, methane (CH_4) 30 per cent, carbon monoxide (CO) 10 per cent, and various *hydrocarbons* such as *benzene* (C_6H_6) and ethylene (C_2H_4) 5 per cent. The residual content includes various other gases, such as ammonia (NH_3) which is now removed for manufacture of nitrogenous fertilizers. What is supplied as "coal gas" is not always the gas which is emitted from coal when heated. It is often mixed with *water gas*, prepared by passing steam over the residue or coke which is left after the coal gas has been distilled off. When steam, which is hydrogen oxide, is passed over coke (which is comparatively pure carbon) it is reduced like a metallic oxide. An inflammable mixture of hydrogen and carbon monoxide is produced thus:

$$H_2O + \dot{C} \rightarrow H_2 + CO$$

The introduction of coal produced a profound change in what the biologist would call the *ecological* relations of mankind. Stores of dead organic material were substituted for products of living organisms previously used as fuel (wood or charcoal) or as illuminants (tallow, bees-wax, whale oil). This displacement was carried further by the emergence of two other industries, shale oil (1848) and American petroleum (1859). The distillation of shale furnished a source of oils ("paraffin") for heating and illumination, lubricating oils, and waxes. These superseded the use of animal and vegetable fats. From crude petroleum, in addition to volatile oils which proved to be so important in the later development of the internal combustion or gas engine, vaselines, solid waxes, and pitch for road making were also obtained.

In the meantime other uses had already been found for coal itself. Besides the gas distilled over and the coke remaining when coal is heated, vapours mixed with the gas condense in the tubes and containers after cooling. The crude mixture which condenses first is called coal tar. To begin with, its appearance was regarded as an incidental nuisance, because it dirtied the pipes. Chemists were set to work on it, at first more in the hope of getting rid of it than of using it. Coal tar is now the basis of the great chemical industries of dyes, disinfectants, modern explosives, synthetic perfumes, drugs, and synthetic resins. By heating, it can be separated into fractions of decreasing volatility. The Light Oil which vaporizes at the lowest temperatures is mainly a mixture of substances known as *benzene, toluene,* and *xylene.* The Middle Oil is a mixture of which the chief constituents are *phenol* or carbolic acid (as we call it in domestic use) and *naphthalene* (moth balls). The Heavy Oil composed of substances called *cresols* is used for winter sprays in fruit culture. Anthracene Oil, the least volatile fraction, is so called because it is mainly made up of a substance called *anthracene*. The final residue is *pitch*. This is now an ingredient of asphalt used in road making, the technique of which had continued unchanged in essentials from Neolithic times till the introduction of coal.

The chemical study of the coal tar derivatives found in these fractions and of compounds easily derived from them progressed rapidly after the 'fifties, when Perkin discovered how to make a cloth dye, "mauve," from impure aniline. Till then the dyeing of all textiles had been carried out with plant juices like madder, "grain," or indigo, and animal excretions like the Tyrian purple of antiquity. In 1868 two German chemists synthesized "alizarin," the colouring matter of the madder plant from anthracene. Within a decade the madder industry of France was ruined. The synthesis of indigo, then a vegetable dye imported from India, soon followed. Several thousands of these synthetic dyes are now produced.

Traditional medicine succumbed in the same way as traditional dyeing. The old herbalists had relied exclusively on the native products of the living plant to concoct preparations sometimes with genuine but more often with supposititious benefits. The manufacture of useful antifebrile drugs, phenacetin, salicylic acid, aspirin, and antifebrin, followed as soon as the chemical constitution of the simpler active constituents of medicinal herbs had been established. A new class of more powerful explosives, of which trinitrotoluene or T.N.T. is an example, emerged as another by-product of coal tar chemistry. The antiseptic properties of coal tar stimulated the search for new antiseptics of which crude "carbolic acid" was one of the first to be introduced. Today coal tar is the source of synthetic scents, synthetic antiseptics, anaesthetics, synthetic narcotics and soporifics (like veronal), explosives, synthetic resins, as well as the enormous variety of synthetic pigments. These substances do not exist because coal tar itself has unique or miraculous resources. The reason why we can put coal tar to so many uses is that when we know how the organic molecule *is built up*, we can generally make it from the disintegration products of *any* organic material.

All the primary products of the coal industry, except the free hydrogen and traces of ammonia, etc., present in the coal gas, are compounds of carbon. What is called organic chemistry today, the chemistry of the carbon compounds, is mainly the outcome of putting chemists to work on coal tar. A new trade in chemical fertilizers (Chapter XX) was also built on the utilization of traces of ammonia in coal gas itself. Pre-existing industries had already conspired to nurse the study of the carbon compounds before the extensive exploitation of coal tar began in the latter half of the nineteenth century. The chemistry of sugar manufacture, of wine fermentation and of brewing have been mentioned in previous references to the original programme of the Royal Society. At the end of the eighteenth century the beet sugar industry had broken the monopoly of the American sugar cane by direct application of new knowledge concerning the chemical characteristics of the sugars. During the first half of the nineteenth century the expanding export wine industry of France (*vide* Chapter XIX) provided a powerful stimulus to the study of alcoholic fermentation, to the production of vinegar, and to crystallographic researches on tartaric acid.

In a private communication Mr. Mackie, who has studied the history of sugar taxation, gives the following details of the rise of the sugar industry. The original sugar cane was a tall rank grass indigenous to the Ganges basin, whence it spread to Southern China. The Chinese Government sent students to Behar (*circa* A.D. 648) to study cultivation and manufacture. Originally canes were crushed for juice, which was then evaporated. Refining of syrup was carried out from the eighth century onwards in Persia. There was an extensive Arabic trade in white sugar from the tenth century. Cultivation thus spread to Spain, Egypt, and Syria, where crusaders became acquainted with it. Its supposed medicinal use in lung disease interested Arabic physicians in chemical methods of refining it. Under Kubla Khan chemists were sent from Egypt to instruct the Chinese in sugar refining. The European trade dates from the fourteenth century, when sugar cane was cultivated in Sicily and carried by Venetian traders from the Levant. Thence followed a European trade in confectionery, sugar candy, etc., perfumed with essence of roses, violets, etc. Henry the Navigator cultivated it in Madeira. After the discovery of America, Portuguese plantations were transferred to Brazil, Guiana, and the West Indies. This was partly because of the climate and partly for getting cheap labour.

Sugar was classed with rice, almonds, and dried fruits as *spice* in early records of the Grocers' Company engaged in Venetian barter trade. Two refineries were set up in London in the middle of the sixteenth century. By 1650 there were fifty English refineries. About 1740 Margraf obtained sugar from beet juice. His pupil Achard improved the extraction process. Frederick William III of Prussia cultivated beet on his estates, and set up factories for Achard in 1801. After the naval blockade of French ports by Britain in 1807, Napoleon ordered the planting of 80,000 acres of beet. Schools were set up for teaching the technique of sugar manufacture, and a flourishing French industry developed. During the 'forties the French beet industry practically monopolized the sugar trade of France.

It is convenient to separate the study of the carbon compounds from the study of others for two reasons. One is that carbon forms a prodigiously large number of compounds, the multiplicity and complexity of which is a fundamental condition of the complexity of living organisms. The other is that the methods of preparation and synthesis employed in the study of this enormous assemblage of carbon compounds are peculiar. In studying mineral compounds three main types of chemical reaction are employed: separation by heat into a volatile and non-volatile portion as in the reduction of an ore or formation of quick lime; decomposition by the electrical current; and precipitation in solution through the free interaction of electrically charged sub-molecules or ions. None of these three methods is used much in studying carbon compounds. If solid they are nearly always volatile. They are rarely electrolytes, as are most soluble mineral compounds. So, unlike electrolytes in solution, they react very slowly and usually require a catalyst to help them to do so. This means that the chemistry of carbon compounds mainly depends on the coal tar method. Mixtures are heated and distillates are collected at different temperatures. The process is repeated till fractions of constant boiling point, the pure constituents, are obtained.

This practical distinction, which emerges when we seek real knowledge bearing fruit in action, is very different from one which philosophers had already made, when the carbon compounds were merely objects of idle curiosity. Long after it had been shown that the carbon dioxide produced in our tissues and exhaled in our breath can be synthesized from atmospheric oxygen and carbon, the carbon compounds continued to provide a refuge for animistic beliefs which obstructed the progress of early chemistry. One stronghold of superstition was the process of fermentation. The chemical study of sugar, which preceded the beginning of the beet industry at the end of the eighteenth century, threw a flood of light on one of the oldest chemical industries. Although mankind had been using catalytic processes in baking and brewing for many millennia, the nature of fermentation was surrounded by mystery till the middle of the nineteenth century. The Arabs had distilled a "spirit"—*alcohol* or spirits of wine—which was known as the "active principle" of intoxicating liquors. Subsequently Black had shown that the bubbles given off in fermentation are "fixed air." Further insight into what goes on during fermentation was checked by absence of knowledge about the nature of yeast before there were good microscopes to reveal the yeast organism, and ignorance about the chemical characteristics of sugar.

Since sour fruit juices ferment as well as those which are noticeably sweet, there was nothing to suggest that sugar is the common basis of the reaction till the chemical properties of sugars were sufficiently well known to make them identifiable in the absence of noticeable sweetness. Thus the fermentation of fruit juices in the absence of yeast appeared to be "spontaneous." About the time when beet sugar was first made, Lavoisier suggested —without proving—that the essence of fermentation is the decomposition of sugar. Although the chemical sequence of events involved (see p. 474) was disclosed soon after this, the discovery of the part played by the yeast organism served only to thicken the air of mystery—the *aura vitalis*—and to discourage the hope that fermentation is a chemical model for human ingenuity to imitate.

This air of mystery which surrounded the process of fermentation left open a last shelter for spiritual agencies in the realm of chemical combination. The useful distinction between carbon ("organic") and mineral ("inorganic") chemistry became a barren metaphysical dogma. So strongly was dogma entrenched that the great chemist Henry could write in the third decade of the nineteenth century:

It is not probable that we shall ever attain the power of imitating nature in these operations. For in the functions of a living plant a directing principle appears to be concerned peculiar to animated bodies and superior to and differing from the cause which has been termed chemical affinity.

In the very next year a German chemist Wöhler (1828) discovered that urea, the principal organic constituent of human urine, can be prepared from the evaporation of solutions of ammonium cyanate, a substance which can be built up from its elements carbon, nitrogen, hydrogen, and oxygen, in the laboratory. One method is to keep sparking nitrogen with carbon electrodes like those of an arc lamp. A highly poisonous gas cyanogen (C_2N_2) is then formed. If cyanogen is passed into a solution of caustic potash a mixture of two salts is formed. One is potassium cyanide (KCN), a well-known poison. The other is potassium cyanate (KOCN). If the latter is treated with a concentrated solution of ammonium sulphate, crystals of ammonium cyanate (NH_4OCN) separate out. Wöhler announced his discovery with the declaration that he could make urea without the help of a man, a dog, or a kidney. Such discoveries drove spirits from their last resting place in the theory of chemistry.

The transition from the use of living animal and plant products to the use of dead organic residues such as coal, shale, or petroleum, as sources of heat, illumination, drugs, dyes, and perfumes, was socially the transition from a predominantly rural to a predominantly urban economy, from the green and pleasant land to the dark Satanic mills of Blake's poem. Technologically it was the transition from the use of substances with *high* molecular weights to substances with *low* molecular weights. The three main constituents of all living matter are classified as *carbohydrates*, *fats*, and *proteins*. The first include the sugars, starches, and what is by far the most abundant organic material in the world, the main dry constituent of plant tissues such as wood fibre, namely *cellulose*. The carbohydrates contain carbon, hydrogen, and oxygen. So also do the fats, a term which includes the animal and vegetable oils. One class of fats, the *lecithins* (of egg yolk), contain phosphorus and nitrogen as well. The proteins all contain nitrogen as well as hydrogen, oxygen, and carbon. Most of them contain sulphur and many contain phosphorus. A few contain other elements, such as iron, which is present in the red protein pigment *haemoglobin* of our blood. The molecular weight of the simplest natural proteins is in the neighbourhood of ten thousand. The molecular weight of the simplest natural sugar, glucose, is 180, which is three times as large as the molecule of common salt and is very small compared with the molecule of cellulose. The molecular weight of the common fats is in the neighbourhood of a thousand. Compared with these figures the molecular weights of the constituents of coal gas or coal tar are small. The molecular weight of methane is 16, and that of carbolic acid, or as we shall henceforth call it *phenol*, is 94.

The organic residues of the new economy were thus the bricks and plaster of the molecules of more complex carbon compounds which exist in living beings. In finding how to make substitutes for living products by using the waste material of the coal gas industry, the chemist was therefore finding how to build with bricks common to any organic matter. The social possibilities of this step go far beyond the incidental use of coal itself in a highly urbanized society. England's green and pleasant land is not incompatible with the fullest use of scientific knowledge.

PECULIARITIES OF CARBON COMPOUNDS

Wöhler's discovery involves one of the characteristics which provides a clue to the amazing multiplicity of the carbon compounds. The two compounds ammonium cyanate and urea are both compounds of which the molecular weight can be easily determined. Both are soluble in water. We therefore know the complexity and composition of their molecules. The one passes into the other without the formation or addition of a third substance. Both have the same percentage composition of identically the same elements, and can be represented by one and the same formula CON_2H_4. In what does the difference lie?

The difference between molecules which are made up of the same atoms or of different atoms in the same proportions may be of two kinds. We have already touched on one of these. When we make electric sparks repeatedly in oxygen the gas becomes more dense. Ordinary oxygen turns into another gas which is one and a half times as heavy as the oxygen in the air or the oxygen usually obtained by heating decomposable metallic oxides. It is called *ozone*. Ozone combines with carbon to form carbon dioxide and nothing else, just as soot or diamond combine with ordinary oxygen to form carbon dioxide and nothing else. So its atoms are the same as the atoms of ordinary oxygen, just as the atoms of diamond and soot are both carbon atoms. Ozone differs from oxygen in having a molecular weight one and a half times as great. If we represent oxygen by O_2, we must therefore represent ozone by O_3. The difference between the two gases simply concerns the number of atoms in the molecule. This cannot be the sort of difference with which we are dealing in the case of ammonium cyanate and urea. Both have the same molecular weight.

Two groups of objects may differ with respect to the *kinds* of them in each group, the *numbers* in each group, and the *arrangement* in each group. The difference between urea and ammonium cyanate does not involve the kind and number of atoms in the molecules. So it can only be a difference of *arrangement*. Although we have not touched directly on the arrangement of atoms in a molecule, we have already had a clue. We have noticed that just as all metallic chlorides have one or more atoms of chlorine combined with a metal, all metallic carbonates have the atom cluster or *radicle* CO_3. Just as all the sodium salts have the hydrogen atom of an acid replaced by an atom of sodium, all "ammonium" salts have the atom cluster or radicle NH_4 of the hydroxide NH_4OH, which is formed when ammonia NH_3 dissolves in water (H_2O). Thus ammonium chloride is NH_4Cl, ammonium carbonate $(NH_4)_2 . CO_3$, and so on. Similarly ammonium cyanate is NH_4OCN just as sodium cyanate is $NaOCN$.

The peculiarity of these radicles is that they are relatively stable collections of atoms which go in and out of chemical reactions *as a group*. Hence substances in which they occur have common characteristics of chemical behaviour. For instance, the addition of a calcium salt in solution to either ammonium or sodium carbonate results in the precipitation of calcium carbonate and the formation of the sodium or ammonium salt of the acid from which the calcium salt was formed (e.g. $(NH_4)_2CO_3 + CaCl_2 \rightarrow 2NH_4Cl + CaCO_3$). Nearly all ammonium salts are extremely soluble. The noteworthy exception is that they form a yellow insoluble chloroplatinate, and are therefore precipitated from solution as a yellow powder when chloroplatinic acid is added. Besides having different physical properties such as its melting point and the shape of its crystals, urea differs from ammonium cyanate in its chemical behaviour. Ammonium salts show the characteristics of electrolytes in solution by taking part in such reactions and by conducting an electric current. The ammonium radicle splits off as an electrically charged sub-molecule or ion. Urea is not an electrolyte. It fails to give a yellow precipitate with chloroplatinic acid. Thus urea does not show most characteristics which we associate with the radicle NH_4 in ammonium salts.

The queer thing about carbon compounds is the enormous number of simple radicles containing a carbon atom, such as CO, CN, CNO, CH_3, C_2H_5, C_6H_5, COOH, CHO, CHOH, CH_2OH, etc. Hence it is possible for many compounds with different chemical behaviour to have the same percentage composition and the same molecular weight. To distinguish them, or to tell what sort of substance a carbon compound is, we have to write the formula so that the atoms are grouped together in radicles. A chemical formula, as we have seen, is a compact way of conveying a mass of information about the physical properties, chemical behaviour, and methods of preparation, of a substance. In the large class of carbon compounds, the elements which are contained in the molecule of a substance are comparatively unimportant. Their behaviour depends more especially on how the atoms are arranged, that is to say, which groups of atoms stick together. Hence the formula of a carbon compound only contains relevant information about its origin and behaviour, if it indicates such a grouping.

For instance, the essential constituent of vinegar, acetic acid, a substance which is a crystalline solid in a cold room and a colourless liquid which mixes freely with water in a warm room, might be represented as $C_2H_4O_2$. While this formula would correctly tell us the proportion by weight of its constituents and the molecular weight of acetic acid vapour, it would not distinguish it from two other substances called methyl formate and glycollic aldehyde. Both of these have the same molecular weight and the same percentage composition, but different physical properties, totally different chemical behaviour, and different methods of preparation. Thus acetic acid is a weak electrolyte turning blue litmus dye red in solution. Like a mineral acid it is capable of decomposing carbonates or combining with caustic alkalis to form salts such as sodium and calcium acetate, in which one atom of hydrogen is replaced by one atom of a monovalent metal. Methyl formate and glycollic aldehyde are not electrolytes. They are not acids. They do not decompose carbonates or combine with caustic alkalis to form metallic salts. So they differ from acetic acid because they have no hydrogen atom which is readily replaceable by an atom of a metal. As a first step we may therefore distinguish acetic acid as $C_2H_3O_2$. H from methyl formate or glycollic aldehyde $C_2H_4O_2$. This indicates that the radicle $C_2H_3O_2$ is common to all acetates like sodium acetate $Na(C_2H_3O_2)$ and calcium acetate $Ca(C_2H_3O_2)_2$, which are respectively formed by the action of vinegar on baking powder and chalk.

The formula $C_2H_3O_2$. H only conveys one set of facts about the chemical behaviour of acetic acid. For instance, the whole atom cluster $C_2H_3O_2$ can be combined with various metals just as the atom Cl of the acid HCl (or Cl . H) can be combined with metals in the salts which we call chlorides, and these *acetates* in general have certain common properties just as the chlorides in general have certain common properties. As it stands this formula gives us no clue to how we might build up acetic acid from its elements. When it is written in the form CH_3COO . H it suggests several ways of building up acetic acid from its elements, when we have mastered one or two quite general rules about the behaviour of carbon compounds. When you have seen the reason for splitting the complex radicle $(C_2H_3O_2)$ into (CH_3COO), you will see how fruitful this device is. For example, it shows us how we could build up acetic acid from the methane CH_4 of coal gas if we wanted to do so. If mixed with chlorine in sunlight, methane combines to form a series of compounds in which one, two, three, or four atoms of hydrogen are replaced by chlorine atoms. One of these is called methyl chloride CH_3Cl, another is the familiar anaesthetic chloroform $CHCl_3$. A similar series of compounds is formed by the substitution of the element iodine, which is very closely related to chlorine in its properties. One of these is methyl iodide CH_3I. Another is the antiseptic iodoform CHI_3. When a chlorine or iodine derivative of a carbon compound is heated with potassium cyanide, the chlorine or iodine atom is generally replaced by the cyanide radicle CN. Thus we can easily convert methyl iodide into methyl cyanide CH_3CN. The cyanide radicle has a peculiarity which is very important. It is easily broken up by boiling in the presence of water. This results in the formation of ammonia and another radicle. For instance, if we go on boiling a solution of potassium cyanide itself we get a different salt, potassium formate, which contains no nitrogen. Its composition corresponds to the formula $K . CO_2H$ or $H . CO_2K$. This is the potassium salt of the formic acid ($H . CO_2H$) found in nettles and in the sting of ants. The acid itself can be formed in an analogous way by prolonged boiling of a solution of the acid (prussic or hydrocyanic acid) of which potassium cyanide is a salt. Prussic acid $H . CN$ becomes $H . CO_2H$. The preparation of either formic acid or potassium formate might be put in a general way, thus:

$$X . CN + 2H_2O \rightarrow X . CO_2 . H + NH_3$$

In the same way methyl cyanide when boiled for a long while with water becomes acetic acid, thus

$$CH_3CN + 2H_2O \rightarrow CH_3CO_2 . H + NH_3$$

Writing the formula of acetic acid in this way tells us first that it is derived from the methane of coal gas by replacing one of the hydrogen atoms of methane CH_4 with the radicle CO_2 . H or as it is more often written COO . H, because in certain circumstances one of the oxygen atoms can be displaced. Further, it tells us that the substance shares all the characteristics common to all compounds with the radicle COOH, i.e. the "organic acids." The tremendous economy of this symbolism depends on two facts. The first is that, since compounds containing a given radicle have certain common characteristics, we can detect what radicles make up its molecule, when we have determined the molecular weight and percentage composition of a compound, if its behaviour is fairly well known. The second is that since there are comparatively few rules about the way in which one radicle can be replaced by another, we can see at once what has to be done to build up any organic compound from any other which we have at our disposal.

We may illustrate this once more by considering an organic acid called succinic acid which occurs in fossil wood and amber. By its molecular weight and composition it is found to be $C_4H_6O_4$. From its chemical behaviour it is recognized to have two COOH radicles and may be represented as $C_2H_4(COOH)_2$. Besides methane, coal gas contains a hydrocarbon called ethylene which is responsible for its luminosity. Its formula is C_2H_4. Ethylene combines to form "addition compounds" with chlorine and iodine represented by the formulae $C_2H_4Cl_2$ or $C_2H_4I_2$ (ethylene chloride and iodide). By heating these with potassium cyanide we get $C_2H_4(CN)_2$ or ethylene cyanide. On boiling this we get succinic acid. So if we know the radicle formula of succinic acid, we see at once that it can be built up from ethylene in a series of steps precisely analogous to those used in building up acetic acid from methane.

The different behaviour of ethylene and methane in their reactions with chlorine or iodine illustrates a device which is very useful in suggesting what sorts of radicles are combined in a molecule. When we say that a radicle behaves like an element in remaining stable through a large variety of chemical changes (so that some radicles have been confused with elements until it has been found possible to build them up from elements), we mean that the same elements persist as a group in the same proportions by weight throughout a series of reactions and that, when present as a group in these proportions in a compound, they confer special characteristics upon it. This is an empirical fact whether we accept or reject the atomic view of matter. We have not yet recognized any general clue to the circumstances in which radicles are formed. The recognition of such a clue proved to be one of the most fruitful developments of the atomic doctrine. It depends on the characteristic called valency (p. 485).

In the last chapter it was said that sodium has a valency of 1, because one atom of sodium replaces one atom of hydrogen in acids like H_2SO_4 or HCl to form salts such as $NaHSO_4$, Na_2SO_4, or NaCl. Likewise calcium is 2-valent because one atom of it replaces two hydrogen atoms, as in $Ca(HSO_4)_2$, $CaSO_4$, or $CaCl_2$. You may look on water as a molecule of oxygen in which one atom is replaced by two hydrogen atoms. Thus oxygen is 2-valent. It comes to the same thing to say that oxygen is divalent, because one atom of oxygen cannot combine with more than two atoms of hydrogen, as in water. Similarly you may say that carbon is 4-valent or quadri-valent, because one atom of carbon cannot combine with more than four atoms of hydrogen as in methane (CH_4). The valencies of many elements, as defined in this way, exhibit a consistent system of behaviour. Thus one atom of oxygen will combine with two atoms of an element like sodium as in the oxide Na_2O, or one atom of calcium as in quicklime CaO. Many elements form two types of compounds in one of which the valency is n, and in the other $8 - n$. Thus chlorine forms a hydride HCl and an oxide Cl_2O_7. In the first it is univalent, in the second 7-valent.

Although there are many exceptions to this simple rule in the behaviour of mineral compounds, it is a safe rule to follow in dealing with the compounds of carbon. Within those limits we may say that any radicle has a definite valency, and any element which can replace a radicle or a group of radicles behaves as if it also had a fixed valency. One atom of the 4-valent element carbon can combine with two atoms of oxygen each of which is equivalent to two atoms of hydrogen, as in CO_2. If it combines with less, as in CO, the resulting compound is *capable of taking on more oxygen*, as when carbon monoxide burns in air to form CO_2. Thus we may pictorially represent the difference between the two oxides as

$$(a)\ O = C = O \qquad\qquad (b)\ ? = C = O$$
(carbon dioxide)   (carbon monoxide)

The question mark represents an invitation to take on more oxygen. Similarly, we may represent methane (CH_4) and ethylene (C_2H_4) pictorially thus

$$
(a)\quad
\begin{array}{c}
\text{H} \\
| \\
\text{H}\!-\!\text{C}\!-\!\text{H} \\
| \\
\text{H}
\end{array}
\qquad (b) \qquad
\begin{array}{c}
\text{H} \quad \text{H} \\
|\quad\ | \\
\text{H}\!-\!\text{C}\!-\!\text{C}\!-\!\text{H} \\
|\quad\ | \\
?\quad\ ?
\end{array}
$$

The question mark indicates that when ethylene reacts with chlorine it simply adds on more atoms to its molecule, forming the *addition* compound $C_2H_4Cl_2$, whereas when methane reacts it can only do so by replacing one or more hydrogen atoms to form *substitution* compounds like chloroform ($CHCl_3$).

This pictorial device is of very great fruitfulness for various reasons. One is that the number of atoms in a simple compound may tell us at once whether it forms compounds by addition or substitution. A second is that if we can spot one radicle by the general properties of a compound, there may be only *one possible arrangement* of the remaining atoms—thus indicating the nature of the remaining radicles—or at least a comparatively small number *of possible arrangements to explore*. A third depends on a curious feature which we encounter when we classify organic compounds.

Carbon compounds may be grouped in various classes distinguished by a common radicle, such as the radicle COOH of the organic acids. Inside these groups the members form an ascending series of increasing molecular weight illustrated by two fatty acids already mentioned. Formic acid is the simplest member of a series of which the second is acetic acid. The difference between the two formulae H . COOH and CH_3COOH is that the second has one carbon and two hydrogen atoms (CH_2) more than the first. Propionic acid (C_2H_5COOH) differs from acetic in the same way. Butyric acid (C_3H_7COOH), found in rancid butter, differs from propionic acid in the same way. When these acids are arranged in serial order from the lowest (with least molecular weight) to the highest, we find a continuous gradation in their physical properties. Thus the boiling points run as follows:

Formic acid	..	..	..	.. 101° C.
Acetic acid	..	..	..	. 118° C.
Propionic acid		..	..	.. 141° C.
Butyric acid {(a)	..	..	..	.. 155° C.
{(b)	..	..	..	.. 163° C.

You will notice at the foot of the list *two* butyric acids. There are, in fact, two substances with the same formula C_3H_7COOH and with similar chemical properties in so far as they are both acids and both form salts containing the radicle COO. In other respects their chemical properties like their physical properties (melting and boiling points, specific gravity in the liquid state, etc.) are not quite identical. The existence of two butyric acids is in accordance with the principle of valency which shows us that the monovalent radicle C_3H_7 can be represented in two ways thus:

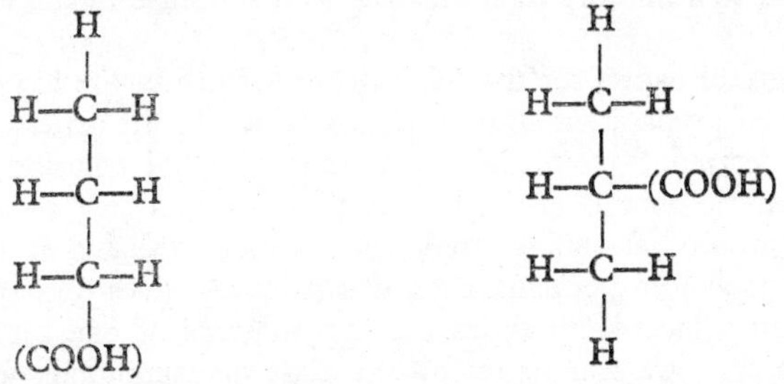

On the other hand the radicle C_2H_5 of propionic acid can only be represented in one way corresponding to the existence of only one known compound of the formula C_2H_5COOH.

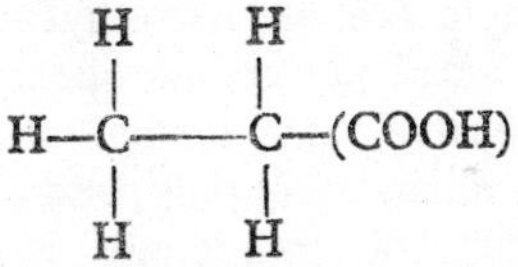

Carbon compounds can thus be grouped in two ways. First, we can divide them and subdivide them into groups with common properties which depend on the possession of the same radicle. Second, we can arrange the members of each class in a "series" in which the complexity of the molecule increases in regular steps by the addition of one carbon and two hydrogen atoms or, if you prefer to put it that way, the replacement of one hydrogen atom by the *univalent* radicle CH_3. We can thus look on every series as starting from the hydrogen molecule (H_2) by replacement of a hydrogen atom in this way:

	Saturated Fatty Hydrocarbons	Saturated Fatty Monohydric Alcohols	Saturated Fatty Monobasic Acids
1.	H CH_3 or (CH_4) (methane)	H OH or (H_2O) (water)	H COOH (formic acid)
2.	CH_3 CH_3 or (C_2H_6) (ethane)	CH_3 OH (methyl alcohol)	CH_3 COOH (acetic acid)
3.	C_3H_8 (propane)	C_2H_5 OH (ethyl alcohol)	C_2H_5 COOH (propionic acid)
4.	C_4H_{10} (the butanes)	C_3H_7 OH (propyl alcohol)	C_3H_7 COOH (butyric acid)

In all such series the physical properties of the members show a consistent gradation. Thus the lowest members of the "hydrocarbon" series beginning with methane are gases at room temperature. The compounds C_5H_{12} and C_6H_{14}, forming the fraction of American petroleum called petrol ether, and the compounds C_6H_{14} and C_7H_{16}, of which the gasoline of American petroleum is a mixture, are liquids boiling just above room temperature, and hence highly volatile. The remaining liquid fractions of American petroleum: naphtha (C_7H_{16}, C_8H_{18}), benzoline (C_8H_{18} and C_9H_{20}), and kerosene ($C_{10}H_{22}$ to $C_{16}H_{34}$) are less volatile. The higher members of the same series are vaselines and waxes. The crude paraffin wax of shale is a mixture of substances with formulae ranging from $C_{18}H_{38}$ to $C_{43}H_{88}$.

The technical names for the substances set forth in the last table suggest their mode of preparation and not their position in the series. Thus methyl alcohol is derived from methane by boiling methyl chloride with caustic potash. Butyric acid is derived from butyl alcohol just as acetic acid is derived from ethyl alcohol, by treatment with an oxidizing agent, i.e. something, like potassium permanganate, which readily gives up oxygen or takes up hydrogen. Since every series goes up in steps of one carbon and two hydrogen atoms, we can represent any class of compounds with common properties depending on the presence of a particular radicle by a general formula C_nH_{2n+1} . R or more briefly X . R where X is the *alkyl* radicle, C_nH_{2n+1}, and R is the radicle characteristic of the group, e.g. CH_3 in the "saturated fatty hydrocarbons," COOH in the saturated monobasic fatty acids, and OH in the simple alcohols, like ethyl alcohol (C_2H_5OH) or "spirits of wine," which with a small percentage of impurities is the same as the familiar "methylated spirits," and methyl alcohol (CH_3OH), the spirit distilled from heating sawdust, wood pulp, and other wood residues.

The classification of carbon compounds is a big task to face. Since laziness is the mother of ingenuity, you will need a good reason before proceeding with it. So before we continue let us be perfectly clear about the *social* meaning of what we are doing. Till the coming of the coal economy man had depended for the essentials of civilized life on a variety of substances produced by animals and plants which (like the silkworm or the madder plant) grew only in one place. Because carbon compounds are all built up from a very small number of elements, we are no longer dependent on limited supplies available in restricted areas. We now know how their molecules are put together. The social art of finding universal substitutes for local organic products involves the discovery of two classes of general rules which make up the essentials of organic chemistry. The first are the rules of constitution which allow us to detect which radicles are present in a carbon compound by the kind of chemical behaviour it exhibits. The second are the rules of synthesis which allow us to replace one radicle by another. By using them we can make a substance when we know what its constitution is.

RULES OF CONSTITUTION

The most important rules of constitution are embodied in the following brief survey of the principal classes of simpler carbon compounds. Some of them, like esters, fatty acids or alcohols, occur commonly in living organisms. Some of them, like the hydrocarbons, are simple disintegration products of organic matter. Some of them occur very little in nature but are easily derived from natural products by simple laboratory reactions, and are of immense importance as reagents to assist in replacing one radicle by another. For instance, the "alkyl halides"* like CH_3I are extremely rare in organic matter. The same is true of the alkyl cyanides like CH_3CN. These substances are easily made from hydrocarbons, as we have seen already; and once made they allow us to build from any hydrocarbon (C_nH_{2n+2}) an alcohol $(C_nH_{2n+1} . OH)$ or an acid $(C_nH_{2n+1} . COOH)$ according to the simple recipe:

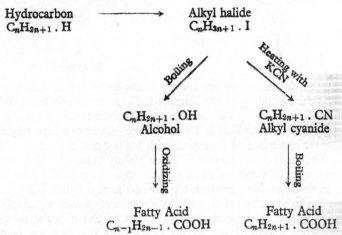

$$\text{Hydrocarbon} \longrightarrow \text{Alkyl halide}$$
$$C_nH_{2n+1} . H \qquad\qquad\qquad C_nH_{2n+1} . I$$

Boiling   *Heating with KCN*

$$C_nH_{2n+1} . OH \qquad\qquad C_nH_{2n+1} . CN$$
$$\text{Alcohol} \qquad\qquad\qquad \text{Alkyl cyanide}$$

Oxidizing   *Boiling*

$$\text{Fatty Acid} \qquad\qquad\qquad \text{Fatty Acid}$$
$$C_{n-1}H_{2n-1} . COOH \qquad\qquad C_nH_{2n+1} . COOH$$

The principal classes of simple carbon compounds may now be set out under the following headings.

(1) *The Hydrocarbons.*—These contain only carbon and hydrogen and fall into two main classes: the fatty, and the aromatic, hydrocarbons, represented respectively by the series

(*a*) Fatty or marsh gas series: CH_4 (methane), C_2H_6 (ethane), C_3H_8 (propane), etc. The higher members are the various volatile spirits, illuminants, vaselines, and waxes, of American petroleum and shale distillate.

(*b*) Aromatic or coal tar series: C_6H_6 (benzene), C_7H_8 (toluene), C_8H_{10} (xylene)—all present in the light oil of coal tar. The next member is mesitylene C_9H_{12}.

There is an important difference between these two series. Unless we take the extreme course of burning it away, the molecule of an aromatic compound always sticks to six of its carbon atoms in any changes it undergoes. In consequence the molecule of an aromatic compound (i.e. a compound in which one or more hydrogen atoms of an aromatic hydrocarbon are replaced by a radicle) is represented pictorially as having a central hexagon

---

* Fluorine, chlorine, bromine, and iodine are called the "halogen" elements, and their derivatives may be referred to collectively as "halides."

of carbon atoms.* Each of the six has one useful valency, as the following formulae for benzene and toluene indicate:

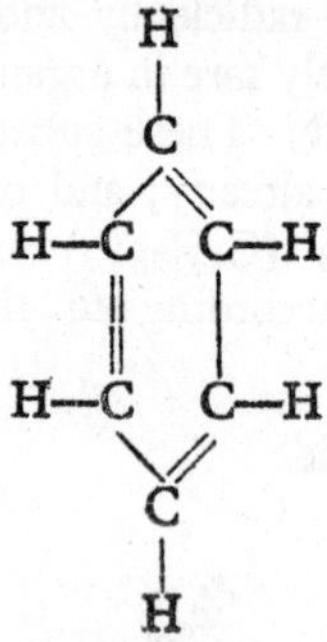

(a) Benzene

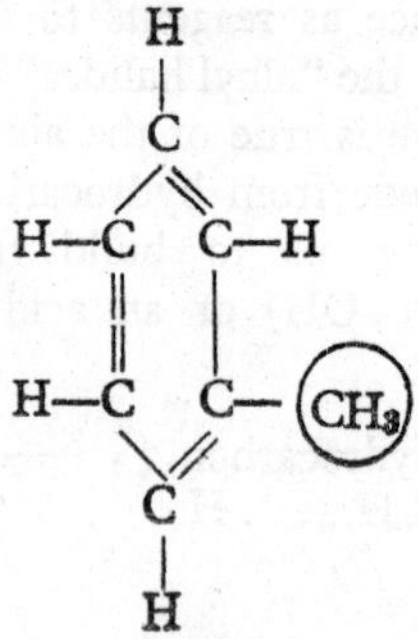

(b) Toluene

With a stable nucleus of six carbon atoms there is only one substance (benzene) corresponding to the formula C_6H_6 and one substance (toluene) with the formula of C_7H_8. On the other hand, there are four substances corresponding to the formula C_8H_{10}. Three of these (the xylenes) are very similar in behaviour and mode of formation, with boiling points between 137° and 140° C. The other (ethyl benzene), with a boiling point 134° C., is made in a different way. The xylenes all have the *methyl* group (CH_3) because they can be made by reaction between toluene and methyl iodide (CH_3I). Ethyl benzene can be made by reaction of benzene with ethyl iodide (C_2H_5I).

This illustrates once again the fruitfulness of the pictorial or valency formula. While it only allows for the existence of one benzene, or of one toluene, the valency formula gives us four possibilities for a substance with six stable carbon atoms in the molecule C_8H_{10}. Thus the ethyl radicle C_2H_5 may replace one of six equivalent hydrogen atoms giving

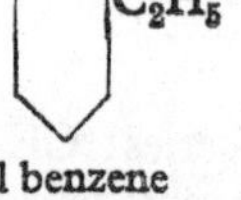

Ethyl benzene

Alternatively two methyl radicles (CH_3) might replace two hydrogen atoms giving three arrangements (see also p. 536) according as the hydrogen atoms replaced are attached to (a) adjacent carbon atoms of the nucleus or to carbon atoms separated by (b) one or (c) two other carbon atoms, thus:

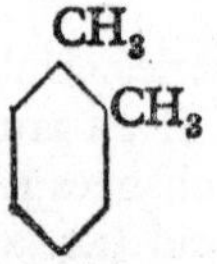

(a) o-xylene

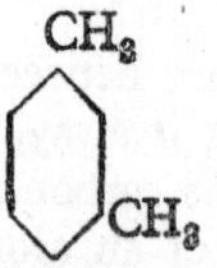

(b) m-xylene

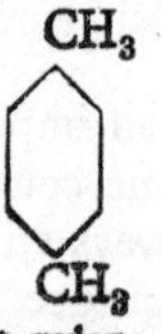

(c) p-xylene

* In the structural formulae of aromatic compounds it is usual to symbolize the benzene ring (or what is left of it) by a simple hexagon. This represents the six carbon atoms and such of the six hydrogen atoms as have not been replaced (as one has in ethyl benzene) by some radicle.

Besides these two basic series which form derivative compounds by replacement or substitution of a hydrogen atom by a radicle, there are other series of "unsaturated" hydrocarbons. Such are the ethylene (C_nH_{2n}) series: ethylene C_2H_4, propylene C_3H_6, etc., and the series C_nH_{2n-2}, of which the first member *acetylene* (C_2H_2) is formed, as we all know, by the spontaneous decomposition of calcium carbide in the presence of water. The peculiarity of these unsaturated hydrocarbons has been mentioned. They form addition compounds with the halogens (chlorine, bromine, and iodine) as if the four valencies of their carbon atoms were not *satisfied*. Hydrocarbons of the ethylene series are obtained by heating alkyl halides with alcoholic solutions of caustic potash, e.g. C_2H_5I gives C_2H_4, C_3H_7I gives C_3H_6 (propylene).

(2) *The Alcohols and Phenols.*—The alcohols are substances in which the "hydroxyl" radicle OH present in caustic alkalis replaces one or more hydrogen atoms in a hydrocarbon. Among aromatic hydrocarbons this may happen in two ways. From benzene (Fig. 270) itself we can make only the substance called carbolic acid or *phenol* (C_6H_5OH) found in the middle oil fraction of coal tar, thus:

From toluene (C_7H_8), or any higher hydrocarbons of the same series, there are two general alternatives which correspond to two different classes of aromatic compounds. Thus there are four compounds having the formula C_7H_7OH, of which three (*a, b, c*) arise by replacement of a hydrogen atom in the "nucleus," and one (*d*) arises from replacement in the "side chain."

TOLUENE

(a) o-cresol   (b) m-cresol   (c) p-cresol   (d) Benzyl alcohol

When a hydrogen atom of the "side chain" is replaced by an OH group the resulting compound is more like a typical alcohol of the fatty series. The product of *"nuclear"* substitution is called a "phenol" and has somewhat different properties, to which we shall refer later.

Corresponding to the saturated fatty hydrocarbons, like methane, we have a series of alcohols with one OH group already mentioned. To this methyl alcohol and ethyl alcohol—the alcohol of our happiest and most hallowed associations—belong. The fifth member of the series, counting methyl alcohol as the first, is *amyl* alcohol (C_5H_{11} . OH) which for reasons already indicated has eight closely allied forms having different physical properties. They also differ chemically in a way which will be mentioned later. The highest members (like *cetyl* alcohol $C_{16}H_{33}$. OH) are waxy substances. Corresponding to ethyl alcohol there is a *di*hydric alcohol $C_2H_4(OH)_2$ called glycol, and corresponding to propyl alcohol (C_3H_7 . OH) a *tri*hydric alcohol $C_3H_5(OH)_3$ which is glycerine. Corresponding to the hydrocarbon C_6H_{14} of gasoline, there are various 6-hydric alcohols C_6H_8 . $(OH)_6$, differing according to the internal arrangement of the hydrocarbon portion of the molecule. All the alcohols are non-electrolytes. They can be formed from corresponding alkyl halides by boiling with caustic potash. The former can themselves be formed from alcohols by boiling them with the halogens (chlorine, bromine, or iodine) in the presence of red phosphorus. On account of the OH group they resemble mineral alkalis in combining with acids to form salts called *esters*. In esters the "alkyl" radicle X, i.e. (C_nH_{2n+1}) of the general formula X . (OH) replaces the hydrogen of the acid as does the metal of an alkali. This does not take place quickly as with reactions of electrolytes. It proceeds slowly after prolonged boiling, the products being separable by distillation. Esters differ from mineral salts in being non-electrolytes like the alcohols. The nitrate of glycerine $C_3H_5(NO_3)_3$ called nitroglycerine is highly explosive. Dynamite is a mixture of nitroglycerine and a porous natural earth called kieselguhr.

(3) *Organic Acids.*—The organic acids all contain the "carboxyl" radicle COOH. The most important series (p. 511) of which the first member is formic acid (H . COOH), corresponds to saturated fatty hydrocarbons in which one methyl group (CH_3) is replaced by COOH. In another series one hydrogen atom is also replaced by COOH. The first is oxalic acid (COOH . COOH), a highly poisonous acid with a very insoluble calcium salt. Crystals of the latter irritate the bladder in the "oxaluria" resulting from eating too much rhubarb or fruits which contain oxalic acid. The next member, *malonic acid*, COOH CH_2 COOH, has the same relation to acetic as has oxalic to formic acid. It is of very great importance in synthesis, especially in the preparation of the large class of soporific drugs called the "barbituric" derivatives.

Another series is that of the "hydroxy" acids in which one hydrogen atom of the molecule is replaced by an OH radicle. Carbonic acid may be regarded as the first. The second member is called *glycollic* (hydroxy-acetic) acid (CH_2 OH . COOH) and the third is *hydracrylic* acid (CH_2OH . CH_2COOH). Hydracrylic acid is one of two hydroxy-propionic acids. The other, called *lactic* acid (CH_3 . CH(OH) . COOH), is the fatigue substance formed in our muscles during exercise. More complex familiar fatty acids include tartaric acid (of grape juice and sherbet), which is a dihydroxy derivative of the third member of the oxalic series, i.e. $C_2H_2(OH)_2(COOH)_2$ (dihydroxy succinic acid or dihydroxy-carboxy-propionic acid). The various aromatic acids in which one or more (COOH) radicles replace one or more hydrogen atoms of the nucleus or side chain of an aromatic hydrocarbon or phenol will be touched on later.

(4) *Esters.*—The structure of an ester has been explained already. This class includes the common flavouring essences of fruit juices. Many of them are compounds formed from simple fatty acids of the acetic series and

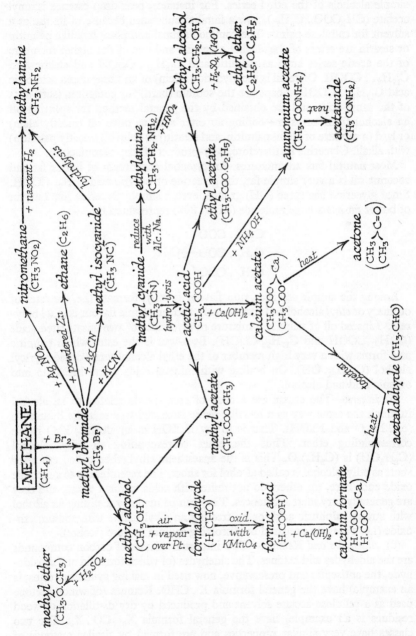

FIG. 264.—SYNTHESES OF PARAFFIN DERIVATIVES FROM METHANE, THE PRINCIPLE HYDROCARBON OF COAL GAS

simple alcohols of the ethyl series. For instance, pear drop essence is amyl acetate ($CH_3COO . C_5H_{11}$), now a familiar substance because of its use as a solvent for cellulose paints. The common animal and plant fats like palmitin or stearin are esters of the alcohol glycerine and one of the higher members of the acetic series such as palmitic acid $C_{15}H_{31} . COOH$ and stearic acid $C_{17}H_{35} . COOH$. Olive oil is the glyceride (olein) of an unsaturated acid oleic acid $C_{17}H_{33} . COOH$. Soaps are the sodium (hard)* or potassium (soft) salts of the same acids and are obtained by the general method for splitting off an alcohol from an ester—boiling an ester such as olive oil (mostly olein) or lard (a mixture of olein, palmitin, and stearin) or palm oil (mostly palmitin) with alkali. Glycerine is, therefore, a by-product of soap manufacture.

Most natural fats are mixtures. An essential constituent of butter fat and coconut oil is a very simple fat, the glyceride of butyric acid $C_3H_7 . COOH$. Since glycerine has three (OH) groups, even a simple glyceride like butyrin of butter fat has a large molecule (M.W. 302) represented by

$$C_3H_7 . COO\diagdown$$
$$C_3H_7 . COO\longrightarrow C_3H_5$$
$$C_3H_7 . COO\diagup$$

Among the simple essences, rum flavour is ethyl formate (i.e. the ester of ordinary or *ethyl* alcohol and formic acid), and pineapple flavour is ethyl butyrate. Linseed oil of paint is a mixture of glycerides of two unsaturated acids ($C_{17}H_{31} COOH$ and $C_{17}H_{29} COOH$). Bees-wax is the ester which palmitic acid forms with a very high member of the ethyl alcohol series called myricyl alcohol ($C_{30}H_{61} . OH$). On boiling with mineral acids esters break up into organic acid and alcohol.

(5) *Ethers.*—The ethers are a class of compounds related to an alcohol in much the same way as a metallic oxide is related to a metallic hydroxide (e.g. Na_2O and $NaOH$). That is to say if XOH is an alcohol, X_2O is the corresponding ether. Thus the ether corresponding to ethyl alcohol (C_2H_5OH) is (C_2H_5)$_2O$. This is the anaesthetic ethyl ether, called ether for short as ethyl alcohol is called alcohol for short. The resemblance to a metallic oxide ends here, for ethers do not unite with acids to form esters, and they are generally very inert substances. They can be made by distilling an alcohol with strong sulphuric acid, or by treating an alkyl halide with sodium ethoxide (i.e. a reagent prepared by dissolving sodium in pure alcohol).

(6) *Aldehydes and Ketones.*—Two important classes of carbon compounds are the aldehydes and ketones. The aldehydes (of which formalin or formaldehyde, the antiseptic and preservative, now used in making synthetic resins, is an example) have the general formula $X . CHO$. Ketones (of which acetone used as a cellulose acetate solvent and produced by dry distillation of wood residues is an example) have the general formula $X_a . CO . X_b$. The two classes have very similar properties and are formed by similar methods of preparation. They both form "addition" compounds with sodium hydrogen sulphite ($NaHSO_3$). They are both "reduced" to an alcohol when treated

* Modern hard soaps may contain up to 40 per cent resin and other substances, e.g. sodium silicate, to give bulk.

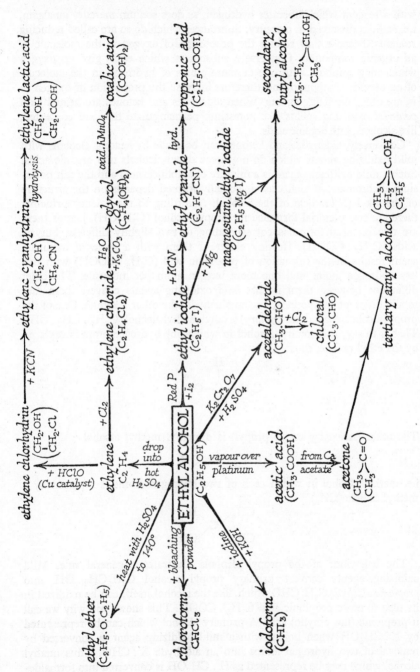

Fig. 265.—Some Simple Syntheses from Ethyl Alcohol which May be Obtained from Fermentation of Grain

with a reagent which liberates hydrogen, as does sodium mercury amalgam, i.e. sodium dissolved in mercury. Substances which do so are called reducing reagents, because they reduce the proportion of oxygen in the molecule of an organic compound. Conversely, substances which easily give up oxygen which may combine with one or more atoms of hydrogen in the molecule of an organic compound, and therefore increase the proportion of oxygen in it, are called oxidizing agents. When aldehydes and ketones are heated with *powerful* oxidizing agents like potassium permanganate they are converted, like alcohols, into organic acids.

Conversely, aldehydes and ketones can be made by heating alcohols with mild oxidizing agents which do not break down alcohols into organic acids. Such a mild oxidizing agent is a mixture of sulphuric acid and the salt potassium dichromate. Which class is actually formed depends on the structure of the alkyl (X) radicle of the alcohol. According to the valency principle there are two pictorial formulae for propyl alcohol (C_3H_7OH), just as there are two pictorial formulae corresponding to two slightly different butyric acids ($C_3H_7 . COOH$). Heating either of them with a *powerful* oxidizing agent results in the formation of propionic acid ($C_2H_5 . COOH$) with two less hydrogen atoms and one more oxygen atom per molecule. The chief difference between them is that *mild* oxidizing agents convert them into totally different compounds, one an aldehyde, the other a ketone. One of the propyl alcohols (called the *primary*) is ethyl methyl alcohol ($C_2H_5 . CH_2 . OH$). That is to say, it is methyl alcohol in which one hydrogen atom is replaced by the ethyl radicle, thus:

$$C_2H_5 - \overset{\displaystyle H}{\underset{\displaystyle H}{C}} - OH$$

The other (*secondary* or iso-propyl) is dimethyl methyl alcohol

$$(CH_3)_2CH . OH$$

i.e. methyl alcohol in which each of two hydrogen atoms is replaced by a methyl radicle (CH_3)

$$\overset{\displaystyle CH_3}{\underset{\displaystyle CH_3}{\diagdown}} C \overset{\displaystyle H}{\underset{\displaystyle OH}{\diagup}}$$

The behaviour of the propyl alcohols illustrates a general rule. Mild oxidizing agents convert primary propyl alcohol $C_2H_5CH_2 . OH$ into *propionic aldehyde* C_2H_5CHO which, like the alcohol itself, can be oxidized in its turn to make propionic acid $C_2H_5 . COOH$. This shows you why we call it propionic (not ethylic) acid. A primary alcohol which can be represented by $X . CH_2OH$ when boiled with a mild oxidizing agent is converted by removal of two hydrogen atoms into an aldehyde $X . CHO$. Thus methyl alcohol which may be represented as $H . CH_2OH$ is converted into formaldehyde $H . CHO$, which is converted by a *strong* oxidizing agent, like potassium permanganate, to formic acid $H . COOH$. Secondary propyl alcohol

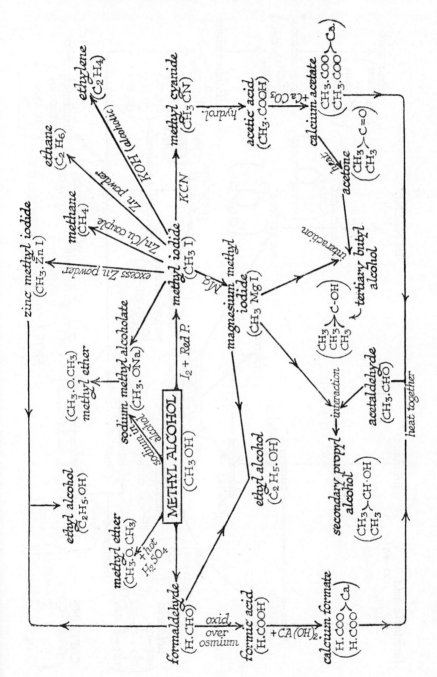

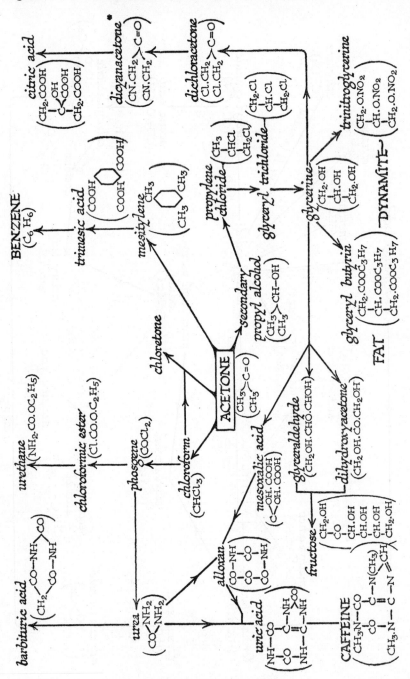

* This cannot be done at one step.

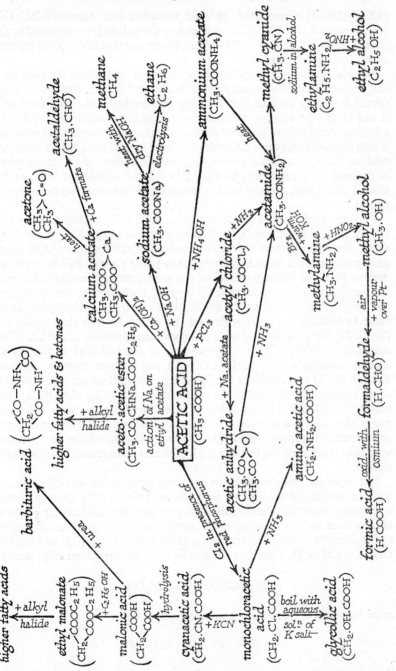

FIGS. 266, 267, AND 268

Some syntheses which may be effected from the three principal products of the dry distillation of wood pulp: methyl alcohol (wood spirit), acetic acid, and acetone. Note that the latter can be made the starting point for the same class of compounds as the coal tar derivative.

[($CH_3)_2CHOH$] is converted by mild oxidation into acetone ($CH_3)_2CO$, better written $CH_3 . CO . CH_3$. A *secondary* alcohol can be represented by the general formula $XY . CH . OH$ and oxidizes to a ketone $XY . CO$ by removal of two hydrogen atoms.

Acetone is a substance with interesting social possibilities. It gives us a link between an urban economy based on coal and a rural economy in which science is used to the full. Acetone along with methyl alcohol and acetic acid is one of the three major products formed by dry distillation of cellulose, e.g. when wood pulp is heated or weeds are burned in a slow fire. On distilling it with sulphuric acid three molecules condense to form *mesitylene* or trimethyl benzene (C_9H_{12}), and thus give us the aromatic nucleus of six carbon atoms in the coal tar constituents. In Figs. 266–8 various syntheses from methyl alcohol, acetic acid, and acetone illustrate why we have outlived the necessity of coal.

Further oxidation of acetone ($CH_3 . CO . CH_3$) yields acetic acid CH_3COOH, in which the *OH* radicle replaces one methyl CH_3 group. This shows you why we write the carboxyl radicle COOH and not CO_2H. Complete oxidation of a secondary alcohol thus yields a lower acid than the one derived from the primary alcohol of the same general formula. Aside from the method of preparation used for making both ketones and aldehydes, one special method is generally applicable for each class. Aldehydes can be made by cooking dry calcium formate ($H . COO)_2Ca$ with the calcium salt ($X . COO)_2Ca$ of a fatty acid. This gives the aldehyde $X . CHO$. Thus acetaldehyde ($CH_3 . CHO$) corresponding to ethyl alcohol is formed by cooking calcium acetate ($CH_3 . COO)_2Ca$ and calcium formate together. Ketones X_2CO are formed by simply cooking the calcium salt ($X . COO)_2Ca$ of an organic acid by itself. Thus calcium acetate ($CH_3 . COO)_2Ca$ gives acetone ($CH_3)_2CO$. The oxidation of alcohols with more than one (OH) group gives rise to a mixture of substances depending on whether a strong or weak oxidizing agent is used. The following table shows how the "dibasic" acids (like oxalic) and the hydroxy acids (like lactic) are related to a dihydroxy alcohol.

Just as we can make an aldehyde or ketone by oxidizing an alcohol we can make an alcohol by *reducing* an aldehyde or ketone, i.e. by treating it with a reducing agent that introduces hydrogen into the molecule or removes oxygen from it. The reducing agent usually used is an amalgam of sodium and mercury in water. This converts a CHO radicle to CH_2OH and the CO radicle to $CH . OH$. Thus on reduction of acetaldehyde we get ethyl alcohol

$$CH_3 . CHO \rightarrow CH_3CH_2OH$$

or on reduction of formaldehyde we get methyl alcohol

$$H . CHO \rightarrow H . CH_2OH$$

On reduction of acetone we get secondary propyl alcohol,

$$(CH_3)_2CO \rightarrow (CH_3)_2 . CHOH$$

DIHYDRIC ALCOHOLS, DIBASIC AND HYDROXY ACIDS

Hydroxy Acid	Aldehyde	Alcohol	Aldehyde	Acid Aldehyde	Dibasic Acid
$OH.CO.OH$ Carbonic acid	⋯	⋯	⋯	⋯	⋯
$CH_2.OH.COOH$ Glycollic Acid	$CH_2OH\ CHO$ Glycollic aldehyde	$(CH_2OH)_2$ Glycol (ethylene glycol)	$(CHO)_2$ Glyoxal	$CHO.COOH$ Glyoxalic acid	$(COOH)_2$ Oxalic acid
$CH_2OH.CH_2COOH$ Hydracrylic / $CH_3CH.OH\ COOH$ Lactic Acid		$CH_2(CH_2OH)_2$ propylene glycol			$CH_2(COOH)_2$ Malonic Acid
		$C_2H_4(CH_2OH)_2$ butylene glycol			$C_2H_4(COOH)_2$ Succinic Acid

NOTE.—*Malic* = hydroxy } succinic acid
Tartaric = dihydroxy }

Citric acid is:
$$\begin{array}{l} CH_2COOH \\ \ \ | \\ COH.COOH \\ \ \ | \\ CH_2\,COOH \end{array}$$

Some relations between the saturated fatty hydrocarbons, simple fatty alcohols, aldehydes, ketones, and simple fatty acids are shown in the following table:

MONOHYDRIC ALCOHOLS AND MONOBASIC ACIDS

CH_4 Methane	CH_3OH ($H . CH_2 . OH$) Methyl Alcohol	$H . CHO$ Formaldehyde	$H . COOH$ Formic Acid
C_2H_6 Ethane	C_2H_5OH ($CH_3 . CH_2 . OH$) Ethyl Alcohol	$CH_3 . CHO$ Acetaldehyde	$CH_3 . COOH$ Acetic Acid
C_3H_8	C_3H_7OH ($C_2H_5 . CH_2 . OH$) Primary Propyl Alcohol	$C_2H_5 . CHO$ Propionic aldehyde	$C_2H_5 . COOH$ Propionic Acid
Propane	$(CH_3)_2 CH . OH$ Secondary Propyl Alcohol	$(CH_3)_2 CO$ Acetone	
C_4H_{10}	Two primary butyl alcohols, C_4H_9OH:— $C_2H_5 . CH_2 . CH_2 . OH$ and $(CH_3)_2 . CH . CH_2 . OH$ Secondary butyl alcohol	Two aldehydes $C_2H_5 . CH_2 . CHO$ $(CH_3)_2 . CH . CHO$	$C_3H_7 . COOH$
Butane	$(C_2H_5) (CH_3) . CHOH$ Tertiary butyl alcohol $(CH_3)_3 . COH$	One Ketone	Two acids (butyric)
C_5H_{12} Pentane	Eight Amyl Alcohols		$C_4H_9 . COOH$ 4 valeric acids

The simplest sugars like glucose or galactose having the general formula $C_6H_{12}O_6$ are aldehydes or ketones of the 6-hydric alcohols $[C_6H_8(OH)_6]$ in which (a) *one* CH_2OH group is replaced by a CHO (aldehyde) radicle, or (b) *one* CHOH group is replaced by a CO (keto) group. Either means eliminating two hydrogen atoms. We might therefore call them alcoholic ketones or aldehydes. The commoner sugars, cane sugar, milk sugar, and malt sugar, are formed by the union of two molecules of a simple sugar with the elimination of a molecule of water ($2 C_6H_{12}O_6 = C_{12}H_{22}O_{11} + H_2O$). When more than two simple sugars unite we get more complex carbohydrates like the dextrin of rice paper, starch (which yields first dextrin, then malt sugar on digestion with saliva and can be converted into dextrin by heat in the process of ironing starched collars) and cellulose, the last being the most complex. The cellulose molecule and that of all the natural carbohydrates except the simple sugars is built up from simple sugar molecules. Many organisms can break down cellulose to sugar, as we break down the starch of our food in digestion. Since garden weeds, sawdust, and textbooks of economics are mainly made up of sugar molecules, importing cane sugar from Java and subsidizing a beet industry in England are both illustrations of the absence of a chemically enlightened imagination at work in politics. On account of its

(OH) groups cellulose forms esters with certain acids. Such are the cellulose nitrates, a series of substances which include collodion and gun-cotton, and cellulose acetate which is prepared in one of the artificial silk processes. Cordite is a mixture of gun-cotton and trinitroglycerine.

All the classes we have touched on so far occur commonly in nature or as objects of domestic use. Those on which we shall now touch are mostly laboratory products which are important as steps in the replacement of one radicle by another. Two of these have been mentioned—the alkyl halides (like methyl iodide) and the alkyl cyanides (like methyl cyanide). The alkyl halides and cyanides are two of many classes of halogen and "cyanogen" derivatives of organic compounds: for instance, the acid chlorides (X . CO . Cl); the chloracids in which a halogen replaces hydrogen in the X radicle or *alkyl* part of the acid, e.g. $CH_2Cl COOH$ (monochloracetic acid); and the chlorhydrins, e.g. $CH_2Cl(OH)$.

The *acid chlorides*, e.g. acetyl chloride used as a cellulose solvent are formed by reaction of a dry acid with a reagent called phosphorus trichloride. Thus acetic acid (CH_3COOH) gives acetyl chloride $CH_3 . CO . Cl$. This is one reason why we write the formula of an organic acid X . COOH and not $X . CO_2H$. With the sodium salt of an organic acid, an acid chloride reacts to produce an acid anhydride, e.g. acetic anhydride $(CH_3CO)_2O$. Acetic anhydride has the same relation to acetic acid as CO_2 has to carbonic acid. Organic acids react with chlorine to form a mixture of *chloracids*, just as hydrocarbons (p. 508) react with chlorine to form alkyl halides. The chlorine atom of either an acid chloride or a chlor-acid can be replaced by the *amino* radicle NH_2 when these compounds are treated with ammonia. Chlor-acids then give rise to *aminoacids*, e.g. mon-aminoacetic acid CH_2NH_2COOH, which are weak electrolytes. Amino-acids are bricks of the protein molecule (which breaks up into them as the result of digestion) just as simple sugars are the bricks of the cellulose or starch molecule. Most proteins yield some amino-acids which also contain an SH or S—S radicle. The action of chlorine in solution on the presence of a copper compound, which acts as a catalyst, converts hydrocarbons of the ethylene (C_2H_4) series into substances called chlorhydrins such as $CH_2 . Cl . CH_2OH$. With potassium cyanide these react to form cyanhydrins such as $CH_2 . CN . CH_2OH$. The CN radicle can be converted into the COOH radicle on hydrolysis, i.e. boiling with water. So this is one way of synthesizing the hydroxy acids like hydra-crylic acid ($CH_2OH . CH_2COOH$).

Other very important classes of reagents in addition to these are the metallo-organic compounds and a series of nitrogen derivatives the amides, isocyanides, nitro-hydrocarbons and amines.

(1) *The Metallo-Organic Compounds.*—Zinc dust and magnesium powder are dissolved by alkyl halides (which are liquid) to form substances such as zinc methyl, represented by the formula $Zn(CH_3)_2$ or magnesium methiodide $Mg(CH_3)I$. These compounds are highly unstable ones. They decompose in water giving off hydrocarbons according to the general reaction

$$2 H_2O + Zn (X)_2 \rightarrow 2XH + Zn (OH)_2$$
$$2 H_2O + Mg XI \rightarrow XH + Mg (OH)I + H_2O$$

(2) *Amides.*—One of the principal reasons why we represent the carboxyl radicle as COOH is that organic acids give rise to a class of crystalline compounds called *amides*. In amides the COOH group is replaced by the complex radicle $CONH_2$. They can generally be formed by heating the ammonium salt of the acid. Thus heating ammonium acetate (CH_3 COO . NH_4) leads to elimination of a molecule of water giving acetamide. This substance has the smell of mice. Its constitution is CH_3 . CO . NH_2. The amides can also be made by treating an acid chloride with ammonia (e.g. CH_3 . CO . Cl becomes CH_3 . CO . NH_2).

The formation of an amide in this way reminds us that we can regard them as substances formed by substituting the acid radicle X . CO of an acid chloride for a hydrogen atom in ammonia (NH_3). Ammonia combines with acids to form salts, and amides do so as well. Urea NH_2 . CO . NH_2 may be regarded as an amide formed by replacement of both OH groups in carbonic acid (H_2CO_3) if we represent the latter as HO . CO . OH. Urea combines with various dibasic organic acids to form a series of very important compounds called ureides. Thus it combines with malonic acid (COOH . CH_2 . COOH) to form malonyl ureide or "barbituric acid"

$$CH_2\big\langle{}^{COOH}_{COOH} + {}^{NH_2}_{NH_2}\big\rangle CO = CH_2\big\langle{}^{CO-NH}_{CO-NH}\big\rangle CO + 2H_2O$$

The important hypnotics and anaesthetics called veronal, medinal, evipan, etc., are barbituric derivatives. Alloxan, a ureide of great importance corresponding to a hypothetical "mesoxalic" acid COOH . CO . COOH, occurs as an excretory product, which is represented by the formula CO . $(CONH)_2$: CO. This forms a second ureide which is uric acid.

The drug caffeine in tea and coffee is a trimethyl derivative of xanthine, a reduction product of uric acid.

(3) *The Amines.*—By boiling an alcohol with a solution of potassium nitrite (KNO_2) we can get an alkyl nitrite. By heating its halogen derivative with dry potassium cyanide, we can make an alkyl cyanide. With the silver salts of *nitrous* acid (silver nitrite or Ag NO_2) and prussic acid (silver cyanide, Ag CN) they form peculiar compounds which have the same molecular weight and percentage composition as the alkyl *nitrites* or cyanides but totally different properties. These classes are respectively called nitro-hydrocarbons and isocyanides. The action of fine bubbles of hydrogen from tin and hydrochloric acid or prolonged boiling with caustic potash converts an alkyl nitrite into the corresponding alcohol. Thus methyl nitrite formed by the action of nitrous acid on methyl alcohol yields methyl alcohol and nitrous

acid. Nitro-methane, which has the same formula (CH_3NO_2) as methyl nitrite, is not decomposed by boiling with caustic potash. An alkyl cyanide yields an organic acid when it is boiled with a dilute mineral acid. An alkyl isocyanide when boiled with dilute acid yields a compound called an *amine*. So does a nitro-hydrocarbon when treated with tin and hydrochloric acid.

The *amines* like methylamine CH_3NH_2 may be regarded either as hydrocarbons with one or more NH_2 radicles in place of one or more hydrogen atoms, or alternatively as ammonia derivatives in which one or more hydrocarbon (alkyl) radicles replace one or more hydrogen atoms. Simple amines of the general formula $X(NH_2)$ like methylamine $CH_3(NH_2)$ are formed: (a) by prolonged boiling of an isocyanide (XNC) with hydrochloric acid; (b) "reduction" of a nitro hydrocarbon (XNO_2) with fine bubbles of hydrogen from tin and hydrochloric acid; (c) action of bromine and caustic soda together on an amide (X . CO NH_2). The reduction of a cyanide (XCN) by sodium amalgam and water also gives an amine (X . CH_2NH_2); but the amine formed is the next higher up in the series.

The amines are substances which generally have a fishy odour. They combine with water, forming hydroxides analogous to ammonia (e.g. $CH_3 . NH_3 . OH$ from $CH_3 . NH_2$); and these hydroxides, unlike alcohols, are electrolytes, forming (as do the amines alone) salts like ammonium salts generally soluble in water. The salts formed by combination of an amine (or its hydroxide) and chloroplatinic acid, like the corresponding salts of sodium or ammonium, are insoluble in water. Although otherwise very stable amines are easily changed into the corresponding alcohols (X . OH) by reaction with nitrous acid (HNO_2). The aromatic amines are of two kinds. If the NH_2 radicle replaces a hydrogen atom of the side chain the resulting compound is a basic compound which forms salts with acids, just as substitution of an OH group in the side chain of an aromatic hydrocarbon yields a typical alcohol. The presence of an NH_2 attached to the nucleus gives a class of compounds which have only feebly basic properties. This is consistent with the behaviour of the phenols which do not readily form esters with mineral acids.

RULES OF SYNTHESIS

When a chemist wants to know the make-up of the molecule of a carbon compound, he first determines its vapour density or its osmotic pressure in solution to ascertain its molecular weight. He then incinerates it in presence of oxygen and determines the weight of carbon dioxide, water vapour, nitrogen, etc., formed from a weighed amount, to get its percentage composition. He thus obtains the number of atoms of each constituent element in the molecule. To see how these are arranged he is guided by three general considerations.

The first is the principle of valency. Suppose a compound has been found to have the composition indicated by the formula $C_2H_4O_2$. As stated earlier, the pictorial representation of this shows that if the valencies of all the atoms are fully satisfied, there are comparatively few ways in which the atoms can be arranged. Thus the arrangement may be:

$$\begin{array}{cc}
H & O-H \\
| & | \\
H-C-C & \\
| & \| \\
H & O
\end{array}$$

$$\begin{array}{c}
H \\
| \\
O-C-H \\
/ \quad | \\
H-C \quad H \\
\| \\
O
\end{array}$$

$$\begin{array}{cc}
H & H \\
| & | \\
H-C-C & \\
| & \| \\
H-O & O
\end{array}$$

(a) $CH_3 . COOH$ (b) $H . COO . CH_3$ (c) $CH_2OH . CHO$

With these preliminary considerations to narrow down the field, the chemist next makes use of what he knows about (i) the physical properties of different classes of compounds, and (ii) their chemical behaviour. One fact which has not been explicitly stated about the physical properties of carbon compounds is that the lower members of series containing an OH radicle—standing alone (c), or as part (a) of the complex radicle COOH—is that they are generally soluble in water. Again, the lower members of series with the complex radicle COOX of the organic esters have a fruity smell. This is a characteristic of methyl formate represented by the middle formula $(H . COO . CH_3)$. Acetic acid (CH_3COOH) and glycollic aldehyde $(CH_2OH . CHO)$ are water soluble. Methyl formate is not.

The chemical behaviour of $C_2H_4O_2$, if an ester, is straightforward. On prolonged boiling with a mineral acid it will give an alcohol (methyl alcohol) and an acid (formic acid). On prolonged boiling with an alkali it will yield an alcohol and a metallic salt (formate). If it were an organic acid it would not be decomposed by boiling with a mineral acid. It would simply form a metallic salt (acetate) if boiled with an alkali. It would decompose a carbonate, and it would combine with ammonia to form a weak electrolyte convertible by heating into an amide. The latter would yield the fishy odour of an amine when treated with bromine and caustic soda. A substance represented by formula (c) would not be an acid and would not decompose carbonates. Having the complex radicle CH_2OH it would be easily oxidized by oxidizing agents like potassium permanganate to form first another aldehyde (glyoxal), and then an acid (oxalic acid), $COOH . COOH$. Having the aldehyde radicle CHO, it would react with ammonia to form a compound which would not be an electrolyte. It would not yield amides on heating.

Suppose now that the substance represented by the formula $C_2H_4O_2$ is also a substance which human beings value as a flavouring essence or perfume, and that the chemist had decided that its make-up is indicated by writing the formula as $H . COO . CH_3$ which shows it to be the ester of methyl alcohol (CH_3OH) and formic acid $(H . COOH)$. We now have two choices. One is to look for some plant in whose juices it occurs as a trace, and cultivate it. Alternatively, we can make it from any convenient source of organic material. Which we decide to do will depend on the kind of social economy in which we live or the kind in which we intend to live.

If we are content with the urban congestion of the steel-coal economy we shall instruct the chemist to make it out of coal. This is easy when he knows that it is an ester of methyl alcohol (CH_3OH) and formic acid. Methyl alcohol is methane (CH_4) of coal gas with one hydrogen atom replaced by the hydroxyl radicle (OH). Formic acid (H . COOH) is methane in which the carboxyl radicle COOH replaces the alkyl (methyl) radicle CH_3.

| Methyl alcohol | *Methane* | Formic acid |

The chemist's problem is then (a) to replace a hydrogen atom by (OH), (b) to replace a methyl radicle (CH_3) by COOH. The general rule for (a) is to replace H by iodine bromine or chlorine. These elements react directly with hydrocarbons to form alkyl halides which can be converted into the corresponding alcohols by boiling with caustic potash. To replace a methyl group by COOH we have first to convert it into CH_2OH. In this instance, this is the same thing as making methyl alcohol itself. The complex radicle CH_2OH when acted upon by a strong oxidizing agent gives place to COOH. So formic acid is obtained by oxidation of methyl alcohol.

Alternatively we may hold that coal exacts too high a price in social comfort, cleanliness, and privacy. If we prefer green fields and forests to the cultural advantages of London fogs we are not compelled to embark on colonial war to secure some exotic plant in which traces of the required substance occur ready made. Methyl alcohol is one of the three major disintegration products when cellulose is subjected to dry heat, the others being acetic acid and acetone. It can be obtained by dry distillation of wood pulp directly, and can be oxidized to formic acid in one step. The technical problem of creating an economy of human welfare with abundance of commodities along with healthy and spacious conditions of life is therefore the problem of replacing one radicle by another in a carbon compound.

We shall now briefly survey the rules for building up any simple carbon compound from any convenient source, under four headings: (a) reagents, (b) substitutions, (c) ascent and descent of series, (d) "nucleus and side chain" transformations.

(a) *Reagents.*—Reagents employed in organic syntheses may be classified according to the class of reactions they bring about. Four most important classes are (a) hydrolysis, i.e. splitting a molecule into bricks combined with the OH or H of the water molecule; (b) dehydrolysis, i.e. removing a molecule of water; (c) oxidation; (d) reduction.

Hydrolysis or prolonged boiling with mineral acids or alkalis with excess of water splits up esters and alkyl halides with the formation of organic acid and alcohol or metallic salt and alcohol, and also replaces the CN radicle by COOH (with production of ammonia) as in making a monobasic acid (X . COOH) from an alkyl cyanide (XCN), a hydroxy acid [X . (OH) . COOH] from a cyanhydrin [X . (OH) . CN], or a dibasic acid [X . (COOH)$_2$] from a cyanacid [X . (CN) . COOH].

Dehydrolysis with phosphorus pentoxide or phosphorus pentachloride converts an amide (X . CO . NH$_2$) into a cyanide (X . CN + H$_2$O). Dehydrolysis with sulphuric acid converts an alcohol into (a) an ether or (b) an unsaturated hydrocarbon $(C_2H_5OH \rightarrow C_2H_4 + H_2O)$, according to the temperature at which it is carried out.

For oxidation, potassium permanganate may be used to convert an alcohol, ketone or aldehyde to an acid. Potassium dichromate and sulphuric acid together are used to convert an alcohol to a ketone or aldehyde. Alcohol vapours passed with air over hot platinized asbestos usually oxidize to the acid (methyl alcohol is only oxidized to the aldehyde by this method). Bromine and potash (or soda) are together used to convert an amide $X . CO . NH_2$ to an anine $X . NH_2$.

For reduction, i.e. introduction of hydrogen into, or removal of oxygen from, the molecule, various reagents are used: (a) tin and hydrochloric acid together make fine bubbles of hydrogen for converting a nitro-hydrocarbon (XNO_2) to an amine (XNH_2), (b) sodium amalgam is used to convert a ketone or aldehyde into an alcohol, (c) zinc dust will convert an alkyl halide into a higher paraffin (e.g. $CH_3I \rightarrow C_2H_6$), (d) the "zinc-copper couple" (zinc dipped in copper sulphate to deposit a thin film of copper) converts an alkyl halide to the corresponding paraffin (e.g. $CH_3I \rightarrow CH_4$).

(b) *Substitutions.*—The most important of the simple radicles in carbon compounds which occur in natural products are —OH, —COOH, —CHO, $=CO$, —O— (ether), —$CONH_2$ (amide), —NH_2 (amine and amino acid). In addition to these are the radicles which are important as steps in the replacement of a hydrogen atom by any of the above, e.g. —Cl or I, —NO_2, —CN (cyanide) or —NC (isocyanide).

The substitution of a halogen for a hydrogen atom in the formation of alkyl halogen substitution products or chloracids is brought about by direct union of a hydrocarbon or organic acid with a halogen. Substitution of a halogen for an OH group in an alcohol (e.g. $C_2H_5OH \rightarrow C_2H_5I$) is effected by action of the halogens in presence of red phosphorus as a catalyst. An OH group in the compound radicle COOH can be replaced by Cl through the action of phosphorus trichloride or pentachloride on an acid (e.g. $CH_3COOH \rightarrow CH_3COCl$). The CN radicle can always be made to replace a Cl atom by heating the halogen derivative with potassium cyanide. The NC radicle (isocyanide) is inserted by using silver cyanide. The OH radicle is introduced by replacing a halogen atom in the hydrolysis of the halogen derivative $(C_2H_5Cl \rightarrow C_2H_5OH)$ or substitution for the NH_2 group by action of nitrous acid. Unsaturated hydrocarbons of the ethylene series combine with hypochlorous acid (chlorine in water) to add one OH radicle and one Cl atom to the molecule. The COOH radicle is introduced by substitution for the CN radicle when a CN derivative is hydrolyzed. The CHO group is introduced by oxidizing a compound containing the complex radicle —CH_2OH, or reducing one with the complex radicle —$CH_2 COOH$. The CO group is introduced by oxidizing a compound with the complex radicle $=CHOH$, or reducing one with the complex radicle $=CH . COOH$. The radicle —O— of ethers or acidic anhydrides [e.g. $(CH_3CO)_2O$] is obtained by treating an alcohol or acid with a strong dehydrating agent. The complex radicle —$CONH_2$ is introduced by heating the ammonium salt of a COOH derivative, or by treating an acid chloride with ammonia. The NO_2 "nitro" group of the nitro-hydrocarbons is introduced by heating a halogen derivative with silver nitrite. By the action of a reducing agent (e.g. tin and hydrochloric acid), the NH_2 group can replace the CN group of a cyanide. By hydrolysis it can replace the NO_2 group of a nitro-hydrocarbon. The NH_2 group can also replace a halogen atom when a halogen derivative is heated with ammonia; or replace the $CONH_2$ radicle by oxidation with bromine and caustic soda. The complex radicle $—CH_2NH_2$ replaces the cyanide radicle when a CN derivative is reduced with sodium in alcoholic solution. These substitutions are summarized briefly in Fig. 269.

(c) *Ascent or Descent of Series.*—The substitution of one alkyl radicle (C_nH_{2n+1}) by another is equivalent to moving up or down in a "series." If we know how to replace the OH radicle of an alcohol or the COOH radicle of an organic acid by the radicles characteristic of other classes of organic compounds, we can do this provided we know how to make an acid or alcohol higher up or lower down in the same series as any particular acid or alcohol. To go up one step, e.g. from methyl to ethyl alcohol, we can make successively (Fig. 269) the halide, cyanide, and higher amine, thus:

(i) CH_3OH (methyl alcohol) to CH_3I (methyl iodide) by heating with iodine in presence of red phosphorus.

(ii) CH_3I to CH_3CN (methyl cyanide) by heating with potassium cyanide.

(iii) CH_3CN to $C_2H_5NH_2$ (ethylamine) by reduction with tin and hydrochloric acid.

(iv) $C_2H_5NH_2$ to C_2H_5OH (ethyl alcohol) by boiling with nitrous acid (HNO_2).

The converse process of stepping down, illustrated by the conversion of ethyl alcohol into methyl alcohol, involves oxidizing the alcohol, making the amide, and converting this into an amine, thus:

(i) C_2H_5OH (ethyl alcohol) to CH_3 . COOH (acetic acid) by oxidation with permanganate.

(ii) CH_3COOH to CH_3 . CO . NH_2 (acetamide) by heating the ammonium salt of the acid.

(iii) CH_3 . CO . NH_2 to CH_3NH_2 (methyl amine) by heating together with bromine and caustic soda.

(iv) CH_3NH_2 to CH_3OH (methyl alcohol) by boiling with nitrous acid.

To make a long jump in a series, as from methyl alcohol of wood spirit to amyl alcohol whose acetic ester is used as a cellulose acetate solvent, or from acetic acid of vinegar to stearic acid of mutton fat and soap, is a long process, if taken one step at a time. There are two important syntheses which make it possible to replace an H by an alkyl radicle traversing as many steps as we wish in one reaction.

Higher alcohols can be synthesized from lower ones by the reaction of metallo-organic compounds with aldehydes and ketones. To make higher primary alcohols a magnesium alkyl halide is treated with formaldehyde thus:

$$H . CHO + X Mg I \rightarrow X . CH_2OH$$

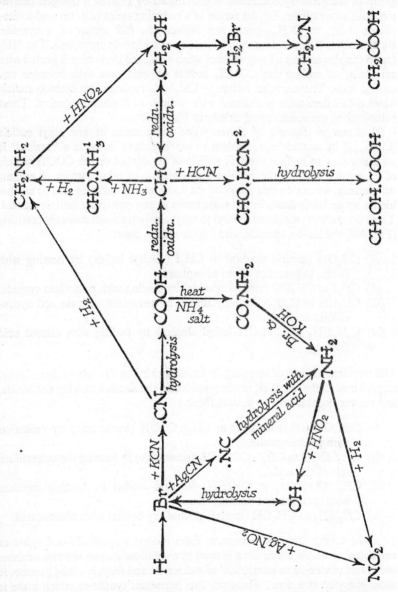

FIG. 269.—ORDER OF SUBSTITUTION OF COMMON SIMPLE RADICLES IN THE HYDRO-CARBON MOLECULE

1 and *2* are so written to indicate that they are *addition* compounds with NH ₃ and HCN respectively. The reaction with HCN can be used to make hydroxy-acids such as lactic acid in which the OH and COOH radicles are attached to the *same* carbon atom.

To make a higher secondary alcohol, a magnesium alkyl halide is treated with acetaldehyde, thus:

$$CH_3CHO + X\,Mg\,I \rightarrow X\,.\,(CH_3)\,.\,CHOH$$

The higher members of a series of alcohols may have the monovalent complex radicle CH_2OH of a primary alcohol, the divalent $CHOH$ of a secondary, or the trivalent COH of a "tertiary alcohol." A tertiary alcohol can be made by treating a ketone with a magnesium alkyl halide, thus:

$$X_a\,.\,CO\,.\,X_b + X_c\,Mg\,I \rightarrow X_aX_bX_cCOH$$

All three types may be illustrated by the preparation of the three butyl alcohols C_4H_9OH. Primary butyl alcohol ($C_3H_7\,.\,CH_2OH$) can be made by treating formaldehyde with magnesium propyl iodide (C_3H_7MgI). Secondary butyl alcohol ($C_2H_5\,.\,CH_3\,.\,CHOH$) can be made by treating acetaldehyde with ethyl magnesium iodide (C_2H_5MgI). Tertiary butyl alcohol, which is $(CH_3)_3\,.\,COH$, is made by treating acetone $(CH_3)_2CO$ with magnesium methyl iodide ($MgCH_3I$). These reactions illustrate the general principle involved in making a series of alcohols with high molecular weight from lower members of the same series, like methyl or ethyl alcohols.

To synthesize higher fatty acids from lower ones either of two important esters, ethyl malonate or ethyl aceto acetate, are used as essential reagents. Both esters react with sodium in alcoholic solution (sodium alcoholate) to form (a) compounds in which one hydrogen atom is replaced by sodium. The sodium derivative reacts (b) with an alkyl halide to form an ester in which the alkyl group replaces the sodium atom. This ester is decomposed by heat, yielding a higher acid. With ethyl malonate (the ester of ethyl alcohol and malonic acid) the process is:

$$(a) \quad CH_2 \Big\langle {{COO\,C_2H_5} \atop {COO\,C_2H_5}} \quad \rightarrow \quad CH\,Na \Big\langle {{COO\,C_2H_5} \atop {COO\,C_2H_5}}$$

Ethyl malonate

$$(b) \quad CH\,Na \Big\langle {{COO\,C_2H_5} \atop {COO\,C_2H_5}} + XI \quad \rightarrow \quad CH\,X \Big\langle {{COO\,C_2H_5} \atop {COO\,C_2H_5}}$$

$$(c) \quad CH\,X \Big\langle {{COO\,C_2H_5} \atop {COO\,C_2H_5}} \quad \rightarrow \quad CH\,X \Big\langle {{H} \atop {COOH}}$$

Thus if the alkyl halide is C_2H_5I (ethyl iodide) we get one of the butyric acids. Ethyl aceto acetate obtained by action of sodium on ethyl acetate and subsequent distillation with acetic acid reacts in a similar way, thus:

$$(a) \quad CH_2 \Big\langle {{CO\,.\,CH_3} \atop {COO\,.\,C_2H_5}} \quad \rightarrow \quad CH\,.\,Na \Big\langle {{CH_3\,.\,CO} \atop {COO\,C_2H_5}}$$

Ethyl aceto acetate

$$(b) \quad CH\,Na \Big\langle {{CO\,.\,CH_3} \atop {COO\,C_2H_5}} + XI \quad \rightarrow \quad CH\,X \Big\langle {{CH_3\,.\,CO} \atop {COO\,C_2H_5}}$$

On heating the alkyl substituted ester we get with caustic potash, it decomposes thus:

$$(c) \quad CH.X\Big\langle\begin{array}{l}CO.CH_3\\[4pt]COO\,C_2H_5\end{array} \qquad \rightarrow \qquad CH\,X\Big\langle\begin{array}{l}H\\[4pt]COOH\end{array}$$

Higher hydrocarbons of the fatty acid series can be made from lower ones by the action of powdered zinc on the alkyl halide according to the recipe:

$$2XI \rightarrow X_2 + 2HI$$

Thus methane can be converted into butane (C_4H_{10}) in the following steps:

$$CH_4 \rightarrow CH_3I \rightarrow C_2H_6(\text{ethane}) \rightarrow C_2H_5I \rightarrow C_4H_{10}$$

(d) *Nucleus and Side Chain Substitutions.*—General rules of synthesis for the derivatives of the fatty series also apply to the aromatic compounds which have a stable nucleus of six carbon atoms. When dealing with the latter it is also necessary to distinguish between substituting a radicle for a hydrogen atom in the side chain and substituting a radicle for a hydrogen atom attached to the nucleus.

The fundamental reason for representing the benzene molecule by a central group of six carbon atoms attached to one another depends on the number of its substitution products. When only one hydrogen atom of benzene is replaced by a radicle, only one compound with the same formula is formed. Thus there is one hydrocarbon $C_6H_5CH_3$ or C_7H_8 *toluene*, one substance $C_6H_5 . COOH$ benzoic acid, one substance C_6H_5OH *phenol*, one substance $C_6H_5 . NH_2$ *aniline*, one substance $C_6H_5 . NO_2$ nitrobenzene, etc. On the other hand, four substances have the formula C_8H_{10}, one corresponding to the substitution of CH_3 in the methyl radicle of the side chain of toluene, and three arrangements resulting from two substitutions of CH_3 in the nucleus of benzene, as explained on p. 514. Similarly there are four substances with the formula C_7H_7COOH, viz. three toluic acids $CH_3 . C_6H_4 . COOH$ and one phenyl acetic acid $C_6H_5 . CH_2 . COOH$. There are four substances with the formula C_7H_7OH, benzyl alcohol $C_6H_5CH_2OH$, and three nuclear derivatives of toluene, the toluic phenols or *cresols*, $CH_3 . C_6H_4OH$. Thus the arrangement of the atoms and radicles in an aromatic molecule raises three problems: (a) how we recognize when a radicle replaces a hydrogen atom in the nucleus or side chain; (b) how we can recognize the various arrangements to which we attribute the existence of different compounds arising by substituting more than one radicle in the nucleus. We can get an answer to the first question by comparing the derivatives of benzene with those of higher hydrocarbons in the same series.

If chlorine is passed into cold benzene in the presence of a catalyst, a substance called monochlorbenzene (C_6H_5Cl) with one substituted halogen atom can be obtained. It is not a typical *halide*. It is not converted into an alcohol by boiling with a dilute alkali. If chlorine gas is passed into cold toluene three substances with different boiling points and a single chlorine atom in each molecule are formed. These *chloro-toluenes* have the same general formula

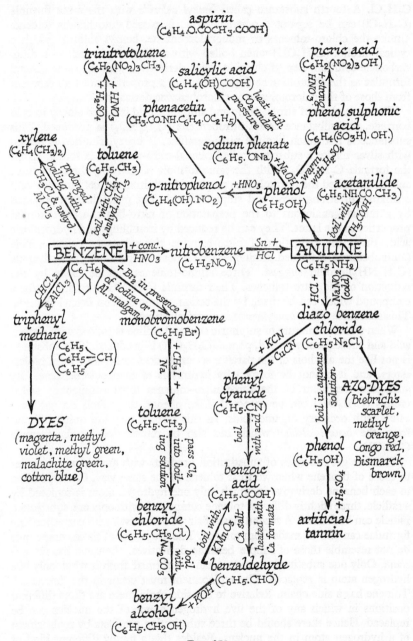

FIG. 270

Simple syntheses from the Benzene which Faraday first identified in Coal Tar

C_7H_7Cl. A fourth substance called *benzyl chloride* with the same formula (C_7H_7Cl) can be separated when chlorine is passed into boiling toluene. Unlike the chloro-toluenes or monochlorbenzene, benzyl chloride yields a typical alcohol (C_7H_7OH) when boiled with a dilute alkali such as sodium carbonate solution. Benzyl chloride yields derivatives with the same general formulae as the chlorotoluene derivatives. Their properties are very different from those of the chlorotoluene or chlorobenzene derivatives.

When a mixture of strong nitric and sulphuric acid is added slowly to cold benzene, one substance called nitrobenzene ($C_6H_5NO_2$) is produced. This substance is not much like the nitro-paraffins. If benzyl chloride is heated with silver nitrite a substance called phenyl-nitro-methane is found. It has the formula $C_7H_7NO_2$. With the same formula ($C_7H_7NO_2$) there are three substances called the nitrotoluenes prepared by "nitrating" cold toluene with a mixture of strong nitric and sulphuric acid. The nitrotoluenes, prepared by a method analogous to the preparation of nitro-benzene, have similar properties to the latter. They can be reduced by iron filings and hydrochloric acid. From the reduction of nitro-benzene the substance called aniline (aminobenzene) is formed. Aminobenzene is not a typical amine, as its formula ($C_6H_5NH_2$) would suggest. Three amino-toluenes can be made by the reduction of the nitro-toluenes. Their formula $C_7H_7NH_2$ also stands for a compound which can be made by the action of ammonia on benzyl chloride. This substance called *benzylamine* is a typical amine.

When a cooled mixture of sulphuric acid and aniline is treated with nitrous acid and subsequently heated, *phenol* (C_6H_5OH) is produced. This substance is not like the alcohols of the paraffin series. It does not readily form typical esters, and it cannot be formed by hydrolysis of monochlorbenzene. By analogous treatment of the three nitro-toluenes three compounds called cresols (C_7H_7OH) can be prepared. Like phenol, the cresols do not form esters with ordinary organic acids. In this respect they are quite different from the *benzyl alcohol* which can also be represented by the formula C_7H_7OH.

Thus we get one class of substitution products with analogous properties to those of benzene when we treat toluene in the same way. Corresponding to each benzene derivative in which only one hydrogen atom is replaced by a radicle, three slightly different toluene compounds with only one substituted radicle can be formed. A second class of single derivatives with corresponding formulae can also be made from toluene. The properties of these compounds do not resemble those of simple benzene derivatives. Benzene has no *side chain*. Only one substitution product can be formed from it when only one hydrogen atom is replaced. The replacement must occur in the "nucleus." Toluene has a side chain. Relative to the side chain there are three different positions in which any of the five hydrogen atoms of the nucleus can be replaced. Hence there should be three substitution products by replacement of a hydrogen atom in the nucleus. Besides this a totally different kind of substitution can occur in the toluene molecule. One (or more) of the hydrogen atoms of the side chain itself can be replaced. Since the class of derivatives of which benzyl chloride is the parent substance do not resemble chlorbenzene compounds, we conclude that the *class of which benzyl chloride is the parent is due to side chain substitution*, and that *side chain substitution leads to the production of compounds with properties more like those of paraffin derivatives.*

The methods of substitution appropriate to each class are summarized in the accompanying table, which calls for a word of explanation. The aromatic hydrocarbons readily combine with strong sulphuric acid to form "sulphonic acid" derivatives in which the radicle (HSO_3) replaces one or more hydrogen atoms of the *nucleus*. These derivatives when heated give rise

METHODS OF SUBSTITUTION

Radicle	Nucleus	Side Chain
Cl, Br	Pass Cl_2 or Br_2 into cold in presence of a catalyst (iodine, etc.).	Pass Cl_2 or Br_2 into boiling fluid.
NO_2	Action of strong nitric acid.	Action of silver nitrite.
CN	KCN on chloro-derivative.	KCN on chloro-derivative.
COOH	(*a*) Oxidation of alkyl group attached to nucleus by $KMnO_4$. (*b*) Hydrolysis of CN derivative.	Hydrolysis of CN derivative.
OH	(*a*) Reduction of NH_2 derivative by nitrous acid. (*b*) Heating sulphuric acid derivative dry with NaOH.	(*a*) Reduction of NH_2 derivative by nitrous acid. (*b*) Hydrolysis of halogen derivative with KOH.
NH_2	Reduction of Nitro derivative with tin and HCl.	Reduction of Nitro derivative with tin and HCl.
Alkyl	Boil with alkyl halide, using anhydrous aluminium chloride as catalyst.	Treat with alkyl halide in presence of sodium.

to phenols, i.e. OH nuclear substitution products. Treatment of aromatic hydrocarbons with either nitric or sulphuric acid may give rise to one, two, or more [e.g. trinitrotoluene $CH_3 C_6H_2(NO_2)_3$] nuclear substitutions according to the time and heat applied. One other point worth mentioning is that any alkyl group in the nucleus of an aromatic compound is converted into the radicle COOH by the action of an oxidizing agent like potassium permanganate. Hence ethyl benzene $C_6H_5 . C_2H_5$ is oxidized to benzoic acid $C_6H_5 . COOH$, but the three xylenes $C_6H_4(CH_3)_2$ are oxidized to the phthalic acids $C_6H_4(COOH)_2$ with two COOH radicles.

Another question which arises when identifying or synthesizing aromatic compounds is how various substances may result from the mutual relations of the same radicles in the nuclear part of the molecule. When there are two radicles as in xylene we distinguish three possible arrangements, called the ortho (*o*), meta (*m*), and para (*p*) forms, which have very similar chemical but

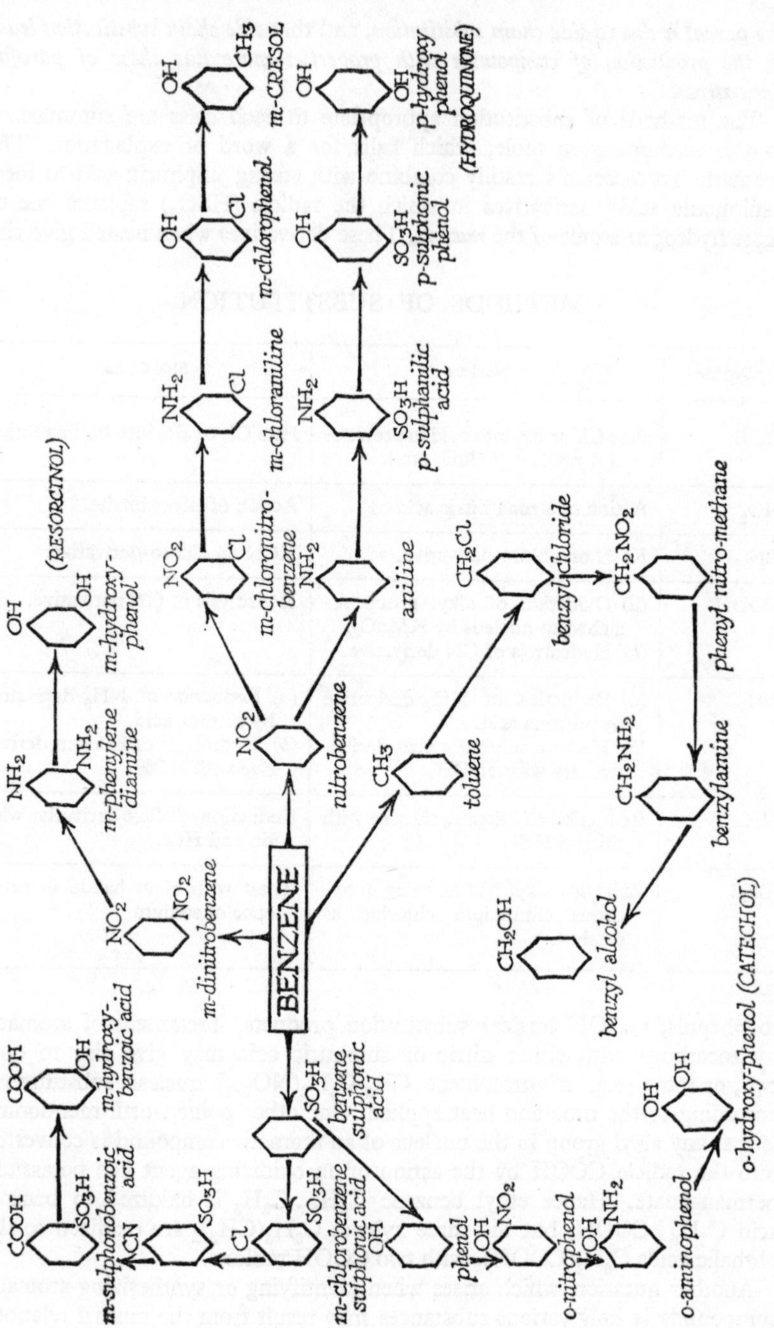

FIG. 271.—SOME BENZENE DERIVATIVES

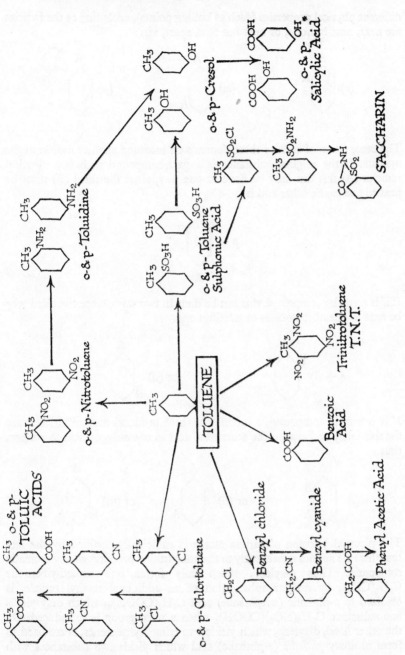

FIG. 272.—SIMPLE SYNTHESES BASED ON THE TOLUENE OF LIGHT OIL COAL TA

* The anti-febrile drug called salicylic acid is the *ortho* compound.

different physical properties (such as boiling points), according as the radicles are next, next but one, or next but two, apart, viz.:

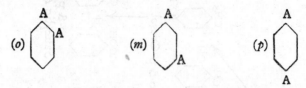

The recognition of each of these depends on inserting another radicle in the nucleus. If the original substance is a para-compound with two identical radicles (A) this can only be done in one way, since the third (B) must be next to one or the other and is

If it is an ortho compound, this can be done in two ways, since the third may be next to one of the others or next but one.

If it is a meta compound, a mixture of three products may result, because the third may be between the other two, next to one only, or next to neither, thus

The pictorial hexagon of carbon atoms is sufficiently justified by the fact that this rule applies consistently to the substitution products of any aromatic compound. Thus *p*-xylene, which only forms one trimethylbenzene $C_6H_3(CH_3)_3$ by nuclear substitution of an additional methyl radicle, is oxidized to *p*-phthalic (*terephthalic*) acid $C_6H_4(COOH)_2$, which only yields one substance $C_6H_3(NO_2)(COOH)_2$ when a nitro group is introduced. On the other hand, *o*-xylene, which yields two trimethylbenzenes, is oxidized to form ordinary *phthalic* (*o*-phthalic) acid which yields two substances with the constitution $C_6H_3(NO_2)(COOH)_2$. The meta form of xylene yields the same two trimethylbenzenes together with a third one, *mesitylene* or 1—3—5 trimethyl benzene. Needless to say, the hexagon figure is merely a diagram. It is not a picture of the molecule, which no one has ever seen. It is a plan of action which, like the ordnance survey map, tells us how to get somewhere and how to recognize when we have got there.

Once having settled how to recognize an ortho, meta or para form we can study the conditions which govern the substitution of radicles to get the best yield of the one we want. Two rules summarize what we have to do, if we wish to get the best yield in substituting a second radicle in the nucleus of a benzene derivative.

(i) A second group prefers the meta position to one of the following already attached to the nucleus:

$$HSO_3 \qquad CHO \qquad CN \qquad COOH \qquad NO_2$$

(ii) A mixture mainly composed of ortho and para compounds is formed if one of the following is already attached:

$$\text{Alkyl, halogen, } OH, NH_2.$$

Hence when we are applying the rules for side chain and nuclear substitution, the route chosen depends on which type of a compound is required. For instance, if we want to make a toluic aldehyde from benzene, we obtain the para form thus:

To get the meta form we proceed thus:

In the less volatile fractions of coal tar there are aromatic hydrocarbons with nuclei of more than six carbon atoms. The two most important are naphthalene $C_{10}H_8$ (also present in Russian petroleum) and anthracene $C_{14}H_{10}$. Anthracene is the parent substance used in the synthesis of alizarin. The simplest are the azo dyes derived from the anilines or nuclear NH_2 substitution products of the benzene series. When the aromatic amines are reduced with nitrous acid they yield alcohols. When the anilines are reduced with nitrous acid they only yield phenols after prolonged boiling. The first product of reaction in cold solution is a "diazo" salt which combines with phenols and various other benzene derivatives to form richly coloured substances.

A PLANNED ECONOMY OF CARBON COMPOUNDS

Although the discovery of benzene in coal tar was made by Faraday in England, where the commercial exploitation of coal tar products first

developed, the development of the British coal tar dye industry was almost
entirely neglected till after the European war of 1914–18. The story of
the dye industry is told by Hale in the following passage from *Chemistry
Triumphant*:

In 1856 occurred a discovery of far-reaching import. Sir William Henry
Perkin, working in the laboratory of A. W. Hofmann, then a professor at the
Royal College of Chemistry in London (1845–65), accidentally discovered
among the oxidation products of aniline with chromic acid a compound exhibiting tinctorial properties. It was the first synthetic dye. Within a year
(1857) a small plant was built by Perkin at Greenford Green and this violet
dye under the name of mauve at once entered commercial production. The
starting point for this dye was aniline ($C_6H_5NH_2$) which is the amino (NH_2)
derivative of benzene; aniline was prepared by reduction of the nitro (NO_2)
derivative of benzene arising by action of nitric acid (HNO_3) upon benzene
itself. These manufacturing steps were fraught with difficulties and expense.
Anything like chemical control was unknown; thus by a mere shift in an
oxidizing agent upon crude aniline a red dye known as magenta made its
appearance. This latter was placed in commercial production in 1859 at Lyons,
France. In 1868 the German chemists Graebe and Liebermann, starting with
anthracene (a hydrocarbon isolated from coal-tar), were able to synthesize a
naturally occurring dye known as alizarin, which when precipitated on fibre
is called turkey red. This dye was then obtained from the roots of the madder
plant. . . . Thus the chemist was brought directly in conflict with one of the
oldest of agricultural pursuits; this dye was used by the ancient Egyptians on
mummy cloths. Still another class of dyes called azo dyes, by reason of their
containing a pair of nitrogen (called azote in French) atoms, was discovered in
Hofmann's laboratory in 1858 by Peter Griess. But this growing interest in
synthetic chemistry was soon to be transferred to Germany whither Hofmann
returned in 1865. From this latter date to 1874 there was not even a professorship in organic chemistry in all England. No instance of such extreme stupidity
on the part of any two nations has ever been recorded in the history of the
world as when France and England gave up the dye industry to Germany.
By 1880 the dye industry, under German tutelage, was rapidly gaining recognition. The uninviting coal-tar distillates constituted the source of its various
hydrocarbon starting points. . . . At about this time von Baeyer's unravelling
of the constitution of indigotine (indigo) turned everyone's attention to its
possible manufacture. Indeed this may be described as the goal of goals among
early chemists. Even after Heumann's discovery in 1890 of the phenyl glycine
process (as in use today) seven more years were required before actual manufacture became feasible; October, 1897, marks the date when this king of the
dyes first entered commercial production. The reasons for such delay were not
far to seek. The state of manufacturing art was low. In the process under
question a concentrated sulphuric acid (H_2SO_4), an abundance of chlorine
(Cl), and a strong caustic soda liquor (NaOH) were absolutely necessary
—to say nothing of the organic chemicals involved. Now these prerequisites
were simply unattainable in quantity. Not till 1901 can the Knietsch contact
sulphuric acid process be described as having attained practicability. Before
1890 there was absolutely no appreciable supply of chlorine in the world. In
that year the Griesheim diaphragm cell, applicable to aqueous salt solutions,
was placed in actual operation. Its development paved the way for indigo. In
this cell an aqueous sodium chloride solution was decomposed by means of
an electric current, yielding chlorine at one electrode and a solution of caustic

soda at the other. . . . This new type of cell, and others following, have all but made the electrolytic chlorine-caustic process supreme. This urge to attain the indigo victory so long in the making—over nineteen years since its first laboratory synthesis, raised the state of chemical knowledge everywhere and pointed to better control in all industry. It was not long before the indigo chemist sought even to better his product beyond that provided by nature through many millennia. In 1909 Friedlaender synthesized 6, 6'-dibromindigotine and found it identical with Tyrian purple of the ancients; over 12,000 molluscs (*Murex brandaris*) were collected on Italian shores to yield 1·4 grams of this dye to confirm his research. And today we brominate indigo directly to a number of valuable fast dyes, notable among which is a tetrabrom indigo (Ciba Blue 2B) far superior to the ancient Tyrian purple of similar constitution. Again in 1905 Friedlaender discovered the beautiful red thioindigo, a direct counterpart of indigotine wherein the imino (NH) groups of the latter are replaced by sulphur (thio) atoms. . . . In general these indigoid dyes constitute our first vat dyes; dyes that are capable of reduction to a soluble leuco or colourless base in "vats" or tube, and from which solutions the immersed textiles absorb the colourless base to be dyed (i.e. impregnated with the original insoluble dye) immediately that they are exposed to the oxidizing action of air. In 1901 R. Bohn discovered another type of vat dye called indanthrene. In brilliance and fastness to light it has few competitors. Furthermore, by halogenation this fastness is enhanced. Possibly no class of dyes has attracted more attention of late than certain of the azo colours; they lend themselves most admirably to development upon the newer silks. . . . We should not forget that discovery is far ahead of practice. We now know the constitution of many naturally occurring compounds for which we have no adequately serviceable manufacturing steps. Perhaps they will continue to be procured direct from nature. We may mention the dye curcumin (from turmeric) used in foods; the dye haematein (from logwood) used on silk; and the interesting but complex insecticide rotenone from derris root.

The synthetic dye industry was nursed into supremacy by the autocratic Prussian state after English chemists had discovered the first coal tar colour. In the closing years of the nineteenth century unrestricted private enterprise was no longer a sufficient guarantee of continued technical progress, and the gap between theory and practice has become much greater since then. A high level of chemical manufacture is now possible without the social pattern of urban congestion which developed in association with the coal economy of private enterprise. Within the existing framework of private enterprise there are already processes which might be developed further to provide the basis of a planned economy of human welfare with due regard to a congenial and healthy distribution of population.

Perhaps the most important facet of recent progress in chemical manufacture regarded from this standpoint is the substitution of cellulose for natural silk. The artificial silk industry is of very recent origin. It is already promoting research into a host of new problems, and among other indirect consequences is likely to revolutionize the production of sugar. Referring to its growth, Hale says (op. cit.):

In 1892 the discoveries of Cross and Bevan in England on cellulose and it conversion into a sodium cellulose, with final transformation by action o carbon bisulphide into a soluble cellulose xanthate, offered immediate possibilities of reprecipitating the cellulose from this "viscose" state into the form of threads. Regenerated cellulose sheet, rendered pliable by admixture with a softener, generally glycerol, is well known under the trade mark "Cellophane." Other methods have come into use. Notably the reduction of nitrocellulose; the dissolving of cellulose in copper ammonium solution and reprecipitation; and particularly the production of cellulose esters (as cellulose acetate or celanese) and their direct employment in the arts. Derivatives of these products by higher acids are now in the making. They will revolutionize the rayon industry. The maceration of woody materials into pulp of high cellulosic content has long been in operation and increasing amounts are in demand. The hydrolysis, however, of cellulose and starch by dilute acids into dextrine and finally glucose is the outstanding development in commercial reversion of one of nature's great steps. The Bergius process for glucose direct from sawdust calls for hydrochloric acid, and the method devised for recovery of this hydrochloric acid makes for an economical operation.

The production of sugar from cellulose or from other complex carbohydrates may in course of time replace the present custom of growing local species which store carbohydrates in the form of sugar (e.g. cane, maple, beet) by the production of any species which manufacture carbohydrates rapidly. Few plants grow so rapidly as the Jerusalem artichoke which has a very wide distribution. The Jerusalem artichoke produces cellulose in the woody fibre of stem and another complex carbohydrate *inulin* which acts as a sugar store in the tubers. This polysaccharide is easily broken down into its ultimate bricks of simple sugar molecules, yielding fructose or levulose (sometimes called levose by American writers) which is three times as sweet as glucose and one and a half times as sweet as cane sugar. Cane sugar yields a mixture of glucose and fructose. Eating levose is less dangerous to diabetics than eating cane sugar. It is absorbed much less quickly than glucose. A small operating plant for producing it already exists in Iowa.

A brief account of the recent manufacture of wood sugar in Germany is given in an article on the *Search for Substitutes* by J. G. Crowther.

Kirchoff, of St. Petersburg, prepared a sugarified starch in 1811. Eight years later Braconnet showed that sugars could be obtained from cellulose with sulphuric acid. In 1855 Mehsens showed that hydrochloric acid could also be used. Bergius and his colleagues have improved the hydrochloric acid process, and it is now in commercial operation. The wood gives a raw product containing 90 per cent of mixed sugars. This may be fed to cattle and fattens pigs well. Its nutritive value is equal to that of barley flour. In May, 1933, a wood-sugar factory, with a yearly output of 6,000–8,000 tons of pure carbohydrates, began production. The wood-sugar industry has been greatly extended since. . . . The lignin residues from the process are used for making buttons and the like. . . . Only half of the wood in trees is used as lumber: the rest is waste. The waste chips, twigs, and sawdust provide an unlimited source of sugar. Bergius states that wood-sugar can be produced in the timber countries, such as the Baltic States and Canada, more cheaply than cane sugar, and give yeast and pure glucose for human consumption besides raw products for cattle fodder. As carbohydrates are the basis of animal and human nutrition he claims that all countries with adequate wood supplies can, if they wish, make themselves self-supporting in food. The Germans hope that cattle fed on wood sugars will provide self-sufficiency in edible fats. The German deficiency in edible fats otherwise remains an intractable problem. The direct synthetic manufacture of edible fats out of mineral oils derived from coal is still remote. Edible fats may be made out of fish oils by hydrogenation, but even fish oils must be imported. There is another important aspect of the wood-sugar process. The glucose provided by it may be fermented by bacteria to give glycerine. Nitro-glycerine, the explosive, is obtained from glycerine by treatment with nitric and sulphuric acids.

The disappearance of localized sugar production is one of many ways in which advancing scientific knowledge is making it possible to break down the sharp line of demarcation between industrial and agricultural communities and to rebuild industry on a biotechnical basis. The dairy bacteriologist has already made the local quality of cheeses an anachronism. Apart from cheese-making, the domestication of bacteria has been applied as an empirical art in the ancient industries of brewing and the practice of crop rotation. Biochemists are daily finding out how fresh processes can be carried out by the agency of organisms which the bacteriologist can culture. Thus the essential hydrocarbon of coal gas itself can be produced in this way. The ensuing quotation is from Hale's book:

The biological hydrogenation of carbon dioxide has been demonstrated as far back as 1910 by Soehngen. Carbon dioxide and hydrogen brought in contact with putrifying bacteria yield methane. Recently Franz Fischer isolated from sewage certain bacteria that actually were able to reduce carbon monoxide with hydrogen into methane. There was found to arise to some extent an equilibrium between carbon monoxide and water as against carbon dioxide and hydrogen. It is possible that carbon dioxide and hydrogen are first converted into formic acid and then into acetic acid as intermediate products; at all events methane was the end product. It is known that fish in some way are able to hydrolyze chlorobenzene into phenol. Who knows but that some day the work of a corps of cold blooded animals will replace a high temperature, high pressure installation as of to-day?

The production of *power alcohol* which has been made the subject of much attention during the recent agricultural depression in America illustrates the rapprochement of industry and agriculture through the application of organic chemistry in another way. Its extensive development would deprive coal and petrol of their predominance as crude articles of commerce, and by so doing encourage the use of other substitutes for the by-products of the coal and petrol industries. How far these tendencies will develop within the economy of private enterprise no one can foresee. There is little doubt that they will progress locally here and there, and that the results will bring forth increasing restrictions and subsidies to reinforce pre-existing processes, where intelligent statesmanship fails to recognize how new resources could enrich human life if their use were rationally planned.

EXAMPLES ON CHAPTER X

1. The formula for acetic acid is written $CH_3CO . O . H$. State (a) two series of reactions which show the presence of the CH_3 (methyl) radicle, (b) two series

of reactions which justify separating one hydrogen from the others, (c) three series of reactions which show the presence of a CO radicle.

2. Two substances, each when vaporized 23 times as dense as hydrogen, have the same percentage composition: C 52·2, O 34·8, H 13. Contrast their reactions by applying what you know about the principle of valency and the characteristics which different radicles confer, and state how one could be made from the other.

3. Compare the properties of *four* substances of molecular weight 75 having the following percentage composition: oxygen 42·7, hydrogen 6·7, nitrogen 18·7, carbon 32. How would you make each of them?

4. How many different compounds with a stable group of six carbon atoms can have the formula C_8H_9Cl? How would you build up each from benzene?

5. Four substances with a stable six-carbon nucleus have the formula C_7H_7OH. Represent how they differ with a picture formula. How would you (a) make them from coal tar, (b) recognize them?

6. Four substances with a stable six-carbon nucleus have the formula $C_7H_7NO_2$. How do their properties differ?

7. Write down the compounds which can have the following formulae with their properties and methods of preparation:

(a) C_2H_4NOCl.
(b) C_2H_5CNO.

SELECTED REFERENCES FOR PART II

For the subject matter of Chapter VII the following are highly recommended text books:
  Houston's *Intermediate physics*. Hadley's *Everyday Physics*.
For Chapters VIII and IX:
  Mellor's *Inorganic Chemistry*. Smith's *Inorganic Chemistry* (revised by Kendall). Findlay's *The Spirit of Chemistry*.
For Chapter X: either
  Cohen's *Organic Chemistry*. Perkin and Kipping's *Organic Chemistry*.
For sources relevant to the social background of Part II:
ALGER, J. G.: *Englishmen in the French Revolution*. (Low.) 1889.
BAILEY, CYRIL: *The Greek Atomists and Epicurus*. (Oxford: Clarendon Press.) 1928.
CLAPHAM, J. H.: *An Economic History of Modern Britain—The Early Railway Age, 1820–1850*. (Cambridge University Press.) 1930.
CROWTHER, J. G.: *British Scientists of the Nineteenth Century*. (Kegan Paul.) 1935.
CROWTHER, J. G.: *The ABC of Chemistry*. (Kegan Paul.) 1932.
DICKINSON, H. W.: *Matthew Boulton*. (Cambridge University Press.) 1937.
DICKINSON, H. W.: *James Watt*. (Cambridge University Press.) 1927.
DIELS, H. *Antike Tecknik*. (Leipzig: Teubner.) 1914.
FINDLAY, A.: *A Hundred Years of Progress in Chemistry*. (Duckworth.) 1937.
HALE, WILLIAM J.: *Chemistry Triumphant*. (Century of Progress Series: Allen & Unwin.) 1931.
HAMILTON, H.: *The English Brass and Copper Industry to 1800*. (Longmans.) 1926.
HAMILTON, H.: *The Industrial Revolution in Scotland*. (Oxford: Clarendon Press.) 1932.
HARTOG, P.: "Bicentenary of Joseph Priestley," *Journ. Chem. Soc.* 1933.

HARTOG, P.: "Date and Place of Priestley's Discovery of Oxygen," *Nature*, vol. 132. 1933.

HARTOG, P.: "Joseph Priestley and His Place in the History of Science," *Royal Inst.* 1931.

HEITLAND, W. E.: *Agricola.* (Cambridge University Press.) 1921.

HOLMYARD, ERIC JOHN: *Makers of Chemistry.* (Oxford: Clarendon Press.) 1931.

JARDINE, G.: "Account of John Roebuck." *Tr. Roy. Soc. Edin.* IV. 1796.

KAY, J.: *A Series of Original Portraits.* (Edinburgh.) 1837–38.

KNOWLES, L. C. A.: *The Industrial and Commercial Revolution in Great Britain During the Nineteenth Century.* (Routledge.) 1930.

LECKY, W. E. H.: *History of the Rise and Influence of the Spirit of Rationalism in Europe.* (Longmans.) 1877.

MANTELL, C. L.: *Sparks from the Electrode.* (Century of Progress Series: Allen & Unwin.) 1931.

MARSHALL, ARTHUR: *Explosives.* (3 vols.) (J. & A. Churchill.) 1932.

MASSON, IRVINE: *Three Centuries of Chemistry.* (Ernest Benn.) 1925.

MOILLIET, A.: *Sketch of the Life of James Kerr, F.R.S.* (Privately Printed.) 1868.

NEEDHAM, JOSEPH: *The Sceptical Biologist (Ten Essays).* (Chatto & Windus.) 1929.

NEF, J. U.: *The Rise of the British Coal Industry.* (Routledge.) 1932.

NEUBURGER, ALBERT: *The Technical Arts and Sciences of the Ancients.* (Methuen.) 1930.

PARKES, S.: *Chemical Essays.* (Baldwin.) 1815.

PROSSER, R. B.: *Inventors and Inventions in Birmingham.* (Privately Printed.) 1881.

PEAKE, HAROLD J.: *Early Steps in Human Progress.* (Low.) 1933.

PARTINGTON, J. R.: *Origins and Development of Applied Chemistry.* (Longmans.) 1935.

READ, THOMAS T.: *Our Mineral Civilization.* (Century of Progress Series: Allen & Unwin.) 1931.

RICKARD, T. A.: *Man and Metals.* (2 vols.) (McGraw Hill.) 1937.

RUSSELL, SIR E. J.: *Soil Conditions and Plant Growth.* (Longmans.) 1932.

RUSSELL, SIR E. J.: *The Farm and the Nation.* (George Allen & Unwin.) 1933.

SINGER, CHARLES: *A Short History of Medicine.* (Oxford: Clarendon Press.) 1928.

SINGER, CHARLES: *A Short History of Biology.* (Oxford: Clarendon Press.) 1931.

SMILES, SAMUEL: *Lives of the Engineers Boulton and Watt.* (John Murray.) 1904.

SMILES, SAMUEL: *Josiah Wedgwood.* (John Murray.) 1894.

SMITH, R. ANGUS: *A Centenary of Science in Manchester.* (Memoirs of the Literary and Philosophical Society of Manchester, Vol. IX.) (Taylor & Francis.) 1883.

STILLMAN, JOHN M.: *The Story of Early Chemistry.* (D. Appleton & Co.) 1924.

THOMAS, JOHN: *The Economic Development of the North Staffordshire Potteries since 1730, with Special Reference to the Industrial Revolution.* (Thesis for Ph.D.) (London.) June 1934. Typescript in London Univ. Liby.

TURNER, D. M.: *The Book of Scientific Discovery.* (Harrap.) 1933.

URE, ANDREW: *The Philosophy of Manufactures.* (Charles Knight.) 1835.

VOWLES, H. P. and M. W.: *The Quest for Power.* (Chapman & Hall.) 1931.

WELLS, H. G.: *Work, Wealth and Happiness of Mankind.* (Heinemann.) 1935.

ZIMMERN, A.: *The Greek Commonwealth.* (Oxford: Clarendon Press.) 1924.

PART III

The Conquest of Power

And did the countenance divine
Shine forth upon our clouded hills?
And was Jerusalem builded here
Among these dark satanic mills?

WILLIAM BLAKE

CHAPTER XI

A CENTURY OF INVENTIONS

The Decline of Wind and Water

ABOUT sixty years ago Alfred Russel Wallace wrote a book called *The Wonderful Century*. Had he called it *A Century of Inventions* he would have been guilty of plagiarism. Three centuries before, the Marquis of Worcester had already used this title for a book in which he described a hundred new devices. Nowadays we are apt to think of rapid technological progress as a special characteristic of capitalism in the nineteenth century. So it is somewhat startling to meet these words in their own context. In a broad sense of the term the sixteenth century had been a century of inventions. Reviewing their consequences in the *Novum Organum*, Bacon wrote:

It is well to observe the force and virtue and consequence of discoveries, and these are to be seen nowhere more conspicuously than in those three which were unknown to the ancients . . . namely, printing, gunpowder and the magnet. For these three have changed the whole face and state of things throughout the world, the first in literature, the second in warfare, and the third in navigation. Whence have followed innumerable changes, in so much that no empire, no sect, no star seems to have exerted greater power and influence in human affairs than these mechanical discoveries.

According to a widely prevalent dogma, the spectacular technological progress which has accompanied the civilization of northern Europe is due to the peculiar attributes of tall people endowed with blue eyes, fair hair, and no sense of humour. The circumstances which abetted the adventurous hopefulness of early capitalism provide very little basis for this belief. The inventions which were crowded into one and the same social context during two centuries before Bacon pleaded for a New Learning included the clock, spectacles, the telescope, the mariner's compass, the printing press, gunpowder, the use of coal as fuel, stringed musical instruments with keys, wind power for corn-mills, and water power to pump flooded mines. Of these there is good reason to regard the first as a device which developed initially to meet the special requirements of northern latitudes and later to serve uses of westerly navigation. Printing, gunpowder, coal as fuel, the compass, water power, and wind power, had long been known to the Chinese. Steam bellows which were now being used in mines had been outstripped by Hero's turbine. The introduction of spectacles and stringed instruments had been sponsored by the ethic and ritual of a religion which was not invented by Nordic man. What was essentially new in the situation which inaugurated the modern era of power production was that circumstances simultaneously forced upon the notice of an expanding literate population a variety of devices which had not become part of the everyday life of the comparatively small group of people competent, elsewhere and in ancient times, to transmit a written record of useful information.

Consider, for example, the single invention which fathered the science of electrical power production. Thales of Miletus, a merchant of Tyrian parentage, knew of the lodestone, and it is not unlikely that he got his knowledge from the Phoenician mariners, from whom he also learned the art of navigating by the position of the stars in the Little Bear. How far the lodestone was used in ancient navigation we do not know. It was familiar to the Chinese, who were not conspicuous for their maritime opportunities or

FIG. 273.—HANSEATIC COG ABOUT 1480

From S. C. Gilfillan's book *Inventing the Ship*.

exploits, before the beginning of the Christian era. The need for it was not imperative so long as the centre of world navigation was located in latitudes where the more ancient technique of star-lore served well enough. We first hear of its use in Scandinavia about the time of Leif Ericcson's renowned expedition to Vinland, beneath the grey skies of a sea route, where stellar or solar navigation would have been utterly impracticable. It becomes an important fact in the social life of mankind when coast-line sailing is giving place to long-distance voyages. Then the manufacture of compasses to meet the needs of expanding merchant enterprise becomes an industry with technological problems which demand access to the written records of the voyages of the time. A Wapping compass maker claims the honour of writing the first printed book exclusively devoted to the phenomena of magnetism. The social conditions for the steady advance initiated by this landmark in the history of scientific magnetism include the expansion of maritime trade, the existence of the printing press and of shops where books are sold, the provision of instruction in the art of reading available to compass makers and ships' pilots, and, at the Court of Elizabeth, an influential body of men whose opulence depended on success in a struggle for colonization and plunder against competitors equipped with Chinese gunpowder and Arabic astronomy.

The material achievement of science in the ancient world was to provide mankind with the knowledge required to regulate the seasonal pursuits of a

FIG. 274.—COLUMBUS' "SANTA MARIA"

From S. C. Gilfillan's book *Inventing the Ship*.

local economy by use of a reliable calendar, and to undertake the exploration of new territories as sources of new materials by equipping ocean transport with the means of localization. No corpus of organized scientific knowledge was available to guide the search for material substitutes nor to provide sources of power to replace human toil.

The social history of power production may be roughly divided into three chapters, the ancient, the middle, and the modern. The signal achievements of the first were the substitution of animal for slave labour and the introduction of the sail as an aid to navigation. Both inventions promoted the diffusion of culture by providing means of trade intercourse between locally self-sufficient communities. The ox was kept to tread corn and to draw sledges or rough carts before civilized man slowly acquired the art of harnessing the horse. In ancient Egypt the horse was not known, till the country became a prey to inroads of Asiatic tribes which had long used it as a steed. Because of their great speed, vehicles driven by horses became a powerful instrument of warfare popularized in the Persian campaigns. Speed created a new technical demand for precision in wheel design; and since the mechanical possibilities of a wheel are not self evident, we may surmise that the exploits of the charioteer were a necessary preparation for a second class of innovations.

The use of the wheel can be traced to the potter's art in the dawn of Mesopotamian civilization. When the Alexandrian age begins, horse-driven chariots had made the wheel a familiar fact of everyday life. During what may be called the middle chapter of the story, knowledge of wheel mechan-

FIG. 275.—TWO PRINTS FROM AGRICOLA'S TREATISE SHOWING HUMAN (TREADMILL) AND MECHANICAL (WATER) POWER USED TO RAISE LOADS FROM MINES

isms for tapping inanimate sources of power spread slowly through the civilized world. Water wheels used for irrigation existed in ancient Babylon. From the description of Vitruvius it appears that power was being transmitted by toothed wheels at the end of the first century B.C.* Windmills, probably of Chinese origin, were known in Persia at least as early as the tenth century of the present era, and water-driven sawmills existed in the Roman Empire as early as the fourth century. By the eleventh century the use of wind and water as sources of power was widely spread throughout Europe.

Modern power production begins with the use of steam in the middle of the seventeenth century. During the eighteenth century steam-driven pumps burning coal as fuel were adapted to maintain a supply of water for mill

* For the history of the water mill see *Ann. d'Hist. Econ. et Soc.* 36 (November 1935), article by Marc Bloch.

wheels in the Potteries, in Scotland, and elsewhere in Britain. The direct production of rotary power by steam was expedited by the fact that water wheels had brought into being a variety of devices depending on heavy sources of power for lifting loads or driving hammers in mining, fulling, metallurgy, and other manufactures. The comparatively rapid extension of water- and wind-driven mechanisms during the three centuries before Bacon's time was therefore a necessary prelude to the technical revolution which began a century later.

A hundred or so devices, including a steam turbine, catalogued by Hero (*circa* 150 B.C.) and the various inventions attributed to Ctesibius (see p. 230) show no lack of ingenuity to explain slow progress in the exploitation of natural power by the Mediterranean world. In *The Quest for Power*, Mr. Vowles and his wife state their view that "the abolition of slavery by the Emperor Constantine and the conversion by Honorius and Arcadius of free distribution of corn to a daily allowance of bread must have greatly stimulated the demand for water power for corn milling purposes." Be that as it may, there is little doubt that slavery acted as a dead weight on the progress of power technology in the civilizations of antiquity. Agricola's treatise gives us many illustrations of the use of water power in mining operations which could no longer rely on abundant sources of cheap labour. The sheer impossibility of extending deep shafts without new sources of power to compensate for lack of cheap and abundant labour brought about a new tempo of mechanical progress towards the end of the Middle Ages.

Steam had been used in ancient metallurgical processes as a substitute for bellows worked by hand. By the seventeenth century it had been largely superseded by the water wheel, which was now being used to drain water from flooded mines. The accumulation of water in mines was a far more serious problem in the humid north than it had been in the deep shaft mining of the ancient world. Indeed it was one of the major technological problems of the period. Steam began to be used as a source of power for pumping in the closing years of the seventeenth century, and the modern use of steam therefore emerges in the same social context as its only use in antiquity.

In the middle of the seventeenth century the development of mechanical power received for the first time a direct impetus from advancing scientific knowledge. In connexion with his experiments on the weight of the atmosphere von Guericke had shown that the vacuum could be used as a means of distributing power at a distance and had (Fig. 276) constructed a model in which a weight was raised by a piston mechanism. Von Guericke's suggestion for communicating power at a distance was a simple application of the new air pump which Hooke was using in England. A similar model, in which the motive force was the external pressure of the atmosphere, seems to have been demonstrated at early meetings of the English Royal Society by Papin, then Curator. It played an important part in the earliest attempts to apply steam power.

The English Royal Society was founded about the time when the first steam pumps were introduced, and its personnel was active in studying problems connected with their use and design. It had begun as informal gatherings of a group of scientific men who met first in the rooms of Sir William Petty, author of the *Political Arithmetic*. An early reference to this group originally called the "Invisible College" is mentioned in the following citation from the *Record* of the Royal Society:

Writing from London on October 22, 1646, to M. Marcombes (who had been his French tutor in England), Boyle alludes to his studies in "natural philosophy and husbandry according to the principles of our new philosophical colledge that values no knowledge but as it hath a tendency to use." He asks his correspondent to bring from abroad with him to England "good receipts or choice books on any of these subjects which you can procure, which will make you extremely welcome to our *invisible college*."

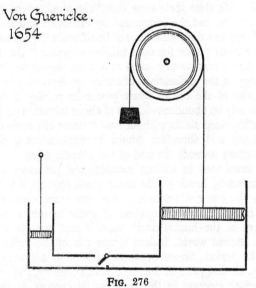

Von Guericke.
1654

FIG. 276

Von Guericke's pump for raising a weight by transmission of reduced pressure is essentially the basis of the vacuum brakes used on trains today.

The first history of the Royal Society by Thomas Sprat, Lord Bishop of Rochester, is redolent with the anxiety of the original fellows to promote the development of mechanical inventions as the foundation of English prosperity. In tracing the beginnings of the Invisible College during the years which immediately preceded the first revolution of Stuart times, Sprat remarks:

I shall only mention one great man who had the true imagination of the whole Extent of this Enterprise as it is now set on foot, and that is the Lord Bacon in whose books there are everywhere scattered the best arguments that can be produced for the Defence of experimental philosophy, and the best Directions that are needful to promote it.

Bacon's defence of experimental philosophy is now a well-thumbed brief. His directions to promote it are forgotten, though "adorned with so much art," as Sprat appraised. It would be hard to find a better statement of what Hessen calls the unity of theory and practice than the passage which opens with the following words in the *Novum Organum*:

> The roads to human power and to human knowledge lie close together, and are nearly the same; nevertheless, on account of the pernicious and inveterate habit of dwelling on abstractions, it is safer to begin and raise the sciences from those foundations which have relation to practice and let the active part be as the seal which prints and determines the contemplative counterpart.

Marquis of Worcester, 1663

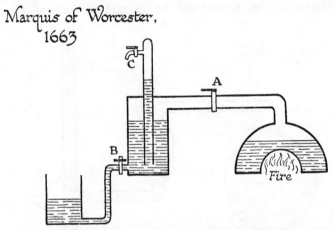

FIG. 277.—SCHEMATIC RECONSTRUCTION OF THE MARQUIS OF WORCESTER'S PATENT FOR RAISING WATER BY STEAM POWER

When all three taps are closed steam collects in the space above the boiler. When A and C are opened, and B is closed, the pressure of the steam drives water out of the cistern. If C and A are turned off, the steam condenses, producing a partial vacuum. When B is turned on water is drawn up from the source below the cistern by the excess atmosphere pressure at the source.

In this spirit the Royal Society began its labours. The project included a conspectus of all the principal technological problems which affected British mercantile supremacy and the theoretical issues relevant to their solution. The exploitation of steam power was one among other contemporary issues which enlisted the enthusiasm of the early Fellows.

"They design," Sprat tells us, "the multiplying and beautifying of the mechanick arts. . . . They intend the perfection of graving statuary, limning, coining and all the works of smiths in iron or steel or silver. . . . They purpose the trial of all manner of operations by Fire. . . . They resolve to restore, to enlarge, to examine Physick. . . . They have bestowed much consideration on the propagation of Fruits and trees. . . . They have principally consulted the Advancement of Navigation. . . . They have employed much Time in examining the Fabrick of Ships, the forms of their sails, the shapes of their keels, the sorts of Timber, the planting of Fir, the bettering of pitch and Tar and Tackling."

The earliest heat engines were devices in which a vacuum was created by filling a closed space with steam, and then forcing the steam to condense by cooling it. In the Marquis of Worcester's patent, and in the later device of Savery (1698), the condenser was in direct connexion with the water which was being pumped away (Figs. 277 and 278). In Newcomen's engine (Fig. 279), which was introduced for draining the Cornish mines in the second decade of the eighteenth century, the condensation of the steam induced the fall of a piston which was connected with the pump rod by a lever of wood.

The steps which led to this combination of the von Guericke (or Papin) principle and the Worcester invention illustrate the close relation between the leaders of English science and the practical problems of mining. An

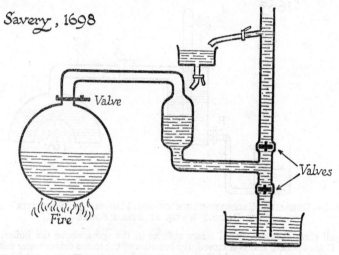

Savery, 1698

Valve

Valves

Fire

FIG. 278.—SAVERY'S PATENT (1698)

This was essentially like that of the Marquis of Worcester. There is an arrangement to cool the steam space by irrigation so as to facilitate condensation.

account of Savery's engine was published in the *Philosophical Transactions* of the Royal Society. In his book on Boulton and Watt, Smiles tells us:

> . . . a draft of Savery's engine having come under Newcomen's notice, he proceeded to make a model of it, which he fixed in his garden, and soon found out its imperfections. He entered into a correspondence on the subject with the learned and ingenious Dr. Hooke, then Secretary to the Royal Society, a man of remarkable ingenuity, and of great mechanical sagacity and insight. Newcomen had heard or read of Papin's proposed method of transmitting motive power to a distance by creating a vacuum under a piston in a cylinder, and transmitting the power through pipes to a second cylinder near the mine. Dr. Hooke dissuaded Newcomen from erecting a machine on this principle, as a waste of time and labour, but he added the pregnant suggestion, "could he (meaning Papin) make a speedy vacuum under your piston, your work were done." . . . Savery created his vacuum by the condensation of steam in a closed vessel, and Papin created his by exhausting the air in a cylinder

fitted with a piston, by means of an air pump. It remained for Newcomen to combine the two expedients—to secure a sudden vacuum by the condensation of steam; but, instead of employing Savery's closed vessel, he made use of Papin's cylinder fitted with a piston.

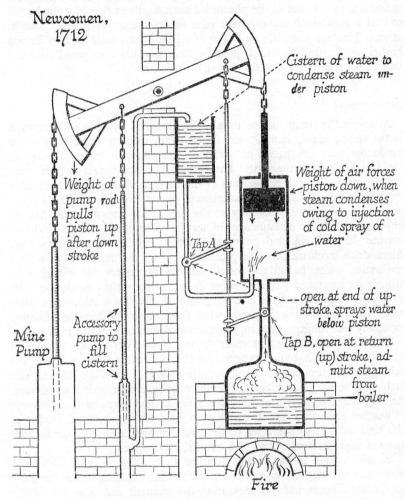

Newcomen, 1712

Cistern of water to condense steam under piston

Weight of pump rod pulls piston up after down stroke

Tap A

Weight of air forces piston down, when steam condenses owing to injection of cold spray of water

open at end of up-stroke, sprays water below piston

Tap B, open at return (up) stroke, admits steam from boiler

Mine Pump

Accessory pump to fill cistern

Fire

FIG. 279.—DIAGRAMMATIC VIEW OF NEWCOMEN'S ATMOSPHERIC OR FIRE ENGINE (1712)

In the earliest models the two valves which admitted (A) the spray of cold water to condense the steam in the piston cylinder, and (B) the steam from the boiler, were worked by hand

The further step of connecting the piston to a fly-wheel did not come till seventy years had passed. Newcomen's engine was used for pumping where water power was not accessible. For other purposes it had little to commend it. An engine based on the von Guericke principle was an exceedingly costly source of power, because of the rapacity with which it devoured fuel. That this greed for fuel was due to a faulty principle of design was not understood until new scientific knowledge was available. Watt's important contribution was to eliminate the colossal wastage which resulted from cooling the cylinder at each stroke of the piston. Hammond tells us that "for one bushel of coal a Newcomen engine could raise on an average $5\frac{1}{2}$ million pounds, at most 7 million pounds, to a height of 1 foot. Watt's early engines for one bushel could raise $21\frac{1}{2}$ million pounds, while his later ones could raise $26\frac{1}{2}$ million pounds." (See also pp. 600-1.)

THERMOMETRY

Although the steam turbine or *aeolipile* described by Hero of Alexandria in the second millennium B.C. was nearer to the modern economy of power production than the patents of Savery or Newcomen, it left no impress on the search for new theoretical knowledge. The first steam engines were not designed with any recognition of the theoretical principles involved in costing the relation of fuel consumption to power production. This, indeed, was not a theoretical possibility at the time. The ancient world had no impetus to study the measurement of heat production, and there could be no balance sheet of fuel and power till units of measurement were settled. Alexandrian mechanics was for practical purposes the mechanics of a slave civilization which lacked the social incentive to explore and exploit substitutes for unnecessary human effort. It was not brought into close contact with the practical problems of mining or with the new mechanics of gases which developed during the period when the problems of deep-shaft mining, especially coal mining, were engaging the attention of scientific men.

The initial impetus to the study of heat came from another source. In pursuance of its Baconian programme the "Invisible College," like the academies which appeared simultaneously in France (p. 285), Holland, and Italy, was seeking new ways and means of promoting maritime supremacy. Among its first projects after the Charter was granted were systematic surveys of weather conditions and of variations in the earth's magnetism. Studies of this kind and others undertaken by the continental academies laid the foundations of scientific meteorology and terrestrial magnetism.

Castelli, a pupil of Galileo, had invented a rain gauge in 1639. Hooke also made one and devised instruments for detecting changes in the humidity of the atmosphere and for measuring the strength and direction of the wind. The barometer was now being used for the first time to study variations in the pressure of the atmosphere. In Italy the Accademia undertook a comprehensive programme of observations of one kind or another involving day-to-day records of changes in the weather. Under Hooke's name one of the earliest publications of the English Royal Society includes "the form of a scheme which at one view represents to the eye observations of the weather for a whole month." Concerted weather records were made at Paris and Stockholm between 1649 and 1651.

The modern science of power production starts from this basis. Economical power production implies a method of measuring heat, and a technique for measuring heat was necessary for weather surveys. At the time there were special reasons which encouraged the study of weather conditions. Although sailing ships are at least three thousand years old, ancient navigation continued to rely very largely on slaves at the oar. The transport of huge cargoes

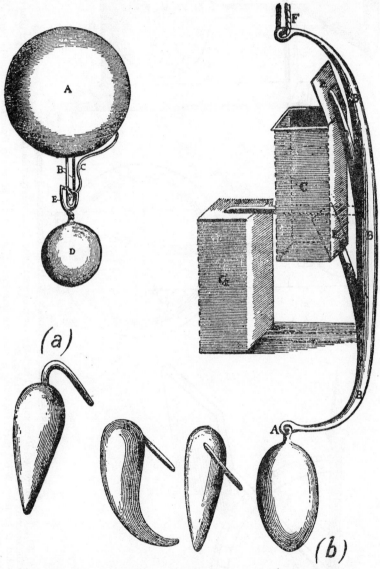

FIG. 280.—TWO OF HOOKE'S MECHANICAL DEVICES FOR SURVEY WORK IN NAVIGATION

(*a*) Sounding instrument (*b*) Water sampler for collecting water at different depths. By kind permission of Professor Wolf, from his *History of Science, Technology, and Philosophy in the Sixteenth and Seventeenth Centuries* (George Allen & Unwin).

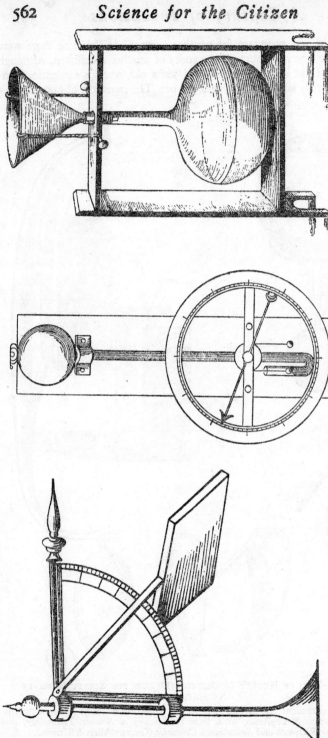

FIG. 281.—THREE OF HOOKE'S WEATHER RECORDING INSTRUMENTS

(*a*) Windgauge (*b*) Wheel barometer (*c*) Rain gauge. The large vacuum space above the mercury in (*b*) minimizes any error due to small bubbles of air trapped in the mercury for the reason shown in Fig. 239. [By kind permission of Professor Wolf, these illustrations and the following Figure are reproduced from his invaluable book on the *History of Science, Technology, and Philosophy in the Sixteenth and Seventeenth Centuries.*]

The Form of a Scheme.

Which at one view reprefents to the Eye Obfervations of the Weather, for a whole Month, may be fuch, as follows.

Days of the Mo-neth, and Place of the Sun	Remarkable hours.	Age and Sign of the Moon at Noon	The Quarters of the Wind, and its ftrength.	The Faces or vifible appear-ances of the Sky.	The Notableft Effects	General De-ductions. Thefe are to be made after the fide is filled with Obfervations, as
June 14 ♊ 12.46′	4 8 12 4 8 12	27 ♉ 9. 46 Perigeum	W · · · · 2 · · · · · · · 3 · · · · · · · · 3½ · · · · · · · · · · WSW 1 · · · · · · · · · ·	Clearblue, but yel lowifh in the N E. Clouded toward the South. Checkered blue.	A great Dew Thunder far to the S. A very great Tyde.	From the laft Quarter of the Moon to the Change, the weather was very tempe-rate, but for the Seafon, cold ; the Wind pretty conftant be-tween N. and W. &c.
15 ♊ 13.40′	8 4 6 12	28 24. 58	NW 3 4 N 2 1	A clear sky all day, but a little check-er'd about 4 P. M. At Sun-fet red and hazy.	Not by much fo big a Tyde as yefterday. A great Thun-der-Showre from the N.	
16 ♊ 14.57 &c.	10	New Moon at 7. 25. A. M. ♊ 10.8 &c.	S 1 &c.	Overcaft and very lowring, &c.	No dew upon the ground, but very much upon Marble-ftones, &c.	

Fig. 282.—Hooke's "Form of a Scheme" for a Continuous Weather Record in an Early Publication of the Royal Society

over vastly greater distances after the discovery of the New World made wind as a source of power supreme. Italian and British scientists, working in close association with the technological problems of navigation, began to study the direction of winds, the nature of storms, and the agencies which contribute to climatic differences.

In doing so they were helped by knowing more about the nature of air than their predecessors had done. The English word "climate" comes from the Greek κλίμα, which was the term used by Alexandrian geographers for what we now call latitude (or more precisely co-latitude, since it was reckoned in degrees from the pole instead of from the equator). The Mediterranean world did not associate differences of climate with anything measurable except the sun's altitude as it varies according to season and latitude. The science of antiquity had no instruments for measuring intensity of heat or cold. When the existence of matter in the third state was clearly established, the significance of many familiar weather phenomena assumed a new aspect, and new instruments like the barometer were now available for research.

The first device which can be described as a thermometer seems to have been made by Galileo. It was a glass bulb about the size of a ping-pong ball with a long stem which dipped into water. The bulb was heated to make the air expand till some was expelled from the tube. On cooling, of course the air contracted, making the water rise up the stem. The warmth of the hand applied to it was then sufficient to make the water level fall owing to expansion of the air in the bulb. Although the stem was graduated in later models, the reading obtained was necessarily arbitrary. It depended entirely on the capacity of the bulb, the initial temperature at which the instrument was calibrated and the atmospheric pressure. A French physician and chemist, Jean Rey (1632), improved on Galileo's instrument and adapted the principle for detecting fever, using water as the thermometric substance. Thermometers with a sealed stem were first made in Italy about fifty years later.

The fact that solids or liquids which have been strongly heated shrink when cooled had presumably been noticed by craftsmen and artificers from earliest times, but the expansion of bodies when subjected to warmth is not an obvious fact of everyday life. The expansion exhibited by gases like air when exposed to slight changes of heat hardly detectable by direct sensation in an instrument, such as the thermometer, or perhaps we should say the *thermoscope* of Galileo, drew attention to the phenomenon, and at once suggested the means of studying the problem of climate from a new angle. If air has weight, and if the same amount of it can occupy a much larger space when warmed, warm air is less dense than cold. It will therefore rise; and if the warmth of the hand suffices to produce a noticeable change in the density of air, how much more does the intense heat of the sun, varying as it does by day and night, winter and summer, or by proximity to the equator? Here, then, was a new instrument for studying how air is set in motion.

The honour of taking the first steps towards a fixed standard for measurement of intensity of heat is due to the Florentine Academy, which was also responsible for an important practical improvement of the thermometer. Rey, as stated, used water as the fluid. For meteorological purposes water is totally unsuitable for two reasons. The first is the obvious fact that a water thermometer cannot be graduated to record degrees of heat below the temperature at which snow melts. Even above this it is unsuitable, because of a very important peculiarity which makes water capable of sustaining aquatic life in the winter. If water at the temperature of melting snow is heated it contracts up to a certain point corresponding to 4° on the centigrade

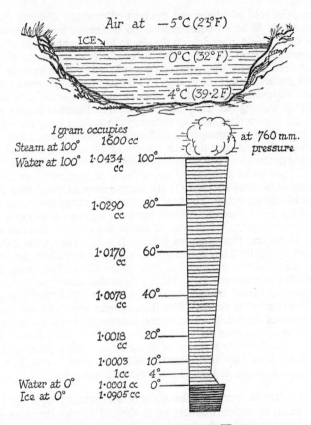

FIG. 283.—THE EXPANSION OF WATER

The upper figure illustrates the freezing of a pond exposed to air below the freezing point of water. As the water is cooled it sinks till the temperature of the bottom is 4°, *at which water is most dense*. Convection is then at a standstill. The top layer freezes and owing to its very low conductivity for heat there is little further change. If water were most dense at 0° C. the pond would freeze to a solid mass whenever the temperature remained appreciably below 0° C. The lower figure shows in a very exaggerated diagram the relative densities of water between 0° and 100° C. At the latter the steam formed expands to 1,600 times the equivalent volume of water. At the former the ice formed expands by nearly 10 per cent. The actual values for the volume occupied by 1 gram are given numerically.

scale, expanding thereafter. That is to say, the maximum density of water is above its freezing point. So water does not sink to the bottom as it approaches the freezing point. If it did so, ponds and rivers would freeze in winter and aquatic life would be extinguished. Alcohol or spirits of wine, which was used in the Florentine thermometers, has a much lower freezing point, and expands continuously over the whole range of temperature at which water exists in the liquid state.

Cajori tells us that the Florentine Academy chose a scale of heat intensity, or as we now say "temperature," based on two

fixed points, the cold of winter and the heat of summer, dividing the intervening space into 80 or 40 equal spaces. To determine more accurately the position of these points, they defined the one to be the temperature of snow or ice in the severest frost, and the other to be the temperature in the bodies of cows and deer. The melting-point of ice was found by them to be invariable, and, in their medical scale, to be at $13\frac{1}{2}°$. In 1829 some of the Florentine thermometers were discovered among old glassware, and Libri actually found them to read $13\frac{1}{2}°$ in melting ice. They had been used in Florence sixteen years in meteorological observations, and by reducing the average temperature to one of the modern scales, and comparing with modern observations, Libri thought he could draw the inference that the climate of Florence had remained unaltered during the two hundred years. The fixed points chosen by the Florentine Academy did not prove satisfactory and all sorts of improvements were suggested. Dalence in 1688 adopted (1) the temperature of air during freezing and (2) that of melting butter. The final adoption of the temperatures of melting ice and boiling water was not reached until the eighteenth century, though Huyghens had recommended the use of one or the other of these as early as 1665. The Florentine thermometers became famous. They were introduced into England by Boyle. They reached France by way of Poland. An envoy of the Queen of Poland was presented in 1657 by the Grand Duke with thermometers and other instruments. Her secretary forwarded one of the thermometers to the astronomer Ismael Boulliau in Paris, and stated that "the Grand Duke always carries one in his pocket." The thermometer was about one decimetre long and contained alcohol. Boulliau himself constructed in 1659 a thermometer in which mercury was used for the first time (so far as known) as a thermometric substance. Recently a record of temperature observations by Boulliau, extending from May 1658 to September 1660, has been found. Next to the Florentine record, begun in 1655, it is the oldest in existence.

For most scientific purposes the scale of temperature now used is the centigrade scale, in which one degree is defined as the intensity of heat required to increase the length of a column of mercury by one-hundredth part of the difference between its length at the melting-point of ice and its length at the boiling-point of water at the mean sea-level atmospheric pressure (760 mm. on the mercury barometer). On the centigrade scale ice melts at 0°, and at 760 mm. pressure water boils at 100°. On the "absolute" scale, often used in connexion with the study of gases and solutions, the corresponding temperatures are 273° and 373°. The centigrade scale was introduced in 1742 by Celsius thirty years after the Fahrenheit scale, in which water freezes at 32° and boils at 212°. The latter is still used in England for clinical purposes and weather records. Since there are 180° F. between the freezing and boiling point of water corresponding to 100° C. the rule for converting temperature from centigrade to Fahrenheit is $F = \frac{180}{100}C + 32$. A third scale on which water freezes at 0° and boils at 80° was introduced by Réaumur, a Dane. It is little used today. One practical development of thermometry before the modern age of power production is indicated by the title (English translation 1750) of a book by Réaumur *The Art of hatching and bringing up domestic fowls of all kinds at any time of the year, either by means of the heat of hotbeds or that of common fire.* Matthew Boulton read it, and busied himself, says Dickinson, "making thermometers for himself and friends."

That Celsius was a Swede draws attention to the influence of climatic studies on the early progress of research into the nature of heat. In this chapter we deal with the technique of measuring heat in connexion with the three main features of climate, viz. winds, wetness, and warmth. Most of us are already conversant with the main conclusion established by experimental enquiry and direct observation during the latter half of the seventeenth and early part of the eighteenth century.

WINDS

Although the direction of the wind changes constantly, continuous record of the weather-cock shows certain prevalent characteristics, of which the two most fully understood are (a) the direction of morning and evening breezes in propinquity to the sea (b) the predominant westward drift of the ocean Trade Winds on either side of the equator. The prevailing direction of coastal breezes during the morning and early afternoon is landward and the prevailing direction of breezes after sunset is seaward. The meaning of this was at once evident when continuous temperature records of land and the sea adjacent to it were kept. The temperature of the sea is far more constant than that of the land. By day it does not rise to the same temperature as the land when there is full sunshine, and by night it does not fall to as low a temperature as the land after the sun sets. As the temperature of the land increases in the morning above that of the sea, warmer air rises because it is less dense, and its place is filled by colder air drawn inwards from the sea. After sunset the converse is true.

In the tropical and sub-tropical seas the predominant direction of air currents near the surface is from the poles towards the equator where the air is hottest, and therefore rises upwards. This major movement is complicated by the fact that the rotational displacement of land from west to east at the equator is vastly greater than it is near the poles (Fig. 285). If you consider a column of air drawn in from, let us say, the latitude of Iceland and dissect its movement by the principle of inertia, you will see that it starts with a movement southwards due to the suction of rising air at the equator and a movement eastwards at the same speed of rotation as the land. As it travels south the earth beneath it is moving more swiftly eastwards. To see what happens imagine two railway trains travelling in the same direction at different speeds. To an observer in the quicker one the slower one will seem to be moving in the opposite direction. So if both are moving towards the east, the slower one will seem to a person in the quicker one to be moving towards the west, i.e. to be coming from the east. Hence the main drift of winds in the neighbourhood of the equator is from the north-east on the north side and from the south-east on the south side. Thus the direction of the Trade Winds which prevail in tropical seas, as first pointed out by Halley, a contemporary of Newton, reinforced the belief in the earth's diurnal motion about its axis.

The basic fact on which the ventilation of the earth's surface, like the ventilation of a room, depends is that warm air is lighter than cold air. Bodies expand when heated. Hence their densities depend on temperature. Bodies which are not rigid, i.e. liquids and gases, are therefore subject to internal movement or *convection* which promotes continuous mixing and circulation of heat (Fig. 284). The direction of the air currents on the earth's surface is modified by two relatively constant agencies, the earth's rotational motion

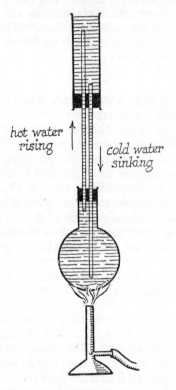

hot water rising ↑   ↓ *cold water sinking*

FIG. 284.—CONVECTION—THE PRINCIPLE OF A CENTRAL HEATING SYSTEM

The method of heat transmission in gases and liquids depends on the fact that they expand when heated, hence the warmer portions, being less dense, rise while the cooler, being more dense, sink.

and the distribution of land and water. The effect of the latter is due to the fact that water maintains a more constant temperature than land. It does not heat up or cool so rapidly. This leads to both daily and seasonal changes in the direction of wind owing to the unequal heating of land and water by day and night or in summer and in winter. In addition to the separate influence of these relatively stable factors various consequences arise from their interaction. Two complications arise from the evaporation of water. Evaporation results in the formation of clouds which affect the distribution of sunshine, and of rain which affects the temperature of the land on which it falls. The distribution of both clouds and rain is affected by atmospheric electrification and by the prevailing air currents resulting from agencies already mentioned. Air currents, which predominate where there are large uninterrupted stretches of land or water, are subject to considerable fluctuations in islands like Britain where land is in close proximity to water. To all these temporary sources of fluctuation we have to add the local one which arises from the expansion of water. This results in ocean currents analogous to the winds. These also modify the relative distribution of heat and cold on land and water.

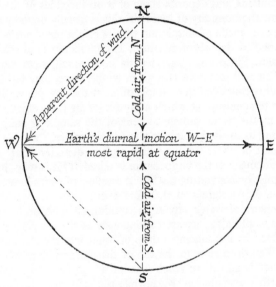

FIG. 285

Trade Winds—due to influence of the earth's diurnal motion on the direction of polar-equatorial convection current.

WETNESS

Scientific knowledge of climate could not progress until the characteristics of matter in the gaseous state began to be studied. The basic experimental fact on which wetness depends is that the liquid state of matter *never exists by itself*. It is always accompanied by the gaseous or vapour state, and the relative amount of the latter depends on the temperature.

This can be illustrated in a general way by the everyday experience of evaporation at temperatures far below the boiling point, and by the fact that when air has been in contact with water (i.e. unless it has been dried by passing over a dehydrating agent like calcium chloride, sulphuric acid or phosphorus pentoxide) it always deposits moisture on the sides of a vessel when cooled sufficiently. This happens, for instance, when warm air comes in contact with cold substances which like metals conduct or absorb heat very efficiently. The exact amount of water vapour which a given volume of air can hold at a given temperature can be measured by bubbling dry air through water at different temperatures. If a known volume of this air is first weighed, then thoroughly dried by passing it over a substance like sulphuric acid, and weighed a second time, the loss of weight shows how much water vapour it contained.

It is not necessary to go through this performance every time we wish to know the water vapour content of the atmosphere. Once we have tabulated the quantity of water vapour which a given volume of air will hold at any temperature, we have only to cool our sample to the temperature called its *"dew point,"* i.e. the temperature at which it just ceases to hold all the water vapour it contains and deposits some of it on the sides of the vessel. If we want to know the humidity of room air, this is usually done by adding ice to water in a vessel made of aluminium till the bright metal surface of the out-side is dimmed by deposit of moisture. The temperature of the water at this point is taken. Since our tables tell us how much water vapour a given quantity of air will just hold at a given temperature, they tell us how much water vapour is contained in a sample of air at the dew point. Since the dew point is the temperature at which a sample of air just ceases to hold all its water vapour, the water vapour content of the sample is simply the figure corresponding to the dew point, as given in the tables.

The amount of water vapour which a given quantity of air will hold in-creases continuously as the temperature is raised. This is why the sun dispels a morning mist by converting the liquid droplets of water into vapour. Since water vapour has weight and therefore exerts pressure, we should expect that the pressure of water vapour in equilibrium with ordinary water in a closed space would also increase continuously as the temperature rises. This is easily proved by introducing a drop of water into the stem of an ordinary barometer. The drop rises to the top of the mercury and there evaporates. If more water is added we reach a point where further addition does not result in further evaporation. Meanwhile the column of mercury has fallen somewhat. At the point where more water added does not vaporize, the fall of pressure represents the pressure of water vapour when the closed space of the barometer can hold no more. If the barometer tube is surrounded by a jacket containing water whose temperature can be varied, it is found that the saturation pressure of water vapour measured in this way is greater when the temperature is greater.

At the boiling point the saturation pressure, or as it is more often called the *vapour pressure*, of a liquid *is the same as the pressure of the atmosphere.* The vapour pressure of a fluid at a fixed temperature is constant, and since it increases as the temperature rises, the boiling point of a fluid is increased if the atmospheric pressure is increased and decreased if the atmospheric pressure decreases. At the top of a mountain the atmospheric pressure is less than at sea-level. So on a mountain-top water boils at a lower temperature than at sea-level.* At the peak of Mont Blanc it boils at 85° C. instead of at

* Papin, a contemporary of the Marquis of Worcester and inventor of a steam engine of the Newcomen type, invented a "digester" for increasing the external pressure, suitable among other uses for cooking according to the authorized rules of the art on a high mountain.

100°. We can therefore determine the height of a mountain without using surveying instruments, or a barometer as explained on p. 381. All we have to do is to find the boiling point of water at the summit. Tables of vapour pressure prepared by the method of Fig 286 tell us the pressure of water vapour at the temperature recorded. This is the same as the atmospheric pressure. From it the height can be calculated, or read off from tables of the variation of barometer readings with altitude.

Generally speaking, water vapour condenses to form water when the

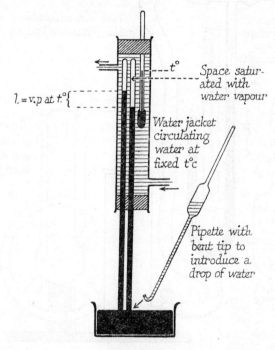

$l = v.p$ at $t°$ {

$t°$ — Space saturated with water vapour

Water jacket circulating water at fixed t°c

Pipette with bent tip to introduce a drop of water

FIG. 286

Hot-water jacket, etc., for finding variation of vapour pressure with temperature.

temperature of the air is cooled to the dew point. This, of course, occurs nightly in hot weather when there is abundant evaporation in the daytime and a relatively big fall of temperature at night. In contrast to this fairly regular deposition of moisture as dew, the more capricious phenomenon of rain depends on circumstances which are not purely local. Incoming currents of air come from regions where the atmosphere is in contact with a large surface of water, and is fully saturated at the temperature of the place where it originates. The circumstances which control their movements are immensely complex, and long-range forecasts of rain depend chiefly on the study of how the pressure of the atmosphere is changing over a wide area (see p. 576).

Immediate prospect of rain at any place is also disclosed by the *relative humidity* of the atmosphere. This is measured by the ratio

$$\frac{\text{Actual Water-Vapour Content of the Atmosphere}}{\text{Water-Vapour Content of Saturated Air at the Same Temperature}}$$

If the dew point has been determined this can be extracted from tables of

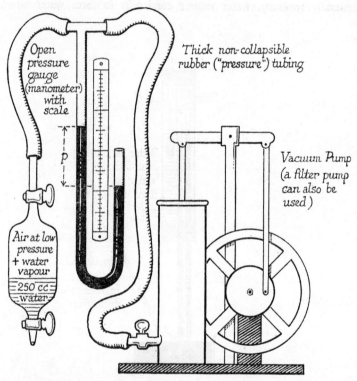

FIG. 287.—RELATION OF SOLUBILITY TO THE PRESSURE OF A GAS

The figure shows how to find the effect of pressure on the solubility of gases. If we wish to know how the solubility of nitrogen or oxygen in water varies with the pressure of the atmosphere, a measured volume of water for analysis of dissolved gases is vigorously shaken with air at various pressures from a high vacuum to 1 atmosphere. When the tap of the air pump is closed the manometer level is noted. When it remains fixed at a height p after shaking for some time, the gases dissolved in the measured quantity are in equilibrium with the gaseous contents of the space. If the atmospheric pressure is P, the gas pressure in the space is $P - p$. This is partly made up of V_t, the vapour pressure of water at the temperature t of the shaker. Hence the true pressure of dry air in equilibrium with the gases dissolved in the water is

$$P - p - V_t$$

Neglect of the vapour pressure of the solvent may give rise to large errors when the temperature is high, or the pressure is low. At 20° C. (temperature of a warm room) the vapour pressure of water is 17·4 mm. If the atmospheric pressure were 760 mm. and the manometer reading (p) were 740 mm., the total pressure in the shaker would be 20 mm., and the "partial pressure" of the air itself $20 - 17·4 = 2·6$ mm. At 0° vapour pressure of water is only 4·6 mm., and the same manometer reading would signify that the partial pressure of dry air was $20 - 4·6 = 15·4$ mm.

the known water content of saturated air at different temperatures. The tables tell us what is the

$$\frac{\text{Water-Vapour Content of Saturated Air at the Dew Point}}{\text{Water-Vapour Content of Saturated Air at the Actual Temperature}}$$

A crude estimate of the relative humidity of the atmosphere can be obtained with a simple device called the wet and dry bulb thermometer. This depends on a most important physical principle which bears on the difference between the Newcomen engine and that of Watt. The fact that water becomes cooler

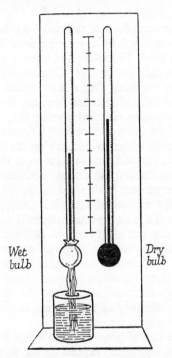

Wet bulb

Dry bulb

FIG. 288.—WET AND DRY BULB THERMOMETERS

as it evaporates is a common experience of everyday life applied in a variety of ways. Thus water is sometimes kept in porous earthenware to encourage evaporation over a large surface, and the sprinkling of water cools a dry room even if the temperature of the water is the same as that of the dry air. Our bodies protect themselves from heat, and maintain a constant temperature when the surroundings are above blood heat, by the secretion of sweat. The electric fan produces the sensation of cold by blowing away saturated layers of air from the moist skin, although it slightly increases the heat of the air by friction and sparking. For the same reason, the actual temperature of summer weather is less important than humidity as an indication of bearable heat. The wet and dry bulb thermometer is simply a pair of ordinary thermometers, the bulb of one of which (Fig. 288) is enclosed in fabric dipping into a vessel of water. If the atmosphere is very dry rapid evaporation occurs on the surface of the wet bulb. It is therefore cooled. Consequently it registers a lower temperature than the dry bulb. A large discrepancy between the two readings therefore indicates that the atmosphere is relatively dry, and that there is no immediate prospect of rain. Any such instrument can be empirically calibrated for future use to determine relative humidity by preparing tables showing relative humidity for different readings of the wet bulb when the dry bulb registers a particular temperature.

WARMTH

Variations in temperature depend primarily on latitude, altitude, and propinquity to water, modified by more capricious factors which depend on the direction of the wind. The relation of latitude to warmth depends on the fact that heat, like light (see p. 174, Chapter III), can be transmitted through a vacuum. The radiating source is of course the sun, and experiment shows that the intensity of radiation from any fixed source depends on the area radiated. A slanting elliptical section cut through a cylindrical beam of sunshine occupies more surface than a circular section cut straight across at right angles to its direction. Hence (Fig. 289) the area radiated by a sunshine cylinder of the same dimensions increases north and south of the parallel of latitude where the sun lies directly overhead. So the same source of heat has to warm a larger area. This accounts for the broad generalization that it is hotter within the tropical belts than it is north or south of them.

In addition, the effect of a radiating source depends on the time of exposure. The relative lengths of day and night vary (p. 196) with season and latitude, and the relation of latitude to climate, therefore, involves the number of hours of sunshine. Near the equator days and nights are nearly always of equal length, and there is no sharp difference between winter and summer. Nearer the poles the winter days are much shorter and the summer days are much longer. So the seasonal disparity of temperature increases with increase of latitude as we travel away from the equator.

The effect of altitude and of propinquity to water (or what comes to the same thing—richness of vegetation) depend on the same peculiarity of heat transmission. This was not understood till the thermometer was introduced. The Italian meteorologists of the seventeenth century showed that equal quantities of different fluids at the same temperature do not melt the same quantity of ice. That is to say, at the same temperature equal quantities of different substances have different powers of imparting heat to others at a lower temperature. Some have a high capacity, i.e. a smaller quantity at the same temperature, or the same quantity at a lower temperature suffices to produce the same heating effect. Such bodies, if heated from one and the same source, gain in temperature more slowly. Water has an exceptionally high capacity, and therefore takes long to warm up or cool down to a given temperature. Two results follow from this fact. One is that during the day in summer the temperature of the sea is lower than that of land at sea-level. The other is that in general the temperature of land at sea-level is subject to much greater diurnal variations of temperature than that of the sea.

Consequently inland climates are far less equable than the climate of coastal areas.

Like the astrolabe or the telescope, the thermometer equips us with a more sensitive instrument than direct sensation for detecting changes in the world, and shows us when the testimony of direct sensation is unreliable. For instance, a room is not cooler when we turn on the electric fan. Although the surface layers of our skin are cooler, the room itself is slightly hotter

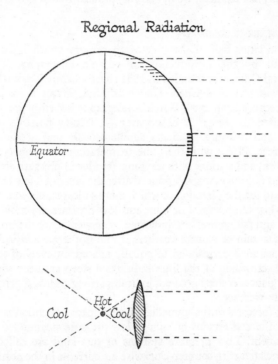

Regional Radiation

FIG. 289.—REGIONAL RADIATION

Below, the burning lens shows that the heating effect of converging beams is due to its great surface intensity. Above, the surface intensity due to a cylindrical shaft of the same dimensions near the poles is less than it is at the equator.

because of sparking and friction. Again, some bodies "feel cold" when we touch them. A fender seems to be colder than a rug at exactly the same temperature, provided both are below the temperature of the hand. If both are above the temperature of the hand the fender is judged to be hotter when the thermometer reading is the same for fender and rug. This is because bodies differ in their power to transmit heat.

The transmission of heat by radiation can occur through a vacuum. Transmission of heat by "convection" can only occur within the substance of a gas or of a liquid. Solids transmit heat without free circulation. Such transmission is called *conduction*. Metals are good conductors, and that is why they feel cold. Common liquids conduct heat very little if the free circulation of parts, i.e. the creation of convection currents, is prevented by heating them from above instead of from below. For instance, if you tie a lead weight to a piece of ice, sink it in a tube of water and apply a flame to the upper end of the column of fluid, the latter can be made to boil for quite a long while before the ice begins to melt noticeably. So if ice were heavier than water it would tend to accumulate from winter to winter at the bottom of ponds. Air is an especially bad conductor. On that account substances which trap air, like feathers, wool, and fur, protect against loss of heat.

MODERN WEATHER RECORDING

During the latter half of the nineteenth century weather recording was revolutionized by the introduction of oceanic telegraphy. The British Meteorological Office was founded in 1854 shortly before Transatlantic communication was first established. Under Admiral Fitzroy it instituted daily telegraphic records from 1860. Wireless telegraphy has since speeded up and vastly increased the range of observation. It is now possible to map out temperature and pressure gradients simultaneously and at short intervals over large areas. Places with the same temperature are connected by lines called *isotherms,* and stations with the same (sea level) pressure are connected by lines called *isobars* on maps produced after the lapse of a few hours. Hence it is possible to see the direction in which more or less stable zones or regions of high and low temperature or high and low pressure are moving. Falling temperature and falling pressure indicated by movement of the isotherms and isobars forecast rain or cloudy weather. If the isotherms and isobars drawn on the weather map correspond to equally spaced intervals of temperature and pressure, crowding of the lines indicates a steep gradient which can be taken in at a glance. A steep gradient indicates strong winds. A gentle gradient forecasts calm weather.

In making forecasts of the immediate future special attention is paid to the movements of closed regions of high or low pressure surrounded by a steep pressure gradient. Low pressure systems of this kind are called cyclones. They are associated with counter-clockwise air currents in the northern hemisphere. Closed high pressure regions called anticyclones are associated with clockwise air currents in the northern hemisphere. The reverse is true of the southern hemisphere, because the direction of the currents like that of the Trade winds depends on the earth's axial motion. The approach of a cyclone as shown by successive weather charts is a signal of storms or heavy rain.

CREATING CLIMATE

Town folk who live in a community where the weather is peculiarly erratic, as it is in Britain or in Massachusetts, may be tempted to underrate the value of meteorological science as a guide to social conduct. So before proceeding to deal with the measurement of heat changes in greater detail, we may pause to notice that the empirical principles which originally emerged from studying the weather have given us many useful recipes for creating our own climate. The same principle of *convection* which underlies the circulation of air and ocean currents is applied to the ventilation of mines and buildings or to the design of central heating and hot water systems (Figs. 284 and 290).

The two facts which we have learned about evaporation are the basis of refrigeration, which has revolutionized the trade in fruit, meat, fish, and other perishable commodities in our time. A liquid boils when its vapour pressure is equivalent to that of the surrounding atmosphere, and can therefore be made to boil by reducing the external pressure till it is equivalent

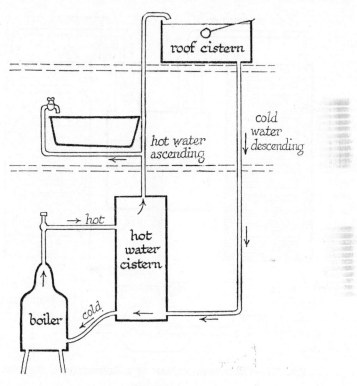

FIG. 290

Simple drawing of hot-water system showing the ascent of hot water to the bath when tap is opened and the descent of cold water from the roof cistern.

to its own vapour pressure. Since rapid evaporation is accompanied by the withdrawal of heat from the surroundings, intense cold can be produced by the rapid vaporization of a liquid under reduced pressure. In a typical refrigerator machine (Fig. 291) a single pump alternately sucks out of one coil and compresses in a second some readily liquefiable gas like ammonia. In the high-pressure coil the gas liquefies at the upstroke, and the fluid circulates into the second coil which is connected with it directly. At the downstroke the liquid evaporates in the low-pressure coil. The latter is in direct connexion with the refrigerating chamber. The high-pressure coil is outside so that the heat given out when the gas is compressed is carried off.

A further constructive application of the phenomena we have just dealt with is the thermos flask which was invented by Sir James Dewar in connexion with experiments on the liquefaction of air. The liquefaction of air raises a special problem. Up to a certain point we can raise the boiling-point of water by increasing the external pressure. The vapour pressure of water increases rapidly after 100°. It is nearly 200 atmospheres at 365°. Beyond this it is so enormous that no further increase of pressure will raise the

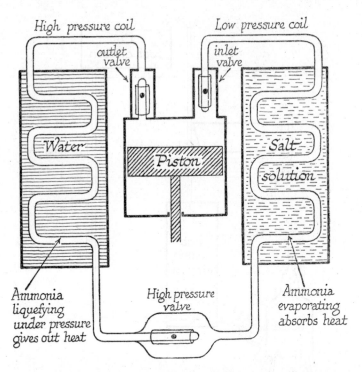

FIG. 291.—DIAGRAMMATIC PLAN OF A REFRIGERATING MACHINE

The pump in the middle sucks ammonia gas from the low-pressure coil through the inlet valve (drawn like a tyre valve) at the downstroke, and sends it through the outlet valve into the high-pressure coil at the upstroke. The connecting (high-pressure) valve does not permit ammonia to pass into the low-pressure coil till the pressure is high enough to liquefy it, while cold water circulates round it to absorb the heat liberated. Intense cold is developed in the tank round the low-pressure coil, where the ammonia rapidly vaporizes under reduced pressure. The tank contains a salt solution (e.g. calcium chloride) which freezes at a temperature well below that of melting ice. This cooled solution circulates in the storage chamber.

boiling-point. Hence it will boil at 366° C. whatever pressure is applied to it. Conversely, steam cannot be condensed into water by mere application of pressure unless it is first cooled below 366° C. This is called the *critical temperature* of water vapour. The critical temperature of air is about 150° below the freezing point of water (i.e. about — 150° C.). That is to say, no application of pressure will liquefy air unless its temperature is brought to this level. So making liquid air depends on keeping it at an exceedingly low temperature.

The thermos flask, as you probably know if you have broken one, is essentially a vessel with double walls silvered on their opposite faces. The interspace is exhausted, so that no heat is transmitted across it by convection or conduction. Since radiant heat, like light, is reflected by a silvered surface, heat transmitted by radiation from one wall to the other is reflected back; thus practically no heat passes from one wall to the other except across the narrow junction at the neck.

EXPANSION

Another empirical principle which was studied before the measurement of heat was put on a satisfactory basis has numerous applications in engineering, and has become especially important since the introduction of heat as a source of power. As most of us know, the engine of a motor bicycle seizes when it gets overheated. A very important consideration in designing any mechanism subjected to large changes of temperature is that the parts must expand as little as possible, and to the same extent. Otherwise warping, friction, etc., interfere with its working, or lead to rupture through internal strains. The same difficulty also arises in the design of all measuring instruments of which the length of the parts must be as nearly constant as possible, e.g. the length of the pendulum of a clock, and in the construction of pipes to convey hot water, of railway lines, and of steel framework of bridges.

In a book called *The Philosophy of Manufactures*, published by Dr. Alexander Ure in 1835, we get a vivid picture of the new demands which the introduction of steam power as the basis of factory production made on the physical science of the period. We also see why the leading industrialists were enthusiastic in promoting a type of education different from what the older seats of learning in England provided at the time. Ure says:

The university man, pre-occupied with theoretical formulae, of little practical bearing, is too apt to undervalue the science of the factory, though, with candour and patience, he would find it replete with useful applications of the most beautiful dynamical and statical problems. In physics, too, he would there see many theorems bearing golden fruit, which had been long barren in college ground. The phenomena of heat, in particular, are investigated in their multifarious relations to matter, solid, liquid, and aeriform. The measure of temperature on every scale is familiar to the manufacturer, as well as the distribution of caloric, and its habitudes with different bodies. The production of vapours; the relation of their elastic force to their temperature; the modes of using them as instruments of power, and sources of heat; their most effective condensation; their hygrometric agency; may all be better studied in a week's residence in Lancashire, than in a session of any university in Europe. And as to exact mechanical science, no school can compete with a modern cotton-mill. When a certain elevation of temperature is made to give pliancy to the fibres of cotton or wool, the philosophical spinner sees the influence of caloric in imparting ductility and elasticity to bodies. The thermometer to indicate the temperature, and the hygrometer the humidity of the air, give him an insight into the constitution of nature unknown to the bulk of mankind. Of the different

dilatations of different solids by increments of temperature, he has daily
experience in the elongation of the immense systems of steam-pipes which heat
his mill apartments, often extending 300 feet in a straight line. On this scale,
the amount of the expansion, and contraction, needs no micrometer to
measure it, for it is visible to the eye, and may be determined by a carpenter's
rule.

One of the most flourishing industries at the time of the English Industrial
Revolution of the eighteenth century played an important part in the demand

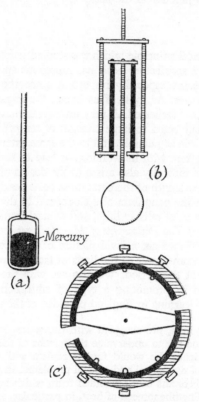

FIG. 292.—COMPENSATING FOR EXPANSION IN CLOCKS

The reliability of clocks of any kind would be affected by seasonal temperature changes
if no allowance were made for the heat expansion of metals. The mercury compen-
sated pendulum (*a*) depends on the fact that the effective length of a pendulum is
approximately from the point of suspension to the mass centre of the weight. If the
latter is a small vessel of mercury, expansion of the latter shifts the mass centre upwards,
while that of the rod shifts it downwards. By using a vessel and quantity of mercury of
suitable dimensions the two effects cancel. In the *grid iron* pendulum (*b*) the grid is
made of rods of different metals, the one represented as black having a higher coefficient of expansion than the other, which is shaded. The grid arrangement is such as
to make the expansion of the former lift the weight upwards, while that of the latter
lowers it. If the dimensions are suitably adjusted the net result is that the length does
not change. The balance wheel of a hair spring watch regulator (*c*) is also made of
concentric strips of metals with different coefficients of expansion. The outer one
expands most, increasing the curvature of the rim, and thus compensating for the
expansion of the spring.

for scientific knowledge of heat. Besides making many experiments in chemistry and maintaining an active interest in geology in the search for suitable materials in the ceramic industry, the great master Potter, Josiah Wedgwood, applied himself to devising thermometers suitable to withstand temperatures at which glass melts. The immediate need which prompted these researches was the determination of the degree of baking required for different qualities of earthenware and china products. His paper on "The Pyrometer or Heat Measuring Instrument," published in the *Philosophical Transactions of the Royal Society,* earned him his election as a Fellow, and was followed by a series of communications on the same general theme.

Various arrangements are devised to guard against displacements and distortions arising from expansion. In any case the important thing is to know in advance how much expansion can occur. As already explained, the expansion of gases is measured by their change in volume. A gas expands

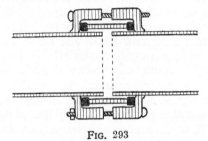

Fig. 293

One type of *Expansion Joint* used for hot water pipes has the gap between the joined ends surrounded by a double collar separated by two rubber rings (black) which make the junction watertight, while allowing the two collars to slide freely lengthwise when made to expand by heat.

by about $\frac{1}{273}$ of its volume at 0° C. when its temperature is raised 1° C. So the gas contained in a cylinder of uniform bore will be increased by the same amount, i.e. approximately 4 in 1,000 per degree if its initial volume is measured at 0° C. This figure $\frac{1}{273}$, or approximately 0·004, is called its coefficient of expansion. The expansion of liquids is measured in the same way. Thus alcohol expands by about 0·0009 and mercury 0·0002 of its volume at 0° C. per degree. So an air thermometer of the same dimensions is about 20 times as sensitive as a mercury one. The expansion of solids is usually measured in units of length. The coefficient of expansion of zinc is 0·00003. That is to say, the length of a bar of zinc increases by 0·00003 of its length at 0° C. for an increase of one degree Centigrade. This is a very high value for a solid. The coefficient of expansion for glass is only 0·000008. For platinum it is 0·000009, for cast iron 0·00001, and for brass 0·00002. Since brass expands twice as much as iron, it is obvious that a brass piston encased in an iron cylinder would soon seize if heated.

Of the various devices to meet problems of this kind some innovations have arisen out of studying the properties of alloys. The most important discovery has been the iron alloy called "*invar,*" which contains 36 per cent nickel. Invar has a coefficient of expansion less than 0·0000001, i.e. an increase of ten degrees only increases the length of a bar by one millionth of its length at 0° C. So for most practical purposes its length is invariable, and its use will supersede some of the ingenious arrangements which have been invented to safeguard against the effects of expansion. Needless to say, the choice of any standard of length for scientific or commercial purposes implies a specification of the temperature. Thus the international standard metre is the distance between two lines ruled on a bar of platinum iridium alloy at 0° C. The bar is deposited in the national archives at Sèvres, so that the fundamental unit of distance can be determined at any time.

NOTEWORTHY TEMPERATURES

A few examples will illustrate the range of temperature encountered in everyday experience. The mean temperature of the North Pole in January is about — 41° C. The temperature of the flame of an ordinary spirit lamp or Bunsen burner lies between 1,700° and 1,900° C. The flame of the oxyacetylene burner often mentioned in crime fiction as part of the cracksman's outfit is 3,000° C. Bodies begin to become just visibly red hot at 526° C. The temperature of white heat is between 1,300° and 1,400° C. The normal temperature of the human body is approximately 37° C or 98·4° F. That of a fowl is approximately 42° C. Among boiling points, that of ammonia is — 33·5° C. (i.e. it would liquefy in the polar winter), that of ether is 34·6° C. (i.e. it will boil in a room kept at blood heat), that of ethyl alcohol is 78° C., of turpentine 159° C., and of mercury 357° C. Ethyl alcohol freezes at — 114° C., and mercury at — 38·9° C.; hence an alcohol thermometer is more suitable for polar exploration than a mercury one. Tin melts at 232° C. before it is red hot, and indeed little above the boiling point of turpentine. Copper melts at 1,083° C., i.e. before it is white hot. Iron melts at 1,530° C., and can just be made white hot without melting. Tungsten melts at 3,400° C., above the temperature of the oxyacetylene flame, and just below the temperature 3,500° C. of the crater of the carbon pencils in the electric arc lamp. It is therefore very suitable for making lamp filaments. Good butter melts at about 30° C., below blood heat, and paraffin wax between 40° and 60° C. according to the quality, i.e. just above blood heat.

For ordinary thermometers in which the liquid is mercury or alcohol (usually coloured to make it more visible) the range is between — 114° C., the freezing point of alcohol, and + 357° C., the boiling point of mercury. The range of an air thermometer is much greater, since air continues to expand uniformly through about 1,000°. A hydrogen thermometer is reliable over a wider range because of its low freezing point. Hydrogen cannot liquefy until it is cooled to — 234·5° C., and expands with comparative uniformity up to + 1,100° C. To register temperature beyond these limits as, e.g., the temperature of the electric furnace, the property of expansion is useless, and the observed effects of heat on other physical properties of matter, e.g. electrical resistance, are used.

THE IMPORTANCE OF GLASSWARE

Readers of detective fiction will be familiar with the threefold formula by which crimes are run to earth. In science the means, the opportunity, and the motive are interdependent and equally necessary for substantial progress. At different places in this book a writer with access to different materials might well have chosen to dwell upon a different aspect of the complex social structure in which scientific enquiry is involved. The course most commonly accepted is to emphasize the *opportunities* created by wealthy patrons of learned academies. In the earlier part of this book more attention has been paid to the *motive*, that is to say, to new social needs which suggest new problems for enquiry. Here and there the part played by improvements in glass manufacture have been mentioned as new *means* of discovery in optics, astronomy, and medicine.

Common threads of opportunity, of means, and of motive, run through optics, chemistry, hydrostatics, and heat measurement, in the last decades of the sixteenth century and in the first half of the seventeenth century, when the centre of intellectual gravity was shifting from Italy to Britain, Holland, and France. The academies which began in Italy have been mentioned in several contexts. The social motive supplied by the needs of navigation has been abundantly illustrated, and in this chapter special attention has been paid to the stimulus which the early study of heat received from meteorology during a period when scientific interest in navigation was actively encouraged by the State. Another feature of the common background of chemistry, optics, hydrostatics, and thermometry, illustrates the coincidence of the motive with the means and with the opportunity. Medicine became a socially organized profession in the early sixteenth century (see p. 822). As such it provided new opportunities of instruction and research into problems which were not themselves new. Other social circumstances created the means for solving them. Two new devices which invested medical research with new powers were the outcome of a new level in glass technology. This fact may throw some light on the scientific pre-eminence of Italy between 1550 and 1650.

Glass is an invention of great antiquity. So it is easy to forget three things about the place of glass in the history of science. Ancient glass was made for ornament. As such it was valued less for its transparency than for its tint. In antiquity it was always a costly luxury. Thus the qualities which we admire in Roman glassware are precisely the qualities which make it useless for scientific instruments to record fluid level with accuracy, or to examine changes of colour or consistency. That Venice was the Mecca of the European glass manufacturers in the sixteenth century is not irrelevant to the fact that Italy took the lead in the invention of the barometer and of the thermometer. Venetian glass manufacture goes back to Roman times, and the initial impetus to its revival in the thirteenth century was the expanding prosperity of the Venetian mercantile classes. By the end of the fifteenth century glass had assumed a new use. The civilization of northern Europe was progressing apace. Prosperity in the Mediterranean could dispense with glass windows, as it had dispensed with wheel-driven clocks. Northern Europe could make little progress from Nordic savagery till glass windows replaced the sombre slits which we still see in the massive stone castle walls of the robber barons. Like the clock, glass windows were probably confined at first to churches and monasteries. By 1450 the prosperous burghers of England

and Germany lived in houses equipped with them. By 1550 the Italian glass trade was a great commercial asset. At the time when Italian science began to flourish, a new social demand for glass had made it a necessity of every-day life, and had set a new standard of transparency. Glass was becoming relatively cheap, and therefore accessible for scientific work. At the same time it was now valued for the quality which makes it suitable for scientific use. After 1620, when flint glass of high transparency was invented in England, Englishmen carried on and eclipsed the Italian tradition of science.

The importance of the glass thermometer as a new instrument of diagnosis in medicine incorporated the study of heat within the medical curriculum of the universities. The next great advance in heat measurement was made by Joseph Black, a professor of medicine in the University of Glasgow. The social context of Black's researches has been touched on in Chapter VIII, where reference was made to the rapid industrialization of Scotland after 1745. Coalmining was an expanding industry, and the Newcomen pump had lately been introduced into Scottish collieries. In repairing a model of the Newcomen engine for use in connexion with Black's lectures, James Watt, a young technical assistant, was led to an invention (p. 429) which revolutionized the conduct of industry. This invention made Black's researches a turning-point in the history of science.

EXAMPLES TO CHAPTER XI

1. If "normal" body temperature is $98 \cdot 4°$ F. what is it (a) on the centigrade scale, (b) on the absolute scale, and (c) on the Réaumur scale (freezing point of water $0°$ and boiling point $80°$ R.)?

2. Convert $- 4°$ C. and $105°$ C. to the Fahrenheit scale and $20°$ F. and $214°$ F. to the centigrade scale.

3. Find roughly at what temperature water will boil at the top of Mt. Blanc (15,800 feet) and Ben Nevis (4,400 feet) if the mercury barometer falls roughly 1 inch for 1,000 feet ascent, and if the vapour pressure of water increases approximately as follows with rise in temperature: $60°$C., 15 cm.; $70°$ C., 23 cm.; $80°$ C., 35 cm.; $90°$ C., 52 cm.; $95°$ C., 64 cm.

4. On successive occasions the shaker of the apparatus shown in Fig. 287 is exhausted till the difference in mercury level of the pressure gauge is $74 \cdot 5$ cm. at $1°$ C., 74 cm. at $9 \cdot 5°$ C., and $74 \cdot 1$ cm. at $23°$ C. The vapour pressure of water is approximately $0 \cdot 5$ cm. at $1°$, $0 \cdot 9$ cm. at $9 \cdot 5°$ C. and $2 \cdot 1$ cm. at $23°$ C. The percentage of oxygen by volume in dry air may be taken as 21 per cent. If the atmospheric pressure was $76 \cdot 25$ cm., what was the partial pressure of oxygen in equilibrium with dissolved gas in each case?

5. A cylinder inverted over water encloses 200 c.c. of oxygen at $20°$ C. when the level of water inside and outside is the same. The mercury barometer reads 74 cm., and tables give for the vapour pressure of water at $20°$ C. $1 \cdot 74$ cm. Use Henry's law (p. 449, Chapter IX) to calculate the volume of dry oxygen at S.T.P. ($0°$ and 76 cm.).

6. Make a graph of the vapour pressure of water from the following data: $1°$ C. $4 \cdot 9$ mm.; $5°$ C. $6 \cdot 5$ mm.; $10°$ C. $9 \cdot 2$ mm.; $15°$ C. $12 \cdot 8$ mm.; $20°$ C. $17 \cdot 5$ mm.; $25°$ C. $23 \cdot 7$ mm. Hence find the relative humidity of (a) air at $16 \cdot 5°$ C. when its dew point is $9 \cdot 2°$ C., (b) air at $21°$ C. when its dew point is $19°$ C.

7. An ordinary steel metre scale agrees with an "invar" rule at 0° C. and the coefficient of linear expansion of the metal is 0·000012. What would be the length of a piece of glass found to be 79·51 cm. with the ordinary steel scale at 150° C., if measured with the "invar" rule?

8. If the coefficient of linear expansion for copper is 0·000017, find how big a gap must be left between the ends of two copper bars, each one metre long and with the *middle* fixed, to allow for expansion over a range of 50° C. above the temperature at which they are fixed.

9. If the length of the tubular railway bridge across the Menai Straits is 461 metres, find how much the total length of steel varies between − 5° C. and + 35° C. (Take the coefficient of expansion as 0·000012.)

10. The coefficients of linear expansion (increase in length per unit length per degree centigrade) of brass and steel are 0·0000187 and 0·000011. If the length of two rods of brass and steel respectively are 1,500 and 1,502 mm. at 0° C., to what temperature must they be heated to make them the same length exactly?

11. A bridge is constructed from 10 girders 50 feet long made of steel whose coefficient of expansion is 0·000012 per degree centigrade. It has to stand a winter temperature which may sink as low as 15° F. and a summer temperature in the sun of 130° F. What must be the length of the gap between each girder at the lower temperature?

12. For every twenty miles of steel rails laid down at 37° F., what will be the total length of the track if the gaps are just sufficient to allow for a summer temperature of 120° F.? Take the coefficient of linear expansion for the rails to be 0·000012.

13. A brass pendulum has a half period of 1 second at 15° C. How much will it gain or lose per day if kept at a temperature of 22° C.?

14. If the density of mercury is 13·596 at 0° C. and its coefficient of cubical expansion is 0·000182, calculate the error in reading a mercury barometer at 10° C. and 25° C. when the true atmospheric pressure is equivalent to a column of mercury 75 cm. at 0°. Neglect the expansion of the glass.

THINGS TO MEMORIZE

1. Temperature F. = $\frac{9}{5}$ (temperature C.) + 32°. Temperature Réaumur = $\frac{4}{5}$ (temperature C.)

2. Relative humidity at T

$$= \frac{\text{Mass of water vapour in given volume of air at T}}{\text{Mass of water vapour in same volume of saturated air at T}}$$

$$= \frac{\text{Pressure of water vapour in air at T}}{\text{Pressure of water vapour in saturated air at T}}$$

If the dew point of the sample has been found, then

Relative humidity at T

$$= \frac{\text{Mass of water vapour in saturated air at dew point}}{\text{Mass of water vapour in saturated air at T}}$$

CHAPTER XII

THE DARK SATANIC MILLS

The Superfluity of Mere Toil

THE invention of the steam engine as a pumping device took place in the closing years of the seventeenth century. The newly-formed Royal Society in England took a conspicuous part both in its theoretical and practical development. During the succeeding half-century, which intervened between the patents of Savery and Newcomen on the one hand and the fruitful partnership of Boulton and Watt on the other, the adventurous hopefulness of early English capitalism declined, and the temper of academic science gravitated away from the original intention of the charter to promote (as Sprat tells us) "a continuous succession of inventors." In the next stage of the theory and practice of power production the scene shifts to Scotland.

Dr. Johnson, who poured contempt on Milton's attempt to introduce the teaching of science during his short employment as a schoolmaster in Aldersgate,* once remarked that education in Scotland is like food in a beleaguered city where everyone has a little and no one has enough. Time will come when Johnson will be remembered, if at all, for his ineptitudes. The first half of the eighteenth century was a decadent period in the history of English social culture. Scientific enquiry languished when concern for its "true and lawful goal" was relinquished. Speaking of Birmingham in Boulton's boyhood, Dickinson (*Matthew Boulton*) remarks: "Here as elsewhere in the country the decay in educational foundations that we find so commonly in the eighteenth century went on almost unchecked." Meanwhile British science renewed its youth in Glasgow and Edinburgh, where Dr. Black was the most noteworthy of several pioneers of modern science. Between the period of Newton, which immediately followed a rapid extension of educational facilities, and that of Davy, Dalton, and Faraday, recruited from a new fund of social personnel, Scotland maintained the predominance of British science when England could chiefly boast of a plethora of prosaic *literati*.†

The debt of British science to John Knox as the pioneer of universal education is a theme which merits more attention than has been given to it. Between the Act of Union and the repeal of religious tests in the English universities the higher seats of learning in England remained the preserve of a small social class with a narrow cultural outlook. The task of supplying man power for the professional services in the colonies largely devolved on the Scottish universities. The latter could thus provide a qualification which

---

* Dr. Johnson's *Lives of the Poets*.

† Cavendish illustrates the adage that one swallow does not make a summer.

was a safe conduct to professional employment. Higher education in Scotland received a powerful impetus from the agrarian and Industrial Revolution in progress at the time when Watt undertook his first experiments, financed by Black. Smiles (*Lives of the Engineers—Boulton and Watt*) refers to the influence of Black in the following passage:

Among his other experiments, he (*Watt*) constructed a boiler which showed by inspection the quantity of water evaporated in any given time, and the quantity of steam used in every stroke of the engine. He was astonished to discover that a small quantity of water in the form of steam heated a large quantity of cold water injected into the cylinder for the purpose of cooling it; and upon further examination he ascertained that steam heated six times its weight of cold water up to 212°, which was the temperature of the steam itself. "Being struck with this remarkable fact," says Watt, "and not understanding the reason of it, I mentioned it to my friend Dr. Black, who then explained to me his doctrine of latent heat, which he had taught for some time before this period (the summer of 1764); but having myself been occupied by the pursuits of business, if I had heard of it I had not attended to it, when I thus stumbled upon one of the material facts by which that beautiful theory is supported." When Watt found that water, in its conversion into vapour, became such a reservoir of heat, he was more than ever bent on economizing it; for the great waste of heat, involving so heavy a consumption of fuel, was felt to be the principal obstacle to the extended employment of steam as a motive power. He accordingly endeavoured with the same quantity of fuel, at once to increase the production of steam, and to diminish its waste. He increased the heating surface of the boiler by making flues through it; he surrounded his boiler with wood, as being a worse conductor of heat than the brickwork which surrounds common furnaces; and he cased the cylinders and all the conducting-pipes in materials which conducted heat very slowly. But none of these contrivances were effectual; for it turned out that the chief expenditure of steam, and consequently of fuel, in the Newcomen engine was occasioned by the re-heating of the cylinder after the steam had been condensed by the cold water admitted into it. Nearly four-fifths of the whole steam employed was condensed on its first admission, before the surplus could act upon the piston.

In other circumstances the researches of Black might have remained unknown. The doctrine of latent heat, which will be explained in this chapter, was never published in a printed form by its author, who announced it verbally in a paper read to the Newtonian Society of Edinburgh in 1762. Its influence on the invention of the new engine illustrates both aspects of the unity of theory and practice in scientific progress. The other side of the relation is indicated in the following passage from Prosser's book on *Birmingham Inventors*. It refers to John Southern. Like Murdock, who was a medallist of the Royal Society, Southern was an employee in the Soho firm, and, like Watt and Boulton themselves, was a Fellow of the Royal Society. Southern, says Prosser,

was an excellent mathematician and very useful to Watt in that capacity. His researches on the elasticity, density and *latent heat of steam, which were undertaken at Watt's request* in 1803, were for a long time the standard authority on the subject. They were printed in Brewster's edition of Robinson's *Mechanical Philosophy*.

The close connexion between Scottish theory and English practice during the critical years of the Industrial Revolution is also illustrated by the business relations of Boulton with Small, Roebuck, and Keir (pp. 424–438). Boulton and Watt were both elected Fellows of the newly-formed Royal Society of Edinburgh before they were admitted (1784) as Fellows of the parent body in London. Wedgwood was elected about the same time in recognition of researches on heat measurement at high temperatures undertaken to ascertain the correct method of baking his pottery products. His relations with the Edinburgh Society are indicated in the ensuing passage from Smiles' *Life of Josiah Wedgwood*:

Wedgwood sent his first paper to the Royal Society on May 9, 1782. His paper was entitled, "An attempt to make a Thermometer for measuring the higher degrees of Heat, from a red heat up to the strongest that vessels of clay can support." A few months after his paper had been read at the Royal Society, Mr. William Playfair, an Edinburgh Professor, wrote to Mr. Wedgwood the following letter (London, September 12, 1782): "Sir—I had the pleasure of being present at the reading of your very ingenious paper on your newly-invented Thermometer before the Royal Society last spring, and of joining in the general satisfaction that such an acquisition to Art gave all present. I have never conversed with anybody on the subject who did not admire your Thermometer, and considered it as being as perfect as the nature of things will admit of for great heat; but I have joined with several in wishing that the scale of your Thermometer were compared with that of Fahrenheit's (so universally used for small degrees of heat), that without learning a new signification, or affixing a new idea, to the term *Degree of Heat*, we might avail ourselves of your useful invention. The method proposed in the enclosed paper occurred to me as one applicable to this purpose, and I lay it before you with all deference to your better judgment of the subject. I should be glad to know where I could purchase some of your Thermometers, as I can get none here in town.—I am, sir, with much regard, your most humble servant—William Playfair." Wedgwood followed Mr. Playfair's advice. In his next papers, sent to the Royal Society, he gave a reduction of the degrees of his Thermometer to Fahrenheit's scale, from which it appeared that the greatest heat he could generate in a small furnace coincided with many thousands of degrees of Fahrenheit—the scale of heat which was registered by his Thermometer being about thirty-four times as extensive as that to which the common Thermometers could be applied.

Through Black, Watt was brought into touch with Roebuck, whose pioneer activities in the manufacture of sulphuric acid at Prestonpans placed him in the forefront of Scottish industrial enterprise. While he was occupied in developing the Carron Ironworks in Stirlingshire, Roebuck supplied capital for the new invention. The venture was a failure owing to defects of workmanship. Practical success did not crown the efforts of Watt until after a visit to Birmingham (p. 429). He was introduced to Boulton by Dr. Small, a Scots physician who was a close friend of Benjamin Franklin. The renowned partnership began in 1775.

A demand for the products of Boulton and Watt came first from the mines and then from the Potteries where the Newcomen engine was already in use. When Watt took out his first patent in 1769, there were already, according to Hammond, "a hundred of Newcomen's engines at work in Northern collieries alone." Successful construction of engines of the new design did not begin till seven years later. Hammond tells us:

In 1776 engines built on Watt's principle were for the first time actually at work. . . . Like Newcomen's engine they worked a rod up and down and were suitable only for pumps or for blowing bellows. . . . The main demand for the engines came from the tin and the copper mines in Cornwall where workings were deep, fuel scarce or dear.

About this time mechanization on the basis of water power was taking a decisive step forward in the textile industry. Several inventions connected with the spinning of fibres into thread ready for weaving coincided independently with the invention of the Watt engine, and prepared the way for using steam as a source of power in the factory. One was Arkwright's "water-frame," patented in 1769, to produce yarn suitable for the warp by using water power. Crompton's mule (1779) served the same end, and was likewise adapted to use of water power. These and other new spinning devices rapidly led to mechanization and factory production which extended more slowly to weaving after the invention of Cartwright (1785), whose power looms only came into use after successive improvements from 1803 onwards. The response of the textile industry is illustrated by the fact that, according to Hammond, it absorbed 114 out of 325 engines produced during the first twenty-five years of their partnership by Boulton and Watt.

Burke spoke of Birmingham in his day as the "toy shop of Europe." John Leland, who visited "Bermigham" in 1538, already noted that "a great part of the Towne is maintained by Smithes who have their Iron and Sea-cole out of Staffordshire." Small *metallic* articles, such as buttons, buckles, candlesticks, medals, and so forth, were prominent articles of its produce in the late seventeenth century, and such "toys," as this class of goods were then called, were the output of Boulton's factory. The Newcomen engine had been adapted already (see p. 429) to produce rotary power by pumping up water for a mill wheel in the Potteries. Boulton conceived the same plan for his hardware factory. It had also been used in Scottish metallurgy. The direct connexion of the piston with a wheel was not patented till 1781. Thenceforward steam was available for any industrial operations based on factory production. That the need, which prompted the Staffordshire Potters or Boulton himself to prepare the way for steam-driven machinery by grafting the Newcomen pump on the pre-existing technology of water power, did not emerge in the more widely distributed industry of clothing, is not surprising. At this time the textile industry had no direct affiliations with the mining interests, nor had it an immediate need for much fuel. Hence it could not serve to bring the problems of pumping and motion into the same technological context. When this happened technical inventions conspired with political events to stimulate the main demand for steam power in textile manufacture.

In the first half of the eighteenth century local English manufacturers were still hampered by the monopolistic wealth of the great chartered companies. Although restriction of monopolistic privileges had been one of

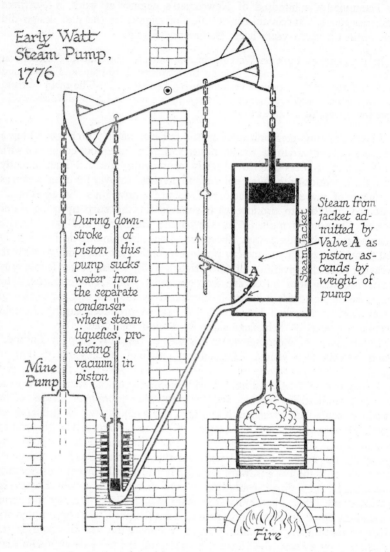

Early Watt
Steam Pump,
1776

*During down-
stroke of
piston this
pump sucks
water from
the separate
condenser
where steam
liquefies, pro-
ducing
vacuum in
piston*

Mine
Pump

Steam Jacket

*Steam from
jacket ad-
mitted by
Valve A as
piston as-
cends by
weight of
pump*

A

Fire

FIG. 294.—AN EARLY WATT MODEL (DIAGRAMMATIZED)

Although Watt's original intention had been to use the direct expansive power of
compressed steam, his engine was really an atmospheric engine, since the pressure
of steam in the boiler was barely in excess of atmospheric pressure. The driving
force, as in Newcomen's engine, was the creation of a partial vacuum, but this was
brought about by the condensation of the steam in a *separate* condenser kept continually in cold water, so that the piston was kept as hot as possible during the entire
cycle. Hence no energy was wasted in making steam to heat up the piston cylinder
after each stroke. For simplicity, the condenser where the steam liquifies and the
pump to suck off the water which thus collects in it are drawn as one unit. Compare
this with Newcomen's Fire Engine (Fig. 279). The earliest Watt engines were sold for
pumping like Newcomen's. The mine pump rod was attached to a wheel for producing rotary motion in the "Sun and Planet" Patent of 1788.

the cardinal sources of conflict with the Crown in the period which preceded the first Revolution of Stuart times, the power of the great colonial trading interests emerged intact from the political struggles of the seventeenth century. The financial and mercantile oligarchy of London exercised a powerful influence in Parliament, and the power of Parliament could still be used to secure monopolies which handicapped local initiative. The great wealth of the "Nabobs" created a fashion for the silks and other fabrics of the East India Company, and so stimulated a demand which the English clothier could not hope to satisfy. A continual conflict went on between local manufacturers and the monopolies. In 1700 the former succeeded in getting an Act passed to forbid the import of cotton goods already printed and dyed, and in 1721 another Act prohibiting importation of goods exclusively composed of cotton for printing and dyeing. In spite of these minor victories the fashion for Indian textiles persisted. During the War of Independence the American middle classes were in one sense fighting the battle of the small English manufacturer as well as their own. Their success, which dealt a decisive blow to the old imperialism, was also a prelude to the rising political power of local English manufacturers. The successive impeachments of Warren Hastings and Lord Clive in the two decades which followed the beginning of the War of Independence and of the partnership of Boulton and Watt were public obituaries on the prestige of the great merchant monopolies. The ethical vehemence with which nascent humanitarian sentiment of the time was enlisted to expose the ill-gotten gains of the Nabobs might have been adapted to expose abuses nearer home, if it had not been usefully employed in making aesthetic fashions inimical to manufacturing interests an object of moral obloquy.

During the period of more intensive mechanization in textile production, the Potteries were active in promoting a transport revolution, which began with the construction of a canal between Manchester and the Duke of Bridgwater's colliery at Worsley in 1760. The new canal system, which grew to meet the needs of a rapidly expanding volume of commodities, and the collieries, where the use of steam power had been so long established, were chiefly responsible for the introduction of steam-driven transport. Symington's steamboat launched on the Forth and Clyde Canal in 1802 was the first of its kind. In the collieries the need for smooth roads suitable for heavy traffic had been solved by putting down iron rails for horse-driven trucks, and the first steam locomotive was tried out on one of these truck railroads at Merthyr Tydvil in 1804. In 1819 the first steamship crossed the Atlantic. A goods line between Stockton and Darlington was authorized by Parliament two years later, and was opened in 1825. In 1830 a passenger line between Liverpool and Manchester initiated the modern English railway system, the main features of which were laid down by 1848.

The Newcomen mechanism was not adapted to rotary motion and, therefore, to the needs of factory production. It was necessarily slow and necessarily wasteful. Steam had to condense in the piston cylinder at each stroke and could not refill the cylinder till the latter had been heated up again. This used up time and fuel. In the Watt patents and in all subsequent steam engines, steam condenses in a separate chamber. There it is prevented from cooling much below the temperature at which it will just pass into the liquid state, and returned to the boiler with as little loss of heat as possible. No fuel is wasted in continually heating up the piston cylinder or continually bringing a large volume of water to boiling point. The introduction of the separate condenser therefore made an engine dependent on atmospheric pressure more rapid, more economical, and—for both reasons—better adapted to produce rotary motion. For this it was only necessary to connect the piston

FIG. 295.—THE RAILROAD SYSTEM IN MEDIEVAL TIMES

In the Middle Ages wooden rails were already used for trucks at the pithead owing to inferior technique of road making. (From Muenster's *Cosmographia Universalis*, 1550.)

rod to a crank or eccentric. Owing to the existence of a patent which protected the crank, the first rotary engines of Boulton and Watt had recourse to more complicated devices such as the "Sun and Planet" gearing.

Watt's original intention, based on Black's teaching, went much further than this. In the Newcomen engine and in Watt's modification with the separate condenser, steam was used to create a vacuum. The effective force of the stroke was limited to the pressure exerted by the atmosphere. At atmospheric pressure the volume of steam created is about 1,600 times that of the boiling water which produced it. Hence very high pressures can be generated when water is heated to boiling point in a confined space. Watt realized that an engine of a given size and fuel consumption would generate more power if the direct pressure produced by the expansion of compressed steam acted on the piston in both directions. His attempts to construct an engine which would use the full force of expanding steam at each stroke were defeated by inferior technique of machine construction. These difficulties were finally overcome by Trevithick's engine, introduced about the year 1800. In modern engines which use the direct power of steam, the latter

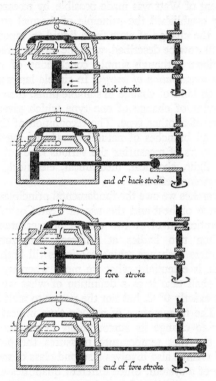

FIG. 296.—DOUBLE-ACTING ENGINE

In the double-acting engine which uses direct steam pressure the slide valve which alternately lets in steam at opposite ends of the piston is worked from the main shaft of the fly wheel by an "eccentric." For clarity a simple lever attachment is here shown. The inertia of the fly wheel carries the piston back or forward during the short interval when the steam is shut off completely at the end of the back and forward strokes. The joints to permit lateral displacement of the rods are not shown.

is let in and shut off alternately (Fig. 296) by suitable valves placed at opposite ends of the piston cylinder.

Nowadays we are all aware that the body uses more fuel in cold weather and when performing hard work. So it is easy for us to see that the Newcomen engine was trying to face the rigours of an arctic winter on an unemployed ration for food and clothing. Commonplace truths of an age when calories crop up in parliamentary debates or in the columns of housekeeping journals were new theoretical discoveries in the eighteenth century. We take it for granted that it is the business of an engineer to draw up a balance-sheet of fuel consumption and power. Nobody did so in Newton's time. Watt's engines were at once the offspring and the parent of scientific knowledge which Newton and his contemporaries did not share.

THE MEASUREMENT OF THERMAL EQUILIBRIUM

The achievement of Watt was made possible by researches which for the first time clearly established the principle of thermal equilibrium and the effect of heat on the change of state from liquid to vapour. Black's investigations, which will now be described, were the dawning recognition of one of the most revolutionary, though simple, conclusions of modern science. It is now called the *conservation of energy*. In simple language this means that if we measure each kind of change in suitable units, there is a fixed relation between the amount of change of one type which gives rise to a certain amount of change of another type. The recognition of this universal truth, which now links all branches of natural knowledge together, rests on discovering suitable ways of measuring the various kinds of changes which we classify as heat, light, chemical, mechanical, electrical, etc., according to their direct or combined effects.

To Black's researches we owe the fundamental principles of a balance-sheet between the source of heat and the use of heat. Costing heat production and fuel consumption involves two classes of measurement. The first is temperature. When two bodies at different temperatures are brought together, each suffers a change which continues till both register the same temperature. This is essentially what we mean when we speak of the flow of heat, and we shall take it as a definition of what we mean by thermal change. Water at exactly 0° C. has not the power to melt ice at 0° C. Water at 100° C. has. The temperature of a body thus indicates whether or not it has the power to change its surroundings in particular ways. For this reason we may say that temperature measures the *potential* of thermal change. Thermal change also involves a second class of measurements called the heat *capacity* of a system. Since different quantities of water at 100° C. will melt different quantities of ice, the heat potential of a body, i.e. its temperature, is not sufficient to tell us how much change it will bring about. This also depends on how large it is and on the nature of the substance.

In the previous chapter we have seen how this was first (p. 566) established half a century before Black's work began. The Italian meteorologists had shown that equal quantities of different substances at one and the same temperature, let us say 100° C., will melt different quantities of ice. Similarly, if we mix the same quantity of water at, let us say, 5° with equal quantities of other substances at 100°, the final temperature when both constituents of the mixture are brought to the same temperature is different for different substances. If the same source of heat (e.g. a hot plate at constant temperature applied to the base of vessels of the same materials and dimensions) acts for the same length of time, the temperatures through which equal masses of different substances are raised are different. Any one of these three methods can be used as a criterion of thermal capacity. The same proportion exists between the masses of a group of different materials which at one and the same temperature will (a) melt a given quantity of ice, (b) raise the temperature of a given quantity of water to a given level, (c) reach a given temperature in a given time when subjected to the same source of heat.

For the purposes of illustration the second of these three gives us the most simple way of studying thermal equilibrium, that is to say, the nature of the final result when no further change occurs. If we mix equal quantities of water at 5° and 15° the resulting temperature is the arithmetic mean 10°. If we mix 5 grams of water at 5° with 15 grams of water at 15° the final temperature of both is the arithmetic mean weighted according to the weight of each constituent, i.e.

$$\tfrac{5}{20} \times 5° + \tfrac{15}{20} \times 15° = 12\tfrac{1}{2}°$$

The second result can be deduced from the first if we make a simple assumption. Divide the water at 15° into two lots of 5 and 10 grams. If we mix the former with the water at 5° the resulting temperature is 10°. We now have left two lots of 10 grams at 10° and 15° respectively. On mixing, these will both reach a final temperature of $12\tfrac{1}{2}°$. Since experiment proves this to be true, we can proceed to examine different types of thermal equilibrium by applying the same convention, i.e. by keeping a separate balance-sheet for whatever happens to each constituent.

If you do this you will notice that the 5 grams of water (A) at 5° has gained $12\tfrac{1}{2}° - 5° = 7\tfrac{1}{2}°$ C., and the 15 grams of water (B) at 15° has gained $12\tfrac{1}{2}° - 15° = -2\tfrac{1}{2}°$ C. Hence its loss is one-third as much as the gain in temperature by A, which is one-third of B by mass. That is to say,

$$-\frac{\text{Temperature gained by A}}{\text{Temperature gained by B}} = \frac{\text{Mass of B}}{\text{Mass of A}}$$

Putting t_a and t_b for the temperatures of A and B at the beginning of the experiment, T for the final temperature, and m_a, m_b for the weights of the constituents,

$$(T - t_a)m_a = - (T - t_b)m_b$$

This reminds you of the law of equilibrium of the lever. On each side we have the product of two quantities. In the rule for the lever the two quantities (distance and force) are ways of measuring different components of mechanical work. In the rule for heat they are ways of measuring different components of thermal change. Just as we measure work done by the product of the load and the distance through which it is lifted, we may therefore measure heat change by the product of the temperature through which a quantity of matter rises or falls and the amount of matter which is involved. The lever is in equilibrium, if the same amount of work is done *on* one weight and *by* the other weight. By analogy, therefore, we say that the common temperature which the two bodies share when equilibrium is established must be such as to make the *amount of heat given up* by one equivalent to the *amount of heat taken in* by the other. The *amount of heat* is measured by the product of the temperature drop and mass, just as the amount of work is measured by the product of vertical distance and weight.

Experiment shows that the law, in the form stated so far, is true only if the constituents of the mixture are made of the same material. Mixing 5 grams of iron at 5° C. with 15 grams of water at 15° C. does not lead to the same result as mixing 5 grams of water at 5° C. to 15 grams of water at 15° C. It takes, in fact, 9 times as much iron at 5° (45 grams) to cool 15° C. of water to $12\frac{1}{2}$° C. Similarly, it takes 9 times as long to raise a given mass of water from 5° to 15° as to raise the same quantity of iron from 5° to 15° using the same source of heat, and it takes 9 times as much iron

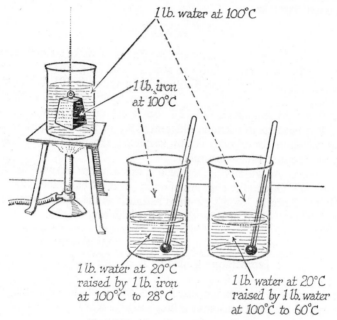

FIG. 297.—SPECIFIC HEAT OF IRON

The specific heat of iron is $\frac{1}{9}$. Hence the heating effect of iron is one-ninth as great as the heating effect of water. 1 lb. of water at 100° added to 1 lb. of water at 20° equilibrates at $\frac{1}{2}(100°) + \frac{1}{2}(20°) = 60°$ C. One lb. of water at 20° mixed with $\frac{1}{9}$ lb. water at 100° equilibrates at

$$\tfrac{9}{10}(20°) + \tfrac{1}{10}(100°) = 28° \text{ C.}$$

as water both at 100° C. to melt a fixed quantity of ice at 0° C. Thus the same quantity of iron at a given temperature can be heated or cooled far more readily than water. For purposes of heat equilibrium 1 gram of iron behaves as if it were one-ninth of a gram (0·11 gram) of water, and we can therefore calculate the thermal equilibrium between iron and water by simply multiplying the mass of iron by 0·11. This index is called the *specific heat* of iron (Fig. 297).

To apply the law of thermal equilibrium to substances other than water we therefore multiply the mass of each by its "specific heat." This gives us its heat capacity expressed as that of an equivalent quantity of water. Water is chosen as the standard because of its very great heat capacity. It will help you to understand why nearness to water results in a more equable climate, or why sandy deserts get so much hotter than regions of rich vegetation exposed to the same duration of sunshine, if you compare the specific heats of a few substances.

Sand	..	..	0·19	Aluminium..	..	0·21
Glass	..	..	0·12–0·20	Mercury	..	0·03
Turpentine..	..	0·42	Brass	..	..	0·09

You will notice that the specific heat of sand is 0·19. This means that it takes roughly five times as much sand to produce the cooling effect of a given quantity of water, that it takes five times as long to heat up water as to heat up the same mass of sand to the same temperature, and that a given quantity of sand cools to the same level five times as fast as the same quantity of water. A mercury thermometer only absorbs one-thirtieth of the heat which is absorbed by a water thermometer of the same dimensions. So it responds more quickly and is more accurate. Mercury has several advantages over water. It does not wet glass, does not evaporate so readily, expands evenly, and has a much wider range between the boiling and freezing points.

To find the specific heat of a liquid the simplest method is to measure the same mass of the unknown and of a standard whose specific heat has already been found (e.g. water sp. h. = 1). If both are brought up to the same temperature and allowed to stand in vessels of exactly the same dimensions in a draughtless room at uniform temperature their specific heats are proportional to the times taken to cool to any fixed temperature. To find the specific heat of a solid it may first be weighed and then put into a vessel containing a known weight of water at a different temperature. If the specific heat of the solid is s, its temperature t_s, and its mass m, the mass of water at a lower temperature t_w being M, the heat capacity of the solid is sm. If the final temperature is T the amount of heat given up by the solid is the product of the fall of potential ($t_s -$ T) and its heat capacity. So the heat loss is $(t_s -$ T). sm. The heat gained by the water is $- (t_w -$ T)M, and according to the principle of equilibrium,

$$sm(t_s - T) = - (t_w - T)M$$
$$\therefore s = \frac{M}{m} \cdot \frac{T - t_w}{t_s - T}$$

As an example of such a determination, suppose 10 grams of lead at 150° C. is added to 40 grams of water at 20° C., and it is found that the final temperature is 21° C. The fall of temperature of the lead is 129° C. (i.e. $t_s -$ T = 129° C.), and the rise of temperature of the water is 1° (i.e. T $- t_w$= 1° C.), so that if s is the specific heat of lead,

$$s = \tfrac{40}{10} \times \tfrac{1}{129} = 0·03 \text{ (approximately)}$$

Strictly speaking, we ought to make allowance for the vessel containing the water. If the weight of the vessel is small compared with the water contained in it, and the material has a very low specific heat like brass, this source of error is very small. To correct for it we have only to add to the mass of water the mass of the vessel multiplied by its specific heat.

In speaking of the amount of heat lost or gained, the international unit is the amount of heat gained or lost when one gram of water is raised or lowered through 1° C. This is called the *calorie*. It follows from the definition that 10 calories are expended in raising 10 grams of water 1°, or 1 gram of water 10°, or 5 grams of water 2°, etc. The commercial value of fuel in Britain is measured by an analogous unit, the British Thermal Unit, which is the amount of heat required to raise 1 lb. of water through 1° F. The "therm" is 100,000 B.Th.U. How we can adjust the supply of gas to the demand for it may be illustrated by a simple example. An iron kettle weighs 3 lb., and the water in it weighs 5 lb. Taking the specific heat of iron as approximately $\frac{1}{9}$, the equivalent weight of water only is $\frac{3}{9} + 5$, or $5\frac{1}{3}$ lb. Hence $5\frac{1}{3}$ B.Th.U. are required to heat it through 1° F. To boil water which has been kept in a room at 62° F., it has to be raised from 62° F. to 212° F., i.e. through 150° F. Thus the heat required is

$$150 \times 5\frac{1}{3} = 800 \text{ B.Th.U.}$$

We can know how much heat (B.Th.U.) is produced by burning 1 cub. ft. of gas once for all by finding the temperature (F.) through which 1 lb. of water is raised by the combustion of a measured volume. Hence we can estimate the quantity of gas required to boil any quantity of water in any kettle of known dimensions. British gas works are required to supply gas having a heating power not less than 450 B.Th.U. per cubic foot. Since 1 lb. of water is 453·6 grams, it takes 453·6 calories to raise 1 lb. of water 1° C. Since a degree Fahrenheit is $\frac{5}{9}$ths of a centigrade degree, it takes $$\frac{5 \times 453\cdot6}{9} = 252 \text{ calories to raise 1 lb. through 1° F. Thus 1 B.Th.U.} = 252$$ calories. For many purposes the calorie is too small a unit, and a unit analogous to the therm is used. This is the "large Calorie" (spelt with a capital C) which is equivalent to 1,000 ordinary calories. When we speak later on about the calorie value of a diet we mean "large" Calories, i.e. 1,000 times the unit defined above.

THE LATENT HEAT OF ICE AND STEAM

The last remarks provide an example of a fixed relation between a definite amount of chemical change (burning 1 cub. ft. of gas) and a definite amount of thermal change (so many B.Th.U.) resulting from it. Clear views about the interconnexion of changes in the physical world actually began with the study of the converse problem, the quantity of another type of physical change resulting from a thermal change. This, of course, was only possible when the study of heat capacity had been undertaken and the principle of thermal equilibrium established through Black's researches, which led on to an enquiry into the relation of heat to change of state, and hence to clearer views about the physiology of the steam engine.

Most of us know that when water is brought to the boiling point it does not turn into steam instantaneously. It remains at 100° C. at atmospheric pressure as it gradually "boils away." Similarly, when a small quantity of boiling water is added to ice at 0°, some of the ice melts to water at 0°. Equilibrium is reached without any change of temperature so far as the ice is concerned. Still, in any intelligible sense, the flame or the boiling water have lost a certain amount of heat, which does not result in a corresponding gain of temperature by the water or the ice. It results in a totally different kind of change, change of *state* from liquid to vapour or solid to liquid.

The simplest way to show that there is a constant relation between both changes when measured appropriately is to apply the same source of heat to a known mass of ice at 0° and note how long it takes to melt the ice, to reach the boiling point, and to boil away completely. You will then find that for a certain period t_1 minutes while the ice is melting you have a mixture of water at 0° C. and ice at 0°. Thereafter, when there is no more ice, the temperature rises nearly uniformly from 0° to 100° C. for a certain period t_2. For a third period t_3, while the water is boiling away, the temperature remains at 100° C. If the experiment has been carried out with 1 gram of ice, the amount of heat used up in the time t_2, when the temperature rises from 0° to 100°, is 100 calories. The source of heat is therefore yielding $100 \div t_2$ calories per minute. In t_1 minutes it therefore gives up $t_1 \times (100 \div t_2)$ calories, and in t_3 minutes $t_3 \times (100 \div t_2)$ calories. Therefore these two quantities represent the amount of heat respectively absorbed in converting 1 gram of ice at 0° into 1 gram of water at 0°, or 1 gram of water at 100° into 1 gram of steam at 100°.

They are called the latent heat of melting and the latent heat of vaporization, and are constant, being 80 and 537 calories per gram respectively. Thus the amount of heat required to convert one gram of water at 100° C. to 1 gram of steam at 100° C. is 537 times as great as the amount of heat required to raise 1 gram of water at 99° C. to 1 gram of water at 100° C. An electric hot-plate which raises water at freezing temperature to the boil in 25 minutes will just melt the same weight of ice at 0° C. in 20 minutes, and will not evaporate the water to dryness till just under two hours and a quarter (134 minutes) after it begins to boil. It takes 8 grams of water at 10° C. to melt 1 gram of ice at 0°. It takes 98 grams of turpentine at 113° C. to convert 1 gram of water at boiling point into steam.

There are many simple applications of these facts in everyday life, as, for instance, the cooling effect of sweat evaporating on the skin. Another is the behaviour of a freezing mixture. All soluble substances depress the freezing point of water. Hence salt water freezes below 0°. So when common salt is added to ice at 0° the mixture is not in equilibrium, and the ice melts. Since ice absorbs 80 calories of heat per gram melted, this can only happen by cooling its surroundings, and a jug of water surrounded by a "freezing mixture" of ice and salt is itself frozen. Conversely, water gives up heat when it freezes. A large pan of water placed near vegetables in a room prevents them from freezing for this reason. The vegetable sap containing solid in solution has a lower freezing point than water. The water therefore freezes first, and in doing so *gives back* the 80 calories per gram which ice takes up in melting, thus helping to keep the temperature of the room above the freezing point of sap.

In his book on the *Theory of the Earth*, the great Scottish geologist Hutton refers to Black's work in words which are appropriate to the results when its implications began to be recognized. "In the abstract doctrine of latent heat" he says "the ingenuity of man has discovered a certain measure for the quantity of those commutable effects which are perceived." Though history has hardly verified his aristocratic assertion that Black's discovery was a "progress of science far above the apprehension of the vulgar," it sufficiently justifies the statement made earlier in this chapter. Although it now seems commonplace to recognize a definite connexion between different kinds of changes like the consumption of fuel, the heating of water and the production of steam, it was not the way in which people looked at the world before Black made the first balance-sheet connecting two different kinds of physical processes.

A new era of physical research now began. In 1777 a Scottish chemist called Crawford, who was associated with Black, showed that the temperature of the same container was raised by $2 \cdot 1$, $1 \cdot 9$, and $1 \cdot 7$ (i.e. approximately the same number of) degrees Fahrenheit for every 100 ounces of oxygen consumed by burning wax, burning charcoal, and the breathing of a live guinea-pig. Three years later Lavoisier and Laplace burned a weighed amount of charcoal in a vessel surrounded by ice and calculated the quantity of heat generated per unit weight of carbon dioxide produced. They did this by measuring the amount of ice which melted. They then made a similar experiment and calculated the amount of heat lost by a living guinea-pig during the production of the same quantity of carbon dioxide, concluding that "respiration is therefore a combustion, very slow certainly, but perfectly similar to that of carbon." The movements of the animal did not affect the measurement. Thus when all movement had ceased the only lasting change was the production of a certain quantity of carbon dioxide and the melting of a certain quantity of ice. In a noteworthy letter to Black, Lavoisier disclosed the results of later experiments, from which he concluded that the oxygen consumption of a man varies with the temperature of the room and his own activity. At 26° C. he found that a man consumed 24,000 c.c. of oxygen per hour. At 12° C. he consumed 28,000 c.c. During exercise he might consume as much as 80,000 c.c. In any case the final result measured as the ratio of a certain amount of carbon dioxide and a certain quantity of heat was practically constant.

The close personal relations between the leaders of Scottish science and English industry during the formative period of the Industrial Revolution have been emphasized for a special reason. Books which adopt the serial obituary method of exposition in dealing with the history of science are apt to dismiss the significance of parallel developments in theory and practice as mere coincidence. The emergence of the energy principle in modern science exhibits the interaction of theoretical discovery and its practical applications both in the character of the major problems and the personal affiliations of the principal actors. Watt's invention was made possible by a certain level of theoretical knowledge. It is hardly too much to say that Lavoisier's experiments were the inescapable sequel to its economic exploitation.

Boulton and Watt had overcome the prevailing prejudice against the steam engine by a curious device for marketing their produce. While the patent remained in force the purchasers agreed to pay a premium representing a one-third part of the savings in fuel effected by replacing the Newcomen by the Watt model. Hence the profit of the partners was directly based on the costing of power production. The arrangement is thus described by Dickinson (*Matthew Boulton*).

There are very few cases where a simple replacement of a common engine by a Watt engine took place and actual measurements could be made, because usually the new engine had to pump more water or it had to pump from a greater depth than the old one; then, too, the mine for which it was wanted might be an entirely new one. To establish a standard of comparison two common engines at Poldice Mine were agreed upon as average and a small committee made the necessary tests. It found that the "duty" which is the Cornish way of expressing the performance of an engine and meant the number of pounds of water raised one foot high per bushel (say 94 lb.) of coal, was seven million. The load on the piston of the common engine when performing its best was 7 lb. per sq. in., while Watt's engine did its best with a load of $10\frac{1}{2}$ lb. In other words, to do the same work the Watt engine was smaller than the common engine in ratio of 3 : 2. Watt drew up a table of sizes of his engine with corresponding sizes of common engines and the appropriate figure was inserted in the agreement that was entered into. To calculate the savings, it only remained to measure the coal consumed and the quantity of water raised. The former was already done on the Cornish mines, because by an Act of Parliament of 1751 a drawback of the duty on exported coal was allowed on all coal consumed in the pumping there. To measure the water pumped, knowing the diameter of the pump barrel and the stroke a figure could be calculated giving the weight of water in pounds delivered by every stroke. It was finally necessary to count the number of strokes and this was done by a mechanical counter fixed to the beam of the engine in a locked box to prevent it being tampered with. Boulton got the idea of this counter in 1777 from a pedometer, made by a firm of Wyke and Green in Liverpool, and made some of them himself at Soho. This method of charging by royalty or premium as Watt terms it, was quite fair because the adventurers only paid so long as the engine was working. If the mine closed down payment stopped. However, the method of calculating the premium was not too readily grasped and much to Watt's chagrin, although probably to Boulton's secret satisfaction, the partners had to give way in favour of a fixed payment annually for each engine according to its size.

The experiments of Crawford were thus a laboratory model of the new task which industry was undertaking on a larger scale. Boulton, says Dickinson in his recent biography,—

states it succinctly towards the close of the partnership in a letter to James Watt, junior, thus (B. and W. Coll. 1796, November 28th):

One bushel (84 lb.) of Newcastle or Swansey coal will—

(1) Raise 30 million lb. of water 1 foot high;
(2) Grind and dress 10, or 11, or 12 bushels of wheat according to the state of it;
(3) Turn 1,000 or more cotton spinning spindles per hour;
(4) Roll and slit 4 cwt. of bar iron into small nailor's rods;
(5) Do as much work per hour as 10 horses.

THE MECHANICAL EQUIVALENT OF HEAT

For several reasons Lavoisier's work was a turning-point in the history of human culture. Science had travelled a long road since *anima* was at once common breath, the human spirit, and vapours materialized in the retort. The changes which occur in the living organism were now seen to be related to changes in the physical world in the same way as similar changes in non-living machines. When Lavoisier's man took exercise, he performed *mechanical* processes. When these had ceased nothing remained except the fact that the *temperature* of the air had been increased and more food had been used up as *fuel*. The increase in temperature illustrates the general fact with which we are sufficiently familiar in an age when motor bicycles are apt to overheat. Mechanical work produces heat just as heat produces change of state or chemical decomposition results in heat. By measuring the net result in calories, Lavoisier applied to the working of the living machine a new physical principle which is the fundamental basis of modern machine design.

To make the best steam engine we want to know how to get as much work as we can out of the least quantity of coal. A standard of efficiency therefore entails knowing how much fuel is required to produce a given amount of heat, and how much heat is used in generating a certain amount of mechanical activity. It might seem an obvious step to ascertain the second, once the first had been taken. The subsequent course of events shows that what was obvious to the working technician was not obvious to theoretical scientists trained in the Newtonian tradition. After the first researches of Crawford and of Lavoisier and Laplace nearly half a century elapsed before the "mechanical equivalent" of heat was actually established.

There were several reasons for this delay. We are reminded of one of them by the way in which we still speak metaphorically of the "flow of heat." Eighteenth-century science was simultaneously growing out of a belief in three very influential spooks, two of which, *anima* and *phlogiston*, have been mentioned. A third, which has not been mentioned, is *caloric* or heat fluid. Caloric passed out of bodies when they were cooled, as phlogiston passed out of bodies when they burned, or as *anima* passed out of the lungs and the contents of the retort. Between a century which believed in caloric and phlogiston and a century which studies energy transformations and chemical reactions there is all the difference between the viewpoint of the engineer who is busy changing the world and that of the philosopher who is content to "interpret" it. Just as spirits continued to preside over fermentation after they had ceased to function in the retort, caloric continued to clog the consideration of changes involving the application or production of heat for three-quarters of a century after Black's work.

Concepts like phlogiston, caloric, and the personal Deity of liberal theology behave like the cat in *Alice in Wonderland*. The smile lingers after the cat has passed out. Black's latent heat, Lavoisier's experiments on exercise, and Priestley's work on the calcination of metals, all telescoped in the three decades preceding the French Revolution, mark the final dissolution of Aristotelian animism in the natural sciences when the stage was already set for an intellectual reawakening, in which clericalism received a far more severe assault than it had suffered from the Reformation. Capitalism was recovering the adventurous hopefulness which accompanied the foundation of the early continental academies and the Invisible College. Science more slowly extricated itself from the scaffolding of metaphor derived from a pre-existing technology which provided no theoretical incentive to costing the available sources of power.

The analogy between water-power and steam-power production is a useful way of drawing attention to what quantities should be measured if we expect to see how one "commutable effect" is connected with another. So we may pause at this point to compare the measurements which affect the total mechanical activity resulting from a flow of water with measurements

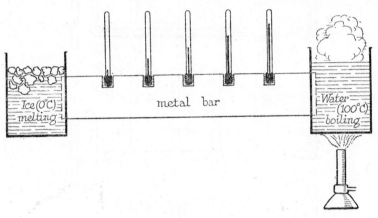

Fig. 298

Temperature gradient along a bar of metal when heat is "flowing."

that affect the final temperature reached when a source of heat is applied. In studying thermal equilibrium we encountered two kinds of measurement which enter into the final result. Analogous measurements enter into problems connected with mechanical work.

When two bodies at different temperature are brought together, the one at higher temperature is cooled, and the one at lower temperature is warmed until both have the same temperature. The existence of difference of temperature alone is therefore concerned with the *power* or potential of the constituents of a system to undergo thermal change. If two reservoirs containing water are connected, water sinks in the one at higher level and rises in the one at the lower level until there is the same head of pressure in each, i.e. till the level of water in both is the same. Difference of level is therefore the only factor which we have to take into account, and represents the *potential* of change. The analogy between temperature and pressure head or water level can be illustrated in another way, if we take into account a very important but not very familiar fact about the flow of fluids. If we heat one end of a bar of iron bored with holes for thermometers at regular intervals along its length, we observe a continuous drop in temperature from the heated end to the opposite end, until both are brought up to the temperature of the source of heat. We then say metaphorically that no more heat flows (Fig. 298). Similarly, if water flows out of a reservoir with a horizontal duct, having a series of upright tubes in its course, there is a continuous fall of pressure head along the length of the duct so long as the water continues to flow (Fig. 299).

This property of flowing fluids is a very important one, partly because it

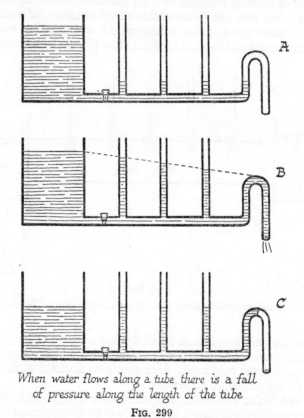

When water flows along a tube there is a fall of pressure along the length of the tube

FIG. 299

Pressure gradient along a tube of water which is "flowing."
(A tap closed, B tap open—water flowing, C equilibrium reached—flow ceases.)

may help you to see how the heat fluid metaphor suggested itself to people who were more familiar with the use of water power than we are, partly because it is still more helpful in explaining why the same metaphor was introduced to describe the electric "current," and partly because of its importance in connexion with a biological phenomenon which was being studied in the eighteenth century for the first time. As most of you know, blood spurts from the thick walled vessels called arteries which lead it away from the heart to the tissues and trickles from the thin walled veins which lead it back from the tissues to the heart. If the artery or vein of an anaesthetized animal is connected with a pressure gauge (or "manometer") the pressure registered by the arterial blood is much higher than that of venous blood. In man the pressure of arterial blood which measures the force of the heart's action is about 110 mm. of mercury. That of venous blood is rarely more than 5 mm., and may sink below zero. This fact, which is simply due to the "resistance" of the long distance through which the blood travels in the minute vessels (capillaries) of the tissues, explains the use of the peculiar valves like watch pockets (Fig. 246) which occur in the course of veins and are absent in arteries. When there is a back pressure in the veins the valves prevent the blood from being sucked away from the heart, and

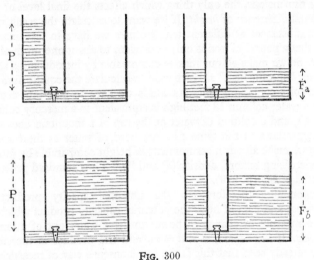

FIG. 300

When water flows between two reservoirs at different pressure heads (P), the final head of pressure (F) depends on the quantity of water in each reservoir as well as on the difference of pressure.

ensure that it only moves forwards towards the heart. The investigation of the pressure of blood in the arteries has led to important discoveries about the properties of drugs which act on the heart or the muscular coats of the blood vessels, and has also led to useful methods of diagnosis.

The second kind of measurement involved in heat changes has been called *heat capacity*. If we are only concerned with one kind of substance this is proportional to *mass*. The relation of mass to thermal equilibrium is shown by the time taken for a body to cool and the final temperature reached when substances at different temperatures are mixed. The time taken for a reservoir to empty depends on its capacity, that is to say the volume of fluid in it, and the illustration above (Fig. 300) shows that if two reservoirs of different capacity are connected the final level of water does not depend merely on the initial difference of pressure head. If the volume of water in the two reservoirs is different, the same difference of pressure may produce different results according as the reservoir at higher potential has higher or lower capacity. Whether we are dealing with heat or the flow of a fluid we thus find two classes of measurement which affect the end result. One, *potential*, which is the temperature difference involved in a heat change, determines the possibility or direction of the change. The other, *capacity*, which is simply volume when we are dealing with the flow of a fluid, determines the time taken for the change to happen.

As long as we are studying the times taken for different quantities of the *same* substance to cool or the final temperature reached, when different quantities of the *same* substance at different temperatures are mixed, the only thing which affects *capacity* for thermal change is *mass*. As long as we are dealing with the flow of one and the *same* fluid between two reservoirs of the *same* dimensions, the only thing which affects the final level or potential is the initial difference of *height*. If we want to calculate the result of mixing different substances at different temperatures we have to take into account the fact that a pound of iron is only equivalent to about one-ninth of a pound of water. So we make all our masses comparable by introducing a standardizing factor "specific heat" s. If we want to calculate the equilibrium between two reservoirs containing different fluids we have to take into account the fact that a water column 13 feet high is equivalent to a mercury column only 1 foot high, and a column of water at the top of a mountain does not exert the same pressure as the same pressure head of water at the bottom of a mine. So we make all our measurements of height comparable by introducing two standardizing factors, density (d) and "g." Thus standard pressure head or potential is hdg (p. 379).

Corresponding, therefore, to the potential-capacity product which measures loss and gain of heat, the potential-capacity product which may be used as a measure of change in power to drive water out of a tank would be $v \times hdg$. If $m =$ mass, $v \times d = m$, and the product is therefore hmg. We have already seen that this is the commonsense way of measuring work, since work done is greater or less according to the weight of the load (mg) and the distance (h) through which it is lifted. So if we are looking for a connexion between heat and mechanical activity, the product mgh suggests itself as a comparable measure of the latter.

In the English system of weights and measures there are two units of force, and consequently two units of work. One unit of force is called the *poundal*, and is the force required to give a mass of one pound an acceleration of 1 foot per second per second. When falling freely to earth, a mass of one pound ($m = 1$) has an acceleration (g) of about 32 feet per second per second. Hence the pulling power of a suspended "weight" of one pound is approximately 32 poundals. This is sometimes spoken of as a force equivalent to a *pound weight*. Two British units of work are used alternatively. Taking one poundal as the unit of force, the unit of work is one *foot-poundal*, i.e. the work done when the point of application of a force of 1 poundal moves through a distance of 1 foot in the direction of the force. It is more usual to use the *foot-pound*, i.e. the work done in raising a mass of one pound through 1 foot against gravity, or the work done by a one pound "weight" in falling through 1 foot under gravity. The force is then 32 poundals acting over one foot. So $32x$ foot-poundals are equivalent to x foot-pounds (e.g. 24,900 foot-poundals is approximately the same as 778 foot-pounds). In the international system, the unit of force is one *dyne*. A force of one *dyne* imparts an acceleration of 1 cm. per sec. per sec. to 1 gram. The unit of work, the *erg*, is the work done when the point of application of a force of one dyne moves through a distance of one centimetre in the direction of the force. Since g is approximately 981 cm. per sec.^{2} at sea-level, a weight of one kilogram falling through a metre performs $1,000 \times 981 \times 100$ ergs.

Just as mechanical activity results in a rise of temperature, pressure on an elastic bag or on the piston in a cylinder may be used to expel a fluid.

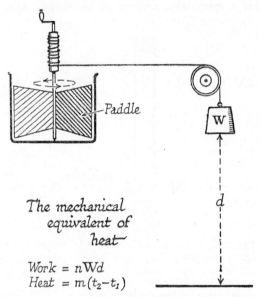

Paddle

The mechanical equivalent of heat

$$Work = nWd$$
$$Heat = m(t_2 - t_1)$$

FIG. 301.—SIMPLIFIED DIAGRAM OF JOULE'S APPARATUS TO FIND THE MECHANICAL EQUIVALENT OF HEAT

The paddle creates heat by friction with the water in a cylinder. If m is the equivalent mass of water (i.e. weight of water + (weight of metal) × specific heat), t_1 the initial and t_2 the final temperature, the heat produced is $m(t_2 - t_1)$. The work done by the falling weight W, if allowed to fall or made to rise n times through a distance d, is nWd. The mechanical equivalent of heat is the ratio of the two.

It does so by diminishing the effective content of the bag or cylinder. If the rise of temperature which accompanies friction is strictly comparable with the expulsion of a material fluid, mechanical activity must therefore exert its effect by *lowering* the thermal content of the substances heated. In one of his earliest experiments Davy put this to a decisive test. This test depends on the fact that heat must be supplied to change ice into water at the same temperature, i.e. the heat content of any mass of water is greater than the heat content of the same mass of ice. When two pieces of ice are rubbed together vigorously water is formed at the surfaces where friction occurs. Describing such an experiment, Davy says:

The fusion took place only at the plane of contact of the two pieces of ice, and no bodies were in friction but ice. From this experiment it is evident that ice by friction is converted into water and according to the supposition that heat is a material fluid its capacity is diminished; but it is a well-known fact that the capacity of water for heat is much greater than that of ice, and ice must have an absolute quantity of heat added to it before it can be converted into water. Friction consequently does not diminish the capacity of bodies for heat.

Davy gave the communication in which these words occur the sub-title "caloric does not exist." Theoretically there was now no obstacle to the recognition that a measurable amount of mechanical work is connected

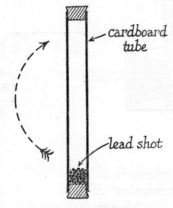

FIG. 302.—THE MECHANICAL EQUIVALENT OF HEAT

Tube rotated quickly through 2 right angles (lead shot remains at end of tube). Wait a few seconds for lead shot to fall to the bottom of the tube. This procedure is repeated, say, 100 times. If h is the height the shots fall,

Potential Energy of shots at top of tube $= mgh$
$= $ Kinetic energy of shots when fallen.
This Kinetic Energy is used up in heating the shots.
If initial temperature of lead shots is t and final temperature of lead shots is T and specific heat of lead shots is s. Then
$$ms(T - t) = \text{Heat generated.}$$
Total amount of Kinetic Energy used is 100 mgh.

$$\therefore \quad \text{Mechanical Equivalent of Heat} = \frac{\text{Energy disappeared}}{\text{Heat generated}} = \frac{100\,gh}{s(T - t)}$$

with a measurable quantity of heat as a measurable quantity of heat is connected with a fixed weight of food or fuel. The first accurate experiments which led to the determination of a fixed ratio of the heat product, i.e. $ms(T - t)$, to the work product (mgh) were not made till forty years later. A simplified form of the apparatus used by Joule in his experiments published in 1843 is shown in Fig. 301. Joule showed that the ratio $\dfrac{\text{work done}}{\text{heat produced}}$ is constant, one B.Th.U. being approximately equivalent to 24,700 foot poundals. Taking g as 32 ft. per sec. per sec., this is the amount of work done in raising

772 lb. one foot, or 1 lb. 772 feet.* In the international system 1 *calorie* is equivalent to approximately 42 million *ergs*.

The accurate determination of this ratio has since been made with various methods, some direct, others indirect. A simple and direct one which gives remarkably constant results is to place a weighed amount (m) of lead shot in a closed cylinder of known length (Fig. 302). The cylinder is inverted quickly several times so that the shot falls vertically to the bottom each time through the length of the tube (h). If this is done n times the total work done is $n(mgh)$. The temperature of the shot is taken immediately before and after. If the rise due to friction is t, and the specific heat of lead is taken as 0·03, the amount of heat gained is $t(0·03\,m)$. The mechanical equivalent of heat (work done ÷ heat produced) is then $ngh ÷ 0·03\,t$.

THERMODYNAMICS AND THE NEWTONIAN SYSTEM

Today we look upon Joule's determination of the mechanical equivalent of heat as the cornerstone of "thermodynamics." Thermodynamics, which has now superseded the mechanics of Newton, is the queen of theoretical science. The position it occupies was not won by discoveries made within the framework of the pre-existing social culture. The researches which led to the determination of the mechanical equivalent of heat were directly prompted by new social requirements, and the leaders of contemporary theoretical science were extraordinarily reluctant to explore their implications. Indeed, the Royal Society refused to publish the greater part of one of Joule's most epoch-making contributions.

The mechanical science which Newton's generation developed was not primarily concerned with how power is generated. It derived its fundamental principles from the "simple machines," i.e. devices like the lever, the pulley, and the inclined plane, for distributing the power supplied by human effort, and from the clock, which moves very slowly, generates very little heat by friction, tells us when to start work, but does not do our work for us. It was less concerned with movement on our own earth, as when the motor engine gets over-heated by the moving contact of solid matter, than with movements of celestial bodies through empty space. In contradistinction to thermodynamics which deals with the relations of different types of change in the physical world, Newton's mechanics was parochial. Its measurements were restricted to motion. It did not concern itself with the measurement of systems which have other characteristics—light, heat, electrical changes, or chemical combination—and it did not deal with the interconnexions of measurements appropriate to systems which exhibit them. In Newton's time the primary sources of inanimate power, wind and the flow of water, had not made friction an important technical problem.

Newton approached the problems of mechanical equilibrium from the standpoint of the means adopted rather than the total result achieved. That is to say, the primary unit of mechanical measurement was *force* rather than work. Thermodynamics is the system of mechanics in which all equations

* According to the best modern determinations one B.Th.U. is equivalent to 778 foot-pounds of work, or about 25,000 foot-poundals taking the more accurate value of 32·2 for *g*.

of mechanical equilibrium are based on the equivalence of heat, mechanical and other changes expressed as the product of two measurements, a potential and a capacity. In Newton's mechanics all the emphasis had been laid on the measurement of potential. The difference between the Newtonian stand-point and the modern outlook may be seen by taking the principle of the lever as an example. The condition of equilibrium is $wd = WD$ (p. 245). This may be expressed by saying the "force of gravity" acting on each weight is inversely proportional to the distances separating them from the fulcrum. Alternatively we may translate it by saying that no work has to be done to produce a slight displacement (see p. 249), since the work done on and by the system balances.

It might seem that this is merely a matter of words, as indeed it would be if the principle of the lever were the only principle of mechanics and if the only kind of motion which is important to measure were the motion of planets through the vacuum of space. Actually we live in a world in which wastepaper falls towards the centre of the earth at a demonstrably slower rate than a cannon ball. Its retardation is not associated with buoyancy, but with the large surface it presents to the air. In Newtonian mechanics the surface offered resistance to another "force," the force of friction. Similarly the fact that nothing we ever see moving on earth continues to go on moving for ever in a straight line was squared with the way in which Newton stated the principle of inertia by asserting that the actual environment in which it moves generates a force of friction which opposes its continued motion.

You must not imagine that this was merely an attempt to dodge the fact that wastepaper falls more slowly than cannon balls, or that the best billiard balls do not go on for ever moving in a straight line on the smoothest billiard table in existence. Newton and his followers carried on experiments to estimate the loss of effective gravitational acceleration on account of surface, and showed how it varied with the speed as well as with the surface area of a moving body. They estimated how much gravitational acceleration a body slipping down a slope loses on account of the roughness of the surface by the limiting angle of tilt at which any motion will begin. So likewise Newton's mechanics represented a rotational movement like that of a fly-wheel as the action of a *couple*, i.e. two equal forces acting in opposite directions at equal distances on either side of the axle, as in the problem discussed on p. 667 in connexion with the deflection of a magnet. Newton's mechanics did not deal with the heat of the boiler which gives the axle the power to move. The difference between Newtonian mechanics and the system of mechanics which has more or less replaced it lies in this. Newton and Galileo did not seek to relate the *measurement of motion* to the *measurement of the heat produced* when motion is stopped. Though they knew as well as we do that heat always accompanies "friction," they did not clearly realize that the production of heat is what decides the loss of work potential or force when, as they would say, a force of friction is acting. Still less did they see that there might exist a numerical equivalence of mechanical activity lost and heat produced if both are measured in the right way.

Imagine a car weighing two tons when put into neutral gear at 30 miles an hour (44 ft. per sec.) and running to a standstill after covering 200 yards

(600 feet). In Newton's mechanics the inertia of the car is opposed by a force of friction which is measured by the product of its mass 2 tons (or 4,480 lb.) and an acceleration in the direction opposite to its motion. This acceleration is (velocity lost) ÷ (time taken). The velocity lost is 44 feet per second. The time taken is (distance traversed) ÷ (mean speed). Since the distance run is 600 feet at a mean velocity $\frac{1}{2}(44 + 0) = 22$ ft. per sec., the time which elapses is 600 ÷ 22 seconds. So the acceleration is:

$$- \frac{44 \times 22}{600} \text{ ft. per sec. per sec.}$$

and the "force of friction" is

$$\frac{4,480 \times 44 \times 22}{600} \text{ poundals}$$

This is the force required to stop the car. Having found it, Newtonian physics can only show how it is connected with the geometry of the environment in which the car moved.

Thus we may begin by dissecting it into "forces" which arise from the contact of the car with the air, with its bearings, and with the surface of the road. We may, for instance, connect the air resistance with the shape of the car by experimenting at the same initial speed over the same stretch, and since our object is to encounter the least resistance, we might use the information to get the best stream-lines. The friction of the bearings, road, and tyres arises from the shape and material of the solid surfaces at which movement occurs. Friction along rough surfaces was measured in Newtonian mechanics by applying the principle of the inclined plane. According to the principle of inertia a body should move downwards if the surface on which it lies is tilted to the least extent from the horizontal position. Actually it is necessary to tilt it through an angle *a* before it begins to slip down. The force of its descent would (p. 257) then be *mg* sin *a*, if there were no friction, and since it does not move till it has reached the position in which gravity exerts this pull down the plane, we may take the force itself as a measure of the greatest frictional resistance in such circumstances.

So far as it goes this device is a useful one. It breaks down when we need a balance-sheet of the running costs of a car. We are then forced to adopt the alternative standpoint, implied in the statement that mechanical "energy" has been converted into heat. To measure the mechanical activity which has been lost, we have to consider what work would have to be done to keep up motion at the same rate, i.e. bring the speed from 0 to 44 ft. per sec. over a distance of 600 feet. This would mean accelerating at $(44 \times 22) \div 600$ ft. per sec. per sec. The force required would be

$$\frac{4,480 \times 44 \times 22}{600} \text{ poundals}$$

So the work done in British units would be

$$\frac{4,480 \times 44 \times 22}{600} \times 600 = \frac{4,480}{2} \times 44^2 \text{ foot-poundals}$$

Thus you will notice that $\frac{1}{2}mv^2$ represents the number of units of work which disappear when the velocity of a body of mass m changes from v to 0. Since 778×32 or about 25,000 foot-poundals represent 1 B.Th.U., this means that the amount of heat generated is

$$\frac{4{,}480 \times 44^2}{2 \times 25{,}000} \text{ B.Th.U}$$

or in calories

$$\frac{4{,}480 \times 44^2 \times 252}{2 \times 25{,}000}$$

This heat (q) which corresponds to the mechanical activity gained in bringing the speed of the car from 0 to 30 m.p.h. comes from the combustion of a measurable quantity of petrol. If we know how much heat (Q) the combustion of the same quantity of petrol produces when no mechanical work is done, we know what fraction ($q \div Q$) of the petrol is used up in producing mechanical activity. This fraction is called the *Efficiency* of the engine. The fraction of fuel $(Q - q) \div Q$ which does not result in doing honest work is used in heating up the engine, and represents the wastage.

KINETIC ENERGY AND MOMENTS OF INERTIA

In the numerical example just given it was noticed that the work done in imparting a velocity v to a body of mass m moving in a straight line is $\frac{1}{2}mv^2$. That this is generally true is easy to see. The work done by the force (F) applied to achieve the result over the distance d through which the body is impelled by it is Fd. If the acceleration imparted is a, this is $m.a.d$. The distance d is the same as the distance through which it would move at uniform velocity equivalent to its mean velocity over the period. The mean velocity $= \frac{1}{2}(v + 0) = \frac{1}{2}v$. Hence $d = \frac{1}{2}vt$, and

$$F . d = m , a . d = m . a . \tfrac{1}{2}vt$$

In the time t taken to move through a distance d starting with zero velocity the velocity gained is v, and the acceleration (a) is $v \div t$, so that

$$F . d = \tfrac{1}{2}mv^2$$

The possibility of making a balance-sheet of heat and work means that this quantity (called the *kinetic energy* of a moving body) represents the work done in making a body at rest acquire a velocity v, if no heat is produced in its motion. It is also the work which could be done if no heat were lost by a body moving with velocity v in the interval during which its motion is being arrested. For instance, if a mass of one hundredweight (112 lb.) moves with a velocity 10 ft. per sec., its kinetic energy is

$$\frac{112 \times 100}{2} = 5{,}600 \text{ foot-poundals}$$

If no heat were produced it could draw up a weight of 10 lb. through a height of about $17\frac{1}{2}$ feet, since the work done in raising 10 lb. through a vertical distance $17\frac{1}{2}$ feet is roughly $10 \times 32 \times 17\frac{1}{2} = 5{,}600$ foot-poundals.

Motions of this kind are rare. So the expression $\frac{1}{2}mv^2$ for the kinetic energy of a moving body is not of much practical use as it stands. However, it can be readily adapted to other problems which have to be solved in engineering. For instance, we can adapt it to the problem of how much "energy" is stored in a flywheel when spinning at a particular speed. Here we have to deal with motion in a curved path. The legend of Fig 303 shows you that a mass m rotating at the end of a string (or thin spoke) of negligible weight and length r has a kinetic energy

$$\frac{1}{2}mr^2\left(\frac{2\pi}{T}\right)^2$$

The kinetic energy of a flywheel can be regarded as the sum of the kinetic energies of all the particles of which it is made up. The kinetic energy of each

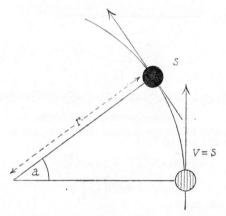

FIG. 303.—KINETIC ENERGY OF A SMALL ROTATING WEIGHT

If a compact body of mass m rotates at fixed speed s at the end of a piece of string of length r, making one revolution in T seconds,

$$s = 2\pi r \div T$$

If the string is cut, the body continues in a straight line with velocity s, numerically equivalent (p. 272) to its former speed, along the tangent grazing its circular path where it was when set free. If it moves in a straight line with velocity s, its kinetic energy is $\frac{1}{2}ms^2$. Since no additional energy is imparted to it, this must also be the kinetic energy which it has at any point on its circular path. Thus its kinetic energy is

$$\frac{1}{2}mr^2\left(\frac{2\pi}{T}\right)^2$$

of these is half the product of two quantities (a) the square of $2\pi \div T$, in which T is the time of a complete revolution, and (b) mr^2. So the total kinetic energy is half the product of the quantity (a), which is fixed by the speed of rotation, and the sum of (b). The sum of all the quantities (b) is called [see Fig. 304 (a)] the *moment of inertia* of the body about some specified axis of rotation. It depends on its shape and on the axis chosen. If we can describe its shape in geometrical terms we can calculate the moment of inertia of any object, and hence its kinetic energy at any given speed of rotation.

It is easier to do this for a long, thin bar. We shall first see how its moment of inertia is calculated before tackling the more difficult case of the flywheel. A bar may be looked on [see Fig. 304 (b)] as if it were made up of thin slabs of equal volume, or, what comes to the same thing and is more simple to deal with, a string of beads whose consecutive centres are one unit of length apart. If the bar swings about an axis through its centre, and each of the n bead units of mass on *either* side of the axis weighs m grams, the total mass

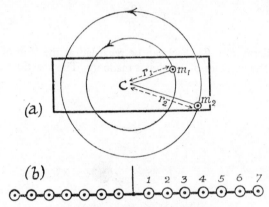

(a)

(b)

FIG. 304.—MOMENTS OF INERTIA

The total kinetic energy of the two particles of mass m_1 and m_2 (a) at distances r_1 and r_2 from the axle of a rotating bar is

$$\tfrac{1}{2}m_1 r_1{}^2 \left(\frac{2\pi}{T}\right)^2 + \tfrac{1}{2}m_2 r_2{}^2 \left(\frac{2\pi}{T}\right)^2$$
$$= \tfrac{1}{2}[m_1 r_1{}^2 + m_2 r_2{}^2]\left[\frac{2\pi}{T}\right]^2$$

For any number of particles it is

$$\tfrac{1}{2}[m_1 r_1{}^2 + m_2 r_2{}^2 + m_3 r_3{}^2 \ldots]\left[\frac{2\pi}{T}\right]^2$$

The quantity $[m_1 r_1{}^2 + m_2 r_2{}^2 + m_3 r_3{}^2 \ldots]$ is called the Moment of Inertia (I), and only depends on its shape. How I is calculated for a bar (b) or a disc (a) like a flywheel is explained in the text.

is $2\,mn = $ M, the mass of the bar, and the moment of inertia on each side of the axis is

$$(m \,.\, 1^2 + m \,.\, 2^2 + m \,.\, 3^2 \,.\,.\,.\, + m \,.\, n^2)$$

Or on both sides together

$$2m(1^2 + 2^2 + 3^2 \,.\,.\,.\, + n^2)$$

Since the sum of the squares of the first n natural numbers is

$$\frac{n(n + 1)(2n + 1)}{6}$$

and since we can regard $n + 1$ and $2n + 1$ as equivalent to n and $2n$ when n is very large, i.e. when the unit of length, and hence the mass of each particle is very small, the last expression can be taken as the same as $n^3 \div 3$; so the moment of inertia (I) of the bar is $2mn^3 \div 3$. Since M the mass of the bar is $2mn$, and $2n$ is the number of units of length, i.e. L, this may be written $\frac{1}{12}ML^2$, and the kinetic energy of a bar of mass M rotating about a centre L units of length from either end is therefore

$$\frac{1}{24}ML^2\left(\frac{2\pi}{T}\right)^2$$

We can imagine the particles of a simple flywheel arranged in discs one particle thick, closely packed. If the particles of each disc are arranged in concentric circles packed as tightly as possible, there will be approximately $2\pi n$ particles in any circle separated by n particles in a straight line from the centre. If there are R concentric circles, the total number of particles is:

$$2\pi(1 + 2 + 3 \ldots + R)$$

Since the sum of the first R natural numbers is $\frac{1}{2}R . (R + 1)$, the previous expression is equivalent to $\pi R . (R + 1)$. If the unit of mass is the mass of one particle, the total mass of all the particles of a disc one layer thick is also $\pi R . (R + 1)$. If the unit of distance is the distance between the centres of two particles, the R concentric rings fill up a space bounded by a circle whose radius is R units of distance. So R stands for the radius of the disc. In any ring separated by n particles from the centre, we have $2\pi n$ units of mass separated by n units of distance from the centre of rotation. So the moment of inertia of the ring is $Mn^2 = 2\pi n^3$. Thus the moment of inertia of all the R rings which make up the disc is

$$2\pi(1^3 + 2^3 + 3^3 \ldots + R^3)$$

The sum of the cubes of the first R natural numbers is

$$\tfrac{1}{4}R^2(R + 1)^2$$

So the moment of inertia of the disc is

$$\frac{\pi}{2} R^2(R + 1)^2 = \pi R(R + 1) . \tfrac{1}{2}R(R + 1) = \frac{M}{2} R(R + 1)$$

If R is very large, $R + 1$ does not differ sensibly from R. So the last expression is equivalent to $\frac{1}{2}MR^2$; and the kinetic energy of the disc is

$$\tfrac{1}{4}MR^2\left(\frac{2\pi}{T}\right)^2$$

All that has been said applies equally to a disc of any thickness. Taking $(2\pi)^2$ as approximately 40, the kinetic energy of a flywheel of uniform thickness, mass M and radius R making one revolution in T seconds is

$$10MR^2 \div T^2$$

If a flywheel of mass 1 cwt. (112 lb.) and 3 feet radius spins at 400 revs. per min.

$$T = 60 \div 400 = 0.15 \text{ sec.}$$

So its kinetic energy is

$$10 \times 112 \times 9 \div (0.15)^2$$
$$= 448{,}000 \text{ foot-poundals}$$

The actual work done in raising a weight of 1 ton through $6\frac{1}{4}$ feet is

$$2{,}240 \times 32 \times 6.25 = 448{,}000 \text{ foot-poundals}$$

If the flywheel spins in a closed space from which no heat could escape, the heat produced when all motion had stopped would be $448{,}000 \div 25{,}000 = 18$ B.Th.U. (approx.). This would raise 1 lb. of water through 18° F., or 10° C. At room temperature it would bring to the boil about 50 grams of water.

THE RATIONAL COSTING BASIS OF HUMAN WELFARE

Thus the substitution of work for force as a measure of mechanical activity enables us to complete the balance-sheet of running costs, and form a clear picture of what economical power production involves. For instance, all the fuel which is used in the steam engine to bring water from the temperature of the air to the temperature at which it boils is sheer waste, eliminated in the internal combustion engine, which uses the increase of volume accompanying the oxidation of gas or petrol as a direct source of power. High efficiency of the steam engine itself implies keeping the cylinder as hot as possible, and returning the water from the condenser to the boiler without lowering it appreciably below boiling point.

The history of the steam engine illustrates how "pure" and "applied" science are mutually dependent. We have seen how Black's work stimulated Watt. In its turn the rapid advance of steam technology revolutionized the principles of physics, in spite of considerable inertia due to the prestige of Newton's methods during the long interval which elapsed between the work of Lavoisier and the first determination of the mechanical equivalent of heat. In his admirable book *British Scientists of the Nineteenth Century*, Crowther sums up the position at the time when Joule began his work in the following passage:

In 1838 the words "energy" and "work" did not have the same meanings as they have today. Young had defined "energy" as one-half of the mass of a moving object multiplied by the square of its velocity. He regarded it mainly as a mathematical function that assisted in the solution of problems in Newtonian mechanics. The theory of mechanics developed by Galileo and Newton was based on the study of the motion of comparatively unresisted objects, such as heavy bodies through air, or planets through empty space. As their formulae had been derived from a study of motions that do not commonly occur on the surface of the earth they had a sort of disembodied quality, and when they happened to apply to such motions, the application was felt to be accidental rather than real. The Newtonian mechanicians were also familiar with the idea of "work" as the product of force and distance, but again mainly as a mathematical function. . . . They used this mathematical equivalence for solving the problems of frictionless motion. The idea of "work" as the product of the distance multiplied by the mean resistance overcome, and hence as a fundamental measure of mechanical action, did not come from the study of celestial motions, but from entirely different sources. This was natural, because no one was interested in the "energy" or *vis viva* of the planet Mars, for example, except as a mathematical function that assisted the solution of problems of solar motions. It was not necessary to evaluate the "energy" of Mars in units because the symbols $\frac{1}{2}Mv^2$ melted away in the process of mathematical transformations of equations. A knowledge of the "energy" of Mars is of no use except in the solution of mathematical problems. It has no direct financial value. . . . The introduction of the steam engine for pumping and factory-driving gave mechanical action commercial value. The industrial notion of "work" was of something that determined the quantity of production. An exact measure of "work" was essential to the foundation of trading in mechanical power. Machine industry naturally arrived at a conception of work in terms of gallons of water raised so many feet in such and such a time, or of foot-pounds per minute. This was a tangible, saleable commodity entirely different from the abstract conception of the Newtonian "work" done by the moon when it fell through a certain distance. The "work" of Newtonian mechanics and the "work" of industrial engineers obeyed the same algebraical laws, but the constellation of other ideas respectively associated with them was profoundly different. The engineers described as "accumulated work" what is now familiar as energy. They considered the work spent in overcoming friction as the measure of mechanical power annihilated.

Before the first determinations of the mechanical equivalent of heat, the requirements of steam technology had already emphasized the need for a new approach to the measurement of mechanical processes. Watt, whose engines were now required to do work previously carried out by animal power, carried out experiments with horses. These experiments showed that a horse pulled a 150-lb. weight suspended from a pulley upward from a coalpit through 220 feet in 1 minute. He decided, therefore, to use as a unit of the rate at which an engine works the power to raise 150 lb. through 220 feet in 1 minute. This unit is called the *horse power*. A force of about 150×32 poundals is required to raise 150 lb. against gravity, and the work performed over 220 feet is, therefore, about $150 \times 32 \times 220$ British work units (foot-poundals). One horse power represents a working rate of about $150 \times 32 \times 220$ foot-poundals per minute.

Horse power must not be confused with efficiency. It measures how quickly we are converting fuel into mechanical activity, and not the proportion of fuel which is used to produce mechanical activity. An illustration will make this clear. If we are told that the efficiency of a 10-h.p. automobile engine is 20 per cent, and that the combustion of 1 gallon of petrol produces 144,000 B.Th.U., these figures suffice to enable us to calculate how long it will take the car to consume any quantity of fuel. The efficiency tells us that $\frac{1}{5} \times 144,000 = 28,800$ B.Th.U. stands for mechanical work per gallon of petrol. The mechanical equivalent of heat tells us that this is $28,800 \times 25,000$ foot-poundals. The horse power tells us that $1,500 \times 32 \times 220$

foot-poundals are used up in one minute. So the time for which the engine can run at full power on one gallon is

$$\frac{28,800 \times 25,000}{1,500 \times 32 \times 220} = 68 \text{ minutes (approx.)}$$

Forty years after Davy's experiment on melting ice (p 607) physicists trained in the Newtonian tradition were still reluctant to relinquish the "peculiar elastic fluid." The first attempt to make a balance-sheet of heat produced as measured by the product $sm(t_2 - t_1)$, and work done (mgh) in producing it by mechanical activity, was attempted by a French engineer, Sadi Carnot. In 1825 Carnot published the first theoretical contribution to the efficiency of the steam engine. Though he did not actually renounce the caloric in this memoir, Carnot introduced a criterion of efficiency which implies the existence of a measurable relation between heat and work. Perfect efficiency according to Carnot's view was reversibility. If a mechanical agency were applied to drive the piston backwards the heat produced in compressing the gas should be just the same as the heat used up in producing the gas which drives the piston outwards in the ordinary course of events. If less heat is produced when the engine is made to work backwards by applying an external force, some of the fuel consumed in normal working is used to produce heat which is a dead loss.

Though Carnot himself made no attempt to assess the actual efficiency of the steam engines in use, he made some estimates of the heat-work ratio in ordinary friction. These were not published till the importance of his memoir was recognized about half a century later. Meanwhile a German biologist Mayer, starting from the similarity of combustion and respiration established by the experiments of Crawford and Lavoisier, had calculated what we now call the mechanical equivalent of heat from physical data which were already in existence. To determine the specific heat of a substance it is necessary to heat it. If it is a gas this means that it will expand when free to do so. If the volume is kept constant it will generate pressure in excess of what is exerted by the surrounding medium. The amount of heat required to raise a gas to a given temperature, if it also does work (e.g. on a piston) by expanding, is greater than the amount of heat required to raise it to the same temperature when its volume is kept constant. At constant volume no heat is being replaced by mechanical work. So the specific heat of a gas which is not allowed to expand is less than that of the same gas when it is free to do so. From Boyle's law it is easy to calculate (see appendix to this chapter) the work done when a piston is driven out by a measured increase of gaseous volume, and Charles' Law tells us the increase of volume per degree. The work done when a gas is free to expand without increase of pressure by raising its temperature through 1 degree centigrade can thus be estimated. The extra heat which disappears when work is actually done can also be calculated from the ratio of the specific heats at constant volume and constant pressure.

Mayer stated his conclusion that a fixed equivalence of heat and work exists in the following passage in a paper published (1842) in a chemical journal:

By applying the principles which have been set forth to the relations subsisting between the temperature and the volume of gases, we find that the sinking of a mercury column by which a gas is compressed is equivalent to the quantity of heat set free by the compression; and hence it follows, the ratio of the capacity for heat of air under constant pressure and its capacity under constant volume being taken as $1\cdot421$, that the warming of a given weight of water from $0°$ to $1°$ C. corresponds to the fall of an equal weight from the height of about 365 metres. If we compare with this result the working of our best steam-engines we see how small a part only of the heat applied under the boiler is really transformed into motion or the raising of weights; and this may serve as justification for the attempts at the profitable production of motion by some other method than the expenditure of the chemical difference between carbon and oxygen—more particularly by the transformation into motion of electricity obtained by chemical means.

At Manchester his contemporary James Prescott Joule was engaged in assessing the relative merits of power production by coal and the only source of electric current used at that time. A year before the publication of Mayer's paper he had written:

With my apparatus every pound of zinc consumed in a Grove's battery produced a mechanical force (friction included) equal to raise a weight of 331,400 lb. to the height of 1 foot, when the revolving magnets were moving at the velocity of 8 feet per second. Now the duty of the best Cornish steam-engine is about 1,500,000 lb. raised to the height of 1 foot by the combustion of a pound of coal, which is nearly five times the extreme duty that I was able to obtain from my electro-magnetic engine by the consumption of a pound of zinc. This comparison is so very unfavourable that I confess I almost despair of the success of electro-magnetic attractions as an economical source of power, for although my machine is by no means perfect, I do not see how the arrangement of its parts could be improved so far as to make the duty per pound of zinc superior to the duty of the best steam-engines per pound of coal. And even if this were attained, the expense of the zinc and the exciting fluids is so great, when compared with the price of coal, as to prevent the ordinary electro-magnetic engine from being useful for any but very peculiar purposes.

Having determined the mechanical equivalent of heat, Joule found that the combustion of one pound of coal produces heat equivalent to 9,584,206 foot-pounds in work units. Most Cornish engines of his time then realized about 1,000,000 foot-pounds of actual work per pound of coal burned. Hence they realized only "one-tenth of the *vis viva* due to the combustion of coal." On comparing this figure with animal work, he found that a horse eats 12 lb. of hay and 12 lb. of corn for an average day's work of 24,000,000 foot-pounds. "From our own experiments on the combustion of hay and corn in oxygen gas," he wrote in 1846, "one quarter of the whole amount of *vis viva* generated by the combustion of food in the animal frame is capable of being applied in producing a useful mechanical effect—the remaining three-quarters being required in order to keep up the animal heat."

The social context of Joule's work, set forth with vivid detail in Crowther's illuminating essay, emphasizes both sides of the two-fold relation of scientific theory and social practice. The new standard of engineering efficiency which Joule introduced has revolutionized the design of the heat engine, and abundantly justified his own assertion that "nothing is more expensive than the endeavour to stumble blindly on an improvement or invention." Conversely it provides a dramatic demonstration of the fact that great theoretical developments arise in response to the requirements of everyday life, and occur when the scientist is in close contact with the world's work.

Joule's relation to the social life of his period is characteristic of the leaders of English science at the time. Like Davy and Faraday, he was not a university man. Like Priestley and Dalton, he had no official connexion with the teaching work of the universities, which were at that time closed to Nonconformists, Jews, and Catholics. These men were representatives of a new social culture. The condition of the established order may be gauged from a pamphlet written by Babbage in 1831. An incident recounted in Babbage's book *The Economy of Manufactures* (1832) is illuminating:

The Duke of Sussex was proposed as President of the Royal Society in opposition to the wish of the Council—in opposition to the public declaration of a body of Fellows comprising the largest portion of those by whose labours the character of English science had been maintained. The aristocracy of rank and of power aided by such allies as it can always command, set itself in array against the prouder aristocracy of science. Out of about seven hundred members only two hundred and thirty balloted; and the Duke of Sussex had a majority of EIGHT. Under such circumstances it was indeed extraordinary that His Royal Highness should have condescended to accept the fruits of that doubtful and inauspicious victory. The circumstances preceding and attending this singular contest have been most ably detailed in a pamphlet entitled *A Statement of the Circumstances connected with the late Election for the Presidency of the Royal Society*, 1831.

Crowther recalls the comment made by Joule when the Royal Society refused to publish his first paper. "I was not surprised," he said, "I could imagine those gentlemen in London sitting round a table and saying to each other: what good can come out of a town where they dine in the middle of the day?" Reference has already been made to the cultural life of Manchester at the beginning of the nineteenth century in another context (p. 419). Living in Manchester during the years when Joule was investigating and expressing his views in public lectures was one man who realized that the physical principle, so tardily recognized by Joule's scientific contemporaries, had an ulterior significance in human affairs. Engels, a prosperous Manchester business man, who had lately completed *The Condition of the Working Class*, welcomed the "work" concept as the beginning of a new chapter in the history of human knowledge, and as the only rational basis for costing the relation of natural resources to the common needs of mankind in a rationally planned economy of human welfare. His views attracted little notice at the time.

"The comprehensive human imagination," says Crowther, "could not be nourished by Joule's discoveries because they sprang from poisoned social sources. They arose out of studies of engines that had been appropriated to the creation of private wealth instead of an increase of human dignity."

Indeed, the sociological implications of the energy balance-sheet, like its biological significance, was recognized before physicists began to appreciate its value. During the period when English scientists were most keenly alive to the social basis of scientific advancement, Sir William Petty, one of the founders of the Invisible College and an original Fellow of the Royal Society, wrote (*Treatise on Taxes and Contributions*, 1662):

Our Silver and Gold we call by several names, as in England by pounds, shillings, and pence, all which may be called and understood by either of the three. But that which I would say upon this matter is, that all things ought to be valued by two natural Denominations, which is Land and Labour; that is, we ought to say, a Ship or garment is worth such a measure of Land, with such another measure of Labour; for as much as both Ships and Garments were the creatures of Lands and mens Labours thereupon.

Benjamin Franklin,* who founded the first American Academy on the same model, wrote in the same sense:

As silver itself is of no certain permanent value, being worth more or less according to its scarcity or plenty, therefore it seems requisite to fix upon something else more proper to be made a measure of values, and this I take to be labour.

The immediate influence of Watt's experiments on sociological discussion is seen in the following citation from Robert Owen's *Report to the County of Lanark* written in 1817. It contains a more explicit statement of the views which Engels' collaborator called the *Labour Theory of Value*:

That the natural standard of value is, in principle, human labour or the combined manual and mental powers of men called into action. . . . And that it would be highly beneficial, and has now become absolutely necessary, to reduce this principle into immediate practice. . . . It will be said, by those who have taken a superficial or mere partial view of the question, that human labour or power is so unequal in individuals, that its average amount cannot be estimated. . . . Already, however, the average physical power of men as well as of horses (equally varied in the individuals), has been calculated for scientific purposes, and both now serve to measure inanimate powers. . . . On the same principle the average of human labour or power may be ascertained; and as it forms the essence of all wealth, its value in every article of produce may also be ascertained, and its exchangeable value with all other values fixed accordingly, the whole to be permanent for a given period. . . . Human labour would thus acquire its natural or intrinsic value, which would increase as science advanced; and this is, in fact, the only really useful object of science. . . . To recreate and extend demand in proportion as the late scientific improvements, and others which are daily advancing to perfection, extend the means of supply, the natural standard of value is required. . . . To make labour the standard of value it is necessary to ascertain the amount of it in all articles to be bought and sold. This is, in fact, already accomplished and is denoted by what in commerce is technically termed "prime cost," or the net value of the whole labour contained in any article of value—the material contained in or consumed by the manufacture of the article forming a part of the whole labour.

* Cited from Crowther's *American Men of Science*.

THE ESSENTIALS OF THERMODYNAMICS

Let us now sum up the change of scientific outlook which followed the Industrial Revolution. Primitive science classified changes which occur in the world by the effects they produce on our sense organs, and apostrophized the source of such changes by agencies such as light which we see with our eyes, heat which we feel on the skin, sound which we hear with the ears. Where the sense organs failed to trace out the sequence of change in the physical world, an earlier, purely animistic, view dominated the science of classical antiquity. Chemical changes were assigned to "spirits," the activities of organisms to "will," "entelechy," and the like. Mechanical changes (i.e. movement from place to place) produced by slave labour, or that of animals, received little attention. While Aristotle's doctrine that some men are born to work and others to enjoy leisure prevailed, there was no social urge to make an inventory of resources for diminishing irksome labour.

In the transition period of the seventeenth and eighteenth centuries various social influences conspired to emphasize the interconnectedness of all natural phenomena. The world was outgrowing Aristotle's sociology as it had already outgrown Aristotle's mechanics. In civilized countries human life was no longer as cheap as it had been in the civilizations of antiquity. The growth of an economy relying more and more on mechanisms which do not depend on the labour of human beings or beasts of burden demanded an understanding of how to produce mechanical changes in the most economical way. In growing out of Aristotle's mechanics and Plato's astronomy science had also outgrown their *idealism*. A more materialistic outlook among men of science was not propitious to the survival of *spirits*, and the discovery of a third state of matter banished spirits from the realm of chemistry altogether. The growth of experimental technique side by side with increasing reliance on mechanism in social life made it more and more clear that the agencies to which we assign specific changes in one or other of our sense organs are not so distinct as they seem to be.

For instance, a source of "light," e.g. a daylight lamp, can be recognized without exerting any direct effect on our eyes. It can produce chemical change in a photographic plate. It can raise the temperature of a thermometer bulb coated with lamp black. It can direct the movements of an insect, and force the green plant to manufacture starch. So soon as we measure "heat" we abandon the skin sensations of hot and cold and substitute a purely mechanical criterion—the length of a column of mercury. Though we usually detect this by using our eyes, it would be quite easy (if we were blind) to construct an apparatus to register increase in temperature by the ringing of a bell.* Experiment teaches us that sound is the way in which one of the sense organs detects mechanical movements of a certain type. We can recognize the same movements with our eyes by strewing lycopodium powder in an organ pipe.

* As Mr. Chesterton sings:
"A man eats clocks in Camberwell;
A man plays billiards in the dark
Entirely by the sense of smell;
. . . But cases of that kind are rare."

A most important signpost in this change of outlook was the study of combustion, which occupied so much attention in the age of coal power. Flame was no longer *something*. It had come to be recognized as one of the ways in which our sense organs detect the complex type of changes which we call *chemical*, affecting several of our sense organs in a variety of ways; and it had become important to measure how much flame can be got from a definite quantity of fuel. When we say that light, heat, sound, electricity, or motion are forms of "energy," or that a lamp, a hot bottle, a coiled spring, a loud speaker, or a dynamo, are *sources* of energy, we mean more than the fact that we recognize light by its effect upon a green plant as well as its effect upon our eyes, heat by the length of a column of fluid as well as by our finger tips, sound by the depth which the recording needle of a gramophone makes on the unfinished record, or an electric current by the movement of a magnet, chemical decomposition, and the heating of a wire. Besides this we mean that *all the changes which occur in the world, however they may be detected by our senses, are related in a way which we can measure, if we choose the right way of estimating the amount of change.* This relation is embodied in the two principles called the Conservation and Degradation of Energy.

The Law of the Conservation of Energy or the First Law of Thermodynamics, which is the common principle of all the natural sciences, is usually expressed by saying that when energy is destroyed in one form, it appears in a corresponding quantity in another form. This is a metaphorical way of stating that in any sequence of changes which occur in nature, the amount of each of them is related to that of its predecessor in a fixed proportion. In other words, we can make an inventory of the resources of mankind for eliminating the necessity of physical labour. In the laboratory the important steps which established the principle were:

(a) Black's discovery of the Latent Heat of change of state, i.e. that a source of heat can produce physical change without rise of temperature.

(b) The discovery of the nature of combustion. Crawford, and after him Lavoisier and Laplace, showed that animal heat or the heat of a candle flame alike bear a constant relation to the amount of oxygen, food, or wax used up.

(c) The determination of the mechanical equivalent of heat by Carnot about 1824, by Mayer, and more exactly by Joule in 1841. This provided an exact theoretical basis for designing the heat engine.

The principle of the Conservation of Energy (sometimes called the First Law of Thermo-dynamics) shows us how to make an inventory of the social efficiency of man's command over nature. A human being is a source of heat, of mechanical activity, and of the manufacture of new materials. There exists a fixed relation between a given quantity of all three and the disappearance of a given quantity of oxygen in the body. This is what we mean when we say that a diet must contain the equivalent of so many Calories for an invalid, or so many Calories for man doing hard manual work, and so many Calories for a nursing mother. The law prescribing that a cubic foot of gas must be equivalent to so many *thermal units* (calories on the Continent) is based on the same equivalence. The fact that so many units of mechanical work (e.g. the rotation of a system of wheels) correspond to so many units of heat means that if we use a certain quantity of heat to drive an engine we know the greatest possible amount of work which we can get out of it. If M is the mechanical equivalent of heat (in ergs per calorie), and W ergs of work are performed, the amount of work done is equivalent to $\frac{W}{M}$ units of heat (calories). If the quantity of coal or petrol consumed is equivalent to H calories, the ratio of the amount of work done to the total source of energy used up is

$$\frac{W}{MH}$$

This is the efficiency of a heat engine, and the problem of economical design is to make this fraction as near as we can to unity.

A special reason for measuring any other kind of change in equivalent units of heat is that the destruction of any form of energy ultimately leads to the production of heat. If a source of light plays on a blackened surface, e.g. a thermometer bulb coated with lamp black, it produces no visible effect on the lamp black. As light it is destroyed. In its place the black surface has acquired "heat." The mercury column shows that it is warmer, if the thermometer is a sensitive one. If a heavy wheel is set going and left to itself in a closed chamber from which heat cannot escape, it keeps going up to a point. However, the principle of inertia is only an approximate truth. The wheel eventually stops. In the mechanics of Newton this was expressed by saying that the inertia of the wheel is opposed by another force called Friction. This friction is only a name for the fact that the bearings and the air around the wheel are being heated up. By the time the wheel is brought to rest, a certain quantity of mechanical energy ("kinetic" energy) has been destroyed. If W units of mechanical work are required to stop the wheel, $\frac{W}{M}$ units of heat will have appeared in the chamber by the time it stops. What will be the ultimate fate of the heat produced? In either of these situations we could conceivably use some of it to do mechanical work, but we know no way *of avoiding a certain amount of leakage.*

In dealing with heat it is impossible to make a reservoir that does not leak. What happens when a leak occurs? In the long run the temperature of the surroundings rises imperceptibly, and the temperature of the thermometer bulb or the closed chamber falls till it is the same as that of its surroundings. Thus we always seem to be losing a certain fraction of our resources for performing work. In the steam engine all the coal which is used to raise the temperature of the water to boiling point is so much waste of calories. When this gross waste is reduced to a minimum the fact remains that the best lubricated wheels get hot, and some of the kinetic energy of the flywheel and every other wheel in a factory is being used to manufacture calories instead of calico.

This universal "degradation of energy" in no way conflicts with the statement that energy cannot be destroyed. The first law of thermodynamics tells us how capacity to produce one sort of change is measurably connected with capacity to produce another. It thus tells us where there is a limit to our efforts in designing a perfectly efficient engine. Experience also assures us that we can never quite reach this goal. A heat engine is a device by which the difference of heat potential between the outside air and the boiler is converted into a difference of work potential, as when a weight is lifted. However much trouble we take to insulate the boiler or to lubricate all the bearings, the system is constantly losing heat. The atmosphere is becoming hotter and the same difference of heat potential is only preserved by using more fuel. Since no known object can for long maintain a fixed temperature in excess of its surroundings, it seems that the temperature of different parts of the universe, as we know it, is continually becoming more uniform, and that its ultimate fate is complete uniformity of temperature with the disappearance of all the changes which we distinguish as electrical, sounds, light, and so forth.

The imagination of a Heath Robinson might easily devise a refrigerating machine to keep all the bearings of another mechanism or the air in contact with the boiler of a steam engine at the same temperature. The refrigerating machine would have to do work to accomplish this result. So the universal degradation of energy or the impossibility of perpetual motion may be stated in another way. Work has to be done to transfer heat from a colder to a hotter body. This is sometimes called the "second law of thermodynamics." On the face of it, there is no obvious reason why we should invest this assertion with the dignity of a law. The need for stating it becomes clear only when we are dealing with complicated changes, the details of which are not fully understood. The so-called second law is then a useful mnemonic to remind the mathematician of the direction in which heat flows in the real world. As such it helps him to keep his bearings. It does not justify pessimism about the human experiment during the next few million years. Lugubrious and somewhat mystical reflections which have been prompted by the degradation of energy and the impossibility of perpetual motion exercise a peculiar fascination. It is difficult to explain their popularity, which may owe something to the fact that human nature shrinks from the imaginative effort of using science constructively. To the extent that it shirks the social challenge of new scientific knowledge, it is forced to belittle the scope of human achievement. One way of doing so is to contemplate a comfortably remote prospect of cosmic bankruptcy.

The Energy Concept links all the processes with which natural science deals in one system of measurements. This means that we can cost the relation between socially organized human activity and resources available for satisfying the common needs of mankind. In the past our use of available substitutes for human effort has been left to the caprice of social institutions which prevailed when irksome toil for the many was a necessary condition of cultured leisure for the few. We could now undertake an inventory of the universe, putting on one side the debt of calories equivalent to human effort expended and on the other the credit of calories in available sources of energy liberated. Thus we could apply an objective criterion to the efficiency of the social machine as we can to the steam engine. We should then have the basis for a scientific economy of social relations in which the concept of free energy would take the place of free trade.

At present we assess the efficiency of our social machine by the results of social practices which mankind adopted before understanding the powers at its disposal. We have been accustomed to say that a scientifically planned economy of food production would not "pay," and that it "pays" to invest in armament shares. To say that it pays to pile up a huge debt of calories in making thermite bombs, poison gas, and concrete shelters is equivalent to saying that the private control of credit by banks is not compatible with a rational system of costing resources for human wellbeing. What is called economics today is mostly concerned with verbal assertions in which words are used in this antisocial sense. Economics will be a science when it adopts a costing system based on natural laws in conformity with Bacon's doctrine that "the true and lawful goal of the sciences is none other than that human life be endowed with new powers and inventions." Since Bacon wrote these words the encouragement of the natural sciences has abundantly justified the expenditure of effort on them. The social sciences cannot hope to enjoy the same prestige till they can also show us how to change the world. The true and lawful goal of the social sciences is that human life be endowed with new discoveries of social organization to use our newly-found knowledge of nature. The history of the steam engine has been a continual progress towards a goal which can never be fully attained. It is merely silly to use the word Utopian as a term of abuse.

The significance of Energetics in social relations will be clearer when we study in the next chapter the results of superseding steam power by electricity. The dynamo which supplies energy for the use of electrically-driven machinery can be driven by waterfalls. From the standpoint of the engineer the efficiency of the dynamo (i.e. the proportion of electrical energy it delivers to the mechanical energy used in driving it) is about three times as high as that of the most efficient heat engine. That is only one side of the question. Once it is made it requires the expenditure of no human labour to replenish the supply of potential energy which drives it. The steam engine must be fed perpetually with fresh supplies of potential energy in the form of coal, which can only be brought from the bowels of the earth and transported to the boiler by human effort. Thus the working of the steam engine involves a certain debt of human calories for every unit of human labour saved in addition to the debt of calories which is paid by the coal. As compared with the dynamo the social balance-sheet of the steam engine would thus reveal a far lower efficiency than the engineer's estimate of its working efficiency. When the economist says that the capital cost of hydroelectric power would exceed the cost of an equivalent quantity of fuel over a number of years, the engineer may reply that society is a continuum and that social planning, unlike *laissez-faire*, need not be limited by the expectation of life of captains of industry. If the Bank of England decides that hydroelectric power would not "pay," the only conclusion to be drawn is that we need to invent new social machinery for capitalizing our resources.

The low efficiency of the best heat engines—less than 30 per cent—is no objection to the use of heat, provided fuel can be supplied without the expenditure of human effort. The heat engines devised so far use the chemical energy of coal and petrol. Its ultimate source is solar radiation which could be applied to power production without wasting human calories in digging it out of the earth. Babbage (1832) hints at one feasible method in the concluding chapter of the *Economy of Manufactures*:

> The discovery of the expansive power of steam, its condensation and the doctrine of latent heat has already added to the population of this small island, millions of hands. But the source of this power is not without limit, and the coal mines of the world may ultimately be exhausted . . . we may remark that the sea itself offers a perennial source of power hitherto almost unapplied. The tides, twice in each day raise a vast mass of water which might be available for driving machinery. But supposing heat still to remain necessary, when the exhausted state of our coal fields renders it expensive, long before that period arrives other methods will probably have been invented for producing it. In some districts there are springs of hot water which have flowed for centuries unchanged in temperature . . . and there can be little doubt that by boring a short distance a stream of high pressure would issue from the orifice. In Iceland the sources of heat are still more plentiful. . . . The ice of its glaciers may enable its inhabitants to liquefy the gases with the least expenditure of mechanical force and the heat of its volcanoes may supply the power for their condensation. Thus in a future age *power* may become the staple commodity of the Icelanders and the inhabitants of other volcanic districts.

Such a scheme could be put into operation by the Soviet Union with its large tract of ice-bound coast line. The temperature of the air in the arctic winter is below the boiling-point of ammonia. Owing to its high heat capacity that of the sea never sinks below it. Hence the difference in temperature between the air and sea in arctic winter could be used to make an ammonia refrigerating machine work "backwards." The stored solar energy of the sea would take the place of a perpetual boiler. The low temperature of the arctic winter air would maintain the external conditions of a condenser. No fuel would be required. The necessary supply of ammonia to replenish inevitable waste could be obtained as a by-product from a long overdue scheme to conserve the world's limited supply of phosphates now wasted by fouling the coastal waters with sewage. While solar radiation continues to supply the basic conditions for the existence of life on our planet, unlimited resources of power now lie within our grasp. Faced with this prospect a decaying social culture is witless enough to welcome the Press lords' appeal for a moratorium on inventions. The result is that a new social orientation is in progress. On the threshold of the modern era of power production science was the ally of capitalism. This was inevitable, as Needham reminds us in his refreshing essay, *Laud, the Levellers, and the Virtuosi*:

> Seventeenth-century science was expanding in the closest relationship with industrial enterprise. The scientific men took, indeed, little or no part in politics, but they definitely depended for their support on the party diametrically opposed to the two groups described above, namely, the Laudian Churchmen and the Levellers. The former were representatives of a dying pre-scientific |

collectivism, the latter were pioneers of a collectivism to which even yet we have not attained. It was inevitable that the scientists should be on the other side, since only capitalism, with its encouragement of technology, would afford science with the means of its development.

Today the economist is the ally of the banks, because it "pays" bankers to endow a humanism with no roots in genuine science. Scientific workers themselves begin to see that the wage system, like chattel slavery, is an obstruction to man's creative ingenuity, and that the future of power production lies in a society with a collective system of natural credit. Only collectivism by its encouragement of technology can now afford science with the means for its further development.

MAYER'S CALCULATION OF THE MECHANICAL EQUIVALENT OF HEAT

It is often difficult to make a direct determination of a physical measurement with great accuracy. When a rough estimate has been made in establishing the new rule, more precise values can be obtained by examining the relation of the rule to other established truths. For instance, the direct determination of g before the days of cinematography and electrical recording apparatus was a very rough-and-ready procedure, and more accurate values were obtained by applying the principle of constant acceleration to the known behaviour of the pendulum. The citation from Crowther given on p. 619 refers to an indirect method by which the mechanical equivalent of heat can be calculated from observations on the specific heat of gases.

That the specific heat of a gas measured in a closed vessel is not the same as its specific heat if measured in conditions permitting free expansion as the temperature is raised, had been known for some time before the work of Mayer and Joule. Hence it is customary to distinguish between two numerical values for the specific heat of a gas. One called the specific heat *at constant volume* is the number of calories required to raise 1 gm. through 1° on the centigrade (or the absolute) scale when the gas is contained in a rigid vessel, so that its pressure increases without any expansion. The other called the specific heat *at constant pressure* is the number of calories required to raise the temperature of 1 gm. through 1° when the gas can expand to the volume it would occupy at the same pressure and the new temperature level.

If the specific heat of a gas at constant volume is S_v, then the heat (H_v calories) required to raise the temperature of 1 gm. from T_1 to T_2 without changing its volume is

$$H_v = S_v(T_2 - T_1)$$

If the specific heat of a gas at constant pressure (e.g. that of the atmosphere) is S_p the heat absorbed (H_p calories) in raising the temperature from T_1 to T_2 is

$$H_p = S_p(T_2 - T_1)$$

In this case besides raising the temperature the volume is increased from v_1 to v_2. In expanding, the gas can do a certain amount of work w (in calories) by pushing out a piston; this must be made good in order to retain temperature T_2 at volume v_2. Hence

$$H_p = H_v + w$$

This expression is only true if all the quantities are measured in the same system of units. If M is the number of work units per calorie (mechanical equivalent of heat) and if W is the work done, in work units, it may be put in work units throughout as follows:

$$\therefore \quad MS_p(T_2 - T_1) = M\, S_v(T_2 - T_1) + W$$
$$\therefore \quad M(S_p - S_v) = \frac{W}{T_2 - T_1} \quad . \quad . \quad . \quad . \quad . \quad \text{(i)}$$

The work done by a gas in expanding from v_1 to v_2 at constant pressure is easy to express. If contained in a cylinder of sectional area A, the piston is pushed out a certain distance d in keeping a constant pressure P equivalent to that of the outside air. The increase of volume ($v_2 - v_1$) is therefore Ad. The force exerted (see p. 369) on the piston head is PA and, since it moves through a

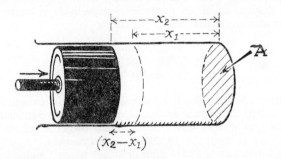

FIG. 305.—WORK DONE IN EXPANSION OF A GAS BY HEAT AT CONSTANT PRESSURE

If the gas is heated so that it expands from v_1 to v_2, pushing out the piston through a distance $x_2 - x_1$, the work done is the product of ($x_2 - x_1$) and the force (F) acting on the piston. The atmospheric pressure against which the piston acts is the force exerted per unit area. Hence F = PA. The work done against atmospheric pressure is

$$PA(x_2 - x_1)$$
$$= P(Ax_2 - Ax_1)$$
$$= P(v_2 - v_1)$$

distance d against this force, the work done by the gas against atmospheric pressure (Fig. 305) is

$$(PA)d = P(v_2 - v_1)$$

According to the gas law (p. 425),

$$\frac{v_2}{T_2} = \frac{v_1}{T_1}$$
$$\therefore \quad v_2 = \frac{v_1 T_2}{T_1}$$
$$\therefore \quad P(v_2 - v_1) = \frac{Pv_1}{T_1}(T_2 - T_1)$$

And since the pressure and volume of n gram-molecules or mols. of a gas are connected by the equation

$$Pv = nRT, \text{ (p. 479)}$$
$$\therefore \quad \frac{Pv_1}{T_1} = nR$$

Hence the work done in expanding from v_1 to v_2 is

$$nR(T_2 - T_1)$$

Substituting this value for W in (i) we have

$$M(S_p - S_v) = nR$$
$$\therefore \quad S_p - S_v = \frac{nR}{M}$$

In deriving this formula the quantity of gas is assumed to be 1 gm. Since one gram molecule of hydrogen is about 2 gm., $n = \frac{1}{2}$ if the gas is hydrogen. According to the best modern determinations at ordinary room temperatures the specific heats of hydrogen determined respectively at constant pressure and constant volume are $3 \cdot 39$ and $2 \cdot 41$. Hence

$$S_p - S_v = 0 \cdot 98$$
$$\therefore \quad 0 \cdot 98 = \tfrac{1}{2}R \div M$$
$$\therefore \quad M = R \div 1 \cdot 96$$

If we wish to get M from this in a particular set of units we must measure all quantities involved in the same system. Specific heats are calculated in calories per gram and ergs in dyne-centimetres. Hence to get M as the number of ergs per calorie R must be expressed in *international* units. We know (p. 479) that 1 mol. occupies $22 \cdot 4$ litres or 22,400 c.c. at 1 atmosphere pressure when the absolute temperature is 273°. One atmosphere pressure is the pressure of 76 cm. of mercury. In units of force this is Hdg where d is the density of mercury, $13 \cdot 6$ gm. per c.c. Since $g = 981$ cm. per sec.[3], 1 atmosphere exerts a force of

$$76 \times 13 \cdot 6 \times 981 = 1 \cdot 014 \times 10^6 \text{ dynes per sq. cm.}$$

For 1 mol.:

$$R = pv \div T$$
$$= 1,014,000 \times 22,400 \div 273$$
$$= 8 \cdot 32 \times 10^7 \text{ in international metrical units}$$
$$\therefore \quad M = (8 \cdot 32 \times 10^7) \div 1 \cdot 96$$
$$= 4 \cdot 24 \times 10^7 \text{ ergs per calorie}$$

Mayer did not get a very accurate value for M because the specific heats of gases had not been determined with great accuracy at that time. The best modern determinations of M by other methods give its value as $4 \cdot 185 \times 10^7$ ergs per calorie. The value $4 \cdot 2 \times 10^7$ is good enough for most purposes.

EXAMPLES ON CHAPTER XII

1. An aluminium vessel weighing 35 gm. contains 125 gm. of water at 21° C. A piece of brass weighing $36 \cdot 5$ gm. transferred from a beaker of boiling water raises the temperature of the water in the aluminium vessel to 23° C. If the specific heat of aluminium is $0 \cdot 21$ calculate that of brass.

2. A copper vessel of mass 20 gm. containing 120 gm. of a liquid is heated to 100° C. and immersed in 300 gm. of water at 13° C. contained in a copper calorimeter of 80 gm. mass. The temperature of the water rises to $27 \cdot 5°$ C. Find the specific heat of the liquid taking that of copper to be $0 \cdot 1$.

3. A copper vessel holds $80 \cdot 2$ gm. of water at $14 \cdot 9°$ C. More water is added at $30 \cdot 2°$ C. till the total water content is $123 \cdot 1$ gm. After stirring, the temperature is $20 \cdot 1°$ C. What mass of water has the same thermal capacity as the copper vessel?

4. A vessel, with water equivalent 20 gm., contains 180 gm. of paraffin oil at $20°$ C. When a piece of ice at $0°$ C. weighing 12 gm. is put into it the temperature of the mixture is $10°$ C. when all the ice has melted. What is the specific heat of the paraffin oil taking the latent heat of water as 80?

5. The temperature of water in a copper vessel, whose thermal capacity together with that^t of the water it contains is equivalent to that of 100 gm. of water alone, is $40°$ C. Find the final temperature after stirring if 30 gm. of water are taken out and replaced by the same quantity at $10°$ C.

6. In a metal condenser weighing 305 gm., and containing the same mass of water at $21°$ C., steam condenses till the total mass of water has risen to $311 \cdot 2$ gm. and the temperature is $32°$ C. If the thermal capacity of water is 9 times as great as that of the metal, calculate the latent heat of steam.

7. A copper calorimeter containing 100 gm. of water at $12°$ C. has 56 gm. of water at $30°$ C. added to it. The temperature of the mixture is found to be $18°$ C. Find the water equivalent of the calorimeter.

8. A metal vessel weighs 50 gm. and contains 68 gm. of water at $15 \cdot 5°$ C. The specific heat of the metal is $0 \cdot 1$. From a beaker at $97 \cdot 5°$ C. a piece of tin alloy is transferred to the vessel and the temperature of the water goes up to $19 \cdot 5°$ C. The vessel is again weighed with the alloy and water contained in it, the total weight being 173 gm. Find the specific heat of the alloy.

9. When a lump of metal weighing 100 gm. is heated to $100°$ C. and immersed in 100 gm. of water at $12°$ C. the resulting temperature of the mixture is $20°$ C. If the water is contained in a calorimeter of water equivalent 12, find the specific heat of the metal.

10. If the specific heat of iron is $0 \cdot 119$, to what temperature must we raise an iron weight of $5 \cdot 2$ lb. so that it raises the temperature of 11 lb. of water from $14°$ to $26 \cdot 4°$ C.?

11. 16 gm. of iron at a temperature of $112 \cdot 5°$ C. are dropped into a cavity in a block of ice, melting $2 \cdot 5$ gm. of ice. What is the specific heat of iron if the latent heat of water is 80?

12. The specific gravity of turpentine is $0 \cdot 87$ and that of ethyl alcohol $0 \cdot 80$. The specific heat of turpentine is $0 \cdot 42$ and that of alcohol $0 \cdot 6$. What is the final temperature if equal volumes of alcohol at $5°$ C. and turpentine at $60°$ C. are mixed?

13. Define latent heat. Find how much ice at $0°$ C. 1,000 gm. of steam at $100°$ C. would melt if the resulting water was at $0°$ C. Take the latent heats of steam and water as 537 and 80 respectively.

14. If 15 gm. of ice at $0°$ C. placed in 150 gm. of boiling water lower its temperature to $83 \cdot 6°$ C. calculate the latent heat of fusion neglecting the thermal capacity of the vessel.

15. A shallow polished vessel supported on three corks contains 1 lb. of hot water. If the temperature falls from $90°$ to $80°$ C. whilst $0 \cdot 25$ ounce is evaporating, calculate the latent heat of vaporization of water, neglecting heat lost by radiation, convection, and conduction.

16. Davy's classical experiment depends on the fact that the thermal content of ice is less than that of water. Using also the data of Example 14, calculate the specific heat of ice from the fact that 15 gm. of ice at $-20°$ C. lower the temperature of 150 gm. of boiling water to $82 \cdot 7°$ C.

17. If the specific heat of ice is $0 \cdot 5$, the latent heat of steam is 537 calories, and latent heat of freezing water is 80 calories per gm., find to what final temperature 120 gm. of water at 15° C. will be raised or lowered if 50 gm. of ice at $- 25°$ C. are put in it and stirred by a current of steam at 100° C. till the total weight of water is 175 gm. after all the ice has melted.

18. Which would be preferable material for a teapot:

(a) A substance with high conductivity and high specific heat?

(b) A substance with low conductivity and high specific heat?

(c) A substance with high conductivity and low specific heat?

(d) A substance with low conductivity and low specific heat?

19. The thermal conductivity (K) of a substance is defined as the quantity of heat which passes in unit time through a cube of unit volume when the difference in temperature between opposite faces is 1°. The quantity (Q) is directly proportional to the temperature gradient, time, and area, and inversely proportional to the thickness (d) of material. Hence if t = time, A = area, and T = temperature

$$K = \frac{Qd}{At(T_2 - T_1)}$$

Calculate the heat loss when an iron boiler of thickness $0 \cdot 5$ cm. and conductivity $0 \cdot 2$ (in international metrical units—cm., secs., degrees centigrade) with a crust of $0 \cdot 4$ cm. thickness and conductivity $0 \cdot 001$ is kept at 300° C. in an atmosphere of 120° C.

20. If the thermal conductivity of copper is $0 \cdot 918$, how much heat is conducted in 1 second through 1 square metre of a copper plate of thickness 3 cm. when one face is kept at 30° C. and the other is kept at $30 \cdot 2°$ C.?

21. Calculate the number of ergs in a foot lb., the number of ergs equivalent to 1 foot-poundal, and the number of ergs equivalent to 1 British thermal unit (= 778 ft. lb.).

22. In a closed metal vessel containing 2,010 gm. of water, $0 \cdot 74$ gm. of petrol is burned. The temperature rises 3° C. If the thermal capacity of the vessel is equivalent to 710 gm., calculate the heat of combustion of the petrol per gram.

23. Find in (i) international units, (ii) foot-poundals,

(a) the work done when a 10-gm. weight falls 10 feet under gravity,

(b) the work done in imparting a velocity of 1 metre per second to a 5-lb. weight.

24. A drop of mercury falls from a height of 15 metres on to a surface which is a very bad conductor of heat. If the specific heat of mercury is $0 \cdot 033$, how much is its temperature raised?

25. Find the heat production in (a) calories (b) B.Th.U. when a 64-lb. weight moving with a velocity 1 km. a second is brought to rest by friction.

26. (a) If 1 gallon of water weighs approximately 10 lb., how many therms are required to prepare a bath of water containing 45 gallons at 120° F., when the original temperature of the water is 52° F.?

(b) If the combustion of 1 gm. of good coal produces 8,000 calories, how much coal would be used if there were no heat loss?

(c) If 1 cub. ft. of gas is equivalent to $0 \cdot 0045$ therm, how much gas would be required?

(d) If 100 cub. ft. of gas costs fourpence, what would be the cost of the bath?

27. A reservoir is 935 feet above a water turbine. Find the potential energy (foot-pounds) of 1 cub. ft. of water in it, taking the weight of 1 cub. ft. of water as $62 \cdot 4$ lb.

28. If a steam engine of 5 per cent efficiency consumes in one hour 56 lb. of coal whose heat of combustion is 36×10^5 calories per lb., find its horse-power, taking 1 ft.-lb. as equivalent to 13,560,000 ergs.

29. Find the horse-power required to give a locomotive weighing 300 tons a velocity of 30 miles per hour in $1\frac{1}{2}$ minutes.

30. How many cubic feet of water will a 10 h.p. engine raise from a mine 300 feet deep in one hour?

31. The specific heat of lead is $0 \cdot 032$. If a lead bullet strikes an iron target which stops it dead at a speed of 350 metres per second, calculate its rise in temperature on the assumption that half the heat developed is given up to the target.

32. If a bar of iron 12 inches long weighing 2 lb. is rotated about an axle 1 inch in diameter through its mid-point by a falling weight attached to a string wrapped round the axle, find (a) how far the weight of 5 lb. must fall to bring its speed up to 1,000 revolutions per minute if no heat is produced, (b) how much heat would be produced, during the time taken for it to run down, when the weight is cut away. *Warning*: Do not forget the kinetic energy of the falling weight.

33. Calculate the moment of inertia of a flywheel 2 feet in diameter weighing 3 cwt. in British and international units, its kinetic energy when it is revolving at 1,000 revolutions per minute, and the heat production when brought to rest (in both systems).

34. If 1 litre of air at $0°$ C. is raised through $1°$, pushing out a piston against an atmospheric pressure of 76 cm., how much work is done in ergs?

35. Taking into account the heat produced by friction in a crane worked by a 10-h.p. gas engine, the efficiency of the latter is 25 per cent. If 1 cub. ft. of gas produces 450 B.Th.U., how many feet of gas will be used in lifting a weight of 1 ton through 100 feet?

36. How much work is required and what is the final pressure if a litre of air measured at 76 cm. pressure is compressed to two-thirds its volume

(a) in a vessel which allows the free escape of heat?

(b) in a vessel which allows practically no heat to escape?

THINGS TO MEMORIZE

1. Law of thermal equilibrium. If M_a grams of substance A, of specific heat S_a, and temperature t_a, are mixed with M_b grams of substance B of specific heat S_b and temperature t_b, and the final temperature of both is T, then

$$S_a M_a (T - t_a) = -S_b M_b (T - t_b)$$

2. 1 calorie = heat required to raise 1 c.c. of water through $1°$ C. This is equivalent in work units to about 42 million ergs.

1 B.Th.U. = heat required to raise 1 lb. of water through $1°$ F. = 252 calories. This is equivalent in work units to about 778 foot-pounds or 25,000 foot-poundals.

3. Efficiency of engine = $\dfrac{\text{heat equivalent of work done}}{\text{heat of combustion of fuel consumed}}$

4. Work done in imparting a velocity v in a straight line to a body of mass $m = \frac{1}{2}mv^2$ = kinetic energy.

5. 1 horse-power = 33,000 foot-pounds or about $1 \cdot 06 \times 10^6$ foot-poundals of work per minute.

CHAPTER XIII

THE SOUTH POINTING INSTRUMENT AND THE LIGHTNING CONDUCTOR

THE eighteenth century was notable in the story of man's conquest of power for the replacement of water by heat as a source of energy. The chemical energy of combustible organic matter superseded the kinetic energy of flowing rivers. The latter half of the nineteenth century initiated a change which is having equally drastic effects on the social habits of mankind. Mobile power is now transmitted over great distances by the grid system, and water power as the means of producing electrical energy is taking the place of coal and petrol. To a far greater extent than in any previous technical development, except the growth of chemical manufacture during the same period, this change is the outcome of new theoretical knowledge gained through the encouragement of scientific research with little *direct* stimulus from a pre-existing technology.

This does not mean that the study of magnetism and electricity received no encouragement in its initial stages from the everyday needs of mankind. During the sixteenth, seventeenth, and eighteenth centuries steady but slow progress in the study of magnetic and electrical phenomena was recorded. What progress occurred between 1600 and 1800 is nevertheless negligible when compared with the strides made between 1800 and 1840. The rapid advance which then occurred was not precipitated by any manufacturing process in which electricity or magnetism played a direct part. It was chiefly fostered by rapidly growing interest in theoretical chemistry during the rise of chemical manufacture, and thus benefited from the outlook of new industrial leaders eager to exploit new discoveries.

The phenomena of magnetism and electricity had attracted little attention in the ancient world. At a very early date the Chinese were familiar with the fact that pieces of certain natural iron ores have the peculiar property of arranging themselves lengthwise along the meridian. The south-pointing instrument was possibly used in navigation before the Christian era. Thales (*circa* 600 B.C.) is reputed to have known that iron ores such as are found near *Magnesia** in Asia Minor attract particles of iron and that when amber (Greek—*electron*) is rubbed it draws to itself light particles of straw and dust. Beyond these elementary facts nothing was known till the end of the sixteenth century in our own era. Aside from thunderstorms which, of course, were acts of God, such phenomena of electricity and magnetism as surround our lives today had no part in the everyday life of early civilizations.

We do not know to what extent the floating magnet or mariner's compass was used in ancient navigation. Probably the Phoenician traders and their successors in the Mediterranean relied exclusively on the bearings of celestial

* " The magnet's name the observing Grecians drew
From the magnetic region where it grew. . . ."
LUCRETIUS.

bodies. It is sometimes stated that the Arabs introduced the mariner's compass into Europe. This is not so. There is a record which shows that the Norwegians were already familiar with its use by the eleventh century of our era. How the Vikings undertook long ocean voyages in which they established settlements in Iceland, Greenland, and even as we now know in Labrador, would be a complete mystery if they had not been able to supplement the uncertain guidance of overclouded northern skies with the testimony of an instrument which they probably knew before there was flourishing commercial intercourse between Northern Europe and the Mediterranean. Be that as it may, the lodestone, mentioned in Chaucer, had already become an important item of navigational equipment during the period when mercan-

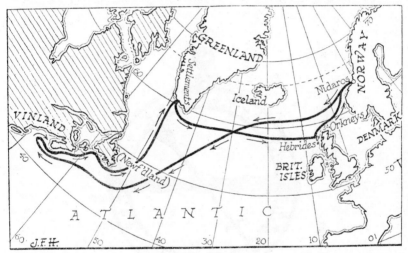

FIG. 306

Map showing probable route of Lief Ericsson's Labrador voyage about the year A.D. 1000.
(After Thordarson's *Vinland Voyages*, American Geographical Soc. Research Series No. 18.)

tile intercourse was expanding between countries of north-western Europe in the fourteenth century, and when the clock, as we may suspect for the same reason, was replacing sundials. By Elizabethan times, the craft of making and designing compasses for use in ships flourished in the large ports, and magnetism was becoming part of the everyday life of the world.

In previous chapters we have seen how two technological problems specially beset the practice of navigation during the period which witnessed the rise of the great scientific academies. One was how to find longitude at sea in the absence of reliable chronometers. The other may be summed up in the phrase "forecasting the weather." What progress in the study of electro-magnetic phenomena occurred between 1550 and 1760 was largely influenced by the same considerations in the order given. To understand how the study of magnetic phenomena became involved in the problem of longitude, it is necessary to know two simple facts about magnets. When a magnetized bar of iron like the compass needle is freely suspended by a thin flexible filament or attached to a float on water, it turns so that one end—the north-seeking pole—points more or less towards the North Pole, and the other—the south-seeking pole—points more or less towards the South Pole. It does not generally lie exactly in line with the true, i.e. *astronomical*, meridian. It is inclined to it at an angle which differs at different places. This deviation called "magnetic declination" or the "variation of the compass" was discovered by mariners, and was already known in the fifteenth century. Columbus among others made careful records of how it varies at any one time from place to place.

Using a mariner's compass is not so simple as our history books condescend to divulge. A ship traversing the course of the Vinland voyagers in

FIG. 307.—DIPPING NEEDLE USED IN SEVENTEENTH-CENTURY NAVIGATION

the year 1932 would start from the coast of Norway, where the needle points 10° west of the true north. Off the Shetlands it would point nearly 20° west of the celestial pole. Near the coast of Iceland it would deviate by 30°, and off Greenland 40°. On the coast of Labrador it would point again 30° west of the true north. So steering a true westerly course by a fixed magnetic bearing is impossible. It can only be done if you possess some knowledge of magnetic declinations. Collecting such information was a practical necessity of efficient seamanship, or any seamanship which relied at all on the use of the compass. We can hardly doubt that Columbus merely repeated a routine which Vikings had long since practised.

During the sixteenth century comprehensive observations of these variations were made in sea voyages throughout the world. Specific instructions that sea captains should record them are contained in the pages of Hakluyt's *Voyages of Elizabethan Seamen*. About this time another fact emerged. If a magnet is suspended about its centre of gravity so that it is free to move vertically, it does not come to rest in the horizontal position along the magnetic meridian. It tilts downwards at an angle called the *dip*, which also

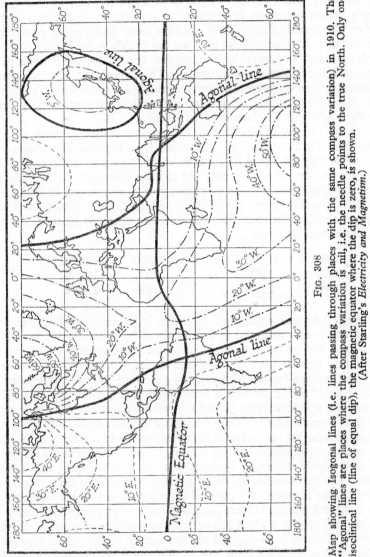

FIG. 308

Map showing Isogonal lines (i.e. lines passing through places with the same compass variation) in 1910. The "Agonal" lines are places where the compass variation is nil, i.e. the needle points to the true North. Only one isoclinical line (line of equal dip), the magnetic equator where the dip is zero, is shown. (After Starling's *Electricity and Magnetism*.)

varies from place to place. In his voyage of 1608, Hudson found that the needle was very nearly vertical at a place on Lat. 75° N. From these local variations of magnetic declination and dip there grew up the belief that the compass might be used to fix an observer's longitude and latitude.

The argument which encouraged this hope depends on the fact that an observer's position can be fixed by any two systems of criss-cross lines like those of latitude and longitude on an ordinary map (Fig. 308). If we could draw across the parallels of latitude lines joining points with the same compass variation (which changes mainly as we move east or west) we should have a second coordinate of reference to supplement observations of the former from meridian altitudes. If we draw across such lines of equal compass variation intersecting lines of equal dip (which varies mainly as we go north or south) we should have a complete specification of position from magnetic and meridian observations alone. This hope dogged nautical science till the end of the seventeenth century, when *The Longitude Found*, published in 1676 by Henry Bond, was severely malhandled two years later by Peter Blackbarrow's book *The Longitude Not Found*.

With the support of the British Government Halley prepared a great world chart for the year 1700. Thereafter hope expired. The reason had been apparently discerned by Flemish manufacturers of compasses in the sixteenth century. Even then they had to make allowance for it. Both the compass variation and the dip vary from year to year as well as from place to place. *Whitaker* gives the following changes in the deviations of the magnetic needle at London from the true (astronomical) North Pole since the Elizabethan age:

1580	$11\frac{1}{4}°$ E	1800	24° W
1665	$1\frac{1}{2}°$ W	1925	$13\frac{1}{8}°$ W
1765	20° W	1935	$11\frac{1}{3}°$ W

Though the quest was doomed to failure, it had results which were ultimately destined to be useful in an entirely different social context, and it encouraged the earliest systematic researches into magnetic and electrical attractions. The literature of magnetism begins with the observations of a Wapping compass-maker, Norman, who published *The New Attractive* in 1581. It is noteworthy because it breaks away from pre-existing astrological speculations which variously located the point of attraction in the Pole Star, the Great Bear, or some mysterious mountain of unknown locality. Norman's suggestion was that the origin of the attraction lies in the earth itself. This was put to experimental test by Gilbert, whose demonstrations delighted the most highly cultivated monarch who has ever occupied the English throne. The *De Magnete*, published in 1600, is noteworthy because it is one of the earliest examples of a physical hypothesis based on the construction of *a small-scale* model. Gilbert (Fig. 309) made a large sphere of magnetic iron over the surface of which he could move a small compass needle suitably mounted. Therewith he mapped out the surface of the sphere into great circles of equal variation from pole to pole and small circles of equal dip parallel to the equator, thus proving that the earth's behaviour is like that of a huge magnet of the same shape.

Gilbert's book and his previous work profoundly influenced Bacon. It is also notable for a hypothesis which, though wrong, exerted a very fruitful influence on later physical research. He supposed that the sun, earth, moon, and planets are all endowed with magnetic properties; and Kepler adopted the suggestion as a possible explanation of planetary motion. Without doubt this prepared the way for the doctrine of attraction at a distance embodied in Newton's principle of universal gravitation, and determined the course of researches towards the end of the eighteenth century, when Priestley and Cavendish showed that magnetic and electrical attractions vary inversely with the square of the distance. The experiments which ultimately proved that the inverse square law applies to magnetic and electrical as well as to gravitational attraction depend on testing devious and indirect inferences from the law. It is easier to see how these discoveries were made, if we recognize at the outset the close connexion between earlier speculations on the same topics, and the ample mathematical development of the theory of gravitational attraction waiting to be used.

The early association of magnetic and gravitational theory explains why

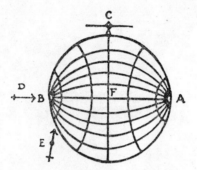

FIG. 309.—GILBERT'S TERELLA

the phenomena of magnetic and electrical attraction engaged the interest of Hawksbee and others in the early days of the Royal Society. It would be consistent with the follies of the racialist doctrines once prevalent in Germany to attribute English leadership in the beginnings of power production, or, equally, American leadership in its more recent phase, to the peculiar natural endowments of the Anglo-American peoples. Such a supposition would be gratuitous. Economic, physiographical, political, and cultural circumstances conspired to give Britain special opportunities in the seventeenth century. Her rich coalfields, isolation from the devastations of the Thirty Years' War which ravaged Germany in the post-Reformation period, the political supremacy of the English mercantile classes, among other circumstances favoured the technology of steam. In her bid for maritime supremacy, England's backwardness in astronomical lore and her northerly situation were both propitious to a new technology of navigation adapted to the experience of her seamen.

The facts about magnetic attractions known by the beginning of the eighteenth century include little that was not established by Gilbert and his immediate successors. They may be summarized under three headings. First, the power to attract iron and to exhibit a polarity when free to move

in the earth's field is possessed by certain natural iron ores, by bars of iron
which have been allowed to rest in line with the magnetic meridian or by
bars of iron which have been rubbed in a definite direction by magnetic
ores (or by other magnets originally prepared in this way). Second, all bodies
which exhibit magnetic attraction have *polarity*, the attractions being of two
kinds (Fig. 311). The north-seeking pole of one suspended magnet repels the
north-seeking pole and attracts the south-seeking pole of another. The
south-seeking pole of one suspended magnet repels the south-seeking and
attracts the north-seeking pole of another one. Third, when a bar of
iron is placed lengthwise in line with the polar axis of a magnet the end

FIG 310.—ELIZABETH WATCHING GILBERT'S EXPERIMENTS

nearest to the nearer of the poles acquires the opposite kind of polarity,
while it remains in that position. This phenomenon is called *magnetic
induction*.

ELECTRIFICATION BY FRICTION

In exploring the nature of terrestrial magnetism Gilbert made experiments
on the traditional property of amber, and showed that resins, crystals,
sulphur, and glass when rubbed acquire the power to attract substances
other than iron. The only important advance on these fragmentary observations made during the seventeenth century was the work of von Guericke,
whose researches on the air pump have been mentioned. Guericke made a
simple frictional machine, a large sphere of sulphur on an iron axle rotated
by a handle and rubbed against the hand during rotation. With this device
he made two new discoveries. One was that when some objects touched the
electrified sphere they were no longer attracted but repelled. The other was

that some objects placed in the neighbourhood of the electrified sphere themselves became "inductively" charged, i.e. capable of attraction and repulsion. Better machines were made by a succession of imitators, of whom Hawksbee will be mentioned later.

The known phenomena described as *electrical* in the middle of the eighteenth century were, in general, effects associated with friction like the above. At first attention was mainly focussed on the phenomena of attraction and repulsion. The main features of electrical attraction and repulsion depend on (*a*) the nature of the materials and (*b*) the nature of electrical induction. Broadly speaking, solids may be divided into two classes. If we hold a fountain pen of vulcanite, a stick of sealing wax, or rod of glass in the

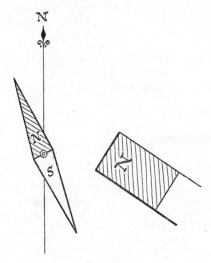

FIG. 311

Like poles repel and unlike poles attract.

hand, it becomes electrified when rubbed against the sleeve, a piece of fur, or a silk handkerchief. A metal rod if held in the hand will not attract small fragments of tissue paper or dust particles when rubbed in the same way. On the other hand, a metal rod will do so if it is mounted on a handle of glass or vulcanite. Thus the two classes of bodies to which belong, on the one hand, substances like glass, amber, resin, sulphur, vulcanite, etc., and on the other hand, the metals, do not differ in ability to become electrified, as Gilbert believed. They merely differ in their power to *retain* the condition of being electrically charged. Some bodies called *insulators* retain their charge and others called *conductors* give it up unless separated from contact with other conductors by an insulating material.

To test the presence of the electrified state a convenient device is made by suspending a small ball of pith from a silk cord. If a small plate of metal mounted on an insulating handle is first applied to the surface of an electrified body, it will attract a suspended pith ball. A glass plate does not do this. So a conducting substance is one which readily acquires as well as one which readily loses charge by contact. Dry pith is a very poor conductor, and when a suspended pith ball is attracted to an electrified body it usually sticks to it. If the suspended pith ball is coated with gold leaf it is violently repelled after it has been allowed to touch the electrified object which at first attracted it.

The circumstances in which attraction and repulsion are seen depend on the nature of the electrified body. If a glass rod is rubbed with silk, it

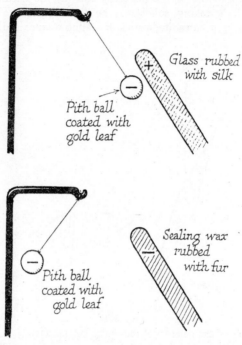

Glass rubbed with silk

Pith ball coated with gold leaf

Sealing wax rubbed with fur

Pith ball coated with gold leaf

FIG. 312

Like charges repel and unlike charges attract. The pith ball coated with gold leaf has the same kind of electrification as sealing wax rubbed with fur.

first attracts, and on touching subsequently repels, a pith ball coated with gold leaf. The same is also true of a piece of vulcanite rubbed with fur (Fig. 312). At first sight the two phenomena are exactly alike, just as the attraction of a piece of iron to the north-seeking or south-seeking pole of a bar magnet is ostensibly the same phenomenon. Further experiment shows that electrical, like magnetic, attraction is of two kinds. If a pith ball coated with gold leaf is repelled by a glass rod electrified by rubbing with silk, it is attracted to a vulcanite rod electrified by rubbing with fur. A similar pith ball which is repelled by a vulcanite rod rubbed with fur is attracted by a glass rod rubbed with silk. Thus the power of electrical attraction is of two kinds, like the two poles of the magnet. Just as like poles repel and unlike poles attract, like charges repel and unlike charges attract.

Since motion towards (attraction) and away from (repulsion) a fixed point may be mathematically distinguished by the positive or negative sign, the two kinds of charge are now distinguished as negative and positive. By convention glass which is rubbed with silk is said to be *positively*, vulcanite rubbed with fur *negatively*, charged. These terms were introduced by Benjamin Franklin. Experiment shows that the silk used to rub the glass attracts the pith ball which is repelled by the latter, and repels a pith ball which has been charged by contact with vulcanite rubbed with fur. Similarly fur used to rub the vulcanite attracts a pith ball charged with the latter and repels

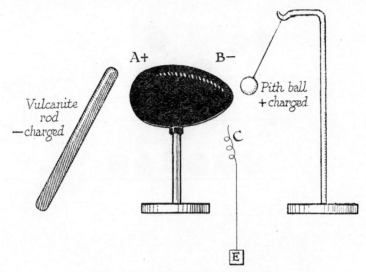

FIG. 313.—ELECTROSTATIC INDUCTION

The egg-shaped metal conductor mounted on an insulated stand is initially neutral. When the negatively charged rod (−) is brought near it the opposite end is negatively charged, i.e. it attracts a pith ball coated with gold leaf previously charged by contact with a positively electrified rod. If the rod is taken away, no attraction occurs. If while the rod is held in position the end B is connected to an *earthed* (E) conductor at C, the attraction ceases, but if the rod is withdrawn *after* the connexion with C is severed, the whole conductor AB is found to be positively charged, and will now *repel* the pith ball.

one which has touched a glass rod rubbed with silk. The fur is positively and the silk negatively charged. In general, when there is friction between bodies of different material, they thus acquire opposite charges.

The reason why a pith ball coated with conducting material is repelled by a charged body when it is allowed to touch it is that it acquires the *same kind of charge* by contact. Why then is it first attracted? The answer to this question lies in the phenomena of induction. To demonstrate the phenomena of induction a convenient device is an egg-shaped metal body mounted on an insulating stand (Fig. 313). When a charged rod is brought near one end (A) the other end (B) will attract an uncharged pith ball, or repel one which has been charged by the electrified rod. One end therefore acquires the same sort of charge as an electrified body brought near the *opposite* extremity. If the rod is removed the charge ordinarily disappears. If the end which is near the pith ball is touched *momentarily* ("earthed") while the rod is held in position the pith ball ceases to react. When the rod is withdrawn, it exhibits the opposite behaviour. It is now repelled. The metal inductor is now electrified with a charge opposite to that which its pointed extremity previously showed.

You can get a clear picture of these seemingly paradoxical effects if you adapt Gilbert's method and make the pith ball a physical model of the phenomena observed. Imagine that matter is made up of particles of two

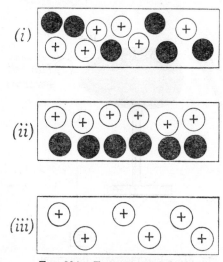

FIG. 314.—ELECTROSTATIC INDUCTION

Pith ball model to illustrate the particular view: (i) an uncharged body with equal numbers of positively and negatively charged particles; (ii) a conductor charged by induction. The positively charged particles are supposed to be held in position by the attraction of a negatively charged body near the upper surface. If the opposite lower surface is now touched with an earthed conductor the excess of negative particles escapes, leaving the conductor (iii) positively charged when the neighbouring negatively charged body is withdrawn.

kinds like pith balls charged to the same attractive power positively and negatively. Whether these particles are molecules, atoms, or smaller than either need not concern us at present. If both kinds are present in equal numbers a body will exhibit no electrical phenomena. When two bodies are rubbed, the loss of one kind, let us say negative particles, by one of them will mean that it has an excess of the other kind, positive particles, and will exhibit positive electrification. Since this loss will entail a corresponding gain to the other body, the latter will be negatively charged. This is in keeping with the fact that the fur and the vulcanite or the glass and the silk acquire opposite charges. If we bring a positively charged rod (e.g. glass rubbed with silk) near an uncharged body, what will then happen? If our particles behave like pith balls one lot, the positively charged ones, will be repelled by the rod, while the other, the negatively charged ones, will be attracted to the rod. Hence there will be an excess of charged particles of opposite sign near the charged rod, and an excess of particles of like charge at the opposite end, which will, therefore, exhibit the same kind of attraction as the rod itself.

If we connect the positively charged end to the earth, negative particles will be drawn into this end by the attraction of unlike charges. Its positive charge will therefore be neutralized, and the end connected to earth will appear to be discharged. If the rod is now removed after connection with the earth has been cut off, there will now be an excess of negatively charged particles on the surface of the inductor, because all the while the positively charged rod was held in position it maintained a concentration of negative

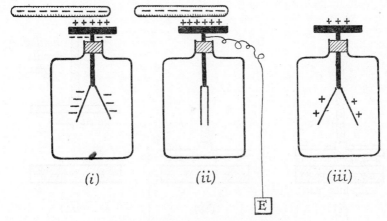

FIG. 315.—ELECTROSTATIC INDUCTION

Charging a gold leaf electroscope positively by means of a negatively charged rod of sealing wax rubbed with fur. The earthed conductor in (ii) must be disconnected before the rod is removed.

particles at the end next to itself. So the inductor will now be charged, and the sign of its charge will be opposite to that of the rod.

You can familiarize yourself with the phenomena of electrical induction by applying the same model to interpret the behaviour of two simple devices, the gold electroscope and the electrophorus, which are also used to demonstrate them. The gold leaf electroscope in Fig 315 is essentially a metal knob or plate connected with a rod at the ends of which two strips of gold leaf are mounted. The rod is fixed on an insulated support, and the leaves are usually protected by a glass window, which may simply be a bottle. If a charged rod is brought near the knob, the leaves, which acquire the same charges by induction, repel one another and diverge like the leaves of a book. If the underside of the knob is touched while the rod is still held near it, the leaves collapse together, but when the rod is withdrawn they once more diverge and remain apart. The electroscope is now said to be charged. If when charged the original charging rod is brought near the knob they collapse again while it is held there; but if a rod of opposite charge is brought near the knob they will diverge more widely. Thus the charged electroscope can be used to test whether a body is negatively or positively charged. Observation shows that the divergence of the leaves is greater or less according to the amount of rubbing and the size of the charged body. The electroscope can therefore be used as a criterion of the extent of charge, and thus to show that when two bodies are rubbed the opposite charges they acquire are of equal strength. One way of doing this is to make a flannel cap just fitting a vulcanite rod. When the two are rubbed together, the flannel cap can be suspended by a thread attached to it side by side with the rod and near the knob of the electroscope. No effect is then produced. Tested separately, each produces equal divergence of the leaves when the knob is not earthed.

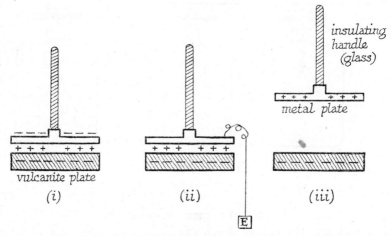

FIG. 316.—ELECTROSTATIC INDUCTION—THE ELECTROPHORUS
The earthed conductor (which can be a finger) must be disconnected before the metal plate is lifted off. A spark can then be obtained by touching the edge.

The electrophorus is worth mentioning, because it demonstrates another feature of electrified bodies. Besides attracting light bodies, von Guericke's frictional machine was noticed to emit minute *sparks with a crackling sound* when touched. Where the atmosphere is very dry, as in Canada, it is often possible to get small sparks by merely rubbing the hair. The electrophorus consists of two parts. One is a disc of vulcanite on a metal base (a gramophone record or the top of a tin filled with sealing wax serves). The other is a metal plate with an insulating handle. The vulcanite disc is rubbed with fur or dry cloth. If the metal plate is now laid on it and then removed, there will be no spark when the edge is touched with the finger. If however the top of the plate is touched while the metal plate rests on the disc the subsequent behaviour of the latter is different. After lifting it, a conspicuous spark is emitted when the edge is touched. This can be repeated an indefinite number of times without rubbing the disc again. To understand the *modus operandi* of this device, you must remember that the metal plate only touches the uneven surface of the insulating disc at a few points, and since the latter is not a conductor it does not give up its charge appreciably through contact. Charging occurs by induction. The reason why we can go on "discharging" the electrophorus repeatedly is that the excess charge of the metal inductor comes from the immense resources of the earth. The reason why the disc eventually loses its charge is that air is not a perfect insulator, and, if moist, conducts appreciably. Hence experiments with frictional electricity can only be relied on to give the results described, if performed in relatively dry conditions.

THE NATURE OF LIGHTNING

If the metal disc of the electrophorus is brought near an electroscope before sparking it is found to be charged. After sparking it is no longer charged. A spark therefore accompanies the *discharge* of an electrified body. Careful observation shows that the spark occurs immediately before the finger touches the edge of the metal plate. Indeed, it is not necessary to touch the plate, if the finger or any earthed conductor is brought near enough. This means that when an uncharged body is brought very near one which is highly charged, the intervening air ceases to insulate and *acquires the power to conduct* electricity, a phenomenon accompanied by the evolution of great heat. The production of light, heat, and sound in the spark without the accompaniment of chemical decomposition of combustible material naturally attracted attention. It did so partly because of its oddity but also because it was the first natural phenomenon which suggested any resemblance to one of the most familiar and hitherto inexplicable characteristics of storms.

The crackle of the spark which occurs when a charge is neutralized by earthing is a miniature thunder clap. In everyday life thunder is commonly followed by rain, and there is nothing unlikely in the supposition that the drops of moisture in clouds acquire an electrical charge by friction with the atmosphere. This view was stated by Wall, a friend of Boyle, in a paper published in the *Philosophical Transactions of the Royal Society* in 1708. In it he suggested that the luminous crackling of rubbed amber "seems in some degree to represent thunder and lightning." A year later Hawksbee published his book *Physico-Mechanical Experiments*, and therein described a glass frictional machine somewhat similar to von Guericke's. Benjamin Franklin, who founded the first American Academy of Sciences at Philadelphia to advance "useful knowledge" in 1743, was fired with interest for the new discoveries and their possible applications to thunderstorms. The damp atmosphere of England and Holland is not well suited for experiments on frictional electrification, because it is not a good insulator. Hence reliable results are difficult to get, and require careful precautions which presuppose some knowledge of the phenomena themselves. Philadelphia, where Franklin began his experiments about 1747, has a more propitious climate because the prevailing north-west winds are deprived of moisture in their passage over the American continent, where the severe frost keeps the air dry in the winter. As Crowther remarks of Franklin and his friends in *American Men of Science*, "striking, easily repeated experiments assisted them to think out clear-cut theories."

Besides being a statesman, Benjamin Franklin was a man of science and a pioneer of secular scientific humanism. It was he who first introduced the terms *positive* and *negative* electricity. He also proved the identity of thunderstorms and frictional phenomena by a classical experiment first carried out in 1752. This experiment was the basis of the first practical application of electricity in everyday life. During a thunderstorm near Philadelphia, Franklin flew a kite provided with a metal point connected with the wet hempen string. To the lower end of the latter a key held by a dry silk cord to a tree was attached. From the metal key sparks were drawn off in rapid succession, whenever it was touched. This at once led to the invention of the lightning conductor. A lightning conductor is simply a metal rod projecting well above a building at its upper end and sunk deep in the earth. When a charged cloud is above, the conductor acquires a charge which leaks to earth. If a discharge does take place the conductor acts like the finger applied to the edge of the charged electrophorus, neutralizing the charge by earthing.

Till the beginning of the eighteenth century these new phenomena exhibited by bodies subjected to friction had been comparatively insignificant. About the middle of the century attempts to improve the insulation of simple frictional machines like those of von Guericke and Hawksbee led to new discoveries about induction and the fortuitous invention called the Leyden Jar. The Leyden jar, so called after the home of its Dutch inventor, added a third to the list of electrical properties of matter, and threw light on another mystery of outdoor life. From ancient times it had been known that certain fishes, like the electric eel, can impart powerful "shocks" which produce violent muscular contraction, and may even kill an animal as lightning sometimes kills men. The inventor of the Leyden jar is alleged to have said that he would not have repeated his principal experiment with it, if he were offered the crown of France.

An experiment with a metal inductor like the one in Fig. 317 helps us to understand the Leyden jar, which is the parent of the "condensers" now used so widely as part of radio equipment. If a charged conductor is connected by a wire with the knob of an electroscope, the leaves will diverge. They do so because they then share the excess of positive or negative charge on the conductor. If another insulated conductor is brought near the first it will have little effect on it unless it is earthed. If it is connected to earth, the divergence of the leaves of the electroscope will noticeably diminish as it approaches it, and return to their original position when it is taken away. Although the conductor connected with the electroscope appears to be less highly charged while the earthed conductor is near it, what happens is not due to the fact that the first has permanently lost any charge. All that has happened is that the distribution of the charge between the conductor and the electroscope connected with it is temporarily changed.

When the same source of heat is applied to two different bodies for the same time, i.e. when two bodies receive an equal "amount" of heat, the temperature they reach is determined by their thermal capacities. So by analogy with what happens in our last experiment, this is described by saying that the "capacity" of the conductor has been increased. The heating effect of two bodies brought to the same temperature (e.g. by immersion in water kept at the boiling point) depends on their thermal capacities. We may therefore press the analogy further by asking whether there is any difference between the electrical effects (attraction or spark) exhibited by conductors of different capacities charged up to the limit from one and the same source, e.g. by repeatedly connecting them with the charged plate of an electrophorus.

A Leyden jar (Fig. 318) or any other "condenser" is simply an arrangement in which a conducting surface is separated by insulating material from another conducting surface which can be earthed. The variable air condenser of radio equipment consists of two sets of parallel metal vanes separated by air. One set may be earthed and the other can be connected with a source of electric charge. The Leyden jar is just a bottle covered up

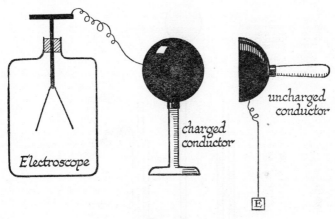

FIG. 317

The fact that the attractive (or repulsive) power of a charged conductor is diminished by the presence of a neighbouring earthed conductor is shown by the fact that the gold leaves diverge *less* when the uncharged metal cup is brought near the charged metal sphere connected with the electroscope.

to the neck on the inside and outside with tinfoil. The outer coat is earth connected. The inner coat is connected with a metal rod held in the neck. The metal rod usually has a knob at its free end, and this can be charged by repeated application of the metal collector of the electrophorus or any other "electrical machine."

To generate large frictional charges, various types of machines had been designed on the same lines as that of von Guericke by his successors. If we go on rubbing two bodies (e.g. a rod of glass and a piece of silk) beyond a certain point no increase of electrification takes place. That is to say, the attractive power is not increased. A crackling sound is heard indicating that further increase is checked by sparking, which allows electric charges to escape. The problem of generating powerful electrification is therefore to let one of the bodies discharge into a conductor of *high capacity*, and to let the other discharge to earth at the same time. How this is done in frictional machines which evolved from that of von Guericke is illustrated by a type

ike Winter's, which can be made with a gramophone record (Fig. 319). The
lcollector of high capacity is a metal knob (A) connected with a pair of metallic
combs, the points of which nearly touch the vulcanite (or glass disc). When
the latter is charged to the limit sparking occurs between the disc and points,
and the collector becomes charged. The disc rotates against a pad of silk or
flannel, which is rubbed with an amalgam (liquid alloy) of mercury and zinc
or tin. This clings to the pad, which is earthed, and carries off the charge to
earth.

When the collector is fully charged bright sparks can be obtained when
the finger or any earthed conductor is brought up to it, and the sparking
continues at regular intervals as long as the machine rotates. If the knob (B)

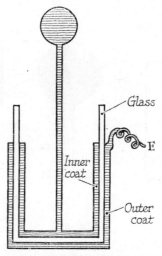

FIG. 318.—SECTION OF A LEYDEN JAR SHOWING THE TWO METAL COATS

of the earthed conductor is brought very near to that of the collector small
sparks follow in rapid succession. If it is withdrawn to a greater distance the
sparks occur at much greater intervals, but they are more bright and more
noisy. Since greater brightness of the spark may be regarded as a sign of more
intense electrification, this means that more intense electrification is required
to break down the insulating power of a long column than to break down
that of a small column of air in the spark gap, and that it takes an appreciable
time to reach the intensity at which sparking occurs. Thus if the gap were
closed by a metal wire the intensity produced would be negligible and
electrification would be dissipated as quickly as it was produced. If the width
of the spark gap is kept the same, and the connector is connected by a wire
with the knob of a Leyden jar whose outer coat is earthed, sparks occur at
longer intervals and are much brighter and louder than before. Also powerful
shocks are obtained by touching the collector. If, when there is no conductor
near the collector to permit sparking, the wire connecting it to the Leyden
jar is disengaged with a glass rod or other insulator, a powerful shock can

still be obtained by touching the knob of the latter. Hence the condenser acts as a *store of electrification,* just as water added to a kettle at the same temperature as itself acts as a store of heat.

Thus every specific feature of a thunderstorm could now be imitated in the laboratory. The rapid progress which ensued after the discovery of the Leyden jar was fostered by the fact that it provided a new instrument of chemical research at a time when chemical industry was emerging and

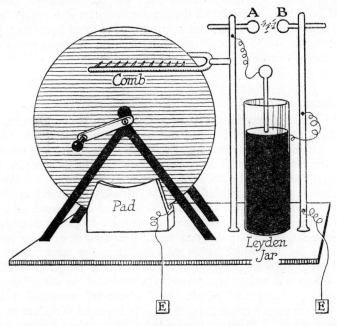

FIG. 319

A simple frictional machine, which can be made out of Meccano parts and a gramophone record. The pad may be flannel on which an amalgam of mercury and zinc is rubbed to conduct away the charge acquired by rubbing against the vulcanite disc by an earthed conductor. When the charge on the disc reaches a certain intensity sparking occurs across the metal comb charging up the conductor A which is mounted on an insulating stand. If B is earthed sparks will occur if the gap AB is small enough. The size of the sparks and the interval between them are increased by inserting the two coats of a Leyden jar across the spark gap.

chemical discovery was progressing rapidly. Priestley demonstrated to a group of his friends the explosion of a mixture of hydrogen and oxygen with a spark from a frictional machine in 1776. Following this clue, in 1781 Cavendish established the composition of water by showing that an electric spark introduced by wires into a closed vessel containing a mixture of "one measure of oxygen with two measures of inflammable air" (hydrogen) produces pure water with no residue. Four years later the great French chemist Berthollet showed that repeated sparking resolves ammonia into its constituent elements, hydrogen and nitrogen.

The ideology of the encyclopaedists also created a favourable atmosphere for further enquiry. The novelty of the shock excited the attention of the physiologist, chiefly perhaps because it raised in a new form a question which had been debated by the French materialist La Mettrie. In everyday life we speak as if death were a quite abrupt change which involves the whole organism. During the first half of the eighteenth century La Mettrie pointed out in *L'Homme Machine* that this is not invariably true. A decapitated fowl which is legally dead may continue to run about for a short while. Clearly the lawyer's definition of the quick and the dead might profit by further elaboration. Since any of the detached muscles of a freshly decapitated frog can be made to contract over a period of many hours by application of electric shocks, experiments with electrical machines showed that death occurs piecemeal, as La Mettrie had argued.

THE ELECTRIC BATTERY

In the course of experiments on frogs, Galvani, an Italian biologist, made a fortuitous observation which had vast and unforeseeable results. Galvani showed that the muscles of the leg of a freshly "killed" frog will contract if touched simultaneously with two different metals, e.g. a piece of zinc and a piece of copper. There is no need to traverse the course of subsequent investigations which quickly led up to the discovery of the cell or battery. It is enough to say that the same result is obtained if we touch a nerve or muscle with the free ends of two wires of the same metal, when their opposite ends are connected to two different metals immersed in a watery solution of salt (like the fluid which bathes the body tissues) or other "electrolyte" (*vide* p. 467). Such an arrangement is called a cell. To get powerful and reliable effects it is better to use several cells connected "in series," that is to say, having an "electrode" of one metal in one cell connected with the electrode of the other metal in the next cell. The invention of such an arrangement of cells called a "battery" was made by Volta, also an Italian scientist, in the closing years of the eighteenth century. Volta's battery or "pile" consisted of circular discs of copper, zinc, and cloth pads soaked in dilute sulphuric acid, arranged in the order copper, acid, zinc, copper, acid, zinc, copper, acid, zinc, etc. With many such plates powerful sparks and shocks could be obtained when wires from the end plates of copper and zinc were brought together.

With Volta's pile, or any other battery in which different elements (zinc and copper, zinc and carbon, etc.) are bathed in a solution of electrolytes, a group of new phenomena were encountered. The same word electrical was applied to them, partly because the spark and the shock were now identified with its use, and also because the sparks and shocks obtained with the battery are only produced by connecting the terminals with conductors such as metal wire. As a matter of fact, many years elapsed before it was possible to prove that all the phenomena produced by an electrical machine can be obtained with a battery, or, conversely, that all the phenomena which are characteristic of a battery can be demonstrated with an electrical machine.

The first of the new phenomena was the discovery that bubbles of gas are produced when the free ends of wires connected with the terminals of a Volta pile are immersed in water. In 1800 two British chemists, Nicholson and Carlisle, accomplished the decomposition of water into its elements by means of the electric "current," a demonstration soon followed by Davy's discovery of the light metals. Till then the study of electrical phenomena had produced no results of great social importance. Henceforth it participated in the new impetus which theoretical chemistry received from the growth of new chemical industries.

The production of sparks and shocks by frictional machines had been

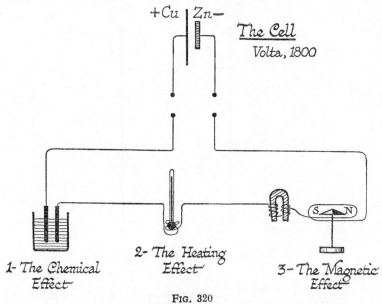

FIG. 320

Diagram showing the principal phenomena of "current electricity."

abrupt and discontinuous. The chemical decomposition produced by a battery is steady, and this is also true of another effect. Heat is produced by a frictional machine when the insulating power of the air is momentarily broken down and a sparking discharge occurs. If the terminals of a battery are connected a steady production of heat is maintained in the wire. For the maintenance of this continuous output of heat and chemical change the word "*current electricity*," in contradistinction to "*frictional electricity*," came into use. The significance of the metaphor will be examined in detail later on.

The second characteristic of current electricity, like the first, led almost immediately to important chemical novelties. About three years after the discovery of the light metals in 1810, Davy observed that a spark from a powerful battery (upwards of two hundred cells) could be maintained between two sticks of charcoal. When the carbon rods are brought close together, the spark causes minute white-hot particles to fly across the gap creating a conducting medium. Once this is established the rods can be drawn apart as far as four inches while still maintaining a brilliantly luminous and continuous spark. With this first arc lamp, such as is still used in magic lanterns, Davy lighted his lecture room at the Royal Institution. In the worn-

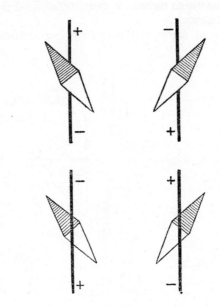

Motion of a magnet in electric field

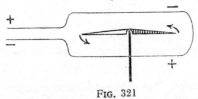

FIG. 321

The deflection of a magnetic needle when a current flows below it or above it through a wire placed along the magnetic meridian. The North Pole is shaded.

out crater at the ends of the carbon rods, he was able to melt platinum, quartz, sapphire, lime, and other substances which had hitherto defied the power of heat. He also succeeded in burning diamonds. This led to the discovery that diamond is elementary carbon.

Ten years later a third group of phenomena of immense importance were discovered on the continent by Oersted and Ampère. Oersted found that a magnetic needle suspended in the neighbourhood of a wire connected with the terminals of a battery is deflected out of its normal orientation along the magnetic meridian. Thus a wire conveying a current has magnetic properties. This observation was followed by the discovery that a piece of iron round which a coil of wire is wound behaves as a magnet while the wire is connected at its ends with the terminals of a battery. Thus a magnet can be made and destroyed by simply turning a switch (Fig. 322) which completes or breaks the circuit of conducting material. A piece of iron mounted on a spring which allows it to move towards another piece when the latter is magnetized by an electric current can itself be made into a switch so that every time it moves contact is broken and attraction ceases. When attraction

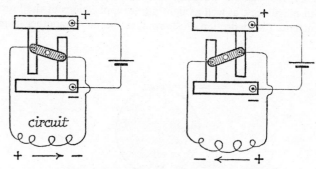

Reversing Switch (commutator)

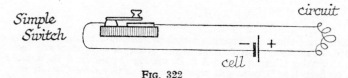

FIG. 322

A simple lever switch (below) for turning a current on and off, and a reversing switch which also changes the direction of a current. Insulating material shaded.

ceases it springs back, remaking contact, and so buzzes to and fro. This is the principle of the electric bell or buzzer (Fig. 324).

FOUNDATIONS OF ELECTRICAL INDUSTRY

These empirical discoveries relating to the phenomena of current electricity lend themselves readily to the invention of a variety of devices. Like the earliest steam engines, such inventions did not in themselves require an elaborate basis of theoretical knowledge. Theory emerged from the needs of practice. Chemical materials of guaranteed purity and economy of output demanded a theoretical basis, when chemical manufacture began to extend. So it was with electricity. Once such inventions had become articles of economic importance, how to produce a guaranteed product and how to achieve economical design, each raised a host of new theoretical issues. In the social context of expanding manufacture—especially in America—manufacturers were more disposed to acquire patent rights and exploit inventions, which now multiplied with astonishing rapidity. The chemical effect was soon adapted for commercial purposes in electroplating, which consists of decomposing the salt of one metal so that particles of metal are deposited on another piece of metal connected with one of the poles of a battery, just as bubbles of hydrogen collect at one "pole" when water is decomposed. As early as 1845 Wright's arc lamp was used to light the streets of Baltimore. Swan and Edison independently made the carbon filament lamp about the year 1879. In contemporary life electric welding, electric cooking, and the electric furnace used in metallurgy, as well as lighting, are applications of the heating effect of the current. The deflection of the compass needle by another magnet

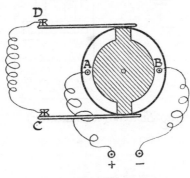

FIG. 323

A simple commutator or reversing switch worked by a handle. Insulating material shaded. As drawn no current flows in the circuit. A slight clockwise turn connects B to C, making C negative, and A to D, making D positive. A slight anti-clockwise turn connects B to D, making D negative, and A to C, making C positive.

had been suggested as a means of signalling in the seventeenth century. While only permanent magnets were available magnetic signalling remained, like so many of the known electrical and magnetic phenomena of the age, a "marvel of science" or more briefly a toy. The possibility of making or destroying magnetic attraction by switching on or switching off a current now made it a practicable device for transmitting messages over long distances.

The discoveries of Oersted and Ampère were immediately applied to this end. Ronald devised a telegraph in 1823, and another was made by Cooke and Wheatstone about the same time. The telegraph was taken up by the railways from the start. Crowther tells us

"its practical value was first demonstrated through its assistance in detaining a murderer who was escaping by train to London. It happened that the telegraph had been set up as a demonstration unit at the station where the murderer boarded the train. A description was wired to London, and he was arrested as he got off the train."

The discovery of electromagnetism happened when Western civilization was undergoing a new revolution in transport. In the ensuing decades the telegraph became essential to the great railway systems throughout the United States, and its improvement offered ample scope for inventive ingenuity. Crowther says that when Edison was employed as a telegraphist on the railways in his youth, night operators were required to send hourly signals to show that they were awake. For his personal convenience Edison devised a clock which made time signals automatically. Edison's later inventions sponsored the far-flung trustification of American industry. The telegraph became "the little mother of the Great Trust," and played a decisive rôle in the triumph of the industrial North during the Civil War. The first cable from Britain to the continent was laid in 1851, and by 1865

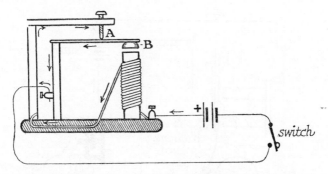

FIG. 324.—PRINCIPLE OF THE MORSE SOUNDER AND ELECTRIC BELL

The current can only flow round the circuit when the switch is pressed if the screw A touches the spring which carries the piece of soft iron B. B is attracted to the iron core of the coil when current flows, forcing down the spring, and so breaking the contact at A. The core then ceases to be a magnet. B springs back and contact is made once more. This goes on as long as the switch is pressed.

cable transmission to America was successfully completed after several attempts beginning in 1857. The earliest telegraphs transmitted signals by deflection of a magnetic needle right or left by reversal of the direction of the current (Fig. 326) with a reversing switch or commutator (Fig. 322). Later the Morse system of signalling by long or short taps with a Morse receiver (Fig. 324) replaced them. Electric motors of the type (see p. 713) first designed on the same principle as the bell and the magnetic crane for lifting steel are further examples of the magnetic phenomena of the current in daily use.

The extensive application of these inventions was limited at first by the fact that current electricity produced by chemical decomposition in the voltaic cell is costly. Until other means of obtaining it were discovered, the use of electricity was therefore restricted to specific purposes for which there were no simple alternatives. In Britain, where the industrial capitalism of the nineteenth century rested on heat as a form of power, heat has con-

tinued to be the main agent of chemical manufacture and of power production. Only during the last fifty years has there been a vastly more efficient
substitute for an economy based on heat. Its extensive exploitation is confined
to countries where vested interests in the pre-existing technology are less
powerful than they are in Britain. We shall come to that in a later
chapter.

FRICTIONAL AND CURRENT ELECTRICITY

It will help us to understand some of the phenomena which we shall meet
later, if we now pause to discuss a question raised earlier. Two of the three
characteristic phenomena exhibited by frictional machines—the production
of sparks and the power to evoke muscular contraction—have been seen to

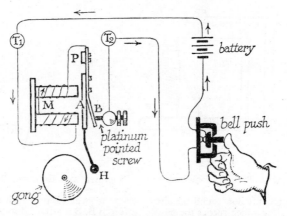

FIG. 325.—THE ELECTRIC BELL

be characteristic of the battery. An additional similarity is that electrical
power from either source can be conveyed by the same classes of substances—
metals and mineral solutions. The most characteristic feature of electrification produced by friction is attractive power, and the two most characteristic
phenomena of the battery are chemical decomposition and the production
of a magnetic field. If the wire from either of the terminals marked on a
battery with the sign + or − is brought near a suspended pith ball or small
fragments of paper no evidence of attraction will be noticed. If wires from
the collector and the unearthed pad of a frictional machine are dipped in a
solution no bubbles are generally noticed, and if the wires are joined there is
no noticeable deflection of a compass needle in the neighbourhood. We are
therefore tempted to conclude that the resemblance between frictional and
current electricity is merely superficial and does not justify the use of the
same word for both.

If we pursue the analogy of flow which proved suggestive in directing
earlier enquiries into thermal equilibrium, there is one circumstance that
helps us to see how a difference might arise between the way in which

electricity is produced. When a conductor like brass is held in the hand, rubbing evokes no display of electrification. If it is insulated by a glass handle, it can be electrified by rubbing just as the insulator itself can. Metaphorically we describe this by saying that when there is no insulator to obstruct its *flow* electrification is conveyed away as quickly as it is produced, and when the *flow* is prevented it accumulates till it reaches a high level of intensity. Experiment shows that when a charged body is touched with an earthed conductor the attraction disappears in the twinkling of an eye. The flow of electricity—to continue the metaphor—is only momentary like the spark. Assuming for the moment that both phenomena are essentially the same, we may therefore draw two provisional conclusions. One is that in the frictional machine the flow of electricity in the spark discharge is of very

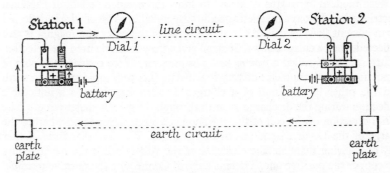

FIG. 326.—TELEGRAPH CIRCUIT

A needle telegraph circuit consists of two magnetic needles mounted on a vertical dial, with electromagnets on either side, two reversing switches, and batteries. Since the current goes through both dials, the operator sees the signal he is transmitting. In 1837 it was discovered that we can dispense with one line if metal plates are sunk deep in the earth which then acts as a sufficiently good conductor.

short duration. The other is that if the pad and the collector are joined by a wire electrification does not amount to a high intensity. So the flow is very slight.

If we make these assumptions two conclusions follow. An ordinary compass needle is heavy. On account of its inertia it needs time in which to move appreciably. If the production of a magnetic field is contingent on the discharge of electricity, the flow must therefore continue for an appreciable time to exert any visible effect. Then again chemical decomposition involves action for some time before it reaches measurable dimensions. Hence we should not expect the momentary discharges obtained by connecting the earth pole and collector of a frictional machine to produce very striking effects. On the other hand, the current which flows through a wire connecting the pad to the collector, when the former is disconnected from earth, may not be sufficiently large to achieve any result unless very sensitive instruments are used. It is quite easy to show both chemical and magnetic effects due to bodies electrified by friction, if we pay attention to these considerations.

A very sensitive indicator of chemical decomposition by the electric current is a strip of paper soaked in a solution of potassium iodide and starch paste. Starch turns deep blue in the presence of iodine liberated by electrolysis, and it is sensitive to extremely minute traces. If the ends of two pieces of wire of very high resistance connected with the collector and pad of a frictional machine are applied to a piece of blotting paper soaked in iodide and starch paste, a blue region is formed round the end of the wire connected with the positively charged conductor. If the generator were a simple voltaic cell with zinc and copper electrodes, the blue colour would appear round the end of the wire attached to the copper plate. For that and other reasons the copper plate is called the positive and the zinc plate the negative electrode of the cell.

With modern apparatus it is easy to show the magnetic effect of frictional electrification. Just as a magnetic needle suspended in a coil of wire is deflected when current flows, a coil free to move between the poles of a magnet is also deflected when a current flows. Such an arrangement can be used for detecting a current, and is called a *moving coil galvanometer*. If we connect one pole of a moving coil galvanometer of very low inertia (i.e. very rapid swing) to earth and the other to the knob of a charged Leyden jar, there is a noticeable deflection during the discharge to earth through the galvanometer circuit. The *initial* direction of the coil of the galvanometer itself depends on whether the charge of the Leyden jar is positive or negative. We have therefore another way of showing that the zinc electrode of the voltaic cell is the negative and the copper the positive one. There is a third. Connecting the positive terminal of a high voltage battery to a sensitive positively charged gold leaf electroscope makes the leaves diverge more.

To demonstrate results comparable to those produced by a flow of a steady current from a dry battery when the generator is a frictional machine, it is important to let the discharge take place slowly through a choke coil of high resistance. Otherwise the surge of current is oscillatory (p. 745) like the contraction of a spring *suddenly* released from tension. It is possible to show this in several ways. For instance, either of two pieces of *low* resistance wire from the terminals of a frictional machine will evoke the blue reaction if we apply them simultaneously to a moist strip of starch-iodide paper.

We can sum up the observed difference between the effects of frictional and current electricity by saying that the former exhibits very powerful momentary (spark or shock) effects or effects (attraction) which do not entail the loss of electrification, while the latter exhibit relatively weak momentary effects or attractions. On the other hand, frictional electrification usually results in very weak effects (magnetic or chemical) which depend on the maintenance of the continuous flow which accompanies chemical (i.e. voltaic) electrification. That there is no incompatibility in their essential identity is easily seen, if we remember what we have learned from the study of heat. Every physical change has two measurable aspects, one which may be described as the intensity factor or potential, the other the capacity factor. A very small change is possible when either of these is large, provided the other is very small. A drop of boiling mercury let fall in a bath of cold water experiences an immense change of thermal potential (temperature). The momentary flow of heat is large, but averaged out over a measurable interval of time it represents a small quantity. A cistern of water at 20° C. emptying rapidly into a half-filled bath at 19° C. till it is full represents a very small change of thermal potential, but a steady flow of heat over a long period; and the change in potential which occurs per unit quantity of matter is actually greater.

An analogous distinction which applies to electrification by friction is

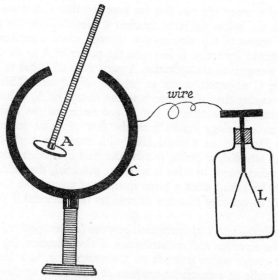

FIG. 327.—FARADAY'S EXPERIMENT TO SHOW THAT THE INDUCED AND INDUCING CHARGES ARE EQUAL AND OPPOSITE

If a charge is induced in the conductor C by the electrified disc A, the leaves of the electroscope remain equally divergent after discharging A by contact with C so that C absorbs all the charge on A.

illustrated by a demonstration first carried out by Faraday and called his "ice pail experiment." To detect electrification an electroscope is connected with a hollow metal conductor (C) mounted on an insulating stand and provided with an aperture at the top through which a small metal disc (A) with an insulating handle can be inserted. To start with, the electroscope is uncharged, and the metal disc A is charged like that of an electrophorus. The experiment may then be carried out as follows:

(i) The disc A is held above and close to the electroscope, the leaves of which diverge widely, and collapse when it is withdrawn.

(ii) It is held carefully inside the conductor C without being allowed to touch it. An opposite charge is induced on the inside of C and the leaves of the electroscope diverge this time *not so widely* as in (i). They collapse when A is withdrawn, since C is not earthed.

(iii) It is again tested by itself, producing more divergence of the leaves of the electroscope than when held inside C. The leaves diverge as widely as in (i).

(iv) It is placed again inside C. The leaves of the electroscope diverge as before (see ii), and they remain in the same position if A touches the surface of C and when A is withdrawn after touching it.

(v) The leaves collapse when the wire connexion is removed and the electroscope earthed. If A is again held over the electroscope and if the surface of A is small compared with that of C it produces no deflection, i.e. it is discharged.

Taking into account the last fact we may say that C becomes as *highly electrified* as A was before the latter touched it. Nevertheless, the power of A to make the leaves of the electroscope diverge when transferred from C through contact or induction is less than the power of A to do so by itself. Regarded as a source of electrification A parts with all it has to C, without conferring on C as much power to produce divergence. This is usually described by saying that after absorbing the charge of A, C has the same charge or quantity of electricity but is not raised to the same *electrical potential*. A close analogy drawn from the flow of water under gravity is illustrated in Fig. 328. In a vessel filled with water the *height* of the fluid determines its *potential*, or power to raise the fluid in another vessel; and the *sectional area* determines to what height, i.e. potential, the fluid content of the vessel can be raised when a given quantity of water flows into it from a tap. The bulk or quantity of water determines the potential if the sectional area is fixed.

So in electrification we can distinguish between (*a*) electrical *potential* which determines the direction and redistribution of electrification, (*b*) quantity of electricity or *charge* which depends on the source (e.g. how long we have turned the handle of a frictional machine or how hard we have rubbed a glass rod), and (*c*) electrical *capacity* which determines how long a source of electrification must be supplied before the potential reaches a particular limit shown by the longer interval between sparking when the two terminals of a Leyden jar or other condenser are connected to those of a frictional machine. The analogy can be pushed farther. A very high pressure head of water will open a spring valve, discharging the contents. So also a limiting potential is reached when further charging results in the breakdown of insulation and an electrical discharge.

Thus frictional electricity is generally associated with high "potential." It can therefore produce intense momentary effects just as a drop of boiling mercury can burn the skin badly though the heating effect on the body as a whole is negligible. On the other hand, battery electricity is not associated with very high potential though its steady character may involve the decomposition of a large quantity of matter. In seeking for a suitable way of measuring electrical output and electrical efficiency, we have first of all therefore to find some way of comparing the intensity level or potential which is *characteristic of the generator*. If the generator is a battery this is sometimes called its electromotive force (E.M.F.). We have also to find some way of measuring the other aspect of electrical change corresponding to thermal capacity. As long as we stick to one kind of matter, thermal capacity is defined in terms of the amount of matter (mass) involved in a thermal change. Similarly, we may take as a criterion of electrical changes the amount of matter decomposed. The amount of matter of a particular kind decomposed in

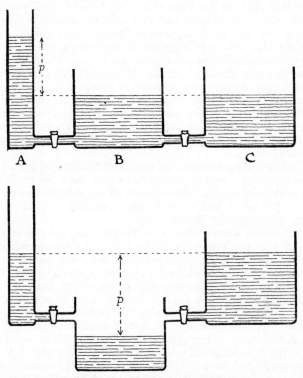

FIG. 328.—FLUID ANALOGY OF ELECTRICAL POTENTIAL, ELECTRICAL CAPACITY AND CHARGE ACQUIRED BY FRICTION

Above.—The *positive* difference of potential *p* between the small vessel A and the large vessel B means that A has the power to raise water in B when the connecting tap is turned on. The difference of potential between the two large vessels B and C is zero, and there will be no flow.

Below.—The potential difference P between A or C and B is the same, but the large quantity of water in C can make B overflow whereas the small quantity in A cannot do so.

unit time corresponds to what is called *current*. The units of potential and current are the *volt* and the *ampère*. By international agreement the volt is chosen so that the E.M.F. of the Weston Standard Cell at 20° C. is 1·0183 volts. By international agreement the ampère is so chosen that 0·001118 gram of silver is liberated in one second from a solution of silver nitrate, when a steady current of 1 ampère passes across the ends of two metal plates dipped in it. In the next chapter we shall see how the voltage of a generator, or the amperage of a circuit in which a current is flowing are measured and why it is useful to do so.

MEASUREMENT OF ATTRACTIONS

The costing of electrical power depends on two ways of measuring it, one by its chemical action, the other by its magnetic effects. In the next two chapters we shall only use the chemical method, because it relies on relatively simple mathematics. On the other hand, the magnetic effects are generally less laborious to record. So there are advantages in using either system of measurement. The chemical system is suggested by analogies which arose naturally out of the pre-existing social context of power production. The magnetic system is based on the earlier mechanics of Newton's period. Although we shall not use it in this book to solve any practical problems, a brief account of the fundamental law of attraction in magnetism and electricity may help to clear up difficulties which the reader may meet in elementary textbooks on the subject. It will also illustrate an important feature of scientific discovery. If it proves difficult, the reader need not be discouraged. The rest of this book does not depend on it.

Fruitful generalizations in science are sometimes the result of piecing together several more restricted rules suggested by direct experiment. Newton's universal gravitation is a rule of this kind. Experiments on falling bodies, on the inclined plane, on the pendulum, and on projectiles, suggested a sequence of simple rules which approximately describe the circumstances of relatively slow terrestrial movements when there is little friction. They are also able to yield results of very high precision when motion occurs in a vacuum without solid contacts. Newton's hypothesis combined them in a more general rule which describes the motions of celestial bodies in empty space. The wave theory of light gave us an example of another way of discovering laws of nature by testing a "hunch" suggested by *analogy*. Scientific laws discovered in this way are liable to mystify us, because books on science do not always explain how the discoverer gets his "hunch." This is particularly true about the law of attractions in magnetism and frictional electricity. The design of experiments first made to test its truth would never occur to anyone, unless he already had a strong disposition to believe it. Confidence of this kind is a common feature of successful experimentation. It is not explained by calling it inspiration, genius, or intuition. On closer examination it is usually seen to be rooted in the social experience and tradition of the scientific worker, the groove in which his intellectual interests run, and the apparatus of symbols which he has been trained to use.

THE INVERSE SQUARE LAW OF MAGNETIC ATTRACTION

The first stage of speculation on the motions of the planets took place when the study of magnetism was beginning; and the analogy of the earth's terrestrial magnetism to the central attraction which keeps the planets moving in curved orbits was raised in the earliest discussions of gravitation by Kepler and his contemporaries. The analogy is not complete, because the pull of terrestrial gravitation applies equally to iron and to non-magnetic substances. So magnetism is not responsible for the motion of the heavenly bodies. Newton's theory attributed the attraction between the planets and the sun to the influence which any piece of matter has on another. This is in direct proportion to its *mass* when the distances are equivalent. Otherwise the effect diminishes in proportion to the square of the distance. Put in symbolic form, with the symbols *m* for one mass, M for the other, D for the distance, and F for the attractive force between their centres it is,

$$F \propto \frac{mM}{D^2}$$

or, if G is a constant for all circumstances of gravitational pull

$$F = G \frac{mM}{D^2} {}^\star$$

In Newton's theory the force exerted on 1 unit of mass by a body of mass M is

$$G \cdot \frac{M}{D^2}$$

This is called the *strength* of the gravitational field at any point on the surface of a sphere of radius D about the centre of M. Newton's followers, who devoted themselves to elaborating the theory of gravitation, introduced a number of such measures for mapping out the intensity of a gravitational field.

When the study of attractions took a new turn at the end of the eighteenth century, scientific workers were therefore accustomed to think of attractions in terms of the inverse square law, and mathematicians had elaborated a variety of ways in which a law of this type can be tested. Though it may not be the first rule which we ourselves would test, it was the first one which they would try out. This being so, the apparently devious route by which the truth of the law is established as a basis for measuring magnetic phenomena was not such a miraculous process of guesswork as a formal statement of the reasoning involved would tempt us to believe. Calculating devices, such as "surface density," "potential," and "field strength," were introduced into the study of frictional charges and magnetic attractions by analogy with corresponding ones in the mathematical elaboration of Newton's theory. All that remained was to adapt one or another aspect of the theory to the limitations of experiment. The chief limitation imposed on experiment by the nature of magnetic phenomena is that two opposite kinds of attraction are inseparable.

In magnetic as in gravitational attractions crude experiments show that we have to deal with two different aspects of force. For instance, one and the same magnet placed at right angles to the magnetic meridian deflects the same compass needle more when it is moved nearer to it, and less when it is moved further away. This shows that the attraction depends on *distance*. On the other hand, different magnets of the same size placed in the same positions may produce very different deflections. At the same distance apart some magnets are stronger than others, just as large masses have more attractive power than small ones. We may express this by saying that the *magnetic power* of one magnet is greater than that of another.

The next thing is to decide how to measure this magnetic power. If magnetic attractions were of one kind only we should be tempted to test out a law of

---

* Since F is 981 dynes per gram at the earth's surface (see p. 258), and the distance of the latter from the earth's centre is $6 \cdot 35 \times 10^8$ cm., and from experiments like that shown diagrammatically in Fig. 189 the mass of the earth is found to be $5 \cdot 94 \times 10^{27}$ grams, the value of G in the international system of grams and centimetres is

$$\frac{(6 \cdot 35)^2 \times 10^{16} \times 981}{5 \cdot 94 \times 10^{27}} = 6 \cdot 66 \times 10^{-8}$$

force in which m_a and m_b would stand for the magnetic power (called their *pole strengths*) of two poles in the formula

$$F = K \frac{m_a m_b}{D^2}$$

If we define pole strength by saying that the repulsive force of a pole of pole strength m_a on one of pole strength m_b is $m_a m_b$ dynes when they are 1 cm. apart, the constant K analogous to G must be unity, so we can rewrite the formula

$$F = \frac{m_a m_b}{D^2}.$$

The *field strength* of a pole m on a pole of unit strength will then be $m \div D^2$.

To carry the analogy further we have to take account of another fact. Except in so far as direction is concerned, a magnetized bar of iron has the same pulling power at both ends. For instance, the weight of unmagnetized iron which each end can just hold against gravity does not sensibly differ if the shape and material is fixed. The angular deflection produced by a bar magnet placed at right angles to the meridian in either of the arrangements relative to the compass shown in Fig. 332 is numerically the same, though opposite in direction, when north and south poles are reversed. The pulling power of the two poles is therefore equal in quantity and *opposite in direction*. Since we can represent movement in opposite directions by opposite signs, we must call the pole strength of the south-seeking pole $-m_a$ if we call that of the north-seeking pole of the same magnet $+m_a$. According to the gravitation analogy the force between two north poles $+m_a$, $+m_b$ at 1 cm. apart would then be $+m_a m_b$, the force between two south poles $-m_a$, $-m_b$ at 1 cm. apart would be $-m_a \times -m_b = +m_a m_b$, and the force between a south pole $-m_a$ and a north pole $+m_b$, or a north pole $+m_a$ and a south pole $-m_b$ at a distance of 1 cm. would be $-m_a \times +m_b = +m_a \times -m_b = -m_a m_b$. Hence the negative sign indicates a force of attraction (unlike poles), and the positive sign indicates a force of repulsion (like poles).

We cannot yet go straight ahead to test the inverse square law in a form suitable for measuring magnetic phenomena by some simple method. You might think that this could be done by investigating the lifting power of a bar magnet at different distances. There are several reasons why this would not be convenient. Iron is heavy, and the distance at which a visible piece of iron can be lifted—except by very powerful magnets—is small. The results obtained at different places would not be comparable, because the dipping needle shows us that the earth's own magnetism has a vertical component. It is therefore better to set about it in another way. The angular deflection of a compass needle is easy to measure accurately, and its behaviour is therefore chosen to test the truth of the rule.

When a very small magnet such as a compass needle is free to rotate in a magnetic field equal and opposite forces act on its two poles. A pair of equal, parallel, and opposite forces pulling on either side of a fulcrum makes a lever rotate, unless it is balanced by a similar pair. In mechanics such pairs are called *couples*. The product formed by multiplying one of the equal and opposite forces with the perpendicular distance between them is called the *moment* of the couple, and two couples balance when their moments are equal and opposite (Fig. 329). If a compass needle is placed in the earth's field (Fig. 330), a couple acts on the two poles except when it lies along the meridian. When it does so, the couple is zero, and the needle can only be at rest when this is so. Fig. 330 shows that if the horizontal component of the earth's field is H, and the pole strength and length of the magnet between the poles are m and $2L$ respectively, then the moment acting on the magnet when it is deflected through an angle a is $2mLH \sin a$.

In practice the position of the poles is rather indefinite, so that it is impossible to determine m or $2L$ exactly. The product $2mL$ or *magnetic moment* (M) of

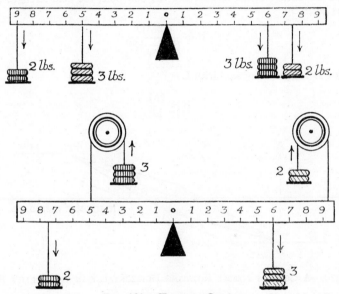

FIG. 329.—TURNING COUPLE

The law of the lever is that (a) a pair of weights pulling in the same direction on opposite sides of the fulcrum, or (b) a pair of weights pulling in opposite directions on the same side of the fulcrum, balance when the product of the weight and its distance from the fulcrum is the same for each pair. In the upper figure a weight 2 lb. 9 inches left of the fulcrum balances a weight of 3 lb. 6 inches right of the fulcrum ($2 \times 9 = 18 = 3 \times 6$) and a weight of 3 lb. 5 inches left balances a weight of 2 lb. $7\frac{1}{2}$ inches right ($3 \times 5 = 15 = 2 \times 7\frac{1}{2}$). In the lower figure 3 lb. 5 inches left pulling the lever up balances 2 lb. $7\frac{1}{2}$ inches left pulling it down, and 3 lb. 6 inches right pulling down balances 2 lb. 9 inches right pulling the lever up. The two 3 lb. weights constitute a turning *couple* which would make the lever rotate clockwise if they were not balanced by the two 2 lb. weights tending to make it rotate anti-clockwise. The law of the balance for two couples (i.e. equal weights pulling in parallel and opposite directions) is that they balance if their *moments* are equal and opposite. The moment of a couple is the product of either of the equal weights and the perpendicular distance between them. Thus the moment of the 3 lb. couple is 3 ($5 + 6$) = 33. The moment of the 2 lb. couple is 2 ($7\frac{1}{2} + 9$) = 33. In more general terms, neglecting signs, the principle of the lever is that if two weights m and M, on opposite sides situated at distances d and D from the fulcrum, balance

$$md = MD$$

If another identical pair weights M and m, suspended over pulleys, also balance at distances S and s on opposite sides of the fulcrum,

$$MS = ms$$

Hence
$$md + ms = MD + MS$$
$$m(d + s) = M(D + S)$$

a magnet can however be determined, and may be defined as the couple that would act on the magnet when placed at right angles to a field of unit strength, so that sin a and H are both unity.

The field strength F at a given point is the resultant force exerted at that point, on a pole of unit strength, by the attraction and repulsion of the two poles of the magnet. Fig. 331 shows how to calculate the value of F in two positions. In position (a) the unit pole is in line with the two poles of the magnet. If M is the magnetic moment of the magnet and D is the distance between the middle of the magnet and the unit pole, the field strength at the latter is given by

$$F = \frac{2MD}{(D^2 - L^2)^2}$$

or where D is great compared with L

$$F = \frac{2M}{D^3}$$

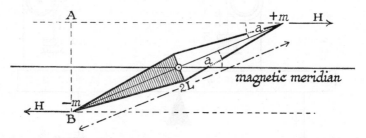

FIG. 330.—A COMPASS NEEDLE ROTATING HORIZONTALLY IN THE EARTH'S FIELD

If H is the horizontal force of the earth's magnetism on unit pole strength, the ends of the needle of pole strength m and $-m$ are pulled (in opposite directions) by forces Hm and $-$ Hm respectively. These forces are numerically equal, and act in parallel and opposite directions. So they constitute a couple like a pair of weights referred to in Fig. 329. The moment of the couple is mH(AB) $= 2m$LH . sin a, where L is half the distance between the poles. There will be no rotation when the moment of the couple is zero, i.e. when AB is zero. That is to say, the balanced position is along the meridian. If shifted from this a couple comes into play restoring the *status quo*.

In position (b), where the axis is at right angles to the line joining the centre of the bar magnet to the unit pole, the field strength is given by

$$F = \frac{M}{(D^2 + L^2)^{\frac{3}{2}}}$$

or where D is great compared with L

$$F = \frac{M}{D^3}$$

We can compare the field due to a magnet with that due to the earth by placing the magnet at right angles to the magnetic meridian and measuring the deflection of a suspended magnetic needle placed in one of the two positions in Fig. 326. In either case we find (Fig. 331) that

$$F = H \tan a$$

In position (a)

$$F = \frac{2M}{D^3} \text{ (approx.)} = H \tan a$$

$$\therefore \quad \frac{M}{H} = \frac{D^3}{2} \tan a$$

In position (b)

$$F = \frac{M}{D^3} \text{ (approx.)} = H \tan a$$

$$\therefore \quad \frac{M}{H} = D^3 \tan a$$

We can use either of these formulae to test the law of inverse squares or to compare the magnetic moment of two magnets, if the law is taken to be correct. To test it we have merely to observe the angular deflections (a_1 and a_2) of the

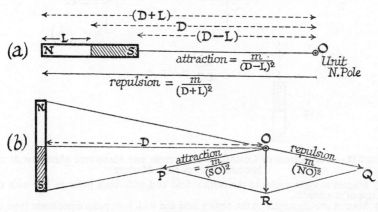

FIG. 331

These two diagrams show how to calculate the strength of the field exerted by a bar magnet on unit pole, assuming that the inverse square law is correct. In position (a) the total force acting on unit pole at O is

$$\frac{m}{(D-L)^2} - \frac{m}{(D+L)^2} = \frac{4mLD}{(D^2-L^2)^2} = \frac{2MD}{(D^2-L^2)^2}$$

In position (b) the attractive force may be represented by $OP = \frac{m}{(SO)^2}$, and the repulsive force by $OQ = \frac{m}{(NO)^2}$. The resultant force is OR, parallel to the magnet.

Since OQR and ONS are similar, $\dfrac{OR}{OQ} = \dfrac{NS}{NO}$.

$$\therefore \quad OR = F = \frac{NS \cdot OQ}{NO} = \frac{m \cdot NS}{(NO)^3} = \frac{M}{(NO)^3}$$

But $(NO)^2 = D^2 + L^2$

$$\therefore \quad F = \frac{M}{(D^2 + L^2)^{\frac{3}{2}}}$$

needle in position (*a*) when the distances of the middle of the magnet from the pivot are D_1 and D_2. In this position the approximate formula gives

$$\frac{D_1^3}{2} \tan a_1 = \frac{D_2^3}{2} \tan a_2$$

$$\frac{D_1^3}{D_2^3} = \frac{\tan a_2}{\tan a_1}$$

This conclusion is true if the law of inverse squares is true, and if the experiment shows that it is true the law of inverse squares may be used. To test the law more severely we should use the formula in its original form and use other

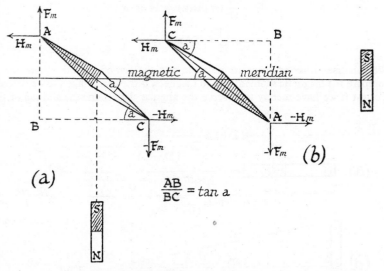

FIG. 332.—DEFLECTION OF COMPASS NEEDLE FROM THE MAGNETIC MERIDIAN IN THE NEIGHBOURHOOD OF A MAGNET

(*a*) Magnet at right angles to the earth's field and with both poles in line with the centre of the needle.

(*b*) Magnet at right angles to the earth's field and with both poles equidistant from the centre of the needle. If m and $- m$ are the pole strengths of the needle, F the field strength of the magnet, and H the horizontal component of the earth's field, the couple due to the magnet is $Fm \cdot BC$ and the couple due to the earth is $Hm \cdot AB$ in the opposite sense. If the needle comes to rest at an angle a from the magnetic meridian, the two couples balance, i.e. $Fm \cdot BC = Hm \cdot AB$

$$F = H \cdot \frac{AB}{BC} = H \cdot \tan a$$

The value of F in position (*a*) will of course be double that in position (*b*) if the distances from the centre of the magnet are the same.

positions of the magnet as well. This does not affect the conduct of the experiment. It merely makes the calculation a little more laborious. Alternatively we may first place the magnet in the position indicated in the upper diagram of Fig. 331, and then in the position indicated in the lower one, keeping D the same. The field strength at the pivot of the compass needle when the bar magnet is in the first position is twice as great as it is when in the second position. If a_1 is the angular deflection in the first and a_2 in the second position, the approximate formulae show that

$$\tan a_1 = 2 \tan a_2$$

According to the approximate formulae the relative magnetic moments (M_1 and M_2) of two magnets placed in the same position at the same distance from the needle which settles at an angle a_1 from the meridian for one and a_2 for the other are

$$\frac{M_1}{M_2} = \frac{\tan a_1}{\tan a_2}$$

All we can get by the method set forth in Fig. 331 is the ratio (M/H) of the magnetic moment of a bar magnet to the horizontal intensity of the earth's field at the place where we make the observation. To determine H alone or M alone we have to employ another method set forth below. Given a value for H at one and the same location, the evaluation of M is merely a matter of simple arithmetic; and if we know the absolute value of M for any one bar magnet, we can use it as a standard to evaluate that of any other by recourse to the $M_1 : M_2$ ratio determined as above. The same method which permits us to evaluate this ratio or to put the inverse square law to the test of experiment, also permits us to get a value for the equivalent length (2L) of a bar magnet. Hence if we know the absolute value of M by recourse to the method we shall deal with next, we can evaluate m the pole strength from the formula: $M = 2mL$.

To determine the ratio M/H it suffices to use the approximate value $\frac{1}{2}D^3\tan a$ based on the deflection a at an *end-on* distance D which is large compared with L. At one and the same measured distance D, the more exact formula for M/H in the two positions respectively shown in Fig. 331 involves L, which we do not know, D which we can measure directly and the corresponding observable deflections a_1 and a_2:

(a) $H \tan a_1 = F_1 = 2MD \div (D^2 - L^2)^2$ $\quad \therefore \frac{M}{H} = \frac{(D^2 - L^2)^2}{2D} \tan a$

(b) $H \tan a_2 = F_2 = M \div (D^2 + L^2)^{3/2}$ $\quad \therefore \frac{M}{H} = (D^2 + L^2)^{3/2} \tan a_2$

We can combine these two relations in a single formula containing only the one unknown L:

$$(D^2 - L^2)^2 . \tan a_1 = 2D(D^2 + L^2)^{3/2} . \tan a_2.$$

From the separate deflections a_1 and a_2 respectively obtained when we place the centre of the magnet at a distance D end-on and at right angles to the meridian, we can thus determine L.

Determination of the value of H.—The *magnetometer* method described above permits us to determine: (1) the *relative* values of the *moment* ($M = 2mL$) of any two magnets; (ii) the ratio (M/H) of M to the horizontal force of the earth's field on a pole of unit strength; (iii) the absolute value of 2L the distance between the poles of any one magnet. To determine the pole strength of a magnet we need to know the absolute value of M for some particular magnet we take as our yardstick of relative values of magnetic moments, or—what comes to the same thing—the absolute value of H at a place where we have determined the ratio M/H for a standard magnet. A method of doing this depends on the restraining force the earth's fields exerts on a suspended magnet free to oscillate in a horizontal plane.

If subjected to a sideways jerk, a bar hanging from a filament executes a *periodic* swing horizontally, as a bar suspended from a spring executes a periodic swing in the vertical plane when subjected to a jerk downwards. The law of elastic resistance to a twist is in fact analogous to the law of vertical stretch (p. 292). The restoring force in the direction of displacement is directly propor-

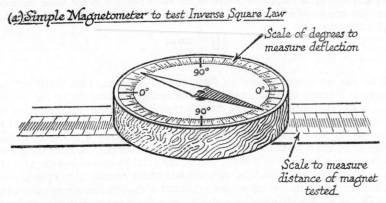

(a) Simple Magnetometer to test Inverse Square Law

Scale of degrees to measure deflection

90°

0°   0°

90°

Scale to measure distance of magnet tested

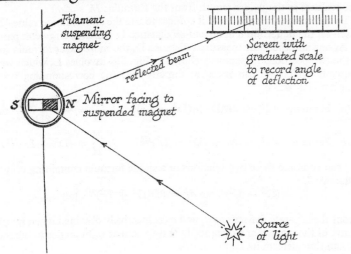

(b) Sensitive Magnetometer with Filament Suspension

Filament suspending magnet

reflected beam

Screen with graduated scale to record angle of deflection

S   N   Mirror facing to suspended magnet

Source of light

FIG. 333.—THE MAGNETOMETER

tional to the angle of twist, and hence the force on any particle supported in the horizontal plane (Fig. 334) is directly proportional to the distance through which it undergoes displacement from its equilibrium position. This we have seen is the law of motion (p. 282) of bodies oscillating with a periodic time T. If a particle of a bar situated at a distance L from the point of suspension has a mass w, a twist through an angle d (radians) from its equilibrium thus invokes a restoring force (Fig. 334) equivalent to:

$$w\text{L}\left(\frac{2\pi}{\text{T}}\right)^2 . d$$

The corresponding moment of this restoring force is:

$$wL^2\left(\frac{2\pi^2}{T}\right).d.$$

For all the particles which make up the bar, the resultant couple is the product of: (i) the total of all quantities defined by wL^2, i.e. the moment of Inertia I (p. 612) of the bar itself; (ii) the common factor $4\pi^2 d \div T^2$. Thus the moment of the turning couple of a suspended bar free to move in the horizontal plane is: $I \cdot 4\pi^2 d \div T^2$. If the bar is a magnet, twisted through d radians from its position of equilibrium in the magnetic meridian, it is subject to a restoring couple MH sin d (Fig. 330) in virtue of the earth's field. If d is small, this is approximately MH d. The couple required to jerk the magnet from its equilibrium position through a twist d is equivalent to the couple due to the elastic recoil of the filament from which it hangs. Thus

$$\text{MH } d = I \cdot 4\pi^2 \cdot d \div T^2$$

$$\therefore \quad T = 2\pi\sqrt{I \div MH}$$

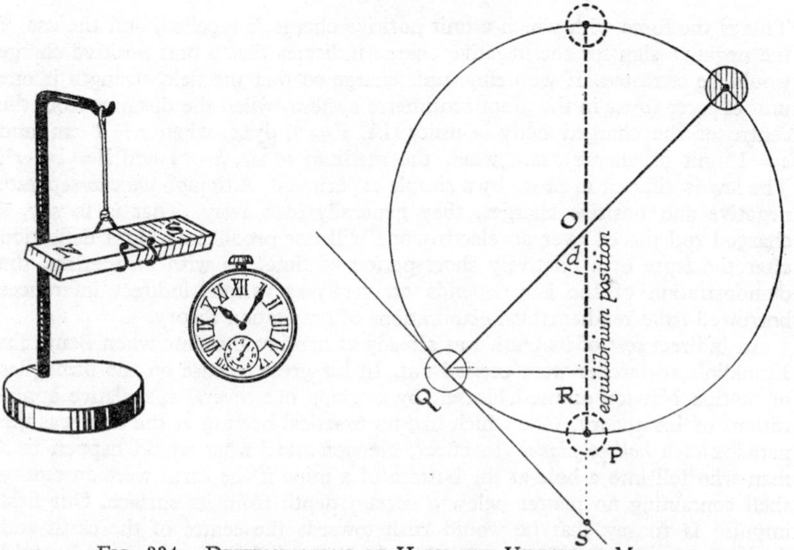

FIG. 334.—DETERMINATION OF H BY THE VIBRATION METHOD

This depends on the restraint the earth's field exerts on the periodic oscillation of a bar magnet in a horizontal plane. Consider a single particle of mass w at equilibrium in the position at a distance OP = L = OQ from the point of suspension. When twisted through d radians to Q it brings into play the elastic resistance of the filament. The force of a jerk in the direction of its *line of motion* (QS) is directly proportional to d, i.e. $f = Kd$; and if d is small, d differs inappreciably from tan d, so that we may put f = K tan d = K . QS $\div$ L. Along the line QR = x this is equivalent to a force $\frac{QR}{QS}.f$

$=\frac{K}{L}$. QR. Now the force is measured by the product of the moving mass (w) and the acceleration (a) imparted to it. Along the line x the equivalent force is $w\ a_x$, so that $a_x = \frac{K}{wL}$. x. With reference to an axis (x) in line with (or parallel to) QR, the acceleration imparted is therefore directly proportional to the displacement. Hence the motion (p. 282) is periodic; and $a_x = \left(\frac{2\pi}{T}\right)^2 x$. Hence K $\div wL = (2\pi \div T)^2$ and:

$$\text{K} = wL \cdot (2\pi \div T)^2.$$

Y

By observing T the period of swing of a suspended magnet whose moment of inertia (I) we can calculate (p. 614) from its dimensions we can therefore estimate the product MH, which we may call A. By the magnetometer method described earlier, we can determine the ratio M/H (which we may call B) for the same magnet at the same location. From determinations of both A and B we can derive the absolute values of either M or H, since $M^2 = AB$ and $H^2 = A/B$.

THE INVERSE SQUARE LAW OF ELECTRICAL ATTRACTIONS

A law identical with the law of gravitational or magnetic attractions also holds good for electrical attractions, if we substitute e representing "charge" or "quantity" of electricity for m or quantity of matter, and k for the gravitation constant in the Newtonian formula. The field strength due to a charged body is then

$$\frac{ke}{r^2}$$

This is the force with which a unit positive charge is repelled, and the use of the negative sign for the negative charge indicates that a unit positive charge would be attracted. If we define unit charge so that the field strength is one unit of force (*dyne* in the gram centimetre system) when the distance from the centre of the charged body is unity (i.e. $F = 1$ dyne, when $r = 1$ cm. and $e = 1$ unit of charge), and when the medium is air, $k = 1$ and $F = e \div r^2$. The law is difficult to prove by a simple experiment. Although we can separate negative and positive charges, they generally leak away. That is to say, a charged rod placed over an electroscope will not produce as big a deflection after the lapse of a relatively short period of time. As with magnetism, the demonstration of the law depends on verifying various indirect inferences borrowed from mathematical elaborations of gravitation theory.

An indirect test of its truth was already at hand at the time when Benjamin Franklin's researches were carried out. In his great treatise on the principles of motion Newton amused himself by working out several speculative applications of his theory. One which had no practical bearing at the time was the paradox of a *hollow planet*. In effect, Newton asked what would happen to a man who fell into a hole at the bottom of a mine if the earth were an empty shell containing no matter below a certain depth from its surface. Our first impulse is to say that he would rush towards the centre of the earth and then come to a stop. On second thoughts we recollect that his speed would carry him beyond it till the opposing attraction reversed his direction, setting up a to-and-fro motion. Neither of these conclusions is consistent with Newton's theory. The surprising thing about gravitation is that the man should not fall, when he stepped through the hole. He would have no acceleration. So if he jumped he would sail steadily through the void at a comfortable fixed speed.

Newton's argument can be followed with the help of Fig. 335, which shows a spherical shell of uniform density, so that the masses M and m of any two small circular patches on its surface are proportional to their areas A and a (i.e. $M : m = A : a$). If the patches are small ones we can consider them to be flat, as we should consider the areas covered by New York and Cape Town to be flat. We can therefore imagine that each is the base of a cone with the common vertex at P, where our imaginary miner is situated, and will remain stuck unless the mass of the patch of earth (A) covered by New York City pulls him harder than the patch of earth covered by Cape Town (or *vice versa*).

Both these cones have the same vertex, and the areas of the bases of cones with the same vertical angle are proportional to the squares of their heights (R and r). Hence M : m :: R² : r²

$$M = mR^2 \div r^2$$

According to the theory of Newton, New York pulls the miner with a force GM $\div$ R² per unit (body) weight, and Cape Town pulls the miner with a force Gm $\div$ r² per unit (body) weight. Since M = mR² $\div$ r²

$$GM \div R^2 = Gm \div r^2$$

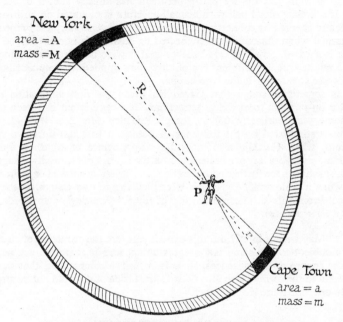

New York
area = A
mass = M

R

P

r

Cape Town
area = a
mass = m

FIG. 335.—THE HOLLOW EARTH PARADOX OF NEWTON

Hence the pull of the patch of earth under New York is exactly the same as the *opposing* pull of the patch of earth under Cape Town. The two pulls cancel one another. So there is no effective pull toward the centre. Because this is equally true of any two corresponding patches, there would be no gravitational pull inside a hollow earth. In other words, the behaviour of the imaginary miner would be the same as if the earth's shell were not made up of matter. The important thing about the hollow earth paradox for the theory of electrical attractions is that this conclusion would not be true if a different law of attractions applied. For instance, we might suppose that matter attracts matter with a force inversely proportional to the cube of the distance. The New York pull would then be GM. $\div$ R³, which would be (GmR² $\div$ r²) $\div$ R³ = Gm $\div$ Rr². This would be different from the Cape Town pull Gm $\div$ r³.

There was a good reason for Newton to bother himself with this imaginary situation. Newton wanted to test the theory that the law of gravitation applies equally to particles of any size. By analogous reasoning, which we need not go into, he came to the conclusion that the miner's behaviour so long as he remained on or above the surface of the hollow earth would be exactly the same as if the earth were solid. That is to say, he would be attracted to it by a pull inversely proportional to the square of the distance *from the centre*. You can therefore look on the earth as an enormous number of layers, each attracting any object outside it with a force inversely proportional to the square of its distance from the same centre, and each exerting no attraction on an object lying inside it.

If applied to electrical attractions, the argument on which the hollow earth paradox is based means that when the outside is electrified, the inside of a hollow spherical conductor behaves as if it had no charge at all. This is very easy to test. In fact the ice pail experiment has already shown us that it is true. If a hollow metal ball with a small aperture is mounted on an insulating stand, and charged by connecting it with a frictional generator, it is immediately discharged when the outside is connected to earth. It is not discharged if the inside is earthed. So the inside behaves as if it were not electrified. Since this would not be true if a different law of attractions applied, we can conclude that the inverse square law is the correct one.

It is sometimes stated that Cavendish made the first application of the Newtonian paradox to electrical attractions. The experiment had been carried out some years earlier (1766) by Joseph Priestley. His interest in electricity had been stimulated by the influence of Benjamin Franklin during a visit to England, when Franklin also made the acquaintance of Matthew Boulton. Franklin, says Miss Turner in her book on the history of electricity, "suggested certain problems for further consideration. . . . Priestley showed experimentally that when a hollow metal vessel is electrified there is no charge on the inner surface. From this he inferred the law of force." Priestley's own words, cited by Miss Turner, are:

"May we not infer from this experiment that the attraction of electricity is subject to the same law as gravitation, and is therefore according to the square of the distances, since it is easily demonstrated that were the earth in the form of a shell, a body in the inside of it would not be attracted to one side more than another."

THINGS TO MEMORIZE

Unit charge is such that when placed at a distance of 1 cm. in air from an equal and similar charge, it repels it with a force of 1 dyne.

Unit field strength is the strength of the field which acts on unit charge with a force of 1 dyne.

The potential difference between two points is unity if one erg of work is done in taking unit charge from one point to the other. One such electrostatic unit of potential is equal to 300 volts.

The *capacity* of a conductor is numerically equal to the charge which must be given to it in order to raise its potential by 1 unit. Hence a conductor of unit capacity has its potential raised by one unit by unit charge. It can be shown that the capacity, in units so defined, of an isolated spherical conductor is numerically equal to the radius in centimetres. Hence the electrostatic unit of capacity is usually called a centimetre. One microfarad (p. 771) is equal to 9×10^5 cm.

CHAPTER XIV

COSTING THE CURRENT

At the end of the third decade of the nineteenth century three powers of the electric battery were well known. It could be used to produce: (*a*) a magnetic field, (*b*) heat sufficient to evoke incandescence, and (*c*) chemical decomposition of metallic salts. The last made it an indispensable part of the chemist's equipment during a period of rapid growth in chemical manufactures which actively encouraged chemical research. The magnetic effect was the first to be exploited commercially. Telegraphy was introduced in the twenties. Its use expanded rapidly in the thirties, more especially in America, where the first electrical invention had been brought into everyday experience. By the end of the fourth decade of the nineteenth century tentative efforts in the commercial exploitation of the heating effect as a source of illumination and of the chemical property of the current as a device for plating with precious or non-corrosive metals made new demands on theoretical guidance.

In its early stages telegraphy raised few fresh problems of far-reaching importance. The extension of the railway system created a new need for rapid communication. No alternative method of signalling over long distances was available. Electricity had no established competitor in the field. For this reason, and also because the expenditure on current by the telegraph was relatively small, the question of costing did not emerge in an acute form until more ambitious undertakings, such as the Atlantic venture, encountered new obstacles. Electric lighting and electroplating had to compete with a pre-existing technique. The aspiring inventor had to count the cost. In short, standards of measurement were indispensable to the commercial exploitation of the heating and chemical properties of the current from the start.

One practical difficulty which beset early experiments in telegraphy was the need for a steady and relatively durable source of current. The first batteries, such as Volta's pile, were seen to be worn down and easily fatigued, or, to use the technical term, *polarized* by bubbles of gas which collected on the metal plates (electrodes). They were therefore replaced by batteries of a more reliable type. Batteries constructed with electrodes immersed in solutions of their own salts do not collect gas bubbles, and are not readily fatigued. In such batteries the two solutions of metal salt are kept apart by enclosing one in a pot of earthenware, sufficiently porous to conduct without much diffusion, except what results from current flow. One type in common use in the first half of the nineteenth century was invented by J. F. Daniell. It had zinc and copper electrodes like those of Volta's pile. The former was immersed in a porous pot containing zinc sulphate solution, and itself immersed in copper sulphate solution contained in a copper vessel which acted as the positive electrode.

The impetus which electrical research received from setbacks to early attempts to establish Transatlantic communication is a story which will be told later in this chapter. Before this happened tentative efforts to use electricity for lighting and plating had been started on a commercial scale, and the economical use of electrical power had been explored with this end in view. The crudest measurements of the chemical or heating action of the electric current bring us face to face with two aspects of electrical phenomena. One depends on the wire used for the circuit. The other depends on the generator. The heat produced in a piece of wire during a fixed interval of time is inversely proportional to its length, and is directly proportional to the square of the number of cells connected *in series* (see p. 699) to make a battery. The heat produced in a uniform piece of wire 1 inch long is three times as great as the heat produced when the terminals of the same battery are connected for the same length of time with a piece of equally thick wire 3 inches long. If the same wire is connected successively with the terminals of a battery of one Daniell cell and with the terminals of a battery of three Daniell cells connected in series (positive to negative) the heat production is increased ninefold.

This rule was first set forth by Joule about the time when arc lighting was introduced in the streets of Baltimore. Joule's experiments on the heat production of the current were part of a wider enquiry which involved the determination of the mechanical equivalent of heat. The social context of the researches which enabled Joule to compare the running costs of a battery and a Cornish engine have been discussed in Chapter XII. This chapter will summarize the main facts about the measurement of current, and will be based on the methods used by Joule and Faraday in the earliest investigations of the heating and chemical properties of the current. In Joule's researches a clear distinction between three kinds of electrical measurements was first made. The units now used, the ampere (current), the volt (potential difference or E.M.F.), and the ohm (resistance) had not yet been settled by international agreement, which did not come about until after the extension of the cable system. When Joule and his contemporaries refer to what we call E.M.F. they do not speak of volts. At that time it was customary to speak of so many *Daniells*, using the name of the generator for the unit itself. So, also when Joule deals with the measurement of what is now called *resistance*, he gives the length of a wire of such and such thickness and material. For our purpose there is nothing to be gained in describing his discoveries in his own words. We shall use the modern terms, and first explain their meaning, illustrating them by simple experiments of the type which Faraday undertook in connexion with his studies (p. 703) on electrochemistry.

It will help us to understand the meaning of the three fundamental units if we pursue a crude analogy suggested by experience of everyday life in the age of water power. It has lost none of its usefulness now that we can no longer subscribe to a literal belief in caloric or the electric fluid of Franklin. The flow of water involves the transference of matter from one place to another at a measurable rate. So also when electrodes of metal connected with the two terminals of a battery or other steady generator are immersed in a dilute solution of an acid, metal is worn away from the positive electrode (anode) and deposited on the negative (kathode). Thus the most direct way of measuring the electric current is to find the weight of a product of chemical decomposition deposited on one or other of the electrodes in unit time.

A paddle or water-wheel will rotate clockwise or anti-clockwise according as the overhead current flows beyond the centre from left to right or right to left. Seen from above, the north seeking pole of a suspended magnet is turned anti-clockwise or clockwise according as a wire placed lengthwise overhead is connected to the negative or positive terminal of the battery at the end beyond the north seeking pole of the compass needle (Fig. 321). Thus the water current and the electric current may respectively be measured by

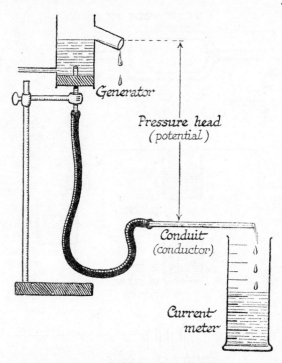

FIG. 336.—POISSEUILLE'S PRINCIPLE

Apparatus for showing how the rate of flow of water varies with the pressure head and resistance of the outflow. The former can be maintained at a constant level by an outflow above, in any position of the "generator." The level can be varied by raising or lowering the generator. Thick or thin, long or short *capillary* tubes can be used for the conduit. The current is measured by the rise of water in a graduated cylinder during an interval of time measured with a stop-watch. If the bore of the conduit is fine so that water only trickles drop by drop the current is increased by increasing the pressure head, and decreased by substituting a conduit of *smaller* cross section or *greater* length.

the power to turn the water-wheel or the compass needle. For reasons which will be explained more fully at a later stage, it is simpler to take the more straightforward definition based on the mass effect. The ampere has already been defined as the current which deposits in one second 0·001118 gram of silver from a solution of silver nitrate.

The accompanying illustration (Fig. 337) will help you to see how the comparison between the electric current and the flow of water can be usefully applied to the measurement of electrical phenomena. If a current of water is flowing at a certain rate, let us say x c.c. per minute through a tube AB which divides at B into two branches, the currents y c.c. and z c.c. per minute respectively flowing through the two branches are together equivalent to the current in AB, $(x = y + z)$. Likewise the currents flowing in two branches of a divided circuit are together equivalent to the current in the common path connected to the generator. This can be proved by putting pairs of

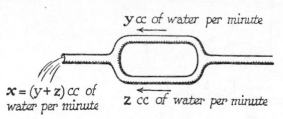

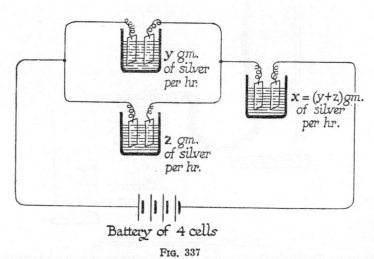

Fig. 337

The sum of the currents through the branches of a circuit is equivalent to the current which flows through a common path.

silver electrodes in solutions of silver nitrate in different parts of the circuit. If the negative electrodes of each "electrolytic cell" are weighed before switching on the current and after switching it off, the weight of silver deposited in the two branches is found to be the same as the weight deposited in the common part of the circuit.

The analogy between electrical measurements and measurements of water flow is very close, when the *bore of the pipes is small*. This can be shown by studying the flow of water in *capillary* tubes, i.e. the sort used for thermometers. The water current or mass of water which issues from the mouth of a narrow tube in unit time depends on two classes of measurements (Fig. 336), one is characteristic of the cistern or dam, and the other of the pipe or orifice which conducts the water away from it. As regards the first, what counts is the head of pressure. If the pipe connecting two cisterns has the same dimensions throughout, the current flowing between them is directly proportional to the difference between the heights of the water in each. Generally both are placed above ground so that this is simply the arithmetical difference of their ground-level heights. When one is above and the other below the earth, the same rule applies, if we measure height above the ground as positive and distance below as negative. If we connect two similar cisterns, each having two taps, one at the bottom at lower, and the other at the top at higher pressure head or water potential, we may do so in two ways (Fig. 338). If connected so that the tap of one cistern at lower potential feeds the tap of the other cistern at higher potential, the effective pressure head is doubled, and

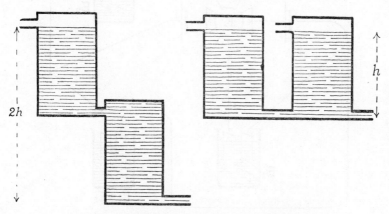

FIG. 338.—CISTERNS IN "SERIES" AND IN "PARALLEL"

the current is proportionately increased. Similarly the electric current measured by the amount of chemical decomposition it produces is doubled if we replace either of two cells which produce the same current by a battery of two cells arranged so that the positive terminal of one is connected with the negative terminal of the other. So if we call the electromotive force or potential difference between the terminals of a single Weston cell $1 \cdot 0183$ volts, the E.M.F. of a battery of two Weston cells connected "in series" is $2 \cdot 0366$ volts. Putting C for current measured in amperes and E for the potential

$$C \propto E$$

The water current which flows from a cistern out of a capillary tube does not merely depend on the pressure head. It also depends on the dimensions of the tube. If the tube is narrow, i.e. if its sectional area is small, the amount of water which escapes in unit time is smaller than if the tube is wide. It is also smaller if the tube is a long one than it is if the tube is a short one. If the terminals of the *same* generator are connected to electrodes dipped in a solution of silver nitrate, the current (i.e. amount of silver deposited in unit time on the negative plate) also depends on the length and thickness of the wire in the same way. The current is decreased if the length of wire is increased, and increased if thicker wire of the same length is substituted. Exact measurement shows that the current is directly proportional to the sectional area of the wire, and inversely proportional to its length, i.e.

$$C \propto a/l$$

If l/a is large the current is therefore small, and if l/a is small the current is large. So we may regard the reciprocal of the ratio on the right-hand side

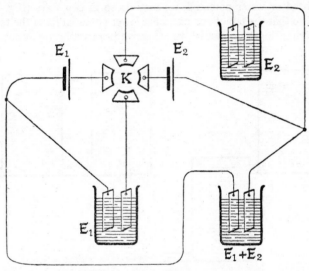

FIG. 339

By insertion of a metal plug in the key K the current is switched on to 3 silver "voltameters" consisting of two pairs of *small* silver plates, placed *far apart* in a *dilute* solution of silver nitrate. If the plates are well separated, the solution is dilute, and the connections are made with thick copper all the effective resistance to the flow of the current is in the voltameters. The sizes of the plates and their distances apart is the same in all three cells, and the same solution is used. Before inserting the plug the negative electrode in each voltameter is weighed. The increase in weight after removal of the plug when the current has been flowing for some time, gives the current in each voltameter. In the arrangement shown the E.M.F. of the first cell (E_1) of a battery of two cells drives current through the lower current meter on the left, the E.M.F. of the second drives current through the upper one, and the current in the lower one on the right is driven by the combined E.M.F. of both cells. If current is directly proportional to E.M.F., the silver deposited on the negative electrode of the last of the three will be found to be equivalent to the total amount of silver deposited on the negative electrodes of the other two.

of the expression just given as a measure of the *resistance* with which the external circuit *opposes* the flow. The corresponding law of capillary flow is not exactly analogous. The water current is inversely proportional to the length of the conduit and directly proportional to the square of the cross section. So the ratio $l \div a^2$ is a measure of the effective resistance offered by the circuit. This is only true if we confine our measurements to the same fluid at the same pressure. At the same pressure different fluids do not flow at the same velocity through the same length of the same pipe. Glycerine or lubricating oil are more sluggish than water. They are said to have greater *viscosity*. The *relative viscosity* of a fluid is simply the ratio of its rate of flow to that of some standard fluid at the same pressure in a capillary tube of the

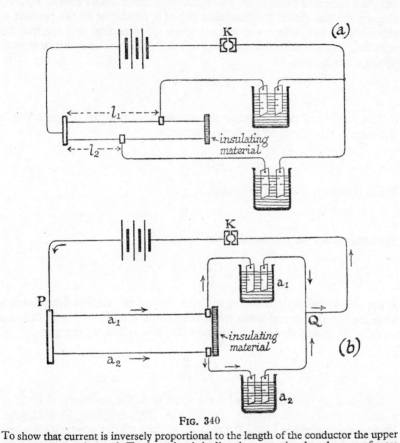

FIG. 340

To show that current is inversely proportional to the length of the conductor the upper arrangement may be used. To show that it is directly proportional to the area of cross section the lower one is designed. In each the current travels through two parallel wires of very high resistance. All other connexions are of thick wire of highly conductive material. The plates are close together, and the solutions are moderately strong. So all the effective resistance is in the two wires. In the upper arrangement the current flows through two lengths l_1, l_2 of two wires of the *same* sectional area. The weights of silver deposited on the kathode in the two silver voltameters give the currents c_1 and c_2 in the same ratio as l_2 and l_1. The two wires in the lower figure are of the same material and length but of different sectional area a_1 and a_2. The current between two points P and Q therefore flows through a_1 and a_2.

same length and cross-section. If we know the rate of flow of the standard fluid in a tube of known dimensions at known pressure, a table of relative viscosities tells all we need for calculating the rate of flow of other fluids when the pressure, the length of the conduit, and its sectional area are specified.

So also we have to take into account a qualitative feature of the resistances which different conducting materials offer to the electric current. To do so we adopt a common device of physical measurement. On pp 594-6 we learnt that the thermal capacity of a substance is proportional to its mass, and that the thermal capacities of equivalent masses of different substances are different. We therefore brought in a standardizing factor called *specific heat*. By analogy we can define the resistance (R) of a conductor as the product of the ratio l/a which fixes the current when the generator and material are specified, and a standardizing factor s called *specific resistance* to take account of the material itself, i.e.

$$R = s \cdot \left(\frac{l}{a}\right)$$

The relation of the current to the external circuit when the generator is the same is then summed up in the statement

$$C \propto \frac{1}{R}$$

When the external circuit is the same

$$C \propto E$$

Both statements are combined in the equation

$$C = k \cdot \frac{E}{R}$$

If the unit of resistance is chosen so that a current of 1 ampere flows through a conductor of unit resistance when there is an E.M.F. of 1 volt between its ends, C, E and R are each one unit. So $k = 1$, and we can put

$$C = \frac{E}{R}$$

This unit of resistance is called the *Ohm*. It is the resistance at 0° C. of a uniform column of mercury 106·300 cm. long, weighing 14·4521 gms. If the unit of length is 1 cm., the ratio l/a is unity when a conductor is 1 cm. long and 1 sq. cm. in cross-section. The resistance R of a conductor with these dimensions is therefore s, and the specific resistance of a metal is the resistance of 1 cm. of uniform wire of 1 sq. cm. cross-sectional area.

The specific resistance of good copper at 20° C. is 0·0000017. A piece of wire 1 mm. (0·1 cm.) thick is $\frac{22}{7} \times (0·05)^2$ sq. cm. in cross-section. So the resistance of 1 cm. of copper wire 1 mm. thick would be about

$$\frac{1 \times 0·0000017 \times 7}{22 \times 0·0025} = 0·00022 \text{ ohm}$$

Hence the resistance of one kilometre would be 22 ohms, and of 1 mile about 35 ohms. The specific resistance of the high resistance alloy "Eureka" is about 0·000048 at the same temperature. Hence the resistance of a filament 0·1 mm.

(0·01 cm.) thick and 30 cm. long would be about 18 ohms. So 12 inches of Eureka 0·1 mm. thick are roughly equivalent to half a mile of copper wire 1 mm. thick.

The rule $C = E \div R$ is called Ohm's law. The importance of it lies partly in the fact that the direct measurement of current is laborious and generally inaccurate. Exact measurement of E.M.F. or resistance is much simpler. Ohm's law tells us exactly what current we shall get, if we know the E.M.F. of the generator and the resistance of the circuit. To design a circuit in which a current of known strength flows we only need to know how to find

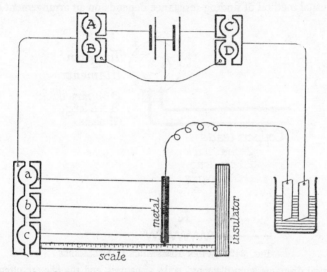

FIG. 341.—COMBINED ARRANGEMENT FOR DEMONSTRATING OHM'S LAW

As in Fig. 340 the whole resistance of the circuit except the three wires in the resistance frame is negligible, if the precautions there stated are taken. The current is measured chemically at fixed resistance when the first cell is used alone by inserting metal plugs in A and D, when the second is used alone by inserting plugs in B and C, and when both cells are used by putting plugs in A and C. This shows that the currents due to generators in series are additive. By inserting plugs in *a* alone, *a* and *b*, *a* and *b* and *c* the sectional area of the resistance is varied. Its length is varied by moving the metal slide.

the E.M.F. (volts) of the generator and the resistance (ohms) of the circuit. To determine E.M.F. or resistance, once we have decided on a standard of E.M.F. (e.g. the Weston cell) and a standard of resistance (a mercury column), we only need to know how to compare a generator of unknown E.M.F. or a circuit of unknown resistance with the standard. Ohm's law shows us how to do either of these things.

MEASURING RESISTANCE

An electric lamp is a metal or carbon filament protected by a glass bulb, which is either exhausted or filled with an inert gas. Using it economically means bringing the filament to the temperature at which it is fully incandescent. According to the rule which Joule established, the heating effect of a current depends on the square of the E.M.F. at the terminals and the reciprocal of the resistance between them. We can therefore calculate the heat production of a piece of wire, when we know its resistance and the E.M.F. applied. If we know the temperature at which the wire becomes incandescent and the specific heat of the material, we can therefore design a filament lamp suitable for a circuit with a particular voltage. All the additional knowledge we need is the resistance of the filament. Ohm's law tells us how to set about finding it.

The usual method of finding resistance depends on an arrangement known

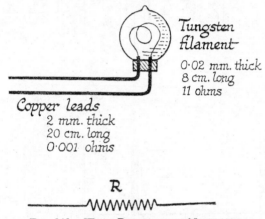

Tungsten filament
0·02 mm. thick
8 cm. long
11 ohms

Copper leads
2 mm. thick
20 cm. long
0·001 ohms

R

FIG. 342.—WHEN RESISTANCE IS NEGLIGIBLE

In electrical diagrams lamp filaments, coils, armatures, and the like are often represented by a zigzag line, as in the figure below. The symbol (here R) for the numerical value of the resistance in that part of the circuit is then treated in calculations, as if the leads had no resistance at all. That this is justified to a very high degree of precision is shown by the fact that one mile of copper wire 2 mm. thick has a resistance of about 8 ohms, as compared with the 1,000-ohm resistance of a 40-watt lamp for a 200-volt circuit.

as Wheatstone's network (Fig. 343). Imagine four conductors of different resistances connected at their ends to form a parallelogram ABCD, of which the points A and C are connected with a cell or other generator of current. The current is then divided at A or C so that current at one amperage (C_1) flows through the resistance R_1 and R_2 (i.e. through a total resistance $R_1 + R_2$) via the branch ABC, and current at a different amperage (C_2) flows through the resistances R_3 and R_4 via the branch ADC. If the voltage between the points A and C is E, Ohm's law tells us that

$$C_1 = \frac{E}{R_1 + R_2} \quad \text{and} \quad C_2 = \frac{E}{R_3 + R_4}$$

$$\therefore \quad \frac{C_1}{C_2} = \frac{R_3 + R_4}{R_1 + R_2}$$

It also tells us the voltages between A and B or A and D, (E_{AB} and E_{AD}), viz.

$$E_{AB} = C_1R_1 \quad \text{and} \quad E_{AD} = C_2R_3$$

If the resistances are so adjusted that $E_{AB} = E_{AD}$ there is no difference of

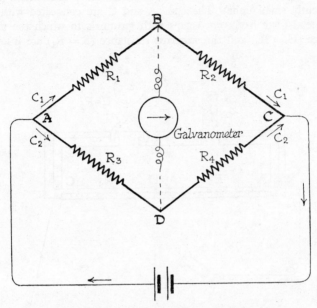

FIG. 343.—THEORY OF THE WHEATSTONE BRIDGE

potential between B and D, so that no current would flow between B and D if they were connected. When this is the case

$$C_1R_1 = C_2R_3$$
$$\therefore \quad \frac{C_1}{C_2} = \frac{R_3}{R_1}$$
$$\therefore \quad \frac{R_3}{R_1} = \frac{R_3 + R_4}{R_1 + R_2}$$
$$\therefore \quad \frac{R_3 + R_4}{R_3} = \frac{R_1 + R_2}{R_1}$$
$$1 + \frac{R_4}{R_3} = 1 + \frac{R_2}{R_1}$$

This means that if the resistances are such that no current flows when B and D are connected

$$\frac{R_4}{R_3} = \frac{R_2}{R_1}$$

Suppose therefore that you want to know R_2, and that you already know R_1, which is your standard resistance. All you have to do is to find a combination R_3 and R_4, which lets no current flow when B and D are connected. For this the instrument usually used is the "Wheatstone bridge" (Fig. 344). It consists essentially of a thin *uniform* wire, AC, of high resistance mounted side by side with a scale marked off in millimetres (or other conveniently small units). The ends A and C are connected with a thick broad metal plate having two gaps with terminals to which the unknown resistance (U = R_2) and the standard resistance (S = R_1) are inserted. In

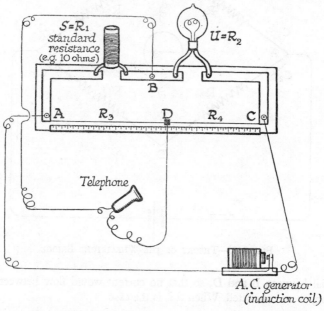

FIG. 344.—WHEATSTONE BRIDGE FITTED TO MEASURE RESISTANCE OF A LAMP

the middle of the metal junction between U and S a terminal is inserted at B. Owing to the thickness of the metal junction, of which the resistance is negligible, all the measurable resistance in the limb ABC is in U and S. A and C are connected with a generator. The terminal B is connected with one terminal of a current detector such as a galvanometer (p. 708), which registers the presence of a current by the deflection of a needle or wire. The other terminal of the detector is connected with a tapping key, which slides alongside of AC. At some point D along AC no current will flow through the detector when the key touches the wire. At this point,

$$\frac{U}{S} = \frac{R_4}{R_3}$$

$$\therefore \quad U = S \cdot \frac{R_4}{R_3}$$

Since the wire is of uniform thickness and material the resistances R_3 of AD and R_4 of DC only depend on the lengths AD and DC, which can be read off on the scale, so that

$$U = S \cdot \frac{DC}{AD}$$

Thus if no current flows when the tapping key is 750 mm. from A and 250 mm. from C and the standard resistance is 10 ohms, the unknown resistance is

$$10 \times \frac{250}{750} = 3 \cdot 3 \text{ ohms}$$

In practice a convenient arrangement is to use the alternating current of a shocking coil as a generator, and a pair of headphones as a detector. When headphones are connected with an alternating current a buzzing sound occurs. When no current passes there is silence, and all you have to do is to slide the tapping key to the point D on the wire where no sound is heard. If you then know the resistance of the circuit and the voltage, the current (C) is calculable from Ohm's law, since $C = E \div R$. Thus if the E.M.F. is 110 volts at each point in a lighting circuit and the resistance of a lamp is 220 ohms, the current which flows through it is $0 \cdot 5$ ampere. With the aid of the Wheatstone bridge we can test the truth of Ohm's law by comparing the resistance of conductors of different lengths, thickness and material without recourse to protracted chemical measurement.

You will notice that the definition of the standard ohm specifies the temperature at which resistance is measured. Resistance does in fact vary with temperature, though not greatly within the customary limits of room temperature. This fact is used in determining very high temperatures. By measuring the resistance at different temperatures registered by an ordinary wire we can ascertain how much the resistance changes per degree, and in this way we can use the resistance of a wire to measure temperatures beyond the limits at which ordinary thermometers, depending on expansion of a fluid or gas, cease to be workable (see p. 582). The resistance of a few substances is also affected by light. This is characteristic of *selenium*, an element allied to sulphur. So it is possible to reproduce differences of light intensity as differences of current strength.

Mechanical vibrations associated with audible sound are converted into current variations in the microphone or telephone transmitter. The construction of the telephone transmitter or microphone depends on the fact that loose contacts between conductors naturally have a high and variable resistance. This is because vibrations bring contiguous surfaces into contact or separate them. For this reason terminals should always be firmly screwed down. The transmitter of a telephone is a box of which one face is a flexible diaphragm. The latter responds readily to sound vibrations. The carbon granules lying against the opposite face are connected, like the diaphragm, in series with the circuit. Between the two the space is lightly packed with carbon granules forming a loose contact. Each mechanical vibration produced by the voice or an instrument therefore produces a change in the resistance of the circuit, and in consequence a corresponding fluctuation of the current when a steady source of E.M.F. is supplied by the generator.

Since the heating effect in a circuit is greatest where the resistance is greatest the high resistance which develops at a loose contact can be used in another way. Electrical *welding* depends on the production of intense heat at the interface between two pieces of metal in loose contact, when a strong current flows across it.

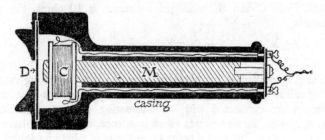

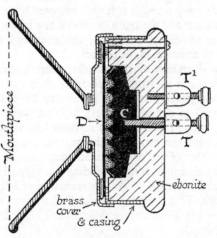

FIG. 345.—TELEPHONE RECEIVER (OR LOUD SPEAKER) ABOVE, WITH MAGNET (M), COIL (C) AND IRON DIAPHRAGM (D). TELEPHONE TRANSMITTER (MICROPHONE) BELOW, WITH CARBON DIAPHRAGM (D) CONNECTED WITH TERMINAL T¹ AND CARBON GRANULES (C) CONNECTED WITH TERMINAL T

THE MEASUREMENT OF POTENTIAL

Two methods of measuring potential or E.M.F. are commonly used when the current supplied is direct and steady. The first is the voltmeter. We have seen that a suspended magnetic needle is deflected by a current flowing parallel to its axis as in a railway telegraph, and it is easy to make a scale showing how much current corresponds to how big a deflection of the needle. Such an arrangement is called a galvanometer. The scale divisions can be graduated by an arrangement shown in Fig. 347. The same current from a battery of known E.M.F. passes through (a) a variable resistance which is a very thin wire of uniform thickness and low conductivity with a sliding contact P; (b) the galvanometer; (c) a "voltameter" of two silver electrodes dipped in silver nitrate. The negative plate of the latter can be weighed at fixed intervals. The steady position of the needle on the scale is noted during each interval, and after each weighing the current is varied by moving the

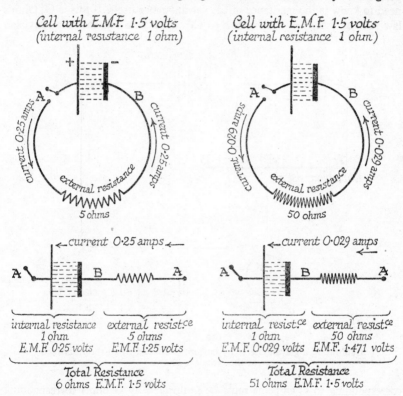

FIG. 346.—E.M.F.

The E.M.F of a cell is the total E.M.F. required to drive the same current from A to B through the external circuit and from B to A through the cell itself *when the key A is closed*. With a current meter we can measure the current which the same cell delivers first with one resistance (e.g. 5 ohms), then with another (e.g. 50 ohms). If the internal resistance of the cell is r, the E.M.F. is E and the two external resistances successively used to give a current C_1 and C_2 are R_1 and R_2:

$$C_1(R_1 + r) = E = C_2(R_2 + r)$$

The value for r so obtained shows that the voltage of the cell is the sum of the voltage which is available for driving the current through the internal resistance of the cell and the voltage for driving the same current through the external resistance. That is to say, Ohm's law applies to the whole circuit. Note particularly that the E.M.F. of the external circuit approaches a limiting value equivalent to the E.M.F. of the cell, when the resistance of the external circuit is large and the current consequently very small.

Check all the calculations in this figure by applying Ohm's law to all parts of the circuit.

sliding contact P, which increases or diminishes the resistance of the circuit. We can thus mark off scale divisions corresponding to so many amperes or fractions of an ampere.

Although an instrument calibrated in this way would not be suitable for finding the current ordinarily flowing in a circuit because its own resistance would reduce the current, it can be used as a *voltmeter* between any two points in the circuit, when its terminals are connected to them. All we need to know is the resistance of the galvanometer itself. If this is G, Ohm's law tells us that $C = E \div G$ or $E = CG$. That is to say, each scale division

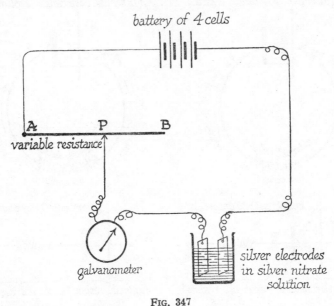

battery of 4 cells

A   P   B

variable resistance

galvanometer   silver electrodes
in silver nitrate
solution

Fig. 347

Calibrating a galvanometer by current produced when the resistance
of the circuit is known.

corresponding to C amperes must be multiplied by G ohms corresponding to the resistance of the galvanometer. This gives us the correct value of E in volts. To get G we have only to put the galvanometer in place of the lamp in one arm of the Wheatstone bridge shown in Fig. 344.

Calibrating a galvanometer by its chemical action is laborious and liable to inaccuracy because of fluctuations in the value of the current. In practice it is therefore better to have an independent way of measuring voltage. An alternative device is called the potentiometer. This consists of two essential parts, a uniform wire, which has its terminals connected to the terminals of a constant source of voltage, e.g. an accumulator, and has a sliding contact like that of a Wheatstone bridge, together with a detector. The detector is a galvanometer, but as it is only used to *detect* current, it need not be gradu-ated accurately, or, indeed, at all. All that matters is that it should be sensitive to very small currents. The use of the potentiometer depends on an analogy between the flow of electricity and the flow of water.

A pipe offers resistance to the flow of water, and there is a continuous drop (Fig. 348) of pressure head along the length of the conduit from a cistern while water is flowing out of it. With a galvanometer we can show that if A and B (Fig. 349) are two points on a wire carrying a current, there is a continuous drop of potential between A and B. That is to say, the deflection is always less when the terminals are connected with A and C, any point between A and B, than when they are connected with A and B. If the galvanometer has been graduated in scale divisions corresponding to volts, as described above, the voltages are proportional to the resistances between the two points to which the terminals are attached. So if the wire AB is of uniform thickness and material the ratio of the voltages $E_{AB} : E_{AC}$ is the ratio of the distances AB : AC.

If we have first satisfied ourselves that Ohm's rule is correct, by testing

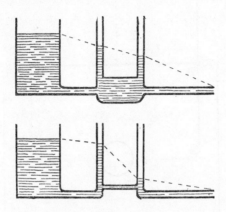

FIG. 348

Drop in pressure head of flowing water, where a high resistance is inserted. For purposes of illustration the gradients are exaggerated.

the resistance of measured lengths of wire on a Wheatstone's bridge, it is not actually necessary to perform the experiment described. The conclusion stated follows from it, if Ohm's law is true of every part of a circuit in which an electric current (c) flows. Thus, if AB is a wire of uniform thickness and material connected to a battery at each end (Fig. 349) the E.M.F. (E_1) between two points A and B separated by the length l_1 of resistance R_1 is cR_1, and the E.M.F. between two points A and C separated by a length l_2 of resistance R_2 is cR_2, so that

$$E_1 : E_2 = R_1 : R_2$$

Since the thickness is uniform the ratio

$$R_1 : R_2 = l_1 : l_2$$
$$E_1 : E_2 = l_1 : l_2$$

The principle of the potentiometer is illustrated in Fig. 350. If two generators with the same E.M.F. are joined by "like" terminals (+ to +

or — to —) a current detector will register no effect. If they are not of the same voltage a small current will flow, and it will be approximately the same as the current produced by a generator whose voltage is equivalent to the difference between the voltages of the cells. If (see lower half of Fig. 350) we connect the positive terminal of a standard cell of known voltage to the positive terminal A of the potentiometer wire AB, and its negative terminal to the negative terminal B, current will flow round the circuit including the standard cell, when its voltage is less than the E.M.F. between A and B.

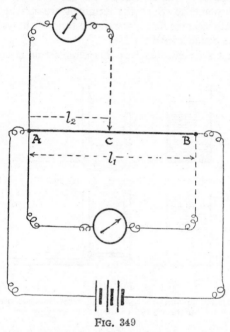

FIG. 349

Drop of potential in a circuit between two points A and B.

This will be shown by deflection of the magnetic needle in a galvanometer placed in series with the standard cell. At some point P the voltage between A and P will be just the same as the voltage of the standard cell, and no current will flow when the cell is connected with P instead of with B. If one terminal of the standard cell is fixed at A, which is connected with the battery terminal of the same sign, the other can be connected to the wire by a sliding key, and by tapping the latter at intervals along the wire we can find the point P situated at a distance l_1 from A. When the standard cell of E.M.F. S has been tested, a cell of unknown voltage (V) may be tested in the same way to find a "null point" C at a distance l_2 from A. Since the voltages E_{AP} and E_{AC} are in the same ratio as the resistances of AP and AC,

$$S : V = l_1 : l_2$$

$$V = \frac{l_2 S}{l_1}$$

The potentiometer method is based on Ohm's rule, and does not require the use of a galvanometer graduated in volts. So it can be used to determine the voltage between two points which give a particular deflection of the galvanometer when connected to its terminals. Hence it can be adapted to graduate a voltmeter directly. Having settled on a simple method of measuring voltage (E.M.F.), ohmage (resistance), and hence, indirectly, of finding amperage (current) without recourse to the laborious method of chemical analysis, we may now examine the various characteristics of current electricity

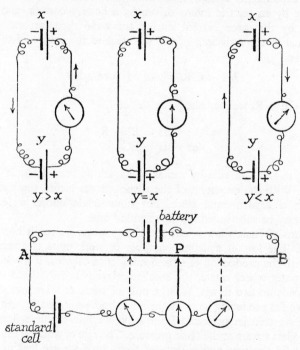

FIG. 350.—PRINCIPLE OF THE POTENTIOMETER

and the use to which they are put. The most important are (*a*) the heating effect, (*b*) the chemical decomposition, (*c*) magnetic phenomena, (*d*) spark discharge through a gaseous medium. The last of these will be left till the next chapter.

THE HEATING EFFECT

If the voltage supplied to a circuit is fixed, Ohm's law tells us that the current which flows through it falls off if a high resistance is introduced into the circuit. Thus long fine wires inserted between the terminals of a cell and electrodes dipped in a solution of silver nitrate result in the deposition of less silver than would be deposited if the electrodes were connected with the battery by short thick wires. In the same way (Fig. 348) a narrow pipe inserted in the outflow from a cistern greatly reduces the rate of flow. Resistance to an electric current or to a water current entails loss of power to do mechanical work, or to produce chemical and magnetic effects, and, as we should expect from the Conservation of Energy, this is associated with the production of heat. The heat is increased if a battery of several cells is substituted for a single cell, and the current which flows is then, of course, greater. Hence the heating produced by a current depends on the strength of the current and the resistance encountered.

In the experiments already mentioned Joule found that the mechanical work done by an electric motor driven by a battery current, and the heat produced by the same current during the same time interval, are both proportional to the resistance of the wire and to the square of the current strength, i.e.

$$kH = C^2R, \text{ where } k \text{ is a constant.}$$

Since $C = E \div R$, we may also write this as

$$kH = E^2 \div R$$
$$\text{or} \quad kH = EC$$

It is easy to test this rule by means of apparatus such as Joule used (see Fig. 351). With the exception of the silver current meter, the parts can be bought in a departmental store. For home-made outfits a secondhand ammeter may be substituted for the chemical one.

The form of Joule's law is not surprising, when we recall how *energy* is measured. The loss of a definite number of work units is associated (see p. 609) with the production of a fixed number of calories. If a water current makes a water-wheel rotate, the mechanical activity in a fixed interval of time depends on two things. A large bulk of water at a low pressure is not as effective for producing work as the same bulk projected at high pressure. Conversely a thin jet projected from a hypodermic needle is less effective than a copious stream at the same pressure. The rate of working thus depends both on fluid pressure and on rate of flow. So if we are looking for units to connect the measurement of heat with the measurement of electrical changes we should expect to find that heat production in unit time depends on the product of voltage and amperage.

The product EC (or what is the same thing C^2R, or $E^2 \div R$) is called the *electrical power* of the circuit. The unit of electrical power is defined as the electrical power of a circuit when the terminals have a potential difference of one volt and one ampere flows between them. Experiment then shows that the heat production is $0 \cdot 239$ calorie per second. Hence

$$k(0 \cdot 239) = 1 \times 1$$
$$\therefore \qquad k = 4 \cdot 18.$$

This means that when the heat production (H) of the circuit is one calorie per second, the number of units of electrical power is $4 \cdot 18$. We have seen on p. 630 that the production of 1 calorie per second involves an output of

$4 \cdot 18 \times 10^7$ ergs per second. So one unit of electrical power is equivalent to 10^7, or ten million units of mechanical power in the international system. Ten million international power units (ergs per second) correspond to one *watt*, which is thus the unit of electrical power as well.

From our definition, the number of watts standing for the power production of a circuit is the product EC (= C^2R = $E^2 \div R$), when E, C, and R are measured in volts, amperes, and ohms. Thus a current of 3 amps.

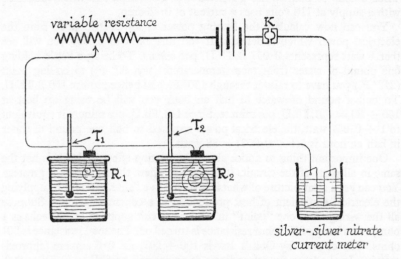

variable resistance

K

T_1

T_2

R_1

R_2

silver-silver nitrate
current meter

FIG. 351.—ELECTRICAL EQUIVALENT OF HEAT

A battery is in series with a silver-silver nitrate voltameter and two known resistances (R_1 and R_2) immersed in the same quantity of water. The electrodes of the silver voltameter are weighed. The key K is inserted to complete the circuit. After ten minutes the key is removed. If the initial temperature was T, it will be found that

$$\frac{T_1 - T}{T_2 - T} = \frac{R_1}{R_2}$$

Since the quantity of water affected is the same, the heat developed is proportional to the rise in temperature, i.e.

$$\frac{H_1}{H_2} = \frac{R_1}{R_2}$$

The electrodes are weighed to see how much silver has been deposited. This gives the average current C in the first experiment. The available current is now reduced or increased by changing the variable resistance. The water is allowed to cool to the temperature T and the key is again inserted. After ten minutes, the new temperatures t_1 and t_2 are recorded, and the electrodes weighed to get the mean current (c) in the second experiment. It will then be found that

$$\frac{C^2}{c^2} = \frac{T_1 - T}{t_1 - T} = \frac{T_2 - T}{t_2 - T} \quad \text{i.e. } C^2 \propto H$$

at a voltage of 50 corresponds to power production at $3 \times 50 = 150$ watts, and a current of 2 amps. flowing through a resistance of 15 ohms corresponds to $2^2 \times 15 = 60$ watts. Lamps are usually marked with the number of watts developed at a given voltage. In effect this tells you the resistance and current at the same time. For example, a lamp may be marked 50 W 110 V. Since $W = E^2 \div R$,

$$R = (110)^2 \div 50 = 242 \text{ ohms}$$

And since $W = E C$

$$C = 50 \div 110 = 0 \cdot 45 \text{ amp.}$$

Thus a lamp so marked has a resistance of 242 ohms, and when connected with a supply at 110 volts uses a current of $0 \cdot 45$ amp.

You can now calculate the heating power of an electric stove from the electrical power which it delivers. If you turn back to p. 598 you will see that 1 watt represents $0 \cdot 057$ B.Th.U. per *minute*. To bring a kettle holding one pound of water from room temperature (say, 62° F.) to boiling point (212° F.) you have to raise it through 150° F., and hence require 150 B.Th.U. To boil a pound of water in half an hour you will be using up heat at $150 \div 30 = 5$ B.Th.U. per minute. Since 1 B.Th.U. per minute is equivalent to $1 \div 0 \cdot 057$ watt, the electrical power required to boil one pound of water in half an hour is $5(1 \div 0 \cdot 057) = 88$ watts.

One important thing to notice about the heating effect is that it is not the same in all parts of the circuit. It is greatest where the resistance is greatest. You can get a clear picture of what is involved in a "short circuit" by applying the electrical equivalent of heat production to a concrete example. Suppose all the wiring from one "point" in a house circuit supplied at 100 volts is 1 ohm, and a lamp of 200 ohm resistance is turned on. The total resistance is 201 ohms. The current by Ohm's law is $100 \div 201$, i.e. $0 \cdot 5$ ampere (approximately). In the lamp the expenditure of power will be $C^2R = (0 \cdot 5)^2 \times 200$, or approximately 50 watts. This represents approximately 12 calories per second. The specific heat of charcoal is about $0 \cdot 25$. If no heat were lost to the surroundings, this would raise 1 gram of charcoal through 48° C. in 1 second, and a carbon filament weighing about one-fortieth of a gram through about 2,000° C. in 1 second. In the rest of the circuit the heating power produced would be $C^2R = (0 \cdot 5)^2 \times 1 = 0 \cdot 25$ watt, or roughly $0 \cdot 06$ calorie per second. The specific heat of copper is about 1/11. Hence 1 calorie raises 1 gram of copper through 11° C., and $0 \cdot 06$ calorie through roughly $0 \cdot 7$° C. If the copper wire connecting the point to the lamp weighed 10 grams, it would therefore be developing heat at less than $0 \cdot 1$° C. per second. Suppose now that the ends of the wires touch, so current is driven through 1 ohm at a potential of 100 volts. The amperage is 100. This means that the production of heating power at the rate of $100^2 \times 1 = 10,000$ watts or 2,390 calories per second. This would raise 10 grams of copper $11/10 \times 2,390°$, or about 2,600° C. in a second, and instantly melt it, incidentally setting the house on fire. To safeguard against this, circuits are always fitted with fuses, i.e. at some point in the circuit a wire with a lower melting point (and rather higher resistance) than the main wires is inserted. When short circuiting occurs, the fuse melts first, thereby breaking the circuit. The practice of replacing a fuse by a lady's hairpin is not advisable.

The connexions of a house circuit raise another problem which also illustrates the use of Ohm's law. From the two terminals at which current is delivered to the house the various points are connected in "parallel" (see Fig. 352). When two resistances r_1 and r_2 are connected in series (Fig. 352), i.e. consecutively with a generator, the whole resistance of the circuit is raised to $r_1 + r_2$, and the current is therefore reduced. When the same two resistances are connected in parallel, i.e. separately to the terminals of the same generator, the result is quite different. The total resistance of the circuit is less than the resistance of any single branch in the circuit. The simplest case to take is a circuit with two branches (Fig. 352). If the total resistance in the circuit is R, the current flowing through the common cables

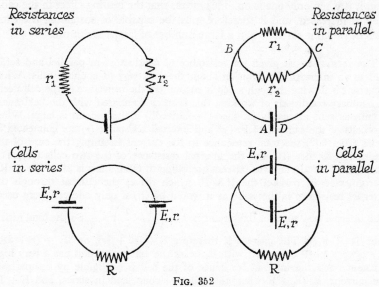

FIG. 352

Resistances and cells in *series* and in *parallel* with connecting cables of thick copper wire.

AB, CD of negligible resistance is $E \div R$. In the branch with resistance r_1 the current is

$$c_1 = E \div r_1$$

and in the branch with resistance r_2 the current is

$$c_2 = E \div r_2$$

Since the total current $C = c_1 + c_2$

$$\frac{E}{R} = \frac{E}{r_1} + \frac{E}{r_2}$$

$$\therefore \quad \frac{1}{R} = \frac{1}{r_1} + \frac{1}{r_2}$$

$$\therefore \quad R = \frac{r_1 r_2}{r_1 + r_2}$$

Thus if r_1 is 10 ohms and r_2 is 15 ohms, the total resistance is $150 \div 25 = 6$ ohms.

Suppose, then, that the generator is a storage cell of 2 volts. When r_1 alone is connected to it the current flowing is $2 \div 10 = 0 \cdot 2$ amp. When r_2 alone is connected the current is $2 \div 15 = 0 \cdot 13$ amp. If however both are connected in parallel the current which flows through the common cable AB and CD (assumed to have negligible resistance) is $2 \div 6 = 0 \cdot 33$ amp. Imagine that the storage cell is a power station, and you will thus see that when all the lights of the house are switched on the current which flows through the cable connecting your house to a distributing station is greater than it is when only one is on. This means that the heating effect in the cable itself is increased, and it therefore must be capable of sustaining the extra current which it carries when a large number of lamps are in use.

The formulae just given for resistance of conductors in parallel and series lead to an interesting conclusion about the best way to connect cells. While a current is flowing through a cell it encounters the resistance of the cell itself. In ordinary conditions of working this is small compared with the "external" circuit, as cells are easily fatigued ("polarized") if the current is large. When two cells of the same E.M.F. (E) and internal resistance (r) are connected in series (Fig. 352) the total resistance to the current is simply the sum of the external resistance (R) and the internal resistance of the two cells ($2r$). The total E.M.F. is 2E, and the current according to Ohm's law is $2E \div (2r + R)$. If connected in parallel the E.M.F. which drives the current through the external resistance is the same as it would be (E) if only one cell were used. The internal resistance of the circuit is $1 \div \left(\dfrac{1}{r} + \dfrac{1}{r} \right) = \dfrac{r}{2}$. So the total resistance is $R + \frac{1}{2}r$. The current is therefore $E \div (R + \frac{1}{2}r)$, or $2E \div (r + 2R)$. If r is very small compared with R, i.e. if the external circuit has a very high resistance and the internal resistance of the cell is negligible by comparison, the current is $2E \div R$ when the cells are connected in series, and $E \div R$, or half as great, when they are connected in parallel. When the external resistance is small and the cells have high internal resistance so that R is negligible compared with r, the current is $E \div r$ when they are connected in series, and $2E \div r$, or twice as great, when they are connected in parallel. In practice the internal resistance of the cell is usually small, and if we wish to maintain a steady current, the external resistance must be large to prevent fatigue, so that the remarks made on page 681 hold good. On the other hand, high tension dry batteries are often made with very high internal resistance, so that in calculating the current produced the latter is relevant (see Examples 1-6).

Calculations of heating power already given illustrate the kind of measurements involved in designing a suitable filament for an electric stove or radiator, and in supplying them with the requisite current. The problem of designing a lamp is essentially similar, since white light is produced by the incandescence of the lamp filament. Lamp filaments are therefore required to sustain much higher temperatures than the filaments of a radiator or stove. This entails two problems. The first is to prevent oxidation of the filament. This used to be done by evacuating the globe. Vacuum globes have two great disadvantages. The first is that they easily burst, and the second is that a very high vacuum is necessary to avoid any oxidation. An alternative procedure is to fill the globe with an inert gas, for which purpose argon is specially suitable, and frequently used. The other problem concerns the best material to use. The filament must have a very high melting-point, and a very low specific heat. While working it is continually losing heat. So heat must be continually supplied to keep it at incandescent temperature (see p. 582).

The first electric lamps had carbon filaments which have a high specific heat. Later the metal tantalum was substituted. To-day *tungsten* filaments are used. This metal has a very high melting-point and (p. 582) a comparatively low specific heat. Thus a carbon filament lamp gives $0 \cdot 25$ candle power (p. 172) per watt (i.e. a 60-watt lamp gives 15 c.p.), while a tungsten filament will give about $0 \cdot 6$ candle power per watt (i.e. a 60-watt lamp gives roughly 35 c.p.). Hence the lighting efficiency of a lamp of the Osram type is more than twice as great as the lighting efficiency of the original Edison type. In the best gas-filled tungsten filament lamps it may be eight times as great. The "half-watt" lamp has an efficiency of from $1\frac{1}{4}$ to 2 c.p. per watt, and lamps giving as much as 500 c.p. are now sold for household use. For main street lighting lamps of 3,000 to 4,000 c.p. have replaced the old carbon arc light.

The *watt* represents the rate at which the circuit is working. It corresponds to a definite amount of heat produced in unit time. Costing electric supply, like costing heat production in terms of B.Th.U., is based on the total energy consumed, and the total electrical energy consumed depends on the time. The Board of Trade unit is taken as an output of 1 kilowatt (1,000 watts) over one hour. Suppose, for instance, the charge is 1d. per unit. This means that 1,000 watts can be used for an hour, or one watt can be used for 1,000 hours at a cost of one penny. If a 16-c.p. carbon lamp is run off 250 volts at an amperage of $0 \cdot 22$ the power required is $250 \times 0 \cdot 22$, or 55 watts ($0 \cdot 055$ kilowatt). The lamp consumes $0 \cdot 055$ unit per hour, and can therefore be used for $1 \div 0 \cdot 055 = 18$ hours for one penny. This is $16 \times 18 = 288$ "candle-hours." A 60-watt lamp can be run for $1000 \div 60 = 17$ hours approximately at the expenditure of one Board of Trade unit. If used six hours a day every day in the year the number of hours is $365 \times 6 = 2,190$, and the cost at a penny a unit is, therefore, $(2,190 \div 17)$ pence, or roughly ten shillings. You can therefore make an estimate of what your lighting bill should be, if you remember to turn off the switch when you leave the room.

Just as it is possible to produce heat by an electric current, it is also possible to produce an electric current by heat. If the two ends of a wire of one metal are joined to the two ends of a wire of another metal, a current flows through the circuit when the temperature of one junction is not the same as that of the other. This is illustrated in Fig. 353. Some metallic junctions are more sensitive to differences of temperature than are others. Antimony and bismuth make a very sensitive combination. For any particular "thermocouple" the E.M.F. between the two junctions depends on the difference of temperature. So if one junction is kept at a fixed temperature the current which flows can be found, and once found used as a means of finding the temperature of the other junction. Since it is possible to make galvanometers which detect very minute currents, the thermocouple is a vastly more sensitive thermometer than a liquid or gas thermometer (see Fig. 355). The best thermocouples are capable of detecting temperature differences as small as one millionth of a degree centigrade.

CHEMICAL DECOMPOSITION

In contradistinction to the heating effect, which varies in different parts of the same branch of a circuit when the resistance is not uniform, the chemical and magnetic effects depend only on the current which flows through any branch. Current is measured by the chemical or magnetic

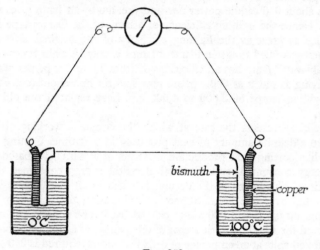

FIG. 353
Current produced by two thermocouples at different temperatures.

phenomena in the branch of a circuit. They are thus the same in all parts of the same branch.

Conductors of electricity may be divided into two classes. Pure metals (and other elements, e.g. carbon, which conducts electricity tolerably well) do not undergo any chemical change either in the solid state or when molten if a current is passed through them, unless of course they are heated sufficiently to undergo oxidation. Compounds which conduct in solution or in the molten state break up into their elements, or into simpler compounds. Metallic salts break up with the liberation of metal deposited on the negative electrode while, generally speaking, acid together with free oxygen bubbles collects at the positive electrode. In the electrolysis of salts like chlorides which contain no oxygen, the non-metallic element is liberated at the positive electrode.

In an earlier chapter we have already referred to the view that substances which conduct electricity in solution break up when dissolved into electrically charged sub-molecules or ions. The conclusion that they do break up is based partly on the facts already explained (p. 480), but was originally suggested by Faraday's researches on the nature of "electrolysis." Faraday discovered two things about chemical decomposition by the current. The first is that if several pairs of electrodes in series with the same generator are placed in solutions of different salts of the same metal (e.g. copper chloride, copper sulphate, and copper nitrate) the amount of metal which is deposited on the negative electrode is the same. This means that the same current liberates the same amount of a metal from any of its salts. The second fact Faraday discovered is that when several pairs of electrodes in series with the same generator are placed in solutions of different metals, the amounts of elements liberated are proportional to their combining weights.

Suppose, for instance, two pairs of platinum electrodes are connected in series with a battery, one pair dipping in a solution of copper nitrate and

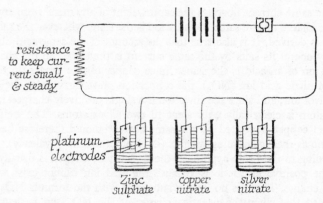

FIG. 354.—APPARATUS FOR DEMONSTRATING FARADAY'S LAWS OF ELECTROLYSIS

one pair in a solution of silver nitrate. In one copper, and in the other silver, will be deposited on the negative electrode, and the ratio by weight of copper and silver will be $31 \cdot 8 : 108$. The atomic weight of silver is 108, and it is monovalent. The atomic weight of copper is $63 \cdot 6$. In copper nitrate $Cu(NO_3)_2$ one atom of copper takes the place of two atoms of silver in silver nitrate. For instance, the reaction between silver nitrate and copper chloride leading to the formation of the insoluble light-sensitive chloride of silver which is precipitated from solution occurs thus:

$CuCl_2$	$+$	$2\ AgNO_3$	$=$	$Cu(NO_3)_2$	$+$	$2\ AgCl$
(1 atom		(2 atoms		(1 atom		(2 atoms
of		of		of		of
copper)		silver)		copper)		silver)

In other words, $63 \cdot 6$ grams of copper replace 2×108 grams of silver in a chemical reaction between their compounds, or $31 \cdot 8$ grams of copper replace 108 grams of silver. This means that when the same current acts for the same length of time on solutions of two different metals, the ratio of the weights of the two metals deposited on the kathode is the ratio of the weights which replace one another in a chemical reaction, such as the double decomposition of their salts.

The ionic hypothesis suggested to account for these facts is that in solution molecules of metallic nitrate break down into sub-molecules or *ions* with equal and opposite electric charges. Like electrically charged pith balls, the positively charged ions are attracted to the negative electrode, and the negatively charged ones to the positive electrode, and since metals go to the kathode (negative electrode) the metallic ion is positive. Thus silver nitrate $AgNO_3$ becomes

$$Ag^+ + (NO_3)^-$$

and copper nitrate, which is $Cu(NO_3)_2$, becomes

$$Cu^{++} + (NO_3)_- + (NO_3)^-$$

Since the same current liberates the same weight of any metal from any of its salts, the charge on the same metallic ion is the same whatever the salt from which it is derived. It is also true that the amount of the same acid liberated from any one of its salts by the same current is the same. So the charge on the acid ion of an acid is the same. Since copper nitrate breaks up to form 2 ions of nitric acid ion (NO_3), the copper ion must carry twice the charge of the silver ion; and since the silver ion is a single positively charged ion one copper atom is electrically equivalent to two silver atoms. The weights of silver and copper deposited by the same current should therefore be in the same ratio as their combining weights (i.e. atomic weight $\div$ valency).

According to the Ionic hypothesis the reason why oxygen is usually given off at the positive electrode is because the acid ion cannot exist when it loses its charge. There is no known substance with the formula NO_3. So it is assumed that when the negative charge of the NO_3^- ion is neutralized at the positive electrode, it may combine with the metal of the electrode which is worn away, but in any case usually combines as well with the water thus—

$$4NO_3^- + 2H_2O = O_2 + 4HNO_3$$

On the other hand, a chloride like NaCl in the Castner process breaks up into $Na^+ + Cl^-$. Two chloride ions can exist as the pure substance chlorine (Cl_2) when the negative charge is removed. So chlorine is given off at the positive electrode. This was how chlorine was discovered to be an element by Davy.

When a current passes through electrodes dipped in any acid which attacks the metal of which the electrodes are made, metal is transferred from the positive to the negative electrode. Thus if silver electrodes are dipped in nitric acid, the ions separated by the current are H^+ and NO_3^-, and at first hydrogen is liberated at the anode. As the reaction goes on silver nitrate is formed at the expense of the silver positive electrode, and this is decomposed with deposition of silver on the kathode. Similarly when platinum electrodes are dipped in hydrochloric acid the positive electrode is worn away by formation of platinic chloride, and a black film of finely divided spongy platinum is deposited on the kathode.

The spongy platinum deposited on a kathode in this way has the power of sucking up hydrogen or any other gas just as blotting paper sucks up ink. This idiosyncrasy makes it easy to understand a phenomenon which is the basis of "polarization," the term applied to the fact that cells become tired when they are allowed to deliver a large current for some time. If two electrodes, both coated with spongy "platinum black," are dipped in a solution of any electrolyte no current flows when they are connected. If a jet of hydrogen bubbles plays on one and a jet of oxygen bubbles on another a current is set up. Thus if suitable arrangements are made to imprison them hydrogen and oxygen behave like the metal plates of a cell, and experiment shows that the hydrogen electrode is the negative one. Since hydrogen is liberated at the positive electrode when a cell of copper and zinc plates dipped in sulphuric acid is working, the effect of this is to set up a current in the opposite direction. So the current delivered by a battery of such cells is rapidly fatigued, regaining its strength after a rest which allows the bubbles of gas to disappear. We might, of course, charge two spongy platinum electrodes with hydrogen and oxygen by immersing them in dilute acid and passing a current through them. Hydrogen then collects on the negative and oxygen on the positive electrode till both are completely saturated. On cutting out the generator and connecting the two electrodes a current can now be obtained from the platinum electrodes. This gives you a picture of the principle involved in the construction of the storage battery with two similar electrodes of spongy lead. Such re-chargeable batteries are now replacing the older type of battery with electrodes of different elements.

Various devices are used to prevent polarization of ordinary cells. In the common "dry cell," one electrode is made of zinc (−) and one of carbon (+) as in the old Leclanché cell of bell circuits, the carbon rod is surrounded by a stiff inner paste of manganese and lead oxides, and the remaining space between this and a zinc cylinder is packed with a thinner paste of plaster of Paris and sal ammoniac (ammonium chloride). Needless to say, the contents are not truly *dry*. If they were there would be no ionization, and therefore no current.

The ionic hypothesis which explains why a current decomposes an electrolyte, also provides an explanation of how the cell works. When two different metals are placed in a solution of electrolyte they do not react with it to the same extent. Hence the concentration of ions at the surface of the two electrodes is different. This implies two things at the same time: a difference of osmotic pressure and a difference of electric charge, and since both are different aspects of one and the same phenomenon there must be a definite connexion between the two. Difference of osmotic pressure means power to do work, which is related in a definite manner to heat production (p. 609), as are also the E.M.F. and current of a cell. So if we know either, the first law of thermodynamics tells us how to find the other. If we know all the chemical reactions involved, the osmotic pressure differences are calculable. Thus the E.M.F. of a cell can be calculated if the ionic hypothesis is correct. This has been done successfully for a few cells in which the chemical changes are fully understood. So the ionic hypothesis gives a correct account both of the chemical changes which result in the production of a current and the chemical changes which result from the application of a current.

z

(a)

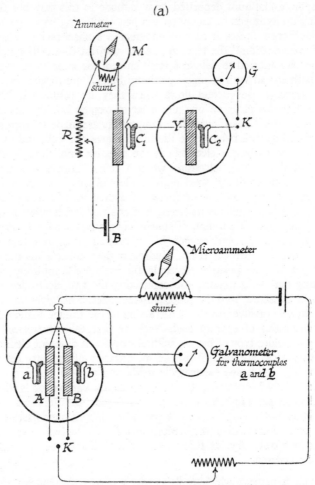

Fig. 355.—Measurement of Radiation Intensity

The top figure (*a*) shows the principle involved in assessing intensity of radiation by the Ångström Pyrheliometer. The shaded rectangles are two pieces of soot-coated metal foil of the same material and dimensions in contact with thermocouples C_1 and C_2. One of them (Y) is exposed to the source of radiation. The other is in series with a battery, an ammeter and a variable resistance (R) to adjust the strength of the current till the temperature of the metal foil is the same as that of Y, i.e. when there is no deflexion of the galvanometer G in circuit with the two thermocouples. If c (amps) is the appropriate current strength and r (ohms) is the resistance of the metal foil in the battery circuit, the rate at which the foil is using energy to maintain itself at the same temperature as Y is $c^2 r = w$ (watts). The calorie equivalent (h) per sec. is given by Joule's law ($w = 4 \cdot 184 h$), and if the area of the strips is a cm.², ($h \div a$) gives the intensity of radiation in cal./sec./cm.² In practice it is difficult to make two pieces of foil of exactly the same dimensions. Consequently it is preferable to take the mean of two values based on alternately radiating each strip and passing the current through its fellow. For this purpose we may mount both on an ebonite ring with a reversible vane hinged at the dotted line in the lower set-up (*b*) to protect from radiation the one in circuit with the battery and micrometer through the key K. The exposed strip receives rays incident at all angles between 0 and 90° to the normal.

THE MAGNETIC EFFECTS OF A CURRENT

In the neighbourhood of a magnet a compass needle does not take up its usual position along the magnetic meridian, unless the magnet is also placed with its axis in line with that of the needle along the meridian. The space in the neighbourhood of a magnet is therefore called a field of magnetic attraction, and the magnetic phenomena characteristic of the electric current are summed up in the statement that the space in the neighbourhood of a conductor, while current is passing through it, becomes a magnetic field. A magnetic field is polar, i.e. exercises equal and opposite effects on the north- and south-seeking poles of a magnet suspended in it. One pole is deflected to the right, and the other to the left of the magnetic meridian, or *vice versa*. If the magnetic field is due to the presence of an ordinary magnet its polarity only depends on the position in which the two poles of the magnet are placed.

The polarity of the magnetic field due to a current flowing through a straight wire depends on the relative position of the ends of the wire with reference to the terminals of the generator. To describe the magnetic effects due to a current it is therefore useful to adopt a convention for the direction of a current. In electrolysis of a metallic salt by electrodes of the same metal the negative electrode is built up at the expense of the positive one, and metal passes from the positive to the negative electrode. For that reason it is customary to speak of the current as flowing *from the positive* terminal *to the negative* one in the external circuit. This is a purely *arbitrary* convenience. It must not be understood to mean anything about the way in which electrically-charged particles shift in a metal conductor. The characteristics of the magnetic field due to the passage of a current may then be summarized under three headings.

(i) If a wire carrying a current lies lengthwise *above* (Fig. 321) the axis of a magnet suspended along the magnetic meridian with the N seeking pole lying towards the end connected with the positive terminal, it is deflected clockwise. If the N-seeking pole lies towards the negative terminal, it is deflected anticlockwise. If we adopt the conventional figure of speech and speak of the current as flowing from positive to negative, both rules are summarized in the statement that *an imaginary man swimming in the current above the compass needle would always see the north-seeking pole deflected to his left*. If the wire lies beneath the needle, an analogous rule applies. The swimmer, now on his back, would still see the north-seeking pole deflected to his left. If the wire is turned back so that the current flows in the opposite direction above and below the compass needle, the deflection is more powerful. If the current passes through several loops, each reinforces the effect. The deflection of the compass needle is then a more sensitive indicator of current.

The sensitivity of the compass needle as a current detector can be further increased by coupling two magnetic needles with unlike poles face to face (Fig. 356). This arrangement or *astatic couple* is unaffected by the earth's field if both needles are equally magnetized. So it is not necessary to arrange the wire along the magnetic meridian. If the coil is wound so that the current first passes above the upper needle, next in the opposite direction below it, and consequently above the second which faces the opposite way, then below the second, and so on, the arrangement is a very sensitive one for detecting the "null point" of a Wheatstone bridge or potentiometer measurement. Such an arrangement is one type of galvanometer.

A galvanometer equipped with an astatic couple can be used to measure current. For making accurate scale divisions showing the amperage corresponding to a particular angle of deflection the method described on page 692 is not a very accurate one, because a very steady current is difficult to get. If the resistance of the coil has been accurately determined we can tap off two currents from two points in a circuit also connected with a potentiometer (Fig. 357), and make practically instantaneous observations on the exact E.M.F. and deflection simultaneously. This gives the scale divisions corresponding to a known E.M.F. and scale divisions corresponding to a known

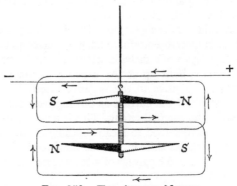

FIG. 356.—THE ASTATIC NEEDLE

amperage are calculated from Ohm's law. Thus if each scale division of a galvanometer whose coil has a resistance of 20 ohms corresponds to $0 \cdot 1$ volt, each scale division also corresponds to $0 \cdot 1 \div 20 = 0 \cdot 005$ ampere.

In practice a galvanometer cannot be used in the same way both for measuring voltage and for measuring amperage. A voltmeter must have a very high coil resistance, or a high resistance must be connected in series with it. If a voltmeter of very low resistance were connected with the terminals of a high-tension supply (e.g. lighting circuit) its wires would melt, or the fuse of the circuit would do so, owing to the high current transmitted. When used for measuring the voltage of a cell, a very high resistance galvanometer is capable of measuring either the total E.M.F. of the cell itself or the E.M.F. available to an external circuit in parallel with the galvanometer (Fig. 358). A current meter (ammeter) must have a very low resistance, so that its presence in the circuit does not appreciably lower the current traversing it. It is not necessary to make the resistance of the coil itself small. If a wire ("shunt") of known low resistance connects the terminals (Fig. 359) a known fraction of the current in the circuit traverses the coil. The same instrument can then be calibrated either for use as a voltmeter, when the shunt is removed, or as an ammeter, when it is connected to both the terminals. Galvanometers with a suspended needle are not used nowadays by the practical engineer, because they have to be kept one way up. An alternative type of instrument will be described later on.

(ii) The characteristic which we have just described is the basis of the old needle telegraph used in railway stations. So many deflections to the right or left in a particular order constituted the letter code, and the transmission was simply carried out by a switch for reversing the current. The principle of the Morse receiver and the electric bell depends on the fact

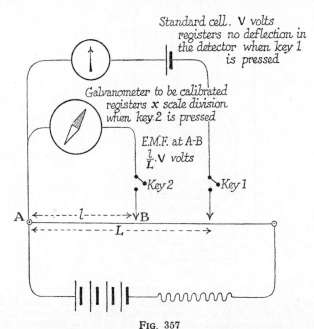

Fig. 357
Calibrating a galvanometer by the potentiometer method.

that a coil of wire through which a current is flowing behaves like a magnet, especially if a core of soft iron is placed inside the coil. Such an arrangement is called an electromagnet. Very strong electromagnets are used for lifting steel rails, and, in occupational surgery, for removing steel filings from the eye. If a coil is wound clockwise away from you with the end of the wire connected with the positive terminal nearest to you, the end of the coil nearest to you is the south-seeking pole. Adopting the usual convention, this is the same as saying that if current flows clockwise away from you the end facing you is the south-seeking pole.

What makes the electromagnet such an important invention is the fact that its magnetism can be destroyed and recreated at will, and can be made greater or less by varying the strength of the current. This is the basis of ordinary telephony. A telephone system consists essentially of a transmitter and a receiver in series with a generator. The transmitter is merely a device by which the vibrations set up by the voice in a diaphragm like that of a gramophone produce corresponding fluctuations of the current in a circuit. The modern transmitter (see Fig. 345) does this by the variation of resistance through loose contact. The receiver is a metal diaphragm placed

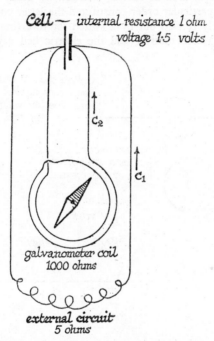

FIG. 358.—GALVANOMETER USED AS A VOLTMETER

When there is no galvanometer in the circuit shown, the total resistance is $1 + 5 = 6$ ohms. If the cell E.M.F. is $1 \cdot 5$ volts the current is $1 \cdot 5 \div 6 = 0 \cdot 25$ amp. The effective E.M.F. in the external circuit is therefore $0 \cdot 25 \times 5 = 1 \cdot 25$ volts. When the galvanometer is connected across the cell terminals, we have two external circuits in parallel and the total external resistance R is given by (p. 699)

$$\frac{1}{R} = \frac{1}{5} + \frac{1}{1000} = \frac{201}{1000} \quad \therefore R = 4 \cdot 975 \text{ ohms}$$

So the entire resistance of the circuit is now $1 + 4 \cdot 975 = 5 \cdot 975$ ohms. Thus the total current in the common circuit is $1 \cdot 5 \div 5 \cdot 975 = 0 \cdot 251$ amp. flowing through the two branches, i.e. $c_1 + c_2 = 0 \cdot 251$ amp. If the E.M.F. available for the two external branches is E

$$5 c_1 = E = 1000 c_2$$
$$c_1 = 200 c_2$$

But
$$c_1 + c_2 = 0 \cdot 251 \text{ amp.}$$
$$\therefore \quad c_2 = 0 \cdot 251 \div 201 \text{ amps.}$$

Hence the E.M.F. at the galvanometer terminals is:

$$(0 \cdot 251 \div 201) \times 1000 = 1 \cdot 249 \text{ volts}$$

This differs by less than one part in a thousand from the E.M.F. available for the external circuit before the galvanometer was connected. Hence the galvanometer can be used to measure voltage available to an external circuit as well as to measure total E.M.F. of the cell (see Fig. 346), if its internal resistance (i.e. that of its coil) is very high.

close to an electromagnet the strength of which varies in unison with the current. In the metal diaphragm this produces vibrations in unison with those set up on the transmitter.

Unlike the ordinary magnet the electromagnet can be used to maintain

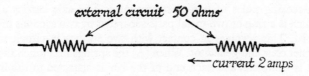

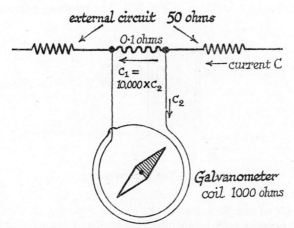

FIG. 359.—GALVANOMETER USED AS AN AMMETER

If the terminals of a galvanometer are connected by a thick wire ("shunt") of known resistance, it can be inserted in a circuit as a current meter without appreciably reducing the flow. Suppose the voltage of the circuit shown above is 100. The current normally flowing in it is $100 \div 50 = 2$ amperes. If the galvanometer with terminals connected by a $0 \cdot 1$ ohm resistance is introduced, the total new resistance (R) added is given by (see p. 699)

$$\frac{1}{R} = \frac{1}{0 \cdot 1} + \frac{1}{1000} = 10 \cdot 001 \therefore R = 0 \cdot 09999 \text{ ohm}$$

So the total resistance in the circuit is increased by less than $0 \cdot 2$ per cent. The same E.M.F. at the terminals of the galvanometer drives a current c_1 through the $0 \cdot 1$ ohm connexion and a current c_2 through the coil of resistance 1,000 ohms, hence by Ohm's law:

$$0 \cdot 1 \, c_1 = E = 1,000 \, c_2$$

If then the galvanometer has been calibrated for a current driven through the coil at known E.M.F., when used as a voltmeter without the connecting wire of $0 \cdot 1$ ohm resistance, each scale division will correspond to 10,000 times as many amps. when the same instrument was used as an ammeter with the $0 \cdot 1$ ohm wire in circuit. Used as a voltmeter without it, a scale division corresponding to 1 volt would be equivalent to a flow of $0 \cdot 001$ amp. through the coil. Used as an ammeter short circuited with a $0 \cdot 1$ ohm resistance, a volt division would be equivalent to 10 amps. The same instrument with a dial calibrated for volts and amps. can be used for either purpose, if the low resistance between the terminals can be disconnected by a switch or put into the circuit as required motion. In the electric bell (Fig. 325) a piece of soft iron is mounted on a spring which brings it back into position when the current is switched off, and in so doing switches the current on again. Various types of electric motors work on essentially the same principle. The simplest type (commonly sold as toys) consists of a soft iron bar (Fig. 361) revolving between the north- and south-seeking poles of two electromagnets. The axle carries a simple switch, which is a ring of two metal parts separated by two sections of insulating material. This revolves in contact with two springs in circuit with the electromagnet coils and generator. When (A) the springs first touch the metal, the circuit is complete, and each end of the bar is attracted to the live pole which it is approaching. In doing so, (B), it brings the insulating material into contact with the springs, breaks contact, and being no longer attracted to the now dead poles of the electromagnet rotates a little further of its own inertia. This again completes the circuit.

An alternative type is shown in Fig. 362. The revolving part carries the

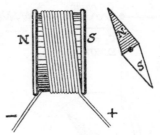

FIG. 360.—THE ELECTROMAGNET

coils which are wound so that when the current is passing the two ends are approaching opposite poles of a strong magnet. The axle carries an arrangement similar to the preceding. The ends of each coil are connected to the opposite metal sectors of the ring. Since the same sector comes alternately into contact with the springs connected to the positive and negative terminals, the direction of the current is reversed at each half turn, and hence the polarity of the electromagnets. Since unlike poles attract each other, the direction of winding is executed so that the electromagnetic arms have the opposite polarity to the permanent magnet ends which they are approaching.

(iii) Electric motors designed like either of the above are not the type much used nowadays to work electrified transport, lifts, lathes, pumps, vacuum cleaners, refrigerators, electric fans, etc. The design of these is generally based on the application of a third characteristic of the magnetic field in the neighbourhood of a conductor carrying a current (Fig. 363). This is the fact that if a coil or loop conveying a current is free to move about the axis of a magnet it rotates about the latter. Seen from above the rotation is clockwise if the direction of current through a wire suspended above a N-seeking pole is downward towards the latter. A simple experiment which shows this property is illustrated in Fig. 363. A modern electric motor consists of an armature of coiled wire arranged radially about the axle of the moving part which is placed between the poles of the permanent magnet (see p. 714, Fig. 362).

The speed of rotation of a conductor so placed in the field of a magnet is directly proportional to the current. This fact is made use of in the construction of an electric meter to measure the number of units consumed in a single dwelling. The meter is in essence a motor geared down like a cyclometer, so that a fraction of a turn of the pointer represents an enormous number of rotations. Since the speed is proportional to the current, the number of turns is proportional to the product of the time and the current.

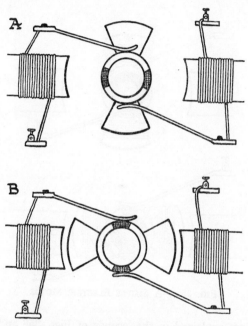

FIG. 361.—A SIMPLE ELECTRIC MOTOR

The electrical energy (kilowatt hours) used is proportional to the product of the time, current, and E.M.F. Since the last is fixed at the terminals of a house circuit the number of turns is proportional to the electrical energy consumed. If it were practicable to make a motor with negligible resistance, as compared with that of the house circuit when all the lamps, etc., are being used, a motor geared down to work a cyclometer dial could therefore be used in series with the house circuit to measure the number of kilowatt hours consumed. This is not practicable. Since the meter coils have a fairly high resistance, it is connected with the circuit like an ammeter. That is to say, the terminals are connected with a low resistance wire, so that a known fraction of the current is tapped through the high resistance of the meter coils. The minute current drawn off does not appreciably affect the consumer's account.

The ammeters and voltmeters of the practising electrician are sometimes based on the fact that a watch-spring placed in a magnetic field undergoes torsion when a current passes through it. This torsion can be used to rotate a dial, and the device is portable. Exceedingly sensitive galvanometers of either type used in research work depend on the movement of a straight wire or coil in a strong magnetic field. Very minute movements which occur when a current traverses the wire can be recorded by focussing a beam of light on a minute piece of silvered glass fixed to it. A spot of light is thus projected on a screen, and a shift is magnified by moving the screen further away. Galvanometers of any design can be used as ammeters or voltmeters

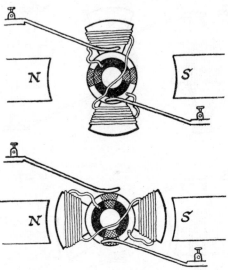

FIG. 362.—A SIMPLE ELECTRIC MOTOR

by the procedure explained in the legends of Figs. 358 and 359, and the same methods for calibrating the dial are equally applicable.

Needless to say, the chemical method of measuring a current employed in the earliest researches into electrical phenomena is useless in everyday life, because it is laborious, lengthy, and unsuitable unless the current is very steady. Similarly the Wheatstone bridge method for finding resistance is only used for very accurate work. In everyday practice the resistance between two points in a circuit is taken as the ratio of the voltmeter and ammeter reading. The potentiometer method of finding voltage, like the Wheatstone bridge method for resistance, is essentially one for standardizing a more convenient type of instrument for everyday use.

We have established the basic principles involved in using such instruments by using the chemical property of the current as a definition of current strength. This leads to a straightforward demonstration of Ohm's rule. If we take the magnetic effect as a basis of measurement, we have to decide at the outset on a suitable unit of deflection. If we adopted the angle itself we should not arrive at a simple relation between the contributions which the generator and the circuit make to the effects observed. Experiment actually shows that the current as we have defined it is proportional to the *tangent* of the angle through which the astatic couple of a simple galvanometer is deflected, and this is in agreement with the results arrived at by elaborate mathematical analysis based on the experimental laws of magnetic attractions and the conservation of energy. To grasp the principle which underlies the use of the magnetic effect it is not necessary to understand the theory of magnetic attractions. We can mark off a dial suitable for quick and convenient measurement of current by its magnetic effect, if we have any independent method of measuring a current, just as we might mark off the scale divisions of a lever weighing machine by trying out the position of the rider and the counterpoise equivalent to different weights on the pan.

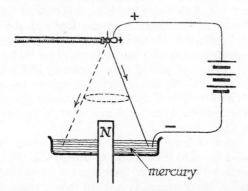

FIG. 363.—MOTION OF A CURRENT IN A MAGNETIC FIELD

If the positive terminal is connected above and the negative terminal below, the wire rotates *clockwise* as seen from *above*.

THE DYNAMO

Babbage, then Lucasian professor in the Newtonian succession, wrote his tract the *Decline of Science in England* in the year 1830. He was concerned with the state of the official organs of English culture. In the ensuing year the future of electrical technology was revolutionized by a group of discoveries made by men who were not products of a well-established social culture. They were made independently and simultaneously in England by Michael Faraday and in the United States by Joseph Henry. The scientific careers of both men were made possible by the creation of new machinery to produce, as Sprat said of the early Royal Society, "a continuous succession of inventors." Faraday followed Davy as head of the Royal Institution, founded in London by an American citizen, named Benjamin Thompson, to encourage the application of science to industrial and domestic economy. Henry became the first director of the Smithsonian Institution, and in that capacity his researches covered a wide range of practical problems, including the invention of a system of fog signals to protect shipping. Vast private fortunes were made as the outcome of their discoveries. Both men gave their advice freely, and subsisted on salaries from which they accumulated no substantial property to leave behind them. As head of the Royal Institution, Faraday received £100 a year with coal and candles.

Their careers thus illustrate a new feature in the history of capitalism. The entrepreneur had ceased to be a man of like stature as Roebuck, Boulton, or Wedgwood. Henceforth how wealth accumulated becomes more and more a tale of how discoveries made by public servants in institutions endowed in the public interest are diverted by credit monopoly to private gain.

The Smithsonian Institution in Washington is a forerunner of the large-scale public laboratories in which the bulk of modern scientific research is conducted. It was, as W. H. Taft put it, the incubator of American Science, and as such its history offers an entertaining footnote to the place of science in contemporary civilization. It was started by a bequest which passed into the hands of the American Government in 1837 under the will of James Smithson, bastard son of Sir Hugh Smithson, first duke of Northumberland. The latter had enlarged his resources by marriage with the Percys, whose estates were rich in minerals. He rapidly accumulated a fabulous fortune by exploiting their coal resources with brutal disregard for the health and safety of the miners of both sexes and all ages. A century and a half have since elapsed. Till January 1947, his family continued to exact its annual toll from the consumer. The British coal industry then became the property of the whole nation. Thenceforward the health and safety of the miner became the responsibility of all its citizens.

The natural father of James Smithson spent his fortune in lavish ostentation, which was a by-word at the Court of George III. His son, a friend of Cavendish, was elected to the Royal Society as a mineralogical chemist three years after Priestley. He prospered in material things, retained a healthy and proper repugnance toward his father and towards George III, and displayed a keen sympathy for the Jacobins and for American democracy. Eventually he disposed of his fortune in a way which may still be commended to the attention of the legitimate branch of his family. He socialized his own property by giving it to the Government of "the United States of America to found at Washington an establishment for 'the increase and diffusion of knowledge among men.' " It was his hope, as Crowther tells us in his own words, that his name "shall live in the memory of man when the titles of the Northumberlands and Percys are extinct and forgotten." In this, it may be that he was unduly optimistic. The British branch of the family have earned their place in the history books for a different reason. They will be remembered for their tenacious resistance to the social exploitation of the nation's mineral wealth.

If the voltaic cell were the only source of current, the use of electricity would be restricted to the chemical laboratory and to a few minor amenities of everyday life, such as railway telegraphs or electric bells. A new era of electricity began with the discovery that current can be generated without the destruction of material resources by chemical decomposition. Chemical decomposition by the current itself depends on analogous changes in the voltaic cell. Any chemical change based on the reaction of electrolytes or ionizable substances can be used as a source of current. So likewise every magnetic effect resulting from the flow of the electric current in a conductor corresponds to some way of producing current. When a current flows through a conductor a magnetic field is set up in its neighbourhood. Conversely, when the magnetic field in the neighbourhood of a conducting circuit is changing, a current flows in the latter. This is called *electromagnetic induction.*

A simple experiment illustrates this. If we connect the ends of a long piece of flexible wire with the terminals of a sensitive galvanometer, and move it quickly between opposite poles of two bar magnets, the galvanometer needle is deflected one way or the other according to the direction of the movement

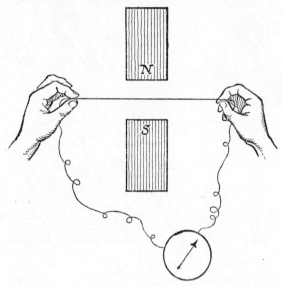

FIG. 364.—INDUCTION OF CURRENT IN WIRE MOVED ACROSS A MAGNETIC FIELD

(Fig. 364). The rotation of a loop of wire about a fixed axis between the poles of a magnet, as in Fig. 365, can therefore be used to maintain a current. Which is the positive and which is the negative end of the wire is difficult to remember without the aid of a rule, like the mnemonic of Ampère's swimmer on p. 707. Imagine the right hand resting on the north pole with one finger pointing to the south pole opposite, the thumb pointed outwards at right angles, and the other fingers downwards over the face of the north pole. The direction of the current (positive to negative) in the further half of the coil is given by the thumb, if the direction of rotation is indicated by the second, third, etc., fingers. If the rotation is clockwise from the south pole to north above the axle as in Fig. 365, and if the ends of the wire are at the end of the coil nearest the observer, the positive terminal is next to the north pole. In the position drawn, *cd* is the nearer half of the coil, and in this position *d* is the positive terminal. After a half-turn *ab* is the nearer half of the coil, and *a* is the positive terminal. Hence if *a* and *d* are connected by flexible wire to a galvanometer the direction of current flowing through it will change at each half turn, and the needle will swing first one way and then the other.

If the axle is rotated repeatedly while the ends *a* and *d* are connected to the terminals of a galvanometer (or any other device which registers the presence of a current) with flex, the latter will become more and more twisted at each turn. To register the current delivered by a continuously rotating loop of wire as in Fig. 365 the two ends *a* and *d* must make movable contact

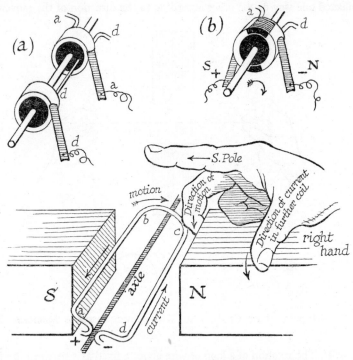

FIG. 365.—PRINCIPLE OF THE DYNAMO
Commutator and brushes for A.C. (*a*) and for unidirectional (*b*)

with the conductors leading the current away. This can be done by connecting them to metal surfaces mounted on insulating material like Bakelite, and revolving in contact with a smooth spring or metal brush.

Such an arrangement may be carried out in two ways—(*a*) and (*b*) in Fig. 365. The two ends (*a* and *d*) of the loop may be connected to separate metal rings so that the same brush or spring is always in contact with the same end as in (*a*). If this arrangement is used the current will flow first one way, then the other at each complete turn since *a* and *d* are alternately negative and positive. It is then said to be an *alternating* current. On the other hand the two ends *a* and *d* may be connected to the two halves of a split ring, as in (*b*), so that the ends *a* and *d* come alternately into contact with one and the same spring or brush. If so one brush or spring is always negative, and the other always positive. While the current delivered from the brush terminals rises and falls, being greatest when the loops are cutting the field between the poles at right angles and least when they move parallel to it (at right angles to the position shown in the figure), it flows in one direction only.

The strength of the current can be greatly increased if many loops of wire revolve simultaneously in the same magnetic field, and if they are wound round a soft iron drum (Fig. 366) which concentrates the field between the poles. Such a drum carrying an enormous number of loops is called an "armature," and a machine in which an armature revolves in a magnetic field is called a magneto or dynamo. According to the type of brush contact

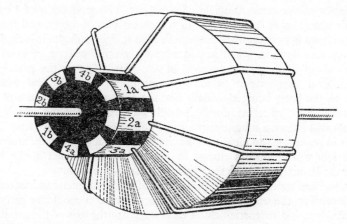

FIG. 366.—DIAGRAMMATIC VIEW OF ARMATURE FOR D.C. DYNAMO OR MOTOR
VERY MUCH SIMPLIFIED

a dynamo gives either an "alternating" (A.C.) or a unidirectional current. If many loops are used (only four are shown in Fig. 366) the brush is practically always in contact with the ends of a loop in which the current is maximal. So the unidirectional current does not appreciably ebb and flow. It is a *direct* current (D.C.) like that of a battery. For heating and therefore for lighting purposes a direct current has no special advantages over an alternating one, since the heating effect does not depend on the direction of the current.

As a source of power to drive an electric motor an alternating current is also equally useful if the motor itself has the right type of contact. Since a conductor carrying a current rotates in a magnetic field (p. 712) a dynamo can be used as a motor if supplied with current of the appropriate kind. An A.C. dynamo will require A.C., and a D.C. dynamo will require D.C., if used as a motor. For chemical purposes a D.C. current is essential, since one terminal of the electrolytic cell must always be positive and the other must always be negative. Since natural magnets of high power are not very reliable and are troublesome a D.C. dynamo has a further advantage. Some of the current can be drawn off to maintain the field magnets. If coils connected with the terminals surround the latter, their small residual magnetism is always sufficient to excite a current when the dynamo begins to work. This increases the magnetic field which rapidly assumes its maximum strength. The advantages of an A.C. dynamo will be explained later.*

ELECTROMAGNETIC INDUCTION

The problem of transmitting electric power, when we have harnessed available natural resources for generating it, raises several technical problems, which will be more easy to grasp when we have looked at other aspects of "electromagnetic induction." In the dynamo, current flows when a conductor moves across the field of a magnet. The production of a current in this way (Fig. 367) is only one of three examples of the general rule that current flows in a circuit when a magnetic field at right angles to it is changing. Current also flows in a coil wound round a magnet when a piece of iron moves about in the neighbourhood of the poles. This is the principle of the original telephone in which the transmitter was identical with the receiver, the latter being essentially like the receiver (Fig. 345) in a modern telephone. Each vibration of a steel diaphragm lying above the pole of a bar magnet will induce a minute current in a coil wound round the latter. If the coil is in series with an identical instrument used as a receiver, each variation of current will produce a change in the field of the magnet in the latter. Thus the attractive force on the diaphragm varies in unison.

A third and more important illustration of electromagnetic induction does not depend on the use of a permanent magnet. Near a conductor carrying a current there is a magnetic field at right angles to the axis of the conductor. When the current is switched on or off there is therefore a changing magnetic field around it. If another conductor whose ends are connected with a galvanometer is placed alongside of it, as in Fig. 367, the effect of breaking or making the "primary current" is equivalent to moving the second conductor across a magnetic field. So the galvanometer needle is deflected in opposite directions when the primary current is switched on and off. It registers no deflection when the current is steadily flowing in the primary circuit. The secondary current is only produced momentarily at the make and break. It flows one way at the "make" and one way at the "break."

When the current is switched on in the primary circuit a current flows momentarily in a parallel secondary circuit in the reverse direction. When the primary current is cut off, the current flows in the secondary in the same direction as the previous flow of current in the primary circuit. If the secondary and primary circuits are straight wires the effect is greatest when they lie parallel, and if one is turned so that it is at right angles to the other no

---

* The numerical value assigned as the voltage of an A.C. circuit is not the maximum E.M.F. between the terminals in either "phase" of the current. It is equivalent to the value of E deduced from the heat production of the circuit and the known resistance in it by applying the formula $E^2 \div R = W$. This is the "effective" (geometric average) E.M.F. between the terminals.

secondary current flows. If a wire with two ends connected to a galvanometer runs the length of a ship, and a cable on the sea bottom is transmitting
an intermittent current the deflection of the pointer is therefore greatest

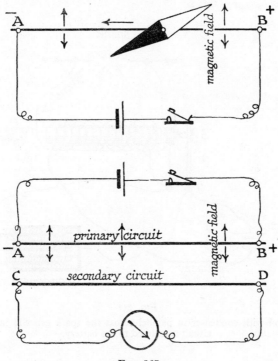

FIG. 367

Above, current producing magnetic field when the key is closed. Below, arrangement to show induced current in neighbouring circuit when the magnetic field is made
or broken by closing the key.

when the ship is running exactly over the cable. Such a device now replaces
the pilot boat to guide ships into port or dock.

The phenomenon of electromagnetic induction can be made more striking
if the primary and secondary circuits are coils wound coaxially around a
soft iron core of circular section. The voltage registered at each kick of
the galvanometer is then dependent on the number of turns in the two
circuits. If the number of turns in the secondary coil is very much greater
than the number of turns in the primary a very high voltage is attained at
the break. Since, however, this means that the length of wire traversed is
greater, the resistance of the secondary circuit is proportionately increased,
and the secondary current is proportionately diminished. If the primary circuit
is fitted with a vibrating switch like the spring of an electric bell or Morse
receiver (Fig. 324) a rapid and regular succession of "make" and "break"
in a primary circuit of low E.M.F. can be made to induce an alternating
current of high E.M.F. in the secondary circuit. This is the principle of

the induction coil devised by Faraday (Fig. 368). When first invented the induction coil was sold to medical practitioners for the supposedly beneficial effect of the unpleasant tingling shocks obtained by holding two metal cylinders attached to the ends of the secondary coil. Today the underlying

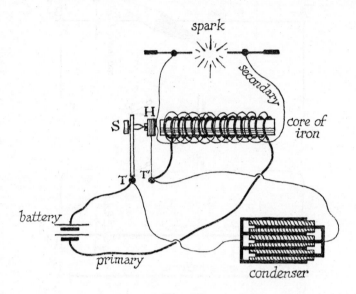

FIG. 368

Induction coil with condenser in parallel across the spark gap SH in the primary circuit connected to the battery.

principle is the basis of the "transformer" in high voltage transmission. The instrument itself is an essential part of X-ray and wireless equipment.

THE SOCIAL SIGNIFICANCE OF THE DYNAMO

Before the invention of the dynamo, the sole source of power available for electrical appliances was the voltaic battery which was costly, cumbersome and ephemeral. The dynamo was more economical and more durable; but the first steam-driven dynamos could not compete economically with the steam engine itself for performance of work which the latter could already carry out. What made demand for electric power so immediately insistent was that it could perform so many new and welcome tasks. After introduction of the telegraph, successive electrical inventions followed swiftly. By the mid-'forties an electro-plating industry was flourishing in Birmingham where the discovery of electro-magnetic induction soon became profitable. In 1842 Woolrich had patented a device for producing a unidirectional intermittent current by the movement of a magnet. This guaranteed a better deposit of silver than is obtainable from the direct current from a voltaic battery; and Faraday had the gratification of seeing it in operation at Prime's works in 1845. In the same decade tentative efforts to exploit Davy's carbon arc lamp stimulated construction of steam-driven magneto-electric machines. By 1862 a dynamo already designed in 1856 had become the source of power for arc lighting in the lighthouse at Dungeness.

Such early dynamos relied on permanent magnets. Great economy of construction came about in 1872 when Granime made a *self-exciting* model. Thenceforth, arc-lighting for railway stations and main thoroughfares was vastly more economical. New electrical appliances now came into use in rapid succession. In 1876 Graham Bell, Edison and Elisha Gray took out patents for telephone design in the U.S.A. By 1879 there were small exchanges in America and in Britain. The carbon filament lamp of Edison (U.S.) and Swan (Britain) became available in that year; and electric light throughout large buildings whose illumination had hitherto made exorbitant demands on man-power with considerable risk of destruction by fire was now at last possible. In 1880 its authorities equipped the British Museum Reading Room with incandescent filament lamps for which a Siemen's steam-driven dynamo supplied the power. In the same year a Ferranti steam-driven dynamo supplied the First Avenue Hotel in Holborn with power for 1,000 lamps. In the next (1881), the Siemens Company exhibited an electric tram-car at an exhibition in Paris. The use of electrical power for transporting growing urban populations to work without exposing the householder to smoke pollution was soon to bring about a revolution of transport by the extension of the underground system in large cities.

Electric power has made it possible to build larger hotels and places of entertainment because of size-limit previously dictated by cost in time and labour for illumination. It has made the sky-scraper possible, because it has also made possible the use of elevators. It has made expansion of towns possible because it has provided them with smokeless transport. Such changes have been realizable because the dynamo can distribute power over vastly greater distances than the belt and pulley system of the old factory steam engine; but they took shape when the dynamo was itself wholly dependent on steam and coal. By 1900, schemes for generating current by water power were in operation and work on the Niagara project was in hand.

Thenceforth, western countries with large natural waterfalls were at once able to adapt the principle of the watermill to rotate the armature. Gigantic schemes for building dams to make water power available are now in operation in all the continents of the world. Once the output has paid off the initial cost, the production of electricity thus involves no further application of human labour to supply fresh stores of energy. The decline of water as a source with the accompanying urban congestion of the coal age had come about because it was not practicable to distribute such power to places where most needed. Now that single generating stations can distribute 1,000,000 horse-power over a radius of 250 miles, we are free to distribute populations in accordance with a high standard of health and more elbow room. As sources of power, coal and petrol called for a continuous output of human drudgery to extract fuel. Hydro-electric power transfers this energy to the credit side of the balance sheet of available leisure. Exposure of workers to heat and soot is no longer the price to pay for more power. Physical conditions of factory labour need be no less congenial than those of the most up-to-date laboratory. Elsewhere, as in the home, electricity can now make unskilled labour an anachronism.

THE INTERNAL COMBUSTION ENGINE

Electromagnetic induction provided the means of revolutionizing the use of heat before superseding it. In the steam engine fuel is used to produce heat, and heat is used to change water into the gaseous state. The second law of thermodynamics reminds us that any process which involves the conversion of heat into work is wasteful. So it is better to convert the stored chemical energy of organic matter into work without the intervening stage of changing a liquid into vapour by heat. This can be done by using the explosive force of any reaction which entails change of volume. Thus when petrol vapour is mixed with air the reaction may be represented thus

$$\underbrace{C_5H_{12} + 8O_2}_{9 \text{ mols}} \rightarrow \underbrace{5CO_2 + 6H_2O}_{11 \text{ mols}}$$

If the pressure and temperature did not change, 9 volumes of explosive mixture would be replaced by 11 volumes of the products of the explosion. Independently of this change, and more important, is the fact that heat liberated in the reaction produces an enormous expansion of the products. To use this expansion it is first necessary to induce combination of the ingredients of the explosive mixture. The discovery of electromagnetic induction made it a simple matter to time a rapid succession of sparks to occur at suitable intervals in conformity with the movement of a piston. This was originally done with an induction coil (see p. 722), which was then superseded by a small dynamo.

Internal combustion became a practical source of power as the result of experiments in 1862, when de Rochas showed that the ignition temperature of an explosive mixture is greatly lowered by previous compression. The way in which an internal combustion engine works is briefly as follows. The cylinder which contains the piston is equipped with sparking points, and with valves to admit the explosive mixture and to let out the products. The main shaft works a small dynamo ("magneto") and a rotating switch ("distributor"), so that the spark exactly synchronizes with the appropriate position of the piston, and the movements of the latter are geared to the valves which open and close successively in unison with the successive phases of the piston movement. A flywheel of high inertia ensures that the piston flies forwards and backwards twice at each explosion, so that the explosive mixture is compressed at the moment when sparking takes place. The valve letting out the products of combustion opens at the end of the outward thrust due to explosion and closes at the end of the inward movement. At the next outward movement, more of the explosive mixture is sucked in, as the mixture is compressed by the return stroke just before the end of which the spark is delivered.

The explosive mixture may be a mixture of air with very fine coal dust, coal gas, or combustible organic vapour. If the engine is not running for long periods a highly volatile substance like petrol is preferable, because it evaporates readily at low temperatures if sprayed through a fine jet (carburettor), but an engine develops sufficient heat after running a little while to vaporize any liquid compound. Paraffin and comparatively heavy oils, as in the Diesel type, can be used for stationary engines or ships. As an alternative fuel, alcohol being universally obtainable from plants releases the heat engine from dependence on localized resources of combustible matter.

TRANSMISSION OF ELECTRIC POWER

A simple induction coil may be adapted to get a higher or lower voltage without greatly reducing the power (W = EC) transmitted. If the secondary circuit of a simple induction coil has a smaller number of turns than the primary circuit, the induced current at the make or break has a smaller voltage. If it has a larger number of turns the voltage at the terminals of the secondary circuit will be greater than the voltage applied to the primary circuit. The current is proportionately increased or decreased by diminishing or adding to the number of turns. If the current in the primary circuit is itself an alternating current, the primary current ebbs and flows of its own account.

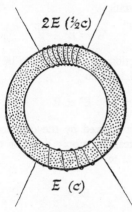

2E (½c)

E (c)

FIG. 369

Transformer formed by two coils wound round a soft iron core. The upper coil has twice as many turns as the lower. To double the E.M.F (and halve the current) attach the lower coil to the supply ("step up"). To halve the E.M.F. (and double the current) attach the upper coil to the supply ("step down"). The two coils are here shown in a simplified way to expose the ratio of the winding. In practice both would be wound all the way round the ring, and 100 per cent efficiency would not be possible unless the secondary completely enclosed the primary, so that all the lines of force from the latter cut the former.

So there is no need to have a contact breaker. Two coils placed side by side may therefore be used as a "transformer" (Fig. 369) to "step up" or to "step down."* The *efficiency* or ratio of power put *in* to power got *out* of a transformer may be as much as 95 per cent.

In distributing electrical power from situations where it is convenient to produce it, a foremost consideration is to economize in the use of wire. At an early stage in the history of telegraphy it was discovered that the earth can be used as one cable if plates connected to terminals are sunk deep in it. So, if one terminal of a generator and one terminal of any instrument using current are both *earthed*, it is only necessary to connect one terminal of the generator to one terminal of the instrument. The problem is then

* The resistance of a transformer is very small compared with that of the external circuit.

to keep the thickness of metal in the single cable as small as possible. If the voltage is very high the latter must be held high above ground to prevent sparking to earth.

Since electrical power (W) is the product of the voltage and current, the same amount of power can be transmitted by using a high voltage and low current, or a low voltage and large current. Thus the transmission of 10 kilowatts (10,000 watts) may mean that a current of 10 amps. is drawn through the circuit by a generator of 1,000 volts, a current of 100 amps. by a generator of 100 volts, or a current of 2 amps. by a generator of 5,000 volts, etc. A current of 100 amps. passed along a thin wire would heat it considerably. So high current transmission means greater expenditure on metal for cables.

You can look on the problem of circuit cost in another way. Since $W = EC$ and $C = E \div R$, in any circuit

$$W = E^2 \div R$$

Hence if the power production of a circuit is to be fixed at a definite figure by the work the generator has to do

$$E^2 \propto R$$

If the length of the circuit is fixed by the distance over which the power is to be transmitted, the resistance only depends on the sectional area (a) being inversely proportional to it, hence

$$E^2 \propto \frac{l}{a}$$

And since the cost $(£)$ is proportional to the sectional area,

$$£ \propto \frac{l}{E^2}$$

Thus the cost of cable is inversely proportional to the square of the E.M.F., e.g. the cost for transmitting the same power from a generator of 100 volts is one hundred times as great as the cost of transmitting it from a generator of 1,000 volts.

Although the D.C. dynamo is in many other respects more useful than the A.C., it has one practical disadvantage. A voltage greater than about 500 is very difficult to maintain owing to sparking across the sections of the commutator (*b* in Fig. 365). The ends of the loops in the armature of an A.C. dynamo are much more readily insulated (as in Fig. 365, *a*), and voltages of 10,000 are comparatively easily maintained. For this reason the A.C. dynamo is used as the primary source for generating power. The voltage is usually raised to a higher level by a step-up transformer and transmitted at very high voltage (e.g. 50,000 volts) to substations where it may be reduced by step-down transformers to work an A.C. motor for driving D.C. dynamos. This entails very little loss of energy by friction. Domestic circuits may have their own step-down transformers when supplied with A.C.

The A.C. dynamos at Niagara generate from 20,000 to 21,000 volts. This is transformed at the source up to 50,000 or 100,000 volts for transmission across country, e.g. as far as Montreal. The London Transport system is supplied by the Chelsea Power Station with about 50,000 kilowatts produced by ten steam turbine-driven alternators at a voltage of 11,000. This is distributed to substations, where it is used to drive motors working D.C. dynamos which supply current for the trains themselves with 600 volts. The giant hydro-electric works set up by the Soviet Government at the Dnieprostroi dam were designed to produce an eventual output of over half a million kilowatts.

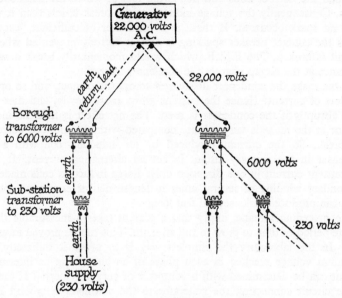

Fig. 370

Simple diagram to show step down in successive stages from the generating station to the house circuit.

THE MEANING OF SELF-INDUCTION

So far, the phenomena of current and frictional electricity have been kept apart. Reasons for regarding them as essentially identical have been given on page 662. There it was suggested that the battery current and the frictional machine spark differ only in one essential feature. Battery current is a steady output of energy at low voltage. The sparks and shocks of electrical machines are momentary discharges at very high voltages. The induced currents produced by an A.C. dynamo or an induction coil provided with an automatic current breaker are essentially successive currents of very short duration involving very high voltages. If the view stated is correct we should therefore expect to find that alternating and intermittent currents produced by electromagnetic induction behave like the discharge from a frictional machine. That this is so is a fact which has results of enormous importance in everyday life.

A condenser can be used to increase the brightness of the spark, the interval between successive sparks and the length of spark obtainable from a frictional machine. A condenser connected across the contact breaker in the primary circuit of an induction coil (Fig 368) has exactly the same effect as a condenser connected with the two knobs of a frictional machine. Perhaps no fact brings out the identity of frictional and current electricity in a more striking way. If there is no condenser across the contact breaker in the primary circuit there is perpetual sparking each time the current is broken. Since a spark involves the passage of a current, this delays the rate at which the current ebbs and hence the rate at which the magnetic field varies. Consequently the voltage induced at the break is less than it would be if no spark occurred. If there is a condenser of sufficient "capacity" across the contact breaker sparking is almost entirely prevented when the current is broken. The E.M.F. which would momentarily break down the resistance at the airgap charges the condenser instead.

At the make the condenser discharges across the contact, and so opposes the flow of current. Hence the current grows more slowly, and dies down more abruptly if the condenser is used. The net effect is that the induced current at the make is very minute compared with the induced current at the break. So the current produced by an induction coil with a large condenser in the primary circuit is not an alternating current. It is an intermittent current in one direction only. Large induction coils made with a secondary winding of several miles in length deliver enormous voltages. They can produce sparks several feet long.

The preceding remarks imply that a current takes a measurable though minute period of time to grow to full strength. This can be proved in various ways. In the laboratory the simplest way is to prove it indirectly. The maximum voltage reached in each phase of an alternating or intermittent current can be determined with a voltmeter of very low inertia. If the wire in the circuit connecting the generator to the voltmeter is wound into a coil the maximum voltage is diminished. The mere fact of winding the wire into a coil does not increase its resistance. The only alternative explanation which experiment suggests is that the setting up of a current in any one turn induces the flow of a current in the opposite direction in neighbouring ones, so that the current does not reach its full strength as quickly as it otherwise would. This is supported by the fact that the maximum voltage is further diminished if a soft iron core is inserted inside the coil. A piece of flex with several parallel strands will exhibit the same phenomenon. It will act as a "choke," steadying the ebb and flow of a rapidly changing current as compared with the flow of current from the same generator through a straight piece of wire of the same resistance. Thus the rate at which a current assumes its full strength when contact is made, or the rate at which a current falls to zero when contact is broken, depends on "self-induction" of opposing currents in the same circuit.

There is also another sort of electrical inertia or damping of the current. The maximum voltage in either phase of the alternating current can be depressed by putting a condenser in parallel between the terminals of the generator. A very long wire surrounded by an insulator is physically equivalent to a condenser, of which the other plate is the earth itself. Thus a cable can damp a current by its *capacity* (p. 649) to store electrification.

One reason why science can only thrive in a community which applies its conclusions to the regulation of social conduct is that industry provides the opportunity of testing theory on a vaster scale than laboratory experiment permits. Alexander Ure's comment upon the expansion of metal pipes in a cotton mill has already shown us how an industrial process can provide spectacular demonstration of phenomena which can only be detected with careful measurement in the laboratory. "On this scale, the amount of the expansion and contraction needs no micrometer to measure it, for it is visible to the eye, and may be determined by a carpenter's rule." An analogous remark applies to the phenomenon of electrical inertia. What is elusive in

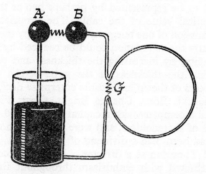

FIG. 371.—INERTIA DUE TO SELF-INDUCTION

A Leyden jar is discharged by bringing the knob B connected to the outer coat near the knob A of the inner coat. If the wire connexion is bent in a loop as shown, a spark may occur across G, in spite of the enormous resistance of the air as compared with the wire loop. The discharge is so rapid that the delay in conduction due to self-inductance chokes off the current in the loop.

the laboratory and can be inferred only from indirect evidence assumed formidable dimensions when the first long-distance cables were laid down. The effect was to stimulate a new field of theoretical enquiry, the immense practical consequences of which may be gauged from the fact that Thomson (afterwards Lord Kelvin) left a fortune of £161,923 from his patents. The story of the cable is well told by Crowther, from whose essay on Kelvin (*British Scientists of the Nineteenth Century*) the following is extracted:

"A cable consists of two conductors, a wire and the sea, separated by an insulator, gutta-percha. Electrically, it behaves like a condenser, or Leyden jar, or the system of two conducting spheres separated by an insulator which Faraday investigated, and with which he proved that a certain period of time must pass before the insulator absorbs a complete charge of electrical energy. The phenomenon of retardation of signals, owing to the preliminary filling-up of the gutta-percha with electrical energy, first became practically noticeable in the Anglo-Dutch cable, which was 110 miles long. In his first paper, *On the Theory of the Electric Telegraph*, Thomson elucidated one of the most important properties of long cables, a knowledge of which is essential to success-ful operation. He showed that if a sharp electrical impulse is given to one end of a long cable, only a small part of its energy reaches the other end almost instantaneously. The impulse gradually spreads out into a wave whose begin-ning reaches the other end very quickly, but whose crest arrives only after a leisurely and almost imperceptible rising, and then fades away. The observer at the receiving end sees only a gentle rise and fall, without the definition necessary for signalling. Thomson showed that the magnitude of this phenomenon depended on the combined value of the electrical capacity and resistance of the cable. As each of these was directly proportional to the length, the effect increased as the square of the length of a cable. If the retardation in a cable one hundred miles long were one-tenth of a second, then that in two thousand miles of the same sort of cable would be four hundred times as great, or forty seconds. Any system of signalling that depended on the observa-tion of the crest of a wave could at the best send only one sign in forty seconds. As a single letter had to be represented by perhaps two or three signs, the delay destroyed the practical value of the cable. The proprietors could not earn profits if the transmission of one telegram was to occupy the cable for the whole of one day. Evidently the retardation could be reduced by reducing the resist-ance and the capacity, by increasing the thickness and purity of the copper wire, and increasing the thickness of the gutta-percha insulating material. In 1856 the promoters of the Atlantic cable enterprise decided they were ready to start construction. J. Brett, Charles Bright, Cyrus Field, and O. E. W. Whitehouse formed a company with a capital of £350,000. The directors were elected by the vote of shareholders, and were to receive no remuneration until the shareholders had been paid a dividend of 10 per cent. The Scottish share-holders nominated Thomson as a director. . . . The successful completion of the cable was celebrated with enthusiasm throughout Britain and America. Immense public expectation had been aroused by the achievement. But the expectation was rapidly disappointed . . . the Queen's cablegram of ninety-nine words had required sixteen and a half hours for transmission from Ireland to America. . . . Whitehouse was suspended, and Thomson was put in charge."

The large scale of this enterprise stimulated the growth of electrical theory in two ways. One is described by Crowther in the following remarks:

"He brought his students into a general investigation of specimens of commer-cial copper, and found that their conductivity varied enormously, and that a small percentage of impurity could reduce conductivity by 30 or 40 per cent. The cable was being manufactured in twelve hundred pieces, each two miles long, and the conductivity of the copper cores of the pieces varied enor-mously. Thomson's investigation of cable copper had several very important consequences. It led to the foundation of the first industrial laboratory for testing materials, and to the study of methods and units of measurement. When Thomson by determined opposition managed to have a clause specifying the conductivity of copper put into future cable contracts, the contractors at first said its fulfilment was impossible. Thomson's work had great influence on the standardization of engineering materials, and on practical measurement, and thus became an important preliminary to the industrial method of mass-production, which can be applied only to uniform raw materials."

Crowther also refers to the cultural impact of telegraphic development in the ensuing passages:

"The establishment of the Cavendish Laboratory at Cambridge in 1874 was in part stimulated by Thomson's achievements at Glasgow. Until the middle of the nineteenth century university science teaching in Britain had not been orientated in directions of interest to the industrialists who had gained the leadership of British society. Before that date university science teaching had been inspired by the mercantilists of an earlier period of British social development. Under their influence astronomy was the branch of physical science with the highest prestige, because safe navigation was dependent on a knowledge of astronomy, and successful sea-trading was dependent on safe navigation. The prestige of physics in British universities did not surpass the prestige of astronomy until the importance of industrialism surpassed the importance of mercantilism. The manufacture of machinery, of steam engines, and later of electrical machines made an exact knowledge of the properties of matter necessary to social progress. Thomson was fond of the term 'properties of matter.' His interest reflected, in a degree, the interests of the industrialist's specialist, the engineers. He was the chief instrument by which the scientific studies of the British universities were reformed to meet the needs of a new governing class. . . . In the early part of the nineteenth century a vast number of new and strange natural phenomena had been observed, and began to require mathematical description. The new and at first ill-defined and often apparently independent facts required very concrete methods of treatment. Their raw, uncouth nature tended to wreck the symmetry of general equations. They could be seized best by short, uniformly clear descriptions of each isolated phenomenon. Thomson's style of short terse papers was suited to their treatment. Thomson and his friend Tait, who had been appointed professor of natural philosophy at Edinburgh, decided to write a *Treatise on Natural Philosophy*, which would expound the mathematical physics suitable to the contemporary demand. They expounded the science of mechanics, unconsciously, from the standpoint of an ideal engineer who was a master of mathematical physics. Maxwell wrote: 'The credit of breaking up the monopoly of the great masters of the spell, and making all their charms familiar in our ears as household words, belongs in great measure to Thomson and Tait. . . .' Thomson and Tait accomplished, on behalf of the educated leaders of the industrial bourgeoisie, the conquest and assimilation of the mathematico-physical culture of the mercantilist class. The influence of the result of this class-struggle in one of the most elevated regions of human endeavour spread down into the teaching of elementary mathematics. Thomson's pupils, Ayrton and Perry, led the movement for the teaching of 'practical mathematics.' They explained that the new class of technician, brought into existence by machine industry, wanted a knowledge of mathematics which would be of practical use to him in his job. They contended that these men should be taught the sort of mathematics which they would find useful. Mathematics was taught at the grammar schools and universities as if it were to be the cultural accomplishment of certain members of a leisured class, and not a technical equipment which would enable its possessors to earn a living. Ayrton and Perry desired, more or less consciously, to conquer elementary mathematics for the large class of the skilled workmen and technicians. Silvanus P. Thompson, the biographer of Thomson, was a leader in the same movement, and wrote the famous book, *Calculus Made Easy*, which was an attempt to wrest the exclusive knowledge of the calculus from the classes educated in grammar schools and universities, and place it at the service of the class of skilled workmen and technicians."

COSTING THE MAGNETIC FIELD OF THE CURRENT

In this chapter, we have made use of three units of current costing: the ohm, the ampere and the volt. The definition of the ohm depends on that of the other two, as does that of a fourth unit the *coulomb*. Thus the ohm is the resistance of a piece of wire through which a current of one ampere flows when

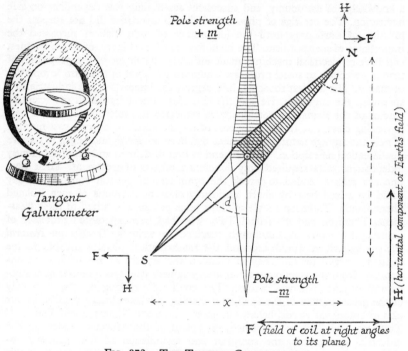

FIG. 372.—THE TANGENT GALVANOMETER

In the right-hand figure: $x = \sin d$. NS and $y = \cos d$. NS.

    H is the horizontal component of the earth's field strength.
    F the field strength of the current at the centre of the coil.

Moment of H $= $ H mx $=$ H $m \sin d$. NS
Moment of F $\;= $ F my $=$ F $m \cos d$. NS

At equilibrium the two moments are equal, i.e.:

$$H\, m \sin d.\, NS = F\, m \cos d.\, NS$$

$$\therefore \quad \frac{\sin d}{\cos d} = \frac{F}{H} = \tan d.$$

$$\therefore \quad F = H \tan d.$$

the p.d. between its ends is 1 volt, and the coulomb is the *discharge* corresponding to the flow of unit current (*one ampere*) for unit time (*one second*). So far we have respectively taken as our standards of the volt and the ampere the p.d. between the terminals of the Weston cell (defined as 1·018 volts) and the quantity of silver deposited at the kathode from a solution of its salt in unit time (*one second*) (0·001118 g). While we are entitled to choose any convenient standard, the reader may well wonder why we do in fact decide to define the p.d. of the Weston cell as 1·018 rather than 1·0 volt, or the ampere as the current which will deposit 0·001118 g rather than 0·001 g per second. The reason is that the original definition of current was fixed by a property which is more amenable to quick measurement and one which was studied before Faraday established the quantitative laws of electrolysis.

The initial definition of current strength by Ampère refers to its magnetic field. Given a unit fixed by this criterion the definition of the volt is fixed by its heating effect when it maintains unit current. In mechanical units this is exactly 10 million ergs per second, and the choice of 10^7, as against 10^6 or 10^8 or any other numerically convenient multiple of 10 makes the unit of p.d. *nearly* that of the terminals of any ordinary electric cell, in particular that of the Weston which is a particularly reliable generator as a standard for a potentiometer set-up. The pivot of the system of electrical units in general use is therefore the *magnetic* definition of current strength.

By observing the magnitude of the deflection of a magnetic needle free to rotate in the horizontal plane in the neighbourhood of a circular coil of wire through which a current flows, while rotating the coil itself about its horizontal and about its vertical axis, we can satisfy ourselves that it behaves like a very flat thin bar magnet whose polar faces lie in the plane of the coil. Thus the magnetic field is at right angles to this plane. When the coil lies vertically in the magnetic meridian (i.e. with its plane in line with the horizontal component (H) of the earth's field) the field strength (F) of the coil, i.e. the mechanical force (dynes) per unit pole, is therefore (Fig. 372) directly proportional to the tangent of the angle of deflection of a magnetic needle free to rotate horizontally on a pivot at the centre of the coil. Without knowing more than this we can proceed to investigate how the field strength at the centre of the circular coil depends on the current. As explained (p. 640), we follow up the analogy of a current of water, assuming that the current produced by two (or three, etc.) generators in series is twice (or three times, etc.) as great as the current due to one alone. We then find that if we double the current in *one and the same* coil, we double the tangent of the angle (*d*) of deflection, if we treble the current we increase the tangent of the angle of deflection three times, and so on. For reasons shown in Fig. 372, the tangent of the angle of deflection is directly proportional to the field strength F at the centre of the coil. That is to say the field at the centre of the circular coil is directly proportional to the current, i.e. F $\propto$ C.

Since the current in the coil is directly proportional to the tangent of the angle of deflection of a magnetic needle at the centre, we can use *tan d* as a measure of the current to investigate the effect of the circuit itself. Between the coil and one of the terminals of one and the same generator we can introduce a resistance (R) of variable length (*l*) and of variable thickness (*t*); and thus show that C = $kt \div l$ in accordance with Ohm's Law. Having established Ohm's Law, we can now determine how the magnitude of the current changes when it flows through 2, 3, or in general *n*, coils of the same radius (*r*), or increase the length of a single coil by increasing its radius. Experiment shows that tan *d* (and hence F) is directly proportional to *n* the

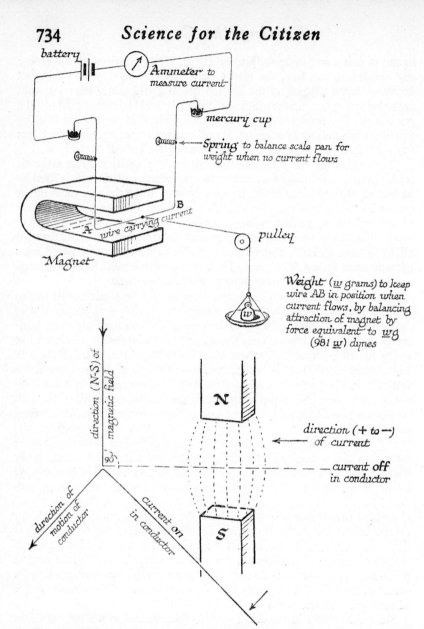

FIG. 373.—PULL OF MAGNET ON LINEAR CONDUCTOR CARRYING A CURRENT

Since a wire carrying a current generates a magnetic field in its vicinity, we should expect to find that a magnet and a wire carrying a current exercise a mutual attraction or repulsion. In fact this is so, and experiment (Fig. 373) shows that there is a simple relation between the mean field strength (F), the current C, and the attractive force (D) when the current flows in a straight line. If we measure current in *amperes*, force and field strength in *dynes* and length in *cm*, the rule is:

$$D = \tfrac{1}{10} \, l.C.F$$

number of complete turns and to r the radius. Thus,

$$F \propto nC \div r \quad or \quad F = KnC \div r.$$

If the radius of a coil of one turn is one unit (1 cm.), $n = 1 = r$ and $F = KC$. The length of a circular coil of radius 1 cm. is 2π cm. At its centre the field strength per unit length of coil is therefore $F \div 2\pi$. If we define our unit (*ampere*) of current so that the field strength *per cm.* at the centre of a coil of radius 1 cm. is 1 dyne, the actual field strength at the centre when a current of one ampere ($C = 1$) flows through such a coil is 2π. Hence $K = 2\pi$, so that

$$F = \frac{2\pi nC}{r}$$

When the coil lies vertically in line with the magnetic meridian the actual value (Fig. 372) of F is given by

$$F = H \tan d.$$

For a galvanometer consisting essentially of a vertical coil in alignment with the horizontal component of the earth's magnetic field and a magnetic needle free to rotate horizontally at its centre (Fig. 372),

$$\frac{2\pi nC}{r} = H \tan d.$$

$$\therefore C = \frac{rH}{2\pi n} \cdot \tan d. = G. \tan d.$$

We know n the number of turns and r the radius of the coil by direct observation. We can determine H at a given location as explained on p. 673 in Chapter XIII. Hence we can determine once for all $rH \div 2\pi n = G$, the numerical value of the *galvanometer constant* at a given place; and can therefore calculate C in amperes by a single direct measurement of the deflection d, a procedure which evidently involves less time and trouble than the measurement of a current by its chemical properties.

EXAMPLES ON CHAPTER XIV

1. A cell of E.M.F. 2 volts and internal resistance 0·5 ohm sends a current through a wire of 11·5 ohms. Find the current.

2. The terminals of a battery of E.M.F. 4 volts and internal resistance 3 ohms are connected through a wire of 9 ohms resistance. Find the potential difference between the terminals.

3. The E.M.F. of a battery is 12 volts on an open and 10 on a closed circuit with a current of 6 amperes flowing. Find the internal resistance of the cell.

4. Two cells, each of internal resistance 3 ohms and 1·1 volt E.M.F. are connected (*a*) in series, (*b*) in parallel with a resistance of 9·5 ohms. Find the current strength in each case.

5. Ten cells, each of internal resistance 3 ohms and E.M.F. 2 volts, are connected (*a*) in one series, (*b*) in two parallel series of 5 cells through a resistance of 20 ohms. Find the strength of the current in each case.

6. A battery in open circuit gives with the electrometer a potential difference of 4 volts between the terminals. When joined with a resistance of 10 ohms the E.M.F. is 3·5. Find the internal resistance of the cell and the current.

'. Twelve cells of E.M.F. 1·1 volt and internal resistance 3 ohms in series are connected through a resistance of 240 ohms. What will be the effect on the current, if we reverse the poles of three cells?

8. Six cells are connected in series with a coil and galvanometer. The internal resistance of the battery is 10 ohms, of the coil is 50 ohms, and of the galvanometer is 20 ohms. If there is a difference of potential at the galvanometer terminals of 2 volts, what is the E.M.F. of each cell?

9. If a pair of torch lamp bulbs are marked 2·5 volts, 0·3 amp., and 3·5 volts, 0·5 amp. respectively, what are their internal resistances?

10. How many Grove cells of 1·8 volts and internal resistance 0·07 ohm each are required to send a current of 10 amps. through a filament of 2 ohms when connected in series?

11. Calculate the length of a coil of resistance wire of uniform calibre if the total resistance is 53 ohms, and a piece 1·2 metres long has a resistance of 0·5 ohm.

12. If the specific resistance of platinum is 0·000011, and of copper 0·00000183, what is the resistance of a cylindrical piece of

(a) platinum wire 0·5 mm. diameter, 328 cm. long,
(b) copper wire 0·42 mm. diameter, 1,000 cm. long.

13. If the resistance of a man's body is found to be 7,500 ohms when the fingers of the two hands grasp opposite terminals, what current will flow through him when he grasps both poles of a battery of 30 Daniell cells in series, each of E.M.F. 1·1 volts and internal resistance 0·3 ohm?

14. The positive pole of a battery A is connected to earth through two resistances AB, 5 ohms, and BC, 10 ohms. The potential difference between the earth and positive pole being 1·48 volts, what current flows through the resistances when the negative pole is also earthed, and what is the E.M.F. between B and C?

15. If a wire could be stretched till its length was doubled, what would be the ratio of its resistance before and after stretching?

16. If three 2-volt accumulators of internal resistance 0·1 ohm are connected in series with a silver voltameter of negligible resistance through a resistance of 6 ohms, find (a) the current, (b) the amount of silver deposited on the kathode in half an hour, (c) the E.M.F. between the terminals of each accumulator while the current is flowing.

17. Two 1·1 volt cells of internal resistance 2 ohms each are arranged (a) in parallel, (b) in series with a wire of 1 ohm resistance. Calculate the current in the latter in each case.

18. During use the voltage falls and the internal resistance of a field telephone battery rises. If a new cell has an E.M.F. of 1·5 volts and internal resistance 0·3 ohm, and an old one has an E.M.F. of 1·2 volts, find (a) what current a new one can drive through a 5 ohm resistance, (b) the internal resistance of the old one in series with a 5 ohm resistance if the ammeter reads 0·1 amp.

19. If the resistance of a 100 metre coil of copper wire of diameter 0·559 mm. is 6·63 ohms at 0° C., calculate the specific resistance of copper.

20. If four 1·5 volt dry cells of internal resistance 0·5 ohm each are in series with a torch bulb of resistance 4 ohms, what is the current flowing through the bulb and the E.M.F. at the terminals?

21. The resistance of the coil of a galvanometer is 108 ohms. If the terminals are connected by a 12 ohm wire, what fraction of the whole current will traverse the coil when the terminals are included in a circuit?

22. If the positive terminal A of a Grove cell of 1·8 volts and 0·2 ohm internal resistance is joined by a wire of 0·3 ohm resistance to the positive terminal B of a Daniell cell of 1·1 volts and internal resistance of 0·4 ohm, and their negative terminals (C and D) are joined by a wire of 0·5 ohm resistance, how many volts would a voltmeter record, if its terminals were connected half-way along AB and half-way along CD respectively?

23. If a carbon filament lamp takes 0·22 amp. from a 250 volt house circuit, what is the resistance of the hot filament?

24. A telegraph line and its instruments have a net resistance of 2,000 ohms, and require a working current of 0·025 amp. (25 milliamps.). If worked by a battery of cells, each of 1·07 volts and internal resistance 8 ohms, how many cells will be necessary?

25. Three cells of voltage 1·2, 1·5, and 1·0, with internal resistances 1, 0·5, and 1·75 ohms respectively, are connected

(a) in series with two parallel external resistances of 5 and 25 ohms.

(b) in series with the same pair of external resistances also arranged in series.

Find the current in each resistance in each case.

26. Three cells A, 1·07 volts 4 ohms internal resistance, B, 1·5 volts 0·4 ohm internal resistance, and C, 2·0 volts 0·3 ohm internal resistance are connected in series with a wire of 83 ohms resistance. The connexions of C are then reversed. Find the current in the circuit in each case.

27. If in the preceding example A and B are connected in parallel to form a battery connected, in series with C, to the same wire, find the current in the latter, and also find what it would be if A and B were alone connected in parallel with an external resistance of 50 ohms.

28. An overhead cylindrical telephone wire of bronze has a specific resistance of 3·37 microhms. If the diameter of the wire is 0·122 cm., what is the resistance in one mile of the wire? A microhm is 10^{-6} ohm.

29. Using the Wheatstone bridge, an unknown resistance is measured against a 5-ohm resistance coil. Find the unknown resistance if there is no galvanometer deflection when contact is made at 28·9 cm. along the metre wire.

30. A current from a battery is allowed to pass for 50 minutes through a variable resistance (as in Fig. 347), an ammeter and a voltmeter, which has copper electrodes in a solution of copper sulphate. The current was kept constant by the variable resistance. The reading of the ammeter was 1·44 amps. and 1·482 grams of copper were deposited on the kathode. Find the current in the circuit if the electrochemical equivalent of copper is 0·0003294 gm. per sec. per amp., and calculate the error in the reading of the ammeter.

31. In measuring the E.M.F. of a cell of internal resistance about 1 ohm, a voltmeter which has a resistance of 2,000 ohms is used. If the current through the voltmeter is neglected, find the percentage error involved.

32. The resistance of a galvanometer coil is one-third of an ohm. The current registered by it when connected with a cell is halved if a wire of 0·1 ohm resistance is placed across its terminals. Find the internal resistance of the cell.

33. Using the Wheatstone bridge an unknown resistance is measured against

(a) a 5 ohm resistance so that balance is obtained when contact is made at 39·7 cm.

(b) a 10 ohm resistance so that balance is obtained when contact is made at 24·7 cm.

Determine the value of the unknown resistance.

34. If the specific resistance of copper is 1·77 microhms at 0° C., what is the resistance in a mile of copper wire of diameter 0·325 cm.? Calculate what the resistance will be when the temperature is 77° F. (Temperature coefficient of resistance of copper = 0·00428 per degree Centigrade.)

35. If the resistance of a galvanometer coil is 20 ohms, what resistance must be shunted between its terminals to reduce the current absorbed by it to 1 per cent of the total current in the circuit? Find also how the current in the rest of the circuit is affected if its resistance is 20 ohms (excluding the shunt), and what further resistance must be put in the main circuit to keep the current unaltered.

36. When a flashlight battery is run for 20 minutes through a wire of resistance 8·85 ohms, the current is found to fall from 0·42 amp. to 0·27 amp., and the E.M.F. as measured on a voltmeter is found to fall from 4·35 volts to 3·0 volts. What are the initial and final values for the internal resistance of the cell?

37. Across the terminals of a galvanometer of 250 ohm resistance a wire of 25 ohms resistance is inserted. A cell of 1·5 volts and no appreciable internal resistance is put in series with it through a 1,000 ohm resistance. If the deflection is 200 scale divisions, find how many amps. correspond to one scale division.

38. Find the length of time it takes for a current of half an ampere to deposit 1 gram of silver from a silver nitrate solution.

39. The tangent galvanometer is used for measuring electric currents by means of the magnetic effects of the current in a coil of wire on a compass needle placed at the centre of the coil.

A constant current passed through the coil of a tangent galvanometer causes a deflection of 35°, and when the same current is passed for half an hour through a copper voltameter containing copper sulphate 1·112 grams of copper are deposited. Find the reduction factor of the galvanometer, i.e. the number by which the tangent of the deflection must be multiplied to bring the current to amperes.

40. A battery is connected in series with a resistance box and an ammeter. When the resistances of 100, 200, 300, and 400 ohms are unplugged in the box, the ammeter gives readings of 99·0, 65·0, 48·3, and 38·6 divisions respectively. Determine approximately what other resistance there is in the circuit.

41. If an ammeter, which reads milli-amps., has a range of 0 to 15 milli-amps. and a resistance of 5 ohms, find the series resistance required so that it can be used as a voltmeter with a range of (a) 0 to 75 volts, (b) 0 to 150 volts.

42. Calculate the cost per hour, if the Board of Trade unit costs 6d., to illuminate a room

(a) by four 16-candle-power carbon lamps requiring 3½ watts per candle,

(b) by two 40-watt metal filament lamps, each giving about 32 candles,

(c) by one 60-watt gas-filled lamp of about 100 candles.

43. A brass vessel of specific heat 0·09 weighs 66⅔ grams, and contains 60 grams of water at 20° C. A current of 4 amps. is passed through with a coil

of 3 ohms resistance immersed in the water. Use the value for the electrical equivalent of heat given on page 696 to find the temperature at the end of five minutes.

44. If 55 grams of water at 15° C. are heated in the same vessel with a heating unit of $2 \cdot 5$ ohm resistance connected to a $1 \cdot 25$ volt cell of negligible resistance, what will be the temperature after ten minutes?

45. How long would it take to boil 1 litre of water at 15° C. with a heating unit of 25 ohms and an E.M.F. of 200 volts if the initial temperature was 15° C.?

46. What is the current passing through the filament of an electric lamp marked 40 W. 230 V., and what is the cost to use this lamp for an hour if the price of the Board of Trade unit is $6\frac{3}{4}$d.?

47. What is the resistance of a 40 W. 250 V. lamp?

48. A lamp of resistance 4 ohms is lit by four Leclanché cells connected in series. Each cell has an E.M.F. of $1 \cdot 5$ volts and internal resistance of $0 \cdot 5$ ohm. Find (a) the current through the lamp, (b) the potential difference at its terminals, (c) how many watts the lamp requires. (1 watt = 1 volt × 1 ampere.)

49. From the above example, find what will be the cost of the zinc dissolved in the four Leclanché cells if the lamp is run for one hour, and if the cost of battery zincs is about two shillings per pound. (1 lb. = $453 \cdot 6$ grams. Electrochemical equivalent of zinc $= 0 \cdot 000343$.)

50. If a tungsten-filament vacuum lamp of 52 candle-power takes a current of $0 \cdot 27$ ampere when the voltage is $232 \cdot 8$ volts, find (a) the resistance of the hot filament, (b) how many watts the lamp consumes, (c) its efficiency in candle-power per watt, and (d) how much it costs to use the lamp for one hour if the charge is 6d. per unit.

51. The temperature of a platinum wire keeps 1° above that of the surrounding objects when a current of one-tenth of an ampere is passed through it. What will be the temperature of the wire when a current of one-fifth of an ampere is passed through it, if you assume that the difference in temperature is proportional to the loss of heat, and disregard the variation of the resistance of the wire with temperature.

52. If the grid of nichrome wire in an electric toaster takes a current of $2 \cdot 28$ amperes when the voltage between its terminals is 245 volts, find (a) the resistance of the hot wire, (b) how many watts it consumes, and (c) how much it costs to use the toaster for ten minutes, if the charge is 6d. per unit.

53. Calculate the temperature-coefficient of nichrome from the previous example if the resistance of the grid at 15° C. is $96 \cdot 9$ ohms, and assuming that the hot wire is at 400° C.

54. If the terminals of a battery, of E.M.F. 15 volts and internal resistance 5 ohms, are connected by a wire the difference of potential between the ends of the wire is 12 volts when the circuit is closed. How many calories are being produced in the wire per minute?

55. If a gas-filled lamp of 200 candle-power takes a current of $0 \cdot 45$ ampere when the voltage is $230 \cdot 9$ volts, find (a) the resistance of the hot filament, (b) how many watts the lamp consumes, (c) its efficiency in candle-power per watt, and (d) how much it costs to use the lamp for one hour if the charge is 6d. per unit.

56. How many watts are expended when a Leclanché cell works at $1 \cdot 46$ volts and produces a current of 1 ampere? If one H.P. = 33,000 ft. lb. per minute, 1 foot = $30 \cdot 48$ cm., and 1 lb. = $453 \cdot 6$ gm., calculate the number of H.P. to which this is equivalent.

57. When a motor-dynamo broke down, current from the 230 volt mains had to be taken to charge a battery of 11 accumulators. If the E.M.F. of each

cell was 2 volts, with negligible internal resistance and the leads could only carry a current up to 8 amperes, (a) how much resistance must be inserted in series with the cells, (b) how many watts are consumed, (c) how many of these watts are put into the cells, and (d) where does the remainder of the power from the mains go to?

58. A power station sends power to a place at some distance from it by means of two lines, transmitting one current at 250 volts and the other at 10,000 volts. Calculate what the ratio of the areas of cross-section of the two lines must be so that there is the same loss of heat in both.

THINGS TO MEMORIZE

1. Ohm's Law. $C = \dfrac{E}{R}$.

2. Resistance, $R = \dfrac{s \cdot l}{a}$, where s is the specific resistance, l the length, and a the cross-sectional area.

3. Resistances in parallel. Total resistance given by $\dfrac{1}{R} = \dfrac{1}{r_1} + \dfrac{1}{r_2} \ldots$

4. Theoretical unit of current = current which, when it flows in an arc 1 cm. long of a circle 1 cm. radius, acts on unit magnetic pole placed at the centre with a force of 1 dyne.

1 ampere = 0·1 theoretical unit = current which liberates per second 0·001118 gm. of silver from a neutral solution of silver nitrate.

5. Theoretical unit of E.M.F. Unit E.M.F. exists between two points in a wire when work equal to 1 erg is done on unit charge in moving it from the one point to the other.

1 volt = 10^8 theoretical units. E.M.F. of Weston standard cell at 20° C. is 1·0183 volts.

6. Theoretical unit of resistance. A conductor has unit resistance when unit E.M.F. produces unit current in it.

1 ohm = 10^9 theoretical units = resistance of a wire in which an E.M.F. of 1 volt produces a current of 1 ampere = resistance of a uniform column of mercury, 106·300 cm. long and of mass 14·4521 gm. at 0° C.

7. Electrical power (watts) = $C^2R = EC = \dfrac{E^2}{R}$

1 watt = rate of working of 1 joule per second = power produced by a current of 1 ampere at an E.M.F. of 1 volt.

CHAPTER XV

THE WAVES THAT RULE BRITANNIA

OUR last chapter ended with the crowning achievements of power production in the latter half of the nineteenth century, and the new means of communication which resulted from the discovery of a new source of power. This one will deal with a discovery which became part of everyday life in the opening years of the century in which we are living. It is sometimes, indeed often, said that the discovery of wireless telegraphy was the direct result of a mathematical theory put forward by James Clerk Maxwell. Such is the story as it is told, and not a few have adorned it with moral. Miss Turner concludes the chapter on Maxwell's work in her useful book, *Makers of Science—Electricity and Magnetism*, with the following comment on:

the unfortunate conclusion that technical inventions and practical applications are the sole justification for the labours of the man of science. . . . The search for knowledge is its own reward. If it leads to applications of benefit to mankind well and good. If not, it is still worth while. The evolution of Wireless Telegraphy affords an example of one who laboured for knowledge alone, one who was a supreme theorist, a visionary, and a dreamer.

Such sentiments, which abound in scientific text-books, perpetuate a mistaken antithesis between individual preferences and the social circumstances which determine how they are exercised, encouraged, or applied. To be a good scientific investigator, a man (or woman) must be intensely interested in his job. That is what makes it worth while from his own point of view. What makes it worth while from the standpoint of other people is whether it endows human life with new powers and inventions, or affords fresh scope for ostentation. Whether the individual investigator succeeds in getting opportunities to do the things which are worth while *to him* depends on whether he can get society or other individuals to believe that what he intends to do is worth while *to them*. To get the fullest advantage of the benefits which science can provide, the citizen must see that those who enjoy making scientific discoveries are encouraged to do so. To get the fullest opportunities for doing the kind of work which is worth while to themselves scientific workers must participate in their responsibilities as citizens. Among other things this includes refraining from the arrogant pretence that their own preferences are a sufficient justification for the support which they need.

This pretence, put forward as the plea that science should be encouraged for its own sake, is a survival of Platonism and of the City-State tradition of slave ownership. It carries with it the nemesis of its origin. Science thrives by its applications. To justify it as an end in itself is a policy of defeat. The fullest use of science cannot be made by a society in which the pursuit of discovery is the toy of a privileged class, or by a society which restricts the benefits of its application to a relatively small group of individuals. Science advances most rapidly when its benefits are keenly recognized because widely shared, especially when it brings new prosperity to a previously unprivileged class. It will attain its highest dignity in a classless society which demands the means of an advancing standard of leisure and well-being for *all its members*. In a classless society ostentatious emphasis on the pursuit of useless activities will no longer be the hallmark of prosperity or good breeding. Discussing whether useless studies are worthwhile for their own sake will be like discussing whether chewing gum is worthwhile for *its* own sake.

The encouragement which the scientific worker gets from the society in which he lives includes far more than his livelihood, the equipment which he can secure and the modicum of respect which sustains the efforts of reasonably modest people. A society facing new practical tasks of industry, agriculture, disease, or protection, forces new problems on the attention of individuals who are capable of solving them. So was it with Maxwell. It was his good fortune to live in a time when new practical tasks made unusual demands on such gifts as he possessed, created special opportunities for their exercise, and was lavish in recognizing their merits. He graduated about the time when the English Channel cable was laid. The severely academic atmosphere of the university in which he studied was mitigated by a tour of British factories undertaken at his father's request. The chair which he subsequently occupied was created in response to the popular demand for modernizing the teaching of science at the older English universities in accordance with the aspirations of the manufacturing classes. It was established during the decade when the struggle to remove them from ecclesiastical control reached its climax in the repeal of the religious tests (see p. 953, Chapter XX).

Indeed, it would be difficult to select the career of a scientific man whose choice of problem, public esteem, and social opportunities were more closely related to contemporary social circumstances. His main achievement is a symbol of the cultural compromise achieved by the creation of the new physical laboratory over which he presided. In Maxwell's treatise the Newtonian mathematics of the older universities was linked to the experimental measurements made by Faraday and Henry in extramural foundations, such as the Royal and Smithsonian Institutions. As with the form, so it was with the substance. From the beginnings of practical telegraphy the possibility of propagating electrical phenomena through space without the aid of conducting material in the ordinary sense continually prompted speculation and experiment. In the adventurous hopefulness of nineteenth-century industrialism, telegraphy without wires was the philosopher's stone and the elixir of youth. Thus far, telegraphic communication was the most spectacular achievement of science. As such it received its full share of recognition in the Great Exhibition which coincided with the Continental Cable venture. Two years later—in 1853—Dering, an inventor whose electrical appliances received an honourable place among the exhibits, referred to "the craving there is at present for wireless telegraphs." This was the year in which Maxwell became second wrangler.

The craving is not difficult to explain. As the distance traversed by electrical communications increased, the total cost became more and more a mere question of outlay on cables. A discovery which had recently resulted in a 50 per cent economy illustrates the close association between theoretical science and the social demand for a cheaper method of transmission. The famous mathematician Gauss was responsible for a project to use the double track of the railroad as a cable substitute. Efforts made by Steinheil to adopt it on the Nuremburg–Fürth line were fruitless owing to faulty insulation. He discovered that this was due to conduction through the earth. By sinking

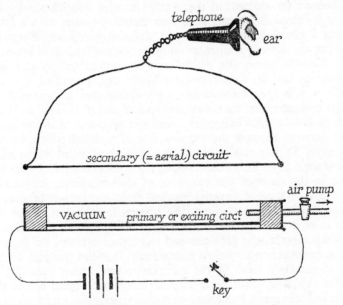

FIG. 374.—ELECTROMAGNETIC INDUCTION IN A VACUUM

In this arrangement the primary circuit runs parallel to the secondary circuit, and is inclosed in a tube exhausted by an air pump. When the key of the primary circuit is pressed or released the current is made or broken. A click heard in the telephone receiver connected to the secondary circuit registers the inductive effect, which is thus propagated through empty space. Telephone wires placed on opposite banks of a river have been used to transmit wireless messages in this way across very short distances. For Morse code signalling it is necessary to have a buzzer, based on the same principle as the electric bell, in the primary circuit. The telephone then registers a long or short succession of clicks corresponding to long or short pressure on the key.

plates deep in the ground Steinheil produced the "earth circuit" (Fig. 326) which made it possible to use one cable to do the work for which two had been necessary. This was in 1838. Thereafter single-line transmission was universally adopted.

Meanwhile Faraday's discoveries about electromagnetic induction had given some substance to the hope that all cost involved in laying down cables could be cut out. An illustration shown in Fig. 374 will make this clear. An alternating or intermittent current generated in an induction coil produces a buzzing sound in a telephone placed in series with the secondary circuit. This buzz, now used to detect current in a Wheatstone bridge circuit, can also be used as a signal in a crude form of wireless communication over short distances. To produce an alternating or intermittent current by induction, the secondary circuit need not surround the primary. It may be placed parallel to it some distance away. In such an arrangement the primary circuit with its key and interrupter constitutes a transmitter, and the secondary circuit with its telephone constitutes a receiver for signals which are communicated without any material connexion. Attempts to devise a practicable system on this basis were made. They were doomed to failure from the start, because the strength of the induced current falls off rapidly as the distance is increased. Transmission over distances greater than a few feet therefore demands enormous coils and tremendously powerful sources of current, or alternatively a far more sensitive detector for induced currents.

The scientific discoveries which brought wireless transmission out of the classroom into the domain of everyday life belong to three classes. One includes certain phenomena which were encountered in connexion with attempts to demonstrate the common characteristics of frictional and current electricity. To this class belongs the *oscillatory* discharge. A second includes devices invented to meet the requirements of practical telegraphy of the earlier type. To this class belongs the lightning protector which was the parent of the *coherer*. To the third belong discoveries prompted by theoretical interest in the common characteristics of electromagnetic induction and light. Some of these discoveries resulted from the pursuit of qualitative analogies before Maxwell's time. His systematic treatment of the whole subject in its quantitative implications undoubtedly increased the confidence with which experimental physicists and technicians explored the application of the wave metaphor to wireless transmission. It is also true that the vindication of Faraday's views by the quantitative tests drawn from Maxwell's formulae would not have been possible unless subsequent empirical discoveries had been made. Purely empirical discoveries which cannot be deduced from Maxwell's teaching furnished the means of testing its credentials; and purely empirical discoveries which were made in connexion with practical telegraphy made it possible to supersede the latter.

THE OSCILLATORY DISCHARGE

In tracing the story of how the craving for wireless telegraphy was at length satisfied, the discoveries which contributed most to success will be dealt with under the three headings already outlined.

The first batteries were regarded as electrical machines capable of maintaining a fixed but small potential, because they were able to reproduce what were then regarded as two of the three most characteristic properties of the latter. They could make sparks and shocks. The chemical and magnetic properties of wires connected with a battery raised a new problem. In 1821 when Ampère and Oersted first discovered the magnetic field of the electric current, Davy set out to test the possibility of producing a magnetic field by the current which flows in a coil of wire connecting the coats of a discharging Leyden jar. Since a condenser discharge is of very short duration, he could not detect the temporary magnetism of a soft iron bar placed in his coil. He then used steel needles. Though less readily magnetized, steel needles retain their magnetism after the current ceases to flow. By repeatedly charging Leyden jars from a frictional machine (see Fig. 319), Davy was able to obtain a detectable magnetic after-effect in the needles.

Subsequent repetition of this discovery by several other investigators, notably Henry (1842), led to the recognition of an unforeseen anomaly. Even when the same terminal of the Leyden jar (Fig 375) was always connected to the same terminal of the machine the result was not exactly the same. Sometimes it would happen that the end of the steel needle nearest the positive terminal of the electrical machine was the north seeking pole. sometimes the reverse happened. As anticipated, the iron became magnetic. Contrary to expectation, its *polarity was indefinite*.

One of two conclusions may be drawn from this. We can infer either

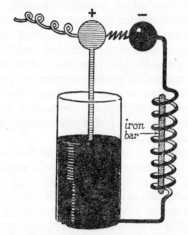

FIG. 375.—APPARATUS TO SHOW INDEFINITE POLARITY PRODUCED BY THE CURRENT OF
THE SPARK DISCHARGE

(a) that electrification by friction and electrification by chemical decomposition are different, or (b) that the current does not flow continuously in one direction during the passage of the spark. It might for instance surge backwards and forwards. There is nothing intrinsically unlikely in this supposition. On the contrary, the mechanical analogies which have suggested other characteristics of the current would lead us to expect something of the sort. In mechanical changes, a rapid drop of potential, as when two columns of mercury at different levels are connected in a U-tube, or when a sudden jerk is applied to a weight suspended by a spring, often results in a periodic motion. Periodic motion of this sort is what the principle of inertia would lead us to expect (see p. 293). The growth of a current has a sluggishness comparable to the inertia of moving matter, as can be seen when a condenser or a choking coil is used in an alternating current (Fig. 371). By analogy we should not expect an impulsive discharge accompanying the disappearance of a large voltage to take place in one step. We should expect it to overstep the mark, so that each terminal would alternately become negative and positive while the difference of potential is being equalized.

Henry, who discovered the phenomenon of self-induction and compared it to the inertia of matter, drew the conclusion that the indefinite magnetic polarity resulting from Leyden jar discharges must be due to the combination of two agencies. One is the effect of a current on the power of iron to retain or forfeit its magnetism. The other is the *oscillatory* nature of the discharge, or, as he put it, "the existence of the principal discharge in one direction and then several reflex actions backward and forward, each more feeble than the preceding until equilibrium is obtained." An alternative and more convincing test of the truth of this explanation is provided by what happens when we use the Leyden jar discharge for showing the ability of the frictional machine to accomplish chemical decomposition. Any part of the circuit containing the coil in Fig. 375 may be replaced by a strip of blotting paper moistened with a solution which conducts electricity. In general, such solutions are partially decomposed by the passage of a current. An extremely sensitive indicator for the latter is a mixture of starch and potassium iodine. Iodine, liberated at the anode during electrolysis, turns starch a deep blue. If the current were to traverse the spark gap in one direction, the region round the free end of wire nearest the positive terminal of the electrical machine would therefore become blue, and the region round the opposite end of wire would not change colour. Experiment shows that the solution becomes equally blue in the neighbourhood of a wire directly connected to either terminal of the electrical machine.

Cinematography makes it possible to take continuous films which show that the discharge of a condenser is an exceedingly rapid succession of short sparks of diminishing brightness. This is equally true of the sparks which occur when a condenser, such as a Leyden jar, is discharged, or of the sparks which are produced between secondary terminals of an induction coil (Fig. 368). A spark is therefore an alternating current accompanied by the production of incandescent heat. Rapid cinematographic films of the spark discharge show that there may be thousands of alternating phases in a single spark discharge, which itself lasts less than a thousandth of a second. From the standpoint of wireless telegraphy *the important thing about spark discharge is that it is an alternating current of enormously higher frequency than of any current produced by a mechanical interrupter.*

Its importance depends on the circumstances which decide the magnitude of induced currents in a secondary circuit. The maximum voltage between the ends of a conductor, in successive phases of the A.C. set up by a variable current in a primary circuit near to it, may be changed in three ways. The brightness of the spark or the length of the spark gap of an induction coil can be decreased by using a less powerful battery to work it, by sliding the secondary coil away from the primary if the former is movable, and by substituting for the spring interrupter another with a lower natural frequency of vibration. Increasing the voltage applied to the primary circuit, decreasing the intervening distance between the two circuits, or raising the frequency of make and break, can each by itself produce a higher induced E.M.F. This means that if the voltage in the primary circuit is fixed, a higher frequency of variation in the primary circuit will exercise the same inductive effect at a greater distance from it.

These considerations may have influenced Henry in a noteworthy experiment which he performed in the forties. In his book *American Men of Science*, Crowther tells us that Henry

connected one end of a coil in his study with the metal roofing on his house and the other end to a metal plate in a deep well near the house. He found that needles put in the coil were strongly magnetized by lightning flashes which occurred "within a circle of at least twenty miles." . . . He showed that the current produced in the house circuit was oscillatory. He found that if a discharge from several Leyden jars was sent through a wire stretched across the campus in front of Nassau Hall, Princeton, "an inductive effect was produced in a parallel wire, the ends of which terminated in the plates of metal in the ground in the back of the campus." The distance between the wires was several hundred feet, and the building of Nassau Hall stood in the intervening space.

Thus Henry discovered the greater efficacy of currents alternating with extremely high frequency, and took the first decisive step in devising what is still the means used to produce them. The spark discharge remains the most powerful way of exciting inductive effects at a distance. The next step in the evolution of a practicable system of signalling without cables was to discover some more sensitive detector of induced currents.

THE LIGHTNING PROTECTOR AND THE COHERER

While the production of cheap cables remained a dominating economic problem of electrical technology, there was a feverish search for new information about the resistance of conductors. One such discovery was first made in the thirties. It played a most important part in the development of cable telegraphy, and made telegraphy without wires a practical possibility. Its connexion with other known facts about electrical phenomenon is still rather obscure. No one who has toyed with electrical equipment needs to be reminded that loose contacts give rise to high resistances. Hence a tube loosely packed with a powder of metallic particles, such as fine copper or iron filings, is a poor conductor to ordinary direct currents. This is not true of its behaviour when traversed by alternating currents of very high frequencies, especially the "oscillatory" currents during the discharge of a Leyden jar. If an oscillatory current is passed through a tube lightly packed with fine copper filings it becomes a good conductor, as if the particles had been made to stick together. Usually they go on *cohering* until the tube is tapped or otherwise shaken. An early application of this fact is indicated in a British patent specification (No. 165 of 1866) under the names of C. and S. S. Varley, who devised a lightning protector for telegraph stations.

One of the embarrassments of the single-line system (Fig. 326), which uses the earth itself as one cable, is that the aerial telegraph wire earth-connected through the fine coils of the recorder is essentially like Benjamin Franklin's lightning protector. When the overhead wire picks up the electrical discharge a powerful current must flow to earth through the sensitive coils of the instrument, unless the latter is in some way protected. Instruments were often fused during thunderstorms before there was a way of avoiding this. Varley's solution, which was widely adopted by telegraph stations, was to put a coherer consisting of a tube of fine copper in parallel with the over-head wire and the earth plate of the circuit (Fig. 376). In ordinary circum-stances its high resistance could not appreciably side-track the current from the instrument. When the overhead wire was struck by the oscillatory

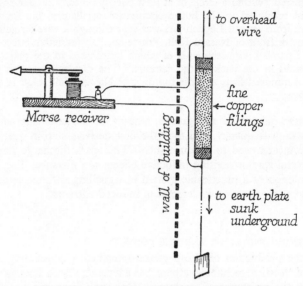

FIG. 376.—THE VARLEY LIGHTNING PROTECTOR

Owing to the high resistance of loose contacts in the coherer, nearly all the current flowing between the underground plate of the earth circuit and the overhead wire ordinarily passes through the coils of the instrument. During a lightning discharge the oscillatory current induced in the circuit immediately induces coherence of the metal particles in the coherer, thus making the latter a much better conductor than the recording instruments. So the lightning discharge is short circuited to earth as in a lightning conductor of the type which Benjamin Franklin introduced.

lightning discharge, it immediately became a good conductor and short-circuited the current which would otherwise flow through the coils of the recorder. The overhead wire then acted as an independent lightning conductor during a thunderstorm without damage to the apparatus.

For use as a lightning protector the sensitivity of Varley's coherer to very minute high-frequency currents was not a matter of importance. What made the coherer an essential step in the subsequent development of wireless telegraphy is the fact that a device of this type can be made to cohere by *extremely minute oscillatory* currents. It is therefore a highly-sensitive detector for high frequency induction. The discovery of this fact was made independently by several electricians, working on the packing of carbon or metallic particles in microphones of the customary type, which depends on the variable resistance of a powdered conductor under mechanical percussion (see p. 689). Fleming tells us of one observation which emerged from work-shop practice at an early stage. Microphones with carbon steel granules will respond by a click to small sparks in the same room. This occurrence embodies all the essential features of the first wireless installations.

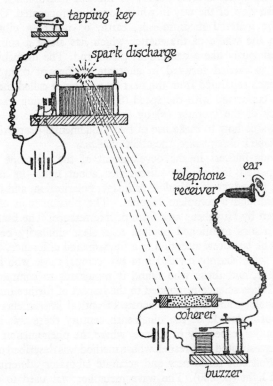

FIG. 377

The fundamental features of Wireless Signalling are exhibited in their simplest form when a coherer is excited by the oscillatory current from the spark gap of an induction coil. The latter can be switched on and off by a key in the primary circuit of the coil. Currents induced in the coherer make the latter a good conductor. So if it is placed in series with a battery and a telephone receiver it will switch the current in the tele-phone on and off, when the key in the transmitting circuit is pressed or released. If a vibrating key of the Morse type is used, a short (dot) and long (dash) succession of sparks can be sent out in accordance with the Morse code.

THE REVIVAL OF THE WAVE METAPHOR

Indeed we can well imagine that wireless telegraphy would have been invented if no new theoretical enquiries into the relation between induction and light had been undertaken. None the less it would be foolish to over-look the fact that theory and practice both contributed to the same result.

The new theories whetted the appetite for discovery, encouraged the hope that science could satisfy the craving for telegraphy without wires, and coordinated the curiosity of numberless investigators to the same focus.

To understand why a new scaffolding of metaphor was erected as a prop to further extensions of electrical knowledge we must now recall what we have already learned in Chapter VI. During the seventeenth century Galileo's mechanics were applied to the study of musical instruments. This led to a more precise view of the way in which sound is propagated. Owing to the inertia of the material medium—air, earth, or water—a vibrating body cannot bring the whole of the matter which lies along a sound track to move simultaneously like a continuous piston rod. The disturbance due to a pure note is carried forward in alternate regions of compression and rarefaction, each separated from the next by a distance called the *wavelength* (W). This is connected with the speed (S) of the advancing track and with the frequency of the vibrator (n) by the simple formula: $S = n\mathrm{W}$. This formula shows us how to make use of two fundamental properties of sound production. One is *interference*, the other *resonance*.

Simultaneous interest in the development of the telescope during the Newtonian period led to new discoveries about light—its finite speed, diffraction at the edges of a shadow or image, polarization, and its ability to pass freely through a complete vacuum. The phenomenon of diffraction was recognized by Huyghens as a form of interference. The first two of the four characteristics mentioned pointed to a clear similarity between light and sound. The last drew attention to a fundamental difference. So scientific theoreticians were sharply divided into two camps, those who adopted the wave metaphor, and those who found it repugnant to common sense, as indeed it is. When science responded to the impact of further improvements in glass technology and the manufacture of optical instruments during the third and fourth decade of the nineteenth century there was a revival of interests in optics, especially in France, where the phenomenon of interference was re-investigated by Fresnel, whose method was described on page 336. Fizeau and Foucault made new and accurate laboratory determinations of the speed of light (p. 330). The wave metaphor was used to explore the visible spectrum for the first time.

Hitherto physical theory had recoiled from a too literal reliance on the analogy between light and sound. The ideological temper of science was ready for a new orientation when Faraday showed that currents may be induced between conductors separated by a vacuum (Fig. 374). Empty space now held out the hope of making money, and gained in substance accordingly. In the social context of flooded mines the important thing about a vacuum was that it had no weight. In the social context of Atlantic telegraphy the important thing about a vacuum was that two sorts of signals could traverse it,—the oldest of all signals, the hilltop beacon, and a new and better substitute for putting the ear to the ground. In Newton's time human nature had just ceased to abhor a vacuum, and was loth to refill it. Faraday and his fellow-workers in science were less squeamish. The distinction between what is matter and what is not matter no longer occupied the centre of the picture. In the latter part of his scientific career Faraday's search for new electrical phenomena was guided by a parable hypertrophied to the limits of sheer paradox.

Apart from the fact that the discovery of new things about light and electricity happened at the same time, there were special reasons why scientific workers could not resist the search for some connexion between them. One depends on the fact that light and induction exhibit different similarities to sound production. Light propagated through empty space can be made to reproduce one of two characteristic phenomena of sound production. That is to say, two beams of light can either reinforce or *interfere*. On that account we can assign to light of different colours a range of wave-lengths. To pursue the analogy further, we should be forced to draw the conclusion that a light wave is produced by vibrations of enormous frequency. From interference measurements we assign to the D_1 line in the sodium spectrum a wave-length of 5896×10^{-8} centimetre. The speed of light is 186,000 miles, or 300 million metres (3×10^{10} cm.), per second. From the formula $S = nW$ we find that $n = 500,000,000,000,000$ (approximately). In the time of Faraday there were no known facts about transmission in a vacuum to give the number n a tangible meaning. This is another way of saying that there was no knowledge of any optical phenomenon analogous to resonance in sound production. Induction provided the first example of a phenomenon analogous to resonance in propagation through empty space.

In sound production resonance may be of two kinds. A vibrator made like a piano wire, an organ pipe, or a tuning fork, has one principal frequency with which it oscillates. It will respond at rest to a vibrator, which produces the same principal note, or to the corresponding subsidiary superimposed vibrations called harmonics. Thus the resonance of a tuning fork or piano wire is *selective*. To make one violin string resonate to the note of another one of different materials or dimensions, we have to shorten or lengthen it till it would have the same natural period of vibration if jerked. A flat circular diaphragm like a drum membrane on the other hand is much less selective. Owing to its shape it will vibrate with different frequencies when struck in different ways. Having a large number of "natural frequencies," it responds to a great range of sound. That is why it is used in the construction of a telephone transmitter or a recording gramophone.

The periodic change of direction of current in the secondary circuit, when an alternating current flows in the primary circuit of a transformer, is analogous to the non-selective resonance of a flat circular diaphragm to the notes of a piano. Taken together, Fresnel's work on the spectrum and Faraday's discoveries about induction showed that disturbances propagated through empty space could reproduce both the outstanding features of sound tracks in a material medium with elastic properties like air or water. Empty space was accordingly filled with an obliging and all-pervading blancmange called the *ether*. The sequel proved two things. The crudest hypotheses can be fruitful if continually refined by use, and curiosity is a far more important asset to discovery than sophistication.

The standpoint of *Science for the Citizen* is that a scientific explanation is one which is vindicated by practice. Laws of science are rules or recipes for the conduct of practical affairs. As such we can distinguish two ways in which they fulfil their use. One is to provide us with a large mass of relevant information in a compact form. The other is to explore common features of seemingly distinct occurrences. The first may be a step towards the second. On the other hand it is not a necessary one. Readers of crime fiction will be familiar with two types of detectives. One adopts the card index method of Bacon, collecting all relevant information piece by piece. The other follows a hunch, like Newton, and, like Newton, abandons it at once when it comes into conflict with observed facts. From time to time the philosophers of science emphasize the merits of one or the other, and write as if one or the other were the true method of science. There is no one method of science. The unity of science resides in the nature of the result, the unity of theory with practice. Each type of detection has its use, and the best detective is one who combines both methods, letting his hunch lead him to test hypotheses and keeping alert to new facts while doing so.

Faraday was in this sense the best detective. Through lack of university education he had never acquired an intellectual faculty for devising arguments against trying out new expedients. Having equipped the vacuum and intramolecular space with his all-pervading blancmange to accommodate light and induction, he drew the inescapable conclusion that electrical or magnetic stresses in the ether must affect the direction in which light waves are free to move. In applying the wave metaphor to light, we can picture a beam as a bundle of skipping ropes with undulations travelling along each (see Fig. 205) in different planes. If a grating is placed in the course of the bundle it will cut out all the undulations except those parallel with the grating. A second grating will not allow any undulations to pass unless placed parallel with the first. So likewise a crystal of tourmaline or Iceland spar placed at any angle will let through *some* of the light when a beam strikes it, while the dimmer beam which emerges will only pass through a second crystal if its corresponding face is parallel to that of the first. The beam which emerges from the first is said to be *polarized*, and differs from an ordinary beam, because it will only pass through a crystal of Iceland spar when the crystal is placed at a certain angle. Faraday passed a polarized beam of light between the poles of a very strong magnet and found that the plane of polarization was rotated. To transmit light the crystal had to be placed at a different angle while the beam traversed the magnetic field.

The scientific study of magnetism had begun with Gilbert's attempt to make a model showing how mariners' observations on the dip and deviation of the compass needle from the true meridian vary in different parts of the world. Gilbert's model was the origin of what later physicists called a "field of force." Gilbert himself used a small compass needle to map out the variation of intensity and direction of magnetic attraction on the surface of his *terella* or spherical lodestone. We can get a more direct picture of the field of force, that is to say, the way in which the intensity and direction of magnetic attraction vary, in the neighbourhood of a bar magnet by sprinkling iron filings over a flat piece of card laid on top of one (Fig. 378). When the bench is lightly tapped the filings take up a characteristic arrangement in curved lines radiating from the poles. If a wire which carries current is passed through a flat piece of card sprinkled with iron filings, the latter arrange

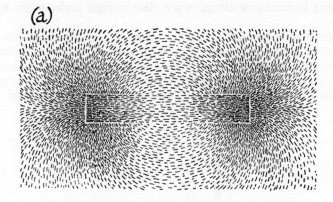

(a)

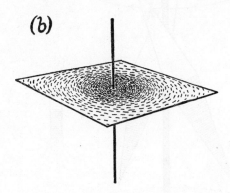

(b)

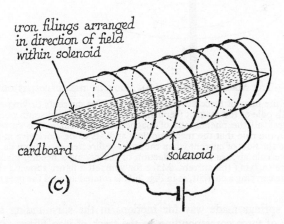

iron filings arranged
in direction of field
within solenoid

cardboard   solenoid

(c)

FIG. 378

The pattern in which iron filings arrange themselves on a flat card in the neighbourhood
of a magnet (*a*), or the magnetic field around a current (*b*, *c*) maps out the direction
and intensity of magnetic attraction. This is one way of saying that each line of filings
corresponds to the course in which an isolated pole would move. The third figure
also illustrates how a bar magnet is made by the orientation of the steel particles
under the influence of the field produced by a solenoid.

themselves in concentric circles in the plane at right angles to the wire as centre.

Faraday's vivid pictorial imagination seized on this to elaborate the ether metaphor in a form which embodies all the rules of the magnetic effects of a current stated on pages 707 and 717. At one stage of his researches he seems to have visualized a magnetic field as a parcel of stretched springs or strands of elastic free to bulge sideways in the empty space between them. Later

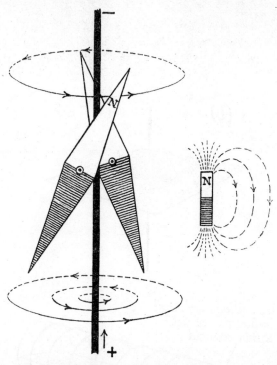

FIG. 379.—THE MAGNETIC FIELD AS AN EDDY IN THE SUPPOSITITIOUS ETHER

If we picture the lines of force around a bar magnet as currents driving a north pole from the north pole of the magnet (repulsion of like poles) to its south pole (attraction of unlike poles), all the phenomena of magnetic movement in the current field are summed up in the rule that the magnetic flow appears to be clockwise in the plane at right angles to the flow of current when the latter is directed away from us. This figure shows how the rule applies to the deflection of the compass needle, placed above or below the wire carrying the current. Make for yourself a figure showing the direction in which a wire carrying a current, as in Fig. 363, is rotated around the pole of a magnet.

these static springs made way for motions in the surrounding space. The curved lines of force corresponding to the track of iron filings from pole to pole came to stand for eddy currents in a viscous medium. If we make the direction of swirl (indicated by the arrows in Fig. 379) correspond to the direction in which a north pole would move, it also represents the direction opposite to that in which a south pole would move. As drawn, the arrows stand for a push exerted on a north pole, or a pull on a south pole. In terms of

The Waves that Rule Britannia 755

the usual convention for current direction (positive to negative) Faraday's rule is illustrated in the figure. The rule is that the rotation of the magnetic eddy is clockwise when we look along a wire conveying current away from us. To get a clear grasp of the wave theory of induction it is necessary to visualize all the implications of this rule for the four positions of the compass needle and current shown in Fig. 321, Chapter XIII. Once you have visualized the direct current surrounded by these concentric eddies of magnetic push and pull, the behaviour of an alternating current offers *two* possibilities.

One may be stated as follows. At one and the same instant of time the direction of current along a wire of any length is the same at every point, as is also the direction of the magnetic eddies in the plane at right angles. In more matter of fact language this means that compass needles placed anywhere along the length *above* the wire and at any distance from it will be deflected to a varying extent in the *same* direction and in the direction opposite to the deflection of all needles placed below it at one and the same instant. In the next instant all the conditions throughout the field will be reversed. If this were so, the periodic nature of the changes would be purely *temporal*. The character of the field would change instantaneously as a whole. The speed with which the inductive effect is propagated would be immeasurably great, literally infinite, if such a thing is conceivable. Experiment shows that this is not true.

There are several reasons for seeking an alternative view. Magnetic and current phenomena have inertia. Then, too, induction has one of the characteristics of radiation. It is propagated through empty space, and all previously known forms of radiation through a vacuum exhibit periodic variations in space, described so vividly by the wave metaphor. We are therefore led to explore another possibility. At one and the same instant of time the direction of current in different parts of a very long wire may vary, as may also the direction of the magnetic eddies in the same plane at different distances from the wire. In matter of fact language this means that at the same distance directly above a very long wire the direction of deflection of compass needles at one and the same instant will be reversed at different points along a line parallel to the wire, or at different distances from the wire in the same plane perpendicular to it. If this is so, the direction of the magnetic field and the direction of the alternating current both vary periodically *in space* as well as in time. This means that electromagnetic induction is not instantaneous. A measurable interval occurs between the rise of a current flowing in one direction in a primary circuit and the rise of the induced current flowing in the opposite direction in a secondary circuit at some distance from it. Fig. 380 shows for simplicity the variation of the magnetic field in one plane at right angles to the current. The next illustration (Fig. 381) shows both variations in the neighbourhood of the spark gap.

Maxwell's mathematical attack on the problem was guided by a vivid realization of these alternative possibilities, and of their implications as they affect electrical and magnetic measurements. Science in his time recognized three sorts of "ether waves," or, as we now say, radiations. These were: rays of longer wave-length than those in the red end of the spectrum, visible light, and rays of shorter wave-length than those in the violet end. The longer were recognized by their heating effects alone, the shorter by their action on silver salts (see p. 173). Maxwell grasped the possibility that there might be other types of radiation, qualitatively and quantitatively distinct from these, including among them a range of wave-lengths recognized by electrical action. Since musical notes are all propagated with the same speed in air, analogy suggested that all waves propagated in the suppositious ether would travel with the same speed, i.e. that of light. Briefly the theory he proposed was: (*a*) that an alternating current is a source of ether waves of immensely long wave length, (*b*) that electromagnetic induction is a form

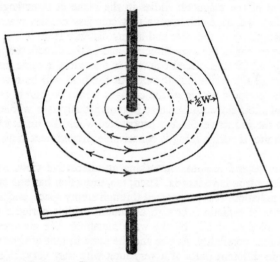

FIG. 380.—MAGNETIC FIELD IN THE PLANE AT RIGHT ANGLES TO AN
ALTERNATING CURRENT

Following the analogy of eddies in a viscous medium the arrows represent the direction of movement of a north pole. If the inductive effect is propagated *periodically* in space, the mid-points of two adjacent regions where the deflections registered by two compass needles at one and the same instant would be opposite are separated half a wave-length. If all disturbances travel with the same speed as light in empty space like different musical notes transmitted through air, the wave-length of a disturbance set up by an a.c. of 100 alternations per second is given by the wave formula $(S = nW)$ in which S is 186,000 miles, or 300,000 kilometres, per second. That is to say $W = 3,000$ kilometres or 1,860 miles, and the half wave-length would be 930, or nearly a thousand, miles. To show that a disturbance is propagated in this way, it would therefore be necessary to devise experiments using alternating currents with immensely high frequency.

of resonance to wave motion propagated with the speed of 186,000 miles, or 3×10^{10} cm., per sec., and (*c*) that a source of light is due to oscillatory currents in the incandescent particles of a luminous body.

The mathematical technique which Maxwell applied to develop Faraday's theories lies outside the scope of this book. All we can do is to be clear about the sort of help Maxwell gave, and, as a mathematician, could give. Physical equations, like chemical formulae, can often serve to expose previously unrecognized connexions between natural events. We have met one good example of this in Chapter V. Periodic motion implies a certain relationship between acceleration and distance from a fixed point. There is a corresponding relation between the pulling power of a spring and the distance through which its end is displaced by a weight. Other circumstances, such as the behaviour of a billiard ball on a slope lead us to conclude that a pull can be measured by the acceleration it imparts. So we can write the law of the stretched spring in a

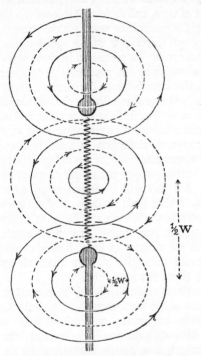

FIG. 381.—VARIATION IN THE MAGNETIC FIELD AND DIRECTION OF CURRENT AROUND AN OSCILLATOR

When currents of immense frequency as obtained from a small spark gap are used as a source of induction, the wave-length corresponding to the simultaneous variation in the direction of secondary current and magnetic deflections in planes at right angles to one another is comparatively short. Owing to limitations of space it has been necessary to compress the figure in one plane. The distance ½W is really the same in both planes. If Maxwell's theory is correct a frequency of 100,000 corresponds to a wave-length of three kilometres or 1·86 miles. A frequency of 100,000,000 which can be obtained from a small spark gap, corresponds to a wave-length of 3 metres or roughly 3⅓ yards. Although we cannot make magnetic needles which move quickly enough to show an instantaneous deflection in opposite directions when separated by a distance of 1·5 metres (half a wave-length) in the plane at right angles to a 100,000,000 frequency oscillator, we can devise experiments based on interference to show that such variations in the field exist.

way which tells us that a weight hanging from its end will perform a to-and-fro movement when it is jerked. At first this does not seem to provide us with new information which we could not get by using our eyes. If you recall what was said on p. 294 you will see that it also exposes a new way of measuring the stretch per unit load. We can now do this by measuring the *time* of the vibration instead of the displacement. If this is easier to do, the mathematical examination of the problem is worth while. The mathematician cannot prove that the weight *must* bob up and down. All he can say is what will happen *if* the pull of the earth on a weight is just the same whether it is tied to the end of a spring, allowed to roll down a slope, or balanced at rest by another one. The observed result is a test of this supposition.

Maxwell examined the rules which govern electrical and magnetic attractions from this point of view, and showed that if we can imagine the existence of an ether having the properties with which Fresnel and Faraday had equipped it, stresses will travel in it with a speed which is the ratio of two units of current. Current can be measured in three ways by using it: (*a*) to decompose a salt and weighing the products, (*b*) to charge a condenser and measuring the attractive force between the plates (see end of Chapter XIII), (*c*) to deflect a suspended magnet and finding the mechanical torsion produced. The last two are respectively called the *electrostatic* and *electromagnetic* units. Maxwell's ratio is the number of electrostatic units of current required to produce the same magnetic deflection as a single electromagnetic unit of current in the same circumstances. The reasoning which led Maxwell to this conclusion and the reasons which prompted practical electricians to define units of current in this way will be found in advanced text-books. Two German electricians, Weber and Kohlrausch, had found the ratio of the units before Maxwell's time. Within the limits of experimental error it is 3×10^{10}. In centimetres per second, the units employed in measuring pulling power, this is the velocity of light. Kelvin obtained the same result by further experiments immediately after Maxwell announced the first outline of his theory about the year 1866.

A coincidence so striking could hardly fail to encourage research suggested by further applications of the wave metaphor. Among these the experiments of Hertz are specially important, and are usually said to have been undertaken to test Maxwell's theory. It is certainly true that Hertz, like other laboratory workers, was greatly stimulated by its publication. It is equally true that the tests which he used might have been devised without recourse to Maxwell's mathematical elaboration of Faraday's views. The method which Hertz used to measure the speed with which electromagnetic induction is propagated starts from an analogy with sound production. If a pipe closed at one end is tapped, a phenomenon known as a *stationary wave* can be demonstrated by sprinkling a fine powder on its floor. The dust accumulates in crests and troughs, as if the air in the pipe were divided into regions of normal pressure separating regions where the pressure is alternately high and low. An analogous phenomenon can be reproduced by making an undulation pass along a rope attached to a rigid support at one end. As the undulation passes forward from the end held by the hand there will be *nodes*, or points with no displacement, at regular intervals along it, and these nodes will be stationary when the undulation is reflected backwards towards the hand. When any "wave" is reflected back along the same path by a flat surface there is interference of this kind at regular intervals which correspond to *half a wave-length* (Fig. 382).

The wave-length of visible light is measured in hundred-millionths of a centimetre and the longest is less than 10,000 of these units. So we cannot detect whether optical interference of this kind exists. If induction is propagated with the speed of light between primary and secondary circuits in which the frequency of double-alternation is, say, 1,000 per second, the converse difficulty arises. The wave-length of an electromagnetic wave from a 1,000-cycle alternator is $3 \times 10^{10} \div 10^3$ cm., i.e. 300 kilometres, or 186 miles. The same objection does not apply to a kind of alternating current which had not been studied much before Maxwell's time. The high frequency or "oscillatory" currents of a spark discharge change their direction with a frequency measured in tens or hundreds of millions per second. If Maxwell's wave exists, an oscillatory discharge alternating 100,000,000 times a second would produce an ether wave with a wave-length of $3 \times 10^{10} \div 10^8 = 3 \times 10^2$ cm., or 3 metres. If reflected along its own path

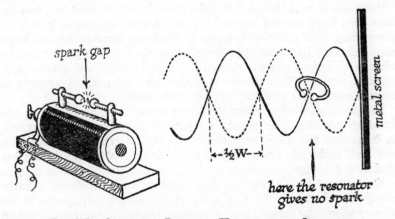

FIG. 382.—STATIONARY REFLECTED WAVES FROM AN OSCILLATOR

Hertz found that if a metal surface is placed parallel to the spark gap, a resonator shows periodic repetition of excitation and indifference in particular positions along the path of the inductive field. We can picture the intervening space as a ripple reflected by a stone causeway. In reflection of boundary waves stationary points separated by a half a wave-length occur. An analogous phenomenon occurs in formation of sound waves in tubes closed at one end.

such a wave would have regions of complete interference 1·5 metres (very approximately a yard and a half) apart. A secondary circuit in these regions would not be excited by discharge.

If the terminals of a secondary coil are brought sufficiently close together they make an effective spark gap across which a spark will pass when an A.C. current is set up in the circuit. Hertz found that a single circular loop of wire will act as a secondary circuit when the spark produced by a Leyden jar, or the secondary circuit of an induction coil, is a primary source of high frequency A.C. That is to say, tiny sparks can be detected between the enas of the loop, when the primary source is excited. Since the sparks are very minute the ends of the loop resonator must be very close, and it must lie parallel with the spark gap of the primary source (Fig. 382) Polished metals act as mirrors for other "ether waves," and shield inductive effects. So Hertz tried out the possibility that they would reflect the waves which spread outwards from the oscillatory discharge. In this way he was able to discover neutral regions, where his resonator would not spark, spaced at definite intervals alternating with regions where the sparks are strongest. These and subsequent experiments by other workers made it possible to assign values for the half "wave-length" of inductive disturbances propagated from an oscillatory discharge. The frequency of the discharge as found by photography gives us the value of n in the wave formula $(S = nW)$. If electromagnetic induction and light are analogous in the same sense as musical notes the product nW determined from the discharge observations should be the speed of light in air. This is found to be true.

THE BEGINNINGS OF WIRELESS TELEGRAPHY

Hertz also showed that an intensified inductive effect could be got at the focus of a large metallic mirror. His experiments stimulated interest in constructing more sensitive detectors of oscillatory currents than his metal loops with their tiny spark gaps. Hertz resonators were soon superseded by coherers of various patterns devised by Branly, Lodge, and several other scientific workers. With the aid of better detectors renewed attempts to transmit signals over long distances were undertaken.

The parent of wireless telegraphy is any arrangement for producing and detecting induction. This may be a primary line in circuit with a battery, an interrupter and a key, separated by air from a parallel secondary line with leads sufficiently near to make a spark. Long or short taps on the key producing prolonged or abrupt sparking can then spell a visible message in the Morse code. The Hertz oscillator and resonator represents a similar arrangement in which the long spark of the former corresponds to the *primary* alternating current. Both devices are useless for transmitting signals over distances greater than a few feet. For an ordinary low-frequency induction circuit a telephone transmitter (see Fig. 345) is a more sensitive detector than a Hertz resonator. Even so, an audible message in Morse code could not be transmitted over many yards. The detector is not sufficiently sensitive.

The experiments of Hertz were completed in 1888. In 1894 Lodge used a Branly coherer to detect signals transmitted over 150 yards. In the following year Rutherford succeeded in transmitting signals across half a mile of Cambridge streets. Popoff, of St. Petersburg, Jervis Smith, Captain Jackson, and others made similar trials elsewhere. In 1896 a young Italian, Marconi, came to England to take out a patent, and persuaded the General Post Office to undertake experiments. During the following May he succeeded in sending messages between two stations separated by nine miles across the Bristol Channel. In 1899 an apparatus which cost less than £100 transmitted messages across the English Channel. In that year the world at large learned that the benefits of the new gains in knowledge were not to be used in the public interest by the General Post Office, which sponsored the final experiments, nor to be reaped by the army of scientific workers who had nursed the initial discoveries which made wireless telegraphy possible. A company had been formed.

The transmission of signals over great distances raises two elementary issues, one of transmission, the other of detection. A beacon must be placed on a hilltop. So likewise a wireless transmitter must throw out its waves of induction in all directions. For doing this a spark gap is of no use by itself. It is used to induce oscillatory currents in a network of wires (the "antenna"). This, as Marconi discovered fortuitously while doing his early experiments under the inspection of the G.P.O., must be lifted high above the ground. The arrangement is shown in Fig. 383. Since there is no fixed connection between the receiver and transmitter, the former must be able to select a particular

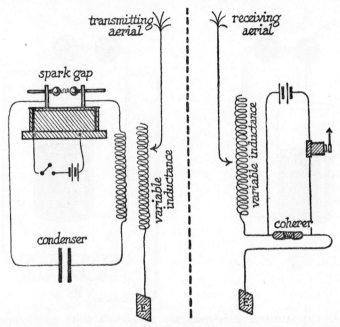

FIG. 383.—WIRELESS TRANSMITTER AND RECEIVER OF THE OLD TYPE FOR TAKING MORSE SIGNALS

one from all messages sent out simultaneously from different stations. His detector must *resonate selectively*. Discovering how to make a sensitive detector resonate was a first essential in the story of wireless telegraphy. How to make a detector resonate *selectively* was the final and most important step. It was made by Lodge before Marconi's minor improvements were patented.

Selective resonance or "syntonic signalling" is a complicated issue, and it is only possible to touch very lightly on it in this chapter. In an inductive field a wire like that of an aerial behaves like the flat thin metal diaphragm of a gramophone. It responds to a large range of frequencies. The wave metaphor suggests how this can be done, and experiments such as those which Lodge carried out (Fig. 384) confirm the analogy. A perfectly selective resonator of sound does not exist. Selective resonators are nearly perfect

if they vibrate with one *audible* frequency, like a tuning-fork. A piano wire
has one principal frequency due to vibration along its whole length. Superimposed on it, there are fainter audible components due to subsidiary vibrations of separate segments. The frequencies of these "harmonics" or overtones
which give "timbre" or richness to the note are simple multiples of the
principal frequency. A long piano wire has more inertia and emits a note of
lower frequency than a shorter one of the same material at the same tension.
So we can change the principal note of a piano wire and therefore the *range*

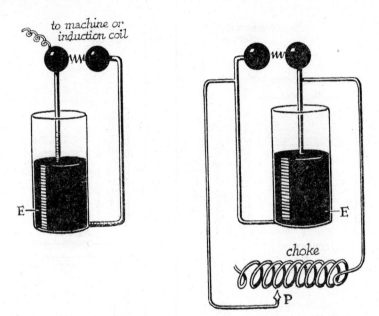

FIG. 384.—DIAGRAMMATIC REPRESENTATION OF LODGE'S EARLY EXPERIMENTS ON
SYNTONIC OR SELECTIVE ELECTRICAL RESONANCE

On one side the "transmitter," a Leyden jar, connected to an electrical machine, the
outer coat being earthed. On the other side the receiver, a neighbouring Leyden jar
with a high inductance in parallel. If this is suitably adjusted sparking occurs across
the gap when the transmitter is in action.

of overtones to which it will resonate by altering its length. If the analogy
holds good the problem of selective resonance is how to give the aerial
circuit of the receiving station more or less *electrical inertia*.

In electrical circuits two phenomena are analogous to the inertia of
material bodies. A rising current in any loop of a coil in series with a
circuit induces a reverse one in any neighbouring loop, thus lengthening
the minute interval requisite to establish a steady flow; and a Leyden jar
in parallel with a circuit has the same effect. It slows down the rate at which
the current grows. Either an inductance in series (see Fig. 383) or a condenser in parallel with the aerial circuit of the receiver can thus be used to change
its inertia, i.e. the time taken by a current to get going. So either a variable

condenser or a variable inductance can be used to make it selectively resonant to a particular range. In practice receiving circuits usually have both. The variable condenser is used for fine and the variable inductance for coarse adjustment.

COSTING THE DISCHARGE

Radio equipment, including as it does condensers and choking coils, raises problems of electrical accountancy not touched on in what has gone before. So far our discussion of the costing of the current has introduced us to three units, the *ampere*, the *volt* and the *ohm*. The last named is the unit of resistance, i.e. of the obstruction which the circuit itself offers to a steady current; and we have seen (p. 687) how to measure it by means of a Wheatstone bridge equipped with a standard and with a suitable detector, i.e. a galvanometer for D.C. or headphones for A.C. To get a satisfactory result it is essential to use either a steady *unidirectional* current or an intermittent current of *low* frequency (e.g. 100 *per sec.*). Alternating or unidirectional intermittent currents of high frequency are impracticable, because it is possible to get a sharp *null-point* only if growth and decline of currents in all parts of the circuit keep in step. This will rarely occur if the frequency is high. Thus circuits offer two kinds of obstruction to flow of electricity, one permanent, i.e. *resistance*, one transitory which we may call sluggishness or (as above) *inertia*. This sluggishness is evident from the fact that condensers or choking coils in parallel with part of a circuit conveying an A.C. of high frequency influence the maximum voltage attainable before its direction reverses. The technical terms for the inertia respectively conferred on a circuit by a condenser and by a choking coil are *capacity* and *self-induction* (inductance). Either is referable to the other in the sense that the combination of a condenser in parallel with a straight conductor can play the same role as a choke coil of the same resistance as the conductor itself. For practical purposes a standard condenser is therefore a satisfactory basis for the determination of either an unknown capacity or an unknown inductance.

We have seen how a condenser in parallel with the terminals of a frictional generator increases the brightness of the spark and the interval between discharges. Though the connexion of a condenser to the poles of a voltaic cell has no detectable effect on prolonged action such as electrolysis produced by a steady current at a fixed E.M.F., it can act visibly as a store, keeping up the surge of an intermittent battery, when in a circuit containing an interrupter and a *low-frequency* (i.e. sluggish) galvanometer. A condenser in parallel with the primary circuit of a shocking coil (Fig. 368) increases both the brightness of the sparks from the secondary terminals and the interval between them. Thus the power of a condenser to store electrification is measurable either by its effect on the behaviour of bodies with a static electrical charge (p. 649) or by its effects on currents of short duration; and the measurement of *capacity*, i.e. storage power, is therefore common territory to battery and to frictional electricity. As such it calls for a thorough examination of the significance of such terms as *charge* and *potential* in either context.

At this point it is therefore necessary to retrace our steps. The essential peculiarities of the electric current produced by a voltaic cell or by a dynamo are: (*a*) liberation of heat; (*b*) chemical decomposition when it flows through the solution of an electrolyte; (*c*) the existence of a magnetic field in its neighbourhood. When discharged to earth the terminal of a frictional machine or the knob of the Leyden jar are each capable of reproducing all three phenomena (p. 660). Leakage of charge from a body electrified by friction is, in short, *a current*, albeit one of momentary duration; and what we mean by the rate of discharge of an electrified body in an incompletely insulated electrostatic field corresponds to what we call the strength of the current in a battery circuit, assessed by the quantity of metal deposited by electrolysis in unit time (*one second*). The quantity of silver so deposited in one second furnishes us with a practical unit of charge, called the *coulomb*. When the mean current strength is one ampere, the charge neutralized is defined as one coulomb. This is therefore (p. 663) the charge associated with $0 \cdot 001118$ g. of silver in a solution of any of its salts.

The energy which would be liberated by the passage of one ampere at a mean E.M.F. of 1 volt is $0 \cdot 239$ ($= 4 \cdot 184^{-1}$) calorie. In conformity with our definition, this is also the amount of heat associated with a discharge of 1 coulomb between terminals whose mean E.M.F. is 1 volt. If we use the symbol Q for charge or quantity of electrification in *coulombs*, C for current in *amperes*, E for E.M.F. in *volts*, W for energy in *ergs* liberated by the passage of the current for t seconds and H for the equivalent heat production in *calories* we may therefore write (p. 696):

$$Q = Ct \quad or \quad C = Q \div t$$
$$H = 0 \cdot 239.EQ \quad or \quad W = 10^7 EQ$$

We have therefore to define units of frictional electricity in such a way as to make the heat visibly liberated as a spark during the discharge of an electrified body directly proportional to the product of the charge removed and the *mean* potential difference involved. The coulomb is a unit chosen for *practical* considerations, and is *not* identical with the mechanical unit defined on p. 674 as that of a spherical body which exerts a field strength of 1 dyne at 1 cm. from its centre. Nor is the corresponding, and so-called *absolute*, unit of potential difference identical with the volt. If Q_a ($= e$ on p. 674) is the *quantity* of charge in absolute units, we define the mean potential difference (E_m) consistently with a straightforward relation between Q_a and W in ergs, viz.: $W = Q_a.E_m$. When Q_a is unity, $E_m = W$, so that the mean potential difference E_m is the *work done by unit discharge*; and the liberation of energy by one absolute unit of charge at a mean p.d. of one absolute unit is one erg.

So defined the unit of p.d. presupposes that we can measure charge *directly* in terms of the mechanical force of attraction or repulsion; but here we are faced with a dilemma we have already experienced in connexion with magnetic measurements referable to a unit of pole strength. As before, we have to seek for a *derived* quantity which is, in fact, *capacity* (K) explicitly defined (p. 676) as the ratio of the charge stored by an electrified body to the potential difference (E_a) between itself and its surroundings, i.e. if earthed, w.r.t. the earth itself. In other words:

$$K = Q_a \div E_a \quad or \quad Q_a = K.E_a.$$

It is important to realize that the *initial* potential difference (E_a) between the knob of the Leyden jar and the earth connected to the outer coat is not the same as the *mean* p.d. (E_m) w.r.t. earth during the discharge. On connecting the two coats, the p.d. falls to zero, so that $E_m = \frac{1}{2} (E_a + 0) = \frac{1}{2} E_a$. Hence we may write:

$$W = \tfrac{1}{2}Q_a . E_a \quad or \quad W = \tfrac{1}{2} K.E_a^2.$$

This distinction is sufficiently important to invoke once more the analogy of water flowing from a tank. If the volume which flows in time t is v, the current or rate of flow is $v \div t$. Accordingly, we have defined our practical units of current and quantity or charge, so that $C = Q \div t$ or $Q = Ct$. The work (W) done by the fall of a mass m through a height h is mgh. Its density (d) is $m \div v$. So we may write the work done as $v.dgh$. Since dgh is the pressure (p) the work done is given by the relation $W = vp$, in which volume takes the place of charge and pressure replaces potential difference w.r.t. earth. To apply our formula to assess the work done when a cistern *at ground level* empties itself by a leak at the base, we have to remember that the whole of the water does not fall through the height h_t of the topmost layer. What happens is that the uppermost layer does so, while the bottom layer does not fall through any distance. A drop of water falls through a mean distance $\frac{1}{2}h_t$; and the outcome is as if half the contents fell through the distance h_t under a constant corresponding pressure head p_t or the whole volume fell through h_t at a corresponding pressure head $\frac{1}{2}p_t$. If p_t stands for the initial pressure head, our formula therefore becomes: $W = \frac{1}{2} v.p_t$. This is consistent with the previous one, in which p stands for the constant pressure throughout the flow, since $\frac{1}{2}p_t$ is the mean pressure, i.e. what the pressure would be if constant throughout a process involving as much work.

If we carry the analogy further, the quantity comparable to capacity as defined above is the ratio of volume to pressure, i.e. $v \div dgh$. If a stands for the sectional area of the tank, this is $a \div dg$.* Since the density of water is unity, the capacity of a cistern so defined involves only its sectional area and a quantity (g) whose exact value depends on the position of the cistern w.r.t. the earth's centre. The analogy between electrical and gravitational attractions therefore leads us to hope that we may be able to define a unit of capacity consistent with the inverse square law of electrification *without recourse to any information other than the physical dimensions of a standard condenser*. That this is so, is in fact deducible by more than one method from the definitions of charge and field strength given on p. 674. What follows pursues an analogy which has proved especially fruitful.

We have seen (Fig. 107) that light diverging from a candle without external interference obeys an inverse square law. This follows from the fact that light pursues a straight path radiating uniformly in all directions from a source. Since the area of a sphere of radius r is $4\pi r^2$, it is evident that n lines spreading out uniformly from the centre cut the surface in such a way that the number (N) per unit area is $n \div 4\pi r^2$. Thus N varies inversely as the square of the distance from the centre. If we identify these lines with what

---

* Notice that electrostatic capacity does not correspond to capacity in the same sense as volume. It corresponds to capacity to do work.

we call *rays* of light from a source at the centre, N is therefore a measure of the intensity of illumination at a surface tangential to the sphere. As such, it does *not* directly depend on the length of the rays themselves. A ray is therefore a geometrical fiction to convey the truth that light does in fact obey an inverse square law, unless we use a slit to pick out a parallel beam or a condensing lens to compel a divergent beam to follow a cylindrical path.

The difficulty of visualizing *action at a distance* when gravitational and magnetic attractions were the focus of scientific interest led early investigators to develop this imagery of lines diverging uniformly from a centre by recourse to a physical model which would almost inescapably suggest itself to Hooke's contemporaries or successors. We replace the pulling power of a magnet, a sun or an electrified body by a set of stretched springs radiating uniformly in all directions from a centre of attraction. In a magnetic field the disposition of these springs or *lines of force* recalls the pattern of iron filings shown in Fig. 378, and we can helpfully compare an electrical conductor to a fluid which allows a spring free movement to contract. A *dielectric*, i.e. insulator, is then comparable to a solid in which an extended spring cannot contract, so that current conceived as free movement of lines of force cannot exist. Such a model makes it possible to visualize electrical calculations of all sorts, and suggests novel possibilities. Indeed, testing the analogy leads to an important and, at first, surprising discovery. If we take to pieces the parts of a detachable condenser such as a Leyden jar and connect the metal coatings, there is no discharge. If we then reassemble the parts the jar discharges, as if nothing had happened. Seemingly, the energy of the spark is *stored* in the dielectric from which it can be released only when in contact with the conducting surface of the metal coats.

To apply to the problem of measuring the capacity of a condenser the reasoning suggested by our spring model, we suppose that two plates (Fig. 382) of equal area A: (*a*) carry equal and opposite charges $+ Q_a$ and $- Q_a$ *absolute* units *separately* conferred on them by one or other terminal of a suitable generator; (*b*) face one another at a considerable distance r cm. apart. They will then attract one another with a mechanical force of M dynes such that (p. 674)

$$M = \frac{Q_a^2}{k.r^2} \quad . \quad . \quad . \quad \text{(i)}$$

If we conceive this attraction in terms of the pulling power of *lines of force* in the medium, we must endow the latter with properties consistent with the known peculiarities of electrical phenomena. To accommodate *induction* (pp. 645–6) we must first assume:

(*a*) that each line of force starts from a body with an independent charge and ends somewhere, however remote, on a surface to which it contributes an equal charge of opposite sign;

(*b*) that such lines of force concentrate wholly in the gap between an independently charged body and a nearby previously neutral conductor connected to earth while it still remains close to the source of its induced charge (Figs. 315 and 316);

(*c*) that such a previously neutral conductor retains a charge equal and opposite to that of the source, if disconnected from earth before removal from propinquity to the inducing charge.

To accommodate the inverse square law of attraction, we have also to assume:

(d) that the mechanical pull on a surface depends only on the number (N) of lines of force impinging on it, being independent of their length (Fig. 107), i.e. $M \propto N$;

(e) that each line of force contributes equally to the pull on a surface at right angles to it;

(f) that lines of force radiate uniformly in all directions from a charged body unless there is a nearby conductor on which they converge to evoke an induced charge.

If we assign n lines of force irradiating in all directions from a body with charge $\pm Q_a$, having no conductor to bring them to focus in its immediate neighbourhood, we must define n consistently with the characteristics of electrostatic phenomena specified above. Between two plates of opposite charge some lines of force arising from each will come to rest on its fellow; and if their distance (r) apart is very great, this will involve no appreciable distortion of their otherwise uniform irradiation. On *unit* area at a distance r from *each* independently charged plate specified above, the number of lines of force will be $n \div 4\pi r^2$; and the total number *per unit area* arising from *both* will be twice this, i.e. $n \div 2\pi r^2$. Since the area of the plates is A, the actual number (N) will therefore be given by:

$$N = \frac{An}{2\pi r^2} \qquad \cdot \quad \cdot \quad \text{(ii)}$$

This involves no assumptions about the numerical relation between N and the charge Q_a. All that our metaphor commits us to is the assumption that M is directly proportional to the number of lines of force between the plates. If a is an arbitrary constant M is therefore equal to aN; and if we assign to a the value of unity, $M = n$. This is consistent with all we know about M, if:

$$N = \frac{Q_a^2}{kr^2} \qquad \cdot \quad \cdot \quad \cdot \quad \text{(iii)}$$

For air (p. 674) $k = 1$; and $N = Q_a^2 \div r^2$. By combining (ii) with (iii) we therefore have:

$$\frac{Q_a^2}{r^2} = \frac{An}{2\pi r^2}$$

$$n = \frac{2\pi Q_a^2}{A} \qquad \cdot \quad \cdot \quad \text{(iv)}$$

Were we now to bring the two plates close together face to face, separated only by a small gap of d cm, all these N lines of force would fill the gap between them. Since n lines of force take their origin from each plate $N = 2n$; and the mechanical pull M ($= $ N) dynes is $4\pi Q_a^2 \div A$. By temporarily connecting one plate—let us say the negative—to earth in this position, we remove its excess and independent charge — Q_a, thereby eliminating n lines of force (Fig. 385). Consequently $N = n$; and

$$M = \frac{2\pi Q_a^2}{A} \quad \cdot \quad \cdot \quad \text{(v)}$$

If pulled together until they touch by their mechanical force, the plates would lose their charge; and the lines of force would contract through d cm. Our

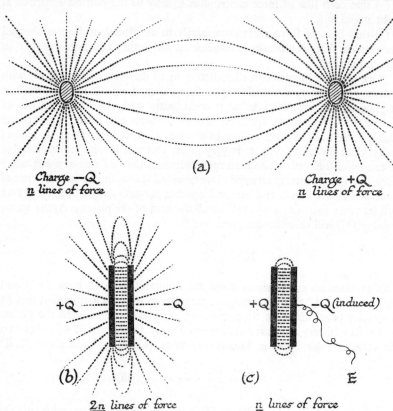

FIG. 385.—LINES OF FORCE IN AN ELECTRIC FIELD

hypothesis is that M depends only on the number of lines of force, being independent of their length. Hence M remains constant throughout the change, and the energy (W) liberated in discharging the plates is Md ergs, i.e.:

$$W = \frac{2\pi Q_a^2 d}{A} \quad \cdot \quad \cdot \quad \text{(vi)}$$

We already know that the energy of discharge is $\frac{1}{2} Q_a . E_a$ ergs; and since the capacity (K) is $Q_a \div E_a$,

$$E_a = Q_a \div K$$

$$\therefore \quad W = \frac{Q_a^2}{2K} \quad \cdot \quad \cdot \quad \cdot \quad \text{(vii)}$$

By combining (vi) and (vii) we get:

$$\frac{2\pi Q_a^2 d}{A} = \frac{Q_a^2}{2K}$$

$$K = \frac{A}{4\pi d} \quad \cdot \quad \cdot \quad \text{(viii)}$$

The last formula (viii) connects the capacity of a simple *air* condenser of parallel flat plates with their area and their distance apart;* and involves recourse to *no* electric measurements as such. It relies only on the area of the plates and their distance apart. This simplifies the measurement of either charge or p.d., because we can calculate either the charge carried by a condenser or the p.d. between the plates, if we know both its capacity and the energy liberated by discharging it, i.e. the heat (in calories) liberated by the spark. Since the capacity of our air condenser (which we can use as a standard for a condenser with any other intervening dielectric) is directly calculable from its dimensions, the energy of discharge therefore gives us a straightforward means of measuring either quantity or potential in the *absolute* system of units, and if requisite the value of *k* the dielectric constant.

This is the rationale of one type of instrument (Fig. 386) employed to measure very large electrostatic potential differences such as the p.d. between the terminals of a frictional machine. The *Attracted Disc Electrometer* perfected by Kelvin is in essence a collapsible air condenser of two parallel plates. One is free to move, being attached to one arm of a balance connected to earth. The other arm of the balance carries a weight sufficient to hold the movable disc at a distance *d* within a *guard ring* which concentrates the field of force at the edges. When the fixed plate receives a charge, another weight ($w = mg$) in the scale pan is requisite to keep the movable disc *d* cm. apart from it by counteracting the force of attraction between the pair. We have seen that this pull (mg) is $2\pi Q_a^2 \div A$. By definition $Q_a = K.E_a$ and by (viii) $K = A \div 4\pi d$, so that:

$$Q_a^2 = \frac{A^2}{16\pi^2 d^2} E_a^2$$

$$\therefore \quad mg = \frac{2\pi}{A} \cdot \frac{A^2}{16\pi^2 d^2} \cdot E_a^2 = \frac{A E_a^2}{8\pi d^2}$$

$$\therefore \quad E_a = d \sqrt{\frac{8\pi.mg}{A}}$$

Given the weight (mg) necessary to counterpoise the attraction of the two plates, we can therefore calculate the potential of the fixed plate w.r.t. earth if we also know the physical measurements (A and *d*) of the set-up.

The attracted disc instrument is suitable for measuring very large potential differences. For the measurement of small electrostatic potential differences, it is sometimes advantageous to use an instrument that does not rely on a steady

* If the dielectric were mica or glass, it would be necessary to introduce the constant *k* (p. 674) into our calculations.

flow of current, as in a magnetic voltmeter (p. 710). The quadrant electrometer (Fig. 387) in one form or another is an instrument of this sort. The main parts are (a) a light vane of aluminium or paper coated with metallic foil suspended by a wire with a mirror attachment; (b) four metal chambers like the four quarters of a pill-box surrounding the vane; (c) an earthed metal case screening the whole. Each quadrant is insulated from its two neighbours and connected by a wire with its opposite. When the instrument is in use, the wire suspending the vane is connected at its attachment to a terminal connected with one electrode of a battery to keep the vane at a constant potential. Adjacent quadrants are connected with sources of un-

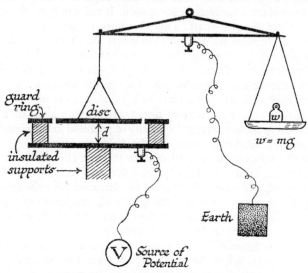

FIG. 386.—ATTRACTED-DISC ELECTROMETER

known p.d. If the needle is positively charged it will be attracted by the quadrants which are negatively charged or of lower positive potential. The experiment with generators maintaining a known p.d. show that deflection (recorded by the displacement of a beam of light) is proportional to the p.d. between the quadrants; and it is possible in this way to calibrate the deflection corresponding to a given p.d.

The formula $(A \div 4\pi d)$ for the capacity of simple air condenser of two flat plates gives it in *absolute* units. The practical unit of capacity for large condensers is the *farad*, which is that of an earthed condenser between whose terminals the p.d. is 1 volt when the charged plate carries 1 coulomb. The link between the two systems of units is the value assigned to the volt. One absolute unit of p.d. is equivalent to 300 volts, i.e. $E = 300 \, E_a$. The heat of discharge (in *ergs*) is proportional to the product of discharge and E.M.F., being $Q_a \cdot E_a$ ergs in absolute units and $10^7 QE$ in the coulombs-volt system. Hence

$$Q_a E_a = 10^7 Q \, (300 \, E_a)$$
$$\therefore Q_a = 3 \times 10^9 Q$$

When $Q = 1$, $Q_a = 3 \times 10^9$. Hence 1 coulomb is 3×10^9 units of charge. By definition, the capacity of a condenser is the ratio of charge to potential difference being $(Q_a \div E_a)$ in absolute units and $(Q \div E)$ farads. Thus K farads are equivalent to

$$\frac{Q_a}{3 \times 10^9} \div 300\, E_a = \frac{Q_a}{E_a} \cdot \frac{1}{9 \times 10^{11}}$$

If $K = 1$ we have $Q_a \div E_a = 9 \times 10^{11}$. That is to say, 1 farad is equivalent to 9×10^{11} absolute units of capacity. For small condensers a more con-

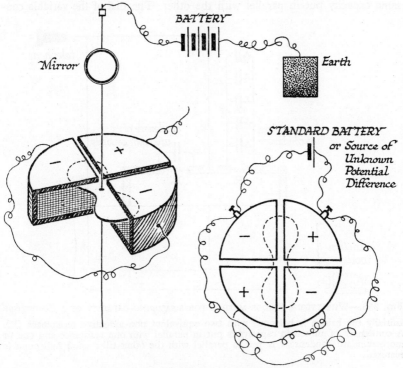

FIG. 387.—QUADRANT ELECTROMETER

venient unit is the *microfarad* which is one millionth of a farad, hence equivalent to 900,000 absolute units. The p.d. required to deflect the leaves of a home-made electroscope noticeably is about 100 volts. By rubbing a fountain pen on the sleeve it is possible to raise its potential to over a thousand volts. To get a spark to pass a 1 millimetre gap between metals balls of 1 cm. diameter the p.d. must be nearly 5,000 volts, and somewhat over 25,000 to spark across a gap of 1 cm.

Having settled on the dimensions of a condenser with a capacity of 1 μF, or of a coil with inductance of 1 henry, a principle used in assigning the appropriate figure for any condenser or choke by comparison with the standard simply depends on the fact that a Wheatstone bridge will not give a clear null point with a high-frequency A.C. unless the inertia of the circuit is the same throughout. Suppose, for instance (Fig. 388), the two arms contain two identical resistances with negligible self-induction, so that the bridge is equally well "balanced" when a low-frequency A.C. or D.C. is applied to it. The insertion of a condenser in parallel with one of the resistances will at once upset the balance when a high-frequency A.C. (10,000 per sec.) is used. To restore it, we should have to put a condenser of the same capacity in parallel with the other resistance. A rough method of comparing two capacities is therefore as follows. A large variable condenser is put in parallel with one resistance, and one, two, three, etc., standard condensers of the same capacity put in parallel with the other. The dial of the variable con-

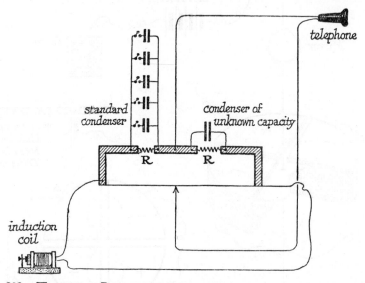

FIG. 388.—WHEATSTONE BRIDGE METHOD FOR MEASURING CAPACITY OF A CONDENSER

Initially the bridge is balanced with two equivalent non-inductive resistances (R). A condenser of unknown capacity is put in parallel with one resistance and one or more standard condensers is put in parallel with the other till a good null point is restored.

denser can be marked for the positions at which a clear null point is obtained for one, two, or more of the standard capacities. The variable condenser can then be used in one arm of the bridge, and adjusted to give perfect balance when a condenser of unknown capacity is put in the other arm.

Similarly, the bridge can be used to compare an unknown inductance with a standard. The principle may be roughly illustrated in this way. Suppose the two arms of a bridge carry a choking coil and a resistance of negligible self-induction so adjusted that it is equivalent to the resistance of the choking coil itself when a D.C. or very low frequency current is used. With a high-frequency current the balance of the bridge will be put out because the inertia of the two parts of the circuit will be different. To restore the balance we have to increase the inertia of the resistance which has no appreciable self-induction, and this can be done by putting a condenser in parallel with it. So the self-induction of a choking coil can be estimated by comparison with the inertia of a condenser of known capacity.

WIRELESS TELEPHONY

The Marconi system of signalling depended on using the coherer as a switch to turn the current of the detector circuit on and off. The recorder in the detector circuit registers long or short taps of the key which releases the oscillatory current at the transmitting station. So many long (dash) or short (dot) taps in a particular order stands for one or other of the twenty-six letters of the Morse alphabet, or for secret code words. The dots and dashes

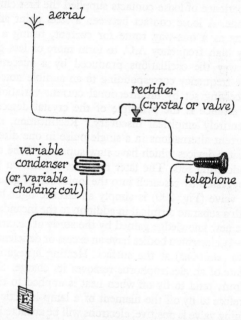

FIG. 389.—WIRELESS RECEIVER WITH CRYSTAL RECTIFIER
The inertia of the circuit is correctly tuned by a variable condenser in parallel.

may be recorded audibly by the duration of the buzz in a telephone receiver, or registered by a Morse instrument (Fig. 383) with a pen writing on a movable tape. The inertia of the coherer is too great to keep step with a rapid succession of oscillatory currents following one another with the frequency of a musical note. Direct speech transmission involves the use of a device called a rectifier.

The frequency of an oscillatory current is immense compared with the frequency of a musical note. Middle C is produced by vibrations of 256 per second. Radio waves of 300 metres wave-length are produced by a current which alternates with a frequency of 1,000,000 per second. A tapper which released them at equal intervals 256 times a second with equal intervals of rest between would send out a succession of oscillatory discharges, each corresponding to roughly 2,000 current alternations. On the face of it there is therefore no insuperable obstacle to the conversion of wireless waves into sounds. In an ordinary telephone receiver the diaphragm vibrates with a frequency corresponding to that of the note which the ear recognizes. The vibrations of the diaphragm correspond to variations in the magnetic field produced by corresponding variations of the current which always flows in one direction. In telephony without wires the problem is how to record a note of, say, 256 vibrations transmitted in 256 equally spaced parcels of, say, 2,000 equally spaced reversals of current in the aerial receiving circuit. This resolves itself into converting each parcel of oscillations into a single pulse of current in *one direction*.

Workshop experience of loose contacts supplied the first clue to show how this could be done. A loose contact between a steel point and a crystal of carborundum acts as a one-way route for current, fusing a succession of phases in a very high frequency A.C. to form more or less coherent single pulses. In this way the oscillations produced by a succession of sparks released with the frequency corresponding to an audible note can be reproduced in the receiving set by unidirectional current variations in the telephone. This in essence is the principle of the crystal detector (Fig. 389), which was an entirely empirical discovery.* Rectification, i.e. fusion of a succession of current alternations in a single pulse in one direction, can also be achieved by later devices which have now superseded the crystal detector of the first broadcasting sets. The later rectifiers depend on the application of a principle suggested by research into the ionization of gases.

The Fleming valve (Fig. 390) is simply an electric light bulb containing a metal plate with a separate terminal in addition to the incandescent filament. According to the new knowledge gained by the study of electrical conduction in gases (pp. 782-4), electrified bodies have an excess or deficiency of negatively charged particles (*electrons*) at the surface. Heating a negatively electrified body like the plate of an electrophorus removes its charge. So we may presume that electrons tend to fly off when heat is applied to the surface of a metal; and therefore to fly off the filament of a lamp in action. If the metal plate of the Fleming valve is positive, electrons will be attracted by its opposite charge. Electrons will be repelled if the plate is negative. This means that if two ends of an A.C. circuit are connected respectively to the metal plate and to the negative terminal of the lamp circuit, current will only pass between filament and plate, and in the A.C. circuit when the plate is positive. Alternate phases are therefore cut out. A unidirectional intermittent current will flow, and if the successive phases of the latter succeed one another with great rapidity they are more or less completely fused into one pulse. Thus a valve acts as a one-way route, converting a succession of high-frequency oscillatory currents into a succession of single pulse currents in one direction, when the oscillatory current is in series with the metal plate and the *negative* terminal of the lamp filament.

The underlying principle of television is analogous to telephony. The essential principle involved in reproducing sound at a distance is that

---

* The crystal detector also acts as a coherer, being sensitive to small oscillatory currents.

variations of sound in the transmitting instrument (microphone) produce corresponding variations in the resistance of the circuit. In the receiver corresponding fluctuations of current produce corresponding fluctuations in the field of an electromagnet. These set up corresponding audible vibrations of a steel diaphragm. The variations of resistance in the transmitter are due to variations of mechanical percussion on a loose contact. Thus the microphone diaphragm is a sort of switch which is turned on and off by sound waves. It is easy to produce light by a current. The problem of reproducing it is to make a switch which can be turned on and off by another source of illumination. This can be done, because the resistance of some

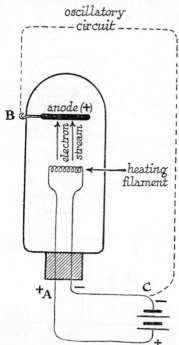

FIG. 390.—THE FLEMING THERMIONIC VALVE

When the positive end of the filament (A) is connected with the plate (B) a current flows between A and B, as can be shown by putting a galvanometer in series with A and B. If instead B is included in the oscillatory circuit current will only flow in the latter when B is positive. Hence the plate acts as a rectifier.

substances, notably *selenium*, is affected by light. Selenium is a good insulator in the dark. In the light it is a poor conductor. So a film of selenium in series with a current acts as a switch or coherer for visible light. If the circuit contains a lamp, light may therefore be used as a stimulus to produce light elsewhere. Neon lamps become incandescent rather suddenly at the critical E.M.F. when ionization of the gas starts. A comparatively small change of resistance in the circuit of a Neon lamp is therefore sufficient to turn the light off or to turn it on, if the current is suitably adjusted.

It is easy to envisage how a visual pattern could be reproduced by an

arrangement involving this principle if you recall the elaborate figures sometimes exhibited as sky signs on high buildings. Imagine a screen studded
with selenium resistances, each connected to a lamp occupying precisely
the same relative position in a second screen, and so adjusted that when
light falls on a particular resistance the corresponding lamp in the receiving
screen will become incandescent. To each stud in the transmitting screen on
which a pattern of light or shade is focussed, there will be a corresponding
point of brightness or darkness on the receiving screen. So the pattern on
the latter will reproduce the image on the former. This is not the mechanism
of transmission actually employed in television. The device which Baird

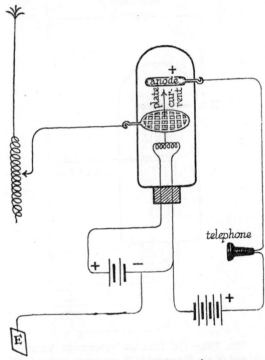

FIG. 391.—THE TRIODE VALVE OR AMPLIFIER

If a "grid" (i.e. wire mesh) is placed between the plate and the filament of a Fleming
valve any variation of the electron current between the filament and grid makes
a large difference to the plate current which flows when the plate is kept at a high
positive potential. In loud speaker circuits the oscillatory circuit is connected with the
grid. The variations in the plate current produce the sounds in the telephone or loud
speaker.

patented depends on the same principle as the cinematograph. That is to
say, the effect of a light stimulus persists on the retina for an appreciable
period of time—about one-sixth of a second. If a succession of points of
light all fall on the retina within this period they give rise to a continuous
sensory pattern. The image of the object to be transmitted falls on a flat
wheel with small orifices arranged in a spiral. Behind the wheel is a photo-

electric cell* which generates a current when a hole lets through light. At the same moment a Neon lamp at the receiving station in direct or radio connection with the selenium cell goes on. If a second wheel rotates at exactly the same speed as the first in front of the Neon lamp in the receiving set a beam of light will issue from a hole in the same position whenever a beam of light penetrates the corresponding hole in the transmitting wheel. Thus a spatial pattern of points of light is translated into a *single succession* of electric impulses, and this in its turn is translated back again into a spatial pattern.

OVERSTRAINING THE ETHER

In the propagation of light and of electromagnetic effects through empty space we encounter various types of periodic phenomena, such as interference bands (Fig. 206) or electrical resonance. These can be observed directly. The spacing of interference bands and stationary nodes in the track of a light beam or train of electromagnetic induction involves any *odd* multiple of a measurable distance. This measurable distance is the actual difference between the paths traversed by two disturbances from the same source. In accordance with the corresponding phenomenon of acoustical interference, this distance is called a *half wave-length*. So far as phenomena of interference are concerned light and electromagnetic induction are propagated like sound waves of compression and rarefaction. For other characteristics of radiation through empty space the analogy no longer holds. The power of polarized light or of an electromagnetic disturbance to traverse a crystal of fluorspar or a grating of metal wires when, and only when, the crystal or wire grid is placed in a particular position recalls the kind of wave motion executed by a skipping rope or circular ripples spreading from a stone dropped into a pool. The characteristic of such wave motion is a periodic *transverse displacement*, i.e. a displacement at right angles to the track of the wave.

The analogy between radiations and "transverse vibrations" of this type is not wholly satisfactory. Familiar examples of the latter are *shape* phenomena characteristic of the *boundary* of a medium in contradistinction to propagation of a disturbance with wave-like characteristics *through the interior* of a medium. A more satisfactory mechanical model is easy to visualize, though it is not easy to construct. We can picture concentric eddies in a viscous fluid swirling at any given instant of time in opposite directions and separated at equal distances by zones where the medium is at rest. We can also imagine how the motion of the current at any point in the fluid may slow down to zero, gain motion in the opposite direction, reach a maximum, slow down to zero, and so on in successive intervals of time. In this model, illustrated in its simplest form in Figs. 380 and 381, there is a periodic transverse displacement at right angles to the radius of the concentric cylindrical eddies. For visualizing the phenomena of interference along the track of a radiation it reproduces all the relevant analogies between radiation and sound waves

* Fig. 399 on p. 802 shows the construction of a *photo-electric cell*, in which a deposit of an alkali metal in a vacuum tube produces a small current under the influence of light.

2B*

of compression and rarefaction. For visualizing the phenomenon of polarization it embodies what is relevant in the analogy between radiation and boundary waves.

Like every other analogy which we can easily visualize this one breaks down at a certain point. It helps us to picture the fact that a wire grating placed in the train of an oscillatory discharge or a crystal acting as a grid for polarized light can obstruct radiation, unless placed in a particular position. On the other hand, it requires a grid with immeasurably long slits. A model which meets all known characteristics of radiation ceases to have any resemblance to mechanisms which we ever meet in real life. This is not because science reveals less orderliness in nature as it grows. It is because science reveals new and unsuspected levels of orderliness. As new stories are added to the edifice of known regularities in the real world, some of the old scaffolding of metaphors which helped to prop it up fall away. Man's first experience of measurable interaction between material things was derived from levers, pulleys, and siphons, which transmit power through the substantial contact of cords, cogs, belts, and pipes. When science was first concerned with changes which are induced without the intervention of ponderable matter, analogies suggested by more familiar measurements met with in more primitive mechanisms pointed the road to unsuspected truths. Once we have adjusted ourselves to the oddities of radiation the all-pervading elastic ether is seen for what it is, a useful device for mapping space, like the lines which Gilbert drew on his *terella*. What remains are the periodic characteristics of measurements on the transmission of power through empty space.

CHAPTER XVI

BEYOND THE ATOM

DURING the past four centuries mankind has blundered into a succession of makeshifts dictated by the impact of scientific discoveries on social organization. There was little prevision of the outcome either by those engaged in the pursuit of new knowledge or by those concerned with its applications. In the partnership between theory and practice, practice has usually been the pacemaker and the patron. Theory has largely relied on the day to day work of the world for clues to follow or problems to assail. The invention of the dynamo was an exception. It was conceived and nursed in the laboratory; and its creation signalizes the emergence of organized scientific research as an institution with a momentum, but as yet a blind momentum, of its own. For few of Faraday's contemporaries gave a thought to the long-range effect of laboratory discoveries on the life of mankind.

Like the dynamo, large-scale use of atomic energy is an outcome of laboratory leadership; but with a conspicuously novel feature. The spectacular horror of the circumstances attendant on the first demonstration quickened an instantaneous premonition of its social consequences throughout the civilized world, not least among participants in the technical tasks involved. Never have human beings responded to the announcement of a new invention with a keener or more widespread concern to protect themselves against its misuse and to take stock of its effect on a social tradition which has treated with indifference or scorn the claims of natural science to a place in education for civic responsibilities. In 1935 it was still necessary to advocate such claims. It was still fashionable for leaders of social thought to discount them. In 1945 it was a commonplace to assert that intelligent decision concerning major issues of social policy presupposes intelligent understanding of the technical possibilities which modern government can exploit for good or evil. Reflective people of whatever traditional background want to know what atomic power is and what it can do in peace and in war. Men of science traditionally disposed to accept the privileges of their vocation with cynical disregard of the social consequences of their discoveries are now deeply anxious about what will be the outcome if statesmen who control its use act without the guidance of those equipped to assess the magnitude of the new opportunities and the new perils.

The atom bomb is a by-product of laboratory research which has led to a new picture of the fine structure of matter. Such research amply paid its own way by inventions—the X-ray tube, the neon lamp, the thermionic valve, the photoelectric cell—which receive mention incidentally in this context or elsewhere. What follows will focus attention on the nature of the problems, as they emerged in the laboratory itself. The parts of what we see in retrospect as a single picture puzzle did not begin to fall into place until the end of the first decade of our own century, and it is not necessary to go back beyond the eighties to pick up the major clues. The most important are three: (*a*) the discovery that certain agents, e.g. heat and ultra-violet light, can make gases capable of conducting electricity; (*b*) the discovery that emanations with peculiar properties accompany the discharge of electricity through gases at low pressure as in an X-ray tube; (*c*) the discovery that certain rare elements, such as uranium and the *thorium* present in gas mantles, give off invisible rays detectable by their effect on a photographic plate.

During the earlier part of the nineteenth century, laboratory researches of investigators engaged in classifying, clarifying and prescribing transformations of substances for the purposes of new chemical industries had vindicated the usefulness of regarding matter as a cloud of particles (*molecules*) themselves built up of different combinations of smaller corpuscles (*atoms*). For practical purposes there was no need for further refinement. The atom was an indivisible entity; and there were no firmly established phenomena to challenge this finality. There were, however, suggestive facts which prompted speculation into novel channels. That the atomic weights of the elements are near to whole numbers more often than pure chance would prescribe prompted an hypothesis which postulated hydrogen as the parent atom and all other atoms as combinations of it; but no hypothesis of atomic structure conceived in such terms could engage the interest of chemists unless able to offer a rationale for *valency*. The study of electrolysis did so, and in so doing implicitly suggested the possibility that the atom is in fact divisible.

THE IMPLICATIONS OF ELECTROLYSIS

Such speculations played a dominant role in later research into the conduction of electricity by gases. Before discussing the latter, it is therefore fitting to recall Faraday's basic discoveries (p. 703) about conduction of electricity by solutions. Earlier work of Davy and others had shown that: (*a*) some substances—*electrolytes*—confer in water the power to transmit a current; (*b*) conduction of the current in such solutions is contingent on their chemical decomposition; (*c*) the products of the breakdown appear at opposite terminals of the circuit.   These phenomena suggest the view that:

(*a*) atoms which make up the molecules of electrolytes stick together by forces of electrical attraction like pith balls of opposite charge;

(*b*) atoms or groups of atoms (*radicles*) detach themselves in solution carrying opposite charges in virtue of which they are susceptible to attraction by an electrode of opposite excess charge and migrate towards it;

(*c*) the process of migration necessarily entails a continuous process of discharge, whence the passage of a current through the solution;

(*d*) the current is, in short, a two-way traffic of electrified particles (*ions*), some carrying a negative charge and moving towards the positive electrode (*anode*), others with a positive charge moving towards the negative electrode (*kathode*).

Faraday's own observations showed that the quantity of an element so liberated at one or other terminal of the circuit by the flow of the same current for one and the same period of time has a simple relation to its atomic weight and to its valency. For equal strength of current of equal duration the actual weights of two elements liberated in electrolysis are in the same ratio (pp. 703–4) as the relative weights by which they combine with one another or displace each other in an ordinary chemical reaction. The combining weight of an element is the ratio of its atomic weight to its valency. Thus the weight of an element liberated from solution by unit current in unit time is directly proportional to its atomic weight and inversely proportional to its valency. If we know W_h the amount of hydrogen liberated by one ampere in one second, A.W. the atomic weight of any other element and V its valency, we can therefore prescribe how much (W_x) of such an element a given current (C) will liberate in a given time (t). For a current of one ampere lasting one second, i.e. for the transference of a charge equivalent to one *coulomb*, the formula is:

$$W_x = W_h. \text{(A.W.)} \div V$$

The amount depends only on the charge $(Q = Ct)$ transferred. If the current is C, the amount displaced in t seconds is:

$$Ct. W_h. \text{(A.W.)} \div V$$

The actual amount of hydrogen liberated by 1 ampere in 1 second, hence the amount of hydrogen associated with a charge of 1 coulomb is $1 \cdot 045 \times 10^{-5}$ gram. Since the A.W. of silver of valency 1 is 108, our formula gives as the weight of silver deposited on the kathode by the passage of 3 amperes for 100 seconds:

$$3 \times 100 \times 1 \cdot 045 \times 10^{-5} \times 108 \times 1 = 0 \cdot 339 \text{ gram}$$

The quantitative law stated above is susceptible of a simple explanation, if we postulate that the ion of an element is an atom associated with V units of charge. If atoms of all *monovalent* elements detached from a parent molecule in solution carry one and the same *charge*, the weight of any such element liberated by decomposition through the agency of the current must depend solely on the size of the atom itself, i.e. its atomic weight. If the atom of a *divalent* element carries twice as big a charge as an atom of a monovalent element, i.e. as that of the hydrogen atom, its liberation from solution will entail a discharge at the electrode of opposite sign twice as great as the corresponding discharge due to the liberation of one atom of a monovalent element, and hence the flow of twice as many units of current in the same interval of time. The weight of a divalent element liberated by a current of a given strength in a given time will therefore be *half* what it would be if its valency were unity. The postulate stated above therefore accounts for the relation of both atomic weight and valency to decomposition by unit current in unit time.

This conception of unit charge implies an *interchange* between atoms in the process of electrolytic dissociation. When the uncharged molecule of calcium chloride ($CaCl_2$) breaks down into an ion of calcium with two units of positive charge and two ions of chlorine each with one unit of negative charge, we must infer one of two things. In so far as a net excess of one positive unit is equivalent to a net deficiency of one negative unit and *vice versa*, our alternatives are: (*a*) that the neutral calcium atom parts with a unit of negative charge to each of the two chlorine atoms of the molecule; (*b*) each of the two neutral chlorine atoms gives up a unit of positive charge to a calcium atom. Either statement implies that an atom of one element can *give up something to an atom of another*. Both signify that the ion of an element is either a *defective* atom or an atom which has *borrowed something* from that of another element. If so, the atom is divisible and the units which enter into its make-up are units which have electrical charge as well as mass. Considerations suggested by quantitative investigations into electrical conduction by solutions thus endowed later study of electrical conduction in the elementary gases with a peculiar interest.

THE LUMINOUS DISCHARGE

In 1740 the French ecclesiastic who was one of the first to study the properties of the Leyden jar (p. 649), made a chance discovery which remained neglected for more than a century. Nollet passed the terminals of an electrical machine inside a container attached to an air pump; and noticed that the customary succession of sparks at atmospheric pressure gives place to a continuous luminous streamer when the air round the spark gap is sufficiently rarefied. In short, a gas will freely conduct electricity at sufficiently low pressure. This is the principle inherent in the design of the now familiar *Neon Lamp* and others of its kind widely used for sky signs. Such lamps have no metal or carbon filament. The terminals end freely in the cavity of the tube, connected by a beam of incandescent gaseous particles when the current is on.

The Abbé Nollet did not himself draw the conclusions stated above. Its importance was not recognized until Faraday embarked on extensive investigations into the discharge of electricity through rarefied gases and stimulated others to do so, notably Crookes, Lenard and Röntgen. The work of this group of investigators showed that discharge tubes of the Neon Lamp type do not conduct electricity according to Ohm's Law, which tells us that the resistance of a metal conductor at a fixed temperature is a fixed characteristic, unaffected by the voltage between the ends of it. They acquire the power to do so only when the voltage between the ends of a column of gas exceeds a certain limit. Where this limit lies depends on the pressure of the gas. With an arrangement such as the one shown in Fig. 392 it is possible to study the effect of reduced gas pressure on (*a*) the potential required to produce a continuous band of light, (*b*) the conductivity of the gas itself, and (*c*) the manifest appearance of the luminous discharge.

If we start with a fixed E.M.F. sufficiently high to maintain a spark at atmospheric pressure, and reduce the pressure in the tube, we reach a stage at which two things happen. The crackling of the spark gives place to a silent broad stream of light between the electrodes. An ammeter reading then shows that the current in the tube has greatly increased. So the gas has become a relatively good conductor of electricity. At very low pressures dark spaces alternate with glowing patches in the track of the luminous discharge, and the glass wall near the negative electrode (kathode) becomes phosphorescent. At still lower pressures there is no stream of light between the electrodes. The entire wall of a straight discharge tube now glows with an eerie phosphorescent light, and a photographic plate in the neighbourhood of the tube is blurred, even if well wrapped up in black paper. At this stage the gas left in the tube retains its power to conduct a current freely. If the pressure is reduced to the lowest attainable limits the phosphorescence ceases, and the space no longer conducts. This fact is important because it shows that the flow of the current depends on the presence of particles of the rarefied gas.

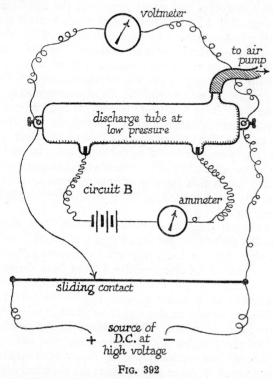

FIG. 392

Arrangement for studying how the reduction of gas pressure affects the sparking potential and how the conductivity of a gas changes during the passage of a continuous luminous streamer. The ammeter in the circuit B gives current strength in a circuit including the ionized gas. When the gas is ionized the current in the circuit increases owing to the fall of resistance. The voltmeter gives the potential at the sparking electrodes. This can be varied by a sliding wire. The usual source of high voltage is the intermittent current of an induction coil with a condenser in the primary circuit to ensure that the main flow of current is in one direction.

The variable resistance of the circuit shown in Fig. 392 makes it possible to find the critical E.M.F. at which the gas is able to conduct readily. The voltmeter reading then shows that reduction of pressure until the gas reaches a highly rarefied condition is accompanied by reduction of the critical E.M.F. Above this limit a rarefied gas becomes more like the solution of a mineral salt, acid, or alkali, and a possible explanation of its behaviour is that the application of a high E.M.F. breaks up its molecules into constituents with opposite charges like the ions of an electrolyte. Since the characteristic effect of a discharge on a sealed photographic plate in its neighbourhood happens only at very low pressures, when its walls begin to show phosphorescence, the radiations responsible for the photographic effect must therefore be due to some secondary action of the electrically-charged particles, as for instance their impact on the walls of the tube. This was the conclusion reached by Röntgen, who accidentally discovered the chemically active radiations in the neighbourhood of a high vacuum discharge tube in 1895.

Earlier work had shown that metal screens in the non-luminous track of a high-pressure tube having the *positive* electrode inserted sideways cast a shadow. That is to say, there is no phosphorescence of the glass opposite to the screen on the side remote from the kathode. The appearance suggests that negatively-charged particles are propelled forward in a *straight line* by repulsion from the negative electrode. The fact that a negatively charged plate (Fig. 394—*upper* half) at high potential in the neighbourhood of the kathode beam makes the latter bend away from it confirms this supposition. If this stream of negative particles exists it must have all the characteristics of a unidirectional current. Early observations had shown that dark spaces which interrupt the luminous stream of a discharge tube at moderately low pressures can be concentrated by a magnet held near it. Röntgen repeated these observations, and found that the area of phosphorescence on the glass end facing the kathode can be made to move by moving a magnet near it (Fig. 394—*lower* half).

Further experiments which led to the modern X-ray tube were guided by the hypothesis that the kathode extrudes a stream of particles with a negative charge. Assuming that the chemically-active penetrating X-rays are produced by the impact of negative particles derived from the gas itself and projected forwards by repulsion from the kathode, Röntgen devised a tube to test whether different radiations are produced by the impact of negative particles on different metals. In this way it is possible to produce X-rays of different wave-lengths (p. 494). The radiations that can penetrate the container of a sealed photographic plate easily penetrate the soft tissues of the animal body. The obvious applications of this discovery in surgical diagnosis (Fig. 393)—on account of the ease with which the chemically sensitive rays penetrate organic substances—excited interest all over the world, and stimulated research which led to the discovery of other characteristics which they possess. One is that they ionize gases, i.e. confer on them the power to conduct electricity. The presence of X-rays in the air around an electroscope has indeed the same effect as sea spray. Its charge leaks away quickly. This discovery, made by Rutherford, at that time engaged in radio research, was followed by attempts to find out more about the negative particles or *electrons* repelled by the kathode.

DIMENSIONS OF THE ELECTRON

That the power of a gas to conduct electricity, like that of a solution, depends on the presence of charged particles in it is a hypothesis which prompts us to press the analogy further; and to ask whether such putative particles are atoms and radicles, like ions in solution, or something smaller than either. The properties of the kathode stream associated with the ionization of rarified gases by the application of a high electrostatic potential provided occasion for the basic measurements which answer this question. The kathode stream bends towards a positively charged body brought up to the discharge tube. The putative particles (*electrons*) which compose it therefore carry a negative charge. To find either the mass of, or the charge

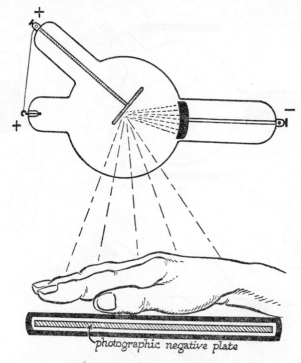

photographic negative plate

FIG. 393.—X-RAY APPARATUS

The negative electrode (kathode) is concave to produce a converging pencil of kathode particles on the metal plate of the positive electrode (anode). The impact of the electrons on the latter make it give off X-rays which penetrate the hand and the black mask containing the unexposed negative.

on, an electron, it is first necessary to measure its speed. This is possible by combined observations on the deflection of the kathode beam by: (*a*) a magnetic field in its neighbourhood; (*b*) a neighbouring electrostatic charge.

(*a*) *Deflection of the Kathode Beam by a Magnet.*—In Chapter V (p. 282) we have seen that we can split the steady motion of a body in a circular arc of radius *r* into two components: (*a*) an initial fixed speed *s* in a straight line; (*b*) a fixed acceleration towards the centre of $s^2 \div r$ cm. per sec. per sec. To sustain its motion at fixed speed in a circular path, a body of mass *m* thus requires a force $ms^2 \div r$ directed towards the centre. The kathode stream in a discharge tube ordinarily follows a straight path; but a magnet can bend it into a circular arc, the radius of which is easily calculated from the deflection (A B in the lower half of Fig. 394) of the fluorescent patch produced by its impact on the glass wall of the tube. If we regard the kathode stream as a volley of particles each of mass m, moving at a speed s in a straight line, the force which the magnetic field exerts on each electron is therefore $ms^2 \div r$. By recourse to the rule on p. 758, where we saw that a magnet exerts an attractive force on a current, we can also measure this

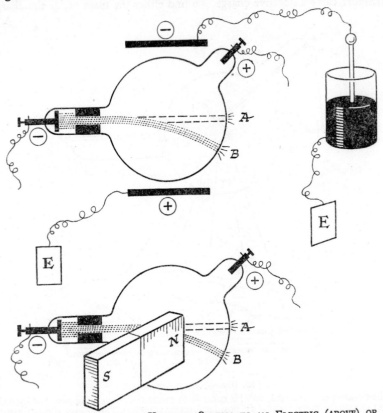

FIG. 394.—DEFLECTION OF KATHODE STREAM IN AN ELECTRIC (ABOVE) OR MAGNETIC (BELOW) FIELD

force in another way. If the current flows in a straight line the force D dynes of a magnet so placed that the field strength is F dynes per unit pole in the neighbourhood of a current of C amperes flowing through l cm. of wire, the rule is:

$$D = 0 \cdot 1 \ \text{F.C.} l$$

Thus the force of the magnet *per unit length* of current is $(0 \cdot 1)$ F.C. Now the appearance of the kathode stream signalizes the passage of a current through the rarified gas in the discharge tube; and if we regard it as a stream of particles each carrying a charge of Q_e coulombs, the current which is itself the *rate of discharge* (p. 659) is the *product* of (a) Q_e; (b) the number of electrons which pass a given boundary in unit time (1 cm.). Let us suppose that there are N electrons in a stretch between two boundaries A and B, separated by s cm., and so situated that an electron at A reaches B in 1 second during which an electron at B has moved s cm. beyond B. Thus s (the distance traversed by an electron in one second) is also its speed. Since N is also the number of electrons which pass the boundary B in 1 second, N.Q_e is the current in amperes. The force exerted *on unit length* of the current by a magnet of field strength F in the stretch AB is therefore 0·1. F.N.Q_e. Since the stretch AB is of length s, the total force on *all the* N electrons between AB is 0·1. F.N.$Q_e s$. Hence the force exerted by the magnet on 1 electron is 0·1. F.$Q_e s$. For the reason stated above, this force is also $ms^2 \div r$. If then we measure m in grams and s in cm.:

$$\frac{ms^2}{r} = 0 \cdot 1 \ \text{F.Q}_e.s.$$

$$\therefore \quad \frac{Q_e}{ms} = \frac{10}{\text{F}r}$$

We can determine directly the field strength (F) of the magnet on the kathode beam by means of a suitable magnetometer, and we can calculate r from the observed deflection. Our equation shows that these are all the data we need for estimating the numerical value of the ratio of the charge (Q_e) of an electron (in *coulombs*) to the product of its speed (s cm. per sec.) and its mass (*grams*). J. J. Thomson first determined this ratio in 1895.

(*b*) *Deflection of the Kathode Beam in an Electrostatic Field.*—By passing a kathode beam between two plates which constitute in essence a simple air condenser of the type discussed on p. 768, it is possible to bend it out of its straight path. This is what we should expect to happen if the kathode stream consists of charged particles constrained to move towards a near-by body with an opposite charge or away from a near-by body of like charge. Since experiment shows that the beam bends away from a negatively charged plate and towards a positively charged one, we have to assume that the putatively charged particles of the kathode beam carry a negative charge. In an experiment of this sort (Fig. 394—*upper* half) it is simpler to have one of the parallel plates earthed and the other at a high negative potential difference w.r.t. earth, say 50,000 volts. We shall here label (Fig. 395) the deflection of the kathode beam as x cm. at a distance l cm. from where it enters the electrostatic field, i.e. l cm. from the vertical level of the edge of the charged plate nearest the kathode itself to the far wall of the discharge tube.

In such a set-up we have an electrostatic field with a drop of potential E_v volts across a gap d cm. between the plates or $E_v \div d$ volts per cm. If a particle moves through a distance x cm. towards the earthed plate by mutual repulsion between its own charge of $- Q_e$ coulombs and the negative charge on the other plate, it moves between two points whose p.d. is $x E_v \div d$. We have defined (p. 681) our units of potential difference and electrical charge strictly in accordance with a *cistern* analogy, so that the work (W) in ergs involved in the transference of a charge of Q coulombs across a p.d.

of E volts is $10^7.EQ$. Thus the work involved in transferring a particle whose charge is Q_e between points whose p.d. is $x.E_v \div d$ is:

$$10^7\, Q_e E_v x \div d$$

To deflect a particle with a charge of Q_e coulombs and a mass of m grams in a circular arc from its motion in a straight path at fixed speed s cm. per sec., it is necessary to give it an acceleration a_r at right angles to its otherwise horizontal track. The force required is ma_r dynes; and the work done in moving it through a distance x is $ma_r x$ ergs. Hence

$$ma_r x = 10^7\, Q_e\, E_v x \div d$$
$$\therefore \qquad a_r = \frac{10^7\, Q_e\, E_v}{md}$$

The evaluation of a_r is strictly analogous to the evaluation of the vertical acceleration of a missile projected horizontally from the edge of a cliff, or that of a bomb dropping from a plane (p. 265). If an electron moves through the horizontal distance l in time t sec. at fixed speed s:

$$s = l \div t \text{ or } t = l \div s$$

If it simultaneously moves through a vertical distance x, its mean vertical speed $u_m = x \div t$. This is half the sum of its initial speed which is zero, and its final speed u_f, i.e.

$$u_m = x \div t = \tfrac{1}{2}\,(0 + u_f)$$
$$\therefore \qquad u_f = 2x \div t$$

This final speed is the speed it has gained along the vertical axis in t seconds. Hence its acceleration along the same axis is $u \div t$; so that:

$$a_r = 2x \div t^2$$

If we now translate t in terms of l the length of the beam and s the speed of the constituent particles by means of the relation $t = l \div s$, as above, we have:

$$a_r = \frac{2x\, s^2}{l^2}$$

$$\therefore \qquad \frac{2x\, s^2}{l^2} = \frac{10^7\, Q_e\, E_v}{md}$$

$$\therefore \qquad \frac{Q_e}{m} \cdot \frac{1}{s^2} = 10^{-7}\, \frac{2xd}{l^2 E_v}$$

All the quantities on the right are measurable, viz. E_v the p.d. in volts between the plates of the electrostatic field, d their distance apart, x the vertical deflection of the kathode beam and l its length. Consequently, a set-up as shown in Figs. 394–5 yields a numerical value for the ratio $Q_e \div ms^2$. If we use the symbol R_e for the ratio of the charge on an electron to its mass we may write this as $R_e \div s^2$. From measurement of the deflection of the beam in a magnetic field we already know the numerical value of $Q_e \div ms = R_e \div s$.

We have now two equations respectively involving the numerical values of $R_e \div s^2$ and $R_e \div s$. If we divide the first by the second we get the numerical value of s. By substituting this value in either the first or the second of the two equations we get the numerical value of R_e ($= Q_e \div m$), the ratio of the charge (coulombs) on an electron to its mass (grams). Numerically, R_e is $1 \cdot 76 - 10^8$ coulombs per gram.

(c) *Constancy of the Ratio R_e.*—Seemingly, the results of experimental measurements of the deflection of the kathode stream in a magnetic and in

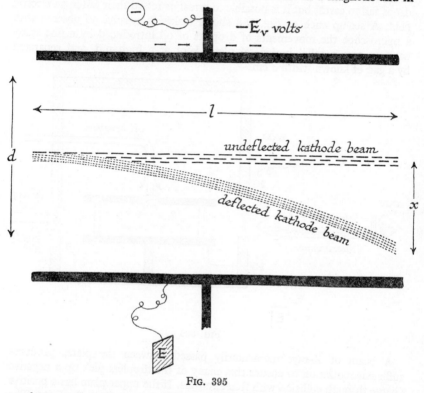

FIG. 395

an electrostatic field do not tell us anything about the absolute size of the electron. All we have so far learnt from them is the *ratio* of its charge to its mass, and we have as yet no standard of comparison with the corresponding ratio of the negative ion in a solution. There is, however, one highly suggestive consequence of repeating such experiments. It turns out that the ratio R_e is the same whether the gas left in the discharge tube is hydrogen, oxygen, nitrogen or any other. To see the significance of this we have to remember that the power of the discharge tube to conduct electricity depends on the residue of rarefied gas inside it. If negative ions of gases like negative ions of solutions were electrified atoms or groups of atoms, carrying a fixed charge or multiple of a fixed charge determined by *valency* alone, the ratio of charge to the mass of the ion would have a different value for each element. That it has the same value for all negative ions of gases indicates that the negative ions (i.e. *electrons*) of all gases are identical. In its turn this signifies that the electron is a constituent common to all atoms. If so, the atom is not an indivisible entity, it is capable of separation into smaller parts.

(*d*) *The Absolute Value of the Charge.*—The common occurrence of a shower after thunder and lightning suggests some connexion between electrification and condensation of moisture. So it is not surprising that the discovery of ionization by X-rays led to investigations into the behaviour of droplets in an ionized gas. Droplets of oil will normally settle under gravity as raindrops fall to earth, but it is possible to arrest or retard their fall in an electric field. A set-up such as Fig. 396 shows makes it possible to observe with a microscope the movements of droplets of oil introduced by a fine spray between two parallel horizontal plates kept at a high p.d. and separated by a gap of known width *d* cm.

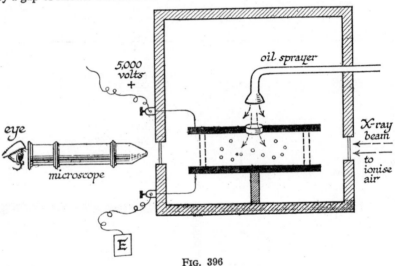

FIG. 396

A beam of X-rays momentarily passed between the plates produces sufficient ionization to ensure that many of the droplets pick up a negative charge through collision with free electrons. If the upper plate has a positive charge it will attract them with a pull antagonistic to that of gravity. The strength of this pull will depend on: (*a*) how many (*n*) electronic units of negative charge (Q_e), i.e. how many electrons, a droplet carries; (*b*) the p.d. (E_v volts) between the plates. The contrary pull of gravity will depend only on the mass (M) of the droplet. This is determinable if we know its volume and the density of the oil. The volume of a sphere of diameter $2r$ is $(4/3) \pi r^3$. So the mass of the droplet can be calculated from microscopic measurement of the diameter.

Let us first suppose that a single droplet falls through a small distance *x* cm. under its own weight. The work done is M*gx*. If pulled through the same distance *x* cm. in the opposite direction the work done is proportional to the product of its charge nQ_e and the p.d. between two points *x* cm. apart, i.e. $xE_v \div d$. If we express Q_e and E_v respectively in coulombs and volts, the work done by the electric field is: $10^7.nQ_e.(xE_v \div d)$. In such conditions, a droplet remains static, when the two attractions counterbalance, i.e.:

$$Mgx = 10^7 nQ_e (xE_v \div d)$$

$$\therefore \quad nQ_e = \frac{10^{-7}mg\,d}{E_v}$$

All the quantities on the right are directly measurable from observations on the dimensions of a droplet which remains suspended in mid-air when the current is on. By making many measurements of the value of nQ_e at different voltages (E_v) between the plates and for particles of various sizes. Millikan found that it is: (a) *never less* than $1 \cdot 6 \times 10^{-19}$ coulomb; (b) always *an exact multiple* of $1 \cdot 6 \times 10^{-19}$ coulomb.

Since the smallest value n can have is 1, when only one electron attaches itself to a droplet, we conclude that

$$Q_e = 1 \cdot 6 \times 10^{-19} \text{ coulomb.}$$

Since $R_e (= Q_e \div m) = 1 \cdot 76 \times 10^8$ coulombs per gram, we can put:

$$\frac{1 \cdot 6 \times 10^{-19}}{m} = 1 \cdot 76 \times 10^8$$

$$\therefore \quad m = (1 \cdot 6 \times 10^{-19}) \div (1 \cdot 76 \times 10^8)$$

$$= 9 \cdot 02 \times 10^{-28} \, gram$$

This then is the mass of an electron.

POSITIVE RAYS

If the kathode of a discharge tube has perforations, there is a luminous region behind it, when the current is on. By using a tubular kathode (Fig. 397) of very fine bore, it is possible to demonstrate a pencil of emanations proceeding backwards to the wall of the tube *behind* the kathode itself, there producing a phosphorescent glow where it impinges on the glass. The patch, or its photographic image, moves sideways in the field of a very strong magnet, and away from a nearby positively charged conductor at high potential. The so-called *canal* rays therefore consist of positively electrified particles. Since the canal rays are much less sensitive than the kathode beam to a magnetic or to an electrostatic field, the positive particles themselves are apparently more bulky or more swift than electrons. They will darken a photographic film by their impact; and a record so obtained shows that they scatter widely under the influence of a magnet or highly charged plate. It would thus appear that the positive particles are not all of the same size or do not all travel at the same speed. Hence the methods which serve for the determination of R_e, the ratio of the charge of the electron to its mass, require some modification to provide a satisfactory evaluation of the corresponding ratio R_p, i.e. the charge per unit mass of the particles which make up the canal rays. Instead of a simple pencil bent into a circular arc by the attractive force of a magnet or electrified plate on the kathode beam, we have to deal with more or less distinct sheaves of canal rays scattered by the same agencies. Each bundle or sheaf of rays yields a different value of R_p. Experiments performed with discharge tubes containing hydrogen as the residual gas show that the maximal value of R_p corresponding to that of the particles which undergo maximum deflection is $9 \cdot 58 \times 10^4$ coulombs per gram. We have already seen that 1 coulomb liberates $1 \cdot 044 \times 10^{-5}$ gram of hydrogen in electrolysis. This then is the mass per unit charge of the hydrogen ion. The charge per unit mass is its reciprocal, and this is $9 \cdot 58 \times 10^4$ coulombs per gram. Evidently, therefore, the lightest particles of the canal rays of a discharge tube containing hydrogen as the residual gas are identical with the *dissolved hydrogen ion*. Maximal values of R_p for other elementary gases are different, the ratio between any two being approximately the inverse ratio of their atomic weights. The smallest positively charged particles of any *ionized* residual gas in a discharge tube are therefore *atoms with a positive charge*.

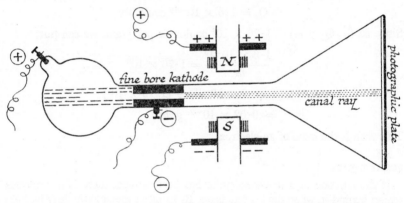

FIG. 397

The extrusion of positively charged particles involves the simultaneous liberation of identical electrons which make up the kathode stream. There is therefore a straightforward explanation of phenomena common to ionization in gases and ionization in solution. That is to say:

(*a*) the positive ion of an element is an atom which has a residual positive charge $+ n.Q_e$ due to the loss of one or more electrons *each* with a negative charge $- Q_e$;

(*b*) these electrons which usually remain free in an ionized gas attach themselves to one or more atoms of another element present in the molecule of an electrolyte to confer on it the excess negative charge of the negative ion.

Accordingly, hydrogen which is *monovalent* has a residual positive charge $+ Q_e$. If then the masses of the electron and of the hydrogen atom are respectively m_e and m_h, the mass of the hydrogen ion is $m_h - m_e$:

$$\therefore \quad R_p = Q_e \div (m_h - m_e)$$

or

$$m_h = (Q_e \div R_p) - m_e$$

From Millikan's experiment we know that:

$$Q_e = 1 \cdot 6 \times 10^{-19} \text{ coulomb}$$
$$m_e = 9 \cdot 2 \times 10^{-28} \text{ gram}$$

We also know that the R_p value for hydrogen is $9 \cdot 58 \times 10^4$ coulombs per gram, so that:

$$m_h = (1 \cdot 6 \times 10^{-19} \div 9 \cdot 58 \times 10^4) - 9 \cdot 2 \times 10^{-28}$$
$$= 1 \cdot 67 \times 10^{-24} \text{ gram.}$$

Thus the ratio of the mass of the hydrogen atom to that of the electron is $1 \cdot 67 \times 10^{-24} : 9 \cdot 2 \times 10^{-28}$. This is nearly 2,000. A single electron therefore contributes very little to the total bulk of the atom.

The preceding argument rests on the assumption that what is apparently the most straightforward hypothesis to account for all the chemical and the electromagnetic phenomena of ionization in gases and solutions is also the correct one. Independent estimates of the size of the hydrogen atom do in fact yield estimates sufficiently close to the figure cited above. One of these relies on the occurrence of the erratic (*Brownian*) movements of fine particles (e.g. Indian ink) suspended in a fluid. To account for diffusion and other physical phenomena, we have to assume that molecules are always on the move. If we postulate that Brownian movement of suspended particles is due to their bombardment by the motion of the molecules, it is possible to calculate the number of molecules in unit volume of solution from observation of the size and speed of suspended particles under the impact. Hence it is possible to infer the size of the molecule from the density of the fluid itself. However, it is not necessary for the reader to take such confirmation on trust. As we shall see at a later stage, direct demonstration that alpha particles from radium are helium atoms with a double positive charge confirm conclusions about the dimensions of gaseous positive ions obtained by measurements of electromagnetic deflections.

To understand all the implications of the outcome of observations on the deflection of positive rays in a magnetic and an electrostatic field, it is necessary to bear in mind the scatter of the rays into more or less distinct sheaves. So far we have concerned ourselves only with the smallest particles, i.e. maximal values of R_p. Other values for the same residual gas may be simple multitudes of this, indicative of the existence of charged molecules as well as of charged atoms; but sufficiently careful study of photographic records of the deflected beam also display distinct bundles of positive rays lying very close together. If Neon (*Atomic Weight* $20 \cdot 2$) is the residual gas, it is possible to distinguish two dark bands on the photographic plates at the extreme (maximal) limit of deflection. The corresponding values of R_p are respectively 1/20th and 1/22nd that of the minimal value of R_p when hydrogen is the residual gas. This means that neon is a mixture of two inert gases whose atomic weights lie close together, each being almost exactly a whole number, i.e. 20 and 22.

Further research on the gaseous elements revealed that others are mixtures of components with indistinguishable chemical properties. In short, an element is really a collection of components whose atomic weights lie close together; and the atomic weight assigned to an element is therefore an *average*. Such constituents called *isotopes*, though chemically indistinguishable, are separable by appropriate methods. Having slightly different atomic weights, they have slightly different densities. Hence they diffuse at different rates through a porous partition. By repeated diffusion, it is therefore possible to concentrate one or another isotope, and hence to confirm the identity of their chemical behaviour. *Chlorine* whose atomic weight is 35·5 is a mixture of two isotopes whose atomic weights are respectively 35 and 37. Accordingly, hydrochloric acid is a mixture of two compounds whose molecular weights are respectively 36 and 38. Their separate identities eluded traditional methods of chemical analysis, because the chemical properties of their compounds are too closely alike. The most suggestive thing about an isotope is that its atomic weight, unlike that of the mixtures to which we assign atomic weights set out in the Periodic Table, is almost exactly a *whole number*. Their discovery therefore brings into focus early speculations which identified the hydrogen atom as the parent of all atoms; but if such speculations have any basis in fact, the chemical behaviour of elements does not depend on the exact number of such units contributory to its bulk. The only number which ties up consistently with the chemical behaviour of the elements is the *atomic number* (p. 496). This takes us into a new domain of discovery.

RADIO ACTIVITY

Experiments on the discharge of electricity through gases have led us to a provisional picture of an atom consisting of a rind of detachable electrons and a more stable core corresponding to the positive ion of an element in solution. They tell us nothing to suggest that this provisional core is itself divisible. In so far as we have split the atom, what we have done is analogous to what happens in chemical reactions between electrolytes, and gives us no hint of the existence of stores of energy other than such as everyday chemical decomposition sets free. The first clear indications of a finer divisibility of the atom, and of the vast stores of energy available by splitting the core itself, came from the study of the *radio-active* elements.

If we leave a piece of gas mantle lying on a sealed box of photographic plates for sufficient time (about a week), it is possible to obtain a clear image of it by developing the plates in the usual way. Evidently, therefore, the mantle contains something which emits chemically active radiations comparable to ultra-violet light, but much more *penetrating*. This property of radio activity is a peculiarity of the compounds of *thorium* present in gas mantles, and of the compounds of certain other heavy metals. In 1896 Becquerel, who discovered this sensitivity of a photographic plate to *uranium* salts in its neighbourhood, encouraged his pupil Marie Curie to investigate natural ores as sources of the metal. Curie discovered that *pitchblende*, an ore rich in uranium, had more radio activity than her analysis of its uranium content could account for. She applied routine methods of solution and precipitation to extract a fraction, the properties of which gave spectacular confirmation to this conclusion and richly rewarded her perseverance. The super-active fraction—less than a gram per ton of pitchblende—was the salt (bromide) of a new element (*radium*), whose intense radio activity stimulated world-wide interest and research.

The two basic peculiarities of the compounds of the radio-active elements are that they evoke both the reaction of the photographic film described above and intense ionization of the surrounding air, so that an electroscope in their vicinity quickly loses its charge. Ultra-violet light, which also has these properties, has relatively little penetrating power. The fact that a photographic plate in a sealed box responds to the presence of the compound of a radio-active element in its neighbourhood shows that the emanations from it have high penetrating power like X-rays; and like X-rays they evoke fluorescence of certain substances, e.g. diamond, zinc sulphide and barium platinocyanide. The study of their penetrating power gave the first clue to their nature. A thin sheet of paper or mica in front of a zinc sulphide screen suffices to prevent fluorescence due to a small quantity of a radium salt in a vessel close to it; but does not appreciably affect the fluorescence of a screen of barium platinocyanide. There are thus at least two sorts of emanations, one called by Rutherford *alpha* rays with little penetrating power, and a residue which proves to be complex by recourse to the same method. Thus a sheet of aluminium 1 cm. thick superimposed on a sheet of mica or paper considerably reduces the fluorescence of a barium platinocyanide screen, but a second sheet of aluminium 1 cm. thick does not very noticeably reduce the residual fluorescence. There are therefore other components—the *beta* and the *gamma* rays. Neither will pass through a thick lead tube.

If sufficiently deep, such a tube therefore serves as a container allowing the escape of a well defined pencil of emanations. This makes it possible to use their impact on a photographic film or fluorescible screen with more refinement. It is then possible to see that a strong magnet or a charged conductor scatter and deflect the mixed emanations. The direction indicates that they are mainly composed of positively charged particles. After screening with a sheet of paper to exclude the alpha rays, the residual pencil moves away from a highly charged plate with a negative charge, and there is no scattering. What still passes through a sheet of lead over 2 mm. thick suffers no deviation in a magnetic nor in an electrostatic field.

Conclusions which it is possible to establish by recourse to fluorescible screens can be put to the test by using either of the two other criteria of the existence of the emanations, i.e. leakage of charge due to ionization of the surrounding air of an electroscope or condenser and activation of a film of silver bromide or other light-sensitive compound. Any such method shows that we are dealing with three classes of radiations:

(*a*) *alpha* rays of very low penetrating power comparable to the positive particles of the canal rays;

(*b*) *beta* rays of negative particles possibly comparable to the kathode rays;

(*c*) *gamma* rays of very high penetrating power seemingly like X-rays.

The determination of the ratio of the charge to the mass of either alpha or beta particles is possible by adaptation of the method of deflection in an electrostatic and magnetic field as set forth already. In this way it is possible to show that the beta ray is in fact, like the kathode beam, a stream of swiftly moving electrons. The ratio of the charge of an alpha particle to its mass is about $4 \cdot 8 \times 10^4$ coulombs per gram, half that of the corresponding ratio for hydrogen. If m_h is the mass of the hydrogen ion and $+ Q_e$ its charge, m_a the mass of the alpha particle and $+ Q_a$ its charge, we may therefore write $Q_a \div m_a = \frac{1}{2} Q_e \div m_h$. If the alpha particle carries a single positive charge equivalent to the loss of *one* electron, this means that its mass is twice as great as that of the hydrogen atom; and this would signify that it is a hydrogen molecule. In fact, it is possible to show that each particle carries an excess positive charge $+ {}_2Q_e$ equivalent to the loss of *two* electrons.

One method relies on the fact that the fluorescence due to the impact of alpha particles on a screen sensitive to them is recognizable under a lower-power microscope as a succession of discrete scintillations. By counting these we know how many alpha particles a given quantity of radium emits per second. By means of an electrometer we can also measure the amount of charge a metal plate acquires under the impact of alpha particles from a fixed quantity of radium in a fixed interval of time. If the charge acquired by the plate is x, and y is the number of particles impinging on the plate in the observed interval, the ratio $x \div y$ is the charge per particle $Q_a \div m_a$. This turns out to be twice the charge on the hydrogen ion, i.e. $+ 2 Q_e$, as stated above. Hence we may replace the equation of the preceding paragraph by:

$$\frac{2 Q_e}{m_a} = \frac{1}{2} \frac{Q_e}{m_h} \quad or \quad m_a = 4m_h$$

This signifies that the mass of the alpha particle is twice that of the hydrogen molecule, corresponding to an atomic weight of 4, that of *helium*; and if the alpha particle is indeed a helium atom with two excess positive charges, it should be possible to detect the accumulation of helium in an evacuated glass vessel containing a radium compound. A beam of light passed through such a vessel before entering the prism of a spectroscope does in fact reveal the characteristic dark lines of the helium absorption spectrum. What we may refer to loosely as the core of the radium atom is thus in process of *slow disintegration* involving the production of atoms of the very light element helium. These atoms, which constitute the particles of the alpha rays, carry a double excess positive charge due to the loss of 2 electrons, the particles of the beta rays. One result of this breakdown is the emission of *gamma* rays comparable to X-rays, their speed being identical with the speed of light.

The last mentioned by-product of the disintegration of radium atoms is reminiscent of the production of light rays by the slow oxidation of phosphorous. Like familiar chemical reactions, the change also entails production of heat; but the amount of heat generated is of an unusually high order of magnitude. The temperature of radium bromide, the original compound extracted by Madame Curie, is always about 2° C. above that of its surroundings. By means of an ice calorimeter, Curie and Laborde showed in 1903 that it parts with about 100 calories per gram per hour. From observations on the rate of emission of alpha particles, we also know that about a gram of radium would have disappeared as such in the course of 3,000 years. Hence it is possible to calculate how much heat would be liberated by the complete disintegration of 1 gram, i.e. about $2 \cdot 5 \times 10^9$ calories. This is between a quarter of a million and half a million times as much heat as the combustion of one grain of coal yields. The performance of this calculation sufficed to convince many scientific workers, notably Soddy and Rutherford, that mankind was now on the threshold of a new age.

The three radio-active elements which occur in appreciable quantities outside the laboratory are *Uranium* (Atomic No. 92), *Thorium* (90) and *Radium* (88). All of these have several radio-active isotopes. The end-products of their disintegration are both helium and one or other of the stable isotopes of Lead (A.N. 82, A.W. 206 or 208). Radium isotopes (A.W. 224, 226 and 228) occur as stages in the breakdown of both the most abundant natural isotope of Uranium (A.W. 238) and that of Thorium (232). The natural Radium isotope (A.W. 226) is a stage in the breakdown of U238. By spectroscopic methods and otherwise, it is possible to identify successive by-products of the disintegration of either in a sequence which involves at a given stage *either* increase of atomic number by unity without change of atomic weight *or* decrease of atomic number by 2 with decrease of atomic weight by 4. Evidently, the latter corresponds to elimination of an alpha particle, the ion of Helium (A.N. 2, A.W. 4). Since the former implies a gain of one positive charge by the nucleus itself, the source of the emitted electron beta particle must be intra-nuclear. Both in the Thorium and in the Uranium sequence, one evanescent breakdown product is Niton (A.N. 86, A.W. 220 or 222), an inert radio-active gas of the Helium–Argon group. In both, later by-products include short-lived radio-active isotopes of Polonium (A.N. 84, A.W. 210, 212, 214, 216, 218), of Bismuth (A.N. 83, A.W. 210, 212, and 214) and of Lead (A.N. 82, A.W. 210 and 214). The thorium sequence is:

1. 90 Thorium 232 $- \alpha =$	2. 88 Radium 228 $- \beta =$
3. 89 Actinium 228 $- \beta =$	4. 90 Thorium 228 $- \alpha =$
5. 88 Radium 224 $- \alpha =$	6. 86 Niton 220 $- \alpha =$
7. 84 Polonium 216 $- \beta =$	8. 85 X 216 $- \alpha =$
9. 83 Bismuth 212 $- \beta =$	10. 84 Polonium 212 $- \alpha$

The uranium–radium sequence is:

1. 92 Uranium 238 $- \alpha =$	2. 90 Thorium 234 $- \beta =$
3. 91 Protoactinium 234 $- \beta =$	4. 92 Uranium 234 $- \alpha =$
5. 90 Thorium 230 $- \alpha =$	6. 88 Radium 226 $- \alpha =$
7. 86 Niton 222 $- \alpha =$	8. 84 Polonium 218 $- \alpha =$
9. 82 Lead 214 $- \beta =$	10. 83 Bismuth 214 $- \beta =$
11. 84 Polonium 214 $- \alpha =$	12. 82 Lead 210 $- \beta =$
13. 83 Bismuth 210 $- \beta =$	14. 84 Polonium 210 $- \alpha =$
15. 82 Lead 206	

Scattering of Alpha Particles.—The possibility of utilizing such vast potential resources of energy presupposes the practicability of speeding up processes such as occur spontaneously, but very slowly, in the normal life cycle of the unstable, i.e. radio-active, elements. That this is now realizable is the outcome of knowledge of the make-up of the atom more precise than the provisional picture which the preceding account has disclosed. The master clue to the new knowledge came from study of the penetrating power of the alpha particles.

By means of one or other appropriate detector, e.g. a fluorescent screen, it is possible to show that alpha particles from radium or uranium have a range less than 7 cm. in the atmosphere, and that a sheet of paper suffices to prevent their further forward motion. In a vacuum they pursue a straight path indefinitely. By reducing the pressure in a suitable vessel containing a radio-active compound, it is possible to show that the range of the alpha particle increases as the density of the gas diminishes. It therefore depends on the number of molecules, and hence also of atoms, which lie in its track. At one and the same pressure the range of an alpha particle is greater in a light gas such as hydrogen than in a heavier gas such as chlorine. It is also possible to show that a corresponding rule applies to penetration of thin metal foil. If we know the atomic weight of a metallic element we can calculate the mass of its atom from that of the hydrogen atom (p. 457). If we also know its density, we can therefore calculate the number of atoms in unit volume of a metal, and hence the *stopping power* per atom in the path of the alpha emanation from a radio-active substance. This turns out to be the same in their compounds as in elementary substances, and is in fact approximately proportional to the square root of the mass of the atom, i.e. to the square root of its atomic weight.

The resistance which a substance offers to the passage of alpha particles is accordingly a property inherent in the atom itself; and the fate of alpha particles which successfully penetrate a sufficiently thin sheet of solid matter gives us a clue to its *modus operandi*. If the incident stream of alpha particles is a narrow pencil, the emergent stream is a cone indicative of more or less *scattering*. Increasing the thickness of the foil increases the proportion of particles deflected through a wide angle and penetration ceases when every particle is in fact deflected through an angle equal to or greater than 90°. In the absence of additional evidence we may interpret such scattering in one of two ways: (*a*) simple collisions between the alpha particles and the atoms of the foil; (*b*) electrostatic repulsion of the former by the positively charged core (nucleus) of the latter. The second possibility implies that the constituent electrons of the atom must lie at a considerable distance from the positive *nucleus*, which therefore constitutes a relatively small part of the space occupied by the atom as a whole. Otherwise the net charge in the neighbourhood of the nucleus itself would be zero, and there could be no deflection of an alpha particle passing close to it.

The scatter phenomenon described in the last paragraph is demonstrable from the distribution of scintillations on a fluorescent screen. A method suggested by the shower which follows a thunderstorm discloses the behaviour of the alpha particles in their passage through a gas. Air or any gas completely free of dust particles will hold water vapour greatly in excess of the normal saturation level. Any ionizing agency, e.g. ultra-violet rays or emanations from radio-active substances, has the power to induce the formation of droplets in such highly supersaturated mixtures; and it is possible to photograph the fine beads of moisture which condense round individual ions in the wake of the radiation or stream of incoming alpha particles. In photographic records obtained from such a *cloud chamber* set-up, it is therefore possible to pick out the tracks of individual alpha particles from the droplets which condense around ions of the gas in their wake.

Distribution of the scintillations produced by alpha particles impinging on a fluorescent screen or tracks disclosed in a cloud chamber provide us with the necessary data for calculating the probability that an individual alpha particle will pass within a given distance of an atomic nucleus, if we also know (a) how many alpha particles impinge on a given area in a given time; (b) how many atoms are present in unit volume of the substance through which they pass. The first of these is directly observable. The other is calculable from the density of the substance, the atomic weights of its constituent atoms and the estimated mass of a single hydrogen atom (p. 793). Calculation of the deflection of an individual alpha particle in virtue of its nearness to a positively charged body (i.e. atomic nucleus) in its path is then a comparatively straightforward application of the inverse square laws of electrical repulsion or attraction. The underlying principle is essentially the same as that which the astronomer employs to determine the gravitational effect of a neighbouring celestial body on the track of a comet, except in so far as: (a) charge plays the role of mass (p. 788); (b) like charges *repel* one another. In this way, it is possible to measure repulsion between alpha particles and atomic nuclei in terms of the positive charge of the nucleus itself, and hence to show that the *number of electrons which the positive nucleus can neutralize is the same as its atomic number*. To say this is also to say that mere collision as opposed to electrical repulsion between alpha particles and nuclei of the atoms of a substance which they traverse does not offer an explanation of the scatter phenomenon.

Against the background of our provisional picture of the atom as an entity with a massive core carrying a positive charge and an outer region of detachable electrons whose mass is trivial by comparison, the facts stated in the last paragraph are highly suggestive, especially if we give due weight to conclusions suggested by electrolysis and the periodic classification of the elements (p. 487). The phenomena of electrolysis suggest that the valency of an element depends on the number of electrons which its atom can give up if it becomes a positive ion, or take on if it becomes a kation. The periodic classification draws attention to the fact that the valency of the elements increases and decreases in a succession of cycles as we pass from those of low to those of high atomic number. Thus a true picture of the structure of the atom has to accommodate the relation of valency to atomic number and to ionization in solution.

We define the valency of an element as the number of its atoms which either combine with one atom of hydrogen or with 2 atoms of oxygen to form stable compounds. The distinction draws attention to an arresting rule. To say that chlorine forms a stable oxide Cl_2O_7 implies that its valency is 7 in accordance with its place in the seventh column of the periodic table; but we are equally entitled to say that it is monovalent since it forms a stable hydride HCl (hydrochloric acid). According to the ionic hypothesis it exists in solution as an anion with a single excess negative charge, i.e. an attached electron, which confers on it a valency of 1. Like its successors (bromine and iodine in the same (7th) column), chlorine has in fact 2 valencies (7 or 1) whose sum is 8. Similarly nitrogen and phosphorous (column 5) have 2 valencies, *five*, as in N_2O_5, or *three*, as in N_2O_3, NH_3, etc.; and in general any element has two valencies whose sum is 8, the lower one corresponding to the number of units of negative charge, i.e. electrons, which its atom can absorb or release. The sum of the two therefore corresponds with the number of columns in the table. In short, each row of the periodic table rings the changes on all possible values from 0 to 8 of two numbers whose sum is 8.

What we have already inferred about the hydrogen atom (atomic number = 1; valency = 1) and the helium atom (atomic number = 2; valency = 0) gives us a first clue to this feature of the periodic table of the elements. In so far as the hydrogen atom which is monovalent has one electron which is detachable in solution, we may regard it as having a core (*the proton*) of mass approximately equivalent to its whole mass, carrying a positive charge of one unit, i.e. a charge capable of neutralizing that of a single electron. The *inert* helium atom has a core (*the alpha particle*) carrying a positive charge of 2 units; but the 2 satellite electrons which neutralize this charge are not detachable, nor can they accommodate electrons which would transform the inert atom into the kation of the dissolved state. So far, it looks as if:

(*a*) the atomic number defines the number of units of charge which the positive core of the atom carries;

(*b*) the complementary electrons associated therewith are of two kinds which respectively do and do not play a part in chemical combinations.

Let us carry such speculation further. Lithium (A.N. = 3) comes next to helium in the sequence of atomic numbers. If our hypothesis is correct its core carries an excess positive charge of 3 units requiring 3 complementary electrons of which only *one* is detachable in solution, since it forms a positive ion with a single unit of charge. Lithium is in fact monovalent, and must accordingly have two other electrons both chemically indifferent like those of the helium atom. Similarly, the *divalent* element *beryllium* whose atomic number is 4 should have 4 electrons of which 2 are detachable. Fluorine, whose atomic number is 9, ends the first cycle. Its valency is 7 or 1, and according to the ionic hypothesis exists in solution as a monovalent kation being able to take on a single electron. In our first cycle, starting with helium, unit increase of atomic number corresponding to unit increment of excess positive charge at the hypothetical core of the atom entails the addition of 1 electron in addition to the 2 electrons of the helium atom, and the number of such extra electrons corresponds to the valency assigned to an element by its column in the periodic table. Accordingly, we may say that an anion is an atom which has expelled its *v valency electrons*, and a kation is an atom which has taken on $8 - v$ electrons conferring an excess negative charge of $8 - v$.

The atomic number of the next element to fluorine is 10. It should thus have 8 electrons other than the two electrons of the helium atom and is in fact the inert gas *neon*, followed by sodium (11) which is monovalent like lithium and has one detachable electron in solution. The cycle which begins with helium and lithium now repeats itself. Magnesium (A.N.=12) is divalent like beryllium and the ionic hypothesis attributes an excess positive charge of two units to its ion due to the loss of two electrons by its atom. The second cycle ends with chlorine (A.N.=17) in column 7. It should therefore have 7 valency electrons and two sets of what we may call *bound* electrons respectively consisting of the 2 electrons of the helium atom and the additional 8 of the neon. In the same way potassium (A.N. = 19) should have 1 valency electron and three sets of bound electrons, the two present in the chlorine atom and the additional set of 8 in the inert atom of argon (A.N. = 18). Inescapably, therefore, the image (Fig. 398) to which speculation from our initial premises leads us is a nucleus with an excess positive charge and successive shells of 8 electrons. The total number of the latter corresponds to the atomic number of the element.

The Photoelectric Effect and Line Spectra.—X-rays, gamma rays and the invisible rays from the ultra-violet lamp can make gases conduct electricity as shown by the discharge of an electroscope when such radiations pass through the air around it. Since their power to ionize gases is due to the liberation of

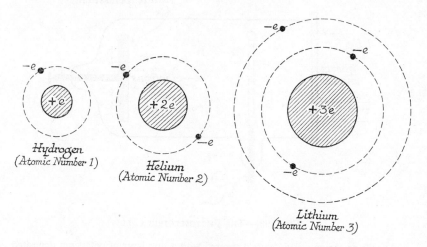

Fig. 398

electrons from their constituent atoms or molecules, we might expect the impact of such radiations on the surface of a metal to impose on it a positive charge. That this is so, is demonstrable by allowing ultra-violet radiation to fall on a metal plate connected with the leaves of an electroscope. A given metal responds only to radiations of a certain minimum frequency usually on the ultra-violet range, but the alkali metals such as potassium respond to radiation within the visible range itself. This is the principle of an important modern invention, the *photoelectric cell* (Fig. 399). The *modus operandi* of the photoelectric cell recalls that of another useful by-product of electronic research, i.e. the *thermionic valve* (p. 775). Since heat, like the impact of radiation, sets free electrons from the atom, it seems as if absorption of energy by the atom excites electrons to jump away from the nucleus. This supposition leads to a new interpretation of a class of physical phenomena which has its basis in the peculiarities of the atoms themselves.

From Coulomb and Priestley to J. J. Thomson and Rutherford, physicists have gained more insight into electrical phenomena by following clues suggested by the laws of celestial motion, in particular the inverse square law which is true in both domains. Before we take the next step, we ourselves shall find it helpful to make the best of what we have learned about them. So we shall now digress. Against the background of the useful application of the inverse square law of attraction as applied to the study of the scattering of alpha particles and of what we otherwise know about the power of alpha particles and of electrons, to pass through matter, the physicist inescapably thinks of matter as a micro-firmament in which there are many solar systems, each alike if we are speaking of the same element, each separated like the galaxies of celestial space by relatively vast distances

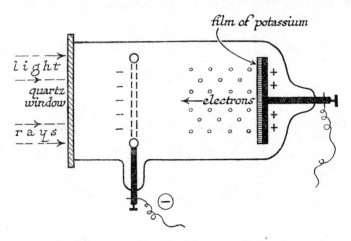

FIG. 399.—THE PHOTOELECTRIC CELL

Light falls on the so-called cathode covered with a thin layer of potassium deposited *in vacuo* to prevent formation of gas films which polarize the cell. The electrons liberated from the surface of the cathode impinge on the anode which is *annular* to permit passage of the beam of light. Thus the anode acquires a negative and the cathode a positive charge. If the two terminals of the cell are connected with those of a galvanometer, it is therefore possible to demonstrate the flow of a continuous current while the cathode is exposed to the beam.

and each of vast size relative to the size of a sun (*nucleus*) or of its satellites (*electrons*). Nothing we know so far is inconsistent with the possibility that electrons remain in fixed orbits when a body is *not* giving off radiation; but our parable breaks down when we take stock of the phenomena of the ionization of gases or of the photoelectric effect. Within the time-scale of our own experience, a planet stays put in its proper orbit. An electron does not.

To make further use of the parable, we may indulge in the fancy that planets sometimes shoot from one orbit to another. So we shall ask ourselves what would happen in a solar system still working to a Kepler schedule. It will then be helpful to characterize each orbit by an *energy level*. This new descriptive device will not be mystifying if we imagine what happened when explosions, such as we can observe in other solar systems, supposedly shot off incandescent masses from our own sun into space. We may arbitrarily dissec the energy thus released in the birth of our own or of our fellow-planets into: (a) the work done in projecting such a mass from the parent body to the orbit in which it moves; (b) the work done to impart the initial speed which it retains in its orbit. The former accommodates the numerical value of the energy a planet would release if transferred instantaneously from a more remote to a less remote orbit without losing speed. The latter takes account of the speed it would then gain, if it subsequently revolved in accordance with the inverse square law.

Alternatively, we may think of the distinction in terms of the projection of an artificial satellite into a pre-assigned orbit. We may then budget for rocket fuel in terms of amounts requisite: (a) to shoot it vertically to a particular distance from the earth; (b) to impart an initial speed at right angles to its path at the end of its vertical trek. The difference between the amount of fuel required to establish it in a nearer orbit at distance d_1 and a more remote orbit at distance d_2 then conveys what atomic physicists mean by a difference between energy levels at d_1 and d_2. We may set out the profit and loss account for this difference by separately considering: (a) the difference between *additional* work done in moving the satellite vertically from d_1 to d_2; (b) the *deficiency* between work done to confer the transverse speed which it will retain in its orbit at d_2 and work done to establish it in an orbit at d_1.

In the Newtonian scheme, a planet of mass m moving with speed s in a circular orbit (as is nearly true of the motion of Venus) retains its position at a fixed distance d from the sun by the balance of two equal and opposite forces: one centrifugal and numerically equal to $ms^2 \div d$, the other centripetal in accordance with the inverse square law. In terms (p. 298) of the mass M of the sun and the universal gravitation constant G, we may write this equality as $ms^2 \div d = GMm \div d^2$ so that $ms^2 = GMm \div d$. Thus its kinetic energy (p. 612) in its orbit is $\frac{1}{2}ms^2 = \frac{1}{2}GMm \div d$. Being inversely proportional to its distance from the sun, that of a more remote planet will be less than that of a nearer one of the same mass; and if two planets of equal mass respectively revolved at distances $d_2(>d_1)$ and d_1 from the sun, the difference between their kinetic energies must be:

$$K_d = \frac{\frac{1}{2}GMm}{d_2} - \frac{\frac{1}{2}GMm}{d_1} = -\frac{1}{2}GMm\left(\frac{1}{d_1} - \frac{1}{d_2}\right)$$

For the fuel budget of the artificial satellite, we may interpret the *negative* sign in the above as the statement that the rocket charge required to set it in a circular orbit under gravitational attraction at d_2 will be less than the rocket charge required to do so at d_1.

The projection of a mass m from d_1 to d_2 along a line through the centre of its sun, will involve work *against* gravitational attraction. We may assign to the force between d_2 where it is $GMm \div d_2^2$ and d_1 where it is $GMm \div d_1^2$ the mean value $GMm \div d_1 \cdot d_2$. The work done (P_d) will be the product of the mean force and the distance, i.e.

$$P_d = \frac{GMm\,(d_2 - d_1)}{d_1 \cdot d_2} = GMm\left(\frac{1}{d_1} - \frac{1}{d_2}\right)$$

The difference between the expenditure of energy involved in establishing the planet in its orbital motion at d_2 and at d_1 respectively will thus be:

$$P_d + K_d = GMm \left(\frac{1}{d_1} - \frac{1}{d_2} \right) - \tfrac{1}{2}GMm \left(\frac{1}{d_1} - \frac{1}{d_2} \right)$$

$$= \tfrac{1}{2}GMm \left(\frac{1}{d_1} - \frac{1}{d_2} \right)$$

If all the planets were of the same size, we might therefore summarize the Newtonian scheme by assigning to a planet distances d_1 and d_2 different energy levels $\tfrac{1}{2}GMm \div d_1$ and $\tfrac{1}{2}GMm \div d_2$.* The difference between the two levels so defined is the amount of energy used up in bringing a planet from an inner orbit at d_1 to an outer orbit at d_2 on the assumption that it there acquired a new speed in accordance with the inverse square law. Conversely, we might say that it represents the amount of energy released if a planet revolving at d_2 in accordance with Kepler's laws jumped into a nearer orbit at distance d_1 where it thenceforth revolved at a new speed in accordance with the same laws. Such is a key to the language which the physicist now uses to describe the relation of electrons to the nucleus.

In such terms, we are more ready to examine the bearing of atomic structure on discoveries made with the spectrograph. When we heat an element till it glows brightly, it gives off radiations in well-defined bands or lines of restricted wave-length (p. 474). If we pass radiation through a cool gaseous element, corresponding black lines or bands appear in its spectrum. Each element has its own characteristic spacing of these bands or lines; and the so-called *line-spectrum* of a compound is merely a composite picture of the line spectra of its constituent elements. From this we infer that a particular line spectrum is a *property of a particular atom.* Against the background of the photoelectric effect and of the ionization of gases by X-rays, it thus seems that the particular radiations an atom can emit, if supplied with energy (as when a body becomes incandescent), or can absorb, if irradiated (as when a body fails both to transmit and to reflect), depends in some way on the freedom of electrons to move towards or from the nucleus.

Already in the eighties of the last century, study of the spectrum of *hydrogen* in the visible region had led to recognition of a simple rule about spacing of the lines. If ν is the frequency corresponding to a bright (emission) or corresponding dark (absorption) line, the spacing in the visible part of the hydrogen spectrum is such that values of ν are in the proportions:

$$\frac{1}{2^2} - \frac{1}{3^2} : \frac{1}{2^2} - \frac{1}{4^2} : \frac{1}{2^2} - \frac{1}{5^2} : \frac{1}{2^2} - \frac{1}{6^2} \quad \text{etc.}$$

Later work showed that the lines in the ultra-violet spectrum conform to the series:

$$\frac{1}{1^2} - \frac{1}{2^2} : \frac{1}{1^2} - \frac{1}{3^2} : \frac{1}{1^2} - \frac{1}{4^2} : \frac{1}{1^2} - \frac{1}{5^2} \quad \text{etc.}$$

* In the electrical model $ms^2, \div r = Ee \div r^2$, so that $K = \tfrac{1}{2}Ee \div r$ $K_d = -Ee \left(\frac{1}{r_1} - \frac{1}{r_2} \right) = \tfrac{1}{2}P_d.$

In the infra-red, they conform to the series:

$$\frac{1}{3^2} - \frac{1}{4^2} : \frac{1}{3^2} - \frac{1}{5^2} : \frac{1}{3^2} - \frac{1}{6^2} : \frac{1}{3^2} - \frac{1}{7^2} \text{ etc.}$$

$$\frac{1}{4^2} - \frac{1}{5^2} : \frac{1}{4^2} - \frac{1}{6^2} : \frac{1}{4^2} - \frac{1}{7^2} : \frac{1}{4^2} - \frac{1}{8^2} \text{ etc.}$$

In the opening years of our own century, another clue to new insight had come from study of the relation of incandescence to temperature. As we all know, visible radiations of different wave-lengths appear as a body becomes hotter; but we have no reason to believe—nor is it true—that the eye is equally sensitive to radiation of different parts of the spectrum in the sense that it can register the same minimum amount of energy absorbed by the same area at different wave-lengths. None the less, physical measurement shows that heat imparted to a body does not result in the emission of equal amounts of radiant energy in different regions of the spectrum—visible or invisible. That it does not do so, follows from nothing we have learned so far. Accordingly, this aspect of the phenomenon of incandescence has prompted much speculation. It eventually led Planck to a conclusion out of step with older views about wave motion. Planck put forward the view that radiant bodies emit waves in separate pulses, that the absorption or emission of a single pulse is equivalent to uptake or release of a fixed amount of energy associated with a particular wave-length, and that the energy uptake or release by absorption or emission of radiation at a fixed wave-length is therefore an *exact multiple* of a unit (*quantum*) characteristic of that wave-length. On Planck's view, this quantum (also called a *photon*) is the smallest quantity of energy which a source can emit or a surface absorb at a given wave-length. It is thus expressible as the product ($h\nu$) of a fixed constant (h) and the radiation frequency (ν). So the quantum of a beam of a particular frequency in the blue (high frequency) end of the visible spectrum is greater than the quantum of a beam of another frequency in the red (low frequency) end.

With this clue to hand, let us return to our planetary parable. We shall first imagine that electrons revolve in fixed orbits distant in the ratio $1^2 : 2^2 : 3^2 : 4^2 : 5^2$ etc. from the centre of the nucleus. Though periodic, this motion cannot be a source of radiation. Otherwise all matter would be radiant at all times. On the other hand, we have reason to conclude that absorption of radiation accompanies displacement of electrons from the neighbourhood of the nucleus; and this leads to the suggestion that absorption of radiation results from the jump of an electron from an inner to an outer orbit. If we now make two bold assumptions, the several pieces of the jigsaw puzzle of line-spectra and quanta fall into place. First, we assume that the single free electron of the hydrogen atom may jump to an outer orbit only from one of the four innermost (distant $1^2 : 2^2 : 3^2 : 4^2$) with absorption of a quantum of radiant energy or *vice versa* with release of one. Second, we assume that it revolves in its new orbit with a new speed in accordance with the inverse square law. To move an electron from an inner orbit at a distance d_1 from the nucleus to an outer one at d_2 against the attractive power of the nucleus, i.e. farther from it, we should have to do work. Its displacement through an equal distance towards the nucleus signifies the release of an equivalent amount of energy. According to the inverse square law, we have seen that this is proportional to:

$$\frac{1}{d_1} - \frac{1}{d_2}$$

Our assumptions thus signify that the above will have values represented by the series:

$$\frac{1}{1^2} - \frac{1}{2^2}, \frac{1}{1^2} - \frac{1}{3^2}, \text{ etc.} \qquad \frac{1}{2^2} - \frac{1}{3^2}, \frac{1}{2^2} - \frac{1}{4^2}, \text{ etc.}$$

$$\frac{1}{3^2} - \frac{1}{4^2}, \frac{1}{3^2} - \frac{1}{5^2}, \text{ etc.} \qquad \frac{1}{4^2} - \frac{1}{5^2}, \frac{1}{4^2} - \frac{1}{6^2}, \text{ etc.}$$

If each jump involves release or absorption of a quantum of radiant energy, this means that $h\nu$ for radiation emitted or absorbed can have only values in the proportions cited above. Since h (*Planck's constant*) is a fixed number, the same is true of the frequency ν. Our assumptions therefore satisfy what we know about the *relative* spacing of the lines of the hydrogen spectrum. To say more, we have to account for a constant on each side of the equation which takes the following form for a particular line in the visible spectrum:

$$h\nu_d = R\left(\frac{1}{2^2} - \frac{1}{d^2}\right)$$

In the gravitational model R would have the value $\frac{1}{2}GMm$. If we insert the numerical value of the corresponding term for the electrostatic model and that of Planck's constant, the equation balances.

What we have said so far applies only to the hydrogen atom with one free electron comparable to the moon of our own planet. If an atom contains more than one, the model must take account of the repulsion between electrons. Bohr first made the hydrogen atom public in 1913. If interpreted as a picture of all atoms of one and the same element, the Bohr model does not embrace all the knowledge since gained. Nor does any other model which we can picture. What we can still say is this. If we regard the Bohr model as a composite picture of the average criminal in contradistinction to the representation of a particular crook, it remains the best picture of the atom in so far as the atom is itself picturable.

★   ★   ★   ★   ★

Selected references for Part III occur as for Part IV on p. 1118.

PART IV

The Conquest of Hunger and Disease

"But it was especially after the ruin spread by the Goths, when all the sciences which before had flourished gloriously and were practised as was fitting, went to ruin, that more fashionable doctors, first in Italy, in imitation of the old Romans, despising the work of the hand, began to delegate to slaves the manual attentions they judged needful for their patients, and themselves merely to stand over them like architects. Then, when all the rest also who practised the true art of healing gradually declined the unpleasant duties of their profession, without however abating any of their claim to money or to honour, they quickly fell away from the standard of the doctors of old. Methods of cooking, and all the preparation of food for the sick, they left to nurses; compounding of drugs they left to the apothecaries; manual operation to barbers." (From Professor B. Farrington's preface to English translation of Vesalius' *De Fabrica humani corporis*.)

CHAPTER XVII

WHEN LIFE IS CHEAP

FROM what we have learned in the opening chapters of this book it will now be clear that the distinction sometimes drawn between ancient science and modern science is a distinction of content rather than of method. If we wish to draw a hard and fast line between craftsmanship and science, we can only draw it at the point when experience has brought forth principles sufficiently comprehensive in scope to demand a permanent written record. In that sense astronomy, the statics of solids and liquids, and geometrical optics are sciences of great antiquity. Chemistry, heat, and electricity are essentially modern.

The scientific study of living organisms on the other hand is both ancient and modern. The written record of medicine goes back almost as far as astronomy. Indeed, the sayings of Hippocrates are household words. In contradistinction to all other learned professions, including even astronomy, the practice of medicine in the Western world records an almost unbroken apostolic succession from the Greek period. Thenceforward there was little conspicuous progress till the beginning of the seventeenth century of the present era. From the publication of Harvey's treatise on the circulation of the blood knowledge of living matter has advanced steadily and continuously.

One reason for this is not far to seek. The continuous existence of medicine as a social institution implies the maintenance of an organized profession with opportunities for capitalizing whatever crumbs fell from the table of other branches of science. How true this is will be sufficiently evident when we recall the title enjoyed by the Moorish doctors and their Jewish successors in Spain, where the doctor was described as "physician and algebraist." So in seeking for the social background of man's conquest of disease, hunger and behaviour, we encounter at the outset two main issues. One is the agencies which have conspired at various times to maintain the continuity of medicine as a secular learned profession, to advance its prestige and to diffuse its influence. The other is the way in which progress in mechanical sciences has placed at the disposal of the medical profession new instruments and, with them, new problems and means of solving them.

The influence of medicine on the mechanical sciences and of the latter on biological studies which medicine has encouraged has emerged repeatedly in previous parts of *Science for the Citizen*. Medical solicitude sponsored the spectacle trade, which in turn revived optical science. Revived interest in optics nursed the microscope, which revolutionized scientific knowledge of reproduction and epidemic disease. Physicians assisted at the birth of two new physical sciences, when the study of gases was the province of "pneumatic chemistry," and the measurement of heat was confined to thermometry. In turn industrial chemistry has made new methods of analysis available for the study of nutrition, and modern engineering has provided a costing system for bodily work. Current electricity began with medical researches on nerves, and practical telegraphy has provided the apparatus for modern discoveries concerned with nervous conduction.

The familiar formula of crime fiction (see p. 582) suggests three aspects of scientific progress. The existence of an organized profession of medicine has provided *opportunities* for the study of living processes. The microscope, the chemical balance, electrical recording instruments, the thermometer and the calorimeter have provided new *means* for solving the problems they suggest. The existence of new technical problems to furnish a fresh *motive* for the pursuit of biological knowledge is perhaps less obvious. A new motive for exploiting the new means which contemporary progress in related sciences placed at the disposal of the physician or the apothecary does, in fact, emerge at the threshold of the modern period.

Researches such as those of Gordon Childe have taught us that the great biological inventions antedate civilization as the term is usually used. The Neolithic was a grain-growing economy, and the domestication of man's chief associates in a self-sufficient system—the horse, the sheep, the goat, the ass, the camel, the ox, the fowl, the bee, the yeast organism—is in almost every instance now known to be as old as city life. Man learned the art of seed scattering, of milking the cow, of bridling the ox, of harvesting the grain—probably of grafting the vine and fertilizing the date—before there was any corpus of recorded scientific knowledge in the world. Aside from a few pedestrian descriptive accounts by writers of the Roman Empire, the record of man's struggle for food had no place in the hieratic or imperial cultures of the Mediterranean world. For one reason or another this neglect ended at the very time when the struggle for new materials was assuming a new aspect.

Cut off from the humble toil of the cultivator, medicine registered no conspicuous progress for two millennia during which scientific husbandry remained at a standstill. Roman agriculture, which was operated on a more imposing commercial scale than agriculture in northern Europe during the sixteenth century, failed to inspire any written record except pedestrian georgics of literati who were not professionally connected with the pursuit of science. It made no enduring contribution to biotechnology. During this period the command of medical skill was the prerogative of those who did not know the pinch of hunger. Mankind had not as yet learned that the health of the few cannot be assured in a community which allows disease to lurk among the many Medicine itself made little progress while the medical profession was exclusively concerned with the well-to-do. When conspicuous progress did begin, the most notable victories concerned diseases whose characteristics compelled attention by the very fact that they interfered with the working life of the community. Hence the social background of man's struggle with disease and hunger must be sought in the agencies which extended the benefits of medical care to the community as a whole and brought the study of medicine and the practice of horticulture and husbandry into one and the same social context.

The period of Harvey, from which the continuous progress of modern medicine dates, was the threshold of a revolution in agricultural technique. It also witnessed the rise of commercial horticulture which begins with the Dutch tulip craze in the sixteenth century. The advance of modern medicine owes a large debt to modern productive biotechnology. In its beginnings, the latter benefited by the existence of a profession interested in encouraging its growth. Harvey's work marks the end of an epoch during which biological studies were exclusively preoccupied with the pursuit of health. Thereafter the conquest of disease is inextricably interwoven with the conquest of hunger.

We have learned from the story of man's conquest of materials that the international economy was showing symptoms of strain, as it approached the pinnacle of its development. The long ages of imperialistic wars, of commercial exploration, of conquest and of colonization were approaching their end. The inventory of nature's ready-made products was wellnigh complete. During all this period scientific culture had been urban, and its most characteristically urban phase of development, the brilliant efflorescence in Alexandria between 300 B.C. and A.D. 300, was relatively barren from the standpoint of biology. Alexandrian science, so brilliant in other fields, was comparatively sterile from the standpoint of biology, and its sterility, like its arrested development in the science of power and materials, is at least partly susceptible of a simple explanation.

So long as slave labour was abundant, the social incentive which led to the systematic study of non-human sources of power and to the discovery of the gaseous state was lacking. Cheap labour and a cheap valuation of human life have never been propitious to rapid development of scientific knowledge. This is more true of biological enquiries than of any other branch of scientific knowledge. In two ways the institution of slavery obstructed biological progress in antiquity. As medical science could not advance while medical services were the exclusive prerogative of the wealthy, scientific husbandry did not advance till a semi-literate class of free cultivators and village Hampdens became socially influential. In the social background of seventeenth-century biology we see the *extension of medical services in a social milieu propitious to biotechnical innovation*.

Though social influences unrelated to public hygiene, notably navigation, stimulated and encouraged the demand for naturalistic knowledge in the dark ages of the Faith, the spread of the Moorish culture which had garnered the fruits of Alexandrian science and Hindu mathematics would scarcely have been possible, if there had not co-existed educational machinery propitious to naturalistic enquiry. Dr. Singer's researches have taught us that the medical schools of the medieval universities were formed by Jewish missionaries of Moorish science. These schools were of pivotal importance to science. They gave naturalistic enquiry a foothold within the precincts of the ecclesiastical culture which was destined to be overthrown by it.

When we recall how little outstanding practical progress was achieved over a period of many centuries during which the medical profession occupied a position of outstanding cultural importance, the continuity of medicine as a learned profession with its own literature is a somewhat remarkable fact of man's social existence. It is hard to say why the physician earned a confidence which could outweigh the very severe inconvenience of being a pagan or heretic. Ancient prescriptions were, with one notable exception,

sheer quackery. Of all the remedies in the classical or Moorish pharmaco-
pœias perhaps the single conspicuous achievement was the use of purgatives
and aperients. For biology it was a felicitous circumstance that the disorder
redressed by this class of remedy is of singularly common occurrence.
Maybe it was pre-eminently in his capacity as surgeon that the practitioner
gained the respect of his fellows. The majority of townsfolk, being little
accustomed to the sight of wounds and fractures, readily succumb to hysteria
or inactivity when brought face to face with them. So they gratefully welcome
the offices of anyone whose regular experience fits him to approach them
with calmness and deliberation, even when beneficial results of his minis-
trations are not self-evident.

Whatever circumstances contribute to the almost superstitious reverence
which the profession of healing has managed to attach to itself, and to retain,
its existence is hardly a matter of dispute. Special circumstances contributed
to enhance it during the three centuries which preceded the publication
of Harvey's works on the circulation of the blood and the generation of animals.
We may refer to two of them respectively as Christianity and metropolitanism.

CATHOLIC DOCTRINE AND THE CARE OF THE SICK

We may trace the social origins of European medicine, as we understand
the term today, to the hospitals and gardens of the monastic orders and to
the medical schools of the ecclesiastical universities. The existence of the
former and the, at that time, singular tolerance which encouraged Jewish
Arabic scholarship in the latter are testimony to a new respect for human life.

We are now sufficiently far removed from the superstitions of Mr. Gladstone's time to take a more detached view of the social significance of Christianity than free-thinkers of fifty years ago could be expected to entertain.
With no temptation to swallow the pietistic apologia of Mr. Hilaire Belloc
in their entirety, we need not shut our eyes to the fact that Catholic Christianity did, on the whole, discourage chattel slavery and indisputably in-
doctrinated Europe with the special beatitude of those who tend the sick
and infirm. Christian metaphysics, being Platonic in origin, was aristocratic
in temper and wholly inimical to the progress of natural enquiry as such.
Christian ethics never completely relinquished its Essene ingredients which
revived in the Spartacist ideology of Wycliffe's poor preachers. As an ethic
Christianity did much to encourage science.

Catholicism contained what Hegelians call an internal contradiction.
Succouring the poor and needy and healing the sick were among the ostensible
objects of the two great monastic orders of Benedictines and Franciscans.
How members of the latter sponsored the only first-rate medical amenity of
the middle ages, and the repercussions of the spectacle industry on the physical science of the period have been pointed out earlier (see p. 132). In the
thirteenth century eagerness to earn the beatitude aforementioned was
sufficiently strong to override the plain duty of compelling the infidel to
come into the fold and to rescue heretical brands from the burning by practical homœopathy. The Jewish and Moorish physicians commanded special
privileges. The early medical schools of Montpellier and Salerno, which

were founded by them, became a focus of the naturalistic movement which bore fruit in the outburst of scientific discovery during the Copernican epoch.

The monastery physic garden was the beginning of a closer union between the practice of medicine and the study of nature. On the same scale, herbal medicine was not cultivated in the urban centres of culture under Roman imperialism. The monastic orders also created a new social institution which was to make systematic and continuous medical study possible for the first time in history. Our oldest hospitals were founded by the monks. In this connexion the following citation from Simon's authoritative work, *English Sanitary Institutions,** emphasizes the significance of new social values as an aspect of the social background of biological progress:

In the parts of the Roman Empire which were soonest affected by the promulgation of Christianity a greatly increased thoughtfulness for the poor, with a great development of charitable service towards them, was a conspicuous first-fruit of the creed: so that, in all early Christian communities, the giving of alms to the poor, of personal tendance to the sick, of shelter to the homeless, and generally of brotherly and sisterly help to persons in necessitous circumstances of mind, body, or estate, became, as it were, a characteristic ritual of the new faith. It was a ritual which the surrounding Roman world may have found the more impressive from the fact that in those early days it required no apparatus of Flamens and Pontiffs, nor even involved any burning of incense; and the Emperor Julian was led to confess something like envy on behalf of his co-religionists, as he saw how they were exceeded in charitable action by votaries of the faith which he despised. In various great centres of population, Christian philanthropy soon showed itself in the establishment of standing asylums and houses of hospitality of different sorts for persons, old and young, who might need them: hospices (in the narrow sense of the term) as places of refuge for strangers and outcasts, almshouses for the helpless poor, homes for orphans and foundlings, and reformatories for women who had gone wrong: and not least among such establishments, hospitals for the sick and wounded, hitherto not precedented in the world, except to some extent in Buddhist India, and in extremely small degree in pre-Christian Greece and Rome, began to appear as Christian institutions. Thus about the year 370, there was founded at Caesarea, by its then bishop, Basil, an immense institution of miscellaneous charity, including a hospital for the sick; and some thirty years later, at Constantinople, a hospital was one of many beneficences which the poor of the city owed to the brief and stormy archiepiscopate of Chrysostom. In minor communities, endeavours of the same sort, though of course on a smaller scale, seem to have been general. *Instantiae lampadis* they indeed were, those early Christianities of action; and they assimilated practice to profession with a sincerity which made them worthy to live. Against their continuance, however, or at least their continuance in the full spirit of their founders, there were obstacles in the nature of the case, and also in the circumstances of the times. The philanthropic ardour which Basil and Chrysostom had awakened was perhaps too impulsive to be equally persistent. Often the founders of special charities would have passed away, and successors like-minded with them would not have risen. Still more, as war spread from region to region, and city after city was whirlpooled in social strife, the urban organizations of charity perished of mere inanition, like the children of slain parents, or were shattered and

* John Murray, London.

trampled under foot as savagely as the fences and gardens. Meanwhile the monastic system had taken root in Europe and was beginning to represent in a somewhat changed way, and for the most part in very changed. local relations, the previous more communal charities. From about the year 529, when the religious order of Benedict of Nursia, with its great monastery at Monte Cassino, was established, and in proportion as the establishment of monasteries more or less after that pattern became general, first in Italy, and then in all parts of Western Europe, the monks, in those parts of Europe, were constant dispensers of help to the poor; and each monastery, besides being a centre of almsgiving to the poor of its neighbourhood, and a home of refuge to many a forlorn wayfarer, served also generally as a hospital for sick and wounded. . . . The Franciscan Order, from the time when it was established, gave a new impulse to the care of the poor in Europe; supplementing in that respect most usefully the action of the monasteries of Benedictine rule. The relations between the Franciscans and Benedictines were habitually relations of much mutual disfavour; and often also on either side there would be relations more or less invidious between brotherhoods following original rule, and brotherhoods purporting to be of "reformed" type: but the two sorts of organization were able to work side by side throughout Europe; and thus working, they together represented, for some centuries, a large proportion of the charity on which the necessitous poor depended for relief. . . . The debt of modern times to the medieval Religious Orders is far more than a mere sentiment of sympathy with the populations which received good at their hands. To say nothing of the obligations which scholars of all sorts acknowledge to the Benedictine and Mendicant Orders in respect of the stores of learning which they transmitted and increased, or of new lights of knowledge and wisdom which came from them—to say nothing of those presages of scientific spirit which dawned among them, as for instance, in the mind of Roger Bacon—there are senses, purely medical, in which the philanthropy of the Middle Ages has been a continuing good to mankind. The hospital system of modern Europe is raised upon that medieval foundation. A large proportion of the noblest hospitals in Europe, giving help year after year to annual millions of the poor, exist by uninterrupted descent from monastic charities: two single instances in our own metropolis, are St. Thomas's Hospital which is the continuation of a monastic charity of the thirteenth century, and St. Bartholomew's Hospital which is of even earlier monastic origin.

MEDIEVAL MEDICINE AND HORTICULTURE

We shall see later (Chapter XX) that the close association between medicine and the systematic survey of plant life arising from somewhat superstitious belief in the healing benefits of herbal preparations was one of the most conspicuous formative influences in the progress of biological science from the sixteenth century onwards. The influence of the monasteries is universally recognized in histories of horticulture. The following quotation is from Amherst's *History of Gardening in England*:

The earliest records of gardens on the Continent (after Roman times) date from the ninth century. In the list of Manors of the Abbey of Saint Germain des Pres, Saint Armand and Saint Remy, in the time of Karl the Great mention is made of various gardens. At other places, as at Corbie, in Picardy, and at St. Gall, near the lake of Constance, there remains more than a mere mention of the existence of a garden. At Corbie the garden was very large; either divided into four, or else four distinct gardens, and ploughs, which had to be contributed annually by certain tenants, were used to keep it in order; while other tenants had to send men from April to October, to assist the monks in weeding and planting. At St. Gall, the "hortus" is a rectangular enclosure, with a central path leading from the gardener's house and a shed for tools and seeds situated at one end, with nine long and narrow beds of equal size on either side. The "herbularis," or physic garden, is smaller, with a border of plants all round the wall, and four beds on either side of the central walk; and the plants contained in each of these beds are carefully noted. In England we have no such exact description of any garden, and it is only by carefully examining the records of the various monasteries that the existence of gardens or orchards in the eleventh and twelfth centuries, and a few of even earlier date, can be proved. A garden was a most essential adjunct to a monastery, as vegetables formed so large a proportion of the daily food of the inmates. Therefore, as soon as monasteries were founded, gardens must have been made around them, and these were probably almost the only gardens, worthy of the name, in the kingdom at that time. Still, the number of plants they contained was very limited, and probably many of those grown on the Continent had not found their way into this country. The monks may have received plants from abroad, as some connexion with religious houses on the Continent was kept up; and in bringing back treasures for their monasteries or churches the garden would not be forgotten. But plants were chiefly brought for medicine, and we may infer that they were imported in a dry state, as our word "drug" is simply part of the Anglo-Saxon verb "drigan," to dry. . . . The earliest view of a monastery garden in this country appears to be that in the plans or bird's-eye views of the monastic buildings at Canterbury, made about 1165, and bound up with the Great Psalter of Eadwin, now preserved in the library of Trinity College, Cambridge. These drawings seem to have been made (probably by the engineer Wibert or his assistants) to record the system of waterworks and drainage of the monastery. One of them shows the Herbarium which occupies half the space between the Dormitory and the Infirmary, surrounded by cloisters; the other the orchard and vineyard which were situated beyond the walls. The first plan records also trees within the wall near the fish-pond, including what was afterwards known as the old convent garden, the site of which was obtained in parcels between the years 1287 and 1368. . . . In all countries, heathen and Christian, and in all ages, flowers have played an important part in ceremonies, such as funeral rites and marriage feasts. England in the Middle Ages was no exception; and the use of flowers in the services of the Church, in crowning the priests, wreathing candles, or adorning shrines, was very general. The gardens within the monastery walls for providing these flowers were under the care of the Sacristan. At Abingdon, he paid the gardinarius four bushels of corn for the rent of his garden. At Norwich, the Sacristan seems to have had more than one garden, as a very cursory glance at the M.S. accounts of that office shows the names of both "St. Mary's" and the "green garden." There was a "gardinum Sacristae" at Winchester as early as the ninth century, and to this day a piece of ground on the east side of the north transept of the cathedral bears the name of "Paradise," and marks the site of the Sacrist's garden. The fifteenth-century doorway, which was the entrance to the enclosure, is still standing. . . . Bede, writing early in the eighth century, says that Britain "excels for grain and trees . . . it also produces vines in some places." In the laws of Alfred, which were chiefly compilations of existing ones, it was notified that anyone who "damaged the vineyard or field of another, should give compensation." . . . In their wanderings in the East during the Crusades, they may have remembered some garden in England, and brought back plants for it, as, for example, the splendid Oriental plane at Ribston, the planting of which tradition attributes to the Templars. The surveys of the manors all over the kingdom belonging to these Orders show the large number of gardens of which they were possessed. . . . Castles were built on the tops of hills, or protection was sought by placing the dwelling behind some river or marsh, when no high ground or escarpments of steep rocks afforded a suitable defence. This was the opposite course from that

FIG. 400.—CITY SANITATION IN MINOAN CRETE, *c.* 1900 B.C.

In the wonderful city of Knossos, with its great Palace of Minos, excavated and restored by Sir Arthur Evans, circular walled pits of large size, called kouloura, were constructed for the sanitary disposal of rubbish from the Palace area. Earth was apparently used in layers to prevent effluvia, and a certain amount of surface water was drained into them. These most effective public rubbish dumps, arranged in line, were built in the period between 1900 and 1750 B.C. on the ruins of houses of the previous Period.

(From *Sixty Centuries of Health and Physick* by S. G. B. Stubbs and E. W. Bligh)

pursued by the monks, who, as a rule, chose a fertile valley in which to place their cloister, and plant their orchards, gardens and vineyards. There was no room for much garden within the glacis of a feudal castle, and as it was not safe for any of the inmates to venture beyond, it was scarcely worth while making any garden or orchard outside, merely to see it plundered by some turbulent neighbour. But, in spite of all these disadvantages some attempt at cultivation of fruit was not unfrequently made.

BEGINNINGS OF SANITARY INSTITUTIONS

The art of gardening, which attained a high level in the civilizations of Mesopotamia and Egypt and at a later date more especially in Islamic Persia, was far older than monastic Christianity. The importance of the monastery garden lies in the fact that it brought into one and the same social context the cultivation of plants for use as food, as ornament and above all as physic. So also the practice of sanitation goes back to Cretan, Assyrian and Egyptian cities, and attained a high level of mechanical contrivance in the Roman Empire. In pre-Christian civilization it was perhaps more a symbol of civic prosperity than a policy of public health. So soon as large cities began to grow the need to ensure a continuous supply of fresh water for drinking purposes, to drain off accumulated rainfall and to dispose of refuse, was inescapable. The urge to make suitable provision in the form of aqueducts and sewers was primarily dictated by the sheer mechanical inconvenience of doing without them. To be sure, there was the beginning of a system of public health officers in Rome itself during the latter days of the Empire, as shown by the edicts of Valentinian about A.D. 370, and by others of Valens. In these edicts we already see the growing influence of the Christian social ethic and the decline of an ideology which was the proper complement to the gladiatorial contest.

The association of sanitary provisions with a public policy of health begins to take shape only when urban life develops in northern climates. Thenceforward there was a progressive recognition that insanitary conditions are propitious to the spread of contagious diseases and epidemics. The following passage from Simon's treatise describes the beginnings of a sanitary policy in medieval England:

In 1357 a Royal Order, addressed to the Mayor and Sheriffs, tells how the King, Edward III, passing along the river, had "beheld dung and laystalls and other filth accumulated in divers places in the said City upon the bank of the said river," and had "also perceived the fumes and other abominable stenches arising therefrom: from the corruption of which, if tolerated, great peril, as well to the persons dwelling within the said city as to the nobles and others passing along the river, will it is feared arise unless indeed some fitting remedy be speedily provided for the same": and the Order forbids the continuance of practices as above, and requires proclamation to that effect to be made: whereupon a new Order for the preservation of cleanliness in the city is proclaimed: and part of it prescribes that "for saving the body of the river, and preserving the quays . . . for lading and unlading, as also for avoiding the filthiness that is increasing in the river and upon the banks of the Thames, to the great abomination and damage of the people," there shall henceforth no rubbish or filth be thrown or put into the rivers of Thames and Flete, or into the Fosses around the walls of the City, but all must be taken out of the City by carts. In 1372, the King again addresses the Mayor Sheriffs and Aldermen of the City: complaining that "rushes, dung, refuse, and other filth and harmful things . . . from City and suburbs are thrown into the water of Thames, so that the water aforesaid and the hythes thereof are so greatly obstructed, and the course of the said water so greatly narrowed, that great ships are not able, as of old they were wont, any longer to come up to the same City, but are impeded therein": and the writ strictly enjoins immediate measures to amend this state of things, and to prevent recurrence: "so behaving yourselves in this behalf, that we shall have no reason for severely taking you to task in respect hereof; and this, as we do trust in you, and as you would avoid our heavy indignation and the punishment which as regards ourselves you may

Fig. 401.—Public Hygiene in India before the Aryans

A brick-built drain, dating from 3000 B.C., at Mohenjo-Daro, where an elaborate civilization, with Sumerian affinities, has been disclosed. This drain ran along a street and the drains from the many well-built houses on the left were connected into it. Sir John Marshall notes that every street, alley-way and passage had its own covered conduits of finely chiselled brick laid with great precision. The whole drainage system was extremely well developed.—Sir John Marshall, Director-General of Archaeology in India.

(From *Sixty Centuries of Health and Physick* by S. G. B. Stubbs and E. W. Bligh)

incur, you are in no wise to omit." Within the first six years of Richard II, the same policy appears in two cases: filth (1379) was not during raintime to be cast into the kennels so as to float away with the water: and (1383) rules are made to preserve the water-course of the Walbrook. Meanwhile, however, latrines, especially public latrines, are again and again named as causing nuisance. In 1346 (20th Edward III) is a royal ordinance in which accusations are alleged against citizens and others smitten with the blemish of leprosy, that they publicly dwell among, and publicly and privately communicate with the other citizens and sound persons, and in some cases actually endeavour by sexual and other intimate intercourse "to contaminate others with that abominable blemish, so that to their own wretched solace they may have the more fellows in suffering": and therefore proclamation is to be made that all the persons having such blemish must "within fifteen days betake themselves to places in the country, solitary, and notably distant from the said city and suburbs and take up their dwelling there; seeking their victuals through such sound persons as may think proper to attend thereto, wheresoever they may deem it expedient." And persons shall not permit lepers to dwell in their houses and buildings in the city or suburbs on pain of forfeiting their houses and buildings, and of other more grievous punishment. And diligent search, with skilled assistants, is forthwith to be made for lepers, in order to their immediate expulsion. On a particular occasion (1372) a leper, who though oftentimes commanded to go, has still been remaining in the city, is made to swear that he will forthwith go and not return, on pain of pillory. In 1375, the porters of the eight city gates, are severally sworn that they will not allow any leper to enter the city or to stay in it or its suburbs, but if any seek to enter, will prohibit him, and if he perseveres, will distrain him by his horse (should he have any) and by his outer garment, the which shall not be given him back without leave of the Mayor, and, if he further endeavour, will attach him bodily and keep him in custody. The porters are to have the pillory if they fail of this ordinance; and the respective foremen of the Hackney and Southwark leperhouses are sworn to aid in giving effect to it.

THE PLAGUE YEARS

The policy developed as a safeguard against the spread of leprosy grew into a more or less stable system of preventive measures in connexion with the devastating epidemics which took a heavy toll from the town populations. This consolidated the prestige of medicine in the period of religious Reformation, when the influence of the monastic orders was destroyed. Simon tells us:

On several occasions during the years to which the Remembrancia relate there was prevalence of Plague in London; and whenever this was or threatened to be the case, the City authorities corresponded about it with the Lords of the Council, and were directed by them what to do in the circumstances. One severe invasion by plague was that of the years 1580–3. In 1580, the disease is raging in Lisbon; and the Lord Mayor, on his application to Lord Treasurer Burghley, is authorized by him to take measures in concurrence with the officers of the port to prevent in regard of arrivals from Lisbon the lodging of merchants or mariners in the City or suburbs, or the discharge of goods from ships until they have had some time for airing, and in the meantime to provide proper necessaries on board ships detained. . . . In 1584 "for the stay of infection in the City . . . it had been thought good to restrain the burials in St. Paul's Churchyard which had been so many, and by reason of former burials so shallow, that scarcely any graves could be made without corpses being laid open. Some parishes had turned their churchyards into small tenements, and had buried in St. Paul's Churchyard. It had been determined to restrain from burial there all parishes having churchyards of their own. . . . The City desired the Council to issue directions to the authorities of the Cathedral accordingly: the order not being intended to prevent any person of honour or worship being buried there, but only the pestering of the Churchyard with whole parishes." Then the Oxford Corporation writes to the Lord Mayor, with reference to the approaching Frideswide Fair, to which it was customary for Londoners to repair with their wares and merchandize, and from which now the Lord Mayor is begged to restrain all citizens in whose houses and families there was infection, or who had not obtained his certificate. With reference to assizes about to be held at Hertford, the Queen through the Lords of the Council expressly commanded the same sort of care to be taken by the Lord Mayor. In 1583, the infection having much increased, the Council pressed upon the City Her Majesty's commands "that they should see that all infected houses were shut up, and provision made to feed and maintain the sick persons therein, and for preventing their going abroad; that all infected houses were marked, the streets thoroughly cleansed, and a sufficient number of discreet persons appointed to see the same done. They desired to express Her Majesty's surprise that no house or hospital had been built without the City, in some remote place, to which the infected people might be removed, although other cities of less antiquity, fame, wealth, and reputation, had provided themselves with such places, whereby the lives of the inhabitants had been in all times of infection chiefly preserved." The City authorities, soon after this communication, informed Sir Francis Walsingham that they have published orders which they intend to execute with diligence; but that, in respect of certain inconveniences—assemblies of people at plays, bear-baiting, fencers, and profane spectacles at the Theatre and Curtain and other like places, to which great multitudes of the worst sort of people resorted, restraints in the City were useless, unless like orders were carried out in the places adjoining; and the Lord Mayor therefore moves the Council to take steps in regard of that difficulty. In connexion with a smaller outbreak which occurred in 1606-7, we find the Lord Mayor informing the Lords of the Council that the following traditional order had been passed: "that every infected house should be warded and kept with two sufficient watchmen, suffering no persons to go more out of the said house, nor no searcher to go abroad without a red rod in their hand." And a marshal and two assistants had been appointed to keep the beggars out of the city. . . . It appears that, during the epidemic of 1625, the Lords of the Council issued orders in restraint of the traffic of carriers and higglers with London; and the Lord Mayor presses on the consideration of their Lordships that if, in consequence of these orders, the City should be restrained of victuals, it was to be feared it would not be in the power of himself, or the few magistrates who remained, to restrain the violence hunger might enforce. In 1629-31, Plague was again in ascendency. In October 1629 precautions were to be taken against arrivals from Holland and France; but at least six months before this, the disease was already spreading in London, and the Lords of the Council advising about it. They had issued a book of instructions. At first they had shut up the sick in their houses, but, on further deliberation, had thought it better the houses should be avoided and shut up, and the inmates sent to the pest-houses. Referring to the poor Irish and other vagabond persons, pestering all parts of the City, they advised steps to be taken to free the City and liberties from such persons: also to see the streets kept sweet and clean, and the ditches in the suburbs within the liberties thoroughly cleansed, and they command the Commissioners of Sewers and the Scavengers respectively to perform their duty. Also, being informed that inmates and ale-houses were in excessive number, they required that the law be enforced against these excesses. They require that infected houses should have guards set at the door, and a red cross or "Lord have mercy upon us" set on the door, that passers-by might have notice. They direct the City Authorities and the Justices of Middlesex and Surrey to prohibit and suppress all meetings and stage-plays, bear-baitings, tumbling, rope-dancing, etc., in houses, and meetings for prize-fencing, cock-fighting and bull-baiting and those in close bowling-alleys, and all other meetings whatsoever for pastime, and all assemblies of the inhabitants of several counties at the common halls of London pretended for continuance of acquaintance, and all extraordinary assemblies of people at taverns or elsewhere. And His Majesty was pleased that the College of Physicians should meet and confer upon some fit course for preventing the infection. At the same time, there being much increase of sickness at Greenwich "all fitting means" are to be used "to stop and cut off all intercourse and passage of people between that town and the City"; and question arises of restricting elsewhere, as from London to Exeter, and from Cambridge to London, the passage of things and persons. . . . In a statement dated December, on proceedings which had been taken in the City under an order made some weeks previously by the Council, the Lord Mayor reports, among other things, these: "that ancient women, reported to be both honest and skilful, had been appointed for visited houses, who appeared by certificate to have carefully discharged their duties, that infected houses had been shut up, the usual marks set upon them, and strict watches appointed so that none went abroad; that persons who had died of the infection were buried late at night; that people who would have followed them had been sent away by threatening and otherwise, and that very few or none went with the bodies but those appointed for the purpose. Some persons had been punished for removing the inscription set on infected houses, and others had been bound over to the sessions to be proceeded against according to justice." . . . In 1636, when there was again much plague, the Lords of the Council ordered "the levying of rates in Middlesex and Surrey for the erection of pest-houses and other places of abode for infected persons; also directing the Justices of the Peace for Middlesex to join with the Lord Mayor and Aldermen in making additional orders, to be printed, for preventing the increase of the infection, and authorizing them to make such further orders thereon as they should see fit; also directing the Churchwardens, Overseers and Constables of every parish to provide themselves with books for their directions, and requiring the Physicians of the City to renew the former book touching medicines against infection, and to add to and alter the same, and to cause it to be forthwith printed." . . . The Attorney General is to draw up a proclamation for the King to sign for putting off Bartholomew Fair on account of the plague. Last come a few entries relating to the terrible visitation of 1663–5, and specially instructive as regards the steps which were now to be taken in the way of developing Quarantine. In October 1663, "the King had taken notice that the plague had broken out in some neighbouring countries, and desired to be informed what course had been taken and means used in like cases heretofore to prevent the conveying and spread of the infection in the City"; and the Lord Mayor, informed to this effect by a letter from the Lords of the Council, replies that "he had found many directions and means used to obviate the spreading of the infection at home, but no remembrance of what course had been taken to prevent its importation from foreign parts. The plague of 1625 was brought from Holland. The Court of Aldermen advised that, after the custom of other countries, vessels coming from infected parts should not be permitted to come nearer than Gravesend, or such like distance where repositories, after the manner of lazarettos, should be appointed, into which the ships might discharge their cargoes to be aired for forty days." As Amsterdam and Hamburg were known to be already under visitation by the pestilence, the matter no doubt seemed pressing; and so, next day, this letter received its answer: "the King acknowledged and approved the Lord Mayor's proposal, but recommended that the lazarettos should not be nearer than Tilbury Hope, and that all ships, English or foreign coming from infected ports, should be liable to be stopped and unloaded if necessary. . . . On the arrival of any infected vessel a list should be made of all persons on board, and, if any should die, the body should be searched before casting it overboard. At the end of forty days, if the surgeons reported the vessel free from contagion —(all the apparel, goods, household stuff, bedding, etc., having been aired in the meantime on shore)—it should be allowed to make free commerce. . . ." Orders, more or less to the effect of the above recommendations, were now issued by the Council, and a first English Quarantine was thus established. It was not enforced during the winter, as the pestilence was for that season lulled; but about Midsummer it was again brought into requisition. On June 27, 1664 (and this is the last communication which appears in the Remembrancia on the present subject) the Lords of the Council inform the Lord Mayor that "the plague had broken out in the States of the United Provinces," and they direct "steps to be taken to prevent the infection from being brought into this country, either by passengers or merchandize, and all ships to be placed in quarantine, according to former orders, until the Farmers of the Customs gave their certificate." Those endeavours to exclude by Quarantine the contagion of the Plague were as ineffectual as if their intention had been to bar out the east wind or the new moon; and, in the sanitary records of the Metropolis, the year 1665 has its special mark as emphatically the year of the Great Plague. Before the middle of the year, the disease was known to be spreading in London: where, as the season advanced, it became more and more prevalent, till, in August and September, when the epidemic was at its height the deaths by it, within the London Bills of Mortality, averaged in each week not fewer than six or seven thousand, and may perhaps once or twice have been as many as ten thousand within the week. What may have been the total fatality of the London Epidemic cannot be exactly known; but the estimate which Macaulay adopts is, that it swept away, in six months, more than a hundred thousand human beings. The subsidence of that terrible epidemic continued during the winter and spring of 1665-6, till the weekly deaths were fewer than fifty; but, as summer advanced, the infection again began to spread; and the London world was fearing what worse renewal of the pestilence might yet come, when suddenly the most drastic of sanitary reformers appeared on the scene, and what had remained of the Great Plague yielded at once to the Great Disinfector. . . . The opportunity which the circumstances afforded for the construction of a fitter city was to some considerable extent turned to account; but, in view of what improvement must cost, improvement was extensively stinted; and especially the public grudged the large expenditure which alone could have brought uncrowdedness of building. Wren, after his survey of the ruins had designed a scheme of reconstruction which would have made the new city a fitting nucleus for the metropolis of later times: would have made it of harmonious plan, with wide convenient thoroughfares, with proper standing-room for its chief buildings, with spacious public quays along the river, and even with reasonable interspaces of mere pleasure-ground; but the largeness of his proposal was beyond his contemporaries.

ORIGINS OF VITAL STATISTICS

Coincident with the public menace of epidemics, which reached a climax in the Great Plague, two significant occurrences which have not been mentioned also merit comment. One is the publication of the *Bills of Mortality* which represent the first recognition that the census of population should be concerned with health as well as with taxation and the mobilization of military resources. The other was the beginnings of *Life Insurance*. These bore fruit in the noteworthy pamphlets of Graunt and Petty and in the construction of the first life table for the calculation of annuities in one of the earliest numbers of the *Philosophical Transactions of the Royal Society* (1693). Halley's Life Table is of dual interest. It signalizes the beginnings of practical encouragement for medical science in conformity with the interests of the financier. It also illustrates the intimate relation of scientific enquiry to contemporary social problems during the period when English science was at the highest level it attained before it received a new impetus from the rise of chemical manufacture.

PREVENTIVE MEDICINE AND THE NEW HUMANITY

The control of epidemic diseases gives us the first picture of a Government in conference with an *organization* of scientific experts, and incidentally also of the circumstances which led to the organization of expert knowledge as a social institution. In the Middle Ages the trained physician and surgeon was still a perquisite of the rich. The common people of England enjoyed the blessings of unrestricted private enterprise, until the Royal College of Surgeons received its Charter from Henry VIII. Thenceforth the barber's operations were confined to the scalp.

Indeed, we may regard the foundation of the Royal Colleges of Physicians and of Surgeons as the first step towards the formation of those academies and institutions which, like the English Royal Society chartered in the reign of Charles II, have made the pursuit of science in some measure a social institution with an internal momentum of its own. This internal momentum of the scientific movement can easily be exaggerated, because, like other social institutions, it has an organic relation to its fellows. The English Royal Society, and not less the French Academy, founded about the same time were both formed by men who believed that "the goods of mankind might be much increased by the naturalist's insight into trades"; and they both suffered a temporary eclipse when their activities became less closely related to live contemporary issues.

The process of conference between the executive and a permanent panel of experts, once begun, has continued ever since. Small-pox and cholera in turn became a public menace sufficient to compel legislation designed to ensure a national minimum of health. The latter led to the appointment of a Central Board of Health, and thereafter local government became increasingly preoccupied with the maintenance of a national minimum. The Act which initiated this Board in England followed half a century after the Board of Agriculture was set up (1793) as a war-time precaution for ensuring food supplies. Together they represent the first two important steps towards a rationally planned organization of the fruits of scientific knowledge. Their existence signalizes an awakening public recognition of our common social responsibility to make available to all the benefits bestowed by scientific knowledge.

The vigorous public measures which were adopted to deal with small-pox and Asiatic cholera in the first half of the nineteenth century coincided with important advances in knowledge of the origins and treatment of epidemic diseases. An incident which occurred in the latter end of the eighteenth century forced on the administration the need for public health measures in a different context. What Florence Nightingale achieved in the middle of the nineteenth century is not more spectacular, if more familiar, than the work of physicians and surgeons like Pringle and James Lind, who began the task of hygienic reform in the fighting services. Lind's essay on the *Health of Seamen* is a landmark in medicine for several reasons.

Till the eighteenth century there had been little classification of diseases as natural phenomena with characteristic individual features. Nothing precise was known about the circumstances which are responsible for the occurrence of the few diseases like ague, or as we now call it malaria, then recognized as distinct clinical entities. This is not surprising when we consider the complexity of the problem in the light of modern knowledge. Liability to disease involves both the constitution of the individual and the environment to which the individual is exposed. Generally speaking it is not easy to decide which is more important without elaborate methods of research. However, there are two classes of diseases which betray their distinctive features to immediate inspection. These are: (a) *regional* diseases which are characteristic of a locality (e.g. malaria and syphilis, when it was apparently brought from the New World and first described by Frascatorius in the sixteenth century); (b) *occupational* diseases which are characteristic of a particular mode of life.

The ailments of the miner (see Chapter VIII) set the problem which led to the first real understanding of respiration. From everyday experience of the world's work biology received a second impetus in combating the ravages of disease among sailors, when protracted voyages were first undertaken in latitudes where supplies of fresh vegetables in winter were difficult to obtain. Vasco da Gama lost 100 out of 160 men when he rounded the Cape in 1498. This death toll was a common occurrence of the Great Navigations. It was mainly due to the disease called *scurvy*, whose characteristic symptoms are swelling and bleeding under the skin and elsewhere with growing weakness and pain. In 1593, Hawkins cured a ship's company of scurvy by making them all drink lemon juice.

At the time when Lind's essay was written, scurvy, says Simon, still used "to cripple fleet after fleet." The importance of Lind's essay does not lie so much in the originality of its contents as in the fact that it brought together the practical experience of enlightened navigators, and proved influential in persuading others to benefit from the bitter lessons which practical experience had taught. Notable among those who responded was Captain Cook. In 1776, when the Royal Society awarded the Copley Medal to Cook in honour of his paper on "The Method taken for preserving the Health of the

Crew of His Majesty's Ship, the Resolution," the president referred in memorable words to the success of Cook's efforts in response to the lead which James Lind had given. They may be commended to those who think that anything is gained by exalting pure science to the detriment of its applications. The reward was

to crown that paper of the year which should contain the most useful and most successful experimental inquiry. Now, what inquiry can be so useful as that which hath for its object the saving of the lives of men and when shall we find one more successful than that before us? Here are no vain boastings of the empiric, nor ingenious and delusive theories of the dogmatist, but a concise, an artless, and an incontested relation of the means by which under the Divine Favour Captain Cook with a company of 118 men performed a voyage of three years and eighteen days, throughout all the climates from 52° North to 71° South, with the loss of only one man by a disease.

Thereafter the Admiralty ordered a supply of lemons in all ships of the British Navy, and scurvy disappeared. As Simon remarks, "since the days of Anson's expedition" it "has become an almost forgotten disease." The work of Pringle and Lind in drawing attention to what may be called the occupational diseases of the army and navy also helped to establish the identity of a group of infectious conditions previously described separately as ship fever, hospital fever, and gaol fever. They are now called *typhus*, a condition which is practically extinct in twentieth-century Britain, though it was rampant in Tsarist Russia.

The social background of this important advance again emphasizes the debt of biological science to high valuation of human life. In Europe and in America the half-century which preceded and that which followed the French Revolution witnessed a rapid and articulate growth of humanitarian sentiment culminating in the abolition of slave owning throughout the British possessions, a succession of reforms in the management of prisons and the wholesale abolition of capital punishment for trivial acts against property. In Britain hanging was still meted out for over a hundred offences, including shoplifting and the felling of trees. These reforms took place in the opening years of the nineteenth century. The exposure of English gaol conditions by Howard in the latter half of the eighteenth century revealed a festering focus of physical, no less than moral, disease in the body politic. He devoted years to the visitation of English prisons, recording with meticulous scientific care the state of affairs which he observed.

Simon says that when the author of the *Winter's Journey* received the thanks of the House of Commons for these years of laborious study, public recognition of his services was no less an *instantia lampadis* of preventive medicine than was the Copley award to Cook. Perhaps no fact bears more striking testimony to the influence of what Simon calls the "new humanity" than the name of the writer who first made a clear distinction between *preventive* and *curative* medicine. History is daily justifying the optimism of Condorcet, as it is daily discrediting the theories of his critic Malthus. Having recognized the debt of medicine to the monastic orders, we should not overlook the fact that the new humanity was essentially part of the social ethic of the French revolution. Partly as such, and partly by its association with Nonconformist bodies it encountered the solid opposition of the bishops' benches when the Romilly bills to abolish capital punishment for trivial offences passed the British House of Commons.

Growing respect for the value of human life, revolt against the toleration of unnecessary suffering, the extension of life insurance and the fear of epidemics bore fruit in one type of legislation which exercised a decisive influence on diagnostic medicine. The mortality bills of the Stuart period, and the Annual Register of births and deaths begun in 1836 in England are milestones in a series of public provisions for the regular collection of medical statistics. Similar provisions were made on the Continent. Their effect was to place on the medical profession the responsibility of giving a precise description of the patient's condition before death. Vague general terms like. plague or the various synonyms by which one and the same disease like typhus was designated gave place to the systematic classification of disease. The search for significant characteristics by which disorders arising from one and the same source could be identified was incorporated in public policy.

Awakening interest in public statistics of health at the end of the seventeenth century drew on other sources. Thus Petty, who ranks with Graunt and Halley as one of the founders of vital statistics, collected mortality figures for the leading French and English hospitals of his time. The importance of such studies in stimulating medical research is sufficiently illustrated by Petty's conclusion as stated in his own words. "If . . . the proportion of those that died out of the L'Hotel de Dieu is double to those that died out of La Charité . . . then it follows that half the said numbers . . . did not die of natural necessity but by the evil administration of the hospitals."

Paradoxical though it may seem, the hospital has advanced preventive medicine till comparatively recent times almost as much by acting as a focus for disease as by providing opportunity for studying curative measures. In the eighteenth century hospitals were a breeding ground for typhus (hospital fever), and in the nineteenth century the maternity ward was still a breeding ground for puerperal fever. Comparison of the records of different hospitals helped to direct attention to the circumstances which promote the occurrence of these conditions, and hence to the necessary measures to. prevent their incidence.

THE NEW ANATOMY

The medical man of the Middle Ages—physician and algebraist—was a person versed in the science of his time. He even had a smattering of astronomy, because the influence of the planets on the organs of the body was still an article of faith. Much of the genuine knowledge he possessed, such as his knowledge of herbs, was hardly more relevant to the success of his professional activities.

The few specifics like mercury compounds introduced for the treatment of syphilis early in the sixteenth century, the half a score purgatives, aperients, and antifebrile herbal preparations making up the bulk of any genuinely remedial treatment the physician had to offer, scarcely required a permanent written record of medical lore. If we ask in what sense medieval medicine was guided by a corpus of knowledge sufficiently comprehensive to merit the name of science we must turn to the practice of surgery. Setting fractures and staunching bleeding from wounds call for some detailed knowledge of the skeleton and the blood system. Along with this, general descriptions of

FIG. 402.—WOOD-CUTS BY DÜRER (1471–1528) ILLUSTRATING THE NEW INTEREST IN THE TECHNIQUE OF ACCURATE REPRESENTATION WHICH WENT HAND IN HAND WITH THE REVIVAL OF ANATOMY

(Albrecht Dürer, *Unterweysung der Messung*, 1525 and 1538)

the disposition of the various organs of the body had been undertaken from the time of Hippocrates onwards. The most notable of the descriptive anatomists of the Roman world was Galen, who lived in the second century of the Christian era. What Ptolemy did for Alexandrian astronomy, Galen accomplished for Alexandrian medicine. Like the Almagest, Galen's Anatomy became a textbook of Moorish science. From the Moorish centres of learning it was introduced into the medieval medical schools.

Two circumstances conspired to awaken interest in anatomy and to stimulate more careful study. Without adequate illustrations the best treatise on anatomy is unintelligible. When the printing trade was able to issue books with competent illustrative material, it was inevitable that the accuracy of the texts would come under closer scrutiny. Simultaneously a new naturalistic motive in the world of art had taken root in Italy. Some of the great masters of the Italian Renaissance, like Leonardo da Vinci, were not less distinguished for their contributions to anatomy than for the works with which their names are customarily coupled. It was now possible to distribute books suitably furnished with pictorial matter, which banished futile disputes about the interpretation of texts.

Italian art made anatomy a live subject, as the cinema might be used to

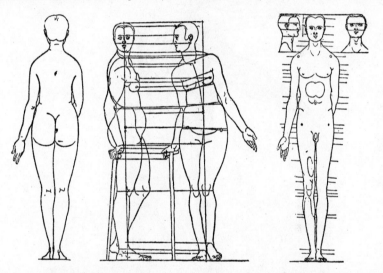

Fig. 403.—Wood-cuts by Dürer to Illustrate the "Canon of Proportion." Dürer, like His Contemporary Leonardo da Vinci, had Used Dissection as an Aid to the Naturalistic Portrayal of the Human Body. He was Equally Successful in the Accurate Representation of Plants

(Albrecht Dürer, *Menschlicher Proportion*, 1528)

make mathematics a live subject if every school were equipped with a projector. The great descriptive treatise which marks the maturity of the study of surgical, as opposed to physiological, anatomy is the *De Fabrica Humani Corporis* of Vesalius published in the same year (1543) as the *De Revolutionibus* of Copernicus and illustrated by a disciple of Titian. The many topographical errors of the Galenic texts were rectified, and a reliable map of the human body was now available for general use.

Between the anatomy of Vesalius and that of the present day there is all the difference between an accurate outline map with the several national areas distinguished and an atlas showing ocean currents, contours, rainfall, winds, exports and natural resources. With a few minor exceptions the bulk of any genuine information contained in the *De Fabrica* about the work which the several regions (organs) of the body do must have been available from the dawn of civilization. Even the elementary fact that muscular contraction involves change of shape without any change of volume of the muscle was

FIG. 404.—ONE OF THE DRAWINGS ILLUSTRATING THE HUMAN MUSCULAR SYSTEM FROM THE *FABRICA* OF VESALIUS

not demonstrated before the work of Swammerdam (Fig. 405) in the seventeenth century. This remained unpublished until 1736. The respiratory organs were simply the channel through which the *anima* escaped. Beyond the fact that the urine flowed from the kidneys into the bladder nothing was known about excretion of urine. The regions of the alimentary canal or gut had long since been named (Fig. 406), and the large digestive glands (salivary, liver and pancreas) were distinguished. With scarcely any chemical science to guide biology, the use of the digestive secretions was totally obscure.

As for the ductless glands about which so many important discoveries have been made in recent times, current beliefs were entirely fantastic. The name of the pituitary gland (p. 1073) is derived from Galen's doctrine that it secretes the phlegm which is in reality produced by the mucous membrane of the nasal tract. Even in the seventeenth century Descartes defended the doctrine that the soul (which had now been detached from the act of breathing) was located in the pineal gland.

The one respect in which Vesalius' knowledge of the *working* of the body

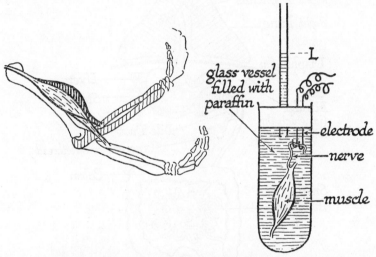

FIG. 405.—MUSCLE CONTRACTION

When movement of limbs is produced by the contraction of a muscle, change of shape is not accompanied by any appreciable swelling (i.e. volume change), as shown by the constant level of fluid (L) in an air-free vessel containing a freshly exercised muscle and attached nerve which can be stimulated by an electric current. In an analogous experiment first done by Swammerdam during the seventeenth century, a fine piece of silk pulled the nerve against a loop of wire to stimulate contraction.

was notably in advance of Galen is important, because his conclusions were based on actual experiments on the part which the nerves play in transmitting messages to the muscles. Recourse to experiment, having once begun, has continued to receive fresh impetus from a succession of new discoveries in the science of materials and of power production and from the elaboration of instruments which the older anatomy could not command.

THE CIRCULATION OF THE BLOOD

Systematic study of how the body works began with the most elementary problem suggested by surgical practice, i.e. *how bleeding occurs*. The discovery of the answer coincided with other advances, and discloses the impact of growing scientific interest in a purely physical problem (Chapter VII, p. 368). The recognition that the heart is a pump came when people began to regard the pump as a device of scientific interest.

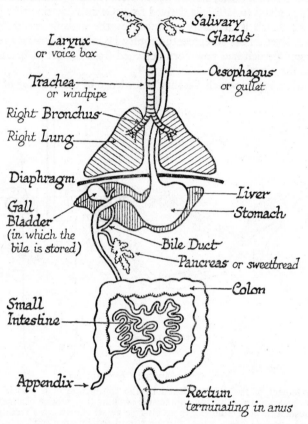

FIG. 406.—THE ALIMENTARY CANAL, ITS ASSOCIATED STRUCTURES, AND THE LUNGS IN MAN

In this, and all similar, figures the organs are seen in ventral view (i.e. from the front, in man), so that the organs of the right side appear on the left of the diagram and vice versa. As drawn, the liver is tucked under the stomach.

In the anatomy of Vesalius, as in that of his predecessors, the blood was supposed to ebb and flow forwards and backwards in the veins and arteries.*

* Galen had taught that the blood of the veins was made from the products of digestion in the liver. The liver was also entrusted with the task of charging it with *natural spirit*. Ebbing and flowing in the veins, it eventually reached the right side of the heart. Here, impurities were supposed to be carried off by the pulmonary artery to the lungs, and it then ebbed back again into the veins. But a small portion of it was held to pass through minute channels in the inter-ventricular septum into the left ventricle, where it mixed with air brought from the lungs by the pulmonary vein. *Vital spirit*, produced by this mixing of air and blood, was then distributed through

The microscope had not yet made it possible to see the blood flowing through the minute vessels called *capillaries* which penetrate all the tissues of the body. Though Vesalius, who dissected the terminal twigs of the branching arteries and the finest tributaries of the venous system, expressed the suspicion that they might be one continuous channel, no direct evidence for this conclusion could be obtained by dissection alone.

That the heart works as a pump, maintaining a continuous flow from the thick-walled arteries through the capillaries into the veins and thence back again, was suggested by a discovery which bears witness to the new temper of precise and patient observation following the decline of mere logic and the authority of the written word. Fabricius, a co-teacher with Galileo at Padua, when Harvey studied there, described the watch pocket valves of the veins (Fig. 246). These valves are constructed so as to prevent blood from flowing away from the heart. Similarly the valves which guard the orifices of the great arteries where they emerge from the heart prevent the blood from going back into it.

The heart of a warm-blooded vertebrate (mammal or bird) consists of four chambers, two thin-walled auricles receiving the main veins, and below them (Fig. 407) two thick-walled ventricles which give off the main arteries. The auricles are separated from the ventricles by valves which only let blood flow into the latter. The two sides of the heart are completely separated. The only communications are between the right auricle and right ventricle—both of which contain dark blood of a purple hue—and between the left auricle and left ventricle—both of which contain bright scarlet blood. Valves (Fig. 407) prevent the blood from flowing backwards from the ventricles into the auricles. The right ventricle only sends out the pulmonary arteries, which supply the lungs. The right auricle receives blood from the two large caval veins (venae cavae) into which smaller veins pour blood from all the organs of the body except the gut and the lungs. The left auricle receives blood from the lungs by the pulmonary veins, and the left ventricle gives off the great artery called the aorta, from which smaller arteries, like the carotid arteries of the neck, take blood to all parts of the body except the lungs.

By various classes of experiments including the exposure of the heart by cutting away the ribs and also the severance of vessels, Harvey obtained direct proof that the blood flows in a continuous circuit.* Direct inspection of the heart shows that the auricles contract, squeezing out blood into the dilated

---

the ebb and flow of blood in the arteries. Reaching the base of the brain, some of the vital spirit was elaborated into *animal spirit* and this was supposed to be distributed through the nerves, which were thought to be hollow.

Vesalius had doubts about the existence of pores in the inter-ventricular septum. Servetus and Realdus Columbus had demonstrated the one-way traffic in the pulmonary circulation. Harvey completed the picture by showing that what is true of the pulmonary circulation is true of the rest of the blood stream.

* One of Harvey's experiments is illustrated in Fig. 247 and is easy to repeat. It shows clearly the falsity of the Galenic doctrine that the blood ebbs and flows in the veins. The arm is bandaged tightly and the veins beneath the skin become distended, the valves appearing as swellings in the course of the veins. If now the blood is pressed along a vein from the valve O to the point H, this part of the vein does not refill from beyond the valve O. The valve prevents the flow of blood away from the heart. Nor can blood be pushed by the finger past a valve in a direction away from the heart.

ventricles, before the latter begin to contract squeezing out blood into the arteries. When an artery is cut, bleeding only occurs on the side connected with the heart. When a vein is cut, bleeding only occurs on the side away

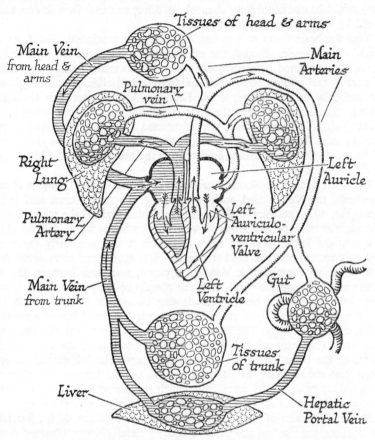

FIG. 407.—DIAGRAM OF MAIN PATHS IN THE HUMAN BLOOD SYSTEM

The smaller arteries connected with the smaller veins by the fine network of capillaries penetrating all the tissues are collectively represented by six spongy masses. Blood comes back from the head and arms, the trunk and legs and from the liver by two main veins which discharge into the thin-walled right auricle. When this contracts, the blood is forced into the right ventricle, till the latter, being filled, is closed by the right auriculo-ventricular valve. The contraction of the right ventricle forces the blood into the pulmonary artery from which it cannot flow back, because of the valves placed at its base. Replenished with oxygen in the lungs, the blood returns to the left auricle by the pulmonary vein. It is then discharged into the left ventricle, then by the main artery or aorta to the organs of the body other than the lungs. The blood from the gut or alimentary canal does not flow back directly to the main vein (post-caval or inferior vena cava) of the trunk. It is collected by a large vein, the hepatic portal, which branches like an artery, discharging its blood through the capillary bed of the liver (see p. 831), so that all the blood-carrying absorbed foodstuff from the intestine has to pass through the liver before it gets into the general circulation. If you have any difficulty in remembering the right and left orientation of the circulation the following mnemonic will help: LIFE-GIVING BLOOD LEAVES LUNGS FOR LEFT AURICLE. REDUCED BLOOD RECEIVED BY RIGHT AURICLE FROM REST OF BODY.

from the heart. Thus the circuit appears to be so arranged that all the blood flows from the right ventricle to the lungs where it becomes bright red, thence to the left auricle, into the left ventricle, and thence to the tissues of the body other than the lungs, returning finally into the right auricle by the smaller veins which coalesce to form the venae cavae. Harvey clinched the matter by a simple calculation. His study of the action of the heart and the arrangement of its valves showed him that the blood could only pass through the heart in one direction. If the left ventricle holds 2 oz. and beats 72 times a minute, it will pump to the body every hour 8,640 oz. of blood, or more than three times the weight of a man. Where, he asked, is all this blood to come from or go to? Clearly it must come in some way from the veins, the same blood circulating again and again.

In a different social context the mere recognition that the blood flows in a continuous circuit might have attracted far less attention. Indeed it is perhaps more remarkable that Harvey's doctrine emerged at such a late date in the history of European medicine. It appears to have been recognized by Chinese physicians at a very early date. It is alleged that the Chinese had even attempted to estimate the rate of flow of the blood. Tson-Tse in the sixth century B.C. is said to have taught that:

the blood flows continuously like the current of a river or the sun and moon in their orbits. It may be compared to a circle without beginning or end. The blood travels a distance of six inches in our respiration, making a complete circulation of the body fifty times a day.*

What is specially significant about Harvey's discovery is that it happened when people were interested in another class of problems which arose from the same social background as the mechanics of the pump. Harvey's discovery came when "the health and accidents of the miner" (pp. 404 and 410) were beginning to direct attention to ventilation and the physiological problems of respiration. Then again, it immediately preceded the introduction of the simple microscope and of a new agricultural economy in Britain. Direct observation of the missing link which is not accessible to inspection of the naked eye came fifty years after Harvey's work, when Malpighi and others used the microscope to reveal the *capillaries* or finest vessels. He saw blood flowing through them in one direction, as is easy to do if we put the web of the frog's foot under a low power magnification.

One inference from Harvey's experiments gave them ulterior importance in relation to new discoveries about the gaseous state. The blood loses its bright red colour in the minute vessels which thread the tissues of the body as a whole and regains it in the capillaries of the lungs which, as Malpighi's observations showed more clearly, are in close contact with the air sucked into the lungs by the act of breathing. In other words, the circulation is arranged so as to ensure that all the blood which goes to the tissues is scarlet and all the blood which goes to the lungs is purple. The work of Hooke and Mayow showed (p. 413) that an animal dies unless its lungs are ventilated

* This passage is cited by Drs. Benkov Kuan Chin Penn and Pei-Lung-tang (cf. *New York Nation*, January 11, 1933). The writer has not checked the source of the reference given.

with fresh air, that this air is as necessary to the activity of the body and the maintenance of the body heat as it is necessary to the continued burning of a candle. Like the latter the lungs replace "nitro-aerial particles" (i.e. oxygen) by fixed air. Thus the lungs are the organs in which the blood loses its purple colour and gives up carbon dioxide. They are also the organs where the blood gains its scarlet colour and takes up oxygen. Slare, a contemporary of Mayow, drew the obvious inference verified more conclusively by Priestley, who showed that scarlet blood shaken in a vacuum becomes purple and regains its original hue, after further shaking if air is readmitted.

So Harvey's work was immediately followed by a new understanding of the work the lungs do. Subsequent advances in the study of respiration emphasize the stimulus derived from enquiry into occupational diseases which excited no concern while medical care remained exclusively a luxury of the well-to-do. After the work of Priestley there was little progress towards further knowledge of the way in which the work of the heart is related to the work of the lungs until the latter end of the nineteenth century. Several facts of social life then conspired to stimulate interest in the nature of respiration. The building of submarine tunnels, like the London underground system, and the use of divers in constructing bridges and laying telegraph cables exposed workers to new risks. In addition the occupational dangers attendant to mining increased as deeper shafts were made.

Passages from Agricola's sixteenth-century treatise dealing with the safety and health of the miner have already given us (pp. 404 and 410) an important clue to the social background of such pioneer researches as those of Hooke and Mayow. The same issue re-emerged with increasing importance in the nineteenth century when Davy's invention of the safety lamp proved a successful safeguard against much avoidable loss of life. In its closing decade the seeds of a rationally planned economy based on real knowledge are beginning to germinate. The Government took a hand in promoting research into coalgas poisoning in British mines. With new analytical technique and instruments which were not available in Priestley's time, J. S. Haldane began researches which have taught us much about coal-gas poisoning and how to prevent it, and have also thrown light on the disorder called *anaemia*. Let us now look briefly at some of these more modern discoveries in the trail which Harvey blazed.

THE RESPIRATORY FUNCTION OF THE BLOOD

The continuous supply of oxygen to the tissues by the pumping action of the heart depends on the fact that the blood of most active large animals contains a "respiratory pigment." In the blood of vertebrates (mammals, birds, reptiles, amphibia and fishes) and in that of many worms the respiratory pigment is the purple-red *haemoglobin* which assumes a bright scarlet hue when combined with oxygen (oxyhaemoglobin). That of many crustacea (lobsters and crabs) and many molluscs (snails, cuttlefish) contains *haemocyanin* which is deep blue when exposed to air and completely colourless when shaken in a vacuum to remove the oxygen.

Both pigments are proteins which contain, in addition to the customary elements present in other proteins, a metal, iron (haemoglobin) or copper (haemocyanin). Their power of combining loosely with oxygen makes them able to give up oxygen in the capillaries, where the dissolved oxygen is scarce, owing to the fact that the tissues are using it up. Their presence in the blood enormously increases the amount of oxygen it can carry. Thus 100 c.c. of human blood at room temperature take up 18 c.c. of oxygen from air at atmospheric pressure. But for the presence of haemoglobin it would not take up more than ordinary water with the same salts as those dissolved in blood, i.e. about three-quarters of a cubic centimetre of oxygen.

Coal-gas poisoning (cf. p. 170) depends on the fact that carbon monoxide combines much more readily with haemoglobin than does oxygen. So a very small quantity of carbon monoxide will drive out oxygen from the blood of red-blooded animals, forming carboxyhaemoglobin which is recognized by its spectrum and bright pinkish hue. The pink flush which the skin exhibits when a person is poisoned with coal gas depends on the fact that the reduced haemoglobin of the blood in the capillaries is more or less completely replaced by carboxyhaemoglobin. The complexity of the protein fraction united to an iron compound in the molecule of haemoglobin is different in different species, and the haemoglobins of different species are not precisely identical. Some have much greater affinity for carbon monoxide than others. Some combine with oxygen more readily than others. Hence some species are much more susceptible to coal-gas poisoning or much more sensitive to oxygen deficiency than others.

The ease with which carbon monoxide combines with haemoglobin is shown by the fact that blood is fully saturated (about 16 c.c. of CO per 100 c.c. of blood), if shaken up with a mixture of 0·5 per cent of the gas and 99·5 per cent nitrogen. It takes at least 15 per cent of oxygen (mixed with 85 per cent nitrogen) to convert all the haemoglobin into oxyhaemoglobin. Air normally contains 21 per cent oxygen. If as little as 1 part in 3,000 of carbon monoxide is present about 30 per cent of the haemoglobin in the blood of a person who breathes it is converted into carboxyhaemoglobin. Beyond this point dizziness supervenes. If the air contains 1 part in 250 of carbon monoxide more than 75 per cent of the haemoglobin is put out of action, and death then results. In a well-ventilated room an ordinary gas leak would not raise the percentage of carbon monoxide above this level, and would rarely be fatal. The appropriate treatment is a simple application of the known facts about the chemical behaviour of haemoglobin. Since coal-gas poisoning in mines (or carbon monoxide poisoning in garages) is due to the fact that a very small quantity of carbon monoxide can compete successfully with the normal concentration of oxygen, the thing to do is to increase the proportion of oxygen taken in, by making the patient breathe pure oxygen, which gradually displaces the carbon monoxide from combination with haemoglobin.

Another occupational condition which depends on the gas-carrying capacity of the blood is *Caisson* disease. This is of importance in connexion with diving, submarine work and making deep tunnels. It can be produced experimentally by putting animals in a chamber under high atmospheric pressure. If the pressure is suddenly released the result is the same as releasing the trigger of a soda-water siphon. The extra gas (nitrogen and oxygen) dissolved in the blood under the extra pressure comes out of solution as bubbles. Frothing in the arteries results in numbness of the limbs. If they collect in the heart, the bubbles may stop the circulation with fatal results. The victim, if still alive, can be cured by raising the atmospheric pressure till the gases are redissolved. If the pressure is then very slowly lowered to the normal level the excess of gases escapes from the lungs without forming bubbles. In using the "diving bell" it is therefore important to lower the pressure very slowly when coming to the surface.

While progress in the study of respiration has been largely due to the impetus derived from the study of occupational diseases, advancing knowledge about other aspects of the circulation illustrates the debt of medicine to the mechanical sciences and to new physical apparatus which they have made available for general use. The pumping mechanism of the circulation ensures a supply of food as well as of oxygen to all parts of the body. The need for oxygen, unlike the need for food, is continuous. This is shown by the fact that it takes very little time to die of suffocation and a very long while to die of starvation. Hibernating animals, like the dormouse or bats, may go for months without food. Hence carrying oxygen to the tissues is much the most important thing about the work the heart does.

This is illustrated in a striking way by the fact that the heart of insects, though built on the same plan as that of their nearest allies, shrimps, crabs, spiders, scorpions, etc., is extremely degenerate, and generally useless. The reason why insects can get along quite well without a functional circulation is that a series of pores on either side of the body lead into a branching system of fine tubes with spiral thickenings, first described by one of the earliest microscopists, Malpighi. These tubes, called *tracheae* (Fig. 459B), penetrate to the innermost tissues, so that oxygen can diffuse into the deepest regions of the body without the intervention of a blood stream. Apparently the diffusion of foodstuffs through the fluids in the cavities which penetrate the tissues meets all the working requirements of the animal.

The food requirements of the animal body will be discussed later. The blood is important in other respects. It carries the chemical telegrams of the body called hormones (Chapter XXIII). It is also concerned with resistance to disease and with heat regulation in warm-blooded animals. The problem of heat regulation has been the subject of research, ever since Harvey's work, which coincided with the invention of the thermometer. From time immemorial excessive warmth of the skin has been recognized as a general characteristic of fever, or as we should now say diseases due to microorganisms. The clinical use of the thermometer made it possible to diagnose the onset of fever by a more delicate test.

THE BLOOD FLOW

The way in which the body temperature of a mammal such as the human species is maintained at fairly constant temperature (about 98° F. or 37° C. in a healthy adult human being) depends on the fact that the arteries and veins have a muscular coat by which the width of the channel can be increased or diminished. The finest vessels or capillaries, which form a network in the tissues connecting the terminal branches of the arteries with the finest tributaries of the veins, are also contractile. As explained on p. 605, the drop of pressure between the large arteries and the veins depends on the bore of the finest vessels (arterioles and capillaries). This was one of the discoveries made when scientific interest in the pump was directing enquiry into the characteristics of fluid pressure and flow.

Stephen Hales, the English physician, whose work on coal gas has been mentioned (p. 418), made the first pressure-gauge measurements on arteries and veins in the early years of the eighteenth century. The study of pressure variations did not progress till the compound microscope revealed the muscle fibres of the finer arteries. If a pressure gauge is connected with a cut artery, the end of which is clipped while the connexion is made, a high pressure will in general signify that the finer blood vessels are constricted, and a low blood pressure will in general signify that they are dilated. Since a fluid communicates pressure in all directions, the blood pressure of a human being can be taken, as is often done at a medical overhaul, by finding the increase of atmospheric pressure necessary to squeeze the large vessels flat so that no pulse is felt (Fig. 408A). An unusually high blood pressure is a premonitory sign of apoplexy.

The amount of blood flowing through an organ varies. How it varies can be studied by recording carefully the blood pressure, the heart rate and the total volume of the organ under various conditions. The volume of an organ can be recorded by closing it with a rubber bag and noting the air pressure in the bag (Fig. 408B). To some extent the blood flowing through an organ is adjusted to the oxygen requirements of the moment. Other things being equal, the rate at which a tissue can take up oxygen depends upon the amount of blood which flows through it in unit time. Now the flow of a liquid through a tube of uniform bore depends upon the force propelling it, the length traversed and the sectional area of the tube. Only the first and the last of these need be considered in connexion with the circulation since the length of tube traversed is approximately constant in the blood vessels. As the activity of the heart is an intermittent quantity, the average force of the heart-beat depends partly on the frequency of the beat, or pulse rate, and partly on the amplitude or strength of the individual beats. Heart muscle reacts to stretching by increased frequency and amplitude of beat, so that any increase in the resistance of the finer blood vessels calls forth more powerful action on the part of the pumping organ.

The heart beat is also regulated by two sets of nerves, branches of the sympathetic system (p. 1056) and of the vagus respectively. The former discharge impulses tending to augment and the latter to inhibit the heart beat. The increased pulse rate following excitement or excessive exercise is due to the action of the former. The variations of heart rhythm that are thus possible affect only the circulation as a whole. Changes in the blood supply of single organs are possible on account of the fact that both the arteries and the veins, like the intestine, have walls with a double coat of plain muscle, one coat with the fibres arranged circlewise and one with the fibres arranged lengthwise.

The extent of contraction of these muscle fibres is under nervous control, and any change in the extent of contraction of the muscular walls of the blood vessels means that the diameter of their bore is increased or diminished.

The capillaries have no muscle fibres in their walls, which are formed of a single layer of cells. The latter possess a measure of contractility. Blushing results from dilation of the smaller arteries and capillaries of the skin of the face, and the flushing of the skin after vigorous exercise gets rid of the surplus

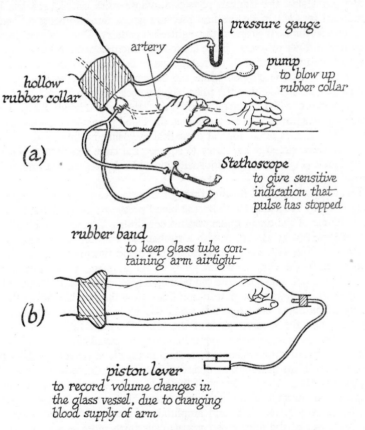

FIG. 408.—(a) MEASURING THE ARTERIAL BLOOD PRESSURE IN MAN
(b) MEASURING THE VOLUME CHANGES OF A LIMB

heat produced. Loss of heat from the surface of the body, when exposed to cold, is reduced by constriction of the blood vessels of the skin, hence the whitening of the surface after bathing in very cold water. Sometimes the capillaries remain dilated while the smaller arteries are almost completely closed up. When this occurs, stagnant pools of blood occur in the capillary network and as their oxygen is used up the blood itself becomes completely reduced. This is what happens when the tips of the fingers become blue on a cold day.

The blood of most animals is never warmer than the atmosphere, and they cannot withstand either great cold or warmth at which birds and mammals can easily live. Our blood is kept at a constant temperature (about 37° C.) in ordinary circumstances. When we are exposed to a warmer temperature or produce excessive heat by muscular activity, secretion of sweat takes place. The evaporation of sweat from the surface of the body absorbs heat, and so keeps the surface cool. Shivering is also a means of regulating body heat. We have lately learned more than we used to know about it owing to promotion of low-temperature research in connexion with cold-storage problems. The skin has nerve endings which are sensitive to extreme cold. When the surface temperature is lowered unduly, they transmit messages which produce muscular twitching. Early in the history of the animal machine Lavoisier's experiments showed (p. 600) that muscles produce more heat when active. So the effect of shivering is to raise the body temperature, and hence compensate the loss of heat at the surface.

THE MARRIAGE OF SURGERY AND HUSBANDRY

The experimental method on which Harvey's researches were based began a new tradition, which was carried on by leaders of the surgical profession like John Hunter during the seventeenth and eighteenth centuries. Gradually the work done by the principal organs of the body began to be understood, and a new horizon of curative treatment unfolded. Guided by a body of theoretical knowledge based on experimental evidence, surgical practice was learning what organs are essential to the maintenance of life, in what circumstances their work could be performed by other organs or by mechanical aids, and what effects their removal would exercise on the general health of the patient. One thing which distinguishes modern surgery from the practice of antiquity is that the modern surgeon can recognize with greater confidence whether harmful results will ensue after removal of a diseased organ which might otherwise infect the whole body, leading to death or chronic illness.

The story of how this knowledge grew will emerge in subsequent chapters. The tempo of progress since Harvey's time depends on the coincidence of many influences. Growing knowledge of chemistry, heat and electricity in relation to social needs and social circumstances which have been discussed in earlier chapters supplied new clues, and the continual invention of new instruments which emerged as a by-product of advancing knowledge in man's conquest of materials and of power again and again put powerful instruments of research in the hands of the medical profession. Meanwhile other aspects of man's social life brought pressure to bear on the search for deeper insight into the behaviour of living matter.

Mere pressure of population in northern Europe was a feature common to the extension of mining and agriculture. The exhaustion of fuel supplies gave a decisive impetus to coal production. Exhaustion of available space for extensive farming of the type which had largely supplanted the more orderly intensive practice of the later Roman Empire may have contributed to the swift improvements in which English agriculturists played a leading part. The seventeenth and eighteenth centuries witnessed a host of innovations

—drainage, winter storage of roots, crop rotation, tillage, manuring, drill sowing, and improvement of domesticated cattle. How Britain assured her independence in a hostile world has been expressed in the epigram that the Battle of Waterloo was won on the turnip fields of England. The expansion of population which accompanied what is usually called the Industrial Revolution and the subsequent beginnings of modern biotechnology were made possible by these improvements.

It is a profound error to dismiss this change as mere empiricism, because, as yet, no embracing biological generalizations had entered into the practice of farming. In the same sense we might say that there was no science of medicine before Pasteur, or before Sherrington, or before Hopkins. What was essentially new in the situation was that there existed close contact between leaders of science and the promoters of the new practice. In an article on the subject, Marshall (*Econ. Hist. Rev.*, Vol. II, 1929) puts the issue very clearly. Referring to the "astonishing intellectual vitality of the century and a half following the Restoration," he writes:

This vitality appears to have been manifested in two bursts round 1660 and 1760 with something of a lapse in between. It was in the highest degree inventive and practical, and reveals a close alliance between pure science and technical economic progress. This was not a dark age starred by two or three prophets of whom it was unworthy. In so far as it was in our particular sphere unresponsive, it had excuse. The picture of the farmer obstinately shutting his ears to the unanimous voice of the experts is false. The experts differed, and wrestled over their differences. . . .

Though two centuries elapsed before advancing knowledge could dispel many of the differences, the practice of agriculture was now ceasing to be regulated by oral tradition alone. It was acquiring a literature, and a literature —unlike the Georgics—with its own language, its own method and that live inquisitiveness which is the offspring of acquisitiveness in the best sense of the word. It was also shaking off painfully the Aristotelian tradition, as chemistry and astronomy had done.

What the monastery physic garden began, the learned academies which followed the growth of an organized secular profession of medicine completed. In England the emergence of the Invisible College (see p. 556) happened when capitalist farming was seeking to exploit new practices. Husbandry no less than navigation and mining was infected with what Clark has called the "adventurous hopefulness" of the times. In 1665 the English Royal Society issued the prolegomena of a scientifically planned economy of food production. Twenty-six "Heads of Enquiries" were printed that they might be "the more universally known" and that persons skilful in husbandry might be "publickly invited to impart their knowledge herein for the common benefit of the country." The topics included "the several kinds of the soyls of England" (sandy, gravelly, stony, clayie, chalky, light mould, heathy, marish, boggy, fenny and cold weeping ground), when each was "employed for arable"; "what peculiar preparations are made use of to these soyls for each kind of grain, with what kind of manure they are prepared; when, how and in what quantity the manure is laid on";

"what kinds of ploughs are used"; "the kinds of grain or seed usual in England"; "how each of these is prepared for sowing," "there being many sorts of wheat . . . and so of oats . . . which of these grow in your county and in what soyl, and which of them thrive best there . . ."; "how they differ in goodness"; "what kinds of grain are most proper to succeed there"; "some of the common accidents and diseases befalling corn in the growth of it, being blasting, mildew, smut; what are conceived to be the causes thereof and what the remedies"; "annoyances the growing corn is subjected to, as weeds, worms, flies, birds, mice, moles, etc., how they are remedied"; "waies of preserving the several sorts of grain"; "how the above mentioned sorts of soyl are prepared when they are used for Pasture or Meadow"; "the common annoyance of these pasture and meadow grounds."

Such are samples of the questions. The replies to them were placed after discussion in the archives of the Society. They have been lately rescued by Lennard, who analyses them in an article in the *Economic History Review* (vol. IV, 1932). Here deliberately and systematically organized science takes stock of the common experience of mankind to formulate problems for which precise solutions are now available. Truly "a brave attempt to link up book learning and scientific research with the experience of practical farmers," as Lennard says. We may go farther and say that it is the first vision of a rationally planned ecology of mankind.

In an essay ostensibly composed to divulge the "Nature and Significance of Economic Science" Professor Robbins justifies his scorn for economists who pursue realistic studies in preference to the so-called analytical method by asserting that they have not as yet produced a single comprehensive generalization. The eighteenth century is littered with the wreckage of comprehensive generalizations with which the protagonists of the phlogiston doctrine, preformationism, vulcanism and a host of minor exploits in elegant deduction from self-evident principles obstructed the steady and piecemeal advance toward the solution of problems clearly conceived by the founders of British empiricism in their relation to vital social needs. If the study of human society ever comes to occupy the prestige and to enjoy the confidence which the natural sciences have rightly established, it also must start with heads of enquiries rooted in the common experience of practical affairs, proceeding by patient examination of innumerable facts in the assurance of Francis Bacon that "the roads to human power and to human knowledge lie close together, and are nearly the same, nevertheless on account of the pernicious and inveterate habit of dwelling on abstractions it is safer to begin and raise the sciences from those foundations which have relation to practice and let the active part be as the seal which prints and determines the contemplative counterpart."

CHAPTER XVIII

REPLENISHING THE EARTH

THE social background of biological knowledge presents a far more intricate problem than that of astronomy, chemistry, or the various branches of experimental physics. Conspicuous contributions of organized biological knowledge to man's social life are of comparatively recent date. Its most signal achievements are hardly more than a quarter of a century old. If we plan the application of resources which are now emerging, they may well seem to be trifling compared with developments which are now taking place, especially in the realm of agriculture. After the first outburst of primitive biotechnology which arose to meet the needs of a localized self-sufficient economy, no important advances occurred. From about 2000 B.C. till the middle of the sixteenth century of our own era, agriculture remained untouched by the growth of theoretical knowledge.

Medicine ranks with astronomy as the oldest learned profession, and it has perhaps a more continuous history as such. In two ways this fact has affected the comparatively steady growth of biological knowledge in the absence of any other social requirement which biological enquiry of one kind or another has gratified. Some departments of biological knowledge which seem to be totally unrelated to medicine, as we know it today, were originally part of the training of a medical man, and were pursued with painstaking care sustained by hopes which proved to be illusory in the long run. Thus the study of botany was encouraged by exaggerated, and sometimes fantastic, beliefs about the curative powers of herbs. If in one sense botany led the physician up the garden, it is also true that the trail was not abandoned till knowledge of plant physiology and breeding had already shown promise of yielding results of equal importance to the horticulturist and to the farmer. Organizations for promoting scientific horticulture and scientific agriculture were already in being before pure chemicals banished herbs from the pharmacopoeia.

The existence of medicine as an independent social institution also guaranteed the presence of a body of men ready to exploit whatever relevant knowledge emerged from a new impetus to discovery in other fields. If a Hooke or Black appeared in the domain of physics or chemistry, there was always a Mayow or a Crawford on the spot. Aside from the indirect impact of new social needs through the influence of theoretical discoveries which have arisen as a by-product, the medical profession has continually benefited from the invention of fresh instruments of practice and thereby of research. Today the maker of scientific instruments keeps a watchful eye on the physician as a market for his wares. It would probably be true to say that this is no new thing, though the rapidity with which seventeenth-century medicine found a clinical use for new instruments like the thermometer was chiefly due to the close contact of the medical colleges with the newer scientific academies of Italy, England, and France.

Both the practice of medicine and new theoretical knowledge have continually benefited in this way. In the past few decades it is sufficient to recall the introduction of X-ray diagnosis into surgery or the new insight into sensory phenomena through the use of the amplifying valve. Between Harvey's treatise and the middle of the nineteenth century, improvements in the construction of a single instrument provided the *means* which contributed to outstanding biological progress. Clear and definite information concerning the nature of reproduction in animals and plants, the discovery of micro-organisms, and a close-up view of the material basis of inheritance were discoveries which paved the way for almost every subsequent and contemporaneous advance of biological knowledge. All three were the direct result of the construction of the microscope.

The story of an advance which was so spectacular in its first stages records delays due to the imperfections of the earliest instruments. The original invention was a side-line of the spectacle industry, doubtless fostered by the utility of the telescope in navigation and its sister science astronomy. A second outburst of biological discoveries followed the production of high-power magnification in the first few decades of the nineteenth century. It is not an accident that the first successful observations on the annual parallax of a fixed star, the announcement of the Doppler principle and rapid progress in the study of optical interference took place in the same decade (1830–1840) as a plethora of new biological discoveries, which include the cell doctrine, the penetration of the pollen tube into the ovule and the recognition of the mammalian ovum. Improvement in the design of microscope and telescope have gone hand in hand, and biological research has benefited from the social demand for the latter.

The invention of the compound microscope at the beginning of the seventeenth century and its equipment with achromatic lenses early in the nineteenth century respectively coincided with new phases in man's conquest of the soil. During the seventeenth century an agricultural innovation which had very profound consequences was spreading from the Low Countries into England. There the first fruits of the new microscopical knowledge were attracting the keenest attention in the newly founded Royal Society, which published communications from some of the most distinguished of the continental microscopists, notably the Dutch merchant van Leeuwenhoek. With reference to the origins of crop rotation, Gras (*History of Agriculture*, p. 182) writes:

The history of such a system is hard to write. Here and there the scientific rotation has come to the front, as the culmination of experiment, trial and error, the experience of cultivators, and the research and theorizing of agricultural students and writers. It arose in ancient China on large estates, perhaps in medieval Lombardy and Tuscany, in parts of Spain, northern France, and Switzerland, in the Rhineland, and notably in Flanders since the fifteenth or sixteenth century. Not far from towns and in districts with a dense population, the scientific rotation, or something like it, first developed. The scientific rotation system that has meant most for the modern world, the model for western Europe and America, was developed in England. Just as the Romans borrowed much agricultural lore from the Carthaginians, and the Spaniards from the Moors, so did the English get from the Flemings the two new essential ingredients of their scientific rotation, clover and turnips. The best known variety of the scientific rotation, and also probably the oldest in England, is the Norfolk rotation of clover, wheat, turnips and barley, developed in the eastern county of Norfolk and at the end of the eighteenth century, made famous in Europe and America by Arthur Young. Like many good things, it was over-done. Found applicable in Norfolk, it was introduced into many other counties where, as William Marshall and Sir James Caird pointed out, some other rotation would have been better. It was the task of the eighteenth century to popularize it, and of the nineteenth century to adapt it to local conditions. In the county of Norfolk, however, it is still the dominant type, though not unchallenged.

Concerning the introduction of the system into England, Ernle (*English Farming Past and Present*) regards the influence of Sir Richard Weston as specially noteworthy. He states (p. 107):

The important change with which Weston's name will always be associated is the introduction of a new rotation of crops, founded on the field cultivation of roots and clover. As Brillat-Savarin valued a new dish above a new star, so Arthur Young regards Weston as "a greater benefactor than Newton." He did indeed offer bread and meat to millions. Whether Weston had visited Flanders before 1644 is uncertain. His attempts to make the Wey navigable by means of locks suggests that he was acquainted with the foreign system of canals. On the other hand, his treatise on agriculture implies that he paid his first visit to the country in that year as a refugee. A Royalist and a Catholic, Weston, at the outbreak of the Civil War, was driven into exile, and his estates were sequestrated. He took refuge in Flanders. There he studied the Flemish methods of agriculture, especially their use of flax, clover and turnips. For the field cultivation of clover he advises that heathy ground should be pared, burned, limed, and well ploughed and harrowed; that the seed should be sown in April, or the end of March, at the rate of ten pounds of seed to the acre; that, once sown, the crop should be left for five years. The results of his observations, embodied in his *Discours of the Husbandrie used in Brabant and Flanders*, were written in 1645 and left to his sons as a "*Legacie*." The subsequent history of the "Legacie" is curious. Circulated in manuscript, an imperfect copy fell into the hands of Samuel Hartlib, who piratically published it in 1650, with an unctuous dedication "to the Right Honourable the Council of State." In the following year Hartlib seems to have learned the name of the author and to have obtained possession of a more perfect copy. He therefore wrote two letters to Weston, asking him to correct and enlarge his "Discourse." Receiving no answer, he republished the treatise in 1651. Eighteen years later, the *Discours* was again appropriated—this time by Gabriel Reeve, who, in 1670, reprinted it under the title of *Directions left by a Gentleman to his Sons for the Improvement of Barren and Heathy Land in England and Wales*. Roots, clover, and artificial grasses subsequently revolutionized English farming; but it was more than a century before their use became at all general.

Not less important as a facet of the social background of growing interest in the problem of reproduction is the rise of commercial horticulture in England. In Holland the bulb industry which began with the tulip cult in the sixteenth century was already a powerful enterprise in the opening years of the seventeenth. Meanwhile the practice of gardening had undergone considerable changes during the Elizabethan period. Amherst (*A History of Gardening in England*) writes:

. . . In the Middle Ages, what we should now call the kitchen garden, was in most cases the only one attached to a house. The idea of a garden, solely for beauty and pleasure, was quite a secondary consideration. In early cookery books, various recipes for serving up vegetables are given, though only a few of these dishes are vegetables cooked alone. But the wealthy, who could afford to get all the ingredients of these many recipes, had so much meat, and such an immense variety of game, cranes, herons, curlews, and other birds, besides those still in use, that they did not care for vegetables served separately, in any quantities, except on fast days. Gardens had chiefly to supply herbs for stuffing and flavouring, and these were freely used. For example, the first recipe in one book is for cooking a "hare in Wortes." . . . There was both a good variety and a fair supply of fruit in the fourteenth and fifteenth centuries. Several new kinds of apple and pear are mentioned by the poets of the day, and must have been well known. Lydgate speaks of the Pomewater, Ricardon, Blaundrelle, and Wueening apples. Gower of another kind, the Bitter-sweet. . . . Cherries and strawberries were hawked in the streets of London, and the cry of "Ripe strawberries" was familiar even in Lydgate's time. . . . Plums are not often mentioned, either by the poets, or in old accounts, but we know that both damsons and bullaces were grown in this country, though probably in no great quantities. . . . In an old recipe for a pudding called "mon amy," the cook is directed to "plant it with flowers of violets, and serve it forth." In another MS. a recipe for a dish called "vyolette" is given. "Take flowrys of vyolet boyle hem, presse hem bray hem smal." This is to be mixed with milk, "floure of rys," sugar or honey, and "coloured" with violets. Not only were violets cooked, but hawthorn, primroses, and even roses, shared the same fate, and were treated in the same way. One recipe, called "rede rose," is simply, "Take the same saue a-lye it with the yolkys of eyroun and forther-more as vyolet." The rose hips were also used, and in a dainty dish called "saue saracen," "hippes" were the chief ingredient. . . . It was only the large landowners who indulged in a garden specially set apart for flowers and pleasure. The garden of every small manor and farm-house in the kingdom was essentially for use. . . . The reign of Elizabeth was a golden era in English history, and abounded in men of genius. Among the many branches of art, science and industry, to which they turned their attention, none profited more from the power of their great minds, than did the Art of Gardening. Bacon's Essay on Gardens is familiar to everyone. Lord Burghley was the patron of Gerard, one of the greatest of English herbalists, and to Sir Walter Raleigh we owe the introduction of our most useful vegetable, the potato. About this time the persecution of the Protestants on the Continent drove many of them to find a safe refuge in England. They brought with them some of the foreign ideas about gardening, and thus helped to improve the condition of Horticulture. The Elizabethan garden was the outcome of the older fashions in English gardens, combined with the new ideas imported from France, Italy, and Holland. The result was a purely national style, better suited to this country than a slavish imitation of the terraced gardens of Italy, or of those of Holland, with their canals, and fish-ponds. There was no breaking away from old forms and customs, no sudden change. The primitive medieval garden grew into the pleasure garden of the early Tudors, which, by a process of slow and gradual development, eventually became the more elaborate garden of the Elizabethan era. . . . The changes in the kitchen, or "cooks-garden," were not so marked as in the "garden of pleasant flowers."

As the flower-garden lay in front of the house, "in sight and full prospect of all the chief and choicest roomes of the house; so contrariwise, your herbe garden should be on the one or other side of the house . . . for the many different sents that arise from the herbes, as cabbages, onions, etc., are scarce well pleasing to perfume the lodgings of any house." This is certainly a change from the gardens of earlier times, when herbs covered more or less the whole area of the average garden, when groundsel was allowed a place with leeks, thyme, and lettuce, and was classed among garden herbs indiscriminately with periwinkles, roses, and violets. . . . A striking proof of the progress gardening was making during this period, was the growing importance of those practising the craft in and around London, until at length, in the third year of King James I, they attained the dignified position of a Company of the City of London, incorporated by Royal charter. In that year all those "persons inhabiting within the Cittie of London and six miles compas therof doe take upon them to use and practice the trade, crafte or misterie of gardening, planting, grafting, setting, sowing, cutting, arboring, knocking, mounting, covering, fencing, and removing of plantes, herbes, seedes, fruit trees, stock sett, and of contryving the conveyances to the same belonging, were incorporated by the name of Master Wardens, Assistants, and Comynaltie of the Companie of Gardiners of London." Thomas Young was appointed first Master, and seven years was the term of apprenticeship to the Company.

The publisher of the *Legacie* was prominent in this movement. Gothein (*A History of Garden Art*, vol. II) says that during the Protectorate:

> . . . kitchen and fruit-gardens were actively encouraged in these years. A certain Hartlib, a Pole by birth, earned a pension of £100 from Cromwell in recognition of the work he had done for the furtherance of agriculture, and especially because he had encouraged gardeners in trade enterprise on a large scale, which was extremely rare, except quite near London.

In the Restoration period John Evelyn communicated a treatise on forest trees to the Royal Society with a view to encouraging the introduction of new trees. In a letter written to Pepys in 1686 he draws up a list of trees to be brought over from the New World. "Evelyn," says Amherst,

> himself tried to procure new seeds and plants from abroad, and also to make those trees he advocated in his *Silva* more plentiful; for many of them such as the Plane and Horse-chestnut were still uncommon in this country, and others, the Larch, Tulip tree and Cedar among the number were scarcely obtainable

The rotation of crops raised a new technological problem. In field production of corn the seed used for propagation of the ensuing crop was part of the harvest. Field production of clover, turnips, and grasses in the four-course system made the culture of plants for seed production a separate operation. Writing in the latter half of the sixteenth century, Googe, who was one of the earliest to advocate root crops, describes pasture sowing by scattering hayseed gathered from the debris of the hayloft. It is clear that in his time seed production for pasture was not as yet commercialized. In the Charter of the Worshipful Company of Gardeners at the beginning of the reign of

James I in England there is reference to regulation and mention of penalties for sale of "bad seeds." In Blith's *English Improver Improved*, published in 1652, it is stated:

Such as are desirous to buy any of the three-leaved grass or lucerne, spurry, clover grass . . . can have them at Thomas Brown's shop at the Red Lyon in Soper Lane.

In conformity with Boyle's concern that "the goods of mankind may be much increased by the naturalist's insight into the trades," the English Royal Society had constituted itself as a Planning Commission collecting "histories of Nature and Arts." About the time when it issued Hooke's programme of systematic and co-operative meteorological research, it also issued "Heads of Enquiries" for agriculture. These, published in the fifth issue of its *Philosophical Transactions*, included such items as:

The kinds of grain or seed usual in England, being supposed to be either wheat, miscelane, rye, oats, pease, beans, fitches, buckwheat, hemp, flax, rape. We desire to know what kinds of grain are sown in your county and how each of these is prepared for sowing. . . .

The first large commercial nursery was founded in 1681. Two years later the practice of drill sowing was introduced into England. By 1750 seed catalogues were already issued. These early nurserymen and seed merchants were botanists as much as salesmen. William Malcolm in his catalogue of seventy-one pages issued in 1776 discusses the nomenclature of plants, and refers to the system of Linnaeus as the best. In Malcolm's catalogue seventeen distinct varieties of peas are offered. Earlier—in 1731—Philip Miller, in the first edition of the *Gardener's Dictionary*, had recorded experiments repeating Bradley's (vide infra) sterilization of tulips by removing the anthers, and also showing that spinach, which, like dog's mercury, bears staminate and pistillate flowers on separate plants, will not produce fertile seeds when the plants are grown apart. Malcolm himself was Governor of the Apothecaries' Company and worked at Chelsea Physic Gardens. Of his *Gardener's and Florist's Dictionary* or *Complete System of Horticulture* Linnaeus said "non erit lexicon hortulanorum sed botanicorum."

While the use of the compound microscope was broadening the Aristotelian conception of sexuality and extending it to the interpretation of seed production in flowering plants, commercial seed production in agriculture was a new technological achievement. In the two decades which preceded and followed the introduction of more powerful compound microscopes (about 1820), horticultural seed production had become the focus of a lively interest in production of new varieties of hybridization (see Chapter XXII). During the intervening period the study of reproductive phenomena in plants received a continued impetus from the practical applications of the new knowledge, an example of which is furnished by the work of Thomas Knight, a president of the newly formed British Horticultural Society, on cross-pollination of apples.

Owing to the recent and deplorable separation of animal and plant biology in the curricula of many universities, it is easy to forget the close inter-relationship of botanical and zoological studies at this time. How intimately progress of enquiry into reproductive phenomena of plants was connected with new knowledge of animal breeding, and *vice versa*, is well illustrated by the opening words with which Knight introduces a paper which he read to the Royal Society in 1809:

> I have been engaged during many years in experiments on fruit trees of which the object has been to discover the best means of forming new varieties, that may be found better calculated for the climate of Britain than those at present cultivated. In this inquiry my efforts have been always most successful, when I propagated from the males of one variety and the females of another; and I was able by the same means to ascertain more accurately the comparative influence of the male and female parents on the character of the offspring. The analogy that subsists between plants and animals in almost everything which respects generation induced me also to attend very minutely to similar experiments in which I engaged on some species of animals. . . .

The introduction of root crops applied a new incentive to sheep and cattle breeding. With adequate winter feeding it was now possible to standardize the environment. An adequate environment made it possible to set up more rigorous standards of hereditary equipment. In England between 1750 and 1790 Bakewell, a practical farmer who practised intensive selective inbreeding for flesh quality and size of cattle, also established the New Leicester breed of sheep. His success became notorious. Continental dukes and Russian princes visited his farm, and "breeders everywhere," says Prothero, "followed his example." This development owed nothing directly to the advance of biological knowledge. The practice and theory of animal and plant breeding reacted successively one to the other. Although it is not possible to trace any direct influence of stock breeding on the scientific study of animal reproduction in its early stages, there is no doubt that the empirical improvement of sheep and cattle in the eighteenth century, associated especially with the name of Bakewell in England, fortified the belief that the same methods might "produce such rare kinds of plants as have not yet been heard of." Knight says in one of his papers:

> I cannot dismiss the subject without expressing my regret that those who have made the science of botany their subject should have considered the improvement of those vegetables which in their cultivated state afford the largest portion of subsistence to mankind and other animals as little connected with the subject of their pursuit. . . . While much attention has been paid to the improvement of every species of useful animals the most valuable esculent plants have been wholly neglected. . . . The improvement of animals is attained with much expense and the improved kinds necessarily extend themselves slowly, but a single bushel of improved wheat or peas may in ten years be made to afford seed enough to supply the whole island.

SPONTANEOUS GENERATION

The first compound microscopes, which provided a free pass into a totally unexplored universe during the mid decades of the seventeenth century,

(1640–1690) belong to the period which also witnessed Römer's discovery of the finite speed of light, the publication of the first maps showing the moon's mountains and the study of the spectrum. The discoveries which they made possible were destined to pave the way for great developments in biotechnology, when the invention of achromatic lenses provided the means for penetrating still further into the domain of things invisible to the naked eye. Of the four major branches of modern biotechnology three which rest entirely on a foundation of these early discoveries are scientific breeding, the control of infectious or contagious diseases, and the domestication of micro-organisms as creative agents of chemical processes.

From the social background of man's earliest attempts to deal with the inconvenience of rain, mud, and the accumulation of excreta, a heap of confused notions about the way in which small organisms are propagated had taken shape. The spiritual attributes of the "effluvia" which exhaled from insanitary dumps were invoked to explain the "spontaneous generation" of the innumerable visible animals which breed among unsavoury surroundings. As time passed, the spontaneous origin of diseases which are encouraged by inadequate sanitation was accepted as a corollary. Although the simple microscope* led to the discovery of micro-organisms such as those which are now known to be responsible for disease, their significance as parasites of man and domesticable animals did not come till higher magnification had encouraged closer study. What immediately accompanied, and in large measure resulted from, the use of the first microscopes was that the doctrine of spontaneous generation was put to the test of direct experiment, and found wanting. The decay of this superstition took place gradually, and its applicability to the micro-organisms was the centre of controversy when achromatic lenses first became available. Its immediate effect was to transform the anthropomorphic conception of sexuality which the *Natural History* of Aristotle had bequeathed to medicine two thousand years earlier.

According to recent research such as Malinowski's account of the Trobriand Islanders, some primitive cultures still fail to recognize the essential rôle of the male parent in reproduction. The recognition of paternity probably arose as the result of domesticating the ox and the ass. Pedigree breeding (Fig. 409) goes back to ancient Mesopotamian cultures, and belongs to the same social context as milking the cow and sowing cereals. Like the last two, grafting of vines and fermentation are also biotechnical inventions of great antiquity. Thenceforward the only important practical advance in the science of breeding was the bulb industry which grew up in Holland at the end of the sixteenth century. In the fourth millennium B.C. civilized man had grasped that bodily intercourse between individuals respectively distinguished as male and female commonly precedes the production of young. That an essentially similar distinction can still be drawn between different individuals of species which do not perform an act of copulation, and that the male performs essentially the same part in the process was not recognized till after the seminal fluid had been subjected to microscopic scrutiny.

* Bacteria were first figured in 1683 by Leeuwenhoek, who used simple lenses of very high magnification in preference to the imperfect compound microscopes of his time.

Aristotle's views on reproduction may be summarized in the following terms. Animals may be divided into those which produce young as the result of sexual intercourse and those which are produced spontaneously from mud, sand, water, excrement or plant juices. In the first group those which produce eggs (which may be hatched inside the body as in the vipers and certain skates and sharks) are distinguished from those which are truly "viviparous" like man and other mammals. By an egg Aristotle means something visible to the eye and more or less reminiscent of the hen's egg, which may be fertile or infertile according as sexual intercourse has or has not taken place. The posture of intercourse, seasonal reproductive habits, oviposition, etc., of a large variety of oviparous vertebrates, birds, reptiles, fishes—are faithfully described in the *Historia Animalium*. There are passages

FIG. 409.—THE FIRST STUDBOOK IN HISTORY

What is probably the world's oldest chart of pedigree horses is this Mesopotamian tablet, dating from many centuries before the beginning of our era. Close scrutiny will reveal the universally adopted sign for "female ♀." (From *Modern Encyclopaedia*, Part I, by permission of The Amalgamated Press.)

of surprising accuracy in Book V where Aristotle discovers the reproductive phenomena of the larger crustacea and molluscs. The following is a sample:

Among the malacostraca, the carabi (crabs, lobsters) are impregnated by sexual intercourse and contain their ova during three months, May, June and July. They afterwards deposit them upon the hollow part of their folded tail and their ova grow like worms. The same thing takes place in the malacia and oviparous fish, for their ova always grow. . . . The malacia produce a white ovum after sexual intercourse. . . . The octopus deposits its ova in holes or pots or any other hollow place. The ovum is like the bunches of the wild vine and of the white poplar. . . . About fifty days afterwards the young polypi burst the eggs and escape like phalangia in great numbers. . . . The cuttlefish also deposits eggs which resemble large, black myrtle seeds. They are united together like a branch of fruit and are enclosed in a substance which prevents them from separating readily. The male emits his ink upon them. The ova are produced in fifteen days and when the ova are produced they remain for fifteen days longer like the small seeds of grapes and when these are ruptured the young sepias escape from the inside. If a person divides them before they have reached maturity, the young sepias emit their faeces, and vary in colour, and turn from white to red with alarm. . . . The crustaceans incubate upon their ova, which are placed beneath them, but the octopus and cuttlefish and such like incubate upon their ova wherever they may be deposited. . . . Each egg produces one small cuttlefish and so also with the teuthis.

Among those animals which produce young as the result of sexual congress, the land Arthropods (i.e. insects especially) occupy a special category, being neither viviparous in the sense that they give birth to young like themselves, nor oviparous. Aristotle seems to have failed to trace back the grub to anything which he could recognize as an "egg." Thus:

Male insects are less than the female; and that the male mounts upon the female, and the manner of their sexual intercourse has been described and the difficulty of separating them. Most of them produce their young very soon after sexual intercourse. All the kinds except some psychae [butterflies and moths] produce worms [i.e. grubs]. These produce a hard substance . . . which is fluid within [i.e. the pupa]. From the worm an animal is produced but not from a portion of it, as if it were an ovum but the whole grows and becomes an articulated animal. . . .

All invertebrate animals which produce offspring by what is now called "external fertilization" were believed to be formed by spontaneous generation. This was asserted to be true of all the molluscs (testacea) except the octopus tribe, of sea anemones, of starfishes, and of sponges. Of these Aristotle says:

The testacea . . . is the only entire class which is not reproduced by sexual intercourse. . . . The purpurae [the sea slug of Tyrian purple fame] collect together in spring and produce what is called their nidamental capsules. . . . These capsules have neither opening for perforation nor are the purpurae produced from them, but both these and other testacea are produced from mud and putrefaction. . . . On the whole all testacea are produced spontaneously in mud, different kinds originating in different kinds of mud. . . .

That the nidamental capsules mentioned in this passage were not recognized as eggs is hardly surprising, when we recall the fact that sexuality was exclusively associated with the act of coition except in so far as the close analogy of the sexual organs in fishes which reproduce by external and internal fertilization led to correct conclusions about the way in which they reproduced. Since many of the animals of the category last mentioned, such as the snail, the barnacle, and the oyster, are hermaphrodite, such errors are excusable. It is less easy to understand the complete disregard for the clues which the comparative method might have disclosed in a passage such as the following:

Some of them are produced from similar animals, as phalangia and spiders from phalangia and spiders. . . . Others do not originate in animals of the same species, but their production is spontaneous, for some of them spring from the dew which falls from plants. . . . Some originate in rotten mud and

dung. . . . Butterflies are produced from caterpillars, and these originate in
the leaves of green plants, especially the rhaphanus, which some persons call
crambe or cabbage. The gnats originate in ascarides [thread worms] and the
ascarides originate in the mud of wells and running waters that flow over an
earthy bottom. At first the decaying mud acquires a white colour, which afterwards becomes black, and finally red. . . .

An even more astonishing lapse is shown when Aristotle relies on second-
hand testimony of the type which used to be accepted as a basis for anthropological discussion. Even of the more familiar groups of which his first-hand
knowledge was usually penetrating, he could write such rubbish as:

Most fish originate in mud and sand. Even of those kinds which originate in
sexual intercourse and ova, some, they say, have appeared both in other marshy
places and in those which once surrounded Coridus which became dry under
the influence of the dog star. . . . The reproduction of mice is more wonderful

FIG. 410.—THE BARNACLE LEGEND

Figure of the Barnacle and Goose in Gerard's *Herball* (1594)

than that of any other animal both in number and rapidity. For a pregnant
female was left in a vessel of corn, and after a short time the vessel was opened,
and a hundred and twenty mice were counted. . . . In a certain part of Persia
the female foetus of the mice are found to be pregnant in the uterus of their
parent. Some people say and affirm that if they lick salt they become pregnant
without copulation. . . .

Accounts of spontaneous generation continued to be credited until the
beginning of the eighteenth century. In the most notable of the English
Herbals, as the works on botanical medicine were called, Gerard (1594) gives
an illustration (Fig. 410) bearing on the following citation:

But what our eyes have seene; and hands have touched we shall declare.
There is a small Island in Lancashire called the Pile of Foulders, wherein are
found the broken pieces of old and bruised ships, some whereof have beene
cast thither by shipwracke, and also the trunks and bodies with the branches
of old and rotten trees, cast up there likewise, whereon is found a certain spume
or froth that in time breedith unto certain shells, in shape like those of the
Muskle, but sharper pointed, and of whitish colour, wherein is contained a

thing in forme like lace of silke finely woven as it were together, of a whitish colour, one end whereof is fastened unto the inside of the shell, even as the fish of Oisters and Muskels are: the other end is made fast unto the belly of a rude masse or lump, which in time commeth to the shape of a Bird; when it is perfectly formed the shell gapeth open, and the first thing that appeareth is the foresaid lace or string; next come the legs of the bird hanging out, and as it groweth greater it openeth the shell by degrees, til at length it is all come forth, and hangeth onely by the bill: in short space after it cometh to full maturitie and falleth into the sea, where it gathereth feathers, and groweth to a fowle bigger than a Mallard and less than a goose having blacke legs and bill or beak, and feathers blacke and white, spotted in such manner as is our magpie . . . For the truth hereof if any doubt, may it please them to repaire unto me, and I shall satisfie them by the testimonie of good witnesses. . . . The bordes and rotten planks whereon are found these shels breeding the Barnakle are taken up on a small Island adjoyning Lancashire, halfe a mile from the main land, called the Pile of Foulders. They spawn as it were in March and April; the Geese are formed in May and June, and come to fulnesse of feathers in the month after. And thus having through God's assistance discoursed somewhat at large of Grasses, Herbs, Shrubs, trees and Mosses, and certain Excrescences of the earth, with other things moe, insident to the historie thereof, we conclude and end our present Volume, with this Wonder of England. For the which God's name be ever honoured and praised.

It is even more illuminating to note the concessions made by those who attacked the Aristotelian tradition in general and current "metamorphoses" in particular. The reader may recall Browne's eloquent passage on the Vulgar Errors:

But the mortallest enemy unto knowledge, and that which hath done the greatest execution upon truth, hath been a peremptory adhesion unto authority; and more especially, the establishing of our belief upon the dictates of antiquity. For (as every capacity may observe) most men, of ages present, so superstitiously do look upon ages past, that the authorities of the one exceed the reasons of the other. Whose persons indeed far removed from our times, their works, which seldom with us pass uncontrolled, either by contemporaries, or immediate successors, are now become out of the distance of envies; and the farther removed from present times, are conceived to approach the nearer unto truth itself. Now hereby methinks we manifestly delude ourselves, and widely walk out of the track of truth.

The same writer, while attacking other accepted cases of spontaneous generation, himself wrote:

Concerning the generation of frogs we shall briefly deliver that account which observation hath taught us. By frogs I understand not such, as arising from putrefaction, are bred without copulation and because they subsist not long are called temporariae [*Rana temporaria, the common frog*], nor do I mean the little frog of an excellent parrot green that usually sits on trees and bushes, and is therefore called Ranunculus viridis [the tree frog], but hereby I understand the aquatile or water frog, whereof we may behold many millions every spring in England.

Sir Thomas Browne was usually in advance of his time. Referring to the doubts he expressed on behalf of Aristotle's story of the mouse, Alexander Ross roundly upbraided him thus:

So may one doubt whether in cheese and timber worms are generated; or if beetles and wasps in cow's dung; or if butterflies, locusts, grasshoppers, shellfish, snails, eels and such like be procreated of putrefied matter which is apt to receive the form of that creature to which it is by formative powers disposed. To question this is to question reason, sense and experience. If he doubt of this let him go to Egypt, and there he will find the fields swarming with mice, begot of the mud of Nylus, to the great calamity of the inhabitants.

The barnacle legend lingered on for more than a century after the issue of Gerard's *Herball*. That canny Scot, Sir Robert Moray, claimed to give the account of an eye-witness in a paper which was published in the *Transactions of the Royal Society*. In it he describes the barnacle shells washed up on the coast of Scotland, and refers therein to the

little bill like that of a goose, the eyes marked, the head, neck, breast, wings, tail and feet formed, the feathers everywhere perfectly shaped and blackish coloured, and the feet like those of other water fowl to my best remembrance.

Less than half a century before Harvey's treatise appeared, Van Helmont, who occupies an honourable place in the history of science, lent his authority to a time-honoured recipe for making mice by putting a few grains of wheat or a piece of cheese along with some dirty linen in a closed receptacle. Important landmarks in the overthrow of the Aristotelian view were the observations of two Italians in the seventeenth century. Redi, a physician and member of a learned society calling itself the Academy of Experience, undertook a detailed study of one of the most firmly accepted examples of spontaneous generation. To test whether the worms which are found in rotten meat really appear spontaneously, he adopted the simple expedient of covering the meat with gauze. Flies attracted by the smell laid their eggs on the gauze and hatched into Aristotelian "worms" without contact with the meat supposed to generate them. A little later Valisneri, a medical professor at Padua, showed that the grubs found in fruit and plant galls (like the marble gall or oak apples) are hatched from eggs deposited by an insect before the fruit or the gall begins to develop.

The influence of the microscope on this change of outlook was both direct and indirect. In various ways it made it possible to recognize similarities which are not accessible to the naked eye. Apart from size, the eggs of insects are just as much like the eggs of a hen, a shark or a lizard as are the eggs of a crab or of an octopus. The doctrine *omnia ex ovo* which Harvey advanced in his last and posthumous work on the *Generation of Animals* was a natural corollary of the new habit of using a lens in his researches. Careless observation of small objects could now be brought to a new tribunal, and unsuspected new facts began to accumulate. Aristotle's division of animals which begin life as worms, animals which begin as eggs and animals which are conceived viviparously was abandoned as direct observation traced the beginnings of all animals to a more or less spherical or ovoid body which has no external resemblance to the adult being.

Simultaneously a flood of light was shed on the nature of sex by one of the most indefatigable of the early microscopists, Leeuwenhoek, who communicated various discoveries to the English Royal Society. These are collected in his *Secrets of Nature*, published in 1695. Leeuwenhoek, who was the first to describe micro-organisms, was also the first to observe that the semen of animals teems with minute vibratile "corpuscles," the spermatozoa or sperms, which are far too small to be seen by the eye.* Although the precise part which the sperm plays in the sexual process was not fully recognized until the coming of achromatic lenses, the discovery of spermatozoa immensely enlarged the conception of sexuality. Till then semen had been recognized as a viscous colourless fluid exuded in the sexual act. Aristotle was aware

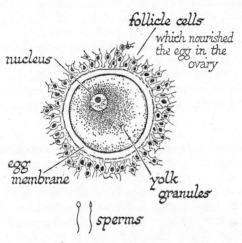

FIG. 411.—HUMAN EGG AND SPERM

The actual size of the egg is less than ·2 mm., and the sperms (below) are drawn to the same scale. The thickened head of the sperm (seen here in two views) contains the nucleus.

that this fluid is not necessarily introduced into the generative cavities of the female. It may, for instance, be squirted over the eggs as they emerge, as is done by the male frog. The traditional view admitted the distinction between male and female animals which do not carry out the fertilization of the egg by the seminal fluid as the result of direct bodily contact, when

---

* According to Cole the first published reference to spermatozoa is made by Huyghens who, besides being foremost in devising the pendulum clock was prominent in the optical researches which received their impetus from the technology of the telescope. Huyghens mentions in a letter dated June 1678 that he had of late devoted his attention to improving microscopes, prompted by observations of a student called Hammius at Leyden. Hammius had discovered animalcules in the semen of animals, and these he (Huyghens) had often seen. It seems that Huyghens obtained this information indirectly from Leeuwenhoek, whose letter written a year earlier, though not published till 1679, he had read. The incident illustrates the close association between the improvement of the microscope and the technology of navigation.

their reproductive organs and seminal fluid respectively exhibited an obvious similarity to those of near relations which practise a recognizable act of coition. On the other hand, Aristotle exempted from any claims to sexuality (*a*) the immense category of marine invertebrates like the oyster, which shed their semen and ova into the sea without parental propinquity and (*b*) the many *hermaphrodite* terrestrial animals, like the earthworm and snail, which combine the production of semen and eggs in one individual.

Without immediately giving birth to a correct view of paternity Leeuwenhoek's discovery provided a new *differentia* of sex, and at once prepared the way for the recognition of universal sexuality. Henceforth maleness is defined as power to produce sperms. Simultaneously as a direct result of new microscopic observations on plant anatomy, including the production of pollen, Nehemiah Grew, whose *Anatomy of Plants* was finally published in 1682, advanced the doctrine that the stamens of the flowering plant are its male organs, that the pistil corresponds to its female parts (Fig. 413), and that pollen performed the same essential function as semen. Though there is some evidence that dusting the pistil with pollen had been carried out by vine-growers in dynastic Egypt, the doctrine of sexuality on which the industrial practice of modern seed production rests was a veritable revolution in the scientific world of the eighteenth century in the Christian era.

Grew says that Sir Thomas Millington, another Fellow of the Royal Society, had arrived independently at the same conclusion. We have no information concerning any experiments they may have performed to test or arrive at their conclusions. They may have been based on microscopic recognition that the dust of the ancient date husbandry was a production essentially common to all flowering plants. A German botanist Camerarius established the doctrine on a firm footing of experimental evidence set forth in his *Letter on the Sex of Plants* (1688). His experiments seem to have been inspired by observations on the habit of the mulberry tree which from time immemorial had been the basis of an important industry, since it is the food plant of the mulberry moth (*Bombyx mori*) whose caterpillar is the silkworm. The mulberry resembles the holly and the willow whose pollen flowers and seed flowers occur on different trees. Wolf summarizes the experiments of Camerarius in the following passage:

Having observed that a fruit-bearing mulberry tree near which there was no pollen-bearing tree produced sterile seed vessels, he decided to investigate the subject experimentally. He chose for this purpose such common plants as dog's mercury having flowers of different sexes. Planting some of its ripe seeds in soil, he saw that they produced two kinds of plants which though similar in many ways differed in this respect, namely, that some of them had stamens but no seeds or fruit, while the others bore fruit but did not have stamens. When he isolated the fruit-bearing plants from the pollen-producing plants, then seed vessels still appeared on the former, but they were sterile. He next experimented with plants in which both stamens and pistils grow on the same plant, such as maize and *Ricinus* (the tropical plant from which castor oil is derived). He found that when their stigmata were removed before the anthers were fully developed, then the seed vessels were always empty and sterile.

It is more than a coincidence that the doctrine of sexuality in plants took shape at a time when scientific men were beginning to take an interest in agriculture, horticulture, and husbandry. In England Grew's work coincided with the introduction of the four-course system or rotation of turnips, grass, clover, and cereals, an innovation sometimes spoken of as the agricultural revolution of the seventeenth century, though some such practice seems to have been of long standing in China. During the long period in which localized self-sufficiency had been displaced by the growth of international trade,

FIG. 412.—THE FERTILIZATION OF THE DATE

This Assyrian bas-relief shows King Ashur-nasir-pal assisting at the pollination rite before a date tree. Behind him is a priest carrying the male seed and in his left hand the pollination tray or basket. (British Museum.)

science had developed as an essentially urban product, and medicine to which biological enquiries owed their primary impetus was cut off from the soil.

Though the fact was never generalized, sexuality in plants was one of the earliest secrets of husbandry. Three of the most important plants which civilized man learned to value—the date, the vine, and the mulberry—produce separate staminiferous and pistillate flowers. Theophrastus, a pupil of the Lyceum and the most renowned herbalist of the ancient world, describes the treatment of date palms in the words:

With dates the males should be brought to the females. For the males make the fruit persist and ripen. . . . When the male is in flower they at once cut off the spathe with the flower and shake the bloom with its flower and dust over the fruit of the female, and if it is thus treated, it retains the fruit and does not shed it.

The fertilizing power of the male catkins of the date palm was familiar in Babylon at a much earlier time. It is represented by a frequent symbol on Assyrian monuments, and is recorded by Herodotus. The practice of artificial pollination in vine husbandry is also of great antiquity. However, there was no recognition of the fact that the stamens or pollen-producing organs in any way resemble the generative organs of the male animal—still less that the flowers of common plants are essentially hermaphrodite structures, as experiments like those of Camerarius established. The complete failure of the pre-microscopic herbalists to generalize the lesson of the date palm is well illustrated by the words of the thirteenth-century Arab physician, Kazwini:

The date has a striking resemblance to man, through the beauty of its erect and slender figure, its division into two sexes, and the property which is peculiar to it, of being fecundated by a sort of union.

The importance of this step was far greater than anyone could have foreseen. An immediate practical result was that it made systematic experiments in plant hybridization possible. Hence it initiated a succession of attempts which laid the foundations of scientific breeding of plants and animals. Its practical importance will be realized more fully when we have surveyed the origins of this important department of modern biotechnology. Here it is sufficient to remark that a contemporary of Camerarius claims the honour of being the first creator of a horticultural product by deliberate interference with the normal course of reproduction.

He was Thomas Fairchild (1667–1729), who owned a nursery at Shoreditch, and left a sum of money to the newly chartered Worshipful Company of Gardeners to provide for an annual discourse. Bradley, then Professor of Botany in Cambridge, wrote in 1718:

The Carnation and the Sweet William are in some respects alike, the Farina (i.e. pollen) of one will impregnate the other, and the seed, so enlivened, will produce a plant differing from either, as may now be seen in the garden of Mr. Thomas Fairchild, of Hoxton, a plant neither Sweet William nor Carnation but resembling both equally, which was raised from the seed of a Carnation that had been impregnated by the Farina of the Sweet William.

A century later the hybrid was still shown as Fairchild's Sweet William in English gardens.

While it is doubtful whether the experiments of Camerarius exerted any effect on English horticulture, it is fairly certain that the issue was being probed about the same time in England. For some years before Bradley recorded this account (1718) of an achievement which might "produce such rare kinds of plants as have not yet been heard of," he himself had carried out experiments essentially like those of Camerarius to test views which had been raised in discussions of the Royal Society by Robert Balle and by Samuel Moreland, who communicated a short paper in the *Philosophical Transactions* of 1703. Bradley had "good fortune to bring it to demonstration by several experiments since which a gentleman of Paris had printed something of the same nature in . . . the year 1711 and 1712."

Moreland acknowledges priority to Dr. Grew as "the only author I can find who hath observed that the Farina . . . doth some way perform the office of the male sperm." He then submits to the "disquisitions and censures" of competent judges and to further enquiry by persons possessed and skilled in the use of "the best microscopes" two further suggestions: (i) the "seeds . . . are at first like unimpregnated ova of animals," and (ii) "this Farina is a congeries of seminal plants *one of which must be conveyed into every ovum* before it can become prolific." The gist of the paper is that wherever seeds are formed arrangements coexist to ensure that pollen is collected on the stigma first. Moreland does not state that he had carried out the crucial test of showing that no seed is formed when pollen is prevented from doing so. The importance of the paper lies in the vivid way in which it bears testimony to the influence of the microscope and new views on the nature of sex in animals.

Though we do not know whether Grew or Moreland established their views by direct experiment, it is clear that experiments on pollination were in progress in England between 1670 and 1710, and that the issue was brought forward several times. The close association of the Fellows with current social movements in the early days of the English Royal Society is illustrated by the title of Bradley's *New Improvements of Planting and Gardening*. Fairchild communicated in the *Philosophical Transactions of the Royal Society* (1724) results of grafting experiments, "designed," says Zirkle, "to demonstrate the ascent of sap." Thomas Knight, founder of the Horticultural Society, returns to the same theme eighty years later.

The experimental study of hybridization in plants is simpler than the experimental study of hybridization in animals (see Chapter XXII) and the material basis of sexuality in plants is easier to recognize. Hence plant hybridization has laid the foundations of what we now know about inheritance in animals. Throughout the past history of mankind efforts to improve plants and produce them on a large scale had been almost exclusively concerned with vegetative propagation, either natural (e.g. the Dutch bulb industry) or artificial (grafting and cuttings). After the introduction of crop rotation seed production became a process of steadily increasing social importance. The part played by the pollen in fixing the character of hybrid offspring, exhibited in the production of new varieties such as Thomas Fairchild's carnation, prepared the way for closer study of heredity. The way in which normal pollination is assured by wind, insect visits and other means was systematically studied by the plant hybridist Koelreuter, who was director of the grand ducal botanic garden at Carlsruhe in the middle of the eighteenth century. His work was followed by similar studies, of which the most noteworthy were Sprengel's observations on the various arrangements which ensure cross pollination of the stamens and pistils of different flowers through the agency of insects.

THE MODERN VIEW OF SEXUALITY

The material basis of parenthood in animals will be set forth in detail later. First let us briefly contrast the modern view based on direct observation through the compound microscope with the Aristotelian doctrine which was held in a more or less modified form long after the universal existence of sex in animals and plants of visible dimensions had been firmly established. Aristotle's view was that some animals are produced sexually, and that, when they are so produced, their resemblance to their parents is due to the nutrient material absorbed by the egg or embryo from the seminal fluid of the male and a supposedly analogous fluid supplied by the mother. The last was

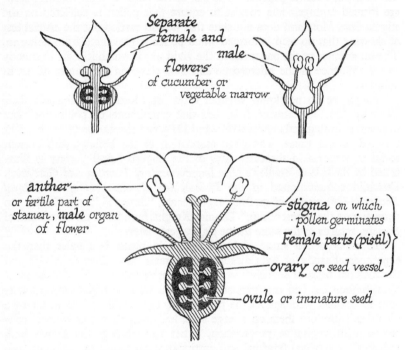

FIG. 413.—SEX IN FLOWERING PLANTS

The figure below shows (below) the parts of a typical flower with a compound inferior ovary containing many ovules or immature seeds. If the stamens are snipped off the young flower before anthers burst and set free the pollen, no seeds will be formed by plants kept under glass to exclude insects or wind-blown pollen. Such castrated flowers will produce normal seed, if pollen is dusted over the stigma with a fine brush. When, as above, there are separate staminate and pistillate flowers, the latter will not form ripe seed, unless there are pollinate flowers in the neighbourhood.

identified with the menstruum of mammals. In contradistinction to this the modern view is that the bodies of all animals and plants ordinarily so described (as distinct from micro-organisms) are built up of microscopic bricks called cells, and the essence of fertilization lies in the fact that two sex cells (*gametes*) produced, one (the sperm) by the male parent and one (the *ovum* or egg-cell) by the female parent, *fuse together bodily*, thereby initiating a process of division which leads to the production of a many-celled embryo.

The gamete which is called the egg-cell or ovum, produced by the parent called female when the sexes are separate, is always larger than the male gamete, and contains more or less storage material. On account of this it may attain considerable dimensions before fertilization ensues, and is then equivalent to what Aristotle calls an egg or nidamental capsule. Ordinary flowers combine in one structure the pollen-producing organs (anthers) and egg-cell-containing organs (ovules). Anthers and ovules are sometimes borne in separate flowers on separate plants (e.g. date, spinach, willow, dog's mercury, and holly) or in separate flowers of the same shoot (stinging-nettles, cucumbers). Similarly semen-producing organs (testes) and egg-producing organs (ovaries) in many groups of animals occur simultaneously (barnacles, earthworms, snails) or successively (oyster, starfish, lamprey) in the same individual.

In some animals such as snails, human beings, and birds, the seminal fluid

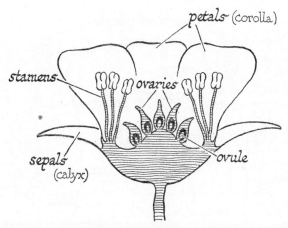

Fig. 414.—A More Primitive Type of Flower than the One Shown in the Previous Figure with Separate Ovaries, Each Containing a Single Ovule

is introduced into the oviduct of the female and the egg is fertilized inside the female body. The male of many land animals has a special organ, the *penis*, which is used to introduce the seminal fluid into the body of the female. The frog and the fowl do not possess one. Many marine animals (e.g. oysters, starfishes, marine worms, sea anemones) shed both eggs and seminal fluid into the sea. There is no act of sexual union between the two parents themselves. Hence the bodily act which brings the semen into contact with the egg is less important to the naturalist than to the dramatist. It has therefore ceased to be regarded as the most characteristic feature of what biologists mean when they talk about sex.

Two links in this chain were by-products of the early microscopes. One was the discovery of the male sex cell or *sperm*. The other was a gradual acquisition. The word *cell* was first used by Hooke in his *Micrographia* to describe the resemblance of cork to a honeycomb, when highly magnified. Leeuwenhoek also noticed that human blood is not a homogeneous fluid. It is a dense suspension of minute bodies, some colourless (white corpuscles), others which are ovoid discs (red corpuscles) containing *haemoglobin*. Subsequent progress in the microscopic anatomy of animals was slow, because animal tissues are soft and yielding. Plant bodies (Fig. 416) are made up of tissues composed of bricks surrounded by a thin wall of cellulose which persists after death, so that even in dead tissue like corn the cellular structure is readily visible. On this account they can be easily sliced with a sharp razor into thin sections which are sufficiently translucent to expose their make-up when examined through the microscope.

HOW ANIMAL BIOLOGY WAS SIDETRACKED

That progress in the study of plant reproduction was closely linked with the practice of horticulture and agricultural seed production is beyond dis-

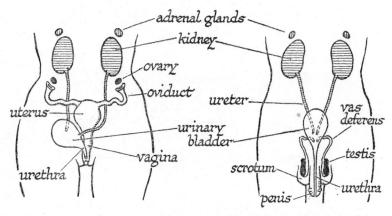

FIG. 415.—RELATIVE POSITION OF THE ORGANS OF NITROGENOUS EXCRETION (KIDNEYS AND BLADDER) AND OF REPRODUCTION IN MAN

On the left, female; on the right, male.

pute. Nor can we doubt the immense stimulus which the elucidation of reproductive phenomena in animals received from parallel enquiries conducted by botanists. The title of Purkinje's treatise published in 1839 *On the analogies in the structural elements in animals and plants* is eloquent testimony to the debt which current knowledge of the material basis of inheritance in animals owes to the recognition of the cellular structure of the plant body. It is equally emphasized by the scope of an important memoir published by Caspar Wolff in the closing years of the eighteenth century.

The importance of Wolff's work recalls an incident, which has been mentioned in an earlier chapter. The brilliant lead of the early English physicists during the latter half of the seventeenth century was sidetracked by the Continental doctrine of phlogiston which came to the rescue of Aristotelian chemistry. Contemporary with Hooke and Mayow, Malpighi had made correct observations on the hen's egg, even describing the formation of the heart from an undifferentiated region of tissue, when classical erudition rehabilitated the remnants of Aristotle's spontaneous generation in the doctrine of "preformation." A being complete in all its essentials lay concealed from view—or from the magnifying power of microscopes then available—in the

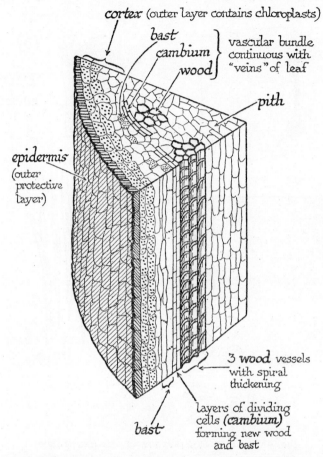

FIG. 416.—CELLULAR STRUCTURE OF THE FLOWERING PLANT.—DIAGRAMMATIC VIEW OF THE MICROSCOPIC ANATOMY OF A YOUNG STEM

The young stem of a flowering plant consists of three main tissues or groups of tissues: (*a*) an outer covering or *epidermis* of thick-walled cells with an outer cuticularized coat protecting the underlying tissues from evaporation; (*b*) thin-walled cells containing abundant fluid and forming a packing (*cortex* and *pith*); (*c*) a ring of *vascular bundles* of conducting tissue continuous with the "veins" of the leaf. Each vascular bundle contains three main tissues: (*a*) the wood, consisting mainly of *wood vessels*. Originally elongated cells with spirally thickened walls, the transverse partitions where they are joined end to end break down, and the cell substance dies, so that hollow tubes of fine bore are formed, running from the roots to the leaves; (*b*) the bast, consisting largely of *sieve-tubes*, elongated, dead conducting cells with perforated ends; (*c*) a few layers of thin-walled *cambium* cells, which multiply to form new wood on the inside and new bast on the outside. As the stem gets older, the cambium may join up to form a complete ring, laying down continuous rings of wood and bast which accumulate from year to year, forming in the case of the wood the *annual rings* of woody plants.

In a young stem the cells just below the epidermis usually contain the green pigment *chlorophyll* concentrated in round corpuscles indicated by black dots in the figure.

egg, or alternatively as the spermatists argued, in the sperm. The alternative view had repercussions on the century-old controversy concerning the conception of the Virgin by the Blessed St. Anne. Since theological ingenuity

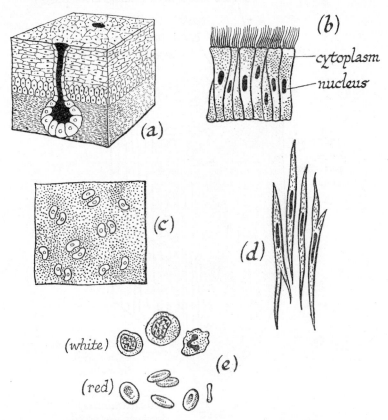

FIG. 417.—CELLULAR STRUCTURE OF THE ANIMAL BODY

(a) Cube cut from the skin of the frog shewing successive layers of cells which make up the outer skin or epidermis, and a simple pit-like gland whose slimy secretion keeps the surface moist.
(b) Lining membrane of the human windpipe; the cells have fine vibratile outgrowths called *cilia*, whose swaying motion keeps the moist film of phlegm circulating.
(c) Cartilage from shoulder blade of frog, shewing cells lying in a gelatinous matrix which they secrete.
(d) Teased out muscle fibres from the human bladder. Each contractile fibre is a single elongated cell.
(e) Three kinds of white blood cells and a group of red blood corpuscles from man.

had not as yet achieved a settlement of the conflicting tenets of the Dominican and Benedictine schools, the issue provided ample scope for manly sentiment and promoted a voluminous literature.

The method of analysis which underlies the exploits of the preformationist writers of the eighteenth century will offer no difficulties to those who have equipped themselves with a knowledge of current economics. If the sperm is the agency by which the manhood of the male parent passes to his son, the recognition of manhood in the sperm is inherent in the original definitions of the subject matter of embryology. To be sure the homunculus was difficult to see with the aid of lenses. What the lens could not do through the limitations of mere empiricism, logic supplemented in the illustrations to the text (Fig. 418) of Hartsoeker and Dalenpatius. A century of phlogistonism intervenes between Hooke and Lavoisier, a century of preformationism between Malpighi and Wolff.

Wolff's microscopic studies showed (i) that the organs of a growing plant develop from uniform cellular regions at the tip of the growing shoot or

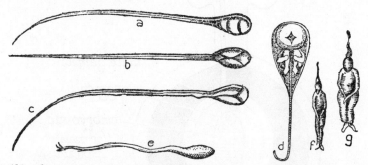

FIG. 418.—Spermatozoa as seen with the Microscope and with the Eye of Faith

a, b, c, Leeuwenhoek from the dog (1679). *d,* Hartsoeker from man showing the "homunculus" (1694). *e, f, g,* Francois Plantades (Dalenpatius) from man. *e,* intact. *f* and *g,* broken to show the "homunculi" (1699). From Dr. Charles Singer's *Short History of Biology* (Oxford).

root; (ii) that the parts of a flower arise from undifferentiated cells as do leaf buds; (iii) that the organs of the chick are gradually evolved from a mass of cellular tissue which is at first indistinguishable.

COMING OF THE MODERN MICROSCOPE

The introduction of achromatic lenses was immediately followed by extensive researches into the details of development, notably the work of Van Baer on the rabbit and other mammals. Its firstfruits were an immense and rapid increase in knowledge about reproduction in plants. Between 1821 and 1830 Amici, an Italian physicist who was foremost in the improvement of microscopic construction as inventor of the "immersion" lens, recorded the way in which the pollen grain germinates on the stigma, and described the pollen tube which grows through the tissues of the pistil, finally making its way into an ovule. In 1846, when the new cell doctrine was already established, he described the single egg cell in the "embryo sac" of the ovule. The importance of this observation, which is fundamental for the theory and practice of modern hybridization, extends far beyond the reproduction of flowering plants. It may well be doubted whether the nature of fertilization in animals would have been elucidated without the previous knowledge that a single pollen grain fertilizes a single ovule.

New facts remained to be discovered before the essential similarities could be fully understood, and these were discovered in the fifties, first by the work of Hofmeister, a German botanist who left school at the age of fifteen to work in a shop, and subsequently by the researches of Pringsheim. The work of these men extended knowledge of sexuality to the flowerless plants. Aside

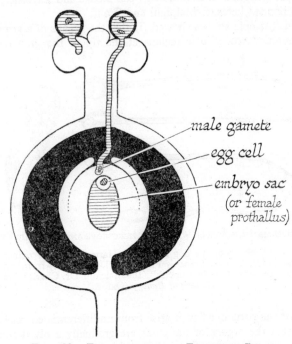

male gamete

egg cell

embryo sac
(or female prothallus)

FIG. 419.—FERTILIZATION IN A FLOWERING PLANT

When the pollen grain leaves the anther it is a single spherical cell with a single nucleus. Here two are seen germinating on the stigma of a flower with an ovary which contains a single ovule. One of the pollen grains has sent out a *pollen tube* which has grown down through the stigma and penetrated the ovule, reaching the ripe "embryo sac" or female prothallus (see p. 978). The sperm nucleus, one of three formed by division of the nucleus of the pollen grain, is about to unite with that of the egg cell. As you will see later from the discussion on p. 978, the "ovary" or seed vessel of a flowering plant does not strictly correspond to the ovary of an animal.

from the impetus which commercial seed production and hybridization supplied, the study of the reproductive phenomena in the lower plants was beginning to attract attention, on account of growing interest in the part played by fungi as agents of plant disease. Thomas Knight concludes a paper delivered to the Horticultural Society in 1815 with the words:

The enormous injury which the crops of wheat sustained in 1814 and other seasons by mildew attaches a great degree of interest to the investigation of the habits of parasitical plants of this tribe.

SEX IN THE LOWER PLANTS

There are three ways in which plants reproduce. Two of these are common to plants and animals. One is *vegetative*, i.e. by a growth or bud from the body of the plant or animal. The bud gradually may assume the form of the full-grown organism before or after it is detached to form a new and separate one. Runners of strawberries, bulbs of daffodils, root-stocks of irises, tubers of potatoes are familiar examples of a process also common among marine sedentary animals which form colonies, as do corals, sea mats, and sea squirts.

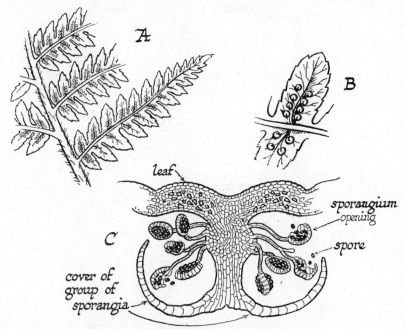

FIG. 420.—ASEXUAL REPRODUCTION IN THE FERN

A, Leaf of fern. The small round objects on the under side of the leaf are the covers of the groups of sporangia, shown more clearly in *B*, which is a portion of the leaf magnified. *C*, group of sporangia cut through the middle.

Some organisms when cut into pieces regenerate the missing organs of each part. Worms and sea anemones sometimes do this and plants can be propagated by artificial vegetative reproduction, as in the practice of "cuttings" and grafts.

In contradistinction to sexual reproduction and vegetative reproduction common to plants and animals, asexual reproduction by fine *spores*, like the dust of the puffball or of mildews, and the fine powder which can be shaken from the underside of the fern leaf or along the edges of the leaflets of the bracken, is peculiar to plants. Till the introduction of the compound microscope, spore production was the only form of reproduction known to exist in the non-flowering plants. Fern spores are single cells. Each is a minute spherical body (Fig. 420), produced in small stalked capsules which are attached to a sort of cushion or pad on the under surface of the leaves. These pads are protected by the folded edge of the leaflets or by a sort of umbrella which is of yellowish brown colour.

It is easy to cut a section of the fern leaf with a safety razor blade if it is pressed between two pieces of pith or the soft stem of a geranium. If the

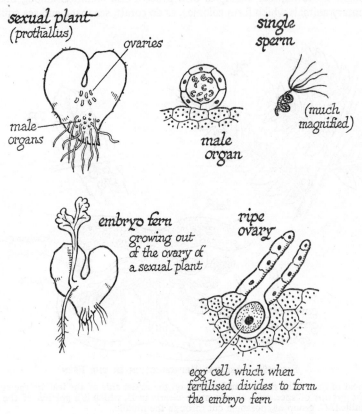

FIG. 421.—SEXUAL REPRODUCTION OF THE FERN

section is mounted on a glass slide in a drop of water and examined under a microscope, the leaf itself is seen to be made up of distinct layers of separate bricks, or *cells*. The cells of each layer have characteristic features in virtue of which they are spoken of as forming distinct "tissues." The spore capsule and its cushion are also made up of separate cells, the walls of the former being flat and thin. When it is young and not fully formed, the spore capsule is a mass of similar cells; from one of the inner mass of cells each spore is formed. When fully formed it has a thick woody coat, but remains undivided until the spore capsule ruptures and sets it free, when ripe.

Blown by the wind, it may settle on damp earth. It then germinates. That is to say, it divides repeatedly to form a flat plate of cells which is green and heart-shaped, rather like a *liverwort* (see Fig. 422) which clings to wet rocks or damp walls. This small green plant, the fern *prothallus* (Fig. 421),

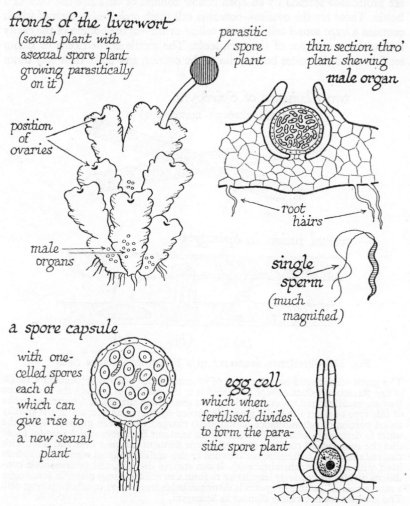

fronds of the liverwort
(sexual plant with asexual spore plant growing parasitically on it)

parasitic spore plant

thin section thro' plant shewing *male organ*

position of ovaries

root hairs

male organs

single sperm
(much magnified)

a spore capsule

with one-celled spores each of which can give rise to a new sexual plant

egg cell
which when fertilised divides to form the parasitic spore plant

FIG. 422.—THE LIFE CYCLE OF THE LIVERWORT, A FLAT AMORPHOUS GREEN PLANT ALLIED TO THE MOSSES AND FOUND GROWING ON MOIST WALLS OR ROCKS BY STREAMS

has no separate shoot, leaves, or root-stock like the familiar spore-bearing form. Apart from the fact that some cells on the lower side—root hairs—are drawn out into fine tubes which penetrate the damp soil, it has no distinct tissue layers like a leaf. At the pointed end on the under-surface, in the film of moisture which separates the prothallus from the soil, small globular masses of cells are formed among the root hairs. These are the male organs or *testes* of the fern—botanists call them *antheridia*. The inner cells of this mass become spirally coiled and their ends become equipped with vibratile filaments or *cilia* by which they can swim about when the wall of the testis bursts. Farther forward on the under-surface of the prothallus are projections formed by an open hollow column of cells like the neck of a bottle. These are the ovaries—botanists call them *archegonia*—each of which contains a large round cell—the egg cell or ovum—at the bottom of the cavity into which the orifice of the neck leads. The motile ciliated cells or *sperms* set free when the testes burst swim to the ovaries, and make their way down

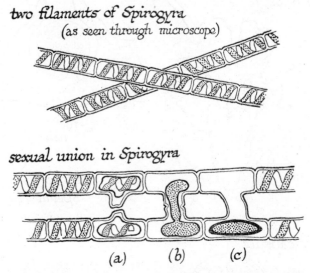

two filaments of Spirogyra
(as seen through microscope)

sexual union in Spirogyra

(a)   (b)   (c)

FIG. 423.—PRIMITIVE SEXUALITY IN A FRESHWATER GREEN ALGA

The green scum found near the edge of stagnant ponds commonly contains a tangle of fine threads just thick enough to be visible to the naked eye. Beneath the microscope they are usually found to consist of long cells arranged in single file. A common species of this type of plant life is the green alga called Spirogyra on account of the spirally coiled portion of cell substance (chloroplast) charged with green pigment. When the water is drying up, adjacent filaments often send out fine tubes which fuse (*a, b*), so that the rounded off contents of a cell of one filament can pass over and unite with those of another. The fertilized cell formed by this undifferentiated sexuality surrounds itself with a resistant membrane (*c*). It can survive drought, and in favourable conditions divides successively lengthwise to form a new filamentous plant. In some algae a motile ciliated gamete or sperm is distinguishable from a non-motile larger egg cell. The gametes are not visibly distinct in Spirogyra.

the neck. One and only one of the many which are swimming near the surface fuses bodily with the egg cell.

The ovum is then said to be *fertilized* and divides into two like a spore. Each daughter cell divides into two—and so on—forming a mass of cells or embryo which does not become a prothallus. It soon develops an up-growing shoot and a down-growing root stock with tissues characteristic of the fern. The prothallus dies as the embryo grows into a recognizable fern plant. Thus ferns show a regular alternation of generations—the sexless green fern plant which is fitted to exposed conditions and produces spores which withstand drought, and the less conspicuous, more ephemeral, sexual prothallus which produces eggs and sperm. Its eggs and sperms resemble those of a human being or an oyster more closely than the eggs and sperms of a shrimp resemble those of a bird. Hence it is not difficult to realize how growing knowledge of the reproduction of the lower plants stimulated the study of reproduction in the lower animals and provided the clue to new features of the sexual process in the higher ones.

Sexual reproduction in the true mosses (as opposed to the club mosses which are really like ferns) and liverworts is very much like that of ferns. There are two generations—a sexual and an asexual. The important difference is that what we ordinarily call the moss plant or the liverwort is the sexual generation. The asexual plant which produces its spores, while still remaining more or less completely parasitic on the sexual generation and still attached to it, like the young fern plant in Fig. 421, never grows true leaves. It dies after producing spores in a single capsule at the end of a leafless shoot, while the sexual plant lives on. The body of the liverworts found on wet walls and rocks by streams has no distinct leaves and is indeed very much like that of the sexual fern plant or prothallus—a flat plate of cells several layers thick with root hairs on the underside (Fig. 422). The ovaries and testes produced on the upper surface are in other ways as much like those of one fern as those of one fern are like those of another, and the spermatozoa are motile with two long vibratile filaments or cilia. The underlying resemblance of reproduction in flowering and non-flowering plants will be discussed later.

ANIMAL REPRODUCTION

The material basis of the reproductive process in animals as we now know it has been advanced greatly by the invention of an instrument called the *microtome*. On a smaller scale a microtome is essentially like the machine used in large grocery stores for cutting rashers of bacon. Animal tissues are generally too soft to be cut by hand into sections of suitable thickness for microscopic study. They are first killed by treatment with a "fixative" mixture, e.g. a saturated solution of picric acid and formalin. This preserves the appearance seen in life without much shrinkage. They are then embedded in wax. To do this the water is taken out of small pieces of fixed tissue by successive immersion in alcohol, which itself freely mixes with wax solvents like benzene or chloroform. They are then put into a wax solvent, and thence transferred to liquid paraffin wax kept just above its melting point.

When the wax block containing the tissue is cut on the microtome, successive sections adhere to form a ribbon, so that the order of the sections is preserved. By means of flat plasticine or beeswax models of a sequence of sections of a small organ or animal, a complete solid picture can then be built up, if required. These wax ribbons produced by the microtome are stuck on a glass slide by a little eggwhite which coagulates when warmed. The wax is then dissolved away with a wax solvent (like chloroform or benzene), and the glass slides are stained with dyes which affect different tissues or parts of a single cell to a different extent. The sections are finally immersed in a mixture called Canada Balsam which sets hard, has the same refractive index as glass and—if the water has been entirely withdrawn by dipping the slides in alcohol—makes the tissues translucent, just as grease makes ordinary paper translucent.

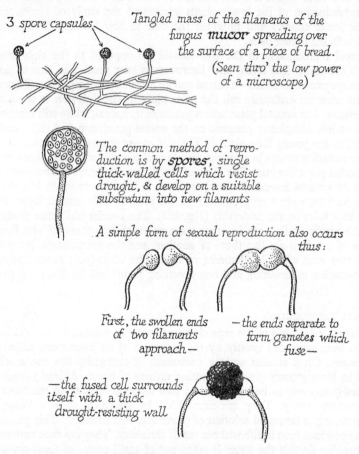

3 spore capsules

Tangled mass of the filaments of the fungus **mucor** spreading over the surface of a piece of bread.

(Seen thro' the low power of a microscope)

The common method of reproduction is by *spores*, single thick-walled cells which resist drought, & develop on a suitable substratum into new filaments

A simple form of sexual reproduction also occurs thus:

First, the swollen ends of two filaments approach —

— the ends separate to form gametes which fuse—

— the fused cell surrounds itself with a thick drought-resisting wall

FIG. 424.—PRIMITIVE SEXUALITY IN A SIMPLE FUNGUS

The simple fungi called moulds on old cheese, bread or jam are filaments like the simple algae. Sometimes the branching filaments which form a mat on the surface of decaying vegetable matter or in animal tissues (like ringworm) are divided into separate cells like those of Spirogyra. Sometimes they contain many nuclei with no separating cell walls. The essential difference between algae and fungi is that the latter have no pigments which enable them to make starch, and are only able to exist by using decaying organic matter or by parasitic habits. They reproduce mainly by forming asexual drought-resisting spores which are single cells. In addition like the algae they have a primitive type of sexuality, as shown in this figure which illustrates the microscopic picture of reproduction in the mould called Mucor which grows on dry bread.

It will clarify the present state of knowledge about the material basis of parenthood in animals, if we base the ensuing account mainly on one common species, the frog, whose reproductive processes are easy to examine. The female frog differs from the male, being somewhat larger than it, and having no horny pad at the base of the thumb. At the breeding season, in Spring, frogs may be found in ponds and streams in pairs. A male tightly clasps a female about the body by the fore-limbs, with his ventral surface in contact with her back. Thus they remain, till the eggs are shed in great numbers embedded in masses of clear jelly, which may be seen floating on the surface of the water. Each egg is almost completely spherical, black in colour towards the pole which floats uppermost, and lighter beneath. As the eggs are laid the male squirts a viscid stream, the seminal fluid, over the surface of the egg.

If the seminal fluid is examined with a microscope, it is seen to swarm with myriads of minute moving sperms. With very high magnification each sperm is seen to be somewhat like a tadpole in shape, having a short, thicker body

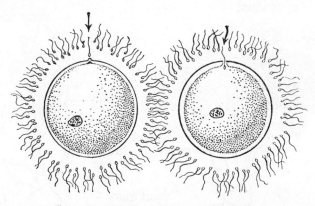

FIG. 425.—FERTILIZATION IN THE STARFISH

Each egg is surrounded by sperms attracted to it by a substance which it gives off into the water. On the left one sperm is approaching the egg which sends out a cone of protoplasm to receive it. On the right, a sperm has entered and a thin membrane is separating from the surface of the egg, keeping the other sperms out.

with a thin whip-like tail or cilium (Fig. 418). The sperm dashes hither and thither by its lashing movements. If the male is taken away from the female before the eggs are laid, and the latter removed from the body of the mother, the eggs will not develop into tadpoles. But if these eggs are placed in a bowl of water in which some seminal fluid obtained from a male is added, they become capable of developing. Seminal fluid from which the sperms have been filtered off through several layers of blotting paper does not possess this fertilizing power.

In 1879 two German investigators, Hertwig and Fol, first observed the process of animal fertilization under the microscope. They were able to see that one sperm, and one only, bores its way into the egg of a sea urchin, as the preliminary to its development into a new organism (Fig. 425). We now know this to be true of *all* animals that reproduce sexually. Development of the egg starts when one of the innumerable minute sperms contained in the seminal fluid ejaculated by the male penetrates into the substance of the egg. *Fertilization*, the process by which the egg starts to develop into a new creature, is, in all animals, the union of one sperm with one egg. All that we now mean by inheritance from the father is the material substance of the sperm. All that we mean by inheritance from the mother is the material of which the egg is composed.

As we now use the terms, an animal that produces eggs is a *female*. An animal that produces sperm is a *male*. The eggs are produced in masses, which are called *ovaries*, within the body of the female. The sperm are produced in a slimy secretion, the seminal fluid, by organs known as *testes* (Figs. 415 and 426). Collectively ovaries and testes are referred to as *gonads*. In the female frog the ovaries occupy a large part of the body cavity in the

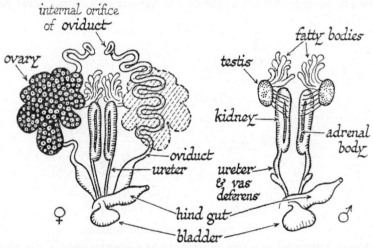

FIG. 426.—ORGANS OF NITROGENOUS EXCRETION AND OF REPRODUCTION IN THE FROG
SEEN IN VENTRAL VIEW

(The position of the left ovary is indicated in shading only.)

trunk region. They are masses of eggs in different stages of growth. Two coiled white tubes (*oviducts*) convey them to the exterior at the breeding season. With the excretory orifices the oviducts discharge into a short tube, the cloaca, between the legs. In the male there are two yellow or white bodies of ellipsoidal shape—the testes—lying over the kidneys and communicating with the exterior by the same duct or passage which conveys the urine to the common excretory orifice (Fig. 426). At the breeding season, when the eggs in the ovaries are ripe, they can be fertilized after removal from the body. If kept in clean water they will not develop, unless a drop of seminal fluid, which can be prepared by crushing up the testis of a male in tap water, is added.

The sperms of nearly all animals are very much alike and are always of microscopic dimensions. Eggs on the other hand vary greatly at the time of fertilization. The egg of an ostrich weighs several pounds. In the human female an egg about half the size of a full stop as printed on this page is liberated into the oviduct once a month, after sexual maturity has been reached (about the age of thirteen). The process regularly occurs about nine days after the monthly renewing of the mucous membrane of the internal

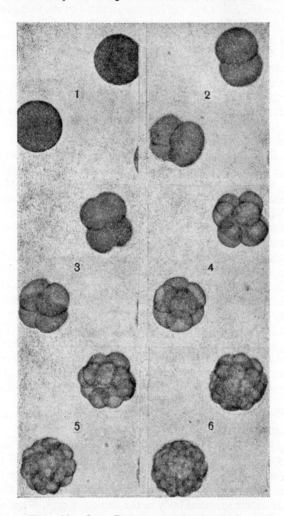

FIG. 427.—CELL DIVISION OF FERTILIZED EGG

Six photographs taken under the microscope with a cinematograph camera showing the first few cell divisions of two fertilized sea-urchin eggs. The time taken from fertilization to the first division is one hour at 20° C. (F. Vlès figure from *Biology* by H. Munro Fox, Cambridge University Press.)

generative passages and its accompanying haemorrhage. The egg of a bird, like the ostrich or fowl, is fertilized before it enters the oviduct. In its passage through the latter the essential part of the egg, the yolk, acquires a slimy coating, the albumen or white, and a chalky shell. In spite of these differences in the fully formed egg, very young eggs from the ovary of different animals are remarkably alike.

The female frog lays her eggs embedded in masses of a clear jelly, analogous to the albumen of a fowl's egg and likewise secreted by the wall of the oviduct. They have no shell. So we can study what follows fertilization more easily in the frog than in an animal whose eggs are protected by an opaque envelope or develop to a late stage in the body of the mother. Once the sperm has made its way into the egg a change occurs in its outermost layer. No other sperm can now penetrate it. In the sea-urchin's egg and that of some lower plants this change is easily visible. A stiff membrane is immediately produced (Fig. 425). About three and a half hours after fertilization a furrow appears on the surface of the frog's egg, which divides into two. The separation is complete about four hours after fertilization. The two halves, which are called *cells*, do not separate to start separate lives of their own. They remain connected and divide again. The process is repeated again and again until, within twenty-four hours after fertilization, the black egg, as can be distinctly seen with a simple lens, is a hollow ball of many such cells (Fig. 428). Thenceforth changes take place in the rate of multiplication of the cells in different regions. From different groups of cells the various characteristic structures or organs of the body begin to take shape.

The details of development vary considerably in different animals. Eggs with a large amount of food stored in them do not divide as a whole. The fowl's egg is an example. After the sperm nucleus has united with the egg nucleus, which lies in the clear circular area on the side of the yolk of an infertile fowl's egg, the combined nucleus divides in the usual way, but only a small part of the fowl's yolk is partitioned off round each cell (Fig. 429). So the embryo is at first a small plate of cells lying on the surface of the remaining yolk and growing at its expense. The domestic fowl lays eggs at definite intervals—in high-laying strains like the White Leghorn about twenty-six hours. The eggs are deposited whether they are fertilized or not.

THE CELLULAR STRUCTURE OF THE LIVING BODY

The cells of the frog embryo are all very much alike at first and resemble a very small egg from the ovary. The cells of different parts of the body in the tadpole or adult frog are not all alike in size or shape. They all resemble one another in possessing a structure known as the *nucleus*, which is very prominent as a clear spherical body in the immature eggs. When cells divide, the nucleus divides in a very characteristic way.

Microscopic sections of the testis show that, like other organs of the body, it is composed of cells. Its cells are constantly dividing to provide new sperm. Each sperm is formed from a single cell of the testis, the head or thick portion of the sperm being the nucleus. In a similar way, eggs are produced by cell division in the ovary. When the sperm penetrates the egg, the tail or flagellum is either sloughed off or absorbed. The body or nucleus swells up and unites with the nucleus of the egg in preparation for the first "segmentation" division (Figs. 427 and 428).

Like the testis or ovary, the substance of all the organs of the animal body is also built up of microscopic bricks called cells (Fig. 417). In some tissues like bone and cartilage the bricks are separated by a good deal of plaster, or to use the technical terms, *matrix*. Others, such as the *epithelia* or lining membranes of all surfaces, internal or external, including the tubular cavities of the glands, consist simply of cells packed closely together. Although the cells of different tissues acquire different shapes and sizes as the development of the frog's egg proceeds, they all arise by division of the undifferentiated cells in the hollow ball stage. The process of cell division involves the partition of the nucleus in the same characteristic manner, described under the term *mitosis* (*vide infra*). Its detailed features were not described till high-power microscopes began to be used.

To recognize the debt which present knowledge of reproduction in animals owes to the progress of botanical studies more directly related to the social needs of the time, it is only necessary to recall a few of the steps which led to the discovery made by Hertwig and Fol in 1879. Although Leeuwenhoek had believed that the sperm impregnates the egg, and botanists had been helped by its discovery to the recognition of sex in plants, prevailing opinion in the early years of the nineteenth century had been swung over by new discoveries of independent micro-organisms to the belief that the sperm is a parasite. In Cuvier's zoological treatise (1817) they are classed under a separate genus, *Cercaria*, with creatures now known to be microscopic larvae of parasitic worms like the liver fluke. The homunculus was in retreat and the sperm was generally supposed to play no essential part in fertilization. Meanwhile botanical science in close relation to practical needs had progressed far ahead of zoology. The great zoologist Owen, writing in 1835, said it was still a matter of doubt whether spermatozoa were comparable to pollen grains or whether they were independent species. Treviranus, who started by inclining to Cuvier's view, adopted a new orientation to the problem in the year (1833) after the cell doctrine of the plant body was established. He compared sperms to the pollen of plants, as Moreland had compared pollen grains to sperm a century earlier, and suggested that they were formed from the tubular walls of the testis as pollen grains are formed from the cells of the anthers.

Kölliker observed that this was true in 1841. The essential part which the sperm plays was experimentally proved by two Frenchmen in 1824—almost immediately after the first microscopic observations on the formation of the pollen tube. They repeated with greater care earlier and, as he thought, inconclusive experiments of Spallanzani. The latter had shown that seminal fluid, filtered through several layers of blotting paper to retain all the sperms, will not fertilize frog's eggs, though the residue of spermatozoa suspended in water will do so. Newport, who confirmed these experiments incontestably in the course of researches started about the time when the fertilization of the flowerless plants with motile sperms was established by Hofmeister, could still write in 1851 (*Phil. Trans. Roy. Soc.*):

We are as yet entirely without proof that any material influence or substance is actually transmitted from the spermatozoon . . . and although not a trace of the spermatozoon is detected in the ovum, we have seen that it remains a long time on the surface.

To observe directly the surprising fact that only one sperm enters the egg of an animal in the act of fertilization calls for good microscopic technique and good powers of patient observation. We may well doubt whether the search would have been brought to a successful conclusion, if the work of botanists had not provided solid ground for hope. When motile sperms were discovered in flowerless plants, plant microscopists were already familiar with the fact that a single pollen grain penetrates a single ovule. They were naturally disposed to explore the possibility that the egg of a fern prothallus or moss plant is fertilized by a single sperm. The discovery of sperms and egg cells, essentially like those of so many marine animals, in mosses and ferns made it difficult to doubt that the union of two cells is the fundamental feature of sexual reproduction common to animals and plants. Progress in knowledge of animal reproduction during the first half of the nineteenth century was a by-product of new social needs which stimulated enquiry into the propagation of plants and of new means of investigation made possible by technical improvements of optical instruments. The new botany furnished the clues for further insight into the knowledge of sex and development among animals. When the twentieth century dawned, the science of animal breeding received a spectacular impetus from the study of plant hybridization, and reaped a rich harvest from the knowledge which had accumulated meanwhile (see Chapter XXII).

THE PHYSICAL NATURE OF FERTILIZATION

The entry of the sperm is a physical event associated with material changes in the egg, and these changes are capable of being imitated. One of them is an increase of permeability to dissolved substances. Physical agents which change the semi-permeable property of the egg periphery are capable of starting the process of cleavage without the aid of the sperm. In 1899 the brilliant American biologist, Jacques Loeb, discovered that eggs of a sea-urchin placed in a mixture of sea water and magnesium chloride about twice the molar concentration of sea water, grew into free-swimming larvae. He found later that this was not due to the specific action of magnesium, since sea water made more concentrated with a variety of substances would do exactly the same. Moreover, the concentration of each substance which was most effective, in producing the greatest number of successes, was found to be such as to exert a definite *osmotic pressure*. It had to have a measurable and fixed power of withdrawing water from the egg. Subsequently Loeb found that by preliminary insertion of the eggs in acidified sea water, 100 per cent fertilization could be obtained. The strength of acid is related to the ease with which it will pass through the fatty outside layer of the egg. By various methods *artificial parthenogenesis* has now been carried out with a variety of species. The frog's egg will develop without the aid of the sperm if pricked with a fine glass fibre. Fatherless tadpoles have actually been raised through the metamorphosis stage to the adult condition.

DEVELOPMENT OF THE ANIMAL BODY

The development of the egg of a frog, as described by Newport and his successors, has a very great advantage over that of other forms as an aid to understanding the way in which the complex architecture of the body is built up. Some of the most important features of the process can be followed with no more elaborate apparatus than a simple hand lens. A few hours after

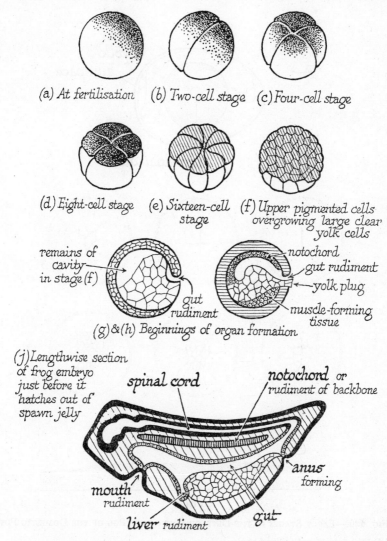

(a) *At fertilisation*   (b) *Two-cell stage*   (c) *Four-cell stage*

(d) *Eight-cell stage*   (e) *Sixteen-cell stage*   (f) *Upper pigmented cells overgrowing large clear yolk cells*

remains of cavity in stage (f)

gut rudiment

notochord
gut rudiment
yolk plug
muscle-forming tissue

(g) & (h) *Beginnings of organ formation*

(j) *Lengthwise section of frog embryo just before it hatches out of spawn jelly*

spinal cord

notochord *or rudiment of backbone*

anus *forming*

mouth *rudiment*

liver *rudiment*

gut

FIG. 428.—STAGES IN THE DEVELOPMENT OF THE FROG'S EGG

fertilization, divisions of the egg into separate compartments or *cells* follow in rapid succession (Fig. 428). At the time of fertilization the egg shows a concentration of black pigment towards the uppermost pole. Division proceeds according to a fixed rule. The first division is parallel to the vertical axis, and the second is also in a vertical plane. The third division is in the horizontal plane, and separates off a tier of cells which contain black pigment from a tier of somewhat larger colourless cells. Successive divisions take place in all planes. A hollow sphere is thus formed. The cells of the lower part are relatively larger and contain no black pigment.

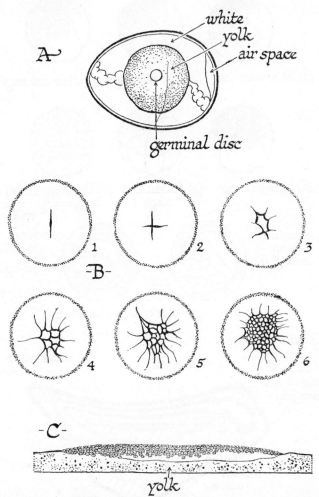

FIG. 429.—EARLY STAGES IN THE DEVELOPMENT OF THE EGG OF THE DOMESTIC FOWL

(*A*) Diagram of unfertilized egg.
(*B*) Six stages in the segmentation of the germinal disc.
(*C*) Vertical section through the germinal disc when segmentation is complete.

Up to this stage the only hint of any differentiation of the immature being, or *embryo*, into separate tissues or organs is the demarcation between the upper zone of smaller black cells and the lower zone (Fig. 428, *f*) composed of a somewhat irregular mass of cells rich in storage material or yolk. Now begins the stage of organ building. Soon almost the entire surface of the embryo is covered with a layer of small pigmented cells, the large unpigmented cells being evident only at one end, the *yolk plug*. This is destined to be the posterior end of the tadpole.

Now begins the differentiation of two systems of organs characteristic of the adult animal—the gut or alimentary canal and the central nervous system. The black outer covering of cells forms a distinct lip over the yolk plug on one side. A small chink beneath this lip grows inwards, enlarging as it grows. This is the rudiment of the alimentary cavity (Fig. 428, *h*) of the

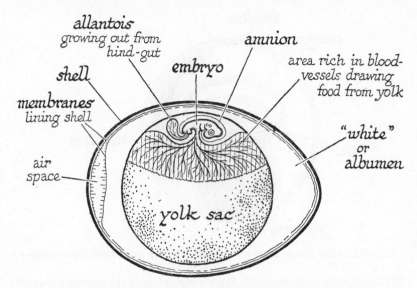

FIG. 430.—THE FOWL'S EGG AFTER FIVE DAYS OF INCUBATION

At first the embryo was flattened against the yolk, and its gut was wide open to the yolk ventrally. Now it has gathered itself together and pinched itself off from the yolk with which, however, it still remains connected by a stalk. A thin layer of highly vascular tissue has spread over the yolk and is drawing nourishment from it. The embryo, which shows the rudiments of eyes, limbs, and gill slits, is protected by a dome-like membrane, the *amnion*, which contains fluid and acts like a water cushion. The *allantois* is growing out from the hind gut. As the yolk-sac and albumen diminish it will grow right round the embryo, becoming connected with the air-space and the shell, and serving as a respiratory organ. At the end of development the stalk of the allantois becomes the urinary bladder.

tadpole. It is the embryonic gut. Meanwhile a groove appears on the surface of the embryo from the region just above the lip already referred to. The groove is wider in front, and as it deepens, its edges grow up, and coalesce, so that a tube is formed beneath a thin covering of cells. This tube, broadest at the future head end, is the rudiment of the spinal cord and brain which retain a cavity throughout life in all vertebrates. While this has been going on, cavitation of the mass of internal unpigmented cells has progressed inwards from the yolk plug.

The original cavity of the sphere has been obliterated. The new cavity excavated inwards from the yolk plug will ultimately become the cavity of the alimentary canal. As cavitation proceeds, a belt of cells is separated off from the mass of colourless cells which form the innermost part of the embryo. This belt of tissue (*mesoderm*) is derived from cells which migrated inwards from the lips surrounding the yolk plug and is destined to give rise to the body musculature, including the walls of the blood vessels which arise as canals in it. Beneath the dorsal rudiment of the central nervous system a rod of tissue is detached from the roof of the primitive gut in the mid-dorsal line.

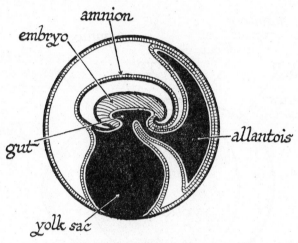

FIG. 431.—THE YOUNG EMBRYO MAMMAL AND ITS ACCESSORY MEMBRANES.—
VERY DIAGRAMMATIC

The double outer membrane in this figure is in part formed at a very early stage, and in part later, as a by-product of the development of the amnion. The "yolk-sac" contains no yolk, but is so called because it corresponds in development and structural relations with the functional yolk-sac of birds and reptiles. In kangaroos and opossums the yolk-sac is large and receives nourishment for the embryo from the uterine wall during the short pregnancy. In higher mammals it may function in this way early in development, but this work is soon taken over by the allantois, which fuses with the outer membrane of this diagram, and with the uterine wall to form the *placenta* (Fig. 432).

The cells of this rod later become vacuolated, and the structure constitutes a stiff skeletal axis, the *notochord*. Around the notochord, which is found in all vertebrate embryos, the vertebral column is built up at a later stage.

The development of the egg of the fowl or of the human being differs in one important respect from that of the frog or of a fish. Segmentation in the fowl and in man leads to the formation of a number of membranes which enclose the embryo before birth, but are discharged at the end of the embryonic life. After fertilization, the nucleus of a fowl's egg divides repeatedly, but as the yolk does not all divide with the nuclei, a thin plate of cells is demarcated on the surface of the remaining yolk (Fig. 429). This plate of cells grows over the surface of the egg, and gives rise to a sac enclosing the yolk and to a series of envelopes which wrap round the embryo proper (Fig. 430). The remains of the yolk sac are often present at the time of hatching.

The human egg cell has practically no yolk, and it develops at first into a hollow ball of cells like the egg of the frog, but only a part of this hollow sphere grows into the body of the embryo. Like the embryo fowl, the embryonic human being is invested with a series of envelopes. These envelopes, more especially the *allantois* (Figs. 429 to 431), enter into very close connexion with the wall of the womb, which is specially well supplied with blood vessels during the nine months during which development completes itself within the body of the mother. The structure formed by this fusion

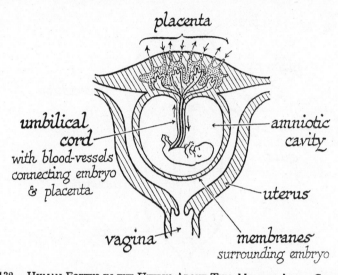

FIG. 432.—HUMAN FOETUS IN THE UTERUS ABOUT TWO MONTHS AFTER CONCEPTION

The black lines in the placenta represent diagrammatically the capillaries containing the blood of the foetus, and the dotted spaces connect with the blood system of the mother. The arrows show the circulation of the blood in both.

of maternal and embryonic tissues is called the *placenta* (Fig. 432). By diffusion of nutrient matter through the thin films of tissue which separate the blood vessels of the mother from those of the embryo, the latter is able to grow in spite of the fact that the egg itself has no storage. A feature common to the development of the fowl and the mammalian egg is the fact that, though it will develop into a land animal, the embryo at a certain stage has clefts on the side of the throat like those through which water passes over the gills of the tadpole or adult fish.

METAMORPHOSIS

After the embryo of the frog has reached the stage when the gut rudiment and the beginnings of the nervous system have been differentiated, it grows more rapidly in the axis parallel to the length of the spinal cord. After about a fortnight the head and tail ends are distinguishable. The muscles of the tail are sufficiently active to enable the embryo to wriggle out of the mass of jelly in which the eggs are laid. Independent existence starts. Unlike ourselves, the frog does not begin its separate existence with an organization very much like the sexually mature form. The human baby at birth is essentially an immature adult. The chief difference is that it has no teeth, and even after it acquires teeth it has to shed one set of them before the permanent set appear. The sexual organs are immature and remain so until about the age of fourteen, when certain minor distinctions between the sexes (*secondary sexual characters*) such as the pitch of voice, presence of hair on the upper lip

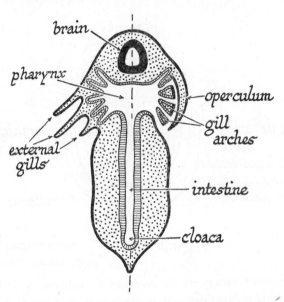

FIG. 433.—VERY DIAGRAMMATIC HORIZONTAL SECTION OF A YOUNG TADPOLE, SHOWING ON THE LEFT AN EARLY STAGE IN WHICH THE EXTERNAL GILLS ARE FULLY DEVELOPED, AND ON THE RIGHT A LATER STAGE, WHEN THE EXTERNAL GILLS HAVE DISAPPEARED, THE GILL-CLEFTS HAVE BROKEN THROUGH AND ARE PROTECTED BY A GILL COVER OR OPERCULUM

and chin of the male, and enlargement of the milk glands in the female, become evident.

Otherwise a human adult is in most respects, anatomically speaking, a grown-up baby. The embryo of the frog, which has hitherto grown at the expense of food or "yolk" stored in the egg, is very different from the adult when it first starts independent feeding. It breathes like a fish by gills and not by lungs. The arterial system is essentially fish-like. It has no fore-limbs and only the tiniest rudiments of hind-limbs. It possesses a tail.

On each side of the throat in the newly hatched tadpole of the frog, shortly after the time of hatching out, there are four clefts which later communicate with the exterior and with the throat, thus letting water pass from the mouth outwards (Fig. 433). The walls between these clefts are known as the gill arches. From the first three gill arches there grow out on either side tufts of filaments well supplied with blood vessels. These "external" gills disappear within a few days. The gill clefts then break through and the sides of the gill arches become covered with folds of skin very richly supplied with blood vessels like the gills of a fish. A fold of skin, the operculum, also similar to that of a fish, grows back over the gill clefts, as in many fishes, and conceals the gill from outside. The tadpole continues to breathe partly by its skin and partly by passing water over the gill clefts, which absorb the oxygen contained in it; and at first it has no true lungs. This state of affairs is not permanent. The tadpole stage of the British common frog lasts only about three months. An abrupt change supervenes; and in a very short time the adult characteristics are assumed. This change is called the *metamorphosis*. The preceding phase or tadpole stage is spoken of as the *larval period*. At metamorphosis the hind-limbs, which in the half-grown tadpole are tiny rudiments, begin to grow rapidly. Then the rudiments of the fore-limbs

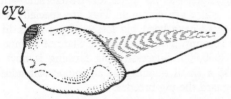

FIG. 434.—ONE-EYED TADPOLE, PRODUCED BY EXPOSING THE YOLK PLUG STAGE TO THE ACTION OF LITHIUM CHLORIDE

break through the skin. Finally the gill clefts begin to close up, and the tail shrinks. A four-legged, air-breathing, tailless adult emerges on to land.

The way in which an animal develops is a very difficult problem to understand, and we are only just beginning to do so. It is possible to experiment with the development of a frog or toad just as it is possible to experiment with the heart or the stomach. We can make the eggs of a frog or toad grow up into individuals with two heads or two tails or with one eye on the top of the head instead of two (Fig. 434). One question about the development of the frog which we are beginning to understand is of considerable importance in medicine and agriculture. This is, what brings about the sudden transformation from the tadpole into the adult form?

In the neck of the human being there is a flat lump of tissue known as the *thyroid gland*. It is represented in the frog by a pair of ovoid bodies on either side of two large veins of the neck region. In both man and the frog the thyroid gland consists of small capsules of a jellyish material, and is very richly supplied with blood vessels. Like the adrenal and pituitary· glands, two other structures which are somewhat like the digestive glands in texture, it has no duct. Such organs are for that reason sometimes called ductless glands. The jellyish material of the thyroid gland is peculiar in that it contains a compound of iodine, an element not found in other tissues of the animal body. When the thyroid gland of any animal is given as food to young tadpoles they start to develop limbs and to lose their tails very rapidly.

A large American frog, which normally lives for two years in water as a tadpole, will undergo metamorphosis within six weeks from hatching, if fed on thyroid gland instead of ordinary meat. The thyroid gland of the tadpole can be removed by a comparatively simple surgical operation about the time of hatching, and tadpoles deprived of their thyroid glands, though otherwise normal, will go on growing for years without undergoing metamorphosis. They never assume the adult characteristics. Among human beings there is a disease of infancy known as *cretinism*. Its characteristics include permanent undergrowth and persistence of childish characteristics. It can now be cured, as these cretin tadpoles can be cured, by giving thyroid gland (dried and in the form of a pill) as medicine. Metamorphosis occurs when the thyroid gland begins to pour its secretion into the blood. Tadpoles can also be prevented from developing into the adult form if kept in water free of any trace of iodine compounds.

The thyroid iodine compound can now be manufactured from pure chemicals in the laboratory. In districts where there is little iodine in the soil or drinking water—as in parts of Switzerland—thyroid deficiency diseases such as goitre are common. Pigs are specially sensitive to iodine deficiency, and there have been big losses of pig stock in certain parts of America on this account. The losses in the State of Montana in 1916 represented about £1,000,000. Successful pig farming is now possible in such localities, because a small quantity of an iodine salt added to the diet is sufficient to safeguard the pig breeder.

HEREDITY AND ENVIRONMENT

There is a local variety of the Mexican salamander, which never grows into the land form in nature. It remains a sort of tadpole called the *axolotl*, and breeds in the immature state. Though a single meal of ox-thyroid suffices to turn it into a land salamander in six weeks, supplying it with iodine does not make it develop into a land form like that of similar salamander larvae in other localities. Its own thyroid does not have the power to use iodine. The Mexican salamander does not develop into the land form in nature, because it *inherits* from its ancestors an inefficient thyroid gland. Tadpoles in mountain lakes sometimes fail to develop because there is insufficient iodine in their *environment*.

This gives us an opportunity for examining two words used very loosely by people who have no biological training. By inheritance we simply mean the stuff which the sperm and the egg contribute to the new being. How that stuff will shape depends partly on what sort of stuff it is, that is to say, on what sort of parents it came from; and partly on the surroundings in which it finds itself. Before the nature of reproduction was understood as we understand it today, it was generally believed that any bodily change which results from a change in our surroundings can be transmitted to our children. Experiment does not support this view, which was commonly believed in the past and was stated in a very explicit form by Lamarck in his *Philosophie Zoologique*. The hereditary stuff does occasionally undergo great changes. Sports appear, and breed true to their new characteristics. Otherwise the same materials are transmitted from generation to generation unchanged through the sperm and the egg. Heredity and environment are different aspects of development. *What we inherit is a capacity to develop in a particular way in a particular environment.*

When the Lamarckian principle was first challenged, even prominent scientists were willing to believe fables such as the story that a cock deprived of one eye transmits eye-defects to all his offspring. When it was conclusively proved that mutilations effected through several generations left no impress on the hereditable characters of the stock, the Lamarckians fell back on the gratuitous defence that only "adaptive" changes could be transmitted. The precise meaning of the adjective was never defined. No reason was forthcoming to suggest how the gonads could discriminate between mutilations and bodily changes that are "adaptive."

The doctrine of Lamarck was first called in question during the decade when the nature of fertilization was finally elucidated. To understand the tenacity with which the belief in the Lamarckian principle has clung to biological thought, we have to remember that the microscopic study of development is the most recently developed branch of anatomical science. So until the middle of the nineteenth century, the current conception of inheritance in biology was closely analogous to the legal notion. The parent was supposed to hand on its characters to the offspring in the same sense as the well-to-do hand on their belongings. While so erroneous a doctrine as preformation could prevail, the so-called inheritance of acquired characters seemed a perfectly reasonable view.

One question of special interest in connection with development arises from one of the earliest biotechnical inventions of mankind. Between the ages of twelve to seventeen there is more or less abrupt development of what we have already called the "secondary sexual characters" in girls and boys. The age of *puberty* may be compared to the period of metamorphosis in the frog. At puberty, so called because of the appearance of hair on the pubic region (i.e. the region where the legs join the trunk), the ovaries begin to liberate egg cells and the testes begin to manufacture seminal fluid. The development of the secondary sexual characters, e.g. bass voice and beard of the male, can be prevented by removal of the gonads, just as the metamorphosis of the frog can be prevented by removal of the thyroid glands.

Just as the loss of the larval characters is dependent on the activity of the thyroid gland in frogs, toads, and salamanders, the assumption of the most obvious differences between the sexes in many other animals also depends on the activity of the *gonads*. In fowls the hen will assume the plumage and spurs of the cock, if the ovary is removed at any time in the life cycle. One result of removal of the gonads (castration) is that the individual tends to deposit fat in the tissues, for which reason castration is practised in agriculture. From ancient times castration was practised in cattle rearing, for which a single normal male suffices to serve a large number of females. It was also carried out on the male of the human species. Such individuals are called eunuchs. Recent experiments have opened up new possibilities in biotechnology by throwing light on the chemical composition of the sex secretions. Before long they will be manufactured in the laboratory, and the discomforts of the menopause may be alleviated.

A number of facts about animals suggest the intervention of some agencies tending to predetermine the sex of the developing organism at a very early stage in development, in fact at the time of fertilization. Some of them are

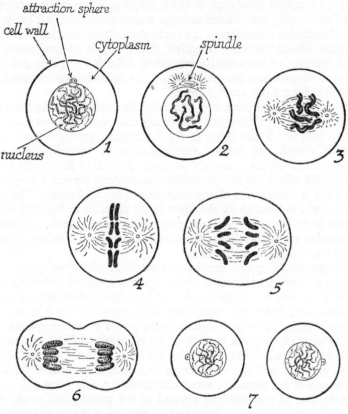

FIG. 435.—CELL DIVISION BY MITOSIS

This figure shows rather schematically the chief stages of mitotic cell division in an organism with four chromosomes in each of the ordinary cells of the body. 1 Resting nucleus just before commencement of division. 2 Spindle forming and the four chromosomes distinct, each with the beginnings of a longitudinal split. 3 The spindle extends across the centre of the cell, the membrane enclosing the nucleus has disappeared, and the chromosomes are becoming short and thick. 4 The compact chromosomes lie along the equator of the cell. 5 Chromosomes separating, cell elongating. 6 Cell beginning to divide, daughter chromosomes beginning to become diffuse and to run together to form two new nuclei. 7 Cell division complete and daughter nuclei entering a new resting phase.

of great importance to the modern practice of crop and stock breeding, as explained in Chapter XXII. One which was known to practical beekeepers in ancient times—indeed Aristotle attacked the belief—is that the male bee or wasp is produced from unfertilized eggs. The female (queens and workers) is produced in the usual way. In some animals the products of the first segmentation divisions separate, and several embryos are produced from one egg. When this happens, as in the production of "identical twins" in the human species, the individuals produced from a single egg are always of the same sex. The nine-banded armadillo produces litters of four young from a single egg. Individuals of the same brood are always of the same sex. In related species of armadillos, which produce litters from several eggs shed at once, individuals of the same litter may be either male or female. Clearly something which happens before segmentation begins decides the sex of the individual.

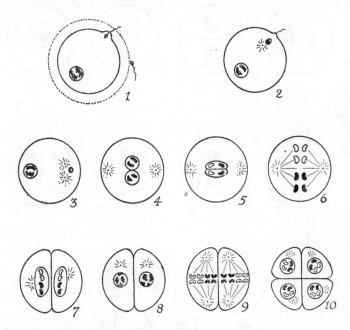

FIG. 436.—FERTILIZATION AND THE FIRST TWO DIVISIONS OF THE EGG

The species shown has four chromosomes in the division of the ordinary body cells. The sperm and egg each contribute two. 1 Penetration of sperm and formation of membrane preventing the entry of other sperms (as in sea-urchins and starfish); 2 and 3 swelling of the sperm nucleus; 4 and 5 union of sperm and egg nuclei; 6–10 the first two cleavage or segmentation divisions of the egg.

The first light on the problem suggested by these facts came when the behaviour of the cell *nucleus* in the process of fertilization and ordinary cell division was studied. In microscopic preparations nuclei of resting cells appear as vesicles containing a tangle of finely-spun threads. At one side of the nucleus is a small area in the cell substance, the *attraction sphere*, whose separation into two parts heralds the inception of cell division (Fig. 435). As the two attraction spheres separate they appear to draw out the surrounding cytoplasm into a *spindle* of fine fibrils. Meanwhile, changes have taken place in the nucleus itself. The tangle of fine threads has resolved itself into a number of readily distinguishable filaments called *chromosomes*, each of which is already beginning to split lengthwise into two halves. They become progressively shorter, assuming the appearance of stout rods or blocks staining deeply with certain dyes such as logwood. The chromosomes next arrange themselves on the equator of the spindle, and the halves of each chromosome separate, passing to opposite ends of the spindle. Then, while the division of the cytoplasm completes itself, they spin out again into fine threads. From these the nuclei of the daughter cells are built up.

Thus each of the chromosomes in the nucleus of any cell is structurally

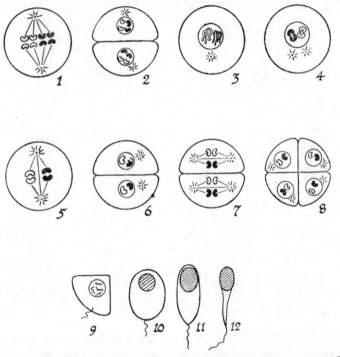

FIG. 437.—REDUCTION DIVISIONS IN THE FORMATION OF SPERMATOZOA IN THE TESTIS OF A SPECIES WITH FOUR CHROMOSOMES IN THE CELLS OF THE DIVIDING EGG

equivalent to a corresponding chromosome in that of the preceding and succeeding cell generations. In every species of organism the number of chromosomes which can be counted in dividing nuclei is constant, and the elaborate method just described by which nuclei divide (*mitosis*) ensures the maintenance of this constancy. The important fact that the nuclei of any one species of animals are made up of a constant number of chromosomes when the cells divide was established during the seventies.

With this discovery a new problem arose. During fertilization, as we have seen (Fig. 436), the nucleus of the sperm united with that of the egg to form a single nucleus of compound origin. Why does this not result in a doubling of the number of chromosomes in the nucleus in each generation? What ensures that each generation has the same chromosome number as the last?

These questions can now be answered. The formation of ripe sperms or eggs is the final stage of a long process of repeated cell-division within the testes or ovaries. All of these divisions except one take place in the manner already described. The last division but one before the formation of the actual ripe gametes is peculiar (Figs. 437, 438). Just before this division, the chromosomes come to lie side by side in pairs—a process known as *synapsis*—and during the subsequent division, when the stage corresponding to 4 of Fig. 435 is reached, it is these pairs which lie on the spindle. Instead of the chromosomes splitting in halves, as is normally the case, the pairs now part company, and one member of each pair goes into each of the daughter cells. Each of the resulting cells, and therefore (as the next division is perfectly normal) each of the gametes, has exactly half the number of chromosomes characteristic of the species. At fertilization the normal number is therefore restored.

So every ordinary cell of an individual organism has a chromosome set

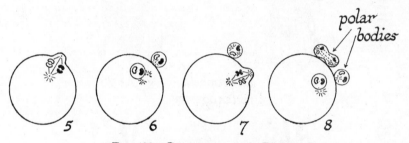

FIG. 438.—REDUCTION IN THE FEMALE

The antecedent stages correspond with stages 1–4 in Fig. 437.

of which half the members are paternal in origin and half maternal. In both sexes the *reduction division*, as this exceptional division of the nucleus is termed, occurs in the same way. In the male it is followed by division of the rest of the cell, and each daughter cell divides again in the normal manner, so that four sperms, each with half the typical chromosome number, result (Fig. 437). In the female, although the nucleus divides twice, just as it does in the male, the rest of the cell does not divide. Only one of the four resulting nuclei is retained within the egg-cell; the other three are extruded and degenerate, constituting the so-called *polar-bodies* (Fig. 438).

In many animals and plants it is possible to distinguish, among the chromosomes, pairs of different sizes and shapes—this is the case, for instance, in the fruit-fly *Drosophila*—and it is possible to see that each gamete receives one representative of each of the four pairs of chromosomes present in ordinary cells (Fig. 439). Thus the nucleus of the fertilized egg divides so that the daughter nuclei of the first cleavage receives two representatives of each pair of chromosomes. Cell divisions follow in rapid succession during the up-building of the embryo. Thus each cell of an individual fruit-fly contains four pairs of chromosomes, one member of each pair derived from the father and the other from the mother. As the result of reduction each gamete receives one component of each pair, that is to say, *with respect to each pair of chromosomes the formation of the gametes involves the segregation of its paternal and maternal components.* We shall find later that this is of the utmost help in understanding how to produce new varieties and breeds by hybridization.

In the fruit-fly there is another feature which calls for further comment. This is the existence, as in many animals, of one unequally mated pair of chromosomes, the XY pair. When this occurs, it occurs in one sex only; in the alternative sex there is a corresponding equal pair (XX). In birds and Lepidoptera (butterflies and moths), the female is the XY, the male the XX

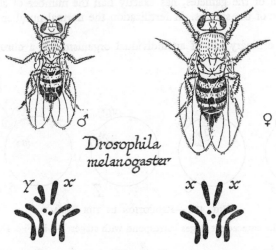

FIG. 439.—THE FRUIT-FLY, *Drosophila melanogaster*, AND ITS CHROMOSOMES

individual. With sufficiently careful measurement the male is usually found in other animals to have an unequal (XY) pair which is equally mated in the female (XX).

This was first noticed, because some animals were found to have an odd number of chromosomes in one sex. This seemed to conflict with the numerical constancy of the chromosomes. In the early years of the present century the American zoologists provided the key to an understanding of the discrepancy. In all such cases the other sex has one more chromosome. The male of *Periplaneta americana*, the large cockroach which haunts our bake-houses, has 33, the female 34 chromosomes. The eggs all have 17 chromosomes, one half of the sperm have 17 the other half 16 chromosomes. If a sperm of the former class fertilizes an egg, the individual produced will be a female (17 + 17 = 34), and if a sperm of the second type fertilizes an egg, the individual produced will be a male (17 + 16 = 33).

Similarly with the XY chromosomes. The male of the human species has 23 equal pairs and 1 unequal pair (XY) of chromosomes in the unreduced nuclei. Thus two types of sperm are produced, X-bearing and Y-bearing respectively, the one female producing, the other male producing. The modern theory of sex determination fits in well with many biological data, and is confirmed by two independent lines of evidence, one of which will be discussed at length later. The other may be mentioned here. In species having an XY pair in the male, measurement of the sperm heads shows that the sperms are of two different sizes. This suggests that it may be possible eventually to separate seminal fluid into portions containing predominantly one or other type of sperm, the X-bearing or Y-bearing. If this could be done the control of the sex ratio would be experimentally realizable. Recent experiments in Moscow record success with the seminal fluid of rabbits.

Some of the new discoveries which have come from the study of fertilization, sex, and allied problems open up radical and far-reaching possibilities in biotechnology, though as yet they have had no practical applications. The rabbit's egg can now be made to develop without sperm as far as the hollow ball stage. It can be grown by tissue culture methods outside the body of the mother till the heart begins to grow. From what we know of other animals it is probable that mammals produced by parthenogenesis would always be females. If the technique were perfected, the hallowed associations of this method of propagation might encourage the fashion of continuing the human race by virgin birth. Perhaps humanity may eventually decide that maleness is an unnecessary complication of agriculture, an obstacle to the control of population growth and a menace to the moral well-being of one-half of the human race.

APPLICATIONS OF THE NEW KNOWLEDGE

The discoveries which resulted from the use of the microscope made possible the production of new horticultural and agricultural varieties by plant hybridization. From the practice of plant hybridization the need for of modern biology. This will be explained in Chapter XXII, where the importance of the purely descriptive phenomena of nuclear behaviour dealt with in the last few pages will be explained. Two technical applications of the new knowledge of fertilization established in the eighteenth century have only been made during the past few decades. These are: (a) the use of pollinators for large-scale production of "self-sterile" varieties of fruits, and (b) artificial insemination.

(a) *Self-Sterile Varieties.*—Many of the best modern varieties of fruit trees have arisen as sports or as hybrids, preserved by grafting on to wild stock. Every single separate tree of some varieties which exist in fruit plantations is descended from the same ovule and pollen grain. As far as sexual reproduction is concerned the entire stock is one individual. This has given rise to an interesting problem which has been successfully solved by applying the knowledge of a discovery which was made by the first investigators who studied pollination. It was early recognized that among species of which the flowers are normally cross-pollinated by insects, dusting pollen from the anthers of a flower on to the stigmas of any flower of the same individual plant often produces a poor yield of offspring, and sometimes produces no seed at all. When no seed is produced the fruit fails to ripen properly. Many of our fruit trees are "self-sterile" in this sense, and since they have been spread by grafting, this means that the self-sterility includes every tree of a particular variety. Thus the choice cherry called "Bigarreau Napoleon" will not form fruit if pollinated by pollen from flowers of any tree of the same variety or that of several other varieties (e.g. Emperor Francis). On the other hand, it forms fruit if the stigmas are dusted with pollen of varieties which may be self-sterile themselves, and are said to be "pollinators" for it (e.g. Belle d'Orléans). Among the best modern varieties of fruit trees those which are self-fertile are a minority. Hence many failures occurred in the first experiments when large-scale fruit production began to replace small mixed orchards. Experiment, guided by correct knowledge of the rôle and agencies of pollination, quickly succeeded in elucidating the facts stated above, and in suggesting the necessary precautions to ensure success. All that need be done is (a) to plant a few trees of the varieties which act as "pollinators" in the vicinity of the self-sterile variety which is the main crop; (b) to encourage the insects which carry the pollen from the pollinator to the latter. Since most of them are bee pollinated, the simultaneous practice of apiculture is a profitable way of doing this.

(b) *Artificial Insemination.*—When the controversy between the "spermatists" and the "ovists" was still going on, Spallanzani, a contemporary of Lavoisier with a remarkably versatile record of first-rate work, undertook experiments in which he filtered off the spermatozoa from the seminal fluid and tested the influence of the several portions on the eggs of frogs. By introducing seminal fluid from a dog into her vagina, he made a bitch pregnant without sexual intercourse. Since then the use of artificial insemination, i.e. introduction of spermatozoa into the female generative passages or into suspensions of eggs, has been frequently used in various classes of biological enquiries as a substitute for normal sexual intercourse.

In the twenties of this century the U.S.S.R. encouraged investigations which have proved the possibility of keeping the seminal fluid of domesticated animals in a fertile condition for some days. Hence small phials of seminal fluid from the best pedigree oxen, horses, etc., can be distributed by air mail over a wide territory for the fertilization of females. The practice of breeding by artificial insemination with semen of exceptionally high quality sires is now (1953) widely used in the United States, in Britain and elsewhere. The U.S.S.R. has taken the lead in applying the method of artificial insemination to selection of the bee. This animal has been used by man for millennia without any attempt to improve the strain by active interference of a kind which has met with extraordinary empirical success in his dealings with other domesticated species. There is little doubt that artificial insemination will make possible improvement in the quality of stock with unexampled rapidity. We may also anticipate that the advance will be conspicuous where society is organized to take advantage of new biotechnical inventions.

CHAPTER XIX

THE MICROBE HUNTERS

THE immediate effect of the introduction of the first compound microscopes was to encourage closer scrutiny into the processes of reproduction. The doctrine of spontaneous generation, as applied to plants and animals of visible dimensions, succumbed in the ensuing century. Besides shedding new light on the material basis of reproduction, the minute structure of the animal and plant body, the microscope also revealed a world of organisms whose existence had been hitherto unsuspected. Some of them—like the smaller water "fleas" (Fig. 440) or minute crustacea in ponds and the surface of sea water—were only miniature examples of a type of bodily organization already well known. Others were new types with a complex bodily organization, having familiar characteristics, though exhibiting an entirely new general plan. Such, for instance, were the wheel animalcules or *Rotifera* of pond water (p. 965). In addition to these there was a class of organisms totally unlike any previously known. Creatures belonging to this last category, now collectively described as *Protista*, in contradistinction to animals and plants as the words are usually employed, were found to appear in great numbers in broths, infusions of organic matter, like pepper and spices, or in water in which hay has been left to soak, especially if contaminated with pond water. Others were found to multiply in rain water left in tubs. They had no structures reminiscent of the sexual organs of known animals and plants. They multiplied prodigiously in suitable media, and being so minute they appeared to come from nowhere.

The ideology of primitive sanitation (see p. 849) made its last stand concerning the generation of the Protista. Its overthrow is associated especially with the work of two men, the variety of whose contributions to science is a noteworthy and instructive commentary on the social background of science. One was Spallanzani. The other was Pasteur. Both worked in France. Separated by three-quarters of a century, their respective failure and success is an eloquent tribute to the debt which the most gifted contributors owe to their social environment.

Protista, as we should define these creatures in the light of the knowledge which the compound microscope confers, *are organisms of which the bodies are not divided up into cells.* There is not a very sharp line of division between the Protista and the simpler sponges which are little more than colonies of similar units equipped with vibratile cilia and embedded in a jelly, or between the Protista and the simpler plant algæ like *Spirogyra* (Fig. 423) and the simpler fungi called moulds (Fig. 424). The simplest animals and plants may in fact be looked on as colonies or companies of which each cell is comparable to a free living *protist*. On this account the Protista are usually spoken of as "unicellular" or *single-celled* organisms. Since the simplest filamentous plants have no separate organs to distinguish them they are chiefly classified by the way they reproduce. Partly for this reason and partly because some filamentous organisms disintegrate into separate cells in suitable culture media, many micro-organisms will be found classified as fungi or algæ in one context and as Protista in another. Thus the yeast organism, which is unicellular —or non-cellular to use the more precise term—is often classified as a fungus belonging to the same group as the mildew which produces "ergot" of wheat.

Some of the largest Protista are called *Infusoria* and can just be seen with the naked eye. The smallest visible with the best microscopes are called *bacteria*. It is difficult to convey their very small dimensions by a single illustration,

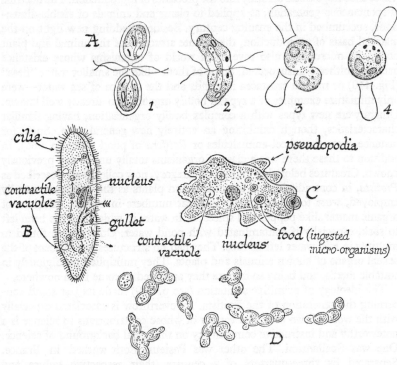

FIG. 440.—FOUR COMMON TYPES OF LARGER PROTISTA

(*A*) A green form, called Chlamydomonas, which progresses by the aid of two long cilia called flagella: four stages in the conjugation of similar gametes.

(*B*) Paramecium. Food particles in clear droplets are seen travelling round the body from the "gullet" to the place where faeces are discharged at a temporary opening in the surface. The "contractile vacuoles" get rid of surplus water which has entered the organism by osmosis.

(*C*) Amoeba, which progresses by a flowing motion in which temporary lobes of the body are pushed out. This specimen is in the act of enclosing another Protist to form a food vacuole in which digestion will take place.

(*D*) Yeast. Successive stages of budding are seen, leading to the formation of chains of cells.

because they vary enormously in size. A typical microbe is so small that it would require about twenty-five billion (25 million million) to balance an ounce weight. Examples of both large and small Protista were seen by Leeuwenhoek, who observed that they split in halves like cells of a developing embryo. Some Protista secrete siliceous or calcareous shells which are superficially like snail shells. The chalk is largely made up of the minute shells of protists called

Foraminifera (Fig. 441). The commonest method of reproduction is the vegetative method of splitting or budding (Fig. 440, D). Splitting into equal halves is characteristic of the Infusoria and the simpler organisms like the formless *Amoeba* (Fig. 440, C) which are not covered with cilia like the Infusoria.

A typical Infusorian of pond life is *Paramecium* (Fig. 440, B). This small organism can usually be found in mud. If samples of mud from several ponds are added to a little pond water in which a few bread-crumbs have been allowed to soak, Paramecium multiplies rapidly. After standing for about a day or two the mud at the bottom, when examined under the microscope, is found to contain little rapidly moving creatures. Each has the shape of a cigar. If you can observe one when it is not moving too quickly you will see that its

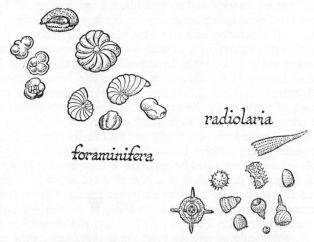

radiolaria

foraminifera

FIG. 441.—SHELLS OF RADIOLARIA AND FORAMINIFERA

Some Protista which live freely in water surround themselves by siliceous (the Radiolaria) or calcareous (the Foraminifera) shells of microscopic dimensions, or just large enough to be visible to the eye. The Chalk has mainly been formed by deposits of Foraminifera, whose dead shells accumulated on the sea bottom.

movements are due to fine flickering outgrowths called *cilia* (because of their resemblance to eyelashes—the Latin word). Cilia cover the whole body. Somewhat similar organisms (*Opalina, Balantidium,* etc.) can always be found living parasitically in the muddy contents in the hindermost portion of the bowel of the frog. When such organisms as these have gone on feeding for a certain time, they become constricted about the middle, and gradually divide into two, just as a drop of fluid will divide into separate drops when it has reached a certain size. Each half becomes a new individual and swims off on its own. Thus every Paramecium arises from another Paramecium. *Like begets like* is a rule that applies to Paramecium, as well as to ourselves.

The yeast organism (*Saccharomyces*) is a small spherical cell with a thick outer coat like the cells of a fungus or any other plant (Fig. 440, D). It reproduces vegetatively by forming buds, which become detached and grow to their full stature subsequently. In addition it forms resistant spores, by division of the body substance within the cell wall into four cells which are each invested with a thicker wall capable of withstanding drought and germinating in a moist situation. This power of forming spores which many Protista, including bacteria, possess accounts for their queer way of turning up when organic material such as broths—or Leeuwenhoek's pepper suspensions—are left freely exposed to air in which the spores are blown about. Needless to say this could not be realized till their reproductive processes were thoroughly understood, and the reproductive processes of the smaller protists can only be seen with very good microscopes.

Before the researches of the pioneer microscopists of the seventeenth century *Protista* had not been known to exist. While it would be true to say that Leeuwenhoek discovered reproduction in the larger Infusoria in the sense that he observed and recorded it, it is quite clear that he did not understand that what he was observing was the way in which these creatures multiply. This conclusion seems to have been first reached in the middle of the eighteenth century by a French botanist de Saussure to whom John Ellis, author of the first clear and comprehensive account of the *Particular Manner of Increase in the Animalcula of Vegetable Infusions*, acknowledges his indebtedness in 1769. There had been much controversy concerning the nature of Protista. In the first half of the eighteenth century it was not yet recognized that they were living creatures, and the issue was only settled when Spallanzani, who taught at Pavia in Italy, carried out an important series of experiments in which he showed that the "organisms of vegetable infusions" are killed by exposure to drought, that they perish like tadpoles, frogs and salamanders at a heat of about 33°–35° C., that they are destroyed by vapours and fluids which poison insects, that some of them— like Paramecium—can take in solid food and digest, and that,—as Spallanzani's biographer and physician Tourdes puts it,—"the electric spark is a thunder clap to the animalcules of infusion : not one of them survives the explosion."

About this time Needham, a Jesuit priest with a predilection for Aristotelian finalities, had sought to put the doctrine of spontaneous generation on a firm basis by showing that micro-organisms appear in vegetable infusions and broths which have been boiled to kill organisms and stoppered afterwards to prevent the entry of fresh ones. The heat used was insufficient. No microscopic check was made to see if the organisms had been killed, and porous corks were used as stoppers. On one bad experiment Buffon, the French naturalist, built up a mountain of metaphysics which dominated scientific teaching for a century. Spallanzani, who was acquainted with de Saussure's observations, entered into a controversy with Needham, and undertook a re-examination of the issue. In his own words:

I repeated that experiment. I used hermetically sealed vases. I kept them an hour in boiling water, and after having opened them and examined their contents within a reasonable time, I found not the slightest trace of animalculae, though I had examined with the microscope the infusions from nineteen vases.

Although Voltaire wrote of the "ridiculous mistake, the unfortunate experiments of Needham, so triumphantly refuted by M. Spallanzani . . ." and declared that "it is now demonstrated to sight and to reason that there is no vegetable, no animal but has its own germ," Buffon's doctrine was generally accepted for the next hundred years. There were, he taught, certain primitive and incompatible parts common to animals and to vegetables. These particles cast themselves into *moulds* or shapes characteristic of different beings. When destroyed by death, the organic molecules become free, over-active, reuniting to form a multitude of new organized bodies. The initial premises rested on unsound experimental foundations. Thereafter the argument proceeded according to rules of evidence which are still acceptable to economists and to the legal profession.

The neglect of Spallanzani's work can hardly be attributed to the lack of esteem in which his scientific work was held. He was perhaps the most truly original experimental biologist of his age. He held successively two important chairs at Reggio and Pavia, travelled and corresponded far afield, receiving many tokens of esteem and recognition throughout Europe. Born in 1729, he had the good fortune to study at Bologna where the professor of natural philosophy was his cousin Laura Bassa. This gifted and remarkable woman was one of the most singular personalities of the eighteenth century. In *Bologna, its History, Antiquities and Art* by Coulson James, we are told that she occupied a university chair, worked at hydraulics and mechanics, and had twelve children to whom she was devoted. When she died at the age of 67, after attending a meeting of the Academia Benedittina on the previous evening, she was buried with great honour in her doctoral robes. Her young cousin and pupil was promoted to a chair at an early age, and in the space of forty years, from 1760 till his death in 1798, he announced a succession of discoveries equally astonishing for their diversity and novelty.

In relation to the immediate growth of biological knowledge he is noteworthy as one of the first workers to carry out systematic experiments on the rôle of the digestive juices. Under the impact of Lavoisier's work he undertook a wide survey of the respiratory organs of the lower animals, and so established the fact that the intake of oxygen and excretion of carbon dioxide are well nigh universal characteristics of complex animals, though the machinery by which the aeration of the blood is effected is diverse. Spallanzani performed the first experiments on the tactile sensations of bats which can thread their way through a network of strings when blinded. He executed the first experiments on artificial insemination. Besides experimenting with the eggs of frogs, toads and silkworms, he injected into the vagina of a bitch, says Tourdes, "nineteen grains of semen taken from a dog of the same breed" and "had, after the ordinary time of gestation, the satisfaction of seeing her bring forth several whelps, likewise of the same breed." He made the daringly mechanistic discovery that, if luminous jelly fish are desiccated and ground to a powder, the latter will emit light when moistened. In his experiments on the regeneration of the head in decapitated snails, he also anticipated modern experimental technique by showing that reproduction by cuttings is not confined to plants.

With the exception of the first two, it may be doubted whether any of his brilliant contributions—many of them so far ahead of the time—exercised any direct effect on the subsequent course of science. When the issue of spontaneous generation was raised by Pasteur in a different social context its solution was demanded by practical necessity, and further progress was ensured by the fact that it immediately became the focus of a host of biotechnical and medical applications in the manufacture of wine, beer and dairy produce, in the control of animal and plant diseases, in the conduct of surgical operations, the organization of hospitals, in veterinary inspection, sewage and interment control, notification of contagious and infectious diseases, immunization and germ-free milk. It had ceased to be an *ideological* squabble between the advocates of the Aristotelian tradition and the rising school of French materialists.

New instruments to allay any uncertainty were available to investigators. Though the larger bacteria had been seen, no satisfactory comparative survey of the Protista could be undertaken before achromatic lenses came into use. A classification of the bacteria appeared in 1838. In the fifties growing scientific interest in agriculture had directed attention to the reproductive processes of the cryptogams (algae and fungi).* Liebig's work on the chemistry of living matter (Chapter XX) had paved the way for analytical measurements of fermentation. Such was the social heritage from which Pasteur's contributions drew their materials.

Another significant fact in the social background of Pasteur's work is that the Crimean war, from which the modern profession of military nursing dates, had focused attention on the problems of sepsis and of food preservation. It was in fact the first great war in which modern methods of food preservation were used. Bremner (*Industries of Scotland,* 1849) tells us:

When Lord Anson reached Juan Fernandes with the Centurion, the Gloucester, and the Tryal, his united crews of 961 men had been reduced by that terrible disease to 626, of whom only a small number were fit for duty; and during last century a Spanish ship was picked up at sea with all her crew dead from scurvy. Cases of this kind might be multiplied to show the loss of human life entailed by want of means for preserving provisions in a fresh state. . . . . To such a height did scurvy attain in the navies and merchant shipping of Britain, France, and other countries, that the attention of the Governments was seriously roused to the importance of doing something to remedy the terrible evil. The French Government took the initiative by offering, in the year 1809, a premium for the invention of a process for preserving meat, so that it would remain fresh for any length of time, and in any climate. In the following year, M. Appert came forward to claim the prize; and, after due investigation, he received £480 for the invention of a mode of preserving both animal and vegetable matter by subjecting them to a certain degree of heat and then sealing them in air-tight vessels. The principle of Appert's system of preserving was known and practised in this country for years before he was made famous as the supposed discoverer of it; but those who were acquainted with the process did not realize its importance, or dream of the application which he made of it. . . . M. Appert claimed to have discovered—"First, that fire has the peculiar property not only of changing the combination of the constituent parts of vegetable and animal productions, but

* Knight begins an address to the Horticultural Society in 1813 with the words: "The little pamphlet upon the rust or mildew of wheat for which the public are indebted to the patriotic exertions of the venerable President of the Royal Society affords much evidence in proof that this disease originates in a minute species of parasitical fungus which is propagated like other plants by seeds" (i.e. spores as we should now say). He then refers to a paper of the same year controverting the prevailing view that rot fungus is produced by "the remaining powers of life in the sap of the unseasoned wood."

also of retarding, for many years at least, if not of destroying altogether, the natural tendency of those same products of decomposition; secondly, that the application of fire in a manner variously adapted to various substances, after having with the utmost care, and as completely as possible, deprived them of all contact with the air, effects a perfect preservation of those same productions with all their natural qualities." The operations by which fire is made available as a preserving agent are stated to be—first, enclosing in bottles the substance to be preserved; secondly, corking the bottles with the utmost care; thirdly, submitting the enclosed substances for a greater or less length of time to the action of boiling water in a water-bath; and fourthly, withdrawing the bottles from the water-bath at the period prescribed. . . . In 1811 an English patent was taken out for Appert's process of preservation. The patent was purchased for £1,000 by Messrs. Donkin, Hall and Gamble, who, in 1812, erected an extensive preservatory at Bermondsey. It is stated that, after a series of experiments made by the patentees for the purpose of testing the accuracy of the process, and ascertaining how far it might be made applicable in a general way for victualling the maritime service occasionally with fresh meat, they found that the system of preservation, so far as it had then been developed, was too defective and uncertain in its results to be made the vehicle of any safe or profitable commercial enterprise. They then made some experiments with vessels of tin, and these were so successful that the art of preserving food was reduced to a certainty. No sooner was the possibility of preserving provisions demonstrated by this firm, than the ships of the navy and of the East India Company were supplied with some of the prepared food; and soon a happy change became apparent in the health of those on board. Emigrant ships were subsequently ordered to carry certain proportions of preserved meats, and now no vessel sails on a voyage that is to extend beyond a few days without having such stores in the lockers. The meat-preserving trade has assumed large dimensions; and the method adopted by Messrs. Donkin, Hall and Gamble is that now followed (with certain modifications in the details of the process) in the great preservatories which supply the shipping of all nations. The meat-preserving trade was introduced into Scotland in 1822, when Messrs. John Moir and Son began business in Aberdeen. . . . During the Crimean war they executed several large contracts for the British and French Governments.

OPTICAL ACTIVITY

Although Pasteur's name is associated with an impressive range of discoveries which have enriched the theory of "pure" chemistry and "pure" biology, it is hardly too much to say that he never took up an enquiry which was not immediately related to dominant technological issues connected with the technical and medical problems of contemporary France. In the greater part of his life-work the funds which made his work possible were specifically given by those who sought his practical assistance. Pasteur's earliest researches were directly related to the wine industry, which became an important factor in national prosperity under the regime of Napoleon III. By the Gladstone agreement of 1860, the English undertook to drink French liquors in return for an agreement which, in effect, committed the French to wear Lancashire petticoats. His first important contribution was a study of the crystal form of tartaric acid which is an important by-product of the wine industry. He created a new branch of chemistry by showing how the pictorial formula of an organic compound is related to its crystalline shape, and how both are related to the effect which crystals exercise on polarized light (p. 333).

In Chapter X no reference was made to one of the most fruitful results of the molecular models based on applying the principle of valency to the behaviour of radicles in the carbon compounds. This directly arose from Pasteur's work on tartaric acid. In the course of it he discovered the pheno- menon of *optical activity* in organic compounds. In Chapter VI the peculiar behaviour of light when it has passed through certain mineral crystals such as fluorspar or tourmaline was described to illustrate the usefulness of the wave metaphor. A beam of light which has passed through a crystal of tourmaline will not pass through a second crystal if its axis is at right angles to that of the first. If we look through the second as we rotate it through 180° from the position in which the two crystal axes are parallel, the light becomes dimmer, disappears, and finally regains maximum brightness.

When a solution of some organic compounds is placed between the two crystals, the "plane of polarization" is shifted. That is to say, we have to twist the second crystal a little farther or not quite so far as 180° to get maximum brightness again. Such compounds are said to be *optically active*. Pasteur found that crystals of tartaric acid salts are not exactly alike. One type of crystal is the mirror image of another. The positions of their faces are reversed from left to right. This inversion is associated with the fact that they show opposite types of optical activity. If a solution of one is placed between two tourmaline crystals with parallel axes, one of the latter must be rotated to the right to get maximum brightness. When the other solution is substituted it must be twisted to the left to get maximum brightness. Many common organic compounds, such as cane-sugar, have this characteristic. Since the angle of twist depends on the strength of the solution, the *polarimeter*, an instrument which is simply an arrangement for rotating one of two polarizing crystals, can be used for quantitative analysis of their solutions.

Many substances which do not differ with respect to any very obvious chemical properties, twist the plane of polarization in opposite directions. Various drugs obtained from plants and drug-like substances (hormones) produced in the animal body are optically active. The natural form nearly always twists the plane of polarization *leftwards*. Their synthetic twins of the modern drug house nearly always twist it to the *right*. The left-handed or natural twin is nearly always much more effective in its action on the body as a poison or as a stimulant.* Several detective novels, such as *The Documents in the Case* by Dorothy Sayers and Robert Eustace, have exploited this theme.

Pasteur himself did not provide the clue which is contained in the picture formula. Substances with the same constitution and similar chemical proper- ties exist in different optically active forms when, and only when, they contain at least *one carbon atom attached to four different radicles*. Thus the

* The existence of the Deity can no longer be deduced from this circumstance alone. Some natural right-handed twins exist and some left-handed twins have been synthesized successfully.

picture formula for lactic (p. 516) acid conveys the information that it must have optically active forms, when it is set out in the following way:

$$
\begin{array}{ccc}
CH_3 & & OH \\
& C & \\
H & & COOH
\end{array}
$$

THE NATURE OF FERMENTATION

In these early researches Pasteur toured the wine manufacturing centres of Europe for material. His motto in research put into other words what Karl Marx called the unity of theory and practice. "Without theory, practice is but routine born of habit" were the words he used when he was appointed to a chair in the University of Lille—"overjoyed," says his biographer, "at being able to do useful work in that country of the distilleries." Of his public audiences, he asked, "where will you find a young man whose curiosity and interest will not immediately be wakened when you put into his hands a potato, when with that potato he may produce sugar, with that sugar alcohol, with that alcohol ether and vinegar."

The reports of the Academy of Sciences for 1861 include a short memoir by Pasteur on the yeast of beer. In it Pasteur recorded experiments which show:

1. Yeast organisms placed in some sweet liquid in contact with abundant air assimilate oxygen, multiply rapidly and produce an insignificant quantity of alcohol. The weight of sugar used up as compared with the weight of the organism—which can be easily determined by separating the latter with a centifuge—is very small.

2. Yeast organisms placed in a sugar solution without air produce alcohol at the expense of the sugar in large quantities.

"Acting out of reach of atmospheric oxygen," concluded Pasteur, the yeast "takes oxygen from the sugar, that being the origin of its fermentative character." Subsequent studies shewed that various moulds like Mucor and Penicillium which grow on bread, jam, cheese, etc., have the same power of switching over from ordinary "*aerobic*" respiration to "*anaerobic*" or intra-molecular extraction of oxygen when deprived of air, and their power to effect the decomposition of the materials on which they grow specially depends on this.

A new understanding of putrefaction was now inescapable. Fermentation is the name customarily given to decomposition of organic matter by micro-organisms like the yeast organism or the cheese bacteria when the end products are suitable to human consumption. So soon as Pasteur was able to shew that vinegar is produced in wine and that butyric acid is produced in rancid butter by the activity of a living organism, the next step was self-evident. Putrefaction is merely the name we have been accustomed to give to anaerobic respiration of micro-organisms when we do not use the end products. The extension of the new doctrine to sepsis and thence to infection seems equally inevitable in retrospect, and the persistence with which Pasteur continued to explore it in the face of violent personal attacks from the French medical profession, illustrates the important truth that great advances in science are less due to great intellectual subtlety than to steadfastness of aim and a robust partiality for unsavoury particulars.

If mildews and moulds could produce poison in the decomposition products from dead organic matter, might not the harm which resulted from the presence of mildews like the rusts or smuts of wheat or the various fungus pests of the orchard—mentioned in the Royal Society's Heads of Enquiries in 1665—be due to their power to liberate similar poisons in the plant body? If so, may not the poisoning which is accompanied by pus formation at cut surfaces of the animal body be due to the fermentative activity of the hosts of micro-organisms which are found in the pus itself? May not the apparently spontaneous character of infection and contagion be due to the fact that the parasites unlike mildews are invisible to the eye?

The clearest answer to all these questions lies in the new body of social practice which has arisen from and constitutes the testing-out of the theory. If putrefaction is a fermentative activity of micro-organisms, it is not a necessary accompaniment of death. All that is necessary, if we want to prevent it, is to stop the growth of the micro-organisms. The modern industry of tinned and canned foods is a practical demonstration that this is so. Likewise, if suppuration of wounds is due to local putrefaction, the way to prevent it is to kill all micro-organisms in the vicinity of the cut surface or exclude them from it. The record of surgical mortality vindicates the truth of the inference. The various steps in the subsequent history of the problem of infectious and contagious diseases were successively and successfully put to the test of social practice in this way.

THE FINAL OVERTHROW OF THE ARISTOTELIAN DOCTRINE

A necessary prelude to further advance was to clear the site for the new foundations. The spontaneous generation of the smaller micro-organisms was still accepted by all the leaders of science in spite of Spallanzani's work. The neglect of the latter is readily comprehensible, if we recall the fact that it had produced no impress on the social practice of his generation. Aided by greatly improved microscopes which Spallanzani's generation did not possess, Pasteur now began enquiries into where the micro-organisms of putrefaction and disease come from and how their multiplication is accomplished. Valery-Radot describes this phase of his work in the following passage: *

Pasteur began by the microscopic study of atmospheric air. "If germs exist in atmosphere," he said, "could they not be arrested on their way?" It then occurred to him to draw—through an aspirator—a current of outside air through a tube containing a little plug of cotton wool. The current as it passed deposited on this sort of filter some of the solid corpuscles contained in the air; the cotton wool often became black with those various kinds of dust. Pasteur assured himself that amongst various detritus those dusts presented spores and germs. "There are therefore in the air some organized corpuscles. Are they germs capable of vegetable productions, or of infusions? That is the question to solve." He undertook a series of experiments to demonstrate that the most putrescible liquid remained pure indefinitely if placed out of the reach of atmospheric dusts. But it was sufficient to place in a pure liquid a particle of the cotton-wool filter to obtain an immediate alteration.

* *The Life of Pasteur* (Constable & Co.).

Pasteur's results were hotly contested by his contemporaries, notably Pouchet who invoked authority, which Browne called the "mortallest enemy unto knowledge and that which has done the greatest execution upon truth." The doctrine of spontaneous generation had been adopted of old by men of genius, said Pouchet, and, besides, how could germs contained in the air be numerous enough to develop in every organic infusion? Such a crowd would surely produce a thick mist, dense as a metal. Pasteur set himself to explore this objection. Radot's account continues:

Pasteur let them laugh whilst he was preparing a series of flasks reserved for divers experiments. If spontaneous generation existed, it should invariably

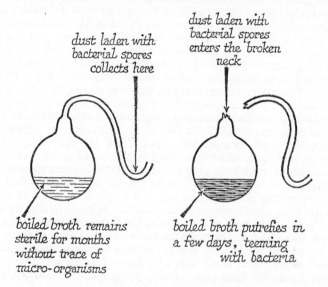

dust laden with bacterial spores collects here

dust laden with bacterial spores enters the broken neck

boiled broth remains sterile for months without trace of micro-organisms

boiled broth putrefies in a few days, teeming with bacteria

FIG. 442.—ONE OF PASTEUR'S EXPERIMENTS

occur in vessels filled with the same alterable liquid. "Yet it is ever possible," affirmed Pasteur, "to take up in certain places a notable though limited volume of ordinary air, having been submitted to no physical or chemical change, and still absolutely incapable of producing any alteration in an eminently putrescible liquor." He was ready to prove that nothing was easier than to increase or to reduce the number either of the vessels where productions should appear or of the vessels where those productions should be lacking. After introducing into a series of flasks of a capacity of 250 cubic centimetres a very easily corrupted liquid, such as yeast water, he submitted each flask to ebullition. The neck of those vessels was ended off in a vertical point. Whilst the liquid was still boiling, he closed, with an enameller's lamp, the pointed opening through which the steam had rushed out, taking with it all the air contained in the vessel. Those flasks were indeed calculated to satisfy both partisans or adversaries of spontaneous generation. If the extremity of the neck of one of these vessels was suddenly broken, all the ambient air rushed into the flask, bringing in all the suspended dusts; the bulb was closed again at once with the assistance of a jet of flame. Pasteur could then carry it away and place it in a temperature of 25-30° C., quite suitable for the development of germs and mucors. In those series of tests some flasks showed some alteration, others remained pure, according to the place where the air had been admitted. During the beginning of the year 1860 Pasteur broke his bulb points and enclosed ordinary air in many different places, including the cellars of the Observatory of Paris. There, in that zone of an invariable temperature, the absolutely calm air could not be compared to the air he gathered in the yard of the same building. The results were also very different: 'out of ten vessels opened in the cellar, closed again and placed in the stove, only one showed any alteration; whilst eleven others, opened in the yard, all yielded organized bodies. . . When the long vacation approached, Pasteur, who intended to go on a voyage of experiments, laid in a store of glass flasks. . . Pasteur started for Arbois, taking with him seventy-three flasks; he opened twenty of them not very far from his father's tannery, on the road to Dôle, along an old road, now a path which leads to the mount of the Bergère. The vine labourers who passed him wondered what this holiday tourist could be doing with all those little phials. . . Of those twenty vessels, opened some distance away from any dwelling, eight yielded organized bodies. Pasteur went on to Salins and climbed Mount Poupet, 850 metres above sea-level. Out of twenty vessels opened, only five were altered. Pasteur would have liked to charter a balloon in order to prove that the higher you go the fewer germs you find, and that certain zones absolutely pure contain none at all. It was easier to go into the Alps. He arrived at Chamonix on September 20, and engaged a guide to make the ascent of the Montanvert. . . The next morning, twenty flasks, which have remained celebrated in the world of scientific investigators, were brought to the Mer de Glace. Pasteur gathered the air with infinite precautions; he used to enjoy relating these details to those people who call everything easy. After tracing with a steel point a line on the glass, careful lest dusts should become a cause of error, he began by heating the neck and fine point of the bulb in the flame of the little spirit-lamp. Then raising the vessel above his head, he broke the point with steel nippers, the long ends of which had also been heated in order to burn the dusts which might be on their surface and which would have been driven into the vessel by the quick inrush of the air. Of those twenty flasks, closed again immediately, only one was altered.

Several decades elapsed before microscopic observation was able to demonstrate the life history of the smallest bacteria and to show how they propagate by simple division. A year after the experiments just described Pasteur devoted his time to the study of putrescence. He showed that butyric acid is formed when butter becomes rancid through the activity of bacteria which need no oxygen and are in fact killed by excess of oxygen. Thus a stream of fresh air suffices to protect against the invasion of the microbe. He proved that production of vinegar from wine is always associated with the presence of a micro-organism and that wine can therefore be prevented from becoming sour by keeping it for a short while at a temperature sufficient to kill the microbe. Radot tells us that in 1864:

As he had more particularly endeavoured to remedy the cause of the acidity which often ruins the Jura red or white wines in the wood, the town of Arbois, proud of its celebrated rosy and tawny wines, placed an impromptu laboratory at his disposal during the holidays of 1864; the expenses were all to be covered by the town. . . . The problem consisted, in Pasteur's view, in opposing the development of organized ferments or parasitic vegetations, causes of the diseases of wines. After some fruitless endeavours to destroy all vitality in the germs of these parasites, he found that it was sufficient to keep the wine for a few moments at a temperature of 50° C. to 60° C. "I have also ascertained that wine was never altered by that preliminary operation, and as nothing prevents it afterwards from undergoing the gradual action of the oxygen in the air— the only cause, as I think, of its improvement with age—it is evident that this process offers every advantage."

MICRO-ORGANISMS OF DISEASE

The results of these researches soon bore fruit in promoting the fortunes of the French wine industry. Further researches on the diseases of wine were curtailed by an incident which eventually turned his attention to the diseases of human beings. An epidemic was ruining the silkworm industry of France. It had begun in 1845. Successive batches of eggs from different localities had proved to be infected till in 1864 healthy stock to replenish the ravages of disease could only be imported from Japan. The *arrondissement* of Alais alone lost 120 million francs in fifteen years. Pasteur was commissioned by the French Government to report and to undertake research on it. Having accepted "full of ardour for the new question of silkworm disease as I was in 1863 when I took up the wine problem," he was lionized by the Empress Eugénie. He succeeded in identifying a new micro-organism as the agent of the silkworm epidemic and prescribed a successful method of microscopical examination of the laying moth, so that no eggs from infected ones should be used for rearing fresh caterpillars.

France and Germany were at war five years after the invitation to undertake this investigation was issued. Paris was besieged. Radot says:

Those who visited an ambulance ward during the war of 1870, especially those who were medical students, have preserved such a recollection of the sight that they do not, even now, care to speak about it. It was perpetual agony. The wounds of all the patients were suppurating, a horrible fetor pervaded the place and septicaemia was everywhere. . . During the siege of Paris, in the Grand Hotel, which had been turned into an ambulance, Nélation, in despair at the sight of the death of almost every patient who had been operated on, declared that he who should conquer purulent infection would deserve a golden statue.

The war of 1870 brought to a climax a situation which, judged by modern standards, seems almost incredible. The surgeon of the first half of the nineteenth century came to the operating table in everyday attire customarily supplemented with a sort of overall coat which was stiff with the coagulated blood of his victims. So long as it was necessary to engage the services of several strong men to hold the victim in a more or less intoxicated condition following a liberal potation of rum, there were practical impediments to the heroic exploits which followed the introduction of anaesthetics. De Quincey's classic reminds us that by the end of the eighteenth century knowledge of opiates which had been used from earliest antiquity in the Mediterranean and Oriental civilizations had become widespread in Europe. No doubt the "New Humanity" helped to stimulate the search for more adequate means of diminishing unnecessary suffering, while the new chemistry was placing a new array of substances at the disposal of the medical profession. Davy, who first ascertained the composition of nitrous oxide, himself recommended its use as a dental anaesthetic after repeated experiments on his own person. It was not used in his own country until American medicine had popularized the use of anaesthetics.

The story of anaesthesia is thus told by Dr. Fishbein in *Frontiers of Modern Medicine:*

Down in Jackson County, Georgia, many miles from a railroad, toward the end of 1841, Dr. Crawford Williamson Long was practising medicine. He was a graduate of the University of Pennsylvania in 1839. He had studied abroad and was recognized as a competent physician. Occasionally young men and women meeting at parties would try the effects of inhaling ether purely as a form of amusement. Dr. Crawford Williamson Long took part in such parties. In the early months of 1842, there came to his office a young man named James Venable who had suffered for some time with a tumor on the back of his neck and who was in great fright over any attempts to remove this tumor by surgery. Doctor Long persuaded the boy to inhale some ether and removed the tumor so that the boy was without pain. Later Doctor Long cut another growth from the neck of James Venable. He then removed two fingers from the burned and mangled hand of a Negro boy, the first finger without ether, the second while the boy was unconscious from inhaling the sleep-producing fumes. . . . In the meantime another investigator in Massachusetts was testing the effects of ether in stopping pain. Dr. William Thomas Green Morton, a dentist who was studying medicine, had observed the attempts of another dentist, Dr. Horace Wells, to use nitrous oxide gas to stop pain during an operation. Those early attempts had failed. A public demonstration in the Massachusetts General Hospital had proved a fiasco, and no one had faith in the use of nitrous oxide. Then Morton asked the famous physician, chemist and geologist, Dr. Charles T. Jackson, if he knew of any substance that might have a more lasting effect. Doctor Jackson suggested to him that he try sulphuric ether. On September 30, 1846, Doctor Morton extracted a tooth painlessly from the mouth of Eben Frost who had previously inhaled some ether. Two weeks later he was given an opportunity by Dr. John Collins Warren to demonstrate the effects of ether during an operation in the Massachusetts General Hospital. It is the morning of October 16, 1846. The scene is the operating room in the hospital where Doctor Warren is getting ready to operate. He is dressed in his best with striped trousers and a long coat. . . . In those days the surgeon had a coat which he wore constantly at operations so that, like a butcher's garment, it became stiffened with dried blood and could almost stand of itself. Near the operating table stood the attendants who were employed ordinarily to hold patients on the table. Other doctors and assistants awaited anxiously the beginning of the demonstration. . . . For some reason Doctor Morton was delayed. The patient had come for an operation on a congenital but superficial vascular tumor just below the jaw on the left side of the neck. Suddenly Doctor Morton entered the room. He had been delayed attempting to perfect a new inhaler. As he came into the room, Doctor Warren said, "Doctor Morton, your patient is ready." Doctor Morton at once proceeded to apply the ether through his inhaler. The patient breathed deeply. He lost consciousness. Then Doctor Morton turned to Doctor Warren and said, "Doctor Warren, your patient is ready " The operation proceeded. A breathless silence pervaded the room. It was obvious to all that the patient was free from pain. The tumour was dissected out in five minutes. After the operation was completed and the patient came back to consciousness, Doctor Warren turned to those who were present and said " Gentlemen, this is no humbug." . . . . One month later, the great Oliver Wendell Holmes, writing to Morton, said: "My dear Sir:—Everybody wants to have a hand in a great discovery. All I will do is to give you a hint or two, as to the names, or the name, to be applied to the state produced and the agent. The state should, I think, be called 'anesthesia.' This signifies insensibility." Thus was born the great discovery of the use of ether as an anesthetic. To Dr. Crawford Williamson Long goes the credit for first using it in an operation. To Dr. William Thomas Green Morton the credit for bringing it to public attention, and for discovering independently its usefulness. . . . To Dr. John Collins Warren goes the credit for first using it in a major operation and to Dr. Oliver Wendell Holmes the credit for giving anesthesia its name. . . . A few months later, Sir James Young Simpson, professor of obstetrics at Edinburgh, used ether in a case of obstetrics for the first time in Great Britain. However, after the passing of a few months he was led to change from ether to chloroform as an anesthetic for obstetrical work and did much to popularize the use of chloroform in Great Britain.

The newest anaesthetics such as the barbiturate "evipan," which induces deep sleep within about five seconds after a completely painless intravenous injection, have eliminated the unpleasantly protracted period of anticipation which was incidental to the earlier methods of inhalation. The patient may now be rendered unconscious in his bed and wake with no knowledge of his presence on the operating table. In the long run anaesthesia has proved to be an immense boon. Its first effect on the contrary was a record of failure which is almost unbelievable in retrospect. One reason for this is easy to see. Experimental physiology had rapidly advanced during the first half of the nineteenth century. It so happens that many animals, especially the rabbit, which —partly on that account—is a favourite subject for laboratory work, do not readily succumb to post-operative infections and suppurating wounds. Emboldened no doubt by the ease with which drastic operations can often be carried out in the laboratory, the surgeon was now free to undertake feats which he could not attempt with patients who struggled under the knife. Many unwittingly helpful precautions of a disinfectant nature had dropped into desuetude. The general mortality from operations rose steadily, so that in 1868 it was higher than 60 per cent.

Two empirical discoveries based on the study of hospital practice paved the way for the advances which rapidly followed the devastating experience of the Franco-Prussian war. A few years earlier a new routine had been introduced into maternity wards of the Vienna hospital by Semmelweis,* a Hungarian physician. He had gained the impression that the disease known as puerperal fever, which at that time commonly followed childbirth with

---

* At the Manchester Infirmary, Dr. Charles White, who wrote, in 1773, a work "On the Management of Pregnant and Lying-in Women and the means of curing but more especially of preventing the principal disorders to which they are liable," instituted similar precautions, but neglected through lack of any theoretical body of knowledge to justify them. This illustrates another side of the "unity of theory and practice."

fatal results, was more common in wards attended by students than in wards from which they were excluded. He also noticed that a form of septic poisoning which he observed to follow a cut hand in the post-mortem room was reminiscent of the same disease. From this he drew the conclusion that infection was spread by products of decomposition and that protection could only be assured by washing with substances like chlorinated lime water—which remove the smell of putrefaction. He therefore instituted a regimen of rigorous washing with thorough disinfectants before entry into his wards. The result was a decisive reduction of maternal mortality. As with the practice of the few enlightened surgeons, like Le Fort (*vide infra*), the general attitude of the time was to ridicule the new sanitary routine.

It was not yet known that all putrefying organic matter contains micro-organisms, that suppurating wounds and pus are analogous in this respect and that the destruction of micro-organisms is a sufficient guarantee against putrefaction of dead organic material or sepsis of exposed living tissue. The regimen introduced by Semmelweis was already beginning to be adopted in America, where Oliver Wendell Holmes in 1843 read to the Boston Society for Medical Improvement a paper entitled "On the Contagiousness of Puerperal Fever," asserting that this disease might be carried from patient to patient particularly by physicians who had made post-mortem examinations or who had attended people with erysipelas. Holmes recommended changing the clothing after taking care of a patient with puerperal fever and thorough washing of the hands with bleaching powder. A French surgeon, Le Fort, instituted similar precautions for operations, abolished sponges, reintroduced alcoholized water for dressings, and exacted scrupulous cleanliness from his students in the Hospital Cochin, where in 1868 he was able to reduce the average mortality to twenty-four per cent.

Alphonse Guérin introduced a new technique in treating the wounded of the Commune at the St. Louis Hospital in 1871. He had decided to try out the possibility that the "purulent infection may perhaps be due to the germs or ferments discovered by Pasteur to exist in the air." So he washed all wounds with carbolic solution or camphorated alcohol, applying thin layers of cotton wool and strong bandages of new linen. Other surgeons were astonished to hear that the majority of his patients had survived serious operations. He enlisted the co-operation of Pasteur, who actively participated in the new hospital policy. Progress in France was not as rapid as it was elsewhere. A few years before Guérin had adopted the suggestion which emerged from Pasteur's work, the same conclusion had been tested in Edinburgh by Joseph Lister, who freely acknowledged his own debt to Pasteur. In Lister's wards the atmosphere was sprayed with carbolic during operations, the wound was washed with it, and dressings made of gauze impregnated with an antiseptic mixture (i.e. one known to kill bacteria) were used to cover the wound. Between 1867 and 1869 Lister reduced the mortality from amputations to fifteen per cent—now an alarmingly high, as then an unbelievably low, figure.

The *antiseptic* technique of Lister and Guérin was fundamentally different from the modern practice of *asepsis* suggested in its essential features by Pasteur himself. They aimed at killing harmful microbes introduced by contact with the instruments, the air and the hands. The resulting gain, though great, had the disadvantage that antiseptics are *de facto* substances which poison living cells. Though they may be much more harmful to bacteria than to the tissues of the body, it is difficult to give enough to ensure killing all micro-organisms without damaging the tissues unnecessarily. The modern way is to take every possible precaution to ensure that the air in the vicinity of the wound, the instruments, the dressings, the hands and clothes of the surgeon, his assistants, and nurses are free from microbes—mainly by using heat to destroy them. "Never make use of an instrument," said Pasteur, "without previously putting it through a flame." He outlined a programme for comparing the results of making several incisions in each of a series of animals, subjecting some to antiseptic, some to aseptic and some to neither treatment.

IMMUNITY AND DISEASE

The next phase in the record of Pasteur's contribution to medical science received a fresh impetus from agricultural problems in which his assistance was again enlisted. In the seventies the flocks of France were being decimated by a disease locally called *charbon*, now *anthrax*. The special characteristic of the condition revealed on autopsy is an excessive enlargement of the spleen, a compact organ which is present in the abdominal cavity of all vertebrates. It has no ducts or glandular tissues, though it resembles a gland in appearance, and its work is mainly concerned with regulating the products of effete red blood corpuscles, and perhaps, since its substance is a porous reservoir of blood without the contractile walls of the finer passages and hence enormously distensible, it also provides a safety valve for the increased blood volume in the main vessels when blood pressure is high. When opened, the spleen of animals (sheep, cattle) which have died of anthrax reveals a black liquid pulp. Anthrax was rife in Europe as a whole at this time. One district of Novgorod in Russia according to Radot lost 56,000 head of cattle between 1867-1870.

Up to this time there had been numerous indications that the presence of micro-organisms was associated with certain diseases and the work of Pasteur on silkworms had placed one instance on a firm foundation. Little advance had been made towards understanding the way in which the smallest visible organisms, bacteria, reproduce or how to cultivate them as pure stocks. A new method of culture for bacteria found in living bodies was developed in the seventies by Koch, who was also working on the anthrax problem. There is no need to retrace the historical steps by which modern methods of cultivating pathogenic bacteria have been perfected. The experimental proof that an animal disease is due to the activities of a microbe depends on (*a*) microscopic observation of the organism in diseased individuals, (*b*) preparation of a "pure culture" of the observed organism and (*c*) production of the diseased condition by inoculating other individuals with a pure culture.

The distinction between one bacterium and another is based primarily on direct observation of the shape or the colour assumed when a smear is stained with a dye. Various types are distinguished (Fig. 443) as bacilli (rod-like), cocci (spherical), spirochaetes (eel-shaped). They are also distinguished by the way they congregate in pairs (diplococci), as tufts like a bunch of grapes (staphylococci) or as single-file filaments (streptococci). The materials used in successfully culturing them, the optimum temperature for growth, and the results of introducing them into the blood also distinguish strains which cannot be recognized as different by microscopic observation.

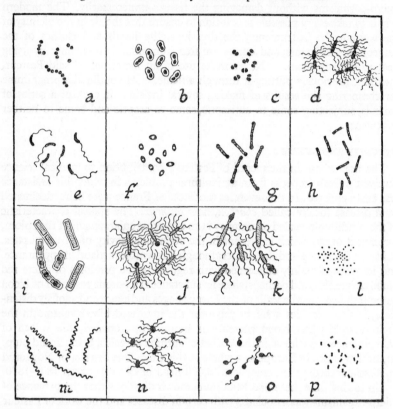

FIG. 443.—BACTERIA AND SOME OTHER MICRO-ORGANISMS

All are magnified a thousand diameters. (*a*) *Streptococcus pyogenes*, which causes septicaemia, puerperal sepsis, tonsillitis, scarlet fever, and many other inflammatory processes. (*b*) *Pneumococcus* of pneumonia. (*c*) *Gonococcus* of gonorrhoea. (*d*) *Bacillus coli*, normally present in the human intestine. The typhoid bacillus is very similar to this one in appearance. (*e*) *Vibrio cholerae* of cholera. (*f*) *Bacillus pestis* of plague. (*g*) *Bacillus diphtheriae* of diphtheria. (*h*) *Bacillus tuberculosis hominis*, which causes tuberculosis in man. (*i*) *Bacillus anthracis* of anthrax. Some of the organisms are forming round spores. (*j*) *Bacillus tetani* of lock-jaw, showing spores. (*k*) *Bacillus botulinus*, which is responsible for the food-poisoning called botulism. (*l*) *Virus* of smallpox. (*m*) *Treponema pallidum*, the organism of syphilis. (*n*) *Bacillus radicicola*, responsible for nitrogen fixation in the root nodules of legumes (p. 922). (*o*) *Nitrosomonas*, which converts ammonium compounds in the soil into nitrous acid. (*p*) *Nitrobacter*, which converts nitrites in the soil to nitrates. All of the above except (*l*) and (*m*) usually count as bacteria.

Culturing them involves finding a medium, e.g. beef tea, in which they multiply rapidly. Nowadays the medium is set in a stiff jelly by addition of "agar" so that it can be laid out in thin plates which are easily protected by a sterile cover from contact with falling dust. A drop of blood or expressed tissue fluid containing the microbe is added to a sterile agar plate. After a while infected areas or colonies where the germs abound are seen as opaque areas on the surface. The colonies sometimes have features characteristic of the type of microbe. It will often happen that the original drop contains one or more other organisms, if it is difficult to get it with completely aseptic precautions. The separation of a pure line is effected by various devices, one being repeated subculture. That is to say, a fragment of a colony is introduced into a fresh sterile agar plate, and a new colony obtained till all the organisms cultivated are identical in shape, staining reaction, or chemical action. Alternatively the cultures, which are usually kept in a "thermostat" or constant-temperature chamber, are made at different temperatures to favour the growth of one or another type of organism present.

In the process of infection, suspensions containing a known number of microbes in a fixed volume are used—so many hundred thousand or million in 1 c.c. This can be done with considerable accuracy without repeated recourse to the laborious method of direct enumeration. The method commonly used depends on the fact that the opacity of a suspension is greater or less according to the number of microbes present in a fixed volume. If a fixed volume taken from a coarse suspension well shaken is diluted to a large volume of fluid, the number in an exactly measured drop of known volume need only be counted once. The number per c.c. in the original suspension is then known. The original suspension can then be diluted successively, and tubes of various dilutions can then be used to match up the opacity of a suspension of unknown strength. This yields results as good as the Registrar-General's returns.

Koch found that microbes in a drop of blood from anthrax victims would multiply rapidly in the fluid (aqueous humour) expressed from the inner chamber of the eye. When cultured in this simple way he observed that they began to lengthen prodigiously, becoming punctuated with fine granules like peas in a pod. These fine granules like the spores of a fern can resist drought. If a drop of the fluid dries, a few flakes of dust from the dried area can be used after a long lapse of time to infect a culture medium, so the bacteria multiply by the method of spore formation. Pasteur took up Koch's method, using household broths or beer yeast as culture media. He discovered that when the process of spore formation occurred and flakes consisting of dense aggregate of swollen filaments appeared in the fluid, a drop of it would infect a second sterile broth, which would then reproduce the appropriate disease symptoms if injected under the skin of a rabbit or guinea-pig. He successively subcultured forty times. Like the widow's cruse the broth continued to produce an inexhaustible store. The toxic power of the broth had also the power of self-multiplication, because, in fact, the power lay in the organism and the organism reproduced its kind.

You will notice that Pasteur had here evolved a method for recognizing the existence of an organism even if—unlike the anthrax bacillus—it is too small to see. Non-living matter is not self-reproductive, and when the power of self-reproduction appears to be exhibited by a non-living system like a pot of broth or a plate of agar we can justifiably infer that an organism is at work. When a micro-organism like those which produce mosaic disease in potatoes, measles in children, and many of the variegated petal types of tulips, cannot be directly seen through the microscope it is called a *virus*. As microscopic construction has improved some organisms have ceased to be viruses and have become microbes. So subsequent history has repeatedly justified the conclusion that self-reproduction is a sufficient test of the presence of an organism.

We can get an idea of the dimensions of a virus by applying the method which Spallanzani devised—unsuccessfully—to test the role of the sperm in

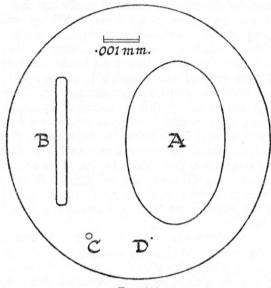

FIG. 444

Outlines of (*a*) head of human sperm; (*b*) tubercle bacillus; (*c*) a filter-passing organism; (*d*) the largest known protein molecule (that of haemocyanin, p. 834); all magnified 10,000 times. They are enclosed in a circle representing the circumference of a human red blood corpuscle, to the same magnification. The microscope can never make visible things so small as *c* and *d*, since the wave length of visible light sets a limit to microscopic vision.

fertilization. He failed to prove what later workers like Prevost and Dumas found, because some sperms will pass through a filter made of a single layer of blotting paper. Filters of various kinds allow particles of various sizes to pass through them and viruses are sometimes called filter-passing organisms, meaning thereby that they have free egress through filters which check the passage of particles just large enough to see with the best microscopes (Fig. 444).

For several reasons the discovery of spore formation by bacteria was a great step forward. It dispelled the objections raised by several workers who had failed to find the anthrax bacillus in its ordinary form and had therefore concluded that its presence was not a necessary condition of the disease. It also threw new light on the way in which contagious diseases are spread. For instance, the fact that the spores of bacteria may retain their power to germinate for a long period, just as seeds of plants do, explained why people who occupy a house which has not been disinfected by agents for killing bacteria will contract a disease from which a previous occupant died. Then, again, the failure of some experiments in which sterilization with the apparent destruction of all bacteria did not prove successful in preventing a new crop appearing received a sufficient explanation, when it was found that spores are much more difficult to kill than the vegetative phase in the life history of the microbe. For instance, anthrax bacilli can be rapidly killed by compressed oxygen and they all die after a few hours' exposure to a temperature of 80° C. The spores are not harmed by oxygen and will resist boiling for some hours.

The two facts last quoted, and similar experience with other microbes, were together responsible for a very prevalent superstition and a signal advance in aseptic and antiseptic precautionary measures. Most bacteria can remain, like the yeast organism, without oxygen in the living state. While the new knowledge was rightly encouraging greater cleanliness, its popularization also fostered an inordinately exaggerated belief in the virtues of fresh air. Air, if infected, owes its power to transmit disease to the presence of highly resistant spores which are unaffected by pure oxygen, and *a fortiori* by the minute differences in the oxygen content of a room with open windows and a room ventilated by the various cracks and small orifices which invariably allow free passage of air currents. Often when a room is said to be stuffy what distinguishes the air in it from " fresh air " is merely the presence of bodily odours, and the horror of stuffy rooms is largely a rationalization of a growing bodily fastidiousness which arose as an unwitting accompaniment of low fertility and the new sanitary tradition.*

The knowledge that bacterial spores can resist much higher temperatures than the vegetative form, has made possible a safe technique of aseptic surgery. Today dressings are kept for some time at a temperature much higher than that of water boiling at atmospheric pressure. One minor contribution to the new sanitation was to crown the investigations of Pasteur and his colleagues in the same field. This was the discovery of anthrax spores in the intestines of earthworms. It seemed plausible to suppose that infected carcasses of sheep and cattle which had been left to die in the open might liberate anthrax spores in the soil. Besides emphasizing the necessity of burning the corpses when such deaths occurred and hence suggesting a new preventive procedure, the fact that the soil laden with spores of pathogenic microbes could be carried about in the bodies of earthworms robbed the country churchyard of its elegiac charm.

In the year 1878 Pasteur announced the general theory that infections and contagious diseases are propagated by micro-organisms which produce their effects by the poisons they make just as the vinegar organism sours good wine. About this time a chicken cholera epidemic was producing serious disquiet in the country-side, and a veterinary surgeon sought Pasteur's help. The method of recognizing and culturing bacteria was now a routine and the identification of the microbe proved simple. An incidental by-product of the enquiry furnished a new clue to the significance of one of the few

* Of course, it is advantageous to keep the atmosphere in circulation to facilitate body temperature regulation by reducing the moistness of air in contact with the skin.

first-rate discoveries of medicine during the eighteenth century. Fresh cultures of the chicken cholera produced invariably fatal results when injected. Sub-cultures which had by chance been allowed to stand produced a comparatively mild disorder from which recovery ensued. Accidentally a benign strain had been isolated from the more malignant type.

In further tests it was shown that the chickens which recovered from the benign form did not succumb to injections of the malignant cultures which were fatal to healthy chickens. In this way Pasteur stumbled on a correct theoretical interpretation of the practice of vaccination and, like any other correct theoretical interpretation of observed phenomena, a *recipe for practice*.

During the eighteenth century smallpox had been one of the most prevalent and deadly diseases. In many countries the majority of people contracted it at some time or another. Hence it came to be noticed that an early non-fatal attack conferred immunity in subsequent epidemics. In the East it was the custom to take advantage of this fact by deliberately exposing people to infection from individuals with a mild form of the disease. In 1798 Jenner, an English country physician, announced the discovery that cowpox, a comparatively mild disorder which like anthrax affects cattle and human beings alike, confers immunity for smallpox; and the practice of vaccination, i.e. deliberately infecting the human body with the milder disease to ensure immunity against the malignant form, was quickly taken up. Smallpox was wiped out in England within a century. Meantime, for nearly a whole century, no clue turned up to suggest the significance of the procedure. Pasteur's work on chicken cholera showed that it is but one example of a general class of reactions which the body shows to infective organisms and to the poisons they produce.

To see whether it was possible to confer immunity for anthrax on cattle, he therefore set about subculturing anthrax bacilli and testing his cultures to obtain a comparatively harmless strain. His laboratory experiments on anthrax satisfied him. They did not satisfy his medical contemporaries in France. In this episode, as at the announcement of his earlier discoveries, the discussions in the Academy had the character of theological debates upon the Arian controversy. Unlike the Trinitarian problem, the microbe question was amenable to public demonstration. As he had done again and again, Pasteur submitted his claims to demonstration before an impartial commission. In one of the tests twenty-five sheep were immunized and injected with a malignant culture which was also injected into twenty-five normal sheep at the same time. All the twenty-five inoculated sheep survived. The twenty-five normal sheep contracted anthrax and died of it.

The final triumph of his career was his work on rabies or hydrophobia. It was the period from which the proverb "mad as a dog" or the expression "dog days" date. The disease was still fairly common, especially among sheepdogs. It was quite incurable, and at one time the horror excited by the symptoms of human beings who had caught the disease after a bite from a mad dog encouraged the practice of smothering or strangling the patient. Such bites were usually fatal. Between the bite and the first symptoms about six weeks elapse. During this interval it is possible to produce "active immunity." Watery suspensions made from brains of infected rabbits which have died of the disease are toxic, and, if fresh, fatal when injected into others. If kept for some time they are less powerful and can be injected without fatal effect. When Pasteur was at last prevailed on to treat children who had been bitten by mad dogs, he used these weak suspensions, injecting strong doses day by day. Thenceforth the usefulness of immunization technique gained general support among the English leaders of medicine.

ARTIFICIAL IMMUNIZATION

Since Pasteur's work in the latter half of the nineteenth century the study of diseases produced by micro-organisms has been extended to plants, with results of great practical importance. Two potato diseases are produced by different *viruses*, for which preventive measures are now available. The mosaic of white and green seen on the leaves of some plants is due to virus infections. Such infections are not necessarily harmful like the mosaic disease of potatoes. If they are not fatal, they may be valued for their ornamental effects. The brilliant patterns of many of our tulips are due to a virus which passes from bulb to bulb, producing its characteristic effect in the petals of the flower.

Among the more common human diseases which are now known to be due to bacteria or other micro-organisms which can be seen with an ordinary high-power microscope are typhoid, tetanus, tuberculosis, scarlet fever, whooping cough, pneumonia, diphtheria, cholera, gonorrhoea, syphilis, anthrax, and infantile diarrhoea. Those which are due to viruses, i.e. micro-organisms which are "filter passers," invisible to direct vision through the microscope, include typhus, rabies, measles, influenza, mumps, smallpox, chicken-pox and encephalitis (sleepy sickness). To these may be added those diseases which result from parasitic protista which are larger than bacteria. Such are amoebic dysentery, trypanosomiasis (tropical sleeping sickness), and malaria.

When some parasitic micro-organisms are cultivated in broths, they set free poisonous substances called *toxins*. This can be shown by injecting broths which have been filtered to remove the organisms or heated sufficiently to destroy them. Successive injections of very small doses of such broths make an animal able to put up with very large doses which would otherwise kill it. Its own blood can then be used to neutralize bacterial poisons in the human system. What we now know of the power of the animal body to produce substances (*anti-toxins*) which neutralize bacterial or virus poisons can therefore be used in two ways. The first, called *active immunity*, is stiffening the resistance of the individual against the possibility of attack by encouraging his own body to make its own *anti-toxin*. The second, called *passive immunity*, is reinforcing the defences of the patient with ready-made anti-toxin from an animal which has been actively immunized in advance.

Protein-free broths heated to kill the micro-organisms or sera containing relatively *weak* strains of a disease virus are called *vaccines*. Vaccines are injected into the human body to produce active immunity as a preventive or "prophylactic" measure. A good illustration of their value gained from the experience of World War I is cited by Campbell. French soldiers were not inoculated with typhoid vaccines during the first sixteen months. Of 96,000 who contracted typhoid fever, 12,000 died of it. British soldiers received the vaccine. Of 2,689 fever cases, only 170 died. Vaccines with genuinely preventive value can be made for smallpox, typhoid, and cholera. They are sometimes recommended for chronic colds and sore throats. As Campbell points out, this is asking more than we have any right to expect of them. The fact that a patient has a chronic condition means that his own body cannot put up a successful fight against the organism or its poisons. Giving him a little more poison is therefore pointless.

To produce passive immunity the blood of an immunized animal is drawn off. The clear fluid or *serum* left behind after clotting is then injected into the patient. It can produce a transitory protection while an epidemic is raging, and, unlike a vaccine, can also be used to cure him, if he has already contracted the disease. Serum treatment succeeds with diphtheria, tetanus, botulism, and bacillary dysentery. Generally speaking, it only works if the organism responsible for the disease liberates its poison into the body fluids.

CHEMOTHERAPY

An alternative protection against micro-organisms is called chemotherapy. Poisonous substances may be broadly divided into three classes. Some, like cyanides and antiseptics, affect all cells. Some affect special classes of cells common to most animals, e.g. strychnine, which acts on nerve cells, and curare (or arrow poison), which acts on nerve endings in muscles. These two classes differ only in degree and the anaesthetics like chloroform and ether which poison all cells, though they affect the nervous system more readily, might be placed in either. Finally a small class like carbon monoxide include substances whose action depends on some chemical peculiarity (see p. 170) which is shared only by restricted classes of animals. The susceptibility of different species to other poisons differs with respect to any one of them, just as the susceptibilities of different types of cell differ in one and the same organism. Thus the amount of *strophanthin* which will stop the heart of the common toad is about one thousand times as great as the amount which will stop the heart of the frog, and the amount of histamine required to kill a white mouse, when injected into the veins, is weight for weight about three hundred times as great as the amount which will kill a guinea-pig ($0 \cdot 0007$ gram) when administered in the same way. If an animal is infected with a parasite, the problem of poisoning the parasite therefore offers two possibilities. One is to find a poison of the carbon monoxide class, i.e. one which only affects certain classes of organisms—attacking the parasite without harming the host. The other is to find a universal poison to which the host is far less susceptible than the parasite.

The first and safest method is relatively simple in dealing with bacteria which will not live in the presence of oxygen. Thus all oxidizing agents like hydrogen peroxide, chlorine and iodine, which combine with water liberating oxygen are useful antiseptics, and a dilute solution of potassium permanganate is used to kill the diplococcus of gonorrhoea in the early stage, when it is possible to irrigate the infected region. Other antiseptic reagents like picric or carbolic acids, cresols (lysol) or formaldehyde are general cell poisons to which bacteria succumb more readily than the host tissues. Since it is difficult to adjust the quantity to secure the first result without the second, they are best used to sterilize instruments rather than for bodily application.

Although the above may be used with more or less success for external application, they are not adapted to internal application. This is so for a variety of reasons. Thus hydrogen peroxide is broken up by a tissue enzyme called peroxidase present in most cells of plants and animals. If it were injected into the blood the circulation would be obstructed by a vigorous evolution of oxygen. On the other hand there are a few highly successful examples of chemical reagents which are much more toxic to particular organisms than to the host itself, and can be used with impunity and often with complete success.

The earliest examples of drugs belonging to this class were entirely empirical discoveries. Peruvian bark was added to the pharmacopoeia by the Portuguese after the discovery of the New World. Its essential constituent, now better known as *quinine*, is a highly effective antidote for the malarial organism. Shortly after, some measure of success in treating syphilis with mercury compounds was achieved. During the past half century systematic search for such relatively specific poisons has been prosecuted with direct encouragement from the drug industry, and has produced several new classes of drugs which have proved highly efficacious for individual diseases. These include the arsenical compounds salvarsan ("606") and neosalvarsan (914), which are highly specific for syphilis, ratbite fever, relapsing fever and yaws. The class of organic compounds known as the *sulphonamides* are highly efficacious for the treatment of puerperal septicaemia, cerebrospinal fever (meningitis), pneumonia and gonorrhoea. Recently *penicillin*, a substance extracted from the blue mould Penicillium (pp. 903 and 924), has proved to be equally efficacious for gonorrhoea, besides being highly toxic to the anthrax bacillus and the bacteria of gas gangrene.

In contradistinction to the preventive use of vaccine, and the curative application of immune sera and a few such chemotherapeutic drugs, intelligent sanitary routine based on the knowledge of how infection occurs is a powerful weapon in the struggle of mankind with micro-organisms. Thus cholera germs are carried in drinking water, and sterilization of water by boiling, by chlorination or other methods used in modern reservoirs is a sufficient safeguard. The micro-organism of yellow fever, which once made white colonization of Central America impossible, is carried by a mosquito whose bite infects the human victim as that of a rabid dog transmits hydrophobia. As with malaria, which is also carried by a mosquito, elimination of the breeding ground of the mosquito by the use of a thin film of paraffin oil on standing water, or by draining swamps, makes infection impossible. The completion of the Panama canal is a direct result of applying this knowledge. Typhus is carried by lice and bubonic plague by the rat flea. The destruction of lice and rats protects a community from the peril of infection with these diseases.

Three hundred years ago the average length of human life in England was thirty years. Today (1953) it is 65 for males, 70 for females. Of a thousand babies born in Bacon's time about three hundred normally died in their first year. Today (1953) only 30 do so; and we may reasonably hope that the number will be half as great twenty years hence. In part such progress achieved is due to poor law reform, to old age pensions, and to other ameliorative measures. In part, it is due to sanitation and drainage under-taken—as with malaria—without any clear theoretical guidance. On the other hand several diseases have been eliminated by definite application of newly found knowledge, or, like smallpox, by the use of immunization before the nature of the technique was understood. Malaria, which was rampant in the fen counties of Defoe's England, disappeared before the part played by a mosquito in transmitting the organism was known. Because we know this now, it is being stamped out deliberately and effectively where it still persists. Unless sanity and sanitation are submerged in world war, cholera, typhoid, diphtheria and infantile diarrhoea will soon be historical or geographical curiosities like typhus, malaria and bubonic plague.

The knowledge which has made it possible to control diseases like these is based on experiments with animals. Those who value the welfare of miners less than that of mice and place the comfort of cats above the safety of children, devote painstaking ingenuity to the plea that all the improvement which has taken place is due to social reform and sanitation. There would be some plausibility in these assertions if our public statistics did not include the record of individual diseases. The tempo of improvement has steadily increased since sanitation has been guided by the new knowledge. Thus the death-rate from typhoid in the United States fell from 36 per thousand in 1900 to 6 per thousand in 1932, and the present figure in the large cities is below 3 per thousand.

While the debt of mankind to the progress of medical knowledge is sub-stantial, there is much to justify a critical attitude to the present organization of medicine. The system of private practice which makes the medical man largely dependent on fees collected for the exercise of knowledge which no one man could possibly carry in his head at once is not adapted to the fullest use of the new knowledge. One result is that the medical man becomes the tool of commercial firms which encourage the belief that their products confer benefits grossly in excess of any claims which the research worker puts forward. The commercialization of medical preparations by private competing firms perpetuates the alchemical elixir. So soon as a new drug or treatment is discovered there is a strong temptation to welcome it as a panacea. Modern practice still encourages many silly illusions of this type. Thus quinine, which is a highly specific and efficacious drug for malaria, is commonly taken for colds and influenza in the absence of the slightest evidence that it has any effect on them. Similarly the success of early work on immunization led to the belief that any disease produced by a micro-organism could be treated successfully by vaccines or immune sera. We now know that this can rarely be done unless the organism liberates its poison into the circulation. In short, there is no single type of treatment which applies to all of them. On the other hand, there is every reason to believe that research can provide an effective weapon against any disease which results from the presence of an organism which can be seen or cultured.

THE NITROGEN CYCLE OF NATURE

Besides providing a powerful stimulus to the study of plant and animal diseases which are produced by the activity of parasitic organisms such as bacteria, viruses, fungi and so forth, Pasteur's work laid the foundations of what is now beginning to prove an important branch of agricultural science. While space does not permit any reference to the practical importance of soil bacteriology, a brief reference to one theoretical issue which the new theory of infection helped to elucidate will prepare the way for further discussion in the ensuing chapter. About the time when crop rotation was beginning to excite interest and discussion in England, Glauber (1656) had discovered a new meaning in the adage "corruption is the mother of vegetation.' "Having found saltpetre in the earth cleared out of cattle sheds," says Sir John Russell, "he argued that it must have come from the urine or droppings of the animals, and must, therefore, be contained in the animals' food, i.e. in plants."

He was thus led to the discovery that saltpetre might be used as a sub stitute for manures to promote plant growth. In England where the *Heads of Enquiries* had directed special attention to the use of manures, Mayow (1674) took up the problem from a new angle, estimated the saltpetre content in the soil at different times of the year and showed that it occurs in greatest quantity in spring when plants are starting to grow. He could find no appreciable quantity "in soil in which plants grow abundantly, the reason being that all the nitre of the soil is sucked out by the plants."

We now know that nitrogen is an essential element of the protein molecule and therefore of the substance of all living matter. The use of nitrates in the soil is the principal way in which the plant gets the nitrogen necessary for making more protein in the process of growth. Hence a fundamental issue which arises from the practice of agriculture is how the soil renews its supply of nitrates "sucked up by the plants." Though crop rotation showed one way in which the renewal occurs in nature without the intervention of artificial manures, the use of leguminous crops, like clover, sainfoin, lucerne or beans, to improve soil depleted of its nitrogenous materials remained a complete mystery till Pasteur's work had shown that useful "fermentations" produced by micro-organisms differ from harmful "putrefactions" only in so far as the results immediately affect the convenience of human beings.

The recognition of the need for greater care in the disposal of sewage sufficiently explains renewed interest in the nature of a process which had defeated all previous enquiries, after interest in the question had been quickened by the work of Boussingault (1841), who had conclusively proved that leguminous plants differ from others in being able to take nitrogen from the air itself. When animal or plant residues putrefy one of the products is ammonia, which can be easily detected in the atmosphere near a manure heap. Nitrates, as Glauber had shewn, are also formed. Pasteur himself had suggested that the production of nitrates is due to bacterial activity ; and this suggestion was put to the test in an experiment by Schloesing and Müntz, who were studying the purification of sewage by land filters during the seventies.

In their investigation a continuous stream of sewage was made to trickle through a column of sand so slowly that it took eight days to pass through it. For the first three weeks the ammonia present in the sewage was not affected. Later on no ammonia was present in the issuing fluid which now contained nitrates instead. The delay could hardly be due to chemical action, and the fact that conversion of ammonia into nitrates was stopped if traces of chloroform were added, indicated that an organism was at work. About the same time an English chemist, Warington, shewed that solutions of ammonium salts can be "nitrified" by adding a trace of soil. The organisms were successfully cultured by Winogradsky ten years later.

These experiments indicated what was proved directly by adding manure or pure nitrates to sand cultures or ordinary crop plants like oats. The manure simply supplies the green plant with nitrates which are formed by the action of bacteria on it. With seeds of leguminous plants like beans, lupins, clover, lucerne, etc., which are used to restore the soil in a crop rotation, the growth is not proportional to the nitrates supplied. Given enough nitrates to start their growth, the seedlings normally establish themselves in a sand culture with no need for any further addition of nitrates, ammonia salts or manure. Such plants differ in an important respect from ordinary crops. Their roots always have little round nodules which are easily visible if you uproot a lupin or sweet-pea plant. Microscopic examination reveals that these root nodules are really small tumours infested with bacteria. So if leguminous seeds are grown in sterilized sand they form no nodules. It is then found that they will not grow unless they are regularly supplied with nitrates like oats or grass seedlings. If a little water which has been shaken up with ordinary soil is added to the sterilized sand cultures, the seedlings develop nodules and no longer require the further addition of nitrates to make them grow.

The fact that they do grow and put on body weight which analysis shows to be partly the result of an increase of nitrogenous material, shows that they must get their nitrogen from the air directly. Thus the root nodule of leguminous plants is a benign, or one may rather say *beneficent* tumour, produced by an organism which can use the nitrogen of the air to make nitrates. Two French workers in the nineties rounded off the story by analysing the air, the soil and the seed for nitrogen at the beginning of an experiment, and the air, the plant and the soil at the end of one. The results of such an experiment are shown below:

	Pea seedlings (milligrams)	Cress seedlings (milligrams)
Nitrogen lost by air	134·6	3·8
Nitrogen gained by soil or plant	152·4	2·0

Apart from what is taken up by free soil bacteria, there is no appreciable loss of nitrogen from the air when cress seedlings grow, and the total nitrogen content of plant and soil does not change when cress seedlings are cultured, because the cress gets its nitrogen from the soil which loses proportionately. On the other hand there is a total gain of nitrogen by the pea seedlings and this gain is offset by a corresponding disappearance of atmospheric nitrogen. This is why soil on which a leguminous crop has been reared contains more nitrates at the end of the season instead of less. The introduction of regular rotation of leguminous and non-leguminous plants was, like the fermentation of wine, an unwitting experiment in what may become a most important development of biotechnology—the domestication of micro-organisms.

The discovery of nitrogen-fixing bacteria stimulated the search for more direct means of tapping the vast reservoir of atmospheric nitrogen for human use at a time when the need was becoming critical. Nitrate deposits are rare in nature. During the eighteenth century the nitrate content of insanitary dumps in India was a coveted source of material for the gunpowder industry. At the beginning of the nineteenth a new source was exploited. Along the western coast of South America enormous deposits of sodium nitrate (Chile saltpetre) formed from accumulations of bird excrement became available for export, and supplied the growing demand for artificial fertilizers. More than 50 million tons have been removed since their discovery. Crookes startled the world of science in 1898 by pointing out that huge populations of industrialized countries could not much longer replenish the nitrogen of the soil from which they got their food, at the rate of depletion which was then taking place. Subsequent history provides a forceful example of the way in

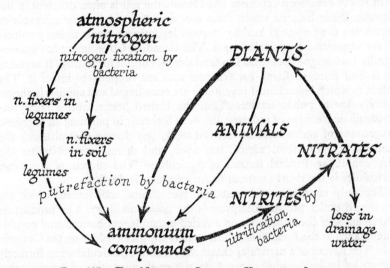

FIG. 445.—THE NITROGEN CYCLE IN UNCROPPED LAND

In this case the plants die where they grow, and the cycle plants : nitrates : plants is complete except for losses in the drainage water. These losses are made good at the other end by nitrogen fixation by bacteria in root nodules or in the soil, and the losses and gains tend in the long run to come into equilibrium. In cropped land, the plants are removed from the soil and with them their nitrogen. Their loss of nitrogen can then be made good by addition of nitrogenous manure or by growing a crop of legumes and ploughing them in, or by letting the land lie fallow or under grass, so that nitrogen fixers in the soil can have time to make good the loss.

which chemical and biological science is continually finding universal substitutes for the ready-made products which Nature supplies in restricted areas.

One method of fixing atmospheric nitrogen, operated on a commercial scale, is the cyanamide process. Finely powdered calcium carbide (used for acetylene lamps) takes up nitrogen when roasted at a high temperature in an atmosphere of the pure gas. The product is poisonous, if laid on too heavily when applied to the soil, and is disadvantageous if the soil already has a high calcium content. Where hydroelectric power is abundant a method which has proved economically adequate is the Birkeland and Eyde process in which air is blown through an electric arc into water. Some of the nitrogen and oxygen unite to form the oxide which dissolves in the water forming nitric acid. The process imitates nature, because traces of nitric acid are formed in air during thunderstorms. The success of the German chemist Haber, whose discovery that nitrogen and hydrogen when heated together at high pressures in the presence of a catalyst such as iron or aluminium oxides form ammonia, made German agriculture independent of Chile saltpetre during the Great War. If the final issue failed to fulfil Glauber's dream (p. 407) of the *Prosperity of Germany*, events could scarcely have furnished a more spectacular vindication of the vision which the discoverer of artificial nitrogenous manures had entertained. After Hitler's rise to power, a grateful Government forced Haber to resign his professorship and research posts, for which he was deemed to be unfitted by his non-Aryan antecedents.

In newly developed countries like Canada the soil is often deficient in the nitrogen fixing bacteria which form root nodules, and is then incapable of permitting the growth of healthy crops of leguminous plants unless a culture of the organisms is sprinkled on it. The Canadian Government has systematically encouraged the farmers to send samples of soil for testing. If found to be free of nitrogen fixing bacteria, cultures are supplied to infect it. The extent to which biotechnical inventions are encouraged and applied is almost entirely due to public services. Thus the United States, with a highly individualistic tradition of industry, has been foremost in pursuing an energetic programme of agricultural advice, test work, and disease control under the gramme of agricultural advice, test work, and disease control under the direction of the Federal Bureau of Agriculture. The success of American agriculture is the *retort courteous* to American individualism.

The only conspicuous constructive biotechnical achievement which has developed under private enterprise is the cheese industry. The production and ripening of cheese depends on a varied assemblage of bacteria and moulds (fungi) such as the *Penicillium* which confers the green colour on the Gorgonzola. The flavour of a particular cheese, like that of a particular wine, formerly known by its local name, depends on the small quantities of organic compounds—chiefly *esters*—formed in addition to the main product of lactification or fermentation by other organisms. The local quality of the milk is mainly important in so far as it provides a suitable culture medium for a particular micro-fauna. When the method of culture is understood, cheese of a particular type—Stilton, Cheddar, St. Ivel, Dorset Blue—can be made under laboratory conditions in any part of the world.

Agriculture is the Cinderella of production in most countries where the capitalist system survives. If our glimpses at the social background of science have taught us anything, biotechnology will not make rapid strides like engineering, chemistry, and physics, till a new social mechanism of food production comes into being. The collectivization of agriculture in the Soviet Union may therefore prove to be a turning point in history, the end, as Lenin put it, of village idiocy. The destiny of the largest national unit in existence is now committed to scientific food production. Future historians may think that the follies and intolerance of a young civilization are trivial in comparison with the momentous achievement of creating a new social impetus to biological discovery.

CHAPTER XX

THE LAWS OF INCREASING RETURNS

THE "Invisible Colledge" which afterwards became the English Royal Society was formed by a group of men inspired by Bacon's eloquent plea that "the true and lawful goal of science is to endow human life with new powers and inventions." Biological no less than mechanical inventions were prominent in the programme to which they set themselves. Among the topics which occupy a prominent place in the "Heads of Enquiries" are the properties of soils and manures. When Bacon wrote the *Advancement of Learning*, it was believed, in his own words, that water constitutes the "principle of nourishment" of the green plant. By an ironical circumstance van Helmont, who first studied carbon dioxide and introduced the word *gas* into the dictionary of science, believed that he had proved that plants need little sustenance except water. He carried out what appears to have been the first, certainly one of the first, experiments on the nature of growth. A young tree shoot was potted in a weighed quantity of soil. "In the end," he tells us, "I dried the soil once more and got the same 200 pounds that I started with, less about two ounces. Therefore the 164 pounds of wood bark and root arose from water alone."

We now know that the green plant, like Shelley's chameleon, "lives on light and air." Shelley's statement would have been nearly true if he had substituted camellias for chameleons. A large bulk of the extra growth in van Helmont's experiment came from the carbon dioxide which is normally present in the air. Admirable in principle, van Helmont's investigation had two other practical defects. He did not weigh the water supplied to see whether 164 pounds of water had actually disappeared, and he underrated the significance of the two ounces of soil.

Further progress towards scientific knowledge of how food is produced resulted from the discovery that saltpetre is present in manure. This discovery, which, like so many others in the history of science, was partly prompted by the search for new ways of destroying human life, led him to another which proved to be the means of conserving it. Glauber found that the saltpetre content of manure is mainly responsible for its power to increase the fertility of the soil. That is to say, saltpetre, or as we now know *nitrates* in general, can be used instead of manure to revive exhausted soils. Mayow (1674) in England seized on this discovery in the spirit of the new programme of "Heads of Enquiries," estimated the nitre content of the soil at different seasons by such methods as were then known, and showed that it is highest in spring when the crops begin to grow.

An early example of the use of precise methods in the study of nutrition is furnished by an experiment in which another Englishman, John Woodward (1699), tracked down the missing two ounces in Helmont's work. Woodward grew spearmint in rain water, Thames water, water from the Hyde Park conduit, and water to which a measured quantity of soil had been added. He then measured the solid content of each sample of water, the water used up, and the gain in weight of each set of plants, after a period of eleven weeks. The historic interest of this enquiry, which shows the use of quantitative methods in advance of contemporary chemical practice till the time of Black and Lavoisier, is instructive, when we recall the powerful impetus which the study of chemistry received from the study of artificial manures (see p. 408). Two typical experiments are cited by Russell, as follows:

| Source of Water | Weight of Plants (in Grains) | | Gain in 11 Weeks | Water Loss | Plant Gain to Water Loss |
	Before	After			
(i) Rain	$28\frac{1}{4}$	$45\frac{3}{4}$	$17\frac{1}{2}$	3,004	1 : 172
Thames ..	28	54	26	2,493	1 : 96
(ii) Hyde Park ..	110	249	139	13,140	1 : 94
Ditto with $1\frac{1}{2}$ ounces garden soil added ..	92	376	284	14,950	1 : 53

With the new air pump of Hooke and Boyle, the English physician Hales showed that air as well as salts and water is necessary for plant growth. In the same social context one of the predominant foci of enquiry was the nature of fluid pressure and flow. In 1727 Stephen Hales published his *Vegetable Staticks* in which he described experiments on the amount of water taken up by the roots and the amount which evaporates from the surface of the leaves. These showed that there is a continuous flow of water from the roots to the leaves. By fixing a pressure gauge to the cut end of the stem of a plant in moist soil or water, Hales measured the actual "root pressure" of the ascending sap. The cells of the fine hairs on the roots are semi-permeable, allowing water to pass inwards more readily than salts (Fig. 446). So water is sucked in by the osmotic pressure of the sugars and salts of the sap.

To an appreciable extent, as Hales discovered, the ascent of sap is due to *capillarity* (see p. 398). Water passes up the stem through the fine vessels called *tracheae*, which make up the bulk of the woody part of the stem and the veins of the leaf. Tracheae (Fig. 416) develop from rows of elongated dead cells with spirally thickened walls. The cells are arranged end to end. The transverse walls between adjacent cells arranged in single file break down, so that continuous tubes of exceedingly fine bore are formed. Hales performed experiments on capillarity with fine glass tubes. The physical phenomena of capillarity and of osmosis were both discovered in connexion with the problems of the movement of water in plants.

We now know that the ascent of sap is not wholly accounted for by the continuous supply of water to the tracheae by the osmotic action of the root, or by the capillary attraction of the wood vessels. A third process, known as *transpiration*, plays an important part, especially where the sap ascends to a considerable height as in trees. The thin-walled cells inside the green leaf lose large quantities of water by evaporation, and as this happens the osmotic pressure of their sap tends to rise, and may reach 10 or 20 atmospheres. Water is consequently drawn into these cells, by osmosis, from the tracheae of the leaf veins. If confined in narrow tubes, water columns are capable of withstanding suction amounting to several hundred atmospheres without breaking. Suction of water in the tracheae of the leaf can thus draw the columns of water, extending through the tracheae from leaf to root, upwards against gravity, as if they were so many solid rods.

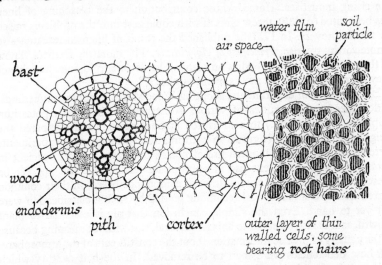

FIG. 446.—PART OF A SECTION THROUGH A YOUNG ROOT

The most important difference between the stem and the root is that the younger parts of the latter are covered by a layer of thin-walled cells, which are readily permeable to water. Many of these cells have fine hair-like outgrowths, the *root-hairs*, which penetrate the moist soil and offer a large surface for the absorption of water and mineral salts in solution. The wood and bast of the young root are arranged on alternate radii instead of together in bundles as in the stem, and the whole vascular cylinder is enclosed in a sheath of cells, the *endodermis*, sometimes found also in stems. The pith is often absent.

During the first half of the eighteenth century interest in manures was temporarily subordinated to mechanical improvements. In England the protagonist of the new methods was Jethro Tull, who introduced the drill, thereby eliminating wind and labour waste due to broadcast sowing. Tull advocated frequent hoeing to pulverize the soil between seedlings planted in uniform rows. His methods, which systematized a variety of local practices in a single routine, spread to other countries, and naturally produced considerable improvement by making more thorough use of available natural resources already present in the soil without recourse to manures. Tull's writings were translated into French, provoked widespread controversy, and made the nourishment of the green plant the pivotal issue of agricultural theory and practice.

Meanwhile Scotland was passing through a rapid phase of agrarian expansion and reorganization described in Dr. Hamilton's book (pp. 434 and 583). In 1723 *The Honourable the Society of Improvers in the Knowledge of Agriculture* was incorporated to carry on a campaign for spreading and sharing information concerning new technique. Scottish agriculture continued to thrive during the process of industrialization which began with the linen industry and proceeded apace in the latter half of the century. Chemical manufacture was beginning. Medical men equipped with chemical knowledge such as Black, Roebuck, and Francis Home were in close contact with the rising industries. Home, whose contribution to the bleaching of linen has been cited (p. 435), threw himself with equal zest into the problems raised by the Improvers. In 1757 he published the result of his own researches in a noteworthy treatise, *Principles of Agriculture*. The more the farmers "know of the effects of different bodies on plants," he declared, "the greater chance they have to discover the nourishment of plants."

Home made pot experiments, adopting Woodward's quantitative methods, added measured quantities of various substances (Epsom salt, potassium sulphate, saltpetre, etc.) to a measured amount of soil, and compared the weights gained by plants grown in each mixture. Though such experiments were the foundation of modern use of potash fertilizers for soil deficient in potassium salts, intelligent use of appropriate fertilizers could not yet be prescribed. A systematic classification of compounds based on their common ingredients and an analytical technique guided by such a classification were not yet to hand. Even the simple conclusion that air is essential to plant growth, as it is also essential to animal survival, was without meaning because of the paucity of precise information about the constituents of the atmosphere.

These deficiencies were soon to be removed. In the half century which followed the foundation of Roebuck's factory for making sulphuric acid, and witnessed the ascent of the first hydrogen balloons, the introduction of coal gas and metallurgical innovations associated with the use of steam power, chemical science grew rapidly. Black's work on carbon dioxide, Rutherford's isolation of nitrogen, the researches of Watt, Cavendish, and Charles on hydrogen, those of Priestley, Lavoisier, and Scheele on oxygen—distinguished the principal constituents of air and the four elements which make up the bulk of plant tissues. They reawakened interest in the problem of breathing and made it possible to analyse the elementary constituents of the atmosphere and of the plant body.

While prosecuting the researches which led to the modern view of metallurgical processes, Scheele, Priestley, and Lavoisier also devoted their efforts to the analogous problem of combustion, breathing, and animal heat: An important by-product of these subsidiary inquiries were two contradictory observations. One was made by Priestley who claimed that mint purifies air made unfit to sustain animal life by breathing. The other was made by Scheele, who asserted that plants like animals vitiate air. In modern terms Priestley claimed that plants remove carbon dioxide, Scheele that they produce it. Spallanzani seems to have been the first to have resolved the paradox by noting that aquatic plants give off bubbles of oxygen in sunlight and do not do so in darkness. Two European workers, Ingen-Housz and Senebier (1779–1782), independently took up the clue, and showed that while plants remove carbon dioxide from the air and give up oxygen to it in sunlight, they evolve carbon dioxide and take up oxygen in the dark. They thus showed that two kinds of gaseous exchange between the green plant and the air occur. One is comparable to *respiration* in animals. The other is essentially different from it.

At Geneva Senebier was associated with the biologist de Saussure, who was in close touch with Spallanzani. In 1804 the son of de Saussure undertook an enquiry on the same lines as the experiments of van Helmont and Woodward, adding two new features which advancing knowledge of the chemistry of gases now made possible. In addition to weighing the dry matter which the soil loses and finding the total gain in weight of the plant itself, he measured the changing composition of the *air* during its growth and analysed the constituents of the ash and combustible matter of the plant separately.

THE COMPLETE ANALYSIS OF GROWTH

The principle of experiments undertaken like those of de Saussure to give a complete balance-sheet of plant growth may be outlined as follows. A group of seedlings is divided into two lots; one is set aside for complete analysis at once. The others are (a) first weighed, then cultured in a closed chamber through which a known volume of air is passed, with their roots in a measured volume containing a mixture of salts (nitrates, phosphates, and sulphates of potassium, calcium, and magnesium) approximating to that of a suitable soil content, (b) weighed a second time after a period of active growth, and then subjected to complete analysis like the first batch of seedlings.

The analysis of the seedlings or of the grown plant involves three operations. Each is weighed, thoroughly dried, and weighed again. The loss of weight represents the uncombined water of the plant juices. The dried plant is incinerated in a hard glass tube through which dry CO_2-free air is passed (Fig. 447). The loss of weight represents the total combustible or "organic" matter in the plant body. The residue is the weight of mineral salts which may be separately analysed. If the air is sucked from the combustion tube into (a) some dehydrating agent like strong sulphuric acid or calcium chloride, or (b) some CO_2 absorbent such as lime or baryta, the total carbon and hydrogen which go to make up the organic matter can be estimated. Since the air drawn through the chamber contains no water vapour or carbon dioxide, the gain in weight of the dehydrating agent is due to water formed by the oxidation of hydrogen in the combustible matter of the plant, and the gain of the lime or baryta is due to CO_2 formed by oxidation of the carbon. One-ninth of water by weight is hydrogen, and three-elevenths of carbon dioxide is carbon. Hence one-ninth of the increase in weight of (a) represents the hydrogen present in the organic material of known weight, and three-elevenths of the increase in weight of (b) represents the carbon. The percentage of carbon, hydrogen, salts, etc., in the seedlings is not found to vary much. If, therefore, the weight of a plant cultured from the same stage in a nutrient solution is known, an accurate estimate of its composition at the beginning of the experiment can be made from the analysis of the first batch.

This is how we can find how much the weights of salts, carbon, hydrogen, etc., increase in a period of growth. To find where they all come from it is necessary to analyse the air and the nutrient solution in which the roots grow. A stock of the latter containing a known weight of each constituent in a measured volume is first made up. If the volume of solution used for each seedling is measured, their initial supply of salts is therefore known. At the end of the experiment each solution used is analysed, and the loss indicates how much has been taken up by the plant. The loss of phosphates, of metallic salt constituents (potassium, calcium, magnesium) exactly corresponds to the

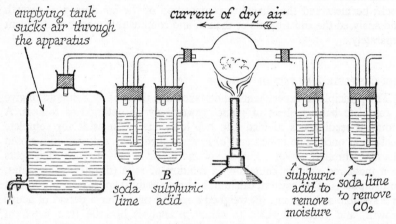

emptying tank sucks air through the apparatus

current of dry air

A
soda lime

B
sulphuric acid

sulphuric acid to remove moisture

soda lime to remove CO_2

FIG. 447.—AMOUNT OF CARBON AND HYDROGEN FIXED IN ORGANIC MATTER IN THE GREEN PLANT

When incinerated in a current of dry air, the organic matter of a dried plant is oxidized with formation of water vapour and carbon dioxide. The sulphuric acid in B absorbs the former, the soda lime in A the latter. If A and B are weighed before and after the experiment, the increase in weight of A gives the carbon dioxide (three-elevenths of which represents fixed carbon), and the increased weight of B gives the water vapour (one-ninth of which is fixed hydrogen).

increased quantity of each in the plant ash. The loss of sulphates and nitrates does not quite correspond to the gain of sulphates and nitrates in the plant body. Part of the sulphur and most of the nitrogen appear as oxides of these elements driven off when the organic matter is incinerated. When this is taken into account all the nitrogen present in the organic matter of the plant is found to come from the nitrates in the nutrient solution.

If the nutrient solution contains no free CO_2, no carbonates nor other soluble compounds of carbon, the gain in weight represented by the carbon of the organic matter does not enter the plant by the roots. Unless living things can manufacture elements out of nothing, or can transmute one element into another, it must therefore come from the air, which as Priestley proved is "purified" by the green plant in sunlight. Experiments show that seedlings will not grow in the dark nor in CO_2-free air once they have thrown off their seed leaves (Figs. 452-3) which contain a store of inorganic material. To show that the carbon content of the combustible matter comes from the carbon dioxide, the air drawn out of the closed chamber (Fig. 448) is passed over a CO_2 absorbent, e.g. slaked lime. The volume of air which is drawn through the chamber while the experiment is in progress is easily measured in the way illustrated in the figure. The increased weight of the tube containing the CO_2 absorbent shows how much CO_2 is present in the air which has circulated around the plant. The CO_2 present in the same volume of ai.

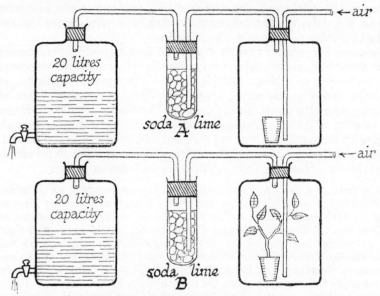

FIG. 448.—FINDING THE CARBON DIOXIDE UPTAKE OF A GREEN PLANT

In the dummy experiment above a fixed quantity of air (e.g. 20 litres) is passed through the apparatus, the carbon dioxide being absorbed by the Soda Lime A. The same quantity of air passed over a green plant during a corresponding period gives up its remaining carbon dioxide to B. The difference between the amounts of carbon dioxide taken up by A and B gives the carbon dioxide uptake of the plant during the interval.

which has not circulated round a plant is determined in the same way, and is found to be greater. The difference is the weight of CO_2 removed from the air by the plant. Three-elevenths of this (p. 451) is the carbon which the plant gains in growth, and corresponds to the gain of carbon determined by incineration.

COMMERCIAL MANURES

De Saussure's work established the revolutionary conclusion that the green plant gets all its carbon from the air and that it can only do so in sunlight. It belongs to the same social context as that of Priestley, Lavoisier, Berthollet, and Davy, whose researches participated in the early stages of chemical manufacture at a time when a new demand for metals to meet the needs of new industry conspired to focus attention on the part played by gases in chemical combination. It also threw new light on the essential mineral constituents of the plant body, in particular lime and phosphates. This paved the way for a new synthesis of practical experience, theoretical knowledge, and industrial enterprise.

Scientific plant nutrition involves three kinds of knowledge: (a) the essential constituents of the plant body, (b) specific variations of the constituents in different classes of crops or garden plants, (c) local variations of the content of these constituents in the soil. Guided by (a) or (b), it is possible to find out the necessary minimum of the various salts which the soil must contain to promote healthy growth, and analysis of a soil sample then tells us in what respect it is deficient. The deficiency can thus be rectified by the application of a suitable dressing of artificial fertilizer.

From another point of view the work of de Saussure and his predecessors from Woodward onwards reflects the interest in soil exhaustion accompanying the growth of capitalist farming and the expansion of population, as capitalist industry extended. Davy, who had an uncanny knack of realizing where the prosecution of theoretical knowledge could best advance the interests of the industrialist, realized the possibilities of further research linking up the nutritional needs of the plant with variations of soil content. In his book *English Farming, Past and Present*, Prothero refers to the enthusiastic interest aroused by Davy's initiative in the following passage:

The dawn of a new era, in which practical experience was to be combined with scientific knowledge, was marked by the lectures of Humphry Davy in 1803. In 1757 Francis Home had insisted on the dependence of agriculture on "Chymistry." Without a knowledge of that science, he said, agriculture could not be reduced to principles. In 1802 the first steps were taken towards this end. The Board of Agriculture arranged this series of lectures on "The Connection of Chemistry with Vegetable Physiology," to be delivered by Davy, then a young man of twenty-three, and recently (July, 1801) appointed Assistant Professor of Chemistry at the Royal Institution of Great Britain. He had already made his mark as the most brilliant lecturer of the day, attracting round him by his scientific use of the imagination such men as Dr. Parr and S. T. Coleridge, and the talent, rank, and fashion of London, women as well as men. His six lectures on agricultural chemistry, commencing May 10, 1803, were delivered before the Board of Agriculture. So great was their success that he was appointed Professor of Chemistry to the Board, and in that capacity gave courses of lectures during the ten following years. In 1813 the results of his researches were published in his *Elements of Agricultural Chemistry*. The volume is now out-of-date, though the lecture on "Soils and their Analyses," in spite of the progress of geological science and the adoption of new classifications, remains of permanent interest. Many passages that were then listened to as novelties are now commonplaces; others, especially those on manures, have been completely superseded by the advance of knowledge. But if the book has ceased to be a practical guide, it remains a historical landmark, and something more. It is the foundation-stone on which the science of agricultural chemistry has been reared, and its author was the direct ancestor of Liebig, Lawes, and Gilbert, to whose labours, in the field which Davy first explored, modern agriculture is at every turn so deeply indebted. It was Davy's work which inspired the choice by the Royal Agricultural Society (founded in 1838) of its motto "Practice with Science."

In England the newly formed Board of Agriculture had been active from its inception in collecting specimens of soil for analysis. The initiative did not come from the commercial firms which began to reap the profits of the new knowledge. From first to last private enterprise has merely exploited a demand due to modern biotechnical discoveries fostered by technical education and advisory work undertaken by Government departments. Besides providing a fresh market for chemical products, the scientific study of plant nutrition also created a new demand for mechanical instruments for tilling, and subsequently for reaping, binding, and threshing. Prothero says:

The changes which have been noticed in modern farming necessitated more frequent operations of tillage, which, without mechanical inventions, would have been too costly to be possible. Here, again, science came to the aid of the farmer, and supplied the means of making his labour cheaper, quicker, and more certain. The Royal Agricultural Society may legitimately pride itself on the useful part which it has played in introducing to the notice of agriculturists the new appliances which mechanical skill has placed at their service. Yet, when the Society was founded, none of its promoters foresaw the importance of the mechanical department. At the Oxford show in 1839 one gold medal was awarded for a collection of implements; three silver medals were allotted; and a prize of five pounds was given for "a paddle plough for raising potatoes." At the show at Gloucester in 1853, 2,000 implements were exhibited. The modern system of farming had, in the interval of fourteen years, built up a huge industry employed in providing the agricultural implements that it required.

The combustible material of a plant or animal body contains four principal elements: hydrogen, carbon, oxygen, and nitrogen. The source of the nitrogen in plants is not a single problem because some green crops, e.g. beans, have bacterial tumours or root nodules due to the presence of nitrogen-fixing bacteria (p. 921). The nitrogen content of the plant substance when the sap has been expressed can be determined by heating the dried tissue with strong sulphuric acid and a trace of potassium permanganate. All the nitrogen is then converted into ammonium sulphate. If the solution is diluted with excess of potash the ammonia can be driven off by heating. If this is passed into a solution of weak acid, the total ammonia produced is found by titrating (pp. 444 and 463) a measured volume of standard acid solution. By weight fourteen-seventeenths of the ammonia is nitrogen. Together with the nitrogen contained in the nitrates present in the sap, this is found to be equivalent to the nitrogen content of the nitrates lost from the soil or culture medium in which a plant is grown. If it is a leguminous plant this is only true when the medium contains no nitrogen-fixing bacilli to infect the roots.

In 1834 the method of carbonization which de Saussure used was adapted to large-scale agricultural inquiries by Boussingault, who made complete analytical estimates of the nitrogen supplied by the manure and present in the crop during various systems of rotation (p. 921). This work was undertaken in association with the eminent French analytical chemist, Dumas. A few years later the results of new insight into the food of plants were broadcast by a book, which laid down the quantitative principles of crop husbandry in the general statement "the crops on a field diminish or increase in exact proportion to the diminution or increase of mineral substance conveyed to it in manure." What Davy had vaguely, though eloquently, foreshadowed Liebig set forth with precision based on analysis of crop and soil in *Chemistry in its Application to Agriculture and Physiology.* This book, says Prothero,

traced the relations between the nutrition of plants and the composition of the soil. . . . (It) revolutionized the attitude which agriculturists had maintained towards chemistry. So great was the enthusiasm of country gentlemen for Liebig and his discoveries, as popularized by men like Johnston and Voelcker, that the Royal Chemical Society of 1845 was largely founded by their efforts. But if the new agriculture was born in the laboratory of Giessen, it grew into strength at the experimental station at Rothamsted. To Sir John Lawes and his colleague Sir Henry Gilbert (himself a pupil of Liebig) farmers of today owe an incalculable debt. By their experiments, continued for more than half a century, the main principles of agricultural science were established; the objects, method, and effects of manuring were ascertained; the scientific bases for the rotation of crops were explained; and the results of food upon animals in producing meat, milk, or manure were tested and defined. On their work has been built the modern fabric of British agriculture. With increased knowledge of the wants of plant or animal life came the supply of new means to meet those requirements. Artificial manure may be roughly distinguished from dung as purchased manures. Of these fertilizing agencies, farmers in 1837 already knew soot, bones, salt, saltpetre, hoofs and horns, shoddy, and such substances as marl, clay, lime, and chalk. But they knew little or nothing of nitrate of soda, of Peruvian guano, of superphosphates, kainit, muriate of potash, rape-dust, sulphate of ammonia, of basic slag. Though nitrate of soda was introduced in 1835, and experimentally employed in small quantities, it was in 1850 still a novelty. The first cargo of Peruvian guano was consigned to a Liverpool merchant in 1835; but in 1841 it was still so little known that only 1,700 tons were imported; six years later (1847) the importation amounted to 220,000 tons. Bones were beginning to be extensively used. Their import value rose from £14,395 in 1823 to £254,600 in 1837.

THE BODY AS A MACHINE

In newly ploughed fields of knowledge, self-evident principles spring up perennially. The work of Home, of Boussingault and of Liebig was the signal for a fresh crop of weeds. A world which had outgrown the slave mechanics of antiquity was not yet ready to discard the slave-owning ethic of Aristotle. The old authority could be sustained if, and only if, scarcity of the essential means of human satisfaction could be reinstated as a natural law. Premonitions of plenty first brought Malthus into the field. Malthus declared that food manufacture must always lag a step behind human fecundity. Then came the astonishing impertinence enshrined in the "law" of diminishing returns. The intrepid Ricardo asserted that nothing can force plant growth to keep pace with human industry. Two systems for costing resources for satisfying common human needs were soon to compete in the open. In disclosing a new substitute for animal labour, science had furnished new scope for investment, and factory technology had adopted horse-power as its current coin. Laboratory workers were now busy with the balance sheet of food required for human effort and fuel (see pp. 601 and 617–21) consumed by the steam engine, while the old axioms consecrated the banker's balance-sheet of owner's receipts.

The experiments of Crawford and of Lavoisier and Laplace (p. 600) showed that the total energy production of the animal body, measured as heat, is accompanied by oxidation of a definite quantity of food, just as the

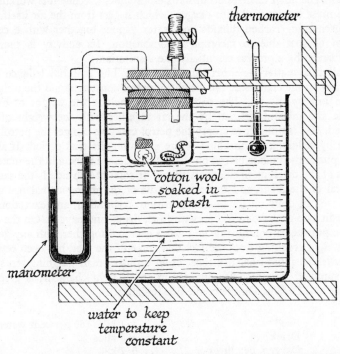

thermometer

cotton wool soaked in potash

manometer

water to keep temperature constant

FIG. 449.—APPARATUS FOR MEASURING THE OXYGEN CONSUMPTION OF A WORM OR OTHER SMALL ORGANISM

The carbon dioxide produced by the organism is absorbed by the potash, and the change in the pressure recorded by the manometer is therefore due to the oxygen consumed. The instrument can be calibrated so that the actual volume of oxygen taken in can be determined.

total energy production of a steam-engine depends on the oxidation of a definite amount of fuel. When a machine is generating both heat and movement we can express the total energy it is giving out either in (ergs) mechanical units or in heat units (calories). If the machine is a motor-bicycle, the total energy (heat and movement) is fixed by the amount of petrol consumed. Whether it is used wastefully or economically from the point of view of the rider, depends on how much of it is used to produce heat without first producing mechanical work. When the engine is running in neutral gear, the engine itself does mechanical work which does not result in mechanical activity of the machine as a whole. The moving parts generate heat by friction with the surrounding air. If the brakes are applied petrol is used to heat up the rim of the wheel. Even with the best management some of it is directly used to heat up the engine, as some of our food is used to keep our bodies warm. Whatever happens the final result is the same. The road surface or air around gets hotter, and this total heat gain is balanced by the quantity of petrol which would produce the same number of calories, if oxidized in any other way.

Meanwhile other changes occur in its environment. While it is working the engine must be supplied with oxygen, which it gets from the air itself. It is also discharging carbon dioxide and water vapour together with a certain amount of soot due to incomplete combustion. Its activity is therefore accompanied by a process essentially like respiration.

In all this, matter is neither gained nor lost. The material balance sheet will show on the credit side the weight of petrol consumed and the weight of oxygen lost by the air. The debit side will include the weight of carbon dioxide and moisture gained by the air together with the weight of soot excreted. If it is difficult to empty the petrol tank, we can get the petrol consumed by weighing the machine before and after the trial period. If all the petrol put in the tank is placed on the credit side, we must add the increased weight of the machine to the debit side. The total of one side is the same as the total of the other, and the same is true of the analogous balance sheet, which we can draw up for human nutrition, respiration, and excretion. On the credit side we have to reckon with food, drink, and oxygen. On the debit side we put the carbon dioxide and water excreted together with any gain of body-weight resulting from the fact that some of the food has been retained for growth. A typical balance sheet of an ordinary man weighing ten stone, when supplied with food for one day in an air-tight chamber, is given by Haldane and Huxley. On the credit side it shows:

Food	..	..	..	.. 1·1 kilos (60 per cent water)
Drink ..	..	..	.. 1·5 kilos
Oxygen, 500 litres or ..	.. 0·7 kilo

This makes a total of 3·30 kilograms. On the debit side we have to reckon with the fact that he excretes during the same period 1·3 kilos of water and 70 grams of solids in his urine. He loses 1·1 kilos of water by evaporation from the skin as sweat. He loses 425 litres of carbon dioxide or 0·82 kilo, making in all a net loss of 3·29 kilos. The difference of 10 grams represents exactly what he has gained in body-weight at the end of the experiment. The carbon dioxide that appears is equivalent to that which would be formed by the same amount of food (allowing for what is retained for growth) if burnt in a flask.

If a human being—or a frog—is placed, like Lavoisier's man, in a heat-proof box or calorimeter, the effect of any movements he may execute is to generate additional heat by friction with the surrounding atmosphere, and all the energy he releases will appear on the balance sheet of energy as an increase of heat in the calorimeter. When this experiment is performed, two things are found. The amount of energy expended is definitely related to the oxygen taken in and the carbon dioxide given off. In addition, the amount of energy generated during the same period is equivalent to the heat which would be generated by combustion of the quantity of food consumed if it were burnt in another calorimeter. In one experiment a corresponding balance sheet for the energy expenditure of Haldane's ten-stone man over the same period was drawn up somewhat as follows. Burnt outside the body, the same amount of food as he takes would yield 2,400 kilocalories. The total heat lost by the body during the period of experiment being 2,190 kilocalories, the difference includes a deficiency, due to incomplete oxidation of food. It can be proved from analysis of the excreta to be equivalent to 150 kilocalories, leaving only 60 kilocalories to account for. This represents the increased potential energy of the body due to stored materials which appeared in the previous balance sheet as increased weight.

Thus the two great mechanical principles called the conservation of energy and the conservation of matter both apply to all man-made contrivances and all physical phenomena. That is why it is right and proper to speak of the *living machine*. We call a dynamo, a water-mill, a steam-engine, and a motor-bicycle machines because they transform energy in accordance with certain definite rules, which are known as the laws of Energetics. We call a frog or man a living machine because it transforms one form of energy into other forms of energy in accordance with the same rules.

The fuel of the animal body is supplied by carbon compounds in its food. This is either derived directly from the green plants on which it feeds or, if it is carnivorous, from the tissues of herbivorous animals. Whichever happens its ultimate source is the same. The plant builds up its complex carbon compounds from the carbon dioxide of the air and the water of the soil. Since oxygen is given off by green plants in sunlight the reaction involved in this process of carbon assimilation or *photosynthesis* is a reduction reaction. Plant tissues also oxidize these products in the process of growth. The parts which are not green (e.g. roots) give off carbon dioxide at all times. The green parts do so in the dark, and may be inferred to be doing so in light, when the universal process of respiration is masked by the simultaneous occurrence of carbon assimilation. Respiration is essentially a combustion. The complex carbon compounds oxidized in respiration give up energy. The reduction reaction of photosynthesis must therefore be regarded as one in which energy is stored up at the *expense of the sun's store*. Thus solar radiation is the basis of all the activities of living creatures.

In addition to fuel an engine needs spare parts. The animal and plant body contain nitrogen and need nitrogen for the continual repairing process which is called growth. The plant ordinarily gets this from nitrates which are formed by the decomposition of animal excreta and from plant and animal remains. Except in so far as the soil is renewed by nitrogen-fixing bacteria the nitrogen content part of the plant and animal body circulates from one to the other and back again. The first important step towards broadening the study of animal nutrition to include the nitrogen intake arose in connexion with the pioneer researches of Boussingault on soil nitrogen and manures.

Besides making an inventory of the nitrogen content of crops, soils, and manures in crop rotation, Boussingault (1839) also made farm experiments on the relation between cattle food and excreta. He determined the amounts of carbon, hydrogen, oxygen, and nitrogen in a milch cow's fodder, and measured how much of each is lost in the urine, faeces, and milk. His experiments showed that about 2 per cent of the food was nitrogen, and of all the nitrogen taken in as food, seven-eighths was excreted, one-eighth being retained. Similar experiments were carried out by Liebig on a company of the Grand Ducal Guards of Hesse Darmstadt.

Liebig's name is associated with the first patent fertilizer and the first patent food ("Liebig's Extract of Meat"). Though neither of them were very successful, they point to the close connexion between the physiology of nutrition and the rise of chemical manufacture. Till the publication of Liebig's treatise on chemistry applied to agriculture little was known about the chemical characteristics of food. In it the three principal classes of "organic" materials which made up the bulk of the dry matter of an animal or plant were first distinguished as *fats*, *carbohydrates*, and *proteins*. Their general characteristics have been stated already. The fats contain carbon, hydrogen, and oxygen. Most of them are simple esters of higher fatty acids and the alcohol glycerine. In a small class, the lecithins (abundant in egg yolk), phosphoric acid, and nitrogenous bases, as well as fatty acids go to make up the molecule. The carbohydrates are the simple sugars and more complex substances built up of simple sugar molecules (e.g. starch, cellulose). They only contain carbon, hydrogen, and oxygen. The proteins are highly complex, being built up mainly of amino acids. They therefore always contain in addition to the three elements of carbohydrates a large amount of nitrogen. Some contain sulphur and phosphorus.

The approximate mean percentage composition of the different classes of food substances is as follows:

	Carbon	Hydrogen	Oxygen	Nitrogen	Sulphur
Fats	77	11·5	11·5	—	—
Carbohydrate	44	6	50	—	—
Protein	52	7	24	16	1

Only two common articles of food, dripping (100 per cent fat) and cane-sugar (100 per cent carbohydrate), belong exclusively to one of these three major groups of organic compounds. Dried white of egg is almost pure protein. The fresh egg albumen contains a large proportion of water. All fresh living matter from the Archbishop of Canterbury to the jellyfish contains at least 60 per cent of water. The relative proportions of the three classes of organic compounds which make up the overwhelming bulk of dry matter may be judged from the table given on p. 939. It gives the proportions in which these main constituents occur in some common articles of human diet, together with the energy content determined by combustion in the laboratory.

Liebig's close relation to the needs of chemical industry gave his work an influential position in continental science. He founded an important scientific journal in which Mayer's paper on the "Conservation of Energy" was published, and made himself the leader of a vigorous school of work. Like Davy, Faraday, Tyndall, Huxley, and many other prominent leaders of science during the period when experimental science was establishing the high prestige to which it has now attained, he also devoted himself to popular expositions which he wrote with compelling passion for his subject,

for the especial purpose of exciting the attention of governments and an enlightened public, to the necessity of establishing Schools of Chemistry; and of promoting a science so intimately connected with the arts, pursuits, and social well-being of modern civilized nations.

Though a German he contrived to express himself in terse and lucid diction. There is sometimes a homely charm in his writing, as when he expresses the hope that his book "may serve to make new friends to our beautiful and useful science."

Food	Water, per cent	Protein, per cent	Carbohydrate, per cent	Fat, per cent	Calories, per lb.·
Lean Beef	69	21·9	—	7·3	715
Breast of Chicken	74	24·6	—	0·2	466
Lean Bacon	56	21·5	—	5·9	649
Eggs	74	12·3	—	11·3	734
Herring..	68	18·6	—	10·9	806
Salmon	64	18·6	—	15·8	1,012
Margarine	14	—	—	84·3	3,556
Butter	14	—	—	81·6	3,442
Brazil Nuts	2·9	13·2	8·1	70·4	3,366
Chocolate	1·0	4·8	59·9	31·1	2,515
Cheddar Cheese	34	25·2	—	33·4	1,939
Milk	88	3·3	4·8	3·6	303
Honey	18	0·4	71·4	—	1,290
Broad Beans	66	9·4	22·8	0·4	616
Brown Bread	44	7·5	45·8	0·1	996
Boiled Potatoes	81	1·9	16·0	—	334
Stoned Prunes..	28	3·0	40·4	0·3	820
Apples	84	0·3	12·5	0·2	246
Plum Jam	24	0·2	70·0	—	1,306
Cabbage	93	1·4	4·5	0·1	114

CARBON ASSIMILATION IN THE GREEN PLANT

During the nineteenth century the pursuit of medicine was stimulated in turn by the growth of commercial horticulture, the sale of fertilizers, food preservation, and the manufacture of wines. Liebig's work on fertilizers and his initiative in producing the first marketable patent food infused new vigour into the study of animal and plant nutrition, and the school of workers associated with him has not yet ceased to exert its influence. Before Liebig's time little was known about the way in which carbon dioxide and water are used to build up the organic materials of the plant, and apart from Spallanzani's observation that the gastric juice secreted by the walls of the stomach dissolves meat, nothing of importance about the changes which the food undergoes in the gut had been found out. His studies on the nature of foodstuffs therefore laid the foundations of new enquiries into carbon assimilation and animal digestion.

By far the largest organic constituent of plants is the complex carbohydrate *cellulose*. Every cell of a plant is enclosed in a wall of cellulose, and the thick walls of the wood vessels up which the sap ascends have the same composition. So wood pulp is almost exclusively made of cellulose, as is also cotton fibre. The cell contents of most green plants contain granules of *starch*, another complex carbohydrate, which like cellulose can be broken down into simple sugars by prolonged boiling with mineral acid or alkali. These granules, easily seen in a thin slice of potato or a fragment of a liverwort when examined with a microscope, were noticed by the first microscopists.

The improvement of the compound microscope early in the nineteenth century brought new information about the organization of plant cells and the minute structure of leaves, where experiment shows that the bulk of carbon dioxide uptake occurs. Microscopic sections across a leaf (Fig. 450) show that it is a spongy mass of thin-walled green cells penetrated at intervals by the woody vessels of the so-called veins and enclosed in a pellicle (or *epidermis*) of thick-walled colourless cells. The epidermis is studded with fine pores (*stomata*) which are usually confined to the lower surface of the leaf and are surrounded by a lip of two cells which are green like those within. In darkness the two cells which form the lips of the pore shrink, and lie slackly together, closing the orifice. In bright light they swell and separate, so that the porous mass of green cells below the epidermis communicates freely with the air.

Thus the structure of a leaf is arranged so that the green cells are in free communication with the air from which the plant removes carbon dioxide in light. They are usually more or less cut off from the air in darkness, when experiment shows that the rate of evaporation from the leaves is reduced, and no CO_2 is taken up. This suggests that the green cells are directly connected with the use of CO_2 and water in manufacturing organic compounds. How to test this in a simple way is suggested by another microscopic observation. In light the green cells contain starch granules which disappear in darkness. Starch is very easily recognized by the fact that it imparts a deep blue tint to a solution of iodine and potassium iodide. If part of a leaf which has been kept in darkness for a few hours is covered with tinfoil, and then exposed for a short period (e.g. an hour) to bright light, soaking the leaf in an iodine solution shows that starch is only formed in the green cells when they are illuminated. The exposed parts are then stained deep blue and the covered part is not. You can, in fact, use the leaf as a sort of photographic plate, and "develop" an image. The iodine test also shows that variegated leaves which present a mosaic of white and green areas only develop starch in the green parts. Hence the green colouring matter called *chlorophyll*, which can be extracted from a leaf if it is soaked in alcohol, plays an essential part in the process of building up carbohydrate from carbon dioxide and water.

Photography depends on the fact that some silver salts undergo a chemical change in light, just as other chemical changes can be accomplished by heating or the application of electricity. Carbon assimilation in the green plant belongs in this sense to the same class of "photochemical reactions."

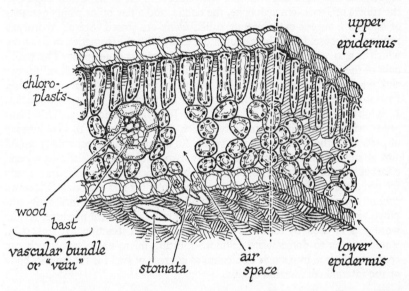

FIG. 450.—DIAGRAMMATIC VIEW OF THE MICROSCOPIC ANATOMY OF A TYPICAL LEAF.

The leaf consists mostly of a spongy mass of cells containing chlorophyll in small round corpuscles called chloroplasts. There are capacious air spaces which permit evaporation and circulation of carbon dioxide and oxygen within the inner mass of cells. They are enclosed between an upper and lower layer of thick-walled cells like the epidermis of the stem. On the under surface of the leaf there are pores called *stomata* guarded by sausage-shaped cells, which swell in certain conditions and especially in the light. Owing to the unequal thickening of their walls, this swelling forces the lips of the pore apart, so that water can freely evaporate from the underlying cells, thus drawing up sap from the veins, while carbon dioxide can freely enter and oxygen escape from the air spaces. In darkness the pores are usually closed, and the starch-forming cells of the spongy interior are protected from water loss. With the exception of the cells which guard the air.pores on the lower side of the leaf, those of the epidermis do not contain chlorophyll.

Chlorophyll may also be compared to the soot used to blacken the bulb of a thermometer for detecting infra-red rays. It "absorbs" light and by so doing makes solar radiation available for building up complex organic matter which liberates heat when broken down into its original constituents. Thus the coal mines and the oil wells of the world are, metaphorically speaking, stores of solar radiation. Solar radiation is therefore the basis of household fuel and of all heat engines. Hitherto man has used solar energy stored up in dead organic residues. We now see that it is not necessary to wait for geological epochs to convert solar radiation into sources of warmth or power. Yeast converts sugar into alcohol which can be used as food for an internal combustion engine or for a methylated spirit burner.

Starch is continually turned back into sugar in the green plant,* and, dissolved in that form, diffuses from the leaves to other regions of the plant. That is why it disappears from the leaf in darkness. Most green plants manufacture starch in the leaves and store their carbohydrates for use in that form. A few, like the sugar-cane and the beet, store it in the form of cane-sugar. In the tubers of Jerusalem artichoke, the dahlia, and a few other plants granules of another complex carbohydrate called *inulin* are stored. Starch hydrolysis produces glucose. Inulin breaks up more easily with the formation of fructose, which is also a simple sugar, sweeter than glucose or cane-sugar. The molecule of the latter is built up from the combination of one molecule of glucose and one molecule of fructose. As compared with cane-sugar or glucose, fructose is very slowly absorbed and can be used with safety by diabetics. It is now being produced in Iowa from Jerusalem artichokes. This plant grows with an astonishing rapidity, which calls attention to the inefficiency of present methods for producing sugar. An economical biotechnology would aim at storing solar radiation as quickly as possible with as little waste and effort as possible. By growing plants like beet which store carbohydrate ready for use there is a large source of waste both in effort and materials. Since we cannot digest cellulose we now waste all the solar radiation indirectly employed in converting sugar into cellulose in our agricultural produce. As the word *pay* is used by scientific workers, in contradistinction to bankers, it would pay us to domesticate cellulose-splitting micro-organisms which can convert cellulose into sugar or alcohol as sources of fuel for the human body or the internal combustion engine.

DIGESTION

Liebig's distinction between the three main classes of organic compounds in the body of the plant or animal opened the door to new researches into the nature of human digestion and the food requirements of a healthy person. The focus of these new enquiries was a discovery made by the French physiologist, Claude Bernard, who discovered the significance of a peculiar feature of the circulation in vertebrate animals. In man and in all vertebrates the vein which takes away blood from the gut does not join up directly with the main veins which take blood back to the heart. It breaks up again in the capillaries of the liver. So all blood from the gut passes first to the liver before joining the general circulation. Comparative tissue analysis following on the work of Liebig's school showed that the liver of a well-fed animal contains a large store of the animal starch called *glycogen*. In the liver of a starved animal there is scarcely a trace of it. Claude Bernard found that the glycogen content of the liver goes up soon after a meal, and then goes down before the next meal. The vertebrate stores starch in its liver just as the potato plant stores starch in its tuber.

* The carbohydrate first formed as a result of photosynthesis appears to be a hexose (sugar), which is then turned into starch for temporary storage in the leaves.

New knowledge of the chemistry of living matter now made it possible to study the fate of the foodstuffs in the animal body with some hope of success. With the exception of the sugars, all these essential constituents of the organic matter of the animal or plant body are either, like the fats, quite insoluble in water, or, like the proteins and starches, soluble but incapable of passing through animal or vegetable membranes (e.g. parchment) as a solution of common salt diffuses through them. Their molecules are too large. So before the food eaten by an animal can get through its tissues to its destination, it must undergo certain changes. This process is known as digestion. Under the incentive of Liebig's agricultural chemistry the study of digestion became a foremost topic of medical research. What we know about it has mainly been found out by work on man's nearest allies to which the following account applies.

From the mouth the food of man or of any other vertebrate animal passes into a winding tube which terminates in a second opening to the exterior, the *anus*, situated dorsally where the legs are joined to the body. This tube, known as the *alimentary canal*, or gut (Fig. 406), has everywhere muscular walls, an inner layer of muscle fibres arranged circle-wise, and an outer coat with a lengthwise arrangement. The slow, rhythmical movements of these muscles help to churn the food, and squeeze it along the alimentary canal to the anus. The inner wall of the gut is lined with a layer of cells which for a great part of its course consists of secreting cells and is folded in pits. The first part of the tube, called the *oesophagus*, or gullet, opens into a capacious bag. This bag, the stomach, leads into a narrower tube, the intestine. The intestine of vertebrates has two distinct portions, one narrower, called the *small intestine*, and the other wider, called the *large intestine*. Its final part, the *rectum*, communicates with the exterior by the anus.

In its passage along the alimentary canal human food encounters the various juices secreted by different parts of the walls of the digestive tract, and also the secretions of two larger glands, the liver and pancreas, which open by a common duct into the small intestine near its anterior end. These digestive juices contain substances, known as *enzymes*, which act on the complex organic constituents of the food, turning them into compounds sufficiently simple to diffuse through the walls of the intestine or sufficiently simple for the cells of the body to build them up into other substances as these may be required. An example familiar to most people, owing to its commercial use, is the *rennin* of the gastric juice. Apart from the fact that they are all derived from living organisms, it is difficult to fix on any single characteristic which will differentiate enzymes from all other types of catalysts. At present their chemical constitution is unknown. Surprisingly small quantities of enzyme are efficacious. Rennet, the gastric juice extract employed domestically for the preparation of junkets and commercially on a large scale in the manufacture of cheese, is able to clot 400,000 times its own weight of the milk protein *caseinogen*. Even this figure gives an imperfect picture of the prodigious activity of the enzyme. The active constituent is very small in proportion to the bulk of the extract.

The first digestive juice to act on human food is the saliva secreted by glands which lie beneath the muscles of the tongue and cheek, discharging by fine ducts into the cavity of the mouth. The saliva contains an enzyme which acts on starch, converting it into the complex sugar of malt extract (maltose). The secretion of the stomach or *gastric juice* contains free hydrochloric acid. It also contains an enzyme *pepsin* which breaks down complex proteins, like albumen, into very simple proteins that are called peptones. It has no action on the starchy or fatty constituents of the food. The bile or secretion of the liver does not contain a digestive enzyme. It contains excretory matter in the form of certain pigments together with alkaline salts which neutralize the acidity of the gastric juice and greatly facilitate the emulsification of fats.

The pancreas or sweetbread is the chief digestive gland. Its secretion contains three important enzymes. One called *amylase* breaks down starch or dextrin into malt sugar. A second called *trypsin* can break down proteins into the organic "amino" acids of which the protein molecule is built up. It thus carries protein digestion a stage farther than is reached in the stomach. A third called *lipase* breaks up fat into fatty acid and glycerol. The intestinal juice secreted by the glandular walls of the small intestine also contains enzymes, one called *erepsin* which acts on the final stages of protein decomposition, completing the work of the pancreatic juice, and a series of others which act on the complex sugars like malt sugar, converting them into simple sugars. The digestive tract of man does not contain any enzyme that breaks down cellulose. Some cellulose is broken down by bacteria in the large intestine, and is wasted. This is a very strong argument against an exclusively vegetarian diet. Another objection to vegetarianism is that the cellulose wall of plant cells makes them much less accessible to the action of the digestive juices than animal tissues.

Any undigested or indigestible matter eventually passes out of the body, along with the bile pigments that confer its characteristic colour, as faeces. In the small intestine the starches have all been absorbed as sugar by the fine blood vessels beneath its lining. The proteins have been broken down into the diffusible substances known as amino-acids (p. 527) and travel to the tissues by the same route. All the blood returning from the alimentary tract passes through the capillary network of the liver *en route* for the heart. The glycogen-storing activity of the liver is its most important role in the economy of the body. The products of fat digestion on the other hand are taken up by the cells of the lining of the small intestine, and given up in turn to the underlying tissue spaces. The lymph spaces in the absorptive wall of the intestine, known as *lacteals*, communicate with a well-defined channel, the *thoracic duct*, which opens into a jugular vein. The lacteals are so called because after a meal of fatty constituents they are found to be gorged with droplets of fat, and it seems that the bulk of the fatty portion of the food is absorbed into the circulation by this indirect route. In the course of the lymph spaces there occur masses of dividing cells which are manufacturing new white blood corpuscles. These are spoken of as *lymph glands*, and are usually enlarged in inflammatory conditions. The tonsils are large lymph glands. The red blood corpuscles are manufactured in the bone marrow.

The bulk of the heat production in man and his nearest allies results from the oxidation of carbohydrates stored as glycogen in the liver and muscles, and also of fats. Thus most of the *nitrogenous* material of the food consumed by a full-grown animal is waste matter. The body can convert the products of protein digestion into carbohydrates by removal of the nitrogenous portion in the form of materials such as urea, $CO(NH_2)_2$. These are eliminated from the body in the urine. The urine is produced by two bodies known as the kidneys, which communicate with the cloaca by tubes known as the *ureters* (Fig. 415). Each kidney is a flattened ellipsoidal structure with a small cavity continuous with the canal of the ureter. Into this cavity open innumerable closely packed tubules of glandular structure which make up the substance of the kidney. These tubules terminate in a flash-shaped swelling whose walls are invaginated to receive a tuft of small blood vessels, this portion being called the Malpighian body, or capsule, after Malpighi (1628–1694), one of the earliest microscopists. In man and most mammals the ureters open into a capacious receptacle with muscular walls, the bladder. This communicates with the exterior by a duct called the *urethra*, separately in the female and along with the male generative ducts in the male.

THE MINERAL NEEDS OF THE LIVING MACHINE

In addition to the three classes of organic materials called carbohydrates, fats, and proteins, the body of plants and animals contains various mineral salts dissolved in the tissue fluids, such as the cell sap of plants, the blood, and the lymph or clear fluid in the body cavities of animals. The mineral needs of the body may be divided under two headings. First come elements which enter into the composition of the organic materials. Thus most proteins contain sulphur. Many contain phosphorus. Haemoglobin contains iron. Haemocyanin, the corresponding blue respiratory pigment of lobsters and snails, contains copper. The plant gets sulphur and phosphorus as it gets the nitrogen necessary to build up the protein molecule from mineral salts (sulphates or phosphates). Animals get their proteins ready made. So the supply of sulphur and phosphorus is usually adequate if the nitrogenous content of the diet is sufficient.

Magnesium is specifically necessary for the green plant because *chlorophyll* is an organic magnesium compound. In vertebrate animals (fishes, reptiles, birds, and mammals) the thyroid gland in the neck manufactures an organic compound of which the molecule contains iodine (see p. 886). On this account iodine is essential to healthy growth. Iodine is not present in appreciable quantities in other animal tissues. For plants and invertebrates it does not seem to be an essential element, though it is present in seaweeds. Near the sea the quantities present in salt carried by the breeze ensures a supply adequate to animal needs. Some inland and mountainous districts of Europe and America have a very low soil iodine content. Thyroid deficiency diseases (goitre, cretinism, etc.) of human beings and livestock are therefore endemic. This is remediable by a very small addition of iodine to the diet. In Switzerland the State provides iodized table salt, the necessary iodine content of which need not be greater than one-millionth of an ounce per daily salt ration of a single person. Iodized rations are also recommended for inland hog rearing, because the pig is very liable to iodine starvation if the soil iodine content is low. The essential secretion of the thyroid gland is a crystalline compound containing 23·2 per cent carbon, 1·4 per cent hydrogen, 1·8 per cent nitrogen, and 65·4 per cent iodine.

A second class of mineral food constituents includes those which appear to exist as salts in the tissue fluids and sap. These include the chlorides of several metals, notably sodium, potassium, calcium, and magnesium. Sodium does not appear to be essential to plants. Potassium, calcium, and magnesium are all essential to them. Which species flourish in different soils under similar climatic conditions is very largely affected by their relative susceptibility to a low local content of one or the other. The addition of a relatively small dressing of the appropriate salt is an important part of the technique of modern soil husbandry.

Potassium and calcium are essential to the life of all cells. This can be illustrated in a very spectacular way (Fig. 451) by perfusing the heart with a mixed solution of salts in roughly the same concentration as they occur in the blood. When a frog's heart is removed from the body it empties itself of blood, and in a few seconds stops beating. If a glass tube is inserted into the main venous orifice so that it can be supplied with a suitable solution of salts of the three essential metals, it at once begins to beat vigorously and will continue to do so for several hours. The mixture used is composed of the chlorides of sodium (6 parts per thousand by weight) and potassium and calcium (1½ parts per ten thousand by weight) together with a little sodium bicarbonate or phosphate to make it slightly alkaline. If the perfusion fluid is replaced by a mixture from which either the calcium or potassium is omitted the heart-beat comes to a standstill. This happens almost instantaneously if no calcium is supplied. After being stopped in this way, the beat resumes almost at once when the heart is supplied with the original mixture. If the solution contains a little sugar the isolated heart can be made to beat for several weeks. Otherwise it gradually uses up its food reserves, and then ceases to be able to work. The same results can be obtained with the sheep's heart, which can also be made to go on working outside the body for at least three weeks, provided the temperature of the fluid is kept near blood heat, i.e. about 36° C. For prolonged experiments of this kind a trace of magnesium is necessary. Lately it has been shown that small traces of manganese may be essential to fertility in mammals. It is not yet known how it is used. Manganese is also necessary to many plants.

Animals are not liable to magnesium deficiency since all green plants contain an abundance of magnesium for their needs. On the other hand, plants which grow on soils with a low lime content may contain a relatively small amount of calcium. Hence herbivorous animals like the pig, which is highly susceptible to calcium deficiency, are liable to various diseases (especially rickets) unless lime fertilizers are applied to the soil or an extra calcium ration is given. The figure already cited with reference to iodine illustrates the general principle that a soil deficiency which might completely exclude the possibility of successful livestock husbandry can often be remedied at a negligible cost. The provision of suitable mineral rations or soil dressings is one way in which advancing biological knowledge is making it possible to break down the natural limitations of locality.

According to the doctrine of free trade as set forth in Tom Paine's *Rights of Man*, it used to be accepted as an axiom that regions which produce particular products produce them because they are inherently adapted to do so. This belief, like the Ricardian superstition, is based on the implicit assumption that biologists will never be able to find out how it happens that things

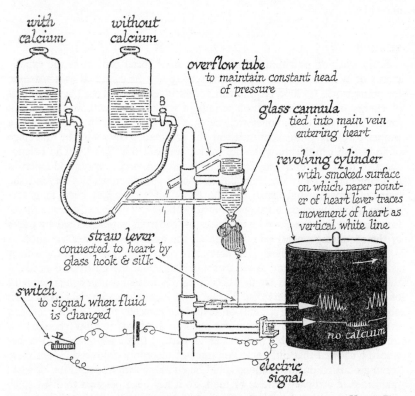

FIG. 451.—SET-UP OF EXPERIMENT TO SHOW THE DEPENDENCE OF THE HEART-BEAT
ON METALLIC IONS

A frog's heart will continue to beat for many hours if supplied with a solution containing the same metallic ions (sodium, potassium, calcium, and magnesium) as blood in the same proportions. By means of the taps A and B the heart can be alternately perfused with a saline mixture of the proper composition and a saline mixture from which one constituent has been left out or added in excess. The figure shows how the heart-beat stops when the heart is perfused with a calcium free fluid, and how it starts to beat normally when the proper saline is supplied once more. A sheep's heart can also be kept beating in the same way, but the fluid must be kept about body temperature.

grow in one place and do not grow in another, what makes them grow best, and how they can be induced to grow at all. There are innumerable limiting factors to growth. If any one of them is lacking successful husbandry of crop or stock is impossible. It may happen that the lack of one of them can be remedied at a trifling outlay, when other contributory agencies are specially propitious to success. For instance, a plant admirably adapted for foliage or root growth and fruit ripening in England may not ordinarily grow there, because the seedlings are susceptible to early frost. If we know this, it may be less wasteful to let the seeds germinate under glass than to import the final product from Honolulu. As with chemistry so with biology, more scientific knowledge means less dependence on nature's ready-made amenities.

VITAMINS

Early work on nutrition belongs to the same social context as the experiments of Watt on horses. The human body was first studied as a machine for doing work. Its food requirements were investigated from the standpoint of energy transformed in short periods of work or rest without regard to a long-range view of national well-being. This limitation of outlook was a proper corollary to the sentiments of the prosperous classes in the first stage of industrial capitalism, when the worker was called a "hand." The balance sheet of food consumption, respiration, excretion, and energy production in experiments of short duration did not show any discrepancies beyond the range of experimental error, and the lesson of scurvy had been long forgotten when the modern study of nutrition began. Till recently it was therefore thought that the three main classes of foodstuffs supplemented by traces of the requisite mineral salts include all the essentials of a healthy diet.

The advance of knowledge has now got beyond the physiology of the worker as *hand*, and is beginning to tell us something about the nutritional needs of the worker as *citizen*. In the first decade of the present century the chemistry of foodstuffs had progressed so far that it was possible to carry out more exact observations by feeding animals on diets of chemically pure protein, fat, and carbohydrate. The animals reared on such diets refused to grow, though they thrived if comparatively small traces of natural foods were added. Further research showed that different symptoms of disorders produced by exclusive feeding on such purified rations could be eliminated by the addition of small quantities of ordinary articles of food. So it has been possible to distinguish different "accessory food factors," the absence of any one of which is associated with a particular defect.

Generically these substances have been called vitamins. The name does not mean that they have anything in common besides the fact that they do not belong to the classes of diet constituents previously believed to be all-inclusive, the fact that the requisite quantities are very small, that they all appear to be organic compounds, and that their chemical constitution was unknown when the word was first introduced. The chemical constitution of several of them is now known, some can be synthesized and others will be synthesized in the near future. Research along these lines was encouraged by the conditions of food shortage during the European war of 1914–18 when "nutritional" diseases like scurvy and rickets came into prominence.

Scurvy is due to the absence of a comparatively simple substance in the diet. It is *ascorbic acid*. Before its chemical nature had been determined it was called "vitamin C." Ascorbic acid has the formula $C_6H_8O_6$. It has alcoholic and ketone characteristics on account of four OH and one CO radicles in the molecule. It is present in most fresh fruit and in many vegetables, especially in oranges, lemons, black currants, green leaves, and potatoes. Since its molecular constitution has been discovered, its commercial manufacture from glucose has been started.

Calciferol, with the formula $C_{28}H_{43}OH$, is one of the known forms of another vitamin, "D." It is produced by the action of ultra-violet light on another alcohol called *ergosterol*. Ergosterol has the same formula $C_{28}H_{43}OH$ with a different internal arrangement of the atoms in its molecule. The exact chemical constitution of both substances is now known. Various fish liver oils contain another form of vitamin D whose formula is $C_{27}H_{41}OH$. So also does butter fat. The D content of the husks of ripe cocoa beans is high, and the latter can be used in cattle feeding to raise the D content of the milk. The absence of D is responsible for the deficiency disease called rickets, still common among the poorer section of the population. Rickets can be cured and, of course, prevented by administering any form of vitamin D, or by exposure to ultra-violet radiation from intense sunlight or a mercury vapour lamp. The exposure leads to the production of D in the skin from pro-vitamins such as ergosterol. Rickets is a deficiency disease affecting especially bone and tooth development in children. They are especially prone to it if brought up in dingy dwellings and sunless cities, unless the lack of ultra-violet light in their normal environment is counterbalanced by a diet containing excess of D, that is to say a diet with plenty of fresh eggs, summer milk and butter with preferably, to make sure, some fish liver oil or calciferol preparation. Pigs are also liable to get rickets. Modern pig-breeders take special precautions to avoid this. In Scandinavian countries glass which transmits ultra-violet light is used for the windows of pig-styes. There has been more progress in the education of Danish pig-breeders than in the education of British politicians.

Scurvy and rickets are the chief diet "deficiency" diseases which have attracted attention in the West. There are several others. Apparently the animal body needs a substance which is abundant in the husk but not in the grain of plant seeds like cereals. Its absence produces severe muscular weakness, especially in birds. A similar condition in human beings is the disease called "beri-beri" to which Japanese peasants who live largely on a diet of polished rice are liable. This is because removal of the husk removes "vitamin B_1." Beri-beri can be cured by the administration of suitable extracts made from these husks, from wheat germ or from yeast. The active chemical constituent, now called *aneurin*, is an organic compound of which the hydrochloride has the formula $C_{12}H_{17}O\ N_4S\ .\ Cl$. To keep animals healthy on diets of pure proteins, fats, carbohydrates, and mineral salts it is essential to add various other substances like the above in minute quantities. One of these, called vitamin A, is present along with D in butter fat, egg yolk, and cod-liver oil, especially in the first two. It is also an alcohol with the formula $C_{20}H_{29}OH$, chemically related to the plant pigment *carotin*. The animal body can convert the latter into A. If the diet is deficient in A, or in carotin its pro-vitamin, animals show general liability to bacterial infections, and an adequate minimum seems to help resistance to diseases like colds and influenza. Lack of *nicotinic* acid (C_4H_4NCOOH), present with aneurin in yeast, as also in pork flesh and in liver, is responsible for *pellagra*, a disease of the digestive system and skin. The composition of what is now called vitamin E, present in cereal oils and green leaves, especially lettuce, is not yet known. If it is absent complete sterility results from degeneration of the testis in the male and resorption of early embryos in the female.

A supply of fresh butter and green vegetables or fresh eggs ensures the presence of sufficient vitamins to meet the requirements of healthy growth. A liberal allowance of milk keeps up an adequate supply of calcium, and of B_2. If the mineral and vitamin content of a diet are safeguarded by this means, or by recourse to the use of pure chemicals such as calciferol or carotin, a diet of soya beans can supply all that is necessary for the physical requirements of a human being. While wheat, barley, and rice appear to be adequate as sources of proteins, maize is not. The reason for this is that digestion of maize protein does not yield one of the amino acids (tryptophane), which is an essential constituent of proteins in the animal body.

Biological knowledge is now approaching the stage at which it will be possible to specify all the necessary constituents of a plant or animal diet composed of chemical pure substances. The result is that a totally new attitude to husbandry is emerging. On the one hand we can plan for an irreducible minimum consumption appropriate to universal human needs. On the other, we can plan for the expenditure of a minimum of human labour in producing the necessary constituents from the soil with the aid of sunlight and bacteria. Two obstacles have stood in the way of using our newly gained knowledge of nutrition in its twofold aspect. One is the obstructive individualism which opposes any interference with planless competitive enterprise in food production. Till lately, we have most of us been less concerned with the proper care of our fellow countrymen than with the provision of a healthy diet for pigs, racehorses, or bullocks. Indeed, the most vocal zoophilists and anti-vivisectionists are found among those who take up human destruction as a profession or profess complete disregard for human well-being by the way they behave in their capacity as voters. In some countries the Colonel Blimps have come now to regard a national minimum of calories as a patriotic gesture; and are thus abreast of scientific knowledge in 1850 or thereabouts.

The calorie standard of nutrition is fitting to a slave civilization in which cheap labour is abundant. "Britons never will be slaves" should not be sung at meetings of parliamentary candidates unless they are prepared to force a national minimum of food for all in sufficient variety to ensure continued growth and health. A standard *minimum* diet is not a sufficient guarantee of national health unless it makes allowance for preferences which result from social habit. To take a horse to the water is one thing. To make it drink is another. So also it is one thing to see that every citizen can get the necessary quantity of vitamins, and another thing to make sure that he can get them in a palatable form. In contemporary society the difference between the quantity and variety of food consumed by the richer and poorer sections of the community is more conspicuous than any difference in the quality of the conversation which accompanies its consumption. Using our knowledge to the fullest extent does not mean that variety need be sacrificed to a narrow definition of efficiency. The mechanical technology of the coal-steel age employed coal tar chemists to furnish thousands of synthetic dyes as substitutes for the few natural colours which primitive biotechnology provided. If biochemists were set to work at the problem, they could produce thousands of new synthetic flavours as substitutes for the limited range of natural ones which are now available for the culinary art. The science of nutrition will receive a new impetus when national food production is planned to safeguard the health of every citizen.

WATER CULTURE AND TANK GARDENING

In its earliest stages the study of plant nutrition was mainly based on potting experiments with the addition of excess of one or other ingredients to a poor soil. The recognition that they can make their own organic materials from the carbon dioxide of the air and the salts and water of the earth led later to a simplification in the technique of studying the dietetic needs of growing plants. A seedling can be brought to maturity by letting its roots grow in water, if the water contains the requisite inorganic salts in a total concentration which does not produce shrinking or swelling of the root cells owing to osmotic pressure. In the last ten years this technique, long familiar as a laboratory device, has been adapted to the economic production of crops both for forage and for human consumption.

The growth of forage crops without soil is described in the following citation from *Nature* (October 1936):

Attention has recently been given to production of green fodder for cattle and other farm stock without the intermediary of the soil. In Great Britain the method advocated is apparently of German origin, and it is claimed that the fodder is grown from seed in ten days. According to published accounts, a layer of seed (maize or other grain) is spread on a perforated metal tray, and the tray is placed in a cabinet, constructed to hold a series of trays. The seed is damped daily by water, containing a small percentage of nutrient salts, from a tank placed on the top of the cabinet, and, when an adequate temperature is maintained, the seed germinates and in 10 days a growth of shoots some 12 inches high is obtained. This growth of shoots, with the mass of rootlets, is then given to the stock. Several trials have shown that this fodder is readily eaten by stock, but carefully controlled experiments are necessary to demonstrate the full nutritive value and the costs of production of this fodder.

This practice does not seem to involve the formation of new material by photosynthesis. It is essentially a rapid way of converting the food stores already present in the grain into a form more suitable for the consumption of farm stock.

Of greater interest are other experiments carried out at the University of California by Professor W. F. Gericke, on the production of crops in shallow tanks of water to which the necessary chemical fertilizers have been added. The seeds are sown in a layer of sawdust or moss on wire netting just above the water into which the roots grow. Even in localities where the soil is good, this tank culture method has the following advantages (Gericke. *Amer. Journ. Bot*, 16, 1929):

Among these are: (*a*) Certain desired compositions of plants can be obtained by growth in water through manipulation of factors that affect absorption of specified elements; (*b*) more economical use of elements by growth in water through manipulation of factors that restrict absorption to definite growth periods; (*c*) more economical use of water, as all that is supplied is available; (*d*) closer planting can be employed; (*e*) complete portability of plants, especially desirable in flowers.

Details of yield obtained by tank culture have been kindly supplied by Professor Gericke in a private communication. Four basins, each providing 25 sq. ft. of water surface, yielded 1,224 lb. of ripe tomatoes. The 28 lb. of chemicals required for this crop cost less than 3 cents a pound. A basin providing one-hundredth of an acre of water surface yielded 24·65 bushels of potatoes. These were grown in the open and required 40 lb. of salts. While large yields can also be obtained with cereals, the cost of chemicals is here so large an item that the method may not justify the cost of the equipment. In general, the crops most suited to tank culture are those with a high water and carbohydrate content.

At present we can only guess at the wider implications of this biotechnical advance. Plant growth is limited by three main factors: light energy, mineral salts, and water. Agricultural production has hitherto been confined to regions where the supply of these three essentials is already adequate, or, as with the last two, where the local supply can be supplemented by manuring or irrigation without too much trouble or loss. The energy of sunlight goes to waste over the hot deserts where rainfall is scanty, and the sand will hold neither water nor salts. Irrigation is costly, and most of the water used sinks through the desert sand, so it is wasted, carrying with it the soluble salts. Tank culture, on the other hand, limits water loss to evaporation.

Some of the most significant advances in the application of science during the past two centuries have been those which have helped us to find universal substitutes for the endowments which Nature distributes in localized areas. It is entertaining to speculate how far tank culture may eventually equalize the potentialities of the sunnier parts of the earth. It is not beyond the bounds of possibility that the Sahara may become a vast open-air factory for storing sunlight in the starch and cellulose of potatoes or artichokes. This could then be converted on the spot into power alcohol and sugar. We are now witnessing the beginnings of a biotechnical revolution that will relegate the Law of Diminishing Returns to the same limbo as phlogiston.

CHAPTER XXI

THE ASCENT OF MAN

THE doctrine of common descent or *organic evolution*, foreshadowed in the world outlook of the Ionian naturalists and their Epicurean successors, was revived in the period of intellectual ferment which preceded and accompanied the French Revolution, when the teachings of the Greek materialists were in favour among scientific investigators. Without attracting much comment from the world at large or exciting much discussion among other naturalists, it was defended in England by Dr. Erasmus Darwin of the Lunar Society (see p. 431), in France by Lamarck and Saint Hilaire, and in Germany by Goethe. The influence of the new doctrine was ephemeral. While the systematic study of·plant life was the professional business of the apothecary, the seed merchant, and nurseryman, that of animals was still a gentlemanly pastime without any professional organization of its own. In the half century before a vigorous controversy raged around the publication of Darwin's *Origin of Species*, the French zoologist, Cuvier, elevated to the rank· of baron by the return of the Bourbons, exerted all his influence as leader of a new school of comparative anatomy to discourage evolutionary speculation.

The accumulation of an immense collection of new data conspired to command the almost universal assent of scientific men, when Darwin expounded it with singular journalistic skill which few scientific writers have excelled. On the other hand, the approval of his fellow naturalists provides no explanation for the fact that Darwin's writings became the focus of one of the greatest intellectual struggles in the history of human knowledge. To understand why this is so we have to recall the fact that England was the centre of the controversy. England was approaching the zenith of a prosperity based on the exploitation of new scientific knowledge, and the new captains of industry had not as yet acquired an effective voice in the policy of the official strongholds of English culture. Nonconformity prevailed among the *entrepreneur* and the new personnel of science. The Test Act of 1673 which imposed the acceptance of the Anglican sacrament on English candidates for public office was not repealed till 1828, and the removal of religious tests which excluded Nonconformists, Catholics, and Jews from the universities was not completed till fifty years later, then only in the teeth of bitter opposition from the Bishops' bench in the House of Lords. Even the condition of the English Royal Society had prompted Babbage, Lucasian Professor at Cambridge in the Newtonian succession, to write his tract (1830) on *The Decline of Science in England*, and years later Faraday's dissatisfaction prompted him to refuse the presidency. H. G. Wells states the position in the following passage:

British science was largely the creation of Englishmen and Scotchmen working outside the ordinary centres of erudition. We have told how the universities after the reformation ceased to have a wide popular appeal, how they became the educational preserve of the nobility and gentry and the strongholds of the established church. A pompous and unintelligent classical pretentiousness dominated them, and they dominated the schools of the middle and upper classes. The only knowledge recognized was an uncritical textual knowledge of Latin and Greek classics, and the test of a good style was its abundance of quotations, allusions, and stereotyped expressions. The early development of British science went on therefore in spite of the formal educational organization and in the teeth of bitter hostility of the teaching and clerical professions.

A few dates and incidents will bring the social *milieu* of the controversy into prominence. In 1854 dissenters were first admitted as students to the Universities of Oxford and Cambridge, in which teaching posts were still restricted by religious tests. The obstruction of the Bishops' bench to complete removal of all religious qualifications for college and university offices (other than chairs in Divinity) was not defeated till 1878. In 1856 the first Atlantic cable was completed. Lord Kelvin (then William Thomson), as a director, laid the foundations of a fortune (see p. 731) which vindicated the plea of Babbage by applying Newtonian mathematics to the measurement of delayed transmission. In 1859 Darwin published the *Origin of Species*. In 1860 Bishop Wilberforce came to the British Association to ask if Huxley claimed descent from a monkey through his grandfather or his grandmother. During the controversy which ensued Disraeli's undergraduate flippancy and the impudent pomposity of William Ewart Gladstone were enlisted in the defence of the Faith.

The Normal School of Science where Huxley taught was not what it now is, the Imperial College of Science and Technology, an institution powerful enough to seduce Sedgwick from the chair of zoology at Cambridge to direct Huxley's former department. In Darwin's time there was no provision for modern scientific instruction in the older British seats of learning. Cambridge did not capitulate till Kelvin had made his fortune. Oral tradition relates how the proposal to equip laboratories for practical teaching in experimental physics was opposed in the senate by a prominent mathematician. He contended that students should be content to accept the testimony of professors who were all communicating members of the Church of England. True or not, the story is representative of the temper of the time. The scientific controversy was carried on while the political struggle over the Test Acts was still proceeding. The intervention of Bishops and of an Anglican Prime Minister inevitably made evolution the ideological symbol of the movement to reshape the key positions of English education in accordance with the aspirations of the new industrial leaders.

A parallel struggle in Germany, where coal-tar chemistry was to provide new opportunities for exploitation, was carried on with Haeckel as the champion of evolution. The following remarks by Humphrey in *The Scientific Worker*, Nov. 1937, describe the German scene:

In Germany supporters of political reform took up Darwinism almost as their catchword. The middle-classes were still oppressed by the remains of the aristocracy, and the Liberals were still hemmed in by the clerical and conservative forces. This reaction became intensified after the 1848 revolution, and so also was the fight for Darwinism. The main popularizers were Johannes Muller and Haeckel. The latter was particularly keen in fighting the doctrine of *ignorabimus* in which he scented political reaction. In 1877 at a scientific meeting at Munich, while the Prussian Government was drafting a new educational law, he gave an address upon the relation of evolution to science in general. In it he expressed the assurance that biology conceived in an evolutionary manner is not an exact but an historic science, and could form a basis for a uniform view of life which would gradually reconstruct the whole of human existence on general humanitarian lines, and which should therefore constitute the foundations for all education. He was opposed by Virchow, who said that Darwinism was largely unproved and that school education should confine itself to indisputable proofs. This view was greeted with cheers by the conservatives. Shortly afterwards the Prussian Minister of Education sent round a circular strictly forbidding schoolmasters in the country to have anything to do with Darwinism, and in the new educational law biology was entirely excluded from the curriculum. The time when German biology held its own in the world came with the immense technical and economic development which followed the unification of the German states into the Empire.

The acceptance of evolution as an ideological gesture of the cultural supremacy of the new manufacturing plutocracy in England and Germany had two effects. One was beneficial to science. The other which was harmful is not sufficiently emphasized, and is only beginning to be apparent to a few biologists. The controversy proved beneficial because it encouraged biological teaching in the universities, attracted benefactions for research and support for the growth of public museums. It helped to raise the pursuit of biology to independent professional status, and supplied funds for apparatus and equipment. This nursed into being new branches of enquiry which had no immediate application in social practice at the time. In doing so, it contributed to the advancement of useful knowledge in the long run. Meanwhile it deflected interest away from the pressing biotechnical problems which had been raised by new horticultural practices in the first half of the century and concentrated attention on the more purely descriptive study of living creatures.

In assimilating evolution to its cultural aspirations, industrial capitalism moulded the direction of biological enquiry in accordance with its material requirements. During the revolutions of Stuart times large-scale farming associated with the enclosure movement which continued throughout the succeeding century offered an outlet for capital investment, reflected in the active interest of the English Royal Society in all aspects of husbandry. When the evolutionary controversy began, only a decade had passed since the repeal of the corn laws. The policy of agricultural self-sufficiency had been abandoned. Cheap bread supplied from undeveloped territories to factory employees in rapidly growing centres of urban congestion was the proper corollary of low wages. Darwin's emphasis on competition as the basis of selection in nature endowed ruthless commercial rivalries with the verisimilitude of natural law, while Ricardian economics placed a flaming sword between the farm and the factory.

Side by side with the work of contemporaries like Mendel whose researches had a close relation to the biotechnical problems of his age, Darwin's experiments on heredity represent a mean order of performance. That French biology received little stimulus from the evolutionary controversy is not surprising. The revolution had long since liberated education from the yoke of an established church. In close relation to the needs of the wine industry and an active policy of agricultural development France experienced a brilliant efflorescence of biotechnical invention, while English and German biologists were preoccupied with filling the lacunae of the evolutionary record. Except in so far as it retained its contact with social practice through medicine, the leadership of Britain and Germany in biological science ended when the larger lacunae had been filled. Striking progress of biology in pursuit of its true and lawful goal has since taken place in countries like the United States, Scandinavia, and more recently the U.S.S.R., where large-scale capitalist farming with paternal encouragement from the Government, co-operative farming and State planning are supplying new problems and the resources for solving them. It is significant that a demand for Government intervention in British agriculture, voiced by eminent biochemists, now comes from a school of biologists whose work lies outside the evolutionary tradition.

The struggle for cultural supremacy and the *laisser-faire* outlook of the manufacturing classes conspired to make the evolutionary problem the focus of a controversy which extended far beyond the boundaries of scientific intercourse, and the thesis which put the match to the bonfire signalizes a new phase in the history of scientific discovery. A slow process of accumulating new facts had occurred during the preceding century at increasing tempo. As with the solution of a picture puzzle, a point was reached at which the general pattern became suddenly and brilliantly clear. During the last half century before Darwin's *Origin of Species* was published three themes had become prominent in biological studies.

THE PRINCIPLE OF UNITY OF TYPE

Of these, a new orientation in systematic classification of living animals and plants might seem to be least related to the social *milieu*. From ancient times the search for medicinal herbs and for ornamental plants sustained a more or less continuous interest in codifying the diagnostic features by which different species can be identified. Between the herbals of Theophrastus in 300 B.C. and of Gerard in A.D. 1600 there was very little genuine progress in content or method. The herbals of the sixteenth century describe many plants which were not known to the Greeks or to the Arabs, and omit others that were. Till the practice of realistic illustration, fostered by the growth of surgery in the sixteenth century, slowly spread to other types of medical treatise, information of this type had a local and ephemeral character. The contents of the herbals waxed and waned simultaneously, and scarcely reached dimensions beyond which *ready reference, without recourse to codification would have been impossible.*

During the seventeenth and eighteenth centuries a new *genre* of botanical treatise reflects the growth of public and private physick gardens, the acquisition of new medicinal and commercial plants such as Peruvian bark (quinine), the potato and tobacco from the New World, the organization of commercial seed production and horticulture, and the invention of the microscope. The new *genre* was in turn both more intensive and more extensive. The herbals of the sixteenth century display hardly a rudiment of systematic classification.

A turning point is signalized by the herbal of Jung of Lübeck in the opening years of the seventeenth century. Jung arranges flowering plants in assem-

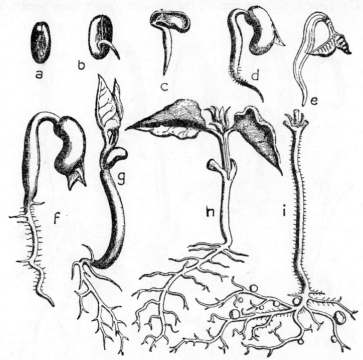

FIG. 452.—MALPIGHI'S DRAWINGS OF THE GERMINATION OF THE BEAN—
A DICOTYLEDON

The two seed-leaves or cotyledons are fleshy food stores between which the young root and shoot are at first concealed. *c* shows the seedling in section, and in *e* both cotyledons have been removed. In *i*, the root nodules characteristic of legumes are figured for the first time.

(This and the next figure reproduced by his kind permission and that of the publisher from Dr. Charles Singer's *Short History of Biology*, Oxford University Press.)

blages which show similar types of flowers. Such are the *Compositae* (daisy family), the *Labiatae* (dead-nettle family), and the *Leguminosae* (pea family). With this end in view he prefaces his arrangement of known plants with descriptive terminology for external characteristics of plant organization such as the inflorescences (spikes, umbels, panicles) for which his own terminology has come down to us. The work of Morison, Professor of Physic at Oxford, represents the intensive type of study. His treatise (1672) on a single family of flowering plants the *Umbelliferae* (parsley, carrot, etc.) emphasizes how far the recognition of new species had extended beyond the range of the ancient herbals. In the herbal of Theophrastus, a disciple of Aristotle, about three hundred plants constituted an exhaustive account of the world's flora. When Ray published the most notable example of the new extensive treatise (*Historia plantarum*) between the years 1684 and 1704, he was in a position to describe nineteen thousand plants divided into one hundred and twenty-five assemblages which included, in addition to the families mentioned above, the *Cruciferae* (wallflower family), the *Rubiaceae* (goose grass family), and

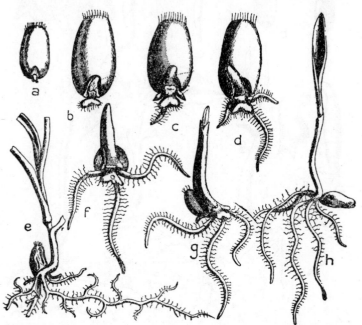

FIG. 453.—MALPIGHI'S DRAWINGS OF THE GERMINATION OF A GRAIN OF WHEAT—A MONOCOTYLEDON

e is the last in the series. Part of the single cotyledon remains within the grain as an absorbing organ, and the rest of it forms the sheath of the first ordinary leaf.

others of which the names survive in botanical works today. The beginnings of a hierarchical arrangement are also seen in the broad division of flowering plants into *Monocotyledons* and *Dicotyledons* (Figs. 452, 453).

The practice of classifying plants for purposes of identification arose naturally from the accumulation of more data than the unaided memory could manipulate. The several social agencies which encouraged systematic description of new species have been indicated sufficiently in previous chapters. Once classification began, an ever-present reality of animate nature stamped itself inescapably on the execution of the task. The principle called *Unity of Type* did not spring into existence suddenly. As more intensive and extensive studies developed side by side, botanists began to realize that some characteristics, e.g. the colour of the flower, are shared by plants with few other common features, while others distinguish groups of species with many common features. Hence it is possible to arrange plants in groups of which the members share a very large number of characteristics which distinguish them from other plants. The dawning recognition of this possibility which expressed itself in a complex hierarchy of resemblances is inherent in a practice which is already found in the herbals of the sixteenth century, though it was not generally adopted. Each plant had two names, one *specific* to it, the other its *generic* name characteristic of others which resemble it very closely.

The arrangement of living creatures in a system based on unity of type may be illustrated by the classificatory position of man and the primrose. Each is a species, i.e. a group of organisms of which the members interbreed freely with one another and do not breed freely with members of other species in nature. In each species there are several local *varieties* or races which preserve their distinct characteristics if they are prevented from inter-breeding by geographical or artificial agencies. Any single species may contain an immense number of such varieties, which can be deliberately perpetuated by breeding like to like as in animal husbandry, horticulture, and crop production. Such varieties would soon lose their distinctive features if left to breed with one another without interference, and the distinction between varieties and species is therefore capable of being put to experimental test. In practice it is difficult to decide whether two distinct forms are actually different, unless they occupy the same locality. There is then no barrier to crossing except their own disability. Two local varieties which are separated by a mountain range or sea may be classified as distinct species though they would freely mix if there were no such obstacle to prevent them.

Both species referred to have two names, a first or generic which it shares with the species most like itself just as we share our surnames with our brothers and sisters, paternal cousins and parents, together with a second or *specific* name which indicates a particular member of the genus just as our christian names distinguish us from our brothers and sisters. Thus Wordsworth was one of the species called *Homo sapiens* and the primrose is *Primula veris*. *Homo sapiens* includes a number of more or less distinct local varieties, e.g. Eskimos and Negroes. Where the natural and social barriers of ocean and tabu have been broken down by commerce and colonization all these varieties mingle and produce fertile hybrids. Some botanists classify the cowslip and the primrose as the same species, because fertile hybrids occur in nature. Since they flower at rather different times and flourish best in different surroundings, they tend to preserve their distinctive characters in the same locality. So other botanists distinguish *Primula veris*, the cowslip, as one species and *Primula vulgaris*, the primrose, as another.

The "binomial" custom which is sometimes wrongly attributed to Linnaeus grew up gradually as the principle of unity of type impressed itself on the herbalists. Gerard's herbal contains several examples of binomial epithets still in use. In the eighteenth century Linnaeus was the first writer to adopt the practice as a universal rule. The immense economy effected may be judged by comparing his name for the Red maple *Acer rubrum* with its earlier title *Acer Americanum, folio majore, suptus argenteo, supre viridi splendente, oribus multis coccineus.*

A name such as this attempts to convey all the relevant information for identifying the species indicated by it. As the herbals grew in size and more plants were distinguished as distinct species the attempt to do this became obviously hopeless. So it was necessary to codify the characteristics of each species by grouping them together. Species were grouped into genera, genera into families or orders, orders into classes, and classes into larger units. Thus *Primula veris* (the cowslip and primrose) and *Primula elatior* (the oxlip), which do not interbreed in nature, resemble each other closely in many respects, on which account they are placed in the genus Primula. On turning up a botanical treatise like Bentham and Hooker's *British Flora*, you will find that the genus Primula is grouped with several other genera such as Anagallis (of which the commonest species is scarlet pimpernel) and Lysimachia (of which yellow loosestrife is one species) in a family or "natural order" called the *Primulaceae* on account of the common features which their flowers share. The *Primulaceae*, with about fifty other families represented in Britain, are all placed in the sub-class *Dicotyledons*, which germinate with two seed leaves and have adult leaves with a branching network of vessels. In contradistinction to these families, *Monocotyledons*, like the lily, have one seed leaf, and adult leaves with parallel vessels. These two sub-classes constitute together the class of *Angiosperms*, or flowering plants, one of the major divisions of plants.

The economy of this codification lies in the fact that you can distinguish an individual plant as a member of one species *Primula veris* among about a quarter of a million of named species now existing, if you know: (a) the characteristics which distinguish *Primula veris* from other primulas, (b) those which distinguish Primula from other genera of the *Primulaceae*, (c) those which distinguish the *Primulaceae* from other families of *Dicotyledons*, (d) those which distinguish *Dicotyledons* from *Monocotyledons*, (e) those which distinguish *Angiosperms* from flowerless plants like conifers, ferns, mosses, mushrooms, or seaweeds. So a hierarchical classification is a key for identifying species in the most economical way.

The procedure used with animals such as *Homo sapiens* arose out of the practice of the botanists and follows similar lines. *Homo sapiens* is distinguished from *Homo neanderthalensis* and other fossil men who preceded him. The genus Homo is associated with other more apelike fossils such as Pithecanthropus (the Java ape man) and Sinanthropus (the Peking man) in the family *Hominidae*. Along with several other families of apes, monkeys, and marmosets, this is placed in the order *Primates*, all of which have grasping hands with nails, forward-looking eyes in a closed bony orbit, and other features which distinguish them from all other *orders* like *Rodentia* (mice, rabbits, etc.) or *Prosboscidea* (elephants), *Chiroptera* (bats), *Cetacea* (Whales) grouped in the *class* (*Mammalia*) of warm-blooded animals which suckle their young. The class *Mammalia* share with birds, reptiles, and fishes common characteristics, on account of which they are placed in the *phylum Vertebrata*, a major division of animals.

The social background of plant classification calls for little comment.

It has been nursed in turn by the practice of medicine and of horticulture. It has a long record of gradual growth encouraged by whatever inventions and social agencies have conspired to promote the progress of medicine and horticulture. Intensive systematic study of animals came much later, and presents a less continuous spectacle of progress. The long break in the record of zoological studies between Aristotle and the seventeenth century suggests the clue to its dominant social incentive.

We may roughly divide the history of systematic interest in animal life into three periods. First comes a period of thirty years or so dominated by the work of Aristotle and his pupils. No further progress is noteworthy till we reach the sixteenth century of our era, when the beginnings of a new literature of zoology can be traced between 1550 and 1750. During this period while the systematic classification of plants made rapid progress, knowledge of animal life expanded notably without conspicuous advance towards a classification analogous to those in vogue today. The third period from 1750 to 1850 saw the rise of hierarchical classification based on the recognition of *Unity of Type*. It is ushered in by the revival of evolutionary speculation, and reaches its climax in the general acceptance of the doctrine of descent.

The fact that no noteworthy zoological progress was made by the brilliant civilization of Alexandria receives a sufficient explanation from its essentially urban character. The failure of the Arabs, who introduced herbalism into Europe, to make any signal contribution cannot be explained in the same way. What the Moorish culture lacks is the impress of a feature common to each of the three periods distinguished in the preceding paragraph. The materials of Aristotle's survey of animals then known were collected during the campaigns of Philip of Macedon. Greek culture was witnessing the irruption of an Asiatic fauna. To the Athenian of Aristotle's time the elephant was a phenomenon as spectacular in its novelty as were the Zeppelins to the inhabitants of London in 1917. The Islamic conquests did not bring a new fauna within the experience of the civilized world, as did the colonization of America in the seventeenth century or the opening up of Australia at the end of the eighteenth, when a rapid development of maritime communications was imminent.

That imperial expansion abetted by improved communications and commercial intercourse has been a decisive social agency promoting interest in the systematic study of animal life, when new faunistic resources have been disclosed thereby, is amply supported by more substantial evidence for what may seem to be a somewhat arbitrary division of the history of zoological enquiries. The materials which Aristotle derived from the Macedonian conquests have been debated too fully to merit further mention (*vide* Singer's *Greek Biology and Greek Medicine*). The active encouragement of biological survey by the Admiralty during the Australian voyages in which Cook was accompanied by the botanist Sir Joseph Banks, is well known, as is also the influence of colonial administrators like Sir Stamford Raffles, who was largely instrumental in starting the London Zoological Gardens after his return from office in Java and Malay. How British Imperialism fostered zoological expeditions in the early nineteenth century, and how the provision of medical attendance for the care of passengers when steam navigation developed conspired to encourage the scientific study of new faunas is told in biographies of the great traveller naturalists.

The formative influence of colonial policy in the preceding period is less fully realized. The social policy which accompanied the colonization of the New World brought into one and the same social context the systematic study of animals and plants. This common social context furnishes a sufficient reason for the classification of animals according to the model which had originated in the practice of the herbalists. A glance at the contents of the proceedings of the older scientific academies is sufficient to draw attention to the characteristic feature of natural history in what has been distinguished as the second period in the history of zoology. Thus the *Philosophical Transactions* of the English Royal Society of 1702 contains *inter alia* "an account of Mr. Sam Brown his Sixth Book of East India plants . . . by James Petive's apothecary . . . To these are added some animals which the Reverend Father George Joseph Camel very lately sent him from the Phillipine Islands." In the same year we find Mr. Strachan's "observations in the island of Ceilon . . . on the ways of catching fowl and deer, of serpents, of the antbear and of cinammon."

These miscellanies were not mere products of idle curiosity. Though mineral prospects largely dominated the aspirations of the Spanish and Portuguese conquerors of the New World, biological products soon became important materials of commerce, the search for which was prominent in the colonial policy of their Dutch and English rivals for maritime supremacy. Contemporaneously with the beginnings of colonization the search for biological products was not confined to the New World. The development of the whaling industry and the emergence of the fur trade belong to the Tudor period. The latter was the special objective of the *Muscovy Company*; and Hakluyt's records give catalogues of plants, animals and minerals, drawn up by ship's captains in the Elizabethan voyages. In 1585 John White, one of the earliest settlers in Virginia, for some time its governor, and lieutenant to Raleigh on several voyages, made drawings, among which is one of the king crab, *Limulus*, an American missing link between the scorpions and the extinct aquatic Eurypterida. It was engraved for de Brys' "America," and is now in the British Museum. The text accompanying the drawing is a translation of Thomas Harriot's *A Brief and True Report of the New Found Land of Virginia*.

A century after the Muscovy company was chartered the Hudson Bay enterprise was started with a similar end in view. The introduction of agricultural products, like the potato, or of medicinal and domestic amenities, like tobacco and Peruvian bark, also prompted more ambitious aspirations. About the same time as Evelyn's proposals for importing new ornamental and useful trees from the British colonies the adventurous hopefulness of early capitalism is illustrated by a suggestion, from which nothing came. It is worth quoting because very similar sentiments recur in the statement of the founders of the Zoological Society at the beginning of the nineteenth century. Robert Childe, principal contributor to Hartlib's *Legacie*, an agricultural work published in 1665, advocated the introduction of black foxes, muske cats, sables, martines, and adds to his list "the elephant, the greatest, wisest, and longest lived of all beast, . . . very serviceable for carriage (15 men usually riding on his backe together)."

The third volume of *New York Colonial Documents* contains a reference to a commission which was specifically requested to draw up a report on the plants of America in 1664. The geranium of our greenhouses and public gardens is derived from the Cape Pelargonium. It bears witness to the close relation between the Dutch East India Company and the flourishing horticultural industry which already existed in Holland during the seventeenth century. The *Hortus Malabaricus,* a monumental work among the herbals of the seventeenth century, was prepared under the aegis of the Dutch governor of Malabar with a skilful staff of Brahmins to assist in the preparation of the figures. The threefold miscellanies of foreign plants, animals, and minerals, in the scientific periodicals of the time are, in fact, the record of an active policy of prospecting the material resources of the colonizing powers. During the period between 1600 and 1750 knowledge of animal life and natural minerals was expanding rapidly, while the new practice of botanical classification was taking shape.

When Linnaeus published the first edition of the *Systema Naturae* in 1735, bringing together all the fruits of the newly accumulated knowledge in his tripartite division of nature into the three "Kingdoms," the method of arrangement which had emerged from the more advanced systematic study of plants was inevitably adopted as a basis for the classification of animals. The Linnaean treatise like the *De Fabrica* of Vesalius is less the beginning of a new phase than the completion of what had gone before. A new era of colonization was ushered in with the irruption of the Australasian faunas into the science of the old world. Several circumstances now combined to stimulate an unprecedented zoological progress in the first half of the nineteenth century. Two call for separate comment.

The first is that Australia yielded types of animal life which differed from previously known ones in a far more striking way than the faunas of America differ from those of Europe and Africa. The duckbilled platypus (Fig. 463) is a spectacular illustration of this, and its discovery was of itself sufficient to act as a focus to the evolutionary speculation of the period.

The second is that progress in the principles of chemistry and electricity had greatly advanced the study of physiology in the eighteenth century. Since the most distinctive features of plant organization concern their reproductive organs, further progress in plant classification after the work of Ray and his contemporaries received its chief impetus from improvement of the microscope, which made it possible to compare the reproductive processes of the flowerless plants. Among animals the character of the reproductive system is far less distinctive of recognizable types of organization. The relations of the muscles to the hard parts co-operating with them in locomotion, the alimentary canal and its associated digestive glands, the arrangements to ensure oxygen supply to the moving parts by the circulation of fluids, the nervous system, all display innumerable common features characteristic of large groups. The recognition of Unity of Type in animals as a whole was not possible till the work of the organs of the body was sufficiently understood to provide a basis for comparison.

As in all other departments of biological knowledge the invention of new instruments which emerged from a different social context played an important part in the birth of zoological classification. During the period of colonizing the New World, the early microscopes had broadened the world outlook of science no less than the telescopes of Galileo and Kepler. A quotation from Stelluti (1630), one of the earliest of the microscopists, cited by Singer vividly emphasizes its influence:

I have used the microscope to examine bees and all their parts. I have also figured separately all members thus discovered by me to my no less joy than marvel, since they are unknown to Aristotle and to every other naturalist.

The broad outlines of a classification of living creatures based on the recognition of unity of type was completed during the three decades which intervened between the introduction of modern microscopes and the publication of Darwin's *Origin*. In the light of the information derived from microscopic studies the twofold division of organisms into animals and plants is now supplemented by a third division, the *Protista*, in which, as explained in Chapter XX, all non-cellular organisms (infusoria, diatoms, bacteria, etc.) are placed. There is no sharp line of demarcation between *Protista* which live in colonies and the simplest types of "animals" like sponges or "plants" such as algae and fungi. Most of the major groups or *phyla* of animals, and some of their subdivisions, together with a few of the distinguishing characteristics which unite the animals placed in them are given below.

Phylum I. Porifera.—This includes the *sponges*, organisms of which the bodies are mainly a gelatinous secretion penetrated by a labyrinth of canals. The canals are lined by cells with vibratile filaments ("cilia") which maintain a constant stream of food particles. Masses of sperms and egg cells are found embedded in the gelatinous body walls along with spicules or horny fibres. There are no separate digestive organs, no blood vessels, nerves, or sense organs.

Phylum II. Coelenterata.—Organisms in which the hollow body consists of two main cellular layers separated by a gelatinous middle region. A single orifice, the mouth, leads into the central cavity, which is usually surrounded by tentacles, and acts as the digestive organ of the body. Digested foodstuffs diffuse through the body substance without the aid of blood vessels to carry them. There may be muscle fibres, more or less distinct from the lining cells of the cellular walls, connected with simple sense organs on the outer surface by a network of nerve fibres. In addition to sexual reproduction, budding is common. Many species form sedentary colonies from which free swimming sexually equipped individuals are liberated. Corals, sea-anemones, jelly-fish, and polyps (Fig. 454) are members of this phylum.

Phylum III. Platyhelminthes.—Flattened worm-like creatures which are, with rare exceptions, hermaphrodite. The gut, if present, has a mouth but no anus. The nervous system consists, as in all the remaining phyla, of a peripheral portion—nerve trunks—and a central mass where nerve cells are concentrated. There are no blood vessels. The muscular system is well developed. There is a system of canals provided with ciliated cells believed to be excretory organs. The three principal classes are: Turbellaria (free-living flat worms found under stones in ponds and in rock pools); Trematoda (parasitic worms called "flukes," including the liver fluke which causes sheep-rot and the worm which

produces the human disease called bilharziasis in tropical countries); Cestoda
(tape-worms—parasites devoid of a gut). Sometimes associated with the Turbellaria is the class of free-living unsegmented marine worms called *Nemer-
tinea*. Unlike the above but like all the remaining phyla they have an anus, and
are sometimes placed in a separate phylum.

  Phylum IV. Nemathelminthes.—Smooth, elongated worms with a tapering
body. They have a mouth and anus, no blood vessels, nor sense organs of vision
and balancing. They are mostly parasitic and include the pin-worm, which
often infects the digestive tract of children, in addition to more dangerous
parasites of stocks and crops and to the human parasite Filaria, which produces
elephantiasis in tropical countries. Species of Tylenchus, Heterodera, and other

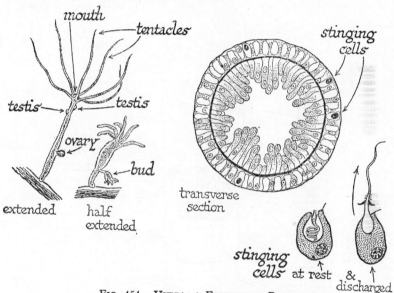

FIG. 454.—HYDRA: A FRESHWATER POLYP

(The figure on the left is magnified from 10 to 20 times.)

genera form galls on wheat, beet, etc. Nearly all the species put in this phylum
are placed in a single homogeneous class, the *Nematoda*, called thread-worms.

  Phylum V. Rotifera (Trochelminthes or Rotatoria).—These are complex
organisms of exceedingly minute dimensions living in fresh water. They have
a well-developed alimentary canal and nervous system and a simple type of
excretory system. Their distinguishing characteristic is a disc fringed with
vibratile cilia in front of the mouth, giving the appearance of a rotating wheel,
whence their name "wheel animalcules." The males, like drone bees, are produced by parthenogenesis or virgin birth, i.e. from eggs which are not fertilized.

  Phylum VI. Echinodermata.—Radially symmetrical marine animals in which
the skin contains calcareous plates which are often joined together to form a
rigid covering to the whole body. Along typically five grooves of the surface are
double rows of pores through which fine muscular suckers, the "tube feet,"
are everted. There are five classes with modern representatives: Asteroidea
(star-fishes), Echinoidea (sea-urchins), Ophiuroidea (brittle stars), Crinoidea

(sea lilies), and Holothuroidea (sea cucumbers). There are many fossil representatives of all the classes, and also several classes which are now totally extinct. The egg is fertilized in the open sea, starts life as a free-swimming larva, which is covered with cilia-bearing cells and passes through a complicated metamorphosis into the adult form.

Phylum VII. Molluscoidea.—In this group are included a number of seden-

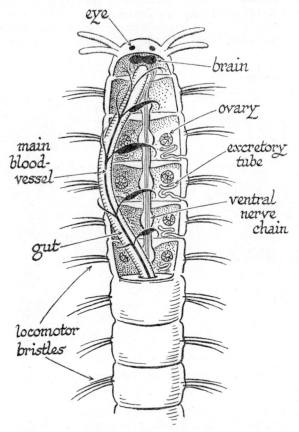

FIG. 455.—MARINE BRISTLE WORM OR POLYCHAETE

The dorsal body wall has been cut away from the first few segments. At the hind end of the dissection, the gut is seen passing through one of the septa which divide the body cavity into a series of compartments. Five other septa, from which the gut has been separated, are seen farther forward.

tary mostly marine organisms with very doubtful affinities, the main resemblance being the circlet or groove of tentacles in the mouth regions. The two principal classes, each with fossil representatives, are the Brachiopoda (lamp shells) and the Polyzoa (sea mats) which superficially resemble hydroids. They are sedentary, often hermaphrodite, and form colonies by budding.

Phylum VIII. Annelida.—These are worms in which the body is segmented and typically provided with bristles by which locomotion is carried out.

There is a well-developed system of contractile blood vessels, and a ventral chain of nerve ganglia. The three main classes are: Oligochaeta (mostly earth worms), Hirudinea (leeches), and Polychaeta (marine bristle worms (Fig. 455)

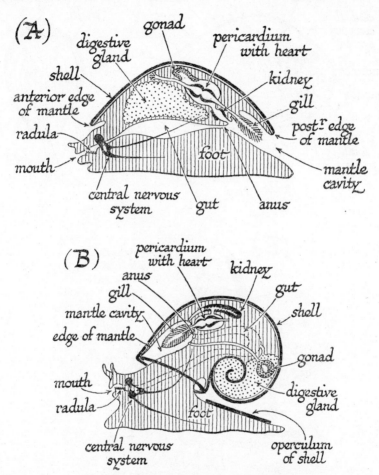

FIG. 456.—UNITY OF TYPE IN THE MOLLUSCA

At first sight representatives of the different classes of Molluscs seem to have little in common. Certain characters are, however, shared by several classes of Molluscs, though not in every case by all, and so the phylum is loosely knit together. We can use these widely distributed features to synthesize an ideal Mollusc (A), from which the existing classes might plausibly have evolved. It is bilaterally symmetrical, and crawls on a flat muscular foot like that of a snail. A flap called the *mantle* runs all round the body like the eaves of a house. Posteriorly, the hollow between the mantle and the foot is large, forming a *mantle* cavity containing a pair or more of gills. The edge of the mantle secretes a shell which therefore grows as the mantle grows. Inside the mouth is a file-like *radula* for rasping off food. Gonad and kidney are connected with the pericardium and open together into the mantle cavity. The central nervous system consists of a number of ganglia, most of them surrounding the oesophagus, but some perhaps lying out in the muscles of the foot and among the viscera. The *Gastropods* (B), such as the whelk and the snail, have gone through a complex process of torsion. The mantle cavity has become twisted round to the front of the animal, and in the snail has become converted into a lung, the gills disappearing.

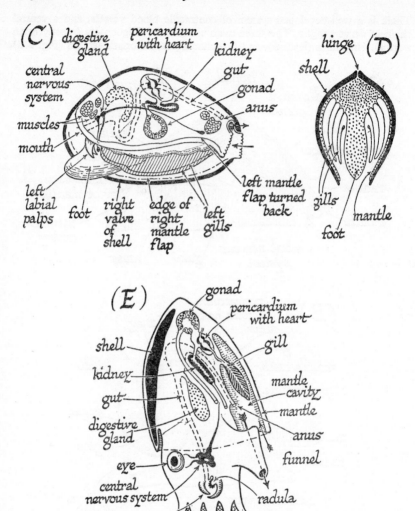

FIG. 456—*continued*

Bivalve Molluscs (C) or *Lamellibranchs*, such as the mussels, cockles, and oysters, have taken to a sedentary life. The mantle is extended into two large lateral flaps, each covered with a separate shell or *valve*, the two valves being held together by muscles. A large mantle cavity is enclosed on each side between mantle and foot. The latter is usually wedge-shaped and used for burrowing. The double gills have moved round into the lateral mantle cavities through which they extend as complex ciliated sheets. Water currents set up by the cilia of the gills carry minute organisms, mostly algae, to the mouth. Respiration is shared between the gills and the mantle. The radula and the well-defined head have disappeared. *D* shows a transverse section with the internal organs omitted. In *Cephalopods* (E) such as the cuttle-fish and the octopus the body has been pulled out in a dorsi-ventral direction. The foot has been made into tentacles and a funnel through which water can be shot out to propel the animal along. The shell is usually enclosed by the mantle and the radula is supplemented by horny jaws.

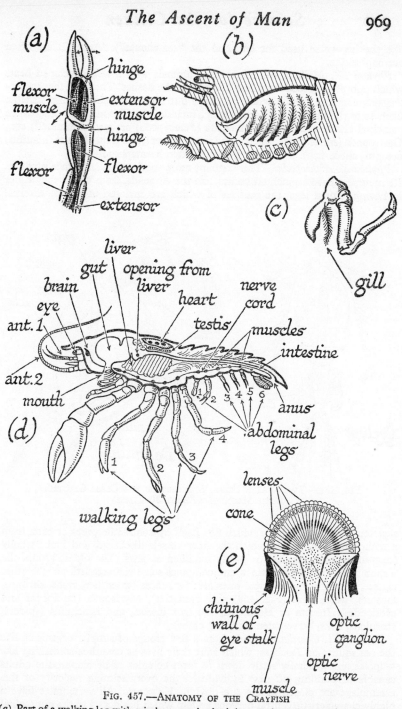

(a) hinge
flexor muscle
extensor muscle
hinge
flexor
flexor
extensor

(b)

(c) gill

(d) liver
gut
opening from liver
brain
heart
eye
nerve cord
ant. 1
testis
muscles
intestine
ant. 2
mouth
1 2 3 4 5 6
anus
abdominal legs
1 2 3 4
walking legs

(e) lenses
cone
chitinous wall of eye stalk
optic ganglion
optic nerve
muscle

FIG. 457.—ANATOMY OF THE CRAYFISH

(a) Part of a walking leg with windows cut in the joints to show the muscles. Note the directions (indicated by arrows) in which each joint is able to move. (b) The gill chamber opened from the side. (c) Walking leg with gill attached. (d) Right half of a crayfish. In the heart, three of the openings which connect the heart with blood spaces can be seen, (e) Longitudinal section through the compound eye.

like the lug-worm used for bait and the "sea mouse"). Annelids are often hermaphrodite.

Phylum IX. Mollusca.—Unsegmented animals with a well-developed heart which pumps the blood from leaf-like gills to the tissues. There are few characteristics common to the whole phylum, but each class shows unmistakable likeness to the small central group which includes the Chitons. The other three principal classes are Lamellibranchiata (Pelecypoda) or oysters, mussels, etc., Gastropoda (snails, slugs, whelks, and many others), and Cephalopoda (nautilus, octopus, cuttle-fish). The Gastropods are often hermaphrodite.

Phylum X. Arthropoda.—This contains more species than any other phylum. Its members have segmented bodies, like the Annelida, from which they differ in having jointed legs, the muscles of which are enclosed in a hard external

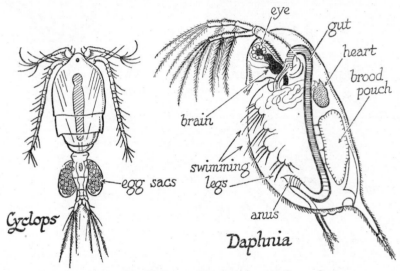

Fig. 458.—Two Water Fleas, Members of the Class Crustacea, Both Magnified About 30 Times

skeleton (Fig. 457), a heart which fills itself by contractile pores or ostia from a main blood cavity into which the finer vessels discharge, and limbs wholly (mandibles and maxillae) or partly modified as jaws. The oldest group, the Trilobita, is completely extinct, and combines some characteristics of the other classes, of which the principal ones are: Crustacea (wood lice, crabs, shrimps, lobsters, water fleas (Fig. 458) and barnacles), Myriapoda (millipedes and centipedes), Insecta or Hexapoda, the true insects, and Arachnida (spiders, scorpions, ticks, harvestmen, and king crabs).

Phylum XI. Chordata.— Aside from a few groups of simpler organisms like the sea squirts or *Tunicata*, which start their lives as creatures something like tadpoles and generally settle down to form colonies of hermaphrodite adults capable of budding off new individuals, the overwhelming majority of this assemblage are placed in the sub-phylum *Vertebrata*. All vertebrates have a highly characteristic central nervous system which lies dorsal to the gut (spinal cord), and expands at the fore end into a brain with a characteristic group of nerves from the great sense organs (eye, internal ear, and nasal organ) of the head, and others supplying the eye muscles, heart, etc. At some stage of life the heart pumps blood forward round a series of vessels surrounding the throat perforated by clefts. These bear gill filaments which are the respiratory organs in the aquatic classes (Fig. 460). Such clefts are present in the embryos of the terrestrial classes, but do not bear gill filaments (Fig. 461). Throughout the sub-phylum there is a characteristic group of organs, the

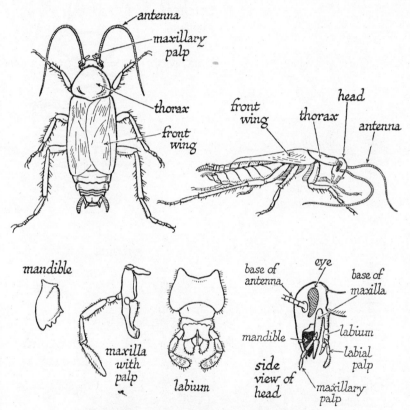

FIG. 459A.—THE ANATOMY OF THE COCKROACH

Above, two views of the whole animal, about 1½ times natural size. The front wings are thickened and protect the thin hind wings which lie folded beneath them. Below, left, the mouth parts. Only one mandible and one maxilla of each pair is shown. The labium is a pair of appendages which have fused in the middle line.

"ductless glands," which include the thyroids, adrenals, etc. The same type of digestive juices are secreted into the alimentary canal by characteristic organs called the liver and pancreas throughout the group, and the system for excretion of nitrogenous waste by two "kidneys" has an essentially similar structure in all members. There are six classes of vertebrata, viz.:

(a) Cyclostomata (hag-fishes and lampreys), which resemble fishes in their respiratory and circulatory arrangements but, unlike fishes, lack jaws, paired limbs, or well-defined vertebrae. The spinal column is represented by a gelatinous rod "notochord," which is present in the embryo of higher vertebrates, but generally disappears in later life.

(*b*) Pisces (fishes). Like Cyclostomes they breathe by gills, and have a

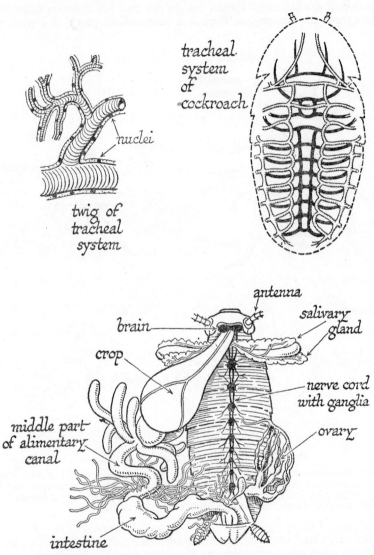

tracheal system of cockroach

nuclei

twig of tracheal system

antenna

brain

crop

salivary gland

nerve cord with ganglia

middle part of alimentary canal

ovary

intestine

FIG. 459B.—THE ANATOMY OF THE COCKROACH—*continued*

heart with only one auricle (except in the lung fishes), receiving the blood from the tissues. They chiefly differ in possessing paired fins.

(*c*) Amphibia (newts, salamanders, frogs, toads). Generally these start life as tadpoles with circulatory and respiratory organs like fishes. They sometimes retain the latter throughout life. They always have lungs (as do some fishes) which usually replace gills in the adult, and, like the three remaining classes of typical land vertebrates, have five-fingered limbs. The heart has separate auricles receiving blood respectively (left) from the lungs and (right) from the rest of the body, but the ventricle which pumps blood out of the heart is not divided as in the remaining groups.

(*d*) Reptilia (crocodiles, lizards, snakes, tortoises). These are cold-blooded land vertebrates with no aquatic larva, the fertilized egg being enclosed in a shell. The body is covered with scales. The heart connects with the main artery of the trunk by two arches, one of which only (left in mammals, right in birds) persists in the next two groups.

(*e*) Aves (birds). These are warm-blooded forms with feathers and fore-

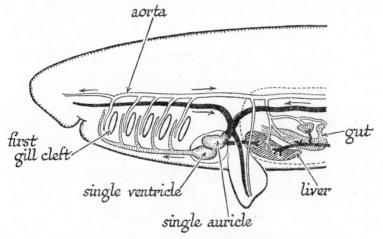

FIG. 460.—BLOOD SYSTEM OF A FISH

The front end only of the fish is shown. The veins are in black and the arteries, which carry deoxygenated blood from the heart to the gills, are lightly shaded. The portal vein, which carries blood from the gut to the liver, is also shown.

limbs modified for flight (Fig. 462). In most other respects their anatomical organization is typically reptilian.

(*f*) Mammalia. Warm-blooded land vertebrates in which the body is covered with hair. The young are suckled and, except in the case of two primitive egg-laying genera—duck-bill (Fig. 463) and spiny anteater—are born alive.

Plants are commonly divided into four great *phyla*, as follows:

I. *Spermaphyta.*—These are the seed-bearing plants, in which fertilization is brought about by scattering pollen. They are generally divided into two sub-phyla:

(*a*) *Gymnosperms*, in which the seed is exposed on the surface of the separate leaflets of the female cone. This group includes the conifers (pine, juniper, yew, etc.), maidenhair tree (*Ginkgo*), and the Cycad palms.

(*b*) *Angiosperms*, in which the seeds are enclosed in ovaries which with the pollen-bearing organs are typically associated together in the structure called the *flower*. The flowering plants are subdivided into two main classes (p. 958). The types included can be inferred from the names of some of the typical orders, viz. *Monocotyledons* (Liliaceae, Gramineae, Iridaceae, Orchidaceae, etc.), *Dicotyledons* (Rosaceae, Primulaceae, Compositae, etc.).

II. *Pteridophyta*.—These exhibit a regular alternation between a separate spore-bearing form, which has much the same vegetative structure (root, stem, and leaves) as the flowering plant, and a simpler more ephemeral sexual structure which produces typical spermatozoa and egg cells like those of animals (see p. 868). This phylum includes ferns, horsetails, and club-mosses.

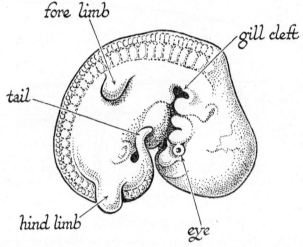

FIG. 461.—HUMAN EMBRYO, ABOUT 4 WEEKS AFTER CONCEPTION,
MAGNIFIED 7 TIMES

III. *Bryophyta*.—These plants exhibit the same type of reproduction with a regular alternation of sexual and spore-producing forms. The spore-producing plant is a parasite on the sexual one, and develops neither root nor leaves. The sexual plant, which may have distinct shoot, leaves, and simple root-like structures, has no wood vessels, and its microscopic structure shows little differentiation of distinct tissues such as occur in the stem and leaves of ferns, flowering plants, and conifers. The phylum includes mosses and liver worts (p. 869).

IV. *Thallophyta*.—This is a rather heterogeneous assemblage of forms, the members of which show various degrees of interrelationship in vegetative structure and reproductive methods, though the group as a whole is difficult to define, except by the fact that none of the plants placed in it exhibit the characteristics of the other three phyla. Their vegetative structure is generally very simple. At best it is little more complex than that of the liver worts. Often the body is merely a filament of cells joined end to end. The *algae*, which are aquatic and possess chlorophyll (which may be masked by other pigments), include seaweeds. Many have motile spermatozoa, but in a few the sexual process is represented by the fusion of two cells of adjoining filaments (Fig. 423) with the production of a resting "spore." Formation of asexual reproductive cells or spores is also common. When there is a regular alternation the two generations do not differ in their vegetative characteristics as do the sexual and spore-

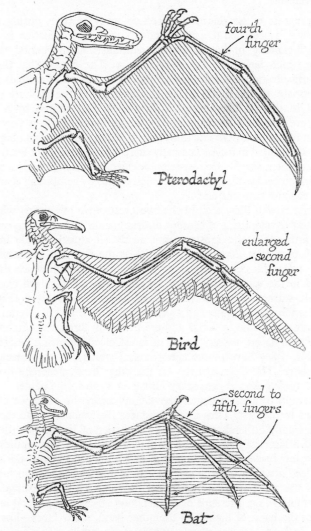

FIG. 462.—VERTEBRATE WINGS

The extinct flying reptiles called Pterodactyls had a wing membrane stretched between the elongated fourth finger and the hind limb. In bats, the second to fifth fingers are long and the hind limb again helps to keep the membrane taut. Birds have feathers, which stand out stiffly on their own account, and the awkward tying up of the hind limbs with the organs of flight is thus avoided.

bearing forms of ferns and mosses. Other thallophyta which live as parasites on plants or animals, or feed on dead organic matter (e.g. moulds on jam, dry bread or cheese, mushrooms on manure) have no chlorophyll and are called *fungi.* Fungi reproduce principally by resistant spores suitable for survival in air. The *lichenes* are associations of a fungus with a simple green Protist, which supplies it with organic material by its power to use sunlight like the complex green organisms.

The progress of classification, based on unity of type, during the three decades which preceded the revival of evolutionary speculation in the mid-nineteenth century, impressed on the naturalists of the period three conclusions, which have now lost their novelty. The first is that the general plan of organization characteristic of the larger classes of animals or plants is appropriate to the mode of life characteristic of the *majority of* species included in them. The second is that each class united by a common architecture also includes many species whose mode of life is very different from that of the majority. The third is that, while the overwhelming majority of animals included in a class generally share a large number of features which distinguish them sharply from species included in other classes, there are also species which bridge the gap between such classes by combining characteristic features of more than one class.

The first is well illustrated in the two great *phyla* of animals which show the greatest development of sensory discrimination and motor co-ordination. Among arthropods the crustacea are nearly all aquatic, while insects are nearly all terrestrial. Associated with this is the fact that crustacea breathe by gills—tufted filaments at the base of the limbs through which the oxygen dissolved in the water diffuses—or by absorption of dissolved oxygen over the whole surface of the body. Insects breathe by *tracheae* (Fig. 459B). Among vertebrates fishes are all aquatic and breathe by gills; reptiles, birds, and mammals breathe by lungs and are nearly all terrestrial. Among plants, the Pteridophyta are usually found in moist places, growing beside streams or swamps. They have motile spermatozoa, which can only reach the egg cell by water. The Spermaphyta, on the other hand, generally live on dry land, and their pollen is carried by insects or wind to the ovule.

The second conclusion stated above emphasizes the existence of striking exceptions to the first. Thus a few crustacea like wood lice and the coconut crab live wholly on land, and a small proportion of insects like the dragon-fly spend a large part of existence wholly in water. A few reptiles like the turtles, a few birds like the moorhen, and, among mammals, the seals and whales, lead a wholly aquatic existence though they continue to breathe air. Some of the most striking anatomical differences which distinguish birds from mammals (e.g. presence of feathers and absence of fingers) are closely related to the habit of flight. On the other hand, a few birds—like the kiwi of New Zealand—are completely unable to fly, while a few mammals, the bats, are completely aerial. Among flowering plants some species, e.g. duckweed, are more completely aquatic than ferns, though they can produce pollen and thus have reproductive arrangements appropriate to terrestrial existence.

Thus the *main* features of the overwhelming majority of species in a class based on common anatomical architecture are appropriate to the mode of life typical of a large proportion of them, and a minority exhibit the same general plan with minor modifications appropriate to a different sort of existence. The picture as a whole presents a series of distinct types of organization each related to a definite habit, and repeatedly modified to meet the demands of a new environment. While each type of organization is distinct in the sense that the overwhelming majority of forms in a class generally share a very large number of common or interconnected characteristics, most groups contain a few species which, while predominantly like the other members, share outstanding characteristics of other groups.

This third rule is well illustrated at every level of classification. Thus the majority of vertebrates are either aquatic like fishes, which breathe by gills and swim with fins, or are terrestrial like reptiles, mammals, and birds, which breathe by lungs and walk on legs with toes. The *Amphibia* (frogs, newts, etc.), on the other hand, are semi-aquatic, having limbs typical of the land form and breathing for the first part of life with gills. Here we have a small group of land vertebrates with gills. Likewise a few species of typical fishes, like the lung fishes and bow-fin, with typical fins and other fish structures have lungs, as well as gills. Or again, while mammals as a whole are

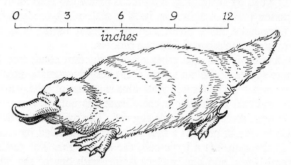

Fig. 463.—The Duck-billed Platypus, a Primitive Egg-laying Mammal

viviparous in contradistinction to reptiles and birds which lay eggs, the duck-billed platypus (Fig. 463), in most respects a typical mammal, lays eggs with a hard shell like the eggs of a lizard or a thrush, and has shoulder bones like those of a typical reptile.

Though the actual number of these living "missing links" is very small in comparison with the many species which fall into sharply defined categories, most groups have a small minority of forms which blur the hard outlines of a classificatory system. In Chapter XVIII we have distinguished two very distinct types of reproduction characteristic of ferns on the one hand, and of flowering plants on the other. While the ferns form the majority of Pteridophytes and the Angiosperms the majority of seed-bearing plants, there is, besides, a series of species which bridge the wide gap between these two extreme and well-defined types of reproductive organization. So far we have spoken of the pollen grain as if it were a single cell comparable to the sperm of a fern or an animal. While it is at first a single cell, the nucleus divides several times before the pollen tube reaches the ovule and only one of these nuclei fuses with the egg cell nucleus of the ovule. In a few seed-bearing plants the cell substance round two of the nuclei in the fully formed pollen tube is separated off, forming distinct sperms. The sperms of the cycad palms and of the maidenhair tree (see p. 973), which are seed-bearing plants, have *cilia* and are motile. Thus the pollen grain is not strictly comparable to the single sperm of a fern.

To see more clearly what it does correspond to, it is necessary to look for other "missing links" in the allies of the fern itself. The latter has a regular alternation of small ephemeral sexual plants (*prothalli*), producing both spermatozoa and egg cells, with spore-producing individuals. Horsetails (*Equisetum*) produce spores like those of ferns, except that they are of two kinds, smaller ones which produce male prothalli and larger ones which produce female prothalli. In the genus of "club mosses," called *Selaginella*, this separation is accompanied by a great reduction of the importance of the sexual generation. The small spores do not germinate to form an independent plant. The sperms are produced *inside* the spore coat, and are set free when it ruptures. The only essential difference between the small spores of the club moss and pollen of a maidenhair tree is that sperms of the former make their way to the egg cell by swimming. No tube is formed to help them to reach it. Thus the pollen grain combines in itself a male-plant-producing spore, an extremely degenerate male plant, and the sperm itself. It is both types of fern reproduction telescoped into one process.

Seed production is also two types of reproduction condensed in a single act. The large spores of the club moss form very degenerate female prothalli when they germinate. The female prothallus is a mass of cells, with a few root hairs, partly enclosed in the spore coat. Each has only two or three ovaries like that of a fern, each with a single egg cell. The ovule which develops into the seed of a flowering plant is a mass of cells surrounded by a capsule, the seed coat. In the centre is a large cell, the *embryo sac*. The nucleus of this divides several times, and one nucleus unites with one of the nuclei in the pollen tube. After that the combined nucleus divides to form the nuclei of the cells, which constitute the embryo. The whole structure—the outer tissues of the ovule, the embryo, and the remains of the embryo sac—represent three generations telescoped into one. The seed coat corresponds to the spore-producing organs on the leaves of a fern. The embryo sac corresponds to a spore, when it is still a single cell. Afterwards, when the nucleus has divided, it corresponds to the very degenerate female prothallus of the club moss. The embryo is the beginning of the next spore-producing generation.

Thus, although the first impression gained from classifying animals or plants is the conclusion that they fall into clear-cut groups with characteristics suitable to the circumstances of their lives, closer study reveals the existence of intermediate, more generalized types, which bridge the gap between different groups, and innumerable features of organization also suggest useless survivals of a former existence. This suggestion becomes more imperative when we compare living species with extinct ones. It then appears that species which seem to show the vestiges of another type of organization came into being later than species in which the same type predominates.

THE PRINCIPLE OF GEOLOGICAL SUCCESSION

Among the Ionian school of materialists, whose brilliant but short-lived tradition has been referred to many times in this book, Xenophanes made observations on the remains of shells and fishes found in rocks far from the sea, and correctly interpreted them as remains of extinct creatures. In the same materialistic tradition Herodotus even went so far as to make an estimate—about ten thousand years—of the time it would take to fill the Red Sea with silt if the Nile opened into it. He correctly interpreted the formation of the delta as the result of solid matter washed down by the flow of the sacred river.

When the materialistic tradition was revived by the English physicists of the seventeenth century, coal mining had become a subject of scientific enquiry. Robert Hooke, perhaps the most fertile scientist in the annals of English culture, advanced the common-sense view of fossil remains and the changing configuration of land and water. Hooke's speculations exerted little direct influence. Close study of the earth's history and of the succession of living creatures which have peopled it made little headway, till new social influences conspired to encourage the exploration of the earth's crust in the closing years of the eighteenth and opening years of the nineteenth century of our own era.

In the intervening time Christian cosmogony elaborated by Milton and Ussher reigned supreme. The world according to the painstaking arithmetic of Ussher, one of Hooke's contemporaries, was six thousand years old. Ussher, as Bury remarks, had proved beyond dispute that the Trinity created man on October 4th, 4004 B.C., at nine o'clock in the morning (winter time). The limits of land and water were finally settled on that date by divine decree. The marine fossils, inconveniently collected at great distances from the coast, were either deposited by Noah's flood, inserted, where found, to test the faith of believers, or left there by itinerant merchants and armies with a partiality for fish diet.

Contemporary with Hooke, Steno, a Dane (once professor at Padua), had, in 1669, issued a tract on *Organic Petrifications within solid rocks.* Steno recognized fossils as remains of long extinct animals, and argued in favour of an originally horizontal disposition of the sedimentary rocks. The ideological temper of the times was not favourable to the birth of a new science. Lyell remarks:

The theologians who now entered the field in Italy, Germany, France, and England were innumerable: and henceforward they who refused to subscribe to the position, that all marine organic remains were proofs of the Mosaic deluge, were exposed to the imputation of disbelieving the whole of the sacred writings. Scarcely any step had been made in approximating to sound theories since the time of Fracastorio, more than a hundred years having been lost, in writing down the dogma that organized fossils were mere sports of nature. An additional period of a century and a half was now destined to be consumed in exploding the hypothesis, that organized fossils had all been buried in the solid strata by Noah's flood. Never did a theoretical fallacy, in any branch of science, interfere more seriously with accurate observation and the systematic classification of facts.

Referring to the controversies which accompanied the birth of geological research in Britain, Lyell adds:

The party feeling exerted against the Huttonian doctrines and the open disregard of candour and temper in the controversy will hardly be credited by the reader, unless he recalls to his recollection that the mind of the English public was at that time in a state of feverish excitement. A class of writers in France had been labouring industriously for many years to diminish the influence of the Clergy by sapping the foundations of the Christian faith and their success, and the consequences of the revolution had alarmed the most resolute minds, while the imagination of the more timid was continually haunted by dread of innovation as by the phantom of some fearful dream. . . . We cannot estimate the malevolence of such a persecution by the pain which similar insinuations might now inflict: for although charges of infidelity and atheism must always be odious they were injurious in the extreme at that moment of political excitement, and it was better, perhaps, for a man's good reception in society, that his moral character should have been traduced, than that he should become a mark for these poisoned weapons.

In this passage Lyell refers specifically to a treatise which might have exerted less influence, if the times had been less propitious. Hutton, whose *Theory of the Earth* (1788) was the first considerable excursion into the formation of the earth's crust, was one of the same group as Joseph Black, Francis Home, and Crawford in Edinburgh (pp. 415 and 600). He belongs to the period when coal mining was asserting itself as a powerful industry in Scotland. Lyell remarks that:

this treatise was the first in which geology was declared to be in no way concerned with questions as to the origin of things, the first in which an attempt was made to dispense entirely with all hypothetical causes and to explain the former changes of the earth's crust by reference exclusively to natural agents.

The main argument is summarized in the following quotation from the first chapter.

The heights of our land are thus levelled with the shores, our fertile plains are formed from the ruins of the mountains and those travelling materials are still pursued by the moving water and propelled along the inclined surface of the earth. These movable materials delivered into the sea cannot for a long continuance rest upon the shore for by the agitation of the winds, the tides, and the currents, every movable thing is carried farther and farther along the shelvy bottom of the sea. . . . But is this world to be considered thus merely as a machine to last no longer than its parts retain their present position, their proper forms, and qualities? Or may it not be also considered an organized body such as has constitution in which the necessary decay of the machine is naturally repaired in the exertion of those productive powers by which it had been formed? . . . We find marks of marine animals in the most solid parts of the earth; consequently those solid parts have been formed after the ocean was inhabited by those animals which are proper to that fluid medium. If therefore we knew the natural history of those solid parts and could trace the operations of the globe by which they had been formed we would have some means for computing the time through which those species of animals have continued to live. But how shall we describe a process which nobody has seen performed? This is only to be investigated first, in examining the nature of those solid bodies, the history of which we want to know, and secondly, in examining the natural operations of the globe in order to see if there now actually exist such operations as from the nature of solid bodies appear to have been necessary to their formation.

Hutton was chiefly interested in the fossil-bearing layers of the earth's crust, now called collectively the sedimentary rocks, and his views recall the brilliant observations of Herodotus two thousand years earlier. The major factors to which he directed attention are (a) *denudation*, i.e. the continual wearing away of land surface by wind, rain, ice, and snow; (b) *deposition* of the loosened matter (sand, mud, or gravel) carried by rivers and glaciers to the sea. Thus the sea is continually being filled up by new rock masses. The displaced water is continually encroaching on the land. The sea floor is being raised to form new land and the land is being submerged to form a sea floor successively.

Emphasis on another class of natural processes which modify the structure of the earth's crust was laid in the teaching of a new school of mining technology, which grew up about the same time in Germany. Besides denudation and deposition, the surface of the earth is changed by laval deposits of volcanic origin and by slow processes of folding or of upward or downward movement affecting the whole thickness of the outer crust. "The art of mining has long been taught in France, Germany and Hungary in scientific institutions established for that purpose, where mineralogy has always been a principal branch of instruction," wrote Lyell in his *Principles*. Werner, who in 1775 was made professor of mining at Freyberg in Saxony,

directed his attention to the natural position of the minerals in particular rocks together with the grouping of those rocks, their geographical position and various relations, and pointed out their application to the practical purposes of mining. They were instantly regarded by a large class of men as an essential part of their professional education and from that time the science was cultivated in Europe more ardently and systematically . . . In a few years a small school of mines, before unheard of in Europe, was raised to the rank of a great university.

Two other social agencies contributed to awaken interest in the problems to which Hutton and Werner had directed attention in the latter half of the eighteenth century. One is referred to in the following extract from the *History of the Geological Society*:

The Agricultural Surveys of the United Kingdom, of which reports were issued by the old Board of Agriculture, commencing in 1794, stimulated enquiry into the soils and subsoils of the British Isles. The report on Somerset, by John Billingsley (1797) contained much geological information, while *The General View of the Agriculture and Minerals of Derbyshire*, by John Farey (2 vols. 1811–13), is a geological classic. Farey (1766–1826) had been a disciple of William Smith, although a somewhat older man than his distinguished master. William Smith (1769–1839) had in the meanwhile been at work for some years, and in 1799 he had coloured geologically the old county survey of Somerset, and a circular map of the country around Bath (the latter preserved in the Library of the Geological Society).

The name of William Smith, a practical surveyor, draws attention to what was perhaps the most important debt which modern geology owes to the everyday life of mankind. In Britain a focal centre of practical geology was north Staffordshire. Plot's seventeenth-century treatise on the natural history of Staffordshire reminds us that the study of "The Earths" in the early days of coal mining and mineral prospecting in the colonies went hand in hand with practical chemistry which had not yet separated itself as a science of "pure" substances. The juxtaposition of boulder clay and coal in the Potteries and the search for better clays in south-west England made the study of outcroppings and seams an issue of technical importance to an industry which originally owed its prosperity to a unique geological site and occupied a position (see pp. 409 and 429) of pivotal importance in relation to all the major themes of scientific research in the latter half of the eighteenth century.

Wedgwood, the Prince of Potters, who was an equally important figure in the scientific and industrial renaissance of the period, frequently went for field excursions in geology with his friend Bentley. As it happened, his industrial policy affected the subsequent history of geology more decisively than the search for clay and fuel. In the early days of the Industrial Revolution one of the major commercial problems was transport, and this was specially felt in the Potteries, because their products were eminently breakable. The pottery owners, who were active in promoting the introduction of the railways, took a leading part in the Transport Revolution which preceded them, when the Trent and Mersey Canal was formed in response to a petition promoted by Wedgwood in 1763.

The rapid development of the English canal system involved a new social demand for large-scale surveying, as did the growth of the railway system in the succeeding half century. It also drew attention to the way in which the natural watercourses are formed. William Smith, who did more than any single man to stimulate the systematic study of geology, developed a method for recognizing the order in which the various layers of the earth's crust have been laid down and took the lead in studying the types of fossil remains characteristic of different sedimentary rocks. Speaking of his contributions, Lyell says:

While the tenets of the rival schools of Freyburg and Edinburgh were warmly espoused by devoted partisans the labours of an individual unassisted by the advantages of wealth or station in society were almost unheeded. Mr. Smith, an English surveyor, published his tabular view of the British strata in 1790, wherein he proposed a classification of the secondary formations in the west of England. Although he had not communicated with Werner, it appeared by this work that he had arrived at the same views respecting the laws of superposition of stratified rocks, that he was aware that the order of succession of different groups was never inverted and that they might be identified at very distant points by their peculiar organized fossils.

It was not wholly an accident that large-scale surveying for canal construction produced the "Tabular View" on which the seriation of the sedimentary rocks is based, nor that geological research was specially developed in Britain during its early formative period. Canal surveying demanded accurate measurements of natural phenomena which play no part in the every-day life of urban communities where science is taught. Town-bred folk take the map for granted, as they take the calendar for granted. They have no first-hand acquaintance with shifting boundaries of land and water. Those who are accustomed to country life will find it more easy to grasp the signi-ficance of William Smith's itineraries.

If you have ever drained a marshy wood you will have watched how the bed is raised by gravel and mud washed down from the tributaries of a stream, how the presence of a log or a bunch of twigs will deflect its course leaving in its wake a mass of silt and vegetation, how a soft waste of mud with branches of trees embedded in it is lifted above the level of the stream and sets to a firm mass, or how masses of granite are exposed by the flow of the current. In canal construction man imitates locally on a small scale what is con-stantly happening in nature, when severe rains produce torrents which wear away new channels. The circumstances which continually, though slowly, and otherwise imperceptibly, modify the aspect of the earth's surface are forced on the imagination with dramatic clarity.

By itself this is perhaps less important than the fact that canal construc-tion in the British Isles involved surveying an area in which there is a unique variety of rocks underlying the superficial layers of soil. Indeed it is hardly possible to find elsewhere the same variety localized within so small a space. This made it possible to test the theory of orderly succession by denudation and deposition under specially favourable conditions. In mining operations we see that the character of the rocks changes as we go deeper. To get coal, for instance, we may have to go through successive layers of gravel and chalk. Where the edge of a land mass has been worn away vertically, as at the face of a cliff, we may also be able to recognize distinct layers, e.g. of chalk overlying green sand or old red sandstone. While these appearances may convey the suggestion that a definite order of succession exists—as, for instance, that chalk was deposited after the coal measures—they provide meagre materials for testing a regular order of the various types of rock which made up the earth's crust. If the arrangement of fossil-bearing rocks has been brought about by the natural processes of denudation and deposi-tion, we should expect that some regions will have been submerged repeatedly while others have been slowly wearing down. So we should not expect to find successive layers corresponding to all the various types of sedimentary rocks at any one place.

The proper test of such a theory is the relative positions which the various classes of rocks occupy where they are brought to the surface by denudation. The accompanying figures illustrate the general principle involved in its simplest manifestation. An upland where the subsoil is chalk is surrounded by a depression where the subsoil is coal. If digging shows that the level of the strata is horizontal, we conclude that the chalk is a later deposition. Thus the first prerequisite for testing the theory, the validity of which rests on the consistency of all such appearances, is the production of a map showing contours and subsoils of an area in which a great variety of surface strata can be found together (Figs. 464, 465, 465A).

The surface survey embodied in William Smith's *Tabular View* (1815) was the foundation of the method on which the modern doctrine of orderly succession by natural agencies rests. A geological map was made by an American

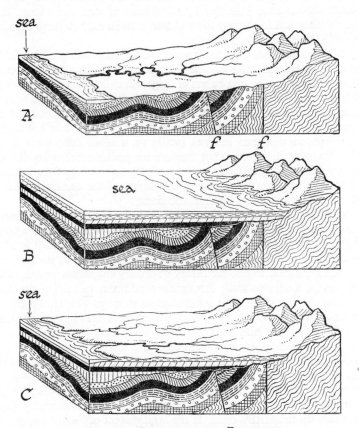

FIG. 464.—DENUDATION AND DEPOSITION

A shows an old land surface. The underlying sedimentary rocks, laid down long before, when this region was under the sea, have become folded by earth movements. Along two planes, *f* and *f*, the strata have become broken across or *faulted*, and the rocks between these *faults* have slipped downwards relative to the rest of the land. Following these subterranean disturbances, the agents of *denudation*, weather, and rivers, have worn down the land surface into a relatively flat coastal plain, on which diverse strata are exposed.

In *B*, the whole region has sunk, the sea has reached to the mountains, and a new series of sedimentary rocks has been deposited on its bottom, and lies in horizontal layers, as yet undisturbed by earth movements. They are separated from the older sedimentary rocks by an *unconformity* corresponding with the old land surface. In *C*, the sea has again retreated, and denudation of the new sedimentary rocks is already beginning.

geologist, Greenough, about the same time. That of Smith, however, was richer in detail, and it was Smith who first drew attention to the fact that different rocks have different fossil types.

If the sedimentary rocks are built from material derived from the wear and tear of wind and rain, land surfaces in one region are worn away while others are accumulating new deposits. So no geological "formation" can

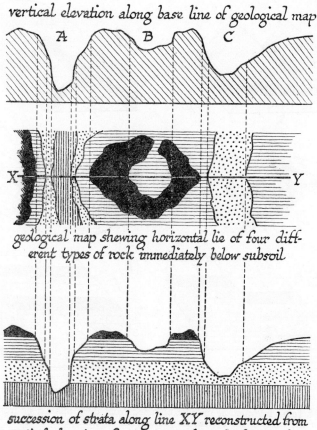

vertical elevation along base line of geological map

A   B   C

X ———— Y

geological map shewing horizontal lie of four different types of rock immediately below subsoil

succession of strata along line XY reconstructed from vertical elevation of outcrops as shewn in figures above

FIG. 465.—THE SERIAL ORDER OF STRATA

The serial order of the strata in the earth's crust is elucidated by combining three main sources of information: (*a*) the distribution or *outcrop* of the different rocks (e.g. chalk, coal, shale, sandstone) immediately below the sub-soil, as exhibited in a geological map, like that in the middle of the figure; (*b*) the relief of the surface, and the vertical elevation of the different outcrops; (*c*) the *dip* or inclination of the strata to the horizontal, in exposures which enable the strata to be seen in section. In the case here illustrated the strata are horizontal, so that the question of dip does not arise. Four superimposed strata are shown. Erosion where the land surface has been worn away by rivers or glaciers (as at A and C), or a river-drained inland lake at B, will expose different strata according to the depth of denudation. If the strata are horizontally placed, the oldest exposed rocks will be those at the surface in low-lying country, and the newest will be those at the surface on the uplands.

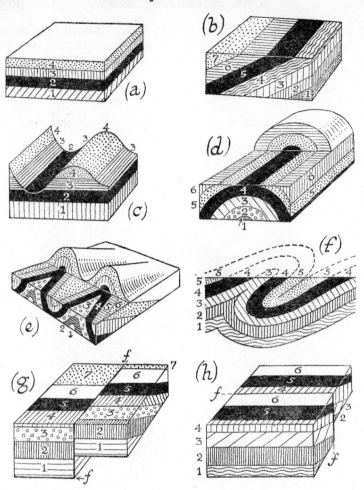

FIG. 465A.—SURFACE, STRUCTURE, AND SUCCESSION

Although some information may be obtained from deep mining, or from borings, much of the work of the systematic geologist is an attempt to translate the *outcrop* of strata on the *surface* into terms of geological structure and succession. Both strata and surface are rarely flat and horizontal as in *a*. More commonly the strata slope at an angle to the horizontal called the *dip*. Then if the surface is flat and horizontal, the outcrops follow each other in bands, the newer rocks showing towards the direction of dip (*b*). The regular sequence may be disturbed if the land surface is undulating (*c*), or if the strata are folded (*d*). In either of these simple cases a stratum may crop out on both sides of a fold. Where the axis of rock folding itself slopes (*e*), a zigzag outcrop is produced if the ground is level. Recumbent folds (*f*) produce an apparent reversal of the succession over a small area, and the true order is only discovered when outcrops further afield are taken into account, or when deep borings are made. *Faulting* in the same plane as the dip (*g*) may displace the outcrop, and faulting across the dip may repeat the outcrop (*h*) or eliminate part of it, according to whether the "downthrow" is up the dip or down. By graphic reconstruction from outcrop, surface contours, dip measurements, and other data, the geologist is able to deduce with some certainty the underlying structure and succession, in spite of these, and many other, complicating factors. Characteristic fossils are useful to him as labels attached to particular layers over a wide area. This does not, as is sometimes supposed, involve a circular argument. The succession of fossils is determined in a number of places where the succession of strata is unambiguous. These fossils can then be used as an aid where other data are less explicit.

be world-wide. Diagrams (like Fig. 467), showing the relative ages of the sedimentary or fossil-bearing layers of the earth's crust, do not correspond to a vertical section at any single place. The names which they bear do not stand for a single type of rock recognizable by its texture or composition as such. While vegetable refuse is forming a hard cake near the estuary of a river, fine silt may be raising the sea-level beyond. In England the mountain limestone of the Pennines, the massive rocks once famous for making millstones and grindstones and hence called by the quarrymen "Millstone Grit," together with the coal seams, make up a threefold interlacing system of contemporary deposits. This whole system of swamp cake and sea grit accumulating here at one time, there at another, corresponds to the single slab of time called the *Carboniferous* or Coal Age. The relative ages assigned to rocks at different depths in one and the same place and to rocks near the surface at different places is based on surface surveys, and on experience derived from mine shafts, from quarrying, and from the aspect of steep cliffs. What rocks are truly contemporary transpires only as a more or less coherent picture unfolds from the combination of evidence from all sources.

Certain regularities are inescapable. In England, for instance, the complex carboniferous system of millstone grit, Pennine limestone, and coal seams lies in many places between thick crusts of "New" and "Old" Red Sandstone, respectively above and below it. Elsewhere coal lies directly covered with marine deposits of chalk which may itself lie directly above layers of New Red Sandstone (*Permian*), where no rocks of the carboniferous system are present. Thus the English chalk assigned to the *Cretaceous* age is a newer deposit than the New Red Sandstone. The latter in its turn is newer than the coal, and the Old Red Sandstone (*Devonian*) is older than all three. Between Hutton and Darwin a century was occupied with the task of sorting out the pieces of a gigantic jigsaw puzzle. An Italian contemporary of Hutton recognized a broad division of three systems of rocks, a *primary*, deepest of all, a *secondary* or middle, and a *tertiary* or more superficial group. Smith himself traced the succession of secondary beds severally formed between the coal age and the chalk age. Thirty years later Lyell and a French geologist, Deshayes, divided the newer or tertiary beds into *Eocene, Miocene* ("less recent") and *Pliocene* ("more recent") levels, while Sedgwick traced out the lowermost level of fossil-bearing rocks. He called it the *Cambrian* because the slates and grits which lie near the surface in North Wales are assigned to it.

When the sedimentary rocks are arrayed in chronological sequence they make up a total deposit of about 400,000 feet. Direct observations on the accumulation of silt at deltas show that an immense period of time must have intervened since the first living creatures lived on earth. We can measure the exact amount of sediment which has been added to the neighbourhood of Memphis since the reign of Rameses II. From this, the rate of deposition by the Nile is found to be 2 feet in a thousand years. At this rate about 200 million years would elapse while 400,000 feet accumulated. It is now possible to get two different historical estimates which agree closely. The *radium* atom is unstable. It continually gives off minute quantities of helium, and its final disintegration product is lead. The rate at which it disintegrates is known from laboratory observation, and the quantities of radium, lead, and helium imprisoned in different strata can be determined by direct analysis. The ratio of radium to helium or radium to lead thus gives a measure of their antiquity. By both methods the end of the Cambrian period is dated at 400,000,000 years with a discrepancy less than 2 per cent. The middle of the coal age occurred 250,000,000 years ago. The chalk age occupied 40,000,000 years, and began about 110,000,000 years ago (Fig. 467).

Smith collected and classified the fossils he found in coal, in quarries, in cliffs, and in gravels, noting which types of shells were common, and which were peculiar to different types of rock. In 1799, when he had completed his preliminary survey of the chief formations from the coal measures to the chalk, he had reached the conclusion that the suites of fossils at different levels "always succeed one another in the same order." Thenceforward a new

FIG. 466.—THE REMAINS OF A GIANT SALAMANDER UNEARTHED IN 1726
BY SCHEUCHZER OF ZÜRICH

It is described in his monograph as "Homo Diluvii Testis" (*Man; Witness to the Deluge*).

systematic study of fossil animals and plants was vigorously prosecuted, especially in France and in England.

The result was the recognition of an orderly pageant of living creatures embodied in what is called the *Principle of Succession*. The prevailing attitude which had been adopted under the influence of Christian cosmogony during the previous century is illustrated by a figure in an early treatise on fossils by Scheuchzer, who in 1726 unearthed the bones of a giant salamander. The remains of this species, closely allied to the extant Japanese *Cryptobranchus japonicus*, abounds in the Upper Miocene of Switzerland (Fig. 466). The figure of his specimen called *Homo diluvii testis* by Scheuchzer bears a motto, which is translated:

Oh, sad remains of bone, frame of poor Man of sin,
Soften the heart and mind of recent sinful kin.

The geological succession of organisms is demonstrated by two classes of data. The first is that many of the more highly specialized and successful groups of the present day did not exist at earlier periods of the earth's history. They were preceded by forms which are intermediate between them and representatives of surviving groups that already existed before them.

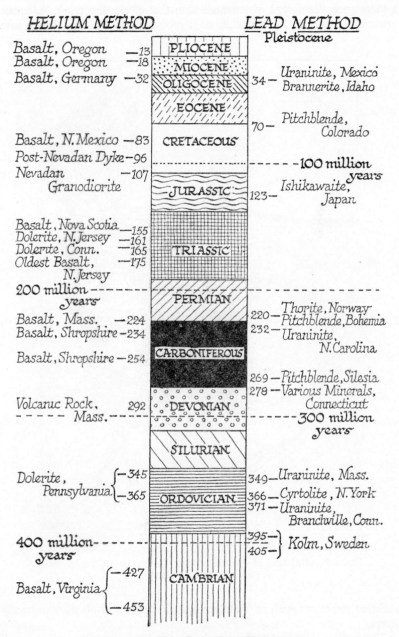

FIG. 467.—THE GEOLOGICAL HOUR-GLASS

As set forth by Holmes in *The Age of the Earth*. The Pleistocene and Recent periods, since the beginning of the Ice Age, are represented by the thickness of the top line of the diagram.

The second is that the earliest members of the great groups usually exhibit a more generalized type of structure than that of existing types. Adequate material for drawing such conclusions is provided only by forms which have

FIG. 468.—REMAINS OF ARCHAEOPTERYX PRESERVED IN SHALE FROM SOLENHOVEN, BAVARIA

resistant structures such as Vertebrates, Arthropods, and plants with woody fibres.

The earliest Vertebrates of the rocks are the Devonian *Ostracoderms*, well preserved forms, whose structure resembles that of the lampreys. That is to say, they were fish-like forms which had not as yet developed paired limbs. Amphibia, the least specialized for terrestrial existence, abound early in the coal age, appearing just before it begins. Reptilian types emerge late in the coal measures. Mammals are found at the end of the Triassic, and primitive birds in the Jurassic period which succeeds it. In the first true fishes there were heavy "ganoid" scales like those of sturgeons and the fins were supported by an extended axis corresponding to the shaft of the limb in a land vertebrate. Early ganoid fishes like *Sauripterus* have many points in common with the lung fishes of today. The bones of their limbs and the structure of their skulls were intermediate between the corresponding parts of modern fishes on the one hand and land vertebrates on the other.

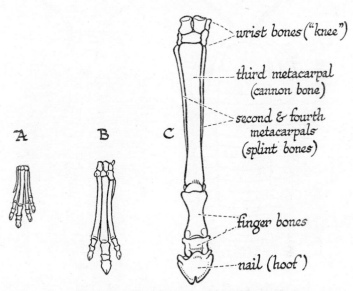

FIG. 469.—FORE FEET OF EXTINCT HORSES

A, the oldest, lived in the Eocene period. B is more recent, and C lived just before the Ice Age, and fairly closely resembles our modern horses in structure.

Through the South African Triassic reptiles (*Theromorpha*) of the Karoo, an unbroken series of forms link up the head, limb girdles, and vertebral column of the ancient amphibia known as *Stegocephali* to the more highly specialized structures of the mammals. The series linking the reptiles to the birds is less complete, but there are definite foreshadowings of the avian limb structures in the earlier Dinosaurs, a fossil order of reptiles. One missing link, beautifully preserved in the Bavarian shale, has many striking reptilian features (Fig. 468). The forelimb has three complete clawed digits with the normal number of phalanges (compare Fig. 462). There was a long tail like that of a lizard. The skull had teeth and distinct sutures. A covering of feathers, however, leaves no doubt about the fact that Archaeopteryx was the authentic early bird.

In the Arthropod series the earliest class to become dominant was the extinct Palaeozoic and very generalized group, the *Trilobites*. They were exclusively aquatic like the majority of modern Crustacea. Crustacean types first emerged in the Cambrian. Winged insects and land Arachnids like land Vertebrates first appear abundantly in the coal measures. A more generalized group of aquatic Arachnids with some Trilobite features or organization (Eurypterids) already existed early in the Palaeozoic.

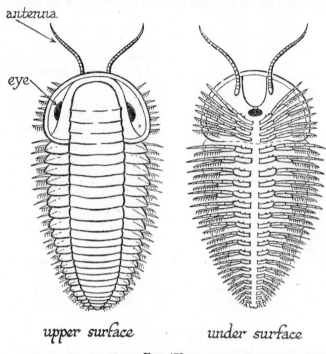

upper surface   under surface

FIG. 470.

The earliest representatives of the phylum Arthropoda found in the oldest sedimentary rocks are the Trilobites, a group which partake of the characteristics of all the more specialized classes which evolved later. Thus they have a single pair of feelers like insects, bifid swimming limbs like crustacea, and no specialized mandibles or biting jaws such as are present in insects and crustacea but absent in the arachnids. The principle of succession is well illustrated in Trilobites, owing to the fact that all parts of the body are enclosed in a hard case which readily leaves its impression on the sediment where it lies or becomes fossilized.

The Trilobites were forms with a head bearing five pairs of appendages and a large number of trunk segments. All the latter were alike, as in Myriapods. There was one pair of appendages in front of the mouth, and as in insects and Myriapods, this pair of appendages was antenniform. The trunk limbs were all two-branched or *biramous*, as are the swimming legs of most Crustacea, the abdominal limbs of the aquatic Arachnid Limulus and the masticatory appendages of insects. All the trunk appendages had basal segments like the masticatory bases ("gnathites") of the anterior appendages of Arachnids. As in Arachnids, no pair of appendages is exclusively subordinated to masticatory activity as are the mandibles of insects, Myriapods and Crustacea. Thus the Trilobites agree with Arachnids in having no mandibles, with insects and Myriapods in having one pair of feelers or antennae, and with Crustacea in the biramous character of the trunk appendages (which are presumably for swimming).

So the predominant group of the Arthropod phylum at the time when the first representatives of any extant groups make their appearance, was a group of species which combine the structural characteristics of all existing groups. The preservation of the Trilobites is so perfect that we know as much about the external anatomy of several genera as we do about that of any extant representative of the Arthropod phylum. The earliest Arachnids (Eurypterida) to become predominant are far more like the Trilobita than are many of the later and now predominant representatives of the same class. The King Crab, Limulus, is the sole surviving representative of an order of Arachnids closely allied to and contemporary with the Eurypterids. An aquatic scorpion Palaeophonus, intermediate between modern scorpions and Eurypterids, occurred before the Carboniferous. Then came typical land Arachnids with remains in the coal measures. In the Carboniferous, insects are abundant, whereas the Myriapods, which may be looked upon as intermediate in many respects between Trilobites and Insects, go back to much earlier rocks.

Just as the earliest Vertebrates and Arthropods were aquatic, the earliest land plants were semi-aquatic species like ferns and horsetails. Extinct ferns include species which bore seeds and thus bridge the gap between the Cycad palms and the earlier type of fern which survives to the present day. Gymnosperms preceded flowering plants, and among the fossil Cycads were species with hermaphrodite cones which are not a far cry from cone-like flowers of an archaic type characteristic of the modern ornamental genus *Magnolia*.

THE PRINCIPLE OF DISTRIBUTION

The principle of succession, which emerged with increasing force as the chronological order of the sedimentary rocks was established, and as their fossil relics were unearthed during the first half of the nineteenth century, showed that the gaps between the well-defined classes of living creatures are filled in by intermediate forms which lived on this earth in past epochs. Different species of animals and plants have lived at different times in the past. Different species of animal and plants live in different places today. The geological record shows that fossil representatives of a group are usually more alike, if they belong to the same strata, i.e. they are more alike, if they lived about the same time. A corresponding generalization is broadly true about related species which live in the same geographical region. For instance, all the species of the kangaroo family live in Australia, and all the species of the Armadillo family live in South America.

The Scorpion family provides a good illustration of the fact that geographical propinquity is generally associated with greater similarity of structure. Six families of Scorpions are commonly recognized. If we exclude the neighbourhood of the Suez Canal and a small part of Morocco, only two families, the *Scorpionidae* and the *Buthidae*, are represented on the African continent. Species belonging to both these families are also found in Asia south of the Himalayas, in Australia and in Central and South America. In the remotest part of the African continent, the Cape Peninsula, the Scorpionidae are represented by one genus, *Opisthophthalmus*, and the Buthidae are represented by three genera, *Uroplectes, Parabuthus* and *Buthus*. *Opisthophthalmus* and *Uroplectes* do not extend north of the Equator. *Parabuthus* extends beyond the Suez into Arabia, and *Buthus* ranges over South Asia. None of these four genera contains species found in Australia or America. The Cape species of Scorpionidae belong exclusively to a genus which has no representatives north of the Great Lakes. The Cape species of Buthidae belong to one genus which is exclusively South African, to one genus with species in the part of Asia nearest to Africa, to one genus with species distributed throughout South Asia, and to no genera with American and Australian representatives.

While belief in special creation was prevalent, the only explanation offered for the connexion between geographical propinquity and structural similarity was that animals and plants have been placed by Providence in the station of life to which they are best fitted. Colonial enterprise and horticulture both show that this is not necessarily true. At the beginning of the nineteenth century there were no rodents in Australia, where the rabbit has become a proverbial pest. A few blackberry seeds transported to New Zealand sponsored a blackberry plague which is a serious agricultural problem. Less than two centuries have elapsed since commerce with New Zealand began. There were then no indigenous mammals on the islands, where twenty-five imported species are now living freely in the wild state.

Exploration and new amenities of transport during the imperial expansion of the nineteenth century provided new opportunities for examining other circumstances associated with the fact that related species live in restricted localities. The two most obvious are: (*a*) the ease with which different groups of species can travel, on account of their locomotory organs or devices for seed dispersal, and (*b*) the physical obstacles which they encounter in spreading far afield. In general, groups of species which can most easily surmount barriers of ocean, mountain or desert spread themselves over wider areas. While bats are cosmopolitan, terrestrial mammals and Amphibia (frogs and salamanders) are not found on islands separated by a wide stretch of deep water from the mainland.

The great traveller naturalists of the nineteenth century made a close study of island faunas; and compared them with the faunas of the nearest adjacent land. The animal and plant populations of some islands are made up mostly of species which also live on the nearest adjacent land areas. Other islands are populated almost exclusively by species which are *endemic*, i.e. are not found elsewhere. Islands of the first class are generally near the mainland and are not separated from it by a great depth of ocean. Islands of the latter class, called *oceanic* islands, are separated from the mainland by a great depth of water. They may be volcanic, and if so have never been connected with the adjacent land area; or they may have remained separate from it for a long period of geological time. The Cape Verde Islands off the west coast of North Africa are volcanic islands. New Zealand, which is separated by a deep channel from the Australian land mass, appears to have been separated from it in Jurassic times.

The following tables taken from Romanes, a contemporary of Darwin, are still representative. St. Helena, Galapagos Islands and the Sandwich Islands are typical oceanic islands separated by a great depth of water from the mainland. In glacial times the British Isles connected with the mainland

A. PECULIAR OR ENDEMIC SPECIES

	Land Molluscs	Insects	Reptiles	Land Birds	Mammals
Sandwich	400	?	2	16	0
Galapagos	15	35	10	30	0
St. Helena	20	128	0	1	0
British Isles	3	149	0	1	0

B. NON-PECULIAR SPECIES

	Land Molluscs	Insects	Reptiles	Land Birds	Mammals
Sandwich	0	?	0	0	0
Galapagos	?	?	0	1	0
St. Helena	0	?	0	0	0
British Isles	83	12,551	13	130	40

of Europe. The British Isles include about a thousand islands large and small. St. Helena is a single volcanic rock.

The geological record furnishes one clue to the meaning of this contrast. We know that the species which now live in Europe have changed very little since glacial times, when the shallow channel between Britain and the mainland was established. In other words, many British species are still identical with European species which already existed when Britain was still part of the European mainland. The vastly deeper channel which separates New Zealand from Australia points to a much longer period of isolation. So fewer existing Australian species are identical with species which existed when New Zealand was part of the same land mass. Of 1,040 species of New Zealand butterflies, 63 are Australian, 24 are cosmopolitan, and the remaining 91 per cent are endemic.

Colonial experience furnishes a second clue to the peculiar faunistic features of oceanic islands. Carnivorous mammals, such as stoats and foxes, which prey on rabbits elsewhere, do not exist in Australia. Circumstances which would contribute to their extinction in other regions were therefore lacking, and they multiplied accordingly. Conversely the introduction of new predatory species by colonists has resulted in the rapid extinction of pre-existing species, like the Dodo. Animals brought at rare intervals by drifting logwood and seeds dropped by birds can multiply on volcanic islands without competition from predatory species on the mainland. So they may survive in their new surroundings, while their relatives on the adjacent mainland are making way for other species.

Families (e.g. Scorpionidae) generally have a more widespread distribution than the genera (e.g. Opisthophthalmus) placed in them; and include species which have been separate for a longer period of geological time than species placed in a single genus. So species placed in different genera of the same family have usually had a longer period for spreading far afield than species placed in the same genus. In short, all the facts of the geological record and of geographical distribution point to the same conclusion. New species are continually appearing and old ones are continually extinct. Four years before Darwin's first book appeared Wallace summed up the known facts about distribution in time and space at the conclusion of his paper entitled *On the Law which has Regulated the Introduction of New Species*: every species has come into existence coincident both in space and time with a pre-existing closely allied species.

THE THEORY OF NATURAL SELECTION

Wallace and Darwin, to whose restatement of the materialist view the prestige which evolution now enjoys is largely due, were primarily preoccupied with the panorama of living creatures disclosed by the great advances in exploration during the preceding century. To the question why do some types exist only in one place and others only in a different locality, their answer was that species unable to survive in competition with others have disappeared, making way for those more suited to the material conditions. In other words, the barriers of ocean, currents, mountain ranges, and the like, perform the same function as the wire netting or fence by which the stock-breeder perpetuates pure varieties. That such pure varieties arise in nature as *sports* or "mutations" which breed true to type when mated *inter se* was inferred from the experience of the breeder, horticulturalist, and fancier. Today it is attested by laboratory experiments under controlled conditions described in the next chapter.

Both Darwin and Wallace evaded the distinction between the separation of locally distinct *varieties* and *species* in the Linnaean sense. They seem to have assumed that when two varieties are separated by a sufficiently diverse assemblage of characteristics they become inter-sterile, and constitute distinct breeding units. In the light of closer acquaintance with evolution in the field and with mutation in the laboratory we can now see that this assumption was gratuitous. True species which do not inter-breed and differ very slightly in their characteristics may, and often do, occupy the same locality. For instance, anyone may see several species of the genus Geranium (Herb Robert, etc.) growing together on a Devonshire wall, several species of Veronica (speedwell) mixed up in a roadside ditch, or the two species of Woodbine (convulvulus) growing intertwined in a hedge in Herefordshire.

Since we now know that mutations which are inter-sterile though fertile when mated to the parent stock arise in experimental cultures of animals and plants, this criticism which was rightly advanced by some of Darwin's critics need no longer prove an obstacle to the common-sense view that the unity of type in living creatures, the record of the rocks and the peculiarities of geographical distribution are the outcome of descent from common ancestors by the natural process of generation and the continuous extinction of forms which cannot survive the continually changing conditions of life on earth.

PLANNED ECOLOGY

The theological temper of the controversy which raged when Darwin's views were first published concentrated attention on the problem of man's past. The vindication of the scientific outlook, which was the outcome of the struggle, was a momentous achievement. It is doubtful whether organized religion will ever regain the power to obstruct the advance of knowledge. Today a more important issue which emerges from the evolutionary doctrine is the future of man as a guiding and directing agent in the process.

The evolutionists of Darwin's time emphasized the way in which competition between species in large geographical areas affects their distribution during long periods of geological time. The study of smaller and more homogeneous units of habitat during shorter periods draws attention to their interdependence. Within any restricted geographical area we encounter well-defined assemblies of species living together in a more or less stable pattern, and similar associations may be found in widely separated regions. Beneath the stones of a garden rockery in Manchester or Montreal, in Camberwell or in Cape Town we find much the same collection made up of local species of the same familiar types, such as millipedes, centipedes, beetle mites, snails and ground beetles. Similar herbs are found in the undergrowth of an oak-birch wood in different parts of Britain and are characteristic of the same association. All the species which make up a relatively stable association can be placed in groups which depend for their existence on others. Unrestricted competition is only possible between species within a single group. The complete elimination of all species in one and the same group would bring disaster to the community as a whole.

A terrestrial life community or *ecological system* such as the population of a garden rockery consists of green plants and nitrogen-fixing soil bacteria converting the inorganic constituents of the soil and atmosphere into organic matter, herbivorous animals and fungi living at the expense of living and dead plants, carnivorous and parasitic animals living on the remains of both larger carnivora and herbivora, putrefying bacteria and saprophytic fungi living on the dead bodies of all these, and nitrifying bacteria converting the simple organic nitrogen compounds liberated by putrefaction into nitrates for the use of green plants. At any level in this closed cycle of chemical synthesis and disintegration several species compete for the means of survival, and every species depends for its survival on the activities of others. Without putrefying bacteria the soil would become exhausted, and incapable of sustaining green plants. Without green plants herbivorous animals would die off, and carnivorous species would be deprived of their prey. Hence intelligent intervention of man as a directing agent in the evolutionary process demands an inventory of all the species with which man competes and all the species on whose continued existence his own depends. The vast assemblage of classified material which the museums of the world have contributed to our present knowledge of the evolutionary drama is the necessary prelude to a planned ecology of mankind.

In establishing himself as a world-wide species man has brought into being a world-wide ecological system with little prevision of his own power to direct the future course of evolution. While he was naturalizing the dog, the sheep, wheat, the silkworm, the horse, and the potato on all five continents of the earth, he took no stock of the prospect which evolution now unfolds. The vast wastage of natural power by blind competition between multitudes of species which are indifferent to human requirements need not continue, if man now applies his scientific knowledge to a deliberately planned project for eliminating species which compete with him for the means of satisfaction, conserving only those which—directly or indirectly—contribute the means of food, of shelter, ornament, and a pleasing prospect.

Extensive social control of productive activities is an essential condition. The outstanding technological problems may be indicated under four main headings. The first is how to control the physical agencies which limit the survival and quality of species which subserve human needs. The second is how to destroy competing species which do not subserve human needs. The third is how to preserve edible species. The fourth is how to improve the quality of propitious species by selection of suitable varieties. This will be dealt with in the next chapter.

Any ecological system ultimately derives its character from the chemical constituents of the soil and such physical conditions as humidity, light, and heat. Reference to the chemical constituents has already been made in the last chapter. The increasing part which the new knowledge plays in the social practice of mankind is illustrated by the fact that the amount of nitrates used in agriculture was trebled between 1903, when the only sources were natural deposits, and 1928 when half the world output was prepared synthetically from atmospheric nitrogen. During the decade ending in 1926 the world's export trade in phosphates increased by 50 per cent. The addition of potash fertilizers has increased the monetary gain on citrus trees by £30 an acre. The use of lime and phosphatic fertilizers has opened up a large area of 200,000 acres of almost desert land in south New Zealand at the cost of £7 per acre.

Tracts of heathland in Cornwall, where the low moor vegetation is due to lack of lime alone, have been made to yield magnificent crops of corn, seeds, and roots by the addition of sea-sand, which is rich in calcium on account of shell fragments. Phosphate excess, which has led to failure of fruit and root crops in Devon, can be completely remedied by the application of potash. Reference to the preservation of livestock in regions with a low calcium or iodine soil content has been made in earlier chapters. Another example is bush sickness in New Zealand, a form of anaemia due to iron shortage. It can be remedied successfully by addition of iron to the diet. Dopiness in sheep, which, like rickets of pigs, is a calcium deficiency disease, can be remedied by an extra calcium ration.

One important general application of chemistry to human ecology is the enormous effect on the quality of pasturage produced by nitrogenous and phosphate dressings. The nitrogen requirements and protein content of different species of grasses vary considerably. The best and worst annual meat production per acre of pasture in Britain is stated by Stapledon to be in the ratio of 1 to 20. By suitable balance of the mineral constituents of the soil we can encourage the multiplication of good grasses (high protein content) at the expense of poor species, and the combination of rotational grazing with nitrogenous dressings is now revolutionizing grass husbandry. High phosphate content favours the selection of clover at the expense of grass, and thus raises the protein content of the hay.

Concerning the physical agencies which limit the survival of species humidity has been mentioned first. The last century has seen large tracts in America converted from desert to rich fruit-growing areas by irrigation projects. Elsewhere, especially in Britain, draining of water-logged areas offers considerable prospects for crop production and grazing. Of late years attention has been paid to the conquest of drought by using deep-rooted crops, such as lucerne and maize. Lord Bledisloe remarks that scientific investigation in Utah

in conserving soil moisture by the systematic cultivation of alternating crops of wheat and lucerne, in arid areas with an annual rainfall not exceeding six inches, and in de-alkalinizing salt-poisoned land, rendering it available for market-garden crops and fruit, has received all too small public recognition, but it has, nevertheless, taken in conjunction with wheat research in Canada, contributed materially to the growing consciousness that the world can continue to increase its population at the present rate for at least another century without any risk of food shortage.

A highly important development in connexion with drought is the discovery of ensilage, i.e. the technique of storing green fodder in a moist condition without putrefaction. For land reclamation the natural hybrid grass *Spartina Townsendii* provides an example of biological control. It grows rapidly even when deeply submerged, collecting tidal silt and thus promoting land accretion.

Of temperature and illumination as physical agencies limiting the survival of species we are only beginning to gain and apply scientific knowledge. Glasshouse protection of food plants has played an increasingly important part in food production during the last half century. With the cheapening of manufactured commodities the cloche system has extended the growing season for vegetables, now cultivated by allotment holders for individual use. In Scandinavian countries it pays the farmer to instal central-heating for pigs, thereby reducing the requisite food ration by 20 per cent. Even in the time of Ricardo it should have been possible to see how mechanical invention would increase the return on food production by increasing the available sources of heat and light. A very recent empirical discovery concerning the influence of the latter may turn out to have much wider application now that a scientific explanation is available. Winter egg production in fowls can be stimulated by exposure of the birds to electric light sufficiently to make it a commercially paying proposition. This appears to be because the pituitary gland, which secretes a hormone regulating the ovary, is reflexly activated by light at the red end of the spectrum.

The systematic destruction of species which compete with man is an essentially new feature of human ecology. Aside from trapping and hunting vermin, mankind accepted the providential dispensation which permitted moth and rust to corrupt, till the systematic study of plant and animal species unravelled the life histories of the common parasites and pests. During the last half century the successful application of this knowledge to the elimination of species which parasitize or devour crops, livestock, garden plants, or human beings themselves, provides many spectacular illustrations of the social importance of a complete inventory of living creatures. Selective elimination of species can be accomplished by various methods, of which the most important are regulation of the physical environment, segregation, specific poisons, and hyperparasitization.

The first depends on the fact that physical conditions make species more or less resistant to attack. For instance, the rust fungus which infests hollyhock grown in potassium deficient soils does not readily establish itself if a dressing is added to the soil. Munro has recently investigated the destruction of forest trees in New Zealand by wood wasps. The real diet of the wood wasp, like that of some other insects which appear to live on wood, is the fungi which infest it. Such fungi do not flourish in the trunk of trees unless they grow in water-logged soil. So draining the soil deprives the wood wasp of its means of existence.

Under the term segregation we may include the simple application of precise knowledge of the life histories of parasites. Many parasites are *heteroecious*, i.e. they spend part of their life cycle in the body of one host species and the remainder in another. For instance, the micro-organisms which are responsible for malaria and yellow fever alternately infect the mosquito and man. The micro-organism which produces sleeping sickness (trypanosomiasis) alternates between man (or cattle) and the Tse-tse fly. The parasitic flat worm (liver fluke) which produces liver rot in sheep breeds one generation in the kidney of the pond snail. The pork tapeworm, as its name suggests is transmitted to man by eating the flesh of the pig. The threadworm *Filaria*, which is responsible for the dread tropical disease called *elephantiasis*, starts its life in a mosquito. The bacillus of bubonic plague is carried by the flea to rodents or human beings which it bites.

When the life history of a heteroecious parasite is fully known the means of exterminating it can often be accomplished by segregation of the intermediate host. For instance, draining marshy land keeps down mosquitoes and pond snails, hence restricting the ravages of malaria, yellow fever, or liver rot. Some parasitic plants have different hosts at different stages of a single life cycle. One of the wheat rusts is heteroecious. It spends part of its life-cycle as a parasite on the barberry. By removing the intermediate host from wheat-growing areas, a policy adopted extensively in America, the danger of infection is practically stamped out. In North Dakota this has resulted in the saving of eighteen million bushels in ten years.

A fatal disease of poultry known as *gapes* is due to a nematode which normally infests turkeys and does not seem to do them much harm. By keeping poultry away from turkeys the danger of contracting the disease is enormously reduced. The menace of the clover seed midge has been eliminated by cutting the first hay crop ten days earlier, thereby preventing the insect from completing its growth. The corn borer and the cotton boll-weevil, which was responsible for a loss of 500,000,000 dollars in the United States during 1921, could have been stamped out if the dead stems had not been allowed to stand during winter. In Texas, with the co-operation of a population of 160,000 persons and the destruction of 40,000 summer-fruiting trees with the consent of their owners, who were in many cases not personally affected, the Mexican fruit-fly pest of citrus has been eradicated. This was achieved by doing away with all other fruit growing in citrus areas and restricting the fruit-bearing period of the citrus trees, so that the insect cannot survive the period between successive fruiting seasons.

The elimination of harmful species by chemical control is illustrated in the latter part of the following passage from Enid Charles' book, *The Twilight of Parenthood*:

We are only beginning to realize the magnitude of wasted effort which arises from witless competition between man and those organisms which are described as weeds, pests, or parasites. Tentative estimates of the total losses which agriculture sustains from the last two have yielded a figure of the order of 25 per cent. Such a figure based on destruction of crops and stock by known pests and parasites probably represents a small fraction of the total loss incurred, partly because it is based upon the damage done by specific agencies such as potato virus or wheat rust rather than non-specific agencies such as wireworms or slugs, and also because the loss through destruction of crop and stock may be small compared with the reduction of quality in what is not destroyed, a fact which has been brought out especially in connexion with apple diseases. Although the effect of the common plant bug, known as the leaf-hopper, on pasture quality cannot be detected by the naked eye, Professor Osborn has shown that when leaf-hoppers are excluded two cows can be kept where there was barely enough for one. A few illustrative data concerning losses may be cited. The destruction of wheat by rusts and of potatoes by virus amounts to between 10 per cent and 20 per cent of world production. These two diseases constitute a small part of the losses which wheat and potatoes suffer on account of parasites and pests. In addition to rusts wheat is attacked by a number of specific organisms such as the Hessian fly, a gall midge, another Dipteran *Oscinus frit*, and the gall thread-worm, *Tylenchus*. It is attacked by several non-specific organisms such as the corn-borer, and large losses to the stored grain are sustained through the ravages of weevils. The potato is attacked by two fatal fungus diseases, potato blight and wart disease, the former of which was the source of the Irish potato famine of 1843–47. Several insects specifically attack the potato, the Colorado beetle in America and the tuber-moth in this country being the most important. In some years a third of the beet crop of

France has been destroyed by the gall thread-worm *Heterodera* alone. Beet, again, has several specific diseases. The Economic Advisory Council estimates that during the last five years locusts have deprived mankind of the fruits of five and a half million working days per annum. The known yearly losses due to insects in the British Empire would feed the entire population of England and Wales. In 1916 the known loss of crops due to insect ravages in the United States represented a total equivalent to a contribution of one dollar per head of the world's entire population. An even more impressive picture of the forfeit man pays in unscientific competition with other species may be obtained by considering the gains resulting when he applies science to their mastery. There are five fairly common fungus parasites of the apple: canker (*Nectria galligena*), scab (*Venturia inequalis*), mildew (*Podiosphaera leucotricha*), brown rot (*Sclerotinia fructigena*), and blossom wilt (*Sclerotinia cinerea*). Of the common insect parasites may be mentioned: Blue bug (Anuraphis), woolly aphis (Eriosoma), apple sucker (Psylla), Capsid bug (Plesiocoris), apple blossom weevil (Anthonoma), codling moth (Cydia), and apple sawfly (Hoplocarpa). Considering two of these alone, three years' trials at Wisbech with spraying against Capsid bug and scab consistently in each case increased the yield over 100 per cent. The new method of growing apples as cordons or espaliers in low hedge formation has the double advantage of increasing fruitage at the expense of vegetative growth and facilitating monthly spraying which guarantees immunity against all the parasites mentioned above. . . . The use of insecticides and fungicides is not the hit-and-miss method which some people imagine it to be. Intensive researches in applied toxicology have been directed to the discovery of highly specific poisons which kill injurious organisms in quantities that do not harm non-injurious ones. The fungus diseases of potato (blight and wart) can both be controlled by spraying with a toxic preparation. Two insect parasites, the bean beetle and black fly, and an acarine which attack beans, the insect parasites of cabbages, carrots, onions, turnips, beet, peas, and potatoes, can now be controlled by spraying of the shoot or soil fumigation. Longley in 1930 collected data from ninety-six apple-growers in Nova Scotia to determine the influence of spraying and dusting on yield. The results demonstrate a clear increase in yield corresponding to an increased amount of spray. This holds good with slight fluctuations from an expenditure of two dollars per acre with an average production of $16 \cdot 2$ barrels to an expenditure of 24 dollars per acre yielding an average production of 85 barrels.

The method of hyperparasitization is referred to in the following citation from the same source:

Experts differ concerning its possibilities. Its importance lies in the fact that when it is successful the cost is utterly negligible compared with the results achieved. Just as the farmer keeps the ferret to check the growth of rodents, the State can breed specific parasites to destroy animals which attack crops or pests. Among notable successes which have been claimed for this method is the destruction of woolly aphis by the insect parasite Aphelinus mali. The earliest successful experiment in biological control was the introduction of the predatory ladybird, *Vedalia cardinalis*, to keep down the scale insect, *Icerya purchasi*, which attacks orange and lemon groves. The citrus mealybug has also been brought under control by the introduction of the coccinellid Cryptolaemus, for the breeding of which there are thirteen insectaries in the infested districts of California. An attempt is now being made to control the pink boll-worm in Egypt by the introduction of a Hymenopteran parasite, *Microbracon Kirk-*

patricki, at an expense of £1,000. If it succeeds the estimated saving will be £5,000,000. For some twenty-five years past the commercial growing of cocoanut on one of the two large islands of the Fiji group has been made impossible by the ravages of a small Zygaenid moth. About seven years ago this moth threatened to invade the adjoining islands. Such an extension would have completely ruined the staple industry of the group, if unchecked. This would have entailed a loss of £400,000 per annum. By the introduction of a Tachinid fly which parasitizes the cocoanut Zygaenid in Malaya the Fiji pest was so completely controlled that in three years' time the moth had become quite a rarity. The cost of this work was approximately £12,000. The late Mr. Frederick Muir estimated that his introduction of the Tachinid parasite of the weevil, borer of sugar-cane into the Hawaiian Islands saved the cane-growers about a million pounds a year. He spent three years in searching for the parasite, eventually got from New Guinea. The total cost of the work was about £10,000.

Essentially similar to hyperparasitization is a new method of weed control. This depends on discovering an insect larva for which the weed is a favourite food plant. "In New Zealand," says Dr. Charles,

scientific knowledge has now introduced the cinnabar moth to stamp out the ubiquitous ragwort. This weed, which has been rapidly invading greater areas of the dairy lands of the Dominions, is doubly disastrous because it leads to hepatic cirrhosis of cattle and horses. Two other exotic insects, *Abion ulicis* and *Antholcus varinervis*, have also been introduced to stamp out gorse and piripiri, the bane of the New Zealand farmer. At the Imperial Entomological Conference in 1930, Dr. Nicholson reported that an area as large as Great Britain now infested with prickly pear is being cleared in Australia by the introduction of the Pyralid moth, *Cactoblastis cactorum*.

Besides these methods of eliminating species which compete with man, the application of scientific knowledge to the production of *resistant* varieties is also important. This will be dealt with in the next chapter. When we reflect on the vast apparatus of chemical and aerial warfare which human ingenuity has elaborated during the past century, it is also salutary to recall the fact that many of the weapons devised for self-destruction can be applied to the conquest of man's natural enemies, if mankind decides to replace witless competition by the social enterprise of creative evolution. When we are at times tempted to blame the inventions of natural science for lack of adventurous inventiveness in social affairs, we should place beside accounts of the horrors of modern warfare the following picture from a recent book on insect control:

As we fly over the orange groves in the gathering dusk we see here and there squads of men erecting tents over the trees. Our guide tells us that these tents will be used during the night for gassing scale insects that are attacking the orange trees. More than $2,000,000 is spent each year in applying poison gas for the control of the scale insects.

CHAPTER XXII

A PLANNED ECOLOGY OF HUMAN LIFE

EVOLUTION unfolds a new horizon of human destiny. Man has it in his power to become an active and intelligent directive agent in the evolutionary process, using his knowledge of the diversity of living creatures to decide which are essential to his own welfare as objects of use or of aesthetic satisfaction, and using his knowledge of the properties of living matter to adjust the environment of the species he chooses as members of a rationally planned ecological system. The biotechnical future of mankind is not limited to these two themes. We also have it in our power to set about creating new types of organisms —and perhaps ultimately of guiding the further evolution of the unborn capacities of our own species.

Within certain narrow limits man has been doing this in a blundering, wasteful and necessarily protracted way throughout the whole history of civilization. Pedigree records of domesticated animals go back as early as the cultures of Mesopotamia (Fig 409) and, from time to time, more or less systematic efforts at improvement of breeds have been undertaken. This happened notably in England during the eighteenth century, when the introduction of root crops had made it possible to keep more cattle alive in winter, hence discouraging the extensive use of veal, while creating a wider demand for fresh meat of good quality. Although success which crowned efforts to improve the various breeds of sheep and oxen had no direct influence on a scientific understanding of animal breeding, its indirect effect was enormous. It acted as a powerful stimulus to the new venture of plant hybridization which had begun as soon as the existence of sex in plants was correctly understood (see pp. 857–9).

Of the beginnings of the human ecological system we know very little, and it is an arrogant pretence to speak of a biological interpretation of man's history while our knowledge is so slight. Overshadowed by the mechanical technology of the age, nineteenth-century archaeology paid a disproportionate attention to the varieties of tools associated with early human remains. Twentieth-century research is now occupied in re-casting the model of cultural progress which the nineteenth century constructed. Minor improvements of tool construction which have been used as the hallmark of various stages in prehistory are negligibly important compared with the several steps in the acquisition of a biotechnology which lasted with very little change from the dawn of history till the eighteenth century of our era. Primitive cultures are essentially self-sufficient, and, as such, moulded pre-eminently by the animals and plants available for food, raiment, drugs, dyes, structural materials, and defence against invasion. These several constituents of man's ecological system supply the primary impetus to an evolving culture. Thus the absence of available ungulates as beasts of burden, or of indigenous cereals, implies the absence of a decisive stimulus to mechanical ingenuity e.g. wheel design) or to a highly developed calendrical practice. The abundance of a narcotic plant or of particular species of parasites or of cereals (e.g. maize) deficient in vitamin content may act as an effective obstacle to sustained progress of any kind.

We still know nothing about how Palaeolithic man hit on the custom of scattering grain. Thanks to the work of Vavilov and others at one time encouraged in the Soviet Union, we are beginning to know something about the distribution of various species of cereals in the dawn of civilization and their relation to the indigenous culture of the seed-scattering "Neolithic" societies. The outstanding fact about the entry of animals into the ecological system of man is that man and the dog are universally distributed together, even in regions as far apart as Greenland and New Zealand. The association of man and the dog in the earliest cave drawings, the existence of the dog in Australia where man and the dog are certainly joint interlopers on a continent cut off from the mainland before placental mammals reached it, the existence of dog remains of considerable antiquity in the Queensland caves, and a variety of other evidence suggest that the disposition of the dog is hardly less decisive than the disposition of man as an agency in the evolution of the human ecological system.

A comparison of the Avebury dog, the Australian dingo, and the Eskimo type suggests that the earliest associate of the dog tribe was something like the Javanese chow, and that this type followed man round the world, breeding with other local species like the wolf and the jackal, which are still apparently interfertile, though commonly distinguished as Linnaean species. Various species of wild dog are addicted to hanging round human dwellings as scavengers, and the beginning of the animal association in the stage when man was a food-gathering creature was probably accidental. The dog as scavenger and unofficial dustman to the kitchen middens of Palaeolithic man participated in, and perhaps encouraged, the habit of hunting other beasts. Where there were indigenous and gregarious ungulates like sheep or cattle, the dog would round them up, keeping them metaphorically in cold storage, so that there was no longer need for hunting far afield. Imperceptibly man would pass from a shell gatherer to a hunter, and from a hunter to a herdsman by virtue of this fortuitous association.

At each stage, the fate of culture would rest on the species of wild animals and plants in his immediate neighbourhood. Once man had blundered into the associations which led to the use of other animals as steeds, sources of meat, milk, fur, and so forth, the several types of association acquired the character of an orderly routine regulated by tradition. This tradition was oral. It progressed without any spectacular changes from the beginnings of settled calendrical culture, and remained outside the urban cultivation of scientific knowledge till commercial seed production during the past three centuries provided the impetus to rational, deliberate, and systematic production of new species propitious to human needs.

PRE-MENDELIAN HYBRIDISTS

There is an admirable survey of the efforts which followed Fairchild's success (p. 858) with the carnation and the sweet-william in Roberts's *Plant*

Hybridization Before Mendel. By the middle of the nineteenth century there had been enough progress to compel the recognition of certain common features of hybrid crosses, and to encourage the search for theoretical knowledge to guide the practice of the seedsman and the nurseryman. As yet the horticulturalist had no certain recipe for fixing a new hybrid type without recourse to the traditional methods of natural or artificial vegetative propagation. The work of Knight (p. 847) shows how the new knowledge of pollination had made it possible to create new varieties for the herbaceous border, the kitchen garden or the orchard. Once created the new varieties could be propagated by cuttings (roses), by grafting them on to parent stock (roses, apples, cherries) or by runners (strawberries). Such hybrids could not perpetuate themselves by seed, and many of our choice fruit trees and ornamental plants keep their characteristics only because they are never propagated by sexual generation.

It was clearly recognized that stable seed varieties may turn up in later generations of hybrid plants. What was lacking was knowledge of how to achieve this result. Malcolm's seed catalogue of 1771 refers to seventeen fixed varieties of kitchen peas, and experiments with pea hybrids led Knight to an observation which was ultimately destined to eclipse his many practical achievements in the improvement of strawberries, currants, grapes, and fruit trees. His reasons for selecting the pea are given in his own words:

None appeared so well adapted to answer my purpose as the common pea, not only because I could obtain many varieties of the plant of different forms, sizes, and colours, but also because the structure of the blossoms, by preventing the ingress of insects and adventitious fauna, has rendered its varieties remarkably permanent.

Knight's experiments continued for thirty-six years, from 1787 to 1823. His general method was to pluck off the stamens of all the flowers of a plant and dust on the stigmas pollen from flowers of another plant. In selecting the pea for his major inquiries he had more good fortune than he could have anticipated. Perhaps because the pea is valued for its seed, the principal available varieties of the pea included many which were distinguished by conspicuous characteristics affecting the seed, such as shape—round, wrinkled, etc.—or colour—white, grey, blue, green, and yellow. Knight found that when individuals of two pure strains, e.g. a white seeded and a grey seeded variety, are crossed by the method stated above, the seeds produced are *uniform*, generally like those of one—the *dominant*—parent rather than the other—the *recessive* (p. 1009). The same results are obtained in reciprocal crosses. Thus if pollen of a white-seeded variety is used to fertilize ovules of a grey-seeded variety, the seeds produced by the maternal parent are all grey, as they also are if pollen from a grey-seeded variety is used to fertilize ovules of a white-seeded variety. When he raised these hybrid plants and tested the effect of pollinating flowers of one hybrid plant with pollen from another of the same generation, Knight found that most pods produced seeds of two kinds—like one (e.g. white) or the other parent (e.g. grey) of the original cross. A few pods contained seeds of one kind only, being exclusively like either one or the other parent of the original cross.

Of itself Knight's discovery of the "splitting of hybrids" did not advance the problem of fixing a new combination of variety characteristics. It was followed by several investigations of the same nature by other horticulturalists, notably in England by Herbert, Goss, and Laxton, who all worked with peas and obtained similar results. In 1820 Goss drew attention to the fact that the recessive type (e.g. white-seeded variety in the previous example) obtained by intercrossing the hybrids was just as pure as the original recessive parent of the hybrid. It perpetuated its kind, uniformly true to type, when self-fertilized or pollinated by its own kind. Laxton, whose work was published by the Horticultural Society in 1872, took the enquiry a step farther by recording crosses involving several characteristics, observed the possibility of fixing particular combinations, and gave rough estimates of the numerical proportions of the several types.

A widespread interest in the technique of hybridization at this time is emphasized by the rewards which were offered for the prosecution of similar researches in France and in Germany. In 1861 the Paris Academy offered the grand prize in the physical sciences for the study of plant hybrids, including among various other issues the question "Do hybrids which reproduce themselves by their own fecundation sometimes preserve invariable characters for several generations, and are they able to become the types of constant races?" Previously in 1819 and 1822 the Royal Prussian Academy had set the prize question, "Does hybrid fertilization occur in the plant kingdom?" In 1830 the Dutch Academy of Haarlem propounded the riddle in the words:

What does experience teach regarding the production of new species and varieties through the artificial fertilization of flowers of the one with the pollen of the other, and what economic and ornamental plants can be produced and multiplied in this way?

The prize offer renewed a second time in 1836 was taken up by Gärtner, who received the award in 1837, carried out numerous crosses with garden plants, and a very extensive enquiry into hybrid peas on the lines of previous work by Knight and Goss. He also worked with maize, and the large number of seeds produced by varieties of this species permitted him to recognize constant ratios of the several types more clearly than did Laxton in his later work on peas.

Of those who contributed solutions to these public competitions Naudin is specially noteworthy for the report presented to the Paris Academy in 1864. Naudin, like Gärtner, made crosses with several plant species, observed phenomena essentially on the same lines as those recorded by Knight, Goss, and Laxton, and proceeded farther towards constructing a hypothesis to guide further research and practice. Naudin's theoretical conclusions, which he devised no new experiments to test, include two significant statements. In his own words these are:

(i) That which is produced is never more than an amalgamation of forms already existing in the parent types. The hybrid is a composition of borrowed pieces; a sort of living mosaic of which each piece, discernible or not, is ascribable to one or the other of the producing species.

(ii) All these facts are naturally explained by the disjunction of the two specific *essences* in the pollen and the ovules of the hybrid. . . . The disjunction takes place in the anther and in the contents of the ovary. . . . Some of the grains of pollen belong totally to the species of the father and others to the species of the mother.

THE PARTICULATE NATURE OF INHERITANCE

It is a very short step from the conclusions established by Goss, Gärtner, Laxton, and Naudin to those which were published (1866) by the Abbé Mendel in an Austrian *horticultural* journal two years after Naudin's memoir. Mendel's special contribution was to bring his results—in themselves essentially identical with those of Goss and Laxton—into relation with the *atomistic* views which were providing an immensely fruitful basis of theoretical knowledge for the new technique of chemical manufacture. Like the particulate doctrine of modern chemistry, the theory which was to provide—in a new social context—satisfactory guidance for biological manufacture rests on two experimental generalizations. In chemistry it was first necessary to establish the law of the conservation of matter, which gained ground through the discovery that air has weight and that matter in the third state exists in many varieties. Then it was necessary to recognize the law of constant numerical proportions, and the several laws of combination by weight and volume. In genetics, the science of plant and animal breeding, analogous principles hold.

What we may call the law of *conservation of genetic materials* is implied in the fact first clearly recognized by Goss. When hybrid offspring of the same parents of pure descent are crossed with one another, it is always possible to reclaim from their progeny individuals which breed true to the *parental* type. If the parents differ in several characteristics, these are combined in various ways in the second hybrid generation, and since some of the individuals showing each combination are capable of breeding true to type, new combinations of variety characteristics can be fixed. The particulate theory of inheritance first advanced by Mendel shows how this can be done.

What we may call the law of *constant proportions* and the several laws of combination which govern inter-crossing hybrids and back-crossing them to their parents was loosely recognized by Gärtner and Laxton. None the less, it is only fair to Mendel to recognize the very special care he took to establish the numerical constancy of the various classes of progeny. When the parents differed with respect to a single characteristic, he found that inter-crossing or self-fertilization of the first hybrid generation (often denoted F.1, which stands for "first filial") gave dominants and recessives in the ratio 3 : 1. When the hybrids were crossed back to the recessive parents equal numbers of dominants and recessives turned up. The following table shows some of the results Mendel got by crossing F.1 hybrids of various matings *inter se*.

MENDEL'S DATA

Structure	Property	Dominant	Recessive	Ratio in F. 2
Seed	Form	5,474 round	1,850 wrinkled	2·96 : 1
Reserve material in Coty-ledons	Colour	6,022 yellow	2,001 green	3·01 : 1
Seed-Coats	Form	822 inflated	299 wrinkled	2·95 : 1
Seed-Coats	Colour	705 grey	224 white	3·15 : 1
Unripe Pods	Colour	428 green	152 yellow	2·82 : 1
Flowers	Position	651 axial	207 terminal	3·14 : 1
Stem	Length	787 tall	277 dwarf	2·84 : 1
		14,889	5,010	2·98: 1 or 3 : 1

There is nothing sacred about these numbers. The important thing is not the actual ratio he obtained, but the fact that what he did obtain could be repeated by anyone else. Here are some results which other workers have got.

Investigator	Yellow		Green		Total
	Number	Per cent	Number	Per cent	
Mendel, 1865 ..	6,022	75·05	2,001	24·95	8,023
Correns, 1900	1,394	75·47	453	24·53	1,847
Tschermak, 1900 ..	3,580	75·05	1,190	24·95	4,770
Hurst, 1904	1,310	74;64	445	25·36	1,755
Bateson, 1905 ..	11,902	75·30	3,903	24·70	15,806
Lock, 1905	1,438	73·67	514	26·33	1,952
Darbishire, 1909 ..	109,090	75·09	36,186	24·91	145,246
Totals	134,736	75·09	44,692	24·91	179,399

Mendel realized more clearly than his contemporaries that this numerical constancy is the clue to a correct understanding of what happens when different strains are crossed, and he did not let the subsidiary issue of dominance—i.e. the fact that hybrids often resemble one parent to the exclusion of the other—distract his attention from what we now know to be the universal feature of hybrid experiments. *Dominance* is not a universal phenomenon. For instance, if we cross individuals from pure stocks of the red and white varieties of the flowering plant popularly known as *four o'clock,* or botanically as *Mirabilis jalapa,* the resulting *first filial* (F.1) generation bear only pink flowers. If these F.1 hybrids are selfed or crossed *inter se,* the resulting *second filial* (F.2) generation is composed of reds, pinks, and whites, in the proportion 1 : 2 : 1. This would correspond to the 3 : 1 ratio if the hybrid types were similar to one or the other type of pure parent.

In crosses between white and black strains of the Andalusian fowl the F.1 individual produced by crossing black and splashed white birds is blue. Consequently the mating of Blue Andalusian fowls results in producing black and white offspring. So if we wish to obtain blue individuals it is more profitable to mate blacks with whites, giving a hybrid generation of blues only. The effect of crossing the blue hybrids among themselves is to raise a progeny of blacks, blues, and whites in the ratio of 1 : 2 : 1. In this example the hybrid is half way between the parental pure-bred types. The inheritance of the white colour of Leghorn fowls illustrates what may be called incomplete dominance. If a white Leghorn mated with an individual of a coloured strain, the hybrid individuals are white with a few coloured tail feathers. Careful measurement of characteristics which can be assessed by numerical standards shows that dominance is never absolutely complete.

However close the resemblance between the hybrid offspring of pure stocks and one or other of the parental types, the hereditary materials remain distinct and recombine to produce pure parental types again in the F.2 generation. Although we still know very little about the physical nature of dominance, analogy can help us to appreciate the issue in its true perspective. Sodium and potassium yield colourless salts with most common acids, but the permanganates of both are purple in solution. The salts of copper are generally of a bluish or greenish tint in solution. In one case the negative, in the other. the positive ion is the dominant agent determining the physical property of colour. In other respects the other component behaves in any reaction with its characteristic efficacy, although its presence is seemingly masked. So in the process of hereditary transmission the recessive factor retains its existence independently of the dominant factor. Dominance is only a matter which concerns their bodily expression.

One of his experiments in which a variety of pea having a dwarf shoot, from a stock breeding true to this feature, was crossed with an individual from another variety characterized by tall shoot, likewise of pure pedigree, may be taken to illustrate Mendel's hypothesis. When pollen from flowers of the one is transferred to the stigma of the other, the same result always occurs. Every seed produced in consequence of such a union gives rise to a tall plant, whichever way the cross is made with respect to the sex of the parents. If these seeds are allowed to germinate and grow into plants, the results of self-fertilizing the flowers of the hybrids, or, alternatively, crossing them with other F.1 plants, is entirely different from the effect of crossing two of the parental pedigree tall plants. Instead of obtaining only tall plants true to type, it is found that three-quarters of the seed produced (F.2 generation) give rise to tall plants, but one-quarter to dwarfs like one of the original parents. Further breeding shows that two-thirds of the F.2 tall individuals breed in the same way, throwing dwarfs in the same ratio. The remainder breed true to type like the original tall parent when self-fertilized, as do the dwarfs of the F.2 generation. When self-fertilized, or crossed *inter se*, the F.2 dwarf plants have only dwarf offspring.

To interpret these observations we must first recognize that the hereditary constitution of the tall individual in the F.1 generation differs from that of the tall parents, inasmuch as it is capable of giving rise to dwarf offspring. It differs presumably in producing gametes which contain some *particle* (without discussing its nature, Mendel called it a factor) responsible for the production of the dwarf condition. We notice too that the proportions of *pure* tall and *pure* dwarf plants are identical in the F.2 generation. That is to say, one-quarter have the factor for tallness only and one-quarter the factor for dwarfness only, so that neither of the gametes from which an individual of either type originates contains the alternate factor. We must also bear in mind that the F.1 tall plants behave in a similar manner whether they get the factor for dwarfness from the maternal or paternal gamete (in the ovule or pollen grain). Mendel drew the conclusion that each F.1 tall plant produces in equal quantities gametes bearing the tall and dwarf factors respectively— but never both; and tested the possibility that there is an equal chance of any pollen grain fertilizing an ovule with the same factor or the factor alternative to that which it contains.

It then follows that the number of individuals produced in the F.2 generation containing both factors for the tall and dwarf conditions will be twice the number containing only the tall or only the dwarf factor. For, if we represent the factor for tallness by T and that for dwarfness by t, T may fertilize T or t, giving TT or Tt; and t may fertilize T or t, giving tT or tt. This, of course, satisfies the conditions, and is an adequate account of the facts so far. Such was the hypothesis Mendel proposed (Fig. 471). Characters distinguishing different hereditary strains were supposed to depend upon separate particles (or *factors*) present in duplicate in all the cells of the body. These particles are what the body inherits from its parents. The members of each pair *segregate* in the formation of the gametes, so that one-half contain the paternal and one-half the maternal factor.

The truth of the particulate hypothesis must stand or fall, like other scientific hypotheses, with its capacity to provide a correct recipe for conduct. Recipes which can easily be tested out are exemplified by crossing back the F.1 impure tall plants with (*a*) the pure tall parents, and (*b*) the dwarf plants— which are all pure. Using letters to denote the hereditary particles at work, the pure breeding tall plants and dwarfs have the constitution TT, tt on the hypothesis outlined, since their character depends on factors inherited from both parents: the impure plants F.1 have the constitution Tt or tT. By crossing Tt with TT we should get two types of offspring TT and Tt, equal numbers of pure and impure tall plants. Also by crossing Tt with tt, we get two types of offspring Tt and tt, equal numbers of impure tall and pure dwarf. Mendel was not a British economist. He was a scientific worker, seriously concerned with getting something done for horticulture. So he *tested* and *verified* these and other implications. He was thus led to this conclusion. Hereditable differences are dependent upon separate particles derived from both parents, remaining distinct throughout the entire life-cycle, and finally separating in the formation of the gametes, so that with respect to any single pair of them one-half of the gametes contain the particle derived from one parent and the other half contain the particle contributed by the alternate parent. This is Mendel's law of *genetic segregation*.

For the sake of convenience we may here introduce some necessary technical terms. An individual which like the "impure" F.1 tall plants receives dissimilar factors from its parents is said to be *heterozygous* in respect of those factors in contradistinction to the *homozygous* (e.g. pure dwarf or pure tall) type. The character which appears to predominate, if its material forerunner is present in the fertilized egg, is said to be *dominant* in contradistinction to the *recessive* character, which is only manifest when both the gametes contribute its material forerunner.

It must not be imagined that every clear-cut characteristic which distin-

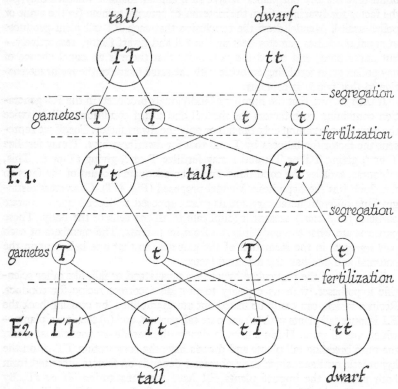

FIG. 471.—MENDEL'S HYPOTHESIS

Each cell of a pure tall pea has two *particles* which are responsible for the difference between it and a dwarf one. Each cell of a pure dwarf pea has two *particles* which are responsible for the difference between it and a tall one. Mendel called these particles "factors." In the formation of the gametes, the members of each pair segregate. So each gamete contains only one member of this pair, T in the case of the tall plant, and t in the case of the dwarf plant. Fertilization yields only one kind of fertilized egg cell (T*t*). This develops into a tall plant. For this reason T is said to be *dominant*, and *t* recessive. At each cell division of the developing plant, the factors divide as well. So every ordinary cell of the hybrid contains the T*t* pair of dissimilar factors. In the formation of the gametes of the hybrid, however, segregation again occurs. Hence gametes containing T and ones containing *t* are produced in equal numbers. Random fertilization yields three classes of offspring—25 per cent pure tall (TT), 50 per cent impure tall (T*t*), and 25 per cent pure dwarf (*tt*).

guishes two related forms need depend on only one factor difference. Mendel was particularly fortunate in hitting upon a form in which there exist a number of strains differing with respect to single pairs of unit factors. Had he studied, for example, the inheritance of the "walnut" type of comb which occurs in the Malay breeds of domestic fowl (Fig. 477), he would have had a more difficult problem. The "rose" comb of Wyandottes and the "pea" comb of the Indian Game breeds are each dominant to the single comb of the Leghorn, Sussex, and Rhode Island breeds. The "walnut" comb can be produced by crossing individuals with the Rose and Pea types of comb. A pure individual with a walnut comb crossed with an individual from a single comb breed would give an F.2 with walnut, rose, pea, and single combs all represented, because the walnut type differs from the single comb in respect of two pairs of factors, namely, those responsible when present alone for the pea and rose types. In the crosses which have been previously discussed, character differences in which only one pair of factors are involved have been deliberately selected for the sake of simplicity. In studying inheritance the geneticist often meets with apparently well-defined characters distinguishing two races of animals or plants which present a multiplicity of factorial differences. It can generally be shown that such apparent exceptions to the law of genetic segregation fall into line, when the data are fully analysed.

The numerical proportions prescribed by the law of segregation are statistical predictions. The physical model which we take as a basis for what happens in fertilization is an urn with an enormous number of otherwise similar counters of different colours in fixed proportions. If the model is a satisfactory one, our conclusions must bear the scrutiny of the mathematical laws of combinations which describe the results of taking counters out of the urn. In our interpretation of a 3:1 ratio, the assumption made is that, since two kinds of egg or sperm are formed in equal numbers by a heterozygous individual, there should be an equal chance of any egg being fertilized by either of two sorts of sperm (one carrying the maternal and the other carrying the paternal factor). Similarly it is assumed that there is an equal chance that any sperm will fertilize one or the other type of egg. On this assumption the 3:1 ratio follows, if one of the parental characters is dominant.

Since the assumption itself involves the idea of *chance*, the conclusion is subject to the laws of chance. Obviously we cannot get a three-one ratio from a litter of three kittens. In experiments on inheritance in a common South African species of bean weevil, Dr. Skaife crossed the dominant black form with a red recessive mutant, and obtained in the second cross-bred generation 466 individuals of which 347 were black and 119 red. For this number the 3:1 ratio of the urn model requires two classes differing from 349·5 and 116·5 by a probable error of approximately 6. This means that if we were drawing counters from an urn containing an immense number of black and red ones in the proportion 3:1, it would happen *less* often that a trial of 466 selections would yield *above* 356 or *below* 343 black counters than that the number of black counters would lie (like the number of black weevils) within these limits.

Mendel's investigations followed up what happens when two different pairs of characters, each dependent on a separate pair of factors, are involved in a cross between pure-bred parents. The actual results of a cross between a strain of peas with green wrinkled seeds and yellow round seeds or of peas with green round and yellow wrinkled seed respectively will be understood by referring to Fig. 472. The ratios of the double dominant, the two classes of single dominants and the double recessives which Mendel obtained in all his crosses was 9 : 3 : 3 : 1, as should occur if the yellow-green factors and the round-wrinkled factors behave quite independently of one another.

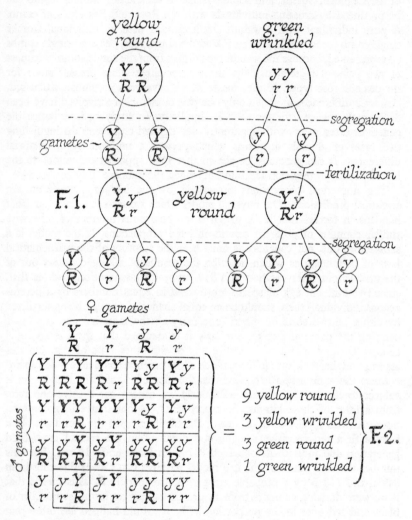

FIG. 472.—INDEPENDENT ASSORTMENT OF TWO PAIRS OF FACTORS

Hybrids represented by the genetic formula YyRr can be produced by crossing the double dominant with the double recessive, or alternatively by crossing YYrr with yyRR. The F_1 hybrid produced the four classes of gametes shown in equal numbers. This is because the assortment of factors in segregation is random in this case, i.e. it is just as likely that Y will go into the same gamete as r, as that Y will go into the same gamete as R. The results of random fertilization of the four classes of x female gametes by the four classes of male gametes, are shown in the chessboard diagram.

Mendel formulated this result as a generalization sometimes known as Mendel's Second Law. It is not, however, a law in the same sense as Mendel's

First Law, of *segregation*, which we have deduced above, for it is only applicable to certain cases, and as we shall see later, the exceptions are of more theoretical interest than the rule. Here again an analogy from chemistry will help. The fundamental law of chemical combination is the law of constant proportions. The law of multiple proportions is no more than a statement of certain experiences that the pioneers of chemistry encountered in dealing with some of the compounds that were first investigated. Had they started with the higher hydrocarbons, they would have encountered no such simple relations. Both the law of multiple proportions and the second law of Mendel are historically important, because they helped to suggest hypotheses which, once stated, were broad enough to take in other possibilities. We shall leave a consideration of the 9 : 3 : 3 : 1 ratio of Mendel's original experiments till a later stage, and now approach the problem of hybridization from a different point of view.

SO-CALLED REDISCOVERY OF MENDEL'S HYPOTHESIS

The publication of Mendel's work produced no discussion, and if it had not been mentioned in a comprehensive and laborious German survey of the existing literature on hybridization undertaken by Focke, it is probable that it would have remained completely unknown, when the principles which Mendel advanced were restated independently by three later workers, de Vries, Correns, and Tschermak. They published their results simultaneously in 1900, and did not know of Mendel's own work, till they had reached their own conclusions. To make a belated and somewhat futile reparation to a scientific worker whose gifts had not been sufficiently recognized by his own contemporaries, there then ensued an apotheosis which went so far as to rechristen the science of breeding. Genetics was called Mendelism, as geometry had been called Euclid.

While Mendel's contribution to the theoretical development of genetics was a conspicuous advance, like that of Avogadro in the theory of chemistry, it had very deep roots in the social preoccupations of his period and in a large body of experimental results which had already been established. To speak of Mendelism and to neglect the work of men like Koelreuter, Knight, Herbert, Goss, Gärtner, Naudin, Laxton—or others like them—is like beginning the history of the atom with Avogadro without any recognition of the contributions of Hooke and Mayow, Black and Lavoisier, Gay-Lussac and Dalton. That Mendel advanced the issue, as he did, is less a matter for comment than his failure to evoke any response from his immediate contemporaries.

No doubt there are several reasons for the arrested development of theoretical genetics during the ensuing generation. Among those which seem specially significant two may be mentioned. One recalls the fate of Spallanzani's admirable experiments on spontaneous generation. The issue had reached a stage when it was necessary *to bring the practical experience of the horticulturalist and seedsman into closer touch with new laboratory discoveries concerning the material basis of inheritance.* This union of theory and practice is what distinguishes Mendel's contribution from that of his predecessors. Events conspired—especially in Britain where so much pioneer work had been carried out on the practical side—to drive a wedge between the worker in the garden or orchard and the worker in the laboratory. The repeal of the Corn Laws signalizes the lopsided development of mechanical technology characteristic of *laissez-faire*, when the restatement of the evolutionary doctrine, coming at the climax of the long struggle for the repeal of religious tests in the Universities, became the focus of an ideological conflict between the cultural aspirations of the rising manufacturing class and the land-owning interests both in Britain and on the Continent. In both ways biological enquiry suffered from the excessive urbanization of capitalism, and our Universities have not yet recovered from the overloading of curricula with the preoccupations of the evolutionary controversy and the separation of biological teaching from any relation to social practice. When the issue was revived, progress was most rapid in America, where large-scale farming was equipped with a lavishly endowed system of technical education.

How the evolutionary controversy diverted interest from the practical problems of horticulture into purely ideological issues is readily seen, if we compare Darwin's work on hybridization with that of Laxton. Darwin did not advance the subject a single step forward, and he might have seen the Mendelian solution in his own data of Antirrhinum crosses, if he had more clearly envisaged how his problem affected the social practice of mankind. Mendel who saw the issue as a practical horticulturalist also saw that a recipe for human interference in the evolutionary process is the necessary basis for a true picture of how evolution occurs. Thus he stated explicitly:

Those who survey the work done in this department will arrive at the conviction that, among all the numerous experiments made, not one has been carried out to such an extent and in such a way as to make it possible to determine the number of different forms under which the offspring of hybrids appear, or to arrange these forms with certainty according to their separate generations or definitely to ascertain their statistical relations. It requires indeed some courage to undertake a labour of such far-reaching extent. This appears, however, to be the *only right way by which we can finally reach the solution of a question the importance of which cannot be over-estimated in connexion with the history of the evolution of organic forms.*

The union of theoretical and practical knowledge set forth in Mendel's solution was more daring than it seems in retrospect. Mendel published his results more than a decade before the work of Hertwig and Fol established the elementary fact that one sperm fertilizes one egg. Even among botanists the implications of the cell doctrine were still on trial. Naudin's "essences" remind us that the older generation of botanists had not been brought up to discuss heredity in terms of gametes. Zoologists (see p. 877) had not yet begun to do so. There was little to indicate that Mendel's conclusions embodied a universal law of plant breeding and far less to suggest that they were universally true of inheritance both in plants and in animals.

Plant breeding on similar lines was continued during the ensuing generation by various enquirers such as Macfarlane and de Vries. When the conclusions of de Vries, Correns, and Tschermak were simultaneously announced, a new interest was immediately awakened. Cuénot in France, and Bateson, who in England had independently and previously urged that the clue to an understanding of hybridity lay in the numerical ratios of the several types of their offspring, immediately announced the applicability of Mendel's hypothesis to animals.

It is not difficult to see how the situation had changed in the intervening time. When Mendel was doing his work on peas, Patrick Shirreff, the first notable hybridizer of wheat, had been labouring in Scotland for many years in a purely empirical attempt to improve cereals by selection. Shirreff refers to Knight as the first individual in Britain known to have crossed wheat, and he seems to have derived encouragement from Knight's work. He succeeded in producing various new varieties of wheat and oats, some of which bore his name. Knight had foreseen (p. 848) the economic results of success in improving cereal yield. We may go so far as to say that when Shirreff published his book on the *Improvement of the Cereals* in 1873 the need for a scientific basis for plant breeding henceforth affected the welfare of everybody, and more especially the future of the grain-growing states of America. The two decades that followed—from 1880 to 1900—established all the essential facts about the material basis of inheritance set forth in Chapter XVIII (pp. 888–893). When Mendel issued his memoir the nature of fertilization in animals was not yet established, and the character of nuclear division in animals and plants was not even suspected. When it was unearthed and applied to animals, the American biologists McClung and Sutton had shown that the paternal and maternal chromosomes sort themselves out in the formation of the gametes precisely in the way that Mendel had envisaged for his "factors."

THE CHROMOSOME HYPOTHESIS

All that is meant by heredity must refer to the contributions which the sperm and the egg make to the new individual. Can we go farther and identify within the sperm or egg the material particles which enter the gametes after innumerable cell divisions? Can we detect the existence of anything which behaves as our "factors" or particles of heredity have been seen to behave?

Hybridization experiments lead us to conclude that the particles of heredity are present in the fertilized egg in duplicate, and that they segregate before the formation of the gametes into maternal and paternal components, one member of each pair and one only being present in each gamete. We now know that the number of chromosomes of any species of animals or plants is twice the number present in the gametes. In many animals (and plants) from the most diverse phyla, the chromosome complex of a species has a definite configuration as well as a definite number. Among the chromosomes it is possible to distinguish pairs of different sizes and shapes (e.g. Fig. 439), and the maintenance of this constant configuration implies that when reduction takes place one member of each pair passes into each gamete (p. 891). In other words, the chromosomes are present in the fertilized egg in pairs, and they segregate in the formation of the gametes into paternal and maternal components, only one member of each pair being represented in each gamete.

The identification of the chromosomes as the material basis of hybrid segregation immensely simplifies the deeper study of genetical phenomena. The most striking advances which have been made of recent years in the study of inheritance are the outcome of discovering this correspondence.

The application of Mendel's principles to animals was first made by Bateson and Cuénot independently. In the same year Sutton's work showed the analogy between the behaviour of chromosomes and the material entities which Mendel had postulated as the basis of bi-parental inheritance. In 1911 Morgan, Muller, and Bridges at Columbia University, New York, commenced a series of investigations on *Drosophila melanogaster*, the fruit fly or banana fly. This little creature has almost every conceivable advantage for the purposes of genetical investigation. It is prolific. It passes through its entire life cycle in little over a week. It is eminently viable. It is easily cultured, and can be fed on rotting banana skins. It has only four pairs of chromosomes, all recognizably different. With *Drosophila* one can do more in a year than could be achieved with cattle in several centuries.

In the Columbia cultures more than eight hundred mutants or sports have appeared, and these mutants or sports, when mated with their like, breed true to type. Thus the interrelation of the mutant characters in their mode of inheritance has been studied with a thoroughness that has no parallel in genetical investigation. To illustrate the more concrete interpretation which the chromosome hypothesis affords, let us take a cross between one of the mutants of Drosophila and the pure wild type. The normal, i.e. wild type, fruit fly has red eyes. One variety which has appeared as a sport is distinguished by its purple eyes. When a purple-eyed mutant is crossed to a wild type individual of pure stock all the F.1 generation are red-eyed (Fig. 473). These red-eyed individuals, when mated among themselves, produce offspring of which one-quarter are purple-eyed and three-quarters are red-eyed. If we mate the hybrids with purple-eyed mutants, half of their offspring are purple-eyed and half are red-eyed.

Let us now suppose that the purple-eyed form originally arose because a sudden change took place in one pair of chromosomes. The individuals of the first filial generation of our original cross will receive one chromosome of this pair from the purple-eyed parent and the other chromosome of the same pair from the wild type parent. So the first filial generation will consist of individuals which possess one pair of chromosomes the two constituents of which are not the same, i.e. a pair of which one member has undergone the change referred to and one member has not. From the result it is evident that an individual will not be purple-eyed unless both members of this particular pair have undergone the change. When reduction (p. 891) occurs in the germ cells of the cross-bred flies a member of this pair carrying the purple-eyed gene will go to one pole and to the other pole a chromosome of the same pair unmodified. So this pair of chromosomes will be represented in one-half of the ripe sperm of the male hybrids by a member that has undergone the change and in the other half by a member that has not.

The same will be true of the eggs produced by hybrid females. If fertilization occurs at random, a sperm which possesses the mutant chromosome will have an equal chance of fertilizing an egg which has it or an egg which has it not. For every sperm which has the mutant chromosome there will be one in which this particular pair is represented by a chromosome unmodified. Sperms of this type will also have an equal chance to fertilize an egg which has the mutant chromosome or an egg which has not. For every fertilized egg which gets a mutant chromosome from its mother and father, there will be one which gets a mutant chromosome from neither, one which gets

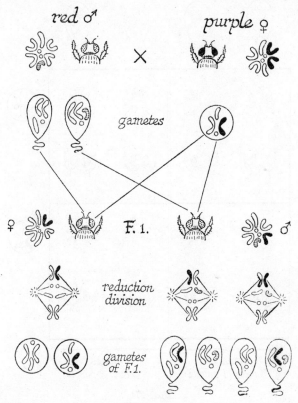

FIG. 473

Diagrammatic representation of the first generation of a cross between the red-eyed wild type of the fruit fly and the purple-eyed mutant. The Y chromosome is shaded, and the chromosome bearing the mutant gene is shown in black.

a mutant chromosome from its mother only, and one which gets a mutant chromosome from its father only. Since an individual has purple eyes only if it gets the mutant chromosome from both parents, this makes the proportion of purple-eyed individuals one-quarter in the F.2. With the aid of the accompanying diagrams you can deduce for yourself the consequences of other types of cross.

Consider now a cross in which two mutant characters are involved. Wild fruit flies are grey in colour and the wings extend beyond the tip of the abdomen. Among the sports of Drosophila are two respectively distinguished by dark body colour and a vestigial condition of the wings. As a matter of fact, there are several mutants of Drosophila which have a dark body colour. The one we shall deal with here is called *ebony*. When either of these sports are crossed to pure wild type flies, the first crossbred generation are wild type. Mated *inter se*, the hybrids in either case yield progeny one-quarter

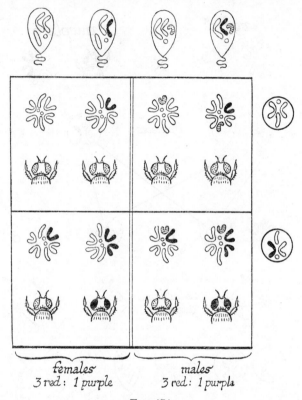

females
3 red : 1 purple

males
3 red : 1 purple

FIG. 474

Continuation of Fig. 473, showing the numerical consequences of mating the first cross-bred generation of flies *inter se*.

of which are of the mutant type. Both mutants are therefore recessive to the respective wild types.

When the ebony mutant is crossed to the vestigial-winged type (for brevity "vestigial") the double hybrids of the first generation are also uniformly wild type (Fig. 475). If sufficient offspring are bred from crosses between these double hybrids, approximately one-sixteenth show both mutant characters, three-sixteenths are ebony, three-sixteenths are vestigial, and nine-sixteenths wild type. Figs. 475 and 476 show how this numerical result follows from the simple assumption that the change which started the ebony condition occurred on a different pair of chromosomes from that on which the change which originated the vestigial type occurred. In the reduction division of the germ cells of the F.1 generation there will be two different configurations according as the mutant members of each pair go to the same or opposite

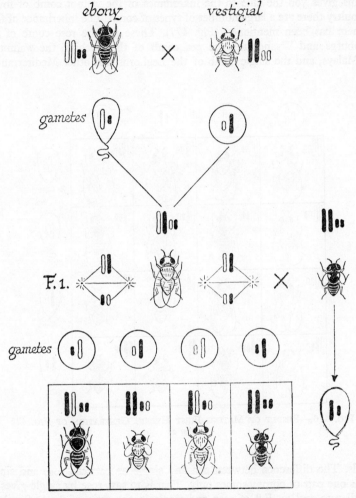

FIG. 475.—CROSS BETWEEN TWO INDEPENDENTLY ASSORTING CHARACTERS IN THE FRUIT FLY

Only the two pairs of chromosomes concerned are shown, distinguished by size for the sake of clearness and with the chromosomes bearing the mutant factors in black. In the lower part of the figure is shown the result of crossing the F.1 flies back to the double recessive type.

poles, and the numerical recombinations can be simply deduced by using a chessboard diagram to show that for every set of four different types of eggs fertilized by one of the four different types of sperm there will be a corresponding quartette fertilized by each of the remaining three types of sperm. If the double hybrid flies are bred with the new type having both mutant characters, the four possible combinations will appear in the progeny in equal proportions (Fig. 475).

This gives you the clue to the inheritance of the walnut comb of fowls. In poultry there are a large number of types of comb. The inheritance of four of them has been mentioned (Fig. 477). These are the rose comb of the Hamburgs and Wyandottes, the pea comb of the Cochins, the walnut of the Malays, and the single comb of the Leghorns and other Mediterranean

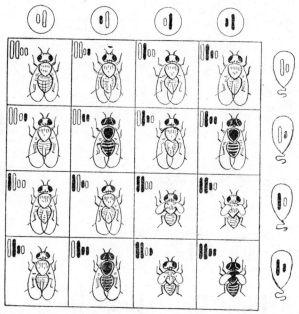

FIG. 476.—RESULT OF MATING FIRST HYBRID GENERATION OF FIG. 475
inter se

breeds. The difference between pea and single or between rose and single affects one pair of chromosomes only. That is to say, rose by single gives an F.1 all rose and an F.2 of rose and single in the ratio of 3 : 1. Similarly with pea and single, pea being dominant. If pure-bred walnut-combed fowls are crossed with singles, the F.1 are all walnut type, the F.2 are walnut, rose, pea, and single in the proportions 9 : 3 : 3 : 1. The same result follows a cross between pure rose and pure pea. The single-combed condition may be taken as the wild type, and the walnut type has arisen by mutant changes affecting two pairs of chromosomes. A change affecting one pair by itself produces the pea condition, and a change affecting the other pair by itself produces the rose condition. Here, it is to be noted, both mutant changes are dominant, i.e. the mutant character is exhibited if only a single member of the modified pair of chromosomes involved is present. You can illustrate this result for yourself with the aid of a diagram like Fig. 472 or 476.

The numerical results of experiments like those of Mendel thus receive a simple explanation on the assumption that the chromosomes are the seat of those changes which lead to the appearance of individuals with new hereditable properties. Further experiments have made it possible to show (1) that the material particle or *gene* responsible for the appearance of a new hereditable property can be identified with a particular chromosome; and (2) that it can be identified with a definite position or *locus* on a particular chromosome.

In everything about which we have concerned ourselves so far it is a

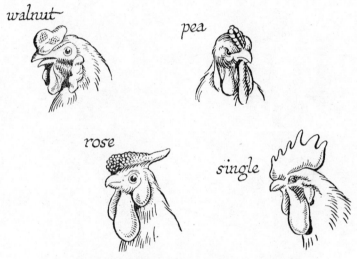

FIG. 477.—FOUR TYPES OF COMB IN THE DOMESTIC FOWL

matter of complete indifference whether the character with which we are dealing is introduced from the maternal or paternal side. We also know that one pair of chromosomes is unequally mated in one sex. So any change which started on this pair is not symmetrically distributed among the sexes. In Drosophila (Fig. 439) the female has one pair of chromosomes (the first pair or XX) represented in the male by one element (X) of similar dimensions and another (Y) of different shape. Thus only half the sperms will carry an X chromosome. Among the mutants of Drosophila there is a large class—more than a hundred—which do not behave like those with purple eyes, vestigial wings, or ebony body colour. Crosses with wild type give different results according as the mutant character is introduced from the maternal or paternal side.

One example of this class has white instead of red eyes. Crossed to pure-bred wild type (red-eyed) females white-eyed males produce offspring all of which are wild type, and when the hybrids are mated *inter se* one-quarter of their progeny are white-eyed (Fig. 478). The only anomaly is that all the F.2 white-eyed flies are males. When white-eyed females are crossed to pure stock wild type males, the result is more remarkable. Only the female offspring of the first generation are red-eyed. The males are white-eyed. When these

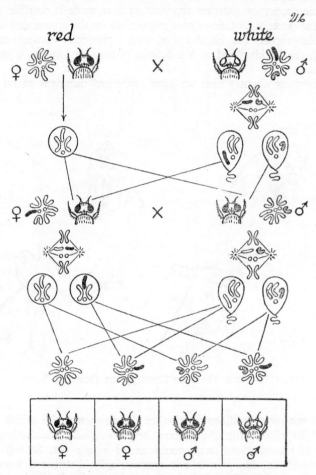

FIG. 478.—SEX-LINKED INHERITANCE IN DROSOPHILA

The male of the mutant stock with white eyes mated with a wild type red-eyed female gives an F.1 all-red-eyed; in the F.2 only males are white-eyed. The X chromosome bearing the mutant factor is shown in black, and the Y chromosome is shaded.

crossbred flies are mated *inter se*, their progeny are one-quarter white-eyed males, one-quarter white-eyed females, one-quarter red-eyed males, and one-quarter red-eyed females. We can interpret this result, if we assume that the mutant gene which is responsible for white eyes is on the X chromosome, and that it can override the effect of all the other chromosomes unless it is paired off with another X chromosome from wild stock. If a mutant X chromosome is present in the male there can be no X chromosome to pair with it. So the mutant condition will always be exhibited. The mutant condition will not be exhibited by the female unless both members of the X pair carry the mutant gene.

The phenomenon of "sex-linked inheritance," as this asymmetrical type

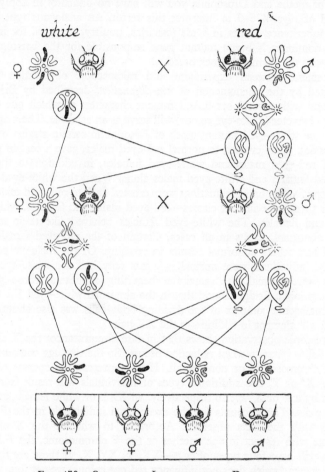

FIG. 479.—SEX-LINKED INHERITANCE IN DROSOPHILA

The reciprocal cross to that shown in Fig. 478. When pure red-eyed males are crossed to white-eyed females the male offspring are white-eyed, and in the F.2 the red-eyed and white-eyed types are present in equal numbers in both sexes.

of transmission is sometimes called, was first discovered by Doncaster (1906) in moths. In Lepidoptera the male is the XX type and the female XY or XO. In the currant or magpie moth Abraxas, there is a pale-winged (lacticolor) mutant in contradistinction to the dark-winged (grossulariata) type. Doncaster set out to find why females of the lacticolor variety are much commoner than males. On breeding he found that dark-winged males crossed to pale females have only dark-winged offspring, which give dark-winged and pale moths in the ratio 3 : 1 when mated *inter se*. All the pale moths of this cross are females. In the reciprocal cross only the males are of the dark type, and the F.2 is composed of dark and pale, males and females, in equal proportions. Bearing in mind the difference (p. 892) between the chromosomes of moths and Drosophila you will have no difficulty in applying the method of Figs. 478–9 to interpret this result. An analogous type of sex-linked inheritance occurs in birds (canaries, poultry, etc.), as, for instance, in the dominant X-borne mutant gene responsible for the barring of the plumage in the Plymouth Rock breed.

Agreement between experiment and microscopic observation is also illustrated by the phenomenon of *non-disjunction*, described by Bridges in connexion with several sex-linked mutant characters of which our original mutant character (white-eye colour) will serve as an example. There appeared among the white-eyed mutant stock of Drosophila certain strains of which the females, when crossed to normal red-eyed males, gave a certain proportion of red-eyed males and white-eyed females, in addition to the usual red-eyed females and white-eyed males alone. When the white-eyed female offspring of such abnormal matings were crossed back to red-eyed males they, in their turn, gave all four classes—red-eyed males and females, white-eyed males and females. The white-eyed females behaved like their mothers, giving abnormal results in all cases. Certain of the red-eyed females gave normal and others abnormal results in crossing. Of the male progeny the red-eyed individuals were normal, whereas only half the white-eyed individuals were normal, the remainder begetting daughters whose progeny was exceptional. Bridges found that in the abnormal white-eyed F.1 females the chromosome complex of the dividing body-cells was also abnormal—it showed a Y element in addition to the XX pair.

Microscopic observation shows that in rare circumstances the X chromosomes fail to separate when reduction occurs. So the ripe egg contains either two X chromosomes or none at all. If we represent the sperms of a red male as X' or Y, two additional types of individuals will result from fertilization by a Y or X' sperm respectively, an XXY or white female, and X'Y or red male. This accounts for the exceptional individuals in the F.1, and accords with the facts observed. According to whether the X elements segregate with respect to one another or the Y chromosome, the F.1 white females will have four types of eggs—XX, Y, XY, X. If these are fertilized by a Y sperm (which does not influence red eye colour) we get four types— (a) XXY white females, which will obviously behave in the same way, thus agreeing with breeding experience; (b) YY—individuals with this constitution cannot live; (c) XYY—white males which should produce XY sperms so that in crossing with normal white female daughters of the XXY type, producing exceptional progeny, would result; (d) XY—normal white males. When the same four classes of eggs are fertilized by an X' sperm carrying the red factor, four red types of offspring would result, as follows: (a) X'XX —a triploid female which usually dies; (b) X'Y—normal red males; (c) X'YX —red females with abnormal offspring; (d) X'X—normal red females. Thus the non-disjunction of the X chromosome in the formation of the eggs of some of the females of the parental white-eyed stock accounts for the entire series of exceptional genetic phenomena which occur in these strains.

THE CHROMOSOME MAP

Such evidence can leave very little doubt about the conclusion that the behaviour of the chromosomes provides the material basis of the numerical proportions found in breeding experiments. There is now abundant evidence of the same kind derived from the study of inheritance in widely different types of animals and plants pointing to the same conclusion. Other experiments have made it possible to locate the changes which are responsible for particular mutant characters on a definite region of a particular chromosome.

The experimental results which lead to this conclusion may first be illustrated by what happens in crosses which involve more than one sex-linked mutant character. There is a yellow-bodied mutant of the fruit fly which behaves, when crossed to wild stock, in a manner analogous to the white-eyed form. That is to say, the yellow females crossed to pure wild stock males give yellow males and grey females, and yellow males mated to pure wild type females give all grey offspring. If we cross a yellow female with white eyes with a pure stock wild type male, the female offspring are wild type, but the males are yellow with white eyes, as we should expect (Fig 480). When these are interbred an unexpected result occurs. A small but definite proportion of yellow individuals with red eyes and grey individuals with white eyes occurs. Since the two properties are separable we can only conclude that the same part of the chromosome is not involved in whatever is responsible for the yellow mutant on the one hand and the white-eyed mutant on the other. The numerical proportions in this case are approximately as follows:

						Per cent
Females:	Wild type	..	..	..	..	24·725
	Yellow-white	..	..	..	..	24·725
	Grey-white	..	..	..	..	0·275
	Yellow-red	..	..	..	..	0·275
Males:	Wild type	..	..	..	..	24·725
	Yellow-white	..	..	..	..	24·725
	Grey-white	..	..	..	..	0·275
	Yellow-red	..	..	..	..	0·275

We can also make a cross involving these two characters in a different way, as when we mate a yellow male and a white-eyed female. The first generation consists of white-eyed males and wild type females. When bred *inter se* these give offspring of all four types:

						Per cent
Females:	Wild type	..	..	..	..	25
	White-eyed	..	..	..	..	25
Males:	Yellow	..	..	..	..	24·725
	White	..	..	..	..	24·725
	Yellow-white	..	..	..	..	0·275
	Wild type	..	..	..	..	0·275

Inspection of the figures for the males in these two crosses shows that the extent (1·1 per cent) to which the yellow and white mutant genes get *detached*, when they are introduced from the *same* parent, is numerically

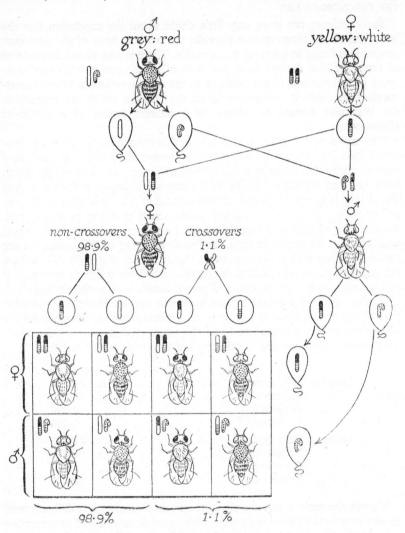

FIG. 480.—CROSSING OVER BETWEEN TWO SEX-LINKED MUTANT FACTORS

The part of the X chromosome containing the gene for yellow body is shown in black and the part containing the gene for white eyes is shaded. The normal X chromosome is left white and the Y chromosome is hooked and stippled.

equivalent to the extent (1·1 per cent) to which they tend to *come together*, when they are introduced in the first place from *different* parents. In a fixed proportion of reduction divisions the two points or *loci*, A and B, where the mutant genes are respectively located, become interchanged in the two members of the X pair of chromosomes (Fig. 481). This is in agreement with microscopic observation. In the pairing before the reduction division, corresponding chromosomes become twisted, and since the split takes place longitudinally, appearances suggest that a crossing over of corresponding segments occurs. Closely neighbouring regions are less likely to get interchanged than regions farther apart. So if the gene has a definite locus on the chromosome, we should expect that genes located in closely adjacent parts would tend to stick together more often than genes whose loci lie farther apart.

The consequences of this conclusion can be seen best with a diagram (Fig. 482). If A B C are three points on the length of a chromosome, and B

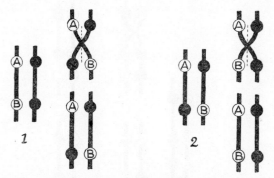

FIG. 481.—DIAGRAM TO EXPLAIN CROSSING OVER BETWEEN TWO LOCI ON A CHROMOSOME

(1) In the cross between yellow, white-eyed female and wild-type male.
(2) In the cross between yellow male and white-eyed female.

is intermediate between A and C, crossing over between the points A and C may take place in one of two ways. The length on which C is located may be displaced with reference to A carrying B with it, or the length on which C is located may be displaced with reference to A not carrying B with it. The first case involves the crossing over of the loci of A and B. The second involves transposition of the loci of B and C. Hence if the three points are located in the order stated the number of cases in which the loci of A and C are transposed will be the *sum* of the number of cases in which A and B cross over and B and C cross over. If the order of A B C is not given, the amount of crossing over between A and C may be the sum *or difference* of the cross over A–B and B–C.

Let us now see how this applies to the example just given. Crossing over takes place between the locus of yellow and the locus of white in 1·1 per cent of the reduction divisions in the formation of the eggs. There is another sex-linked mutant characterized by possession of wings which do not extend beyond the tip of the abdomen. It is referred to as *miniature*. In yellow miniature matings which produce a very large generation of flies, the cross-over percentage (cross-over value or C.O.V.) is found to be 34·3, and in the white miniature cross the C.O.V. is 33·2. The difference 1·1 corresponds to the cross-over value for yellow and white. Thus the locus of white lies between the locus of yellow and miniature 1·1 units of length from the former and 33·2 units from the latter. This relation holds good for all the sex-linked mutant genes of Drosophila. So it is possible to construct, as Morgan and his collaborators have done, a map (Fig. 485) of the X-chromosome.

Thus far we have confined our attention to one group of mutant characters which have their origin in changes which occur at definite loci on the X or first pair of chromosomes in Drosophila. Now Drosophila has four pairs of chromosomes, all of which have been mapped out on the same principle.

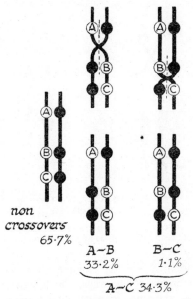

FIG. 482.—LINEAR ARRANGEMENT OF THE GENES

All that we have learned about the other chromosomes so far is that the genes for vestigial, ebony, and purple eye are not on the first (X) pair, and that ebony and vestigial are not on the same pair. Besides ebony there is another dark-coloured mutant which is referred to as black. When a "black" fly with vestigial wings is crossed back to the wild parent stock, the F.1 individuals are grey with long wings as in the ebony vestigial cross (Fig. 483, right). If the F.1 males are mated with females of the black vestigial type, the entire progeny are either grey with long wings or black with vestigial wings (1 : 1). A different result is obtained in the F.2 generation of a cross between a black mutant with normal long wings and a grey fly with vestigial wings (Fig. 483, left). As before, the hybrid progeny are grey with long wings. If these F.1 males are crossed back to the black vestigial females, half the offspring are grey with vestigial wings and half of them are black with long wings. The results of both crosses can be interpreted as before, if we assume that we are dealing with mutant genes located on the same pair of chromosomes. This conclusion is reinforced by further experiments.

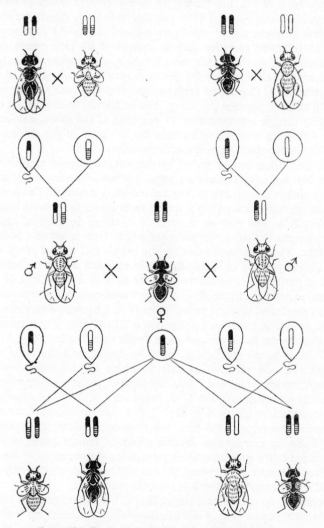

FIG. 483.—LINKAGE IN A NON-SEX-LINKED CROSS

Effect of back-crossing to the double recessive *female*, the *male* offspring of a *black* X *vestigial* mating. The region of a chromosome containing a *black* gene is shown in black, the part containing a *vestigial* gene is shaded, and the parts containing the genes for *grey* and *long* are left white. On the left the black and vestigial genes entered from opposite parents, and on the right they came in together. In mating the males from either cross with the double recessive female, the original linkages appear un-altered in the offspring. Compare Fig. 484.

If instead of crossing back the F.1 males to the double recessive females, we make the reciprocal mating of the F.1 females to the double recessive male type, the result is slightly different. What happens when both the recessive genes (black and vestigial) are brought in from the same parent, is that the back cross of the F.1 females to double mutant males produces 41·5 per cent black vestigial and 41·5 per cent grey long, together with 8·5 per cent black long and 8·5 per cent grey vestigial. If the F.1 females of a cross in which only one recessive gene is introduced by each parent (Fig. 484) are crossed back to the double recessive male, the progeny, instead of being 50 per cent black long and 50 per cent grey vestigial, are 41·5 per cent black long and 41·5 per cent grey vestigial, together with 8·5 per cent black vestigial and 8·5 per cent grey long. The numerical results can be explained by saying that in approximately 17 per cent of reduction divisions in the female a crossing over occurs between the two parts of the chromosome on which the two mutant genes respectively occur.

This conclusion can be tested by the method already applied to white eye, yellow body, and miniature wing mutants. The mutant with purple eyes is a simple recessive to the normal red-eyed condition. The mutant with the bent-up "curved wing" is a simple recessive to the normal long-winged condition. In a cross between individuals involving the vestigial and curved-wing characters the cross-over percentage of 8·2 was based on a generation of 1,861 flies. The cross-over value for the purple and curved genes was 19·9 based on a generation of 61,361 flies. The expected cross-over between vestigial and purple genes would therefore be $19·9 \pm 8·2^* = 28·1$ or 11·7. In an actual experiment in which 15,210 flies were reared, the cross-over value between purple and vestigial proved to be 11·8. The cross-over value for black and purple is 6·2, based on a generation of 51,957 flies. The expected cross-over value for the black vestigial cross would therefore be $6·2 \pm 11·8 = 18$ or 5·6. In an actual experiment, based on 23,731 flies, the value 17·8 was obtained. To add yet another case in which the interrupted wing vein character, known as "plexus," was investigated, the cross-over value for the purple and plexus factors was 47·7, based on 350 flies. The expected value for plexus-black would thus be $47·7 \pm 6·2$, i.e. 53·9 or 41·5. In an actual experiment, involving 2,460 flies, the cross-over percentage was found to be 41·9. So we can arrange another group of mutant genes in a definite order on one of the remaining three pairs of the chromosomes of the fruit fly. The locus of purple lies between the loci of black and vestigial about twelve units of length from the latter and six from the former.

Experiments up to date have shown that all the mutant genes of Drosophila fall into four groups (Fig. 485). Members of the same group tend to stick together—completely in the male, and with a definite amount of crossing over in the female. Members of different groups behave in a manner analogous to the ebony-vestigial cross, i.e. they show "free assortment" in segregation. Thus the number of *linkage* groups corresponds to the number of pairs of chromosomes, and of these four groups one, the smallest, can be identified with the small "fourth" pair of chromosomes in Drosophila on account of abnormal genetical results obtained in crossing flies in which one member of this pair of chromosomes was found to be absent. Recently

* The sign $\pm$ in this context means that the expected cross-over value exceeds (+) or falls short (−) of the preceding figure by the amount stated.

Punnett has shown the existence of seven linkage groups in the sweet-pea which has seven pairs of chromosomes. So the arrangement of the genes in linear series has been shown to hold good for the sweet-pea. Considerable

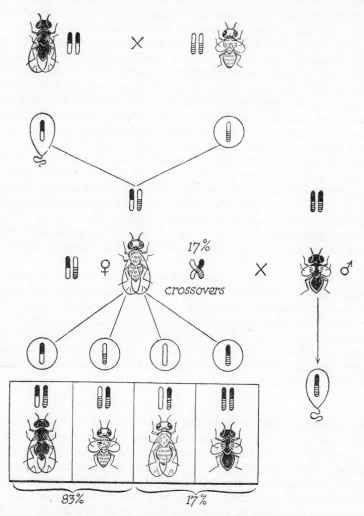

FIG. 484.—CROSSING OVER IN THE BLACK-VESTIGIAL CROSS

Here the *female* F1 of a black X vestigial mating are crossed with the double recessive *male*. The original linkages are broken by crossing over in the formation of 17 per cent of the eggs. Chromosome conventions as in Fig. 483.

progress has also been made towards a chromosome map of maize and the Chinese Primrose.

The results obtained with experiments on the fruit fly apply to a wide range of living creatures. When Mendel's principles were first rescued from obscurity, few, if any, biologists would have been so bold as to assert that they apply to all types of heredity, and the majority were only willing to concede grudgingly a restricted validity to the Law of Segregation. Many continued to speak as if there were two sorts of inheritance, Mendelian and non-Mendelian. Every year since the beginning of this century has witnessed a wider extension of the principle which Mendel first announced.

At one time a great deal of confusion arose through the use of the mis-leading term "unit *character.*" A single clear-cut anatomical *difference* may involve one or many genes. There is no relation between the magnitude of the one and the extent of the other. The inheritance of the walnut type of comb in the domestic fowl illustrates a clear-cut character difference which involves two mutant genes. If a character difference involves two mutant genes on different pairs of chromosomes, we should expect nine instead of four distinct types in the F.2 generation, if there were no dominance, and the analysis of this result would not be at all obvious at first sight. If three dominant or recessive genes on different pairs of chromosomes determine a single character difference, the F.2 individuals would fall into one class with all three dominant characters, three classes with two dominant characters, three classes with one dominant character, and one class with no dominant characters in the ratio 27 : 9 : 9 : 9 : 3 : 3 : 3 : 1. If neither member of any of the three pairs of characters show dominance the number of classes will be twenty-seven instead of eight.

So extremely complicated cases may arise, when only a few genes are involved in the inheritance of some discrete anatomical or physiological difference distinguishing two strains. If only four genes on different pairs of chromosomes come into play, and none is dominant to its alternative, the number of classes in the F.2 is 81. Even so, we have only exhausted a small fraction of problems that present difficulty at first sight. The successful analysis of such difficult cases justifies the confidence which Mendel's principle now enjoys.

APPLICATION OF GENETICS TO HUMAN ECOLOGY

In the absence of definite knowledge about hereditary transmission the improvement of stock and seed-producing crops was accomplished by in-breeding and by artificial selection. Individuals with the selected character-istic were propagated by repeated mating of close relatives having the same characteristic. If this is carried on for many generations pure lines of homo-zygous individuals can be established. What could only be achieved by a long process of selection and inbreeding can now be brought about by systematic testing in two or three generations. The difference between the two methods can be illustrated by taking an example analogous to comb inheritance in poultry (p. 1022 and Fig. 477).

In rabbits two varieties, Blue Bevran and Chocolate Havana, are dis-tinguished by the slate and reddish brown colour of the fur. If pure individuals of both types are crossed, the hybrid is black. When the black hybrids are mated with one another four colour types of offspring are produced, namely black, blue, chocolate, and a fourth whose pale silvery coat is called "lilac."

The fact that there are four types shows that we are dealing with two mutant genes. One recessive gene (*b*) makes black fur slate-blue, the other (*c*) makes black fur reddish brown, both together make black fur lilac. The F.1 hybrids receive b from their blue and c from their chocolate parents respectively. They have neither in duplicate. So if b and c are assumed to be recessive, the F.1 hybrids should be black. All the possible genetic types which may occur may be represented in the letter symbols thus:

Black	..	.. BB CC		BB Cc	
		Bb CC		Bb Cc	
Blue ..	..	.. bb CC		bb Cc	
Chocolate ..		.. BB cc		Bb cc	
Lilac	..	..	bb cc		

Suppose now that black rabbits had been produced for the first time by crossing the Blue Bevran and Chocolate Havana. The fancier or furrier of the old school would first mate the F.1 black hybrids *inter se*. About 9 out of every 16 of their offspring would be black and these would include all the four "genotypes" indicated above. There will therefore be 10 types of possible matings of black litter mates as indicated in the ensuing table.

	BB CC	BB Cc	Bb CC	Bb Cc
BB CC	(i)	(ii)	(iii)	(iv)
BB Cc	(v) = (ii)	(vi)	(vii)	(viii)
Bb CC	(ix) = (iii)	(x) = (vii)	(xi)	(xii)
Bb Cc	(xiii) = (iv)	(xiv) = (viii)	(xv) = (xii)	(xvi)

Of these ten types only one BB CC × BB CC will yield offspring which will infallibly breed true to type by continued interbreeding. If he relies on inbreeding to get a pure stock the breeder has to go on breeding black brother to black sister, rejecting parents which throw blue, chocolate, or lilac offspring, till one of the stocks has been observed to produce no throwbacks for several generations. After about twenty generations this result will usually have been achieved. Selective inbreeding is an exceedingly wasteful way of getting it, because there is a simple way of deciding to which genotype an F.2 black hybrid belongs. By making a chess board diagram (see Fig. 472) you will see that when mated to lilac (bb cc),

BB CC gives progeny all black
BB Cc gives progeny 50 per cent black and 50 per cent chocolate
Bb CC gives progeny 50 per cent black and 50 per cent blue
Bb Cc gives progeny 25 per cent black, 25 per cent chocolate,
        25 per cent blue, and 25 per cent lilac.

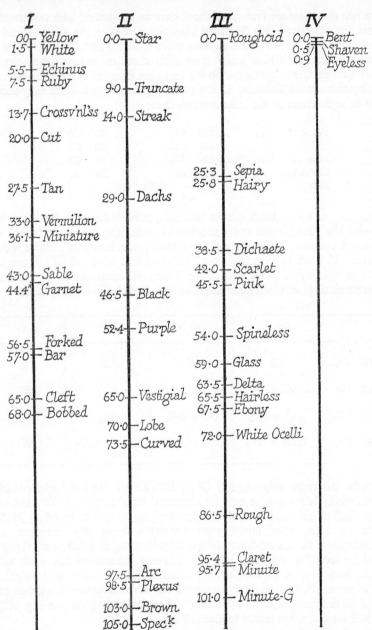

I	II	III	IV
0·0 Yellow	0·0 Star	0·0 Roughoid	0·0 Bent
1·5 White			0·5 Shaven
			0·9 Eyeless
5·5 Echinus			
7·5 Ruby	9·0 Truncate		
13·7 Crossv'nl'ss	14·0 Streak		
20·0 Cut			
		25·3 Sepia	
		25·8 Hairy	
27·5 Tan	29·0 Dachs		
33·0 Vermilion			
36·1 Miniature		38·5 Dichaete	
		42·0 Scarlet	
43·0 Sable		45·5 Pink	
44·4 Garnet	46·5 Black		
	52·4 Purple	54·0 Spineless	
56·5 Forked		59·0 Glass	
57·0 Bar			
		63·5 Delta	
65·0 Cleft	65·0 Vestigial	65·5 Hairless	
68·0 Bobbed		67·5 Ebony	
	70·0 Lobe	72·0 White Ocelli	
	73·5 Curved		
		86·5 Rough	
	97·5 Arc	95·4 Claret	
	98·5 Plexus	95·7 Minute	
	103·0 Brown	101·0 Minute-G	
	105·0 Speck		

FIG. 485.—MAP OF SOME OF THE MUTANT GENES OF DROSOPHILA

So if each F.2 hybrid black is mated once to a lilac individual the production of an all black litter makes it almost certain that it is a pure black (BB CC). The odds are at least 127 to 1 in a single litter of seven and 4,095 to 1 if two successive all black litters of seven are reared. At one step we can therefore determine which of the F.2 hybrids are pure stock, and so achieve the result required in the second generation from the original cross.

You will also see that there is no need to inbreed twenty generations of lilac rabbits to get a pure stock. All lilac rabbits must be pure, since they are double recessives. If we had started, knowing only the black and lilac colour varieties, we should, of course, get the same result in the F.1 and F.2 of a cross between lilac and pure black. Some of our blue and chocolates would be impure. If we wanted to build up pure stocks of either we could test the blues and chocolates for further use by mating to lilac, when

    BB   cc   would give all chocolate
    Bb   cc   would give 50 per cent chocolate and 50 per cent lilac
    bb   CC   would give all blue
    bb   Cc   would give 50 per cent blue and 50 per cent lilac.

This is an exceedingly simple example of the practical application of genetic principles. The fact that thirteen genes which affect the growth of the pollen tube are now known to be involved in the phenomenon of self-sterility in cherries will help you to get a picture of the scope of modern genetical research. Just as he can combine the genes of varieties with pea and rose comb to produce a pure walnut and single comb stock of poultry, or the genes for blue and chocolate to get a pure stock of black and lilac rabbits, the modern geneticist can combine the genes responsible for high resistance to a parasite (e.g. virus or rust) and for high yield of fruit, or for high yield and high baking quality of grain.

Among the first achievements of this kind were Biffen's rust resistant wheat called "Little Joss" and his later "Yeoman" wheat with good yield and "hardness," i.e. good baking quality. American geneticists have produced good strains of beans which are resistant to a "mosaic" (virus) disease. Salaman has produced a potato immune to wart disease. Cotton growers in the Sudan are now using a strain which has been built up for resistance to the virus disease "leaf curl." Curly Top is a virus disease of beet, mainly confined to the United States, which has a very disastrous effect, and in some parts of the country has put hundreds of thousands of acres out of cultivation. The United States Department of Agriculture has now produced two resistant (not immune) varieties which allows deserted areas to be replanted.

An important technique which is coming into use is the method of crossing a cultivated strain of high yield with a local wild variety which is suited to local conditions. In this way the genes which make a crop resistant to local diseases, climatic or soil conditions can be combined with productive capacity. In applying this method a spectacular result was recently achieved in Java, where a mosaic disease threatened the sugar industry. On crossing the cultivated sugar-cane to a local wild type with high immunity, a new variety turned up. The following remarks by Sir J. Russell illustrate how existing social machinery uses the bounty which scientific knowledge makes possible:

"One could dilate," said Sir John, "on the achievement of the Dutch in Java, in producing their new sugar-cane which quadrupled the output and so lowered the price of sugar that the West Indies are in terrible distress, the sugar-beet industry of Great Britain is threatened, and all Europe would be in trouble but that they artificially keep out the new sugar."

One important conclusion which emerges from the contribution which genetics can make to the evolution of the human ecological system is that the possibilities of economic self-sufficiency in restricted geographical areas are increasing daily. Scientific chemistry has made *Toledo* steel and *Castille* soap anachronisms. Scientific biotechnology is making the *Jersey* cow and the *Cheddar* cheese anachronisms. It would hardly be too much to say that we can foresee only one limit to the evolution of productive and ornamental varieties of animals and plants which are adapted to local conditions. The great obstacle to progress in biotechnics is the lopsided development of mechanical science imposed on us by industrial capitalism.

EXAMPLES ON CHAPTER XXII

1. A purple-eyed mutant of Drosophila crossed to pure wild stock which has red eyes, always gives offspring all red-eyed. In one experiment the hybrids were mated *inter se* and gave offspring 107 red-eyed and 38 purple-eyed. Interpret this with the aid of a diagram. How would you test the genetic constitution of the red-eyed animals?

2. A fruit fly with vestigial wings and ebony body colour is crossed to wild type. The F.1 flies are back crossed to the double recessive (ebony-vestigial) and the result is:

>   wild type 32
>   ebony (normal wing) 29
>   vestigial (grey body colour) 30
>   ebony vestigial 31

Interpret this result with the aid of a diagram. What would be the result of mating the wild type in the last experiment *inter se*?

3. All the F.1 generation of a cross between a fowl with single and a fowl with walnut comb (pure bred) have walnut combs. Back crosses of walnut to single gives the following:

>   walnut comb 73
>   rose comb 71
>   pea comb 74
>   single comb 75

Interpret this result by means of a diagram. What would be the result of mating those with walnut combs *inter se*?

4. The white plumage of leghorn poultry is dominant to coloured, feathered shanks is dominant to clean, and pea comb is dominant to single. What would be the result of back crossing the F.1 of a pure white, feathered, bird with a pea comb and a black, clean, bird with a single comb to the triple recessive?

5. A race of black rabbits mated to lilac gives black hybrids which, when mated to their lilac parents, yield black, blue, chocolate and lilac offspring in approximately equal numbers. Four black offspring of black *hybrid* parents behaved as follows. Buck A crossed with a lilac female had one surviving offspring which was lilac. When crossed with Doe B, the same buck sired three

successive litters, including in all 13 black and 3 blue offspring. With Doe C it also sired three litters including in all 6 chocolate and 13 black offspring. With Doe D it sired only black offspring in four successive matings. Interpret these data, giving the genetic constitution of the four individuals.

6. A Yellow male mutant of Drosophila crossed to wild type (grey) females always gives grey offspring. A yellow female mutant crossed to pure-bred wild type male has offspring half of which are grey females and half yellow males. Interpret this result with the aid of a diagram. What will result if flies from each of the F.1 are mated *inter se*?

7. Barred plumage is a sex-linked character of the Plymouth Rock breed dominant to the black of the Ancona breed. A black Ancona hen is crossed with a Plymouth Rock cock and the F.1 males are crossed back to the mother, the F.1. females being crossed back to the father. What are the results obtained? What would be the result of an analogous experiment in which the reciprocal cross was the starting point in the parental generation.

8. White eye is a sex-linked recessive in Drosophila. White-eyed females are crossed to wild type males and the F.1 flies are mated *inter se*. What is the result in the F.2? How would you test the constitution of each of F.1 females without the use of white-eyed males?

9. Interpret the following experiment on Drosophila hybrids with the aid of a chromosome diagram:

Pure stock sable male by Pure stock wild type female gave only wild type offspring. These hybrids when mated *inter se* gave offspring as follows:

wild type males 146　　　　sable males 155
wild type females 305　　　sable females 0

What results would you expect in the reciprocal cross?

10. Interpret the following experiments with the aid of a diagram: A pure wild stock of male Drosophila was crossed to the mutant white-eyed stock, and its progeny when mated *inter se* yielded a generation composed of:

white-eyed females 76　　　white-eyed males 73
wild type females 69　　　　wild type males 68

With another white-eyed female the same type of experiment was carried out and the second generation was composed of:

white-eyed females 97　　　white-eyed males 46
wild type females 91　　　　wild type males 93

11. Construct a diagrammatic solution of the following problem:

In Drosophila vermilion eyes are referred to a sex-linked recessive mutant from the red-eyed wild stock. Certain vermilion-eyed females have vermilion-eyed male and female and red-eyed male and female offspring when crossed to wild type. These females have a Y chromosome in addition to the normal XX group. How would you test their offspring in a cross with red-eyed males to detect differences in genetic constitution of outwardly similar individuals?

12. Yellow (body colour), vermilion (eye colour) and sable (body colour) are sex-linked mutants of Drosophila. A yellow vermilion male is crossed to a wild type female, and the female offspring crossed to a wild type male. The result is:

wild type females 120
yellow vermilion males 38
wild type males 42
yellow males 21
vermilion males 23

A vermilion male is crossed to a sable female and the female offspring crossed to wild type males. The result is:

wild type females 144
vermilion males 64
sable males 62
vermilion sable males 8
wild type males 6

What would be the result of crossing the female offspring of a sable yellow female and a wild type male to wild type males?

13. Two dark-bodied strains of Drosophila were homozygous for vestigial (i.e. both strains were vestigial). When crossed together these strains gave vestigial wing and grey body (wild type). Each of these strains was then crossed to wild type and the F.1 males back crossed to their own double recessive parent. The results were as follows:

Strain A.
dark body 23
vestigial 21
dark body vestigial 20
wild type 25

Strain B.
dark body 0
vestigial 0
wild type 75
dark body vestigial 81

Interpret these results with the aid of a diagram.

14. A laboratory worker forgot to label new culture bottles of dark-body and vestigial used in the previous examples. In order to rectify this, males from each were crossed to wild type females and the F.1 males were then crossed back to respective double recessives. The temperature regulation of the incubator went out of order, and the temperature rose to a very high level killing the parent flies. One yielded 12 W.T. and 10 others all double recessive. The second yielded two flies only, both of which were dark-bodied with normal wings.

Use this information to identify your unlabelled cultures, giving reasons. Supposing these flies had been dark-bodied with vestigial wings could he have labelled his bottles? Give reasons.

15. Illustrate the principle of the linear alignment of the genes by means of the following experiments on Drosophila mutant. (*a*) Female offspring of **vestigial** by black back-crossed to the double recessive male gave:

vestigial 416   wild type 87
black 421   black vestigial 91

(*b*) Female offspring of vestigial-purple back-crossed to the double recessive male gave:

vestigial 336   wild type 44

purple 325   purple vestigial 42

(*c*) Female offspring of black-purple back-crossed to the double mutant male offspring gave:

black 464   wild type 28

purple 488   black purple 32

16. In a cross between the yellow-bodied mutant and a male of the vermilion eyed mutant stock of Drosophila the F.2 generation produced by mating the hybrids *inter se* was as follows:

yellow females 103   wild type males 36

wild type females 98   vermilion-eyed yellow-
                                           bodied males 33

vermilion males 66

yellow males 64

Explain this result with a diagram, and determine the probable percentage of the following types:

wild type male and female;

vermilion, yellow male and female;

vermilion male and female;

in the F.2 generation of the cross between a wild type female and a vermilion-eyed bodied male.

17. A black purple vestigial female was crossed to a wild type male, and the F.1 females were crossed back to black purple vestigial males. The following results were obtained:

black purple vestigial 105

wild type 104

black 6

purple vestigial 8

black purple 15

vestigial 17

black vestigial 1   ⎫
purple 1   ⎬ (double crossover)
             ⎭

Interpret this by means of a diagram. Note the small number of double crossovers.

18. In a series of linkage crossovers the X chromosome yellow was found to be 36 units (% crossover between yellow and miniature) from miniature, white was found to be 36 units from miniature and yellow was found to be 1 unit from white. The numbers on which this was based was small. The experiment as it stands yields no information as to the order of yellow, white, and miniature. Female offspring of yellow males and white miniature females were crossed to wild type males. The following was the result:

wild type females 105
white miniature males 37
yellow males 34
wild type males 1
yellow white miniature males 1
yellow miniature males 20
white males 19
white yellow males 0
miniature males 0

What is the order of genes concerned? What conclusions could you draw if there had been no yellow white miniature, no wild type, no miniature, and two yellow whites.

19. A purple vestigial strain in Drosophila was crossed to wild type, and the offspring were found to be all wild type. The F.1 females were mated singly with single purple vestigial males and two cultures gave the following result:

Culture I	*Culture II*
purple vestigial 80	purple vestigial 57
wild type 82	wild type 104
purple 11	purple 11
vestigial 9	vestigial 25

Interpret these results with the aid of a diagram, and state what experiments you would set up to prove your hypothesis. You may assume that animals suitable for mating were retained in both cultures.

PART V

The Conquest of Behaviour

"In this search for information about myself from eminent thinkers of different types, I seem to have learned one lesson, that all science and philosophy and every form of human speech is about *objects* capable of being perceived by the speaker and hearer, and that when our thought pretends to deal with the subject it is really dealing only with an object under a false name. The only proposition about the *subject*, namely I am, can never be used in the same sense by any two of us, and therefore it can never become science at all."

JAMES CLERK MAXWELL

CHAPTER XXIII

ANIMAL MAGNETISM
or
The Telegraphy of the Body

MODERN society depends for its day-to-day existence on a large corpus of organized and recorded knowledge. Much of it has come into being during the past two centuries. In this sense it is true to say that the pre-eminence of the scientific outlook is characteristic of our own civilization in contradistinction to the civilized societies of antiquity. The fullest use of science for human well-being will be possible only when our knowledge of material resources is supplemented with genuine scientific knowledge of human needs. If we possessed such knowledge, a concluding section of this book dealing with the story of man's *Conquest of Behaviour* might be entitled to more space than two remaining chapters. The little that can be said at this stage has little relevance to the most pressing problems of man's social relations and to his future. What importance it has lies less in showing us how to solve problems of human conduct than in suggesting how they must be stated, if we hope to get an intelligible answer to them. Along the short road which we can traverse as yet, there are no conspicuous milestones of progress. All that we can hope to see are a few legible signposts pointing ahead of us. The legend they bear is *The Scientific Outlook*.

At any stage in the story of science conspicuous advances depend on the coincidence of a variety of circumstances the effects of which reinforce one another. There must be economic provision for the livelihood of the investigator and the social apparatus for maintaining a necessary minimum of literacy and continuity with past experience. Natural and social agencies must conspire to force a certain class of problems on the attention of a sufficiently large number of people with the requisite access to pre-existing sources of knowledge. The social structure must be sufficiently plastic to allow powerful social groups to reap the advantages of new discoveries and make provision for rewarding them and encouraging them. These are conditions of scientific progress common to ancient societies and to our own. Today, as in ancient times, scientific enquiry attracts the largest emoluments, enlists the largest reserves of ability, and secures the most favourable opportunities for large-scale tests of the truth of its hypotheses in departments where socially fruitful discoveries are being made. In ancient times, as now, great activity in one department of knowledge generally leads to incidental discoveries destined to become the keystone of new sciences in a different social context. Such incidental discoveries are the present substance of a science of behaviour.

Two features specially distinguish the relation of knowledge to social organization in modern and ancient civilization. One is that universal education increases the tempo of discovery and diminishes the danger of colossal wastage which accompanied the destruction of a civilization in ancient times. The other is that we are becoming aware of the social conditions which guarantee the continued progress of human knowledge. In earlier societies the restriction of education to a small caste limited the application of discoveries to a restricted context, and checked the co-ordination of technical advantages inherent in different local practices. In the caste-ridden societies of antiquity the encouragement of discovery was therefore local and sporadic. Had the discovery of artificial fertilizers been made in the Alexandria of Erasistratus there would have been no system of American agricultural colleges and primary schools to diffuse the new knowledge over half a continent in a single generation. It would have been impossible to enlist an organized world-wide body of trained workers to develop it farther.

Scientific research, endowed from a variety of sources, now embraces a much wider field of interest. The work of scientific investigators employed in Government or industrial laboratories, in universities and technical colleges, is co-ordinated by a world-wide medium of intercourse through specialist journals in which discoveries are made public. Scientific research thus begins to assume the aspect of a separate social institution. While it still has external relations to navigation, to manufacture, and to husbandry, it has internal characteristics. Its internal characteristics arise partly from the immediate effect of discoveries made by one group on the problems which other groups of scientific workers can undertake, and partly from the social influence which scientific workers collectively exert on the policy of public education.

In studying the social background of scientific discovery, our perspective therefore changes as we approach the present century. In ancient times everyday work in fields, in mines, in military defence, and in ships at sea furnished the raw materials of any organized body of recorded knowledge; and immediate social needs supplied the incentive for any special encouragement of inventive capability or for professional interest by a literate personnel. Tasks carried out in scientific laboratories are now an increasingly important part of the world's everyday work, and they supply the clues which lead to new branches of scientific knowledge. Intelligent anticipation of useful applications encourages research which is not directly prompted by new or urgent social needs, so the tempo of discovery in new fields of research depends less on the external demand for its applications and more on the external demand for scientific knowledge of other kinds.

This is specially true of scientific knowledge about the sense organs, the nerves, the ductless glands and their relations to *behaviour*. Before the beginning of the nineteenth century what little we knew about sensation in animals was circumscribed by the five senses of introspective philosophy. We knew next to nothing about how our nerves control digestion, balancing, the act of breathing or the blood supply to the tissues, and nothing at all about the *hormones* or chemical messengers of the body. Apart from a few minor applications in surgery, the knowledge we now possess does not yet influence the practice of medicine or agriculture, and no new problems of public health or of animal husbandry have conspicuously prompted the search for new information. The problems which will be discussed in this chapter have excited the interest of the medical profession from time immemorial. Until the beginning of the nineteenth century advancing knowledge in other fields of science had not provided the necessary instruments for solving them.

Elsewhere our narrative has kept close to discoveries which have been, or may well be, instrumental in creating amenities which minister to common human needs. Scientific knowledge also influences the social practice of mankind when it comes into conflict with vested interests in forbidden topics. The problems of animal behaviour with which we shall now deal are significant in this way. Between the trial of Galileo and the controversy provoked by the writings of Darwin no major conflict between science and superstition had arisen. In France and Italy the Catholic Church retreated unobtrusively to a more advantageous position by condoning the latitude permitted by their Protestant neighbours. The intellectual ferment which followed the trial of Galileo called for a face-saving formula, and a face-saving formula was forthcoming in the writings of a Catholic mathematician. The new deal of Descartes satisfied Catholic statesmen, Protestant theologians, and the personnel of the new academies by fixing the boundary between faith and reason where there was no imminent danger of a frontier dispute.

The Cartesian compromise relinquished the Pauline distinction between terrestrial bodies and celestial bodies which had lately presided over chemical reactions and human respiration. The spirits of the retort were repatriated, and the universe of rational discourse was partitioned between souls and bodies. Souls, being eligible for salvation, were the concern of the Church sustained by moral philosophy as its customs official. Bodies, which include dead matter, the brute creation, and the human frame, were to be the province of natural science. Since the brute creation is not eligible for salvation, the actions of animals have no intrinsic moral value, and require no Cartesian soul to supervise them. How they behave is fair game for the naturalist, who can gain second-hand knowledge about what decides their actions by using his eyes, ears, and hands. In contradistinction to this second-hand knowledge of bodies, Cartesian teaching also recognized a different and higher sort of knowledge, with which moral philosophy sustains conviction in revealed truths. Human actions which have moral value are decided by the Cartesian soul. We can get first-hand knowledge of the way it works by shutting our eyes and keeping quiet. As far as science is concerned, the Cartesian soul was a forbidden topic.

The controversy over Darwin's teaching therefore raised issues of much wider interest than the literal truth of a Hebrew narrative. Bishop Wilberforce and his supporters saw which way the wind was blowing before the *Descent of Man* set forth the affinities of the human species with other animals. If the basic ingredients of man's intellectual activities can be traced to the social behaviour of gregarious apes, the old familiar landmarks between the proper sphere of scientific observation and the parish of moral philosophy disappear, and their respective claims must be judged by their fruits.

Some time elapsed before the implications of Darwin's doctrine were fully realized by his own supporters. There were foolish controversies between partisans who asserted that "mind" has evolved from "matter" and others who said that matter has evolved under the guidance of a universal mind. Opposing factions floundered in a morass of abstract nouns with no agreement about their meaning. Their disputes could have no practical outcome, because scientific enquiry is not concerned with the distinction between mind and matter. It deals with a changing world in which we recognize characteristic patterns of behaviour and label them with appropriate adjectives. When we have done so, we add nothing to our previous information by transforming one part of speech into another. We may, for instance, distinguish the *automatic* activity of a cash register from the *intellectual* activity of the cashier; but, when we have done so, nothing is gained by saying that one is "caused" by its automatism, and the other is "caused" by his intelligence. So also it may be useful to distinguish the conscious behaviour of a man when he is talking to a friend from his unconscious behaviour when he is walking in his sleep, or to distinguish his mental behaviour when he is writing a book from his material behaviour when he is falling off a ladder. We lose our grip on the essential fact that we are talking about a man, when we say that we are studying consciousness or unconsciousness, mind or matter.

WHAT IS MEANT BY ANIMAL BEHAVIOUR

In this broad sense of the term everything which has been dealt with in the last few chapters is part of the study of how living creatures behave. Behaviour is generally used by biologists in a more limited sense, more especially to call attention to a class of characteristics which conspicuously distinguish animals from plants or non-living things.

One obvious characteristic of an animal as such is its great *reactivity*. It is changing its shape, its position, its hue, its texture, continually and reversibly. Often these changes can be traced to relatively insignificant events in its surroundings, and its great *receptivity* to slight changes in its neighbourhood is another characteristic which distinguishes it from a relatively complicated man-made machine. A flash of light, a draught of cold air, a soft sound, or a slight jerk which would have no effect on the motion or appearance of a motor bicycle may have drastic effects on a racehorse. Knowing how to control an animal is therefore vastly more complicated than knowing how to control a single machine. A far better metaphor would be a deserted factory with a variety of machines and generators, radio equipment, telephone and lighting arrangements. The problem of animal behaviour is to find out where the switches and self-starting devices are placed, where the fuse boxes are located, how the wires are connected, and what sort of work each machine carries out.

The active responses of animals are carried out by different parts of the body. The organs associated with the various types of reactivity which animals display are collectively called *effector* organs. The three most common are: (*a*) *muscles* which execute the mechanical *movements* of talking and walking, peristalsis (the squeezing of food along the gut) or the beating of the heart; (*b*) *glands* which *produce chemical products or secretions* such as the saliva, sweat, or tears, the shell of the fowl's egg, the ink of the cuttle-fish, the poison of a snake, or the slime of the slug; (*c*) *ciliated epithelium* which *maintains fluid motion* over body surfaces such as the inside of the human windpipe or the gills of a clam. These three types of reactivity are exhibited by nearly all animals and nearly all animals possess the effector organs responsible for them.

In addition, many animals, e.g. cold-blooded vertebrates and crustacea, exhibit *reversible colour changes* for which the chameleon is undeservedly notorious. These are brought about by the presence of branching cells in the skin. These cells or *chromatophores* contain pigment which can concentrate in compact masses at the centre, leaving most of the skin surface clear, or flow out into the branches where it forms an interlacing network of light absorbing material (Fig. 486). Many marine animals and some insects (fireflies and glow worm larvae of ground beetles) *produce light* by *photogenic* effectors which manufacture an intermittent supply of phosphorescent material. A few fishes like the electric eel have *electrical effector organs* by which they can administer serious shocks to other creatures.

That *Receptivity* is also localized is easy to see when any of these responses can be traced to some occurrence in the surroundings of an animal. Researches of this kind teach us that impersonal observation can lead to correct

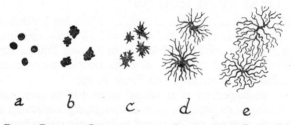

FIG. 486.—BLACK PIGMENT CELLS FROM THE SKIN OF THE FROG, SHOWING FIVE DEGREES OF EXPANSION OF THE PIGMENT ALONG THE CELL BRANCHES, WHICH ARE ONLY CLEARLY VISIBLE WHERE THE PIGMENT FILLS THEM

conclusions, when what is wrongly called "direct" or "immediate" knowledge of "our own sensations" leads to entirely false ones. We can see this clearly if we consider a type of behaviour which human beings do not exhibit. The external agencies which influence colour change in the lower vertebrates have now been ascertained with sufficient thoroughness to enable us to state what steps must be taken, if we wish to make an animal respond in a particular way. It can be evoked by a variety of external agents, notably light, humidity, change in temperature, and certain forms of mechanical and electrical stimulation. In the laboratory each of these agencies can be varied, while the others are kept constant. Their separate contributions can be distinguished and their mutual relations determined. When a supply of oxygen, adequate diet, and the general conditions essential to the efficient working of the bodily machine are satisfied, we can prescribe how to make a chameleon or a frog turn dark olive or pale yellow, just as we can prescribe how to make litmus dye turn red or blue.

Chameleons, if undisturbed, remain dark in a well-illuminated situation so long as the temperature is well below that of the human body. They will become completely pale after suitable stimulation by a succession of electric shocks or by mechanical pressure. Two blunt pins connected with the terminals of a toy shocking-coil to act as stimulating "electrodes" can be used for the first and a glass rod for the second. If the skin of the surface of the body, the roof of the mouth, and the anal orifice are respectively stimulated by a series of electric shocks, or by hard rubbing with a glass rod, the results obtained may be tabulated thus:—

COLOUR CHANGE IN THE CHAMELEON

Stimulus	Area	Response
Electrical	Skin of surface	Local pallor
	Roof of mouth	Generalized pallor
	Anus	Generalized pallor
Mechanical	Skin of surface	No effect
	Roof of mouth	No effect
	Anus	Generalized pallor

This shows that there are two definitely localized regions where the application of an electrical stimulus evokes the response of generalized pallor. In modern nomenclature they are spoken of as *receptor* areas, in the older terminology as sense organs. Only one of them is a receptor area for mechanical stimulation.

Between a temperature of 10° C. and 20° C. a chameleon is uniformly pale in darkness, and responds to bright light by becoming dark. Anthropomorphic prejudices would lead us to assume that this response depends on the eye. This is not so. It has no definite receptor organ associated with it. It can be elicited in a restricted area of the body subjected to *local* illumination, and is unaffected by blinding or blindfolding the animal. As far as this response is concerned the chameleon behaves as if it had *skin-sight*.

Analogous remarks do not apply to the colour changes which are shown by frogs or minnows when transferred from white to black vessels or vice versa. The English common frog can change from a blackish to a bright yellow hue in appropriate situations. The contrast, which is no less striking than the proverbial changes of the chameleon, has attracted less comment because many hours elapse before it is complete. Its relation to light has been studied very thoroughly in one of its near cousins, the South African clawed toad (*Xenopus laevis*), which lives in water and is much less susceptible to the influence of temperature. The skin colour of normal clawed toads kept under normal conditions of temperature with uniform illumination in white tanks is invariably pale and in black tanks invariably dark. The behaviour of normal and blinded individuals is contrasted in the following table:—

COLOUR CHANGE IN *XENOPUS LAEVIS*

	White background	Black background
Normal animal	Very pale	Very dark
Animal after removal of eyes or destruction of the "retina."	Intermediate	Intermediate

This experiment shows that the internal disturbance which underlies colour response to light in the clawed toad is initiated in a restricted area of receptive tissue, the *retina* of the eye. In this sense we are entitled to say that the eye of the frog is an organ of vision. In saying so, we do not introduce any notion which belongs to the domain of our personal feelings. We mean that one localized region in the body of the clawed toad is the starting point of the train of events which culminates in colour change when light impinges upon it.

Such a statement is analogous to saying that a button which, when pressed, sets the engine in motion is situated on the floor of a car. The biologist investigates the sense organ as he would deal with the self-starter of a car if he were ignorant of its mechanism. If he allowed himself to be led by the analogy of his own experience, he would be driven to incorrect conclusions about the way in which light influences colour change in the chameleon, whose skin responds directly to incident illumination. The study of vision in frogs and toads also contains pitfalls for the unwary introspectionist. The clawed toad will collect at the dark end of an aquarium which is unequally illuminated. This is true of eyeless individuals as well as normal ones. Whereas the eye of the toad is the receptor organ for response to "background" by change of colour, the whole of the skin is a receptor organ for the activities which bring the animal into a shady situation.

The phenomena of colour change provide a further illustration of the localization of a familiar form of receptivity in an unusual situation. Drought and humidity in frogs, especially tree frogs, tend to produce pallor and darkening of the skin respectively when other factors are maintained constant. In human beings the response to drought is mainly localized in the mucous membrane of the throat. Biedermann states that the influence of humidity and drought on colour change in the tree frog is completely abolished by painting the pads at the extremities of the toes with cocaine, a drug which paralyses receptivity. "Toe-thirst" is therefore a definite problem for investigation and control, though no conceivable effort of imagination could introduce any meaning into a discussion of what a frog *feels* like when its toes are thirsty. When we are concerned with how to make an animal behave in a particular way the traditional terminology of feeling, will, and purpose have as little relevance to our task as the spirits of alchemy have to the processes in the retort.

Thus the problem of behaviour as the word is used in biological science includes (a) the discovery of physical events (*stimuli*) which initiate active responses, (b) the localization of the *receptive* area on which the stimulus operates, (c) the *modus operandi* of the *effector* organ which executes the visible response, and linking up (b) with (c) the processes which make it possible for a localized stimulus acting on *one* part of the body to elicit a localized response in *another* part of the body. This aspect of behaviour is called *co-ordination*.

The study of co-ordination depends on being able to isolate a single unit of behaviour starting with a definite stimulus and ending in a characteristic response. Such a sequence of events is called a *reflex*. A reflex that is very easy to demonstrate in the frog is the withdrawal of the foot, when the toes are allowed to dip into water warmed to about the temperature of the human body. If we suspend a frog which has been pithed (i.e. the brain destroyed) with the legs hanging downwards, and bring a beaker of water gently into position so that the toes just dip into the water, we find that nothing happens if the water is at the temperature of the room; but the leg is pulled up if the water has been previously warmed to about 40° C. If we time the interval between the immersion of the toes and the withdrawal of the limb, we find that it is a matter of seconds. Something has been happening during those seconds. *What and where* is the aspect of behaviour implied by the term co-ordination?

Examples of simple reflexes, most of which can be easily studied in our own persons, are given in the table below:—

Action	Receptor	Effector
Quickening of heart when its blood supply increases.	Nerve-endings in right auricle	Heart muscle
Contraction of pupil in strong light.	Retina	Plain muscle of iris
Secretion of saliva on smelling food.	Olfactory organ	Salivary glands
Sneezing after pepper.	Olfactory organ	Muscles of chest and diaphragm
Knee jerk	"End organs" in tendon	Extensor muscles of thigh.

The chief means of transmission of the disturbances set up in the receptor organs to the effector organs that carry out the ensuing responses is the *nervous system*. An instructive experiment can be carried out if we hang up five decapitated frogs in the manner indicated above after snipping away the bone known as the urostyle (at the end of the vertebral column). This exposes two groups of shining white cylindrical trunks which are then seen to pass from the backbone downwards to the muscles of the legs. We can now learn what is the path by which the disturbance set up in the temperature receptors of the skin of the toes travels to the muscles of the thigh.

In one frog the white trunks (*sciatic nerves*) of both sides are left intact. In a second the sciatic nerve of the right side is cut. In a third frog the sciatic nerve of the left side is cut. In a fourth frog the sciatic nerves of both sides are cut. And in a fifth frog neither are cut, but a wire is passed down the canal of the backbone to destroy the nerve stem or *spinal cord*. Having done this we may try the effect of letting the toes of both feet dip into warm water. Both legs of the first frog are withdrawn. Only the left leg of the second and only the right leg of the third frog is withdrawn. Neither leg of the other two frogs is withdrawn. From this we conclude that the *something* which is happening between the immersion of the toes and the withdrawal of the foot travels by a definite road, namely, along the sciatic nerve; and further that it travels first up to the spinal cord and then down to the leg muscles. This something is called the *nervous impulse*.

THE SOCIAL BACKGROUND OF NERVE PHYSIOLOGY

That the nerves are the pathway of communication involved in the co-ordination of the reflex stimulus with its appropriate response was recognized by some of the earlier Alexandrian surgeons such as Herophilus (*c.* 300 B.C.). It was established by the experimental work of Vesalius, who observed that cutting nerves sufficed to paralyse all movements. In the succeeding century of medical research the essential part played by the central nervous system (spinal cord and brain), as opposed to the peripheral nerves which. carry impulses from the receptor organs to it and impulses from it to the effector organs, was discovered by such experiments as the foregoing. It was also found that a frog's muscle removed from the body along with an attached nerve trunk will continue to contract for many hours in a moist atmosphere whenever the nerve is stimulated by mechanical pressure or by chemical irritants.

Little more than this was known before the closing years of the eighteenth century. All authentic knowledge about nervous co-ordination available at that time could be demonstrated by consecutive experiments lasting less than half an hour. Three agencies specially contributed to the knowledge which has accumulated since then. The first was the discovery of current electricity. The second was the revival of microscopic enquiry which accompanied the introduction of achromatic lenses. The third was the impact of the evolutionary speculation.

We have already learned that progress in the study of electricity during the eighteenth century was closely connected with medical enquiries. The spark and crackle of the Leyden jar reproduced the physical phenomenon of lightning in miniature, and the powerful shocks which accompanied its discharge recalled the peculiar activity of the electric eel, a phenomenon known to naturalists from the time of Aristotle. The production of the shock itself became an object of special interest when it was found that an isolated muscle will contract after frictional discharge through it or through its attached nerve trunk. In the course of such studies Galvani made the observations which ultimately led to the discovery of current electricity (p. 652). From his time till the present day knowledge of the nervous system has continually reaped new benefits from advances in electrical science, and has responded to the social forces which have encouraged research into all kinds of electrical phenomena.

Galvani's discoveries stimulated interest in the characteristics of nervous tissue, when the comparative anatomy of animals was advancing, and by so doing contributed to its advance. Before Cuvier's time the discovery of sexuality in plants had been the only notable contribution to new principles of biological classification, and nothing was known about the nervous system of the lower animals. The geological record shows that plants have accommodated themselves to new conditions of life by adopting new methods of reproduction, and their reproductive organs are of primary importance in a classification based on unity of type. This is less true of animals, whose evolution has been associated more particularly with new methods of locomotion, escape, and search for food. The peculiarities of the sense organs, the effector mechanisms and the nervous system which links the two provide the master-key to unity of type in animals, and no substantial progress in animal taxonomy could be made until a comparative study of the nervous system had been undertaken. In his dissections of molluscs, arthropods, and echinoderms, Cuvier paid special attention to the nervous system and carried out experiments to identify it.

The work of Darwin's predecessors was continued by his followers with a new end in view. While the status of the human species occupied the centre of the stage, a satisfactory theory of evolution could not rely exclusively on anatomical evidence. Although the anatomical characteristics which distinguish a mathematician from a marmoset are trifling in comparison with the anatomical characteristics which distinguish a marmoset from a mouse, few evolutionists could commit themselves to a corresponding statement about the characteristics of their behaviour; and they would not have been wise to do so. Their only course was to seek for more information about how new patterns of behaviour evolve and how they are connected with the characteristics of the nervous system.

The comparative study of behaviour in a wide range of living creatures brought about a new orientation. Most of us believe that we know how we make decisions, and we bring the same prejudices into action when we watch the behaviour of a sheep-dog. We can study how the leaves of a sensitive plant "decide" when to open or close without doing so, and we are not easily tempted to believe that we have discovered anything new about the behaviour of a plant when we have added a new abstract noun to our vocabulary. So the training we get from studying organisms which have little resemblance to ourselves teaches us the pitfalls of verbal analogies and the need for careful observation.

"An impetus," says Pavlov, "was given to this transition by the rapidly developing science of comparative physiology, which itself sprang up as a direct result of the theory of evolution. In dealing with the lower members of the animal kingdom, physiologists were of necessity compelled to reject anthropomorphic preconceptions and to direct all their efforts to the elucidation of the connections between the external stimulus and the resulting response. . . . This led to the development of Loeb's doctrine of Animal Tropisms; to the introduction of a new objective terminology to describe animal reactions and finally it led to the investigation by zoologists, using purely objective methods, of the behaviour of the lower members of the animal kingdom."

THE REFLEX ARC

Renewed attention to minute anatomy associated with technical improvements of the microscope during the twenties and thirties of the nineteenth century bore fruit in the elucidation of the "reflex arc," that is to say, the path which the nervous impulse traverses in the central nervous system between the receptor and the effector organ. If we tease a nerve like the sciatic nerve of the frog with needles we can separate it into a large number of cylindrical fibres, each of microscopic thickness and each surrounded by a minute sheath of fatty material. By tracing these fibres back to the spinal cord, we eventually find that they are simply attenuated processes of branching cells. Some of them originate from branching cells in the *grey matter* or core of the spinal cord, where their finer branches are closely connected with the terminal branches of other nerve cells or *neurones*. Branching cells of this type also occur in the central nervous system itself. Their fibres run up and down the outer rind or white matter of the spinal cord, carrying nervous impulses from one level to another. Others of the fibres of a mixed nerve, i.e. a nerve carrying impulses both to and from the cord, like the sciatic nerve of the frog, do not have their cell bodies within the spinal cord. Their cell bodies are in swellings known as the *dorsal root ganglia*, situated near where the nerve is joined to the cord (Fig. 489). The cells of the dorsal ganglia send branches into the spinal cord, where they arborize around the cell bodies found in the grey matter. A single nerve fibre, with its sheath, in a vertebrate animal, is not more than a hundredth of a millimetre in thickness, though in ourselves it may be as much as a yard in length.

The experiment cited on p. 1057 indicates that a nerve like the sciatic nerve of the frog is a bundle of fibres, some carrying nervous impulses in either

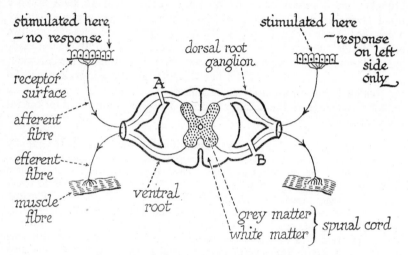

FIG. 487.—DIAGRAM TO ILLUSTRATE MÜLLER'S EXPERIMENT

Dorsal root cut at A; ventral root cut at B.

direction. It does not tell us whether impulses normally travel in both directions in the same neurone or whether some neurones are *afferent*, carrying impulses from the receptor to the cord, and others *efferent*, carrying impulses from the cord to the effector organ. Other experiments show that most nerve trunks contain two different types of neurone.

If we trace any nerve back to the spinal cord, we find that it is connected with it by two separate trunks, the dorsal and ventral roots, the former of which are swollen and contain, as stated, cells, from which fibres pass in both directions, towards and away from the cord (Fig. 489). If we cut a spinal nerve at its peripheral end, muscular contractions can be elicited by electrical stimulation of the nerve *on the central side of the cut*. After cutting the dorsal root these reflexes will not be obtained. This shows that all the afferent impulses pass into the cord by the fibres whose cells are located in the dorsal root ganglion. If the dorsal root of the cut nerve is left intact, section of all other dorsal roots of the remaining spinal nerves does not interfere with the reflex response obtained by stimulating its central end. This shows that all the efferent fibres leave the cord by the ventral root. The separate connections of the afferent and efferent neurones to the C.N.S. were finally established by Johannes Müller (1834), who severed all the dorsal roots on one side of the body of a frog and all the ventral or motor roots on the other side (Fig. 487). Such an animal shows complete indifference to stimuli on the side on which the dorsal roots are cut and complete inability to respond by active movement on the opposite side, but stimuli applied to the side on which the dorsal roots are intact will evoke response on the side whose motor roots are intact. The presence of separate afferent and efferent roots is a peculiarity of the nerves of vertebrates (fishes, amphibia, reptiles, birds, and mammals) and experiments like the one just described have been carried out on representatives of all the Vertebrate classes.

Microscopic sections or teased-out preparations of a mixed nerve are not sufficient to justify the inference that all the fibres of a dorsal root have their

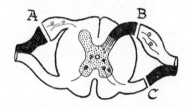

Fig. 488.—Diagram to Illustrate Effect of Section in Nerve Degeneration

Degenerated regions black. A, dorsal root cut on peripheral side of ganglion; the afferent fibres to the left have degenerated. B, dorsal root cut on central side of ganglion; the ends of the afferent fibres carrying impulses into the grey matter of the spinal cord have degenerated. C, ventral root cut; the efferent fibres to the right have degenerated.

cell bodies in the dorsal root ganglion or that all the fibres in the ventral root have their cell bodies in the grey matter of the cord. The microscope enables us to see that fibres from the cells in the dorsal ganglia pass a certain distance towards and away from the C.N.S. and that the fibres of the cells in the grey matter pass out into the ventral root. We can only trace them by direct observation for a small fraction of their course, and then lose track of them. Here experiment comes to our aid (Fig. 488). If we cut a mixed spinal nerve, and keep the animal alive, microscopic examination shows that all the fibres on the side of the nerve remote from the C.N.S. undergo degenerative changes in the course of a few days. If we cut the dorsal root on the *central* side of the ganglion (i.e. nearest to the cord) all the fibres on the *central* side of the cut degenerate. If we cut it on the *peripheral* side of the ganglion all the fibres on the *peripheral* side of the cut degenerate. If we cut the ventral root, we find that degeneration occurs only on the side *remote from* the central nervous system. This means that if cell bodies occur in any tract of nerve tissue, the fibres degenerate on the side of section remote from the seat of cell bodies. In other words, a fibre not connected with its cell body undergoes degeneration. By applying the method of degenerative section combined with direct observation of microscopic preparations we are, therefore, able to reconstruct the nerve paths involved in a reflex (Fig. 489). The simplest possible path of a reflex (reflex arc) is by the way of a fibre having its cell in the dorsal ganglion, into the cord, across the thin membrane (or *synapse*) separating the ultimate branches of such a fibre in the grey matter from the branched cell body of an efferent neurone, whose fibre passes out by the ventral root. The latter fibre is bound up with many other fibres, carrying impulses inwards or outwards, in a nerve trunk.

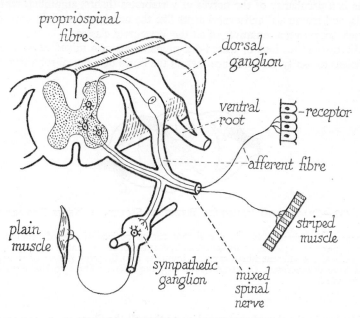

FIG. 489.—DIAGRAM OF THE REFLEX ARC

Such is a very simple type of nerve path involved in reflex action. Generally a reflex path involves additional neurones, which are confined within the C.N.S. There are large numbers of neurones whose whole length is confined to the C.N.S., running up or down, carrying impulses from afferent neurones at one level to efferent neurones at another. Two great meeting places within the C.N.S. for neurones which run forwards to the head and backwards to the posterior extremity of a Vertebrate are the two parts of the brain known as the cerebrum and cerebellum (Fig. 492). When the brain is destroyed these paths are eliminated: and partly for this reason, partly for others which will be referred to later, the behaviour of the pithed frog is much simpler, and therefore more suitable for the study of reflex action than that of the normal animal.

The existence of nerve tracts running up and down the spinal cord can be demonstrated in a very simple way When a dark chameleon, i.e. a chameleon which has been kept a few minutes in bright light in a cool room, is stimulated by an alternating current from a shocking coil by electrodes applied either to the roof of the mouth or to the anal orifice, the animal becomes extremely pale after about a minute. If the spinal cord has been cut with a pair of dissecting scissors about the level of the eighth vertebra generalized pallor does not result from stimulating the mouth. The skin becomes pale only in the half of the body in front of the cut (Fig. 490). After stimulating the cloaca the body becomes pale only on the posterior side of the cut.

The nerve fibres that supply the striped muscles of the limbs, etc., have their cell bodies in the grey matter of the cord. The nerve supply of the

FIG. 490.—EFFECT OF ELECTRICAL STIMULATION OF THE ROOF OF THE MOUTH IN THE CAPE CHAMELEON WHEN THE SPINAL CORD IS SEVERED AT C

smooth muscles, of the muscles of the heart, and of the glands (as well as that of the pigment cells of the chameleon or fish) is somewhat different. Connected with each pair of spinal nerves by fine trunks known as *rami communicantes* are certain swellings of nervous tissue containing nerve cells as well as fibres and therefore called ganglia, or usually *sympathetic ganglia* (Fig. 489). When the rami or ganglia themselves are stimulated by an electrical current from a shocking coil, characteristic responses of the musculature of the gut, walls of the arteries and generative passages, glands, etc., occur. When the ganglia are painted with the drug nicotine, stimulation of the rami does not evoke these responses. Since painting the nerves themselves does not prevent their ability to transmit impulses, nicotine appears to act primarily on nerve cells which occur in the ganglia. These nerve cells belong to neurones which supply the gut, glands, etc. They can be distinguished from efferent neurones which supply striped muscle *via* the spinal nerves and from the nerve fibres which pass out of the cord to the ganglia *via* the rami communicantes, because no fatty sheath (*medulla*) surrounds the fibre itself. The nerve fibres that originate in the ganglia are therefore called non-medullated fibres. The fact that nicotine prevents the conduction of nervous impulses beyond the ganglia by paralysing their nerve cells shows that plain muscle, glands, etc., of the body are not directly innervated by the fibres with cells in the grey matter of the cord. Impulses leaving

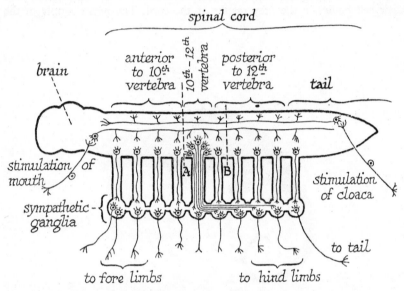

FIG. 491.—DIAGRAMMATIC REPRESENTATION OF THE NERVE PATHS INVOLVED IN THE CONTROL OF THE PIGMENTARY EFFECTOR SYSTEM OF THE CHAMELEON

For the purpose of diagrammatization the number of ganglia is reduced, and the ascending and descending afferent paths from cloaca and mouth respectively are represented in each case by a single neurone. Section of the cord alone anterior to *A* restricts the pallor following stimulation of the mouth, to the region in front of the cut. After section of the cord alone at the level indicated by *B*, stimulation of the roof of the mouth produces generalized pallor of the whole animal with the exception of the tip of the tail.

the C.N.S. for effector organs other than striped muscle pass in the ganglia to a second relay of neurones. Thus the sympathetic ganglia are distributive centres which permit impulses arriving from the cord along a single fibre to set up relay impulses in large numbers of non-medullated fibres going to different destinations.

In the region of the spinal cord—the part of the C.N.S. of a vertebrate enclosed by the spinal column—a pair of nerves with motor and ganglionated roots arises between each pair of vertebrae. The main nerves to the limbs, such as the sciatic nerve, are formed by the union of several of these. The anterior end of the C.N.S. is considerably swollen and enclosed within the skull. From this region, the brain (Fig. 492), ten pairs of nerves called *cranial nerves* come off.* These nerves—especially those of the anterior end of the brain—are not built on the same plan as the spinal nerves. The same nerve does not always contain both afferent neurones and efferent neurones supplying striped muscle. They have various names, but are conventionally denoted more briefly by Roman numerals. Starting from the most anterior pair they are: I the Olfactory nerves from the nasal receptor surface: purely afferent.

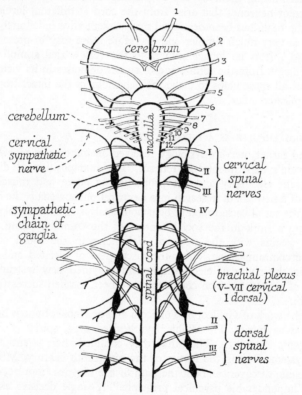

FIG 492.—DIAGRAMMATIC REPRESENTATION OF THE CENTRAL NERVOUS SYSTEM OF MAN

II the Optic nerves from the retina: purely afferent. III, IV and VI are efferent nerves supplying the striped muscles which move the eye in its socket. All vertebrates have six of these in each eye socket or orbit. The remaining cranial nerves, V, VII, IX, and X contain afferent neurones—V from the skin of the face, and in mammals the pulp cavities of the teeth, VII from the skin of the face, and in mammals the receptive surface of the tongue, IX and X from the respiratory and digestive tracts. They also carry medullated fibres with cells in the brain itself. Some of these go to the muscles of the face and

* Two additional nerves, numbered XI and XII, are incorporated in the skull cavity in man and other mammals.

throat. Others end in connexion with short non-medullated neurones in the musculature of the gut or heart. Stimulation of the Xth or Vagus nerve of the frog, as in our nearer allies (e.g. rabbit or dog), always results in slowing and enfeebling of the heart beat. This nerve exerts a restraining influence on the rhythm of the heart

The brain is, therefore, the part of the C.N.S. which receives impulses from the most important receptor organs—the eye, ear, and olfactory membranes, transmitting them by the descending neurones within the C.N.S. to the efferent neurones that arise from the cord at different levels. A frog in which the brain has been destroyed may be kept alive indefinitely; and its behaviour is very much simpler and therefore more easy to prescribe after careful study. It is no longer subject to the very varied stimuli of everchanging images from the retina, and of smells or noises in its vicinity. The interplay of all these helps to make the behaviour of the intact frog a much more complicated affair.

THE NERVOUS IMPULSE AS A PHYSICAL EVENT

As stated earlier, nerve physiology received an impetus to renewed study from Galvani's experiments on reflexes. The juxtaposition of discoveries about current electricity and the properties of nerve and muscle at the threshold of a new era of research into electrical phenomena is the dominant feature in the social background of behaviour analysis. Modern biology began with Harvey's work in the social context of the common pump. Modern neurology begins with the work of Helmholtz in the social context of telegraphic communication. After the discoveries of Oersted and Ampère, progress in the study of electromagnetism provided new instruments for the study of problems which could not have been assailed successfully at an earlier date.

Before the work of Galileo, of Torricelli and of Hooke, human breath had been *anima* or spirits. Till Wöhler synthesized urea, spirits continued to haunt organic chemistry. Thereafter they confined their attentions to the nervous system. During the forties of the nineteenth century, Müller, who made valuable discoveries about the path of the nervous impulse, described it as an "imponderable psychical principle." A single decisive experiment carried out by a physicist whose name is associated with discoveries in current electricity exorcized the spirits of the reflex arc. This was in 1851, when the cross-Channel cable was laid, and only five years before the Atlantic Company of Cyrus Field was registered.

The task of Helmholtz had been made easier by the progress of moral philosophy in the preceding century. A German philosopher called Kant had devised new tests for identifying spirits. One was that they are not bothered about punctuality and have no respect for clocks. The invention of the electromagnet made it easy to devise new methods for signalling the beginning and end of a process which occupies a very short interval, and therefore to decide whether the nervous impulse is a genuinely Kantian spook.

In measuring the speed of sound we can use light signals, because the speed of light is enormous compared with the speed of sound. The speed of the electric current is of the same order as the speed of light, and electric signals are used for finding the speed of sound in a liquid. This was the principle of the method which Helmholtz used in the first determination of the speed of the nervous impulse. To measure the time between stimulation of a nerve by an electric shock and the contraction of its attached muscle the essential apparatus (Fig. 493) is: (*a*) an electromagnet to signal (see also Fig. 451) when the shock is given, (*b*) a tuning fork (see also Fig. 196) to record time, and (*c*) a lever touching a revolving drum coated with lamp-

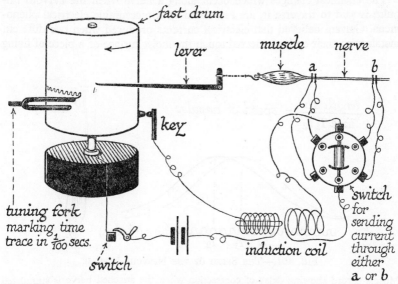

FIG. 493.—APPARATUS FOR DETERMINING THE SPEED OF THE NERVOUS IMPULSE

A pin on the fast drum makes and breaks contact with the key when the tip of the lever is at the same point in each revolution. The current in the secondary is strongest at the break, and it is this which stimulates the nerve. Two records are taken, one with the secondary current passing through *a* and the other with it passing through *b*. The records are then compared as shown in Fig. 494.

black to trace out the shortening of the muscle. There is a measurable delay between the shock and contraction, and the delay is less if the shock is applied *nearer* to the muscle. If we stimulate at two points and divide the distance between them by the delay, we get the rate at which the nervous impulse travels (Fig. 494). In the frog at 12° C. the speed of the nervous impulse is about fifty miles an hour.

In this sense the nervous impulse is a physical event like the production of an echo or the flash of an explosion, and it has other physical characteristics, among which is the fact that it is not *imponderable*. Just as we can weigh the carbon dioxide produced by a time fuse of gunpowder, we can weigh the carbon dioxide produced in the passage of the nervous impulse along a nerve. With apparatus used for the experiment described in Figs. 493-4 we can also show that its speed is affected by raising or lowering the temperature, like the speed of an ordinary chemical reaction.

Like other physical phenomena it is accompanied by the production of heat. The discovery of this fact is another illustration of how progress of nerve physiology depends on progress in electrical science. The heat produced is minute and momentary. It can only be measured with the use of suitable thermopiles and highly sensitive galvanometers, which now make it possible (see p. 701) to estimate a momentary rise in temperature of one ten-millionth of a degree centigrade.

The chemical changes which occur along a nerve when the nervous impulse is said to traverse it, are associated with measurable electrical phenomena. Galvani believed that electrical currents produced when two different metals with their ends connected touch the moist surface of a piece of living

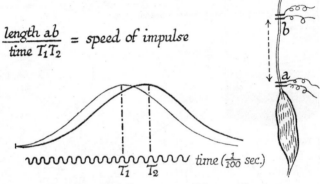

FIG. 494.—THE SPEED OF THE NERVOUS IMPULSE

Muscle record showing delay of contraction when the attached nerve is stimulated at different points (A and B) along its length.

tissue are due to the activity of the living nerve. Volta showed that this is not so. None the less Galvani's belief that electrical phenomena are characteristic of the nervous impulse was well grounded, and it may be that he had good reasons for his belief. A simple experiment which suggests this can be performed by laying one nerve-muscle preparation across another. If the nerve of one of them is stimulated by mechanical pressure, as by pinching with forceps, the contraction of its own muscle will often be accompanied by the contraction of the other one. In his own time it was not possible to follow up the experiments of Galvani, because there were no sensitive devices for detecting currents of short duration. When photographic recording and sensitive galvanometers responding to short-lived currents were introduced, the study of electrical phenomena in tissues was renewed, notably by du Bois Reymond and Burdon Sanderson. This was about the time when Helmholtz first measured the speed of the impulse.

If two electrodes (i.e. metal points) in circuit with a sensitive galvanometer are placed close together at any point along a nerve the galvanometer registers an instantaneous deflection when the end of the nerve is pinched. If two pairs of electrodes are placed at a measured distance along the nerve the deflections can be photographed on a revolving film. If the vibrations of a tuning fork, to act as a time marker, are also recorded on the film, it is possible to measure the interval between the first deflection of the galvanometer connected to the electrodes farthest away from the muscle and the second, which occurs in the galvanometer connected to the electrodes farthest from the point of stimulation. The measured distance separating the electrodes divided by the time interval gives the speed of the local electrical change. This agrees with the speed of the nervous impulse.

Like the nervous impulse, the phenomenon of receptivity, i.e. what occurs in the "sense organ" or receptor area when a stimulus acts on it, is itself an electrical phenomenon. The physical change which occurs in the receptive area, when the appropriate stimulus is applied to it has been investigated most extensively in connection with sight. When a beam of light falls on the retina, it gives rise to a difference in electrical potential between the illuminated region and the surrounding tissue which is not stimulated. This potential difference persists while the stimulus is applied and disappears when the source of light is cut off. It is not constant during the period of stimulation, but shows a very characteristic variation. In the frog's eye it has three well-defined phases each with its own duration, magnitude, and latency, corresponding to successive and separate photochemical reactions occurring in the retina, when it is stimulated by light. The photoelectric reaction of the eye was first discovered by Holmgren in 1866. Such potential differences can only be detected, recorded, and measured accurately with galvanometers of high frequency and great sensitivity. So progress along this line of enquiry has marched in step with electrical discoveries. Recently the technique of these measurements has been greatly improved by Adrian. Forbes, and others who have adopted the use of amplifiers such as are employed in wireless transmission. With such apparatus it is now possible to detect electrical changes in the human brain, when it is involved in carrying out intellectual tasks.

THE STUDY OF "SENSATIONS"

Of four methods which have been used to identify the localization of receptivity in the lower animals the one which is easiest to apply depends upon the possibility of isolating some type of response invariably associated with the application of a specific external agent. The study of colour change in frogs and toads has already provided an illustration of its use. The task of isolating a response which can be relied on to manifest itself under specifiable conditions involves extensive preliminary enquiry. Two types of response are easily handled in experiments of this sort. One is the normal balancing movements by which the body maintains the characteristic orientation to its surroundings implied in stating that it is the "right way up." The other is the highly characteristic posture which many animals adopt when subjected to angular acceleration in the horizontal plane.

Normal balancing movements usually involve orientation with reference to three distinct external agencies—the direction of incident illumination, the mechanical pressure exerted by the weight of the body on the surface with which it is in contact, and finally—in some respects most important of all—the direct influence of the earth's gravitational field. Receptivity to gravitational attraction (georeceptivity) completely eluded introspective speculation concerning the sense organs, until the experiments of Flourens on the internal ear of birds in 1828. These provided a clue to the significance of dizziness in the human subject.

The identification of the receptive fields is sometimes facilitated by the circumstance that one or other of these agencies exerts a predominant influence on bodily equilibration. When this happens the animal is said to display phototaxis, stereotaxis, or geotaxis according as the influence of light, contact, or gravity predominates. Thus barnacle larvae collect at the bottom in darkness and at the surface of a container in light. Their positive geotaxis in

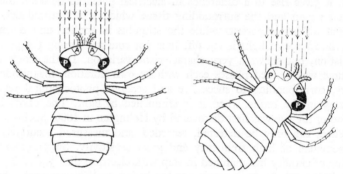

FIG. 495.—DIAGRAM TO ILLUSTRATE MOVEMENT OF INSECT (HOVER FLY) TOWARDS THE LIGHT

darkness is completely overruled by their positive phototaxis in light. When the influence of either light, or gravity, or contact predominates over the other two, the receptive fields can be defined by a process of exclusion.

Pronounced phototactic reactions are well seen in some insects. The flight of the moth to the candle is proverbial. Insects are one of the few groups of familiar animals in which no georeceptors have been located. In flight their tactile receptivity does not come into play. Their orientation to their surroundings then appears to be largely determined by light. In general the phototactic movements of insects depend on two facts: (*a*) light acting on the same region of the same eye reflexly increases the tension of muscles on one side of the body and reflexly relaxes the same ones on the other; (*b*) light acting on one part of the eye produces *contraction* of a particular group of muscles and light acting on another part of the same eye produces reflex *relaxation* of the same group of muscles. Thus if one eye of the hover fly, *Eristalis*, is blackened, a beam of light focused on the anterior margin (A, Fig. 495) of the other eye makes the animal bend the legs of the same side forwards and the legs of the other side backwards, so that the body tilts away from the side illuminated. If a beam is directed on the posterior edge (P, Fig. 495), the legs of the opposite side are bent forwards and the legs of the same side backwards so that the body tilts towards the side illuminated. A comparatively feeble beam acting on the posterior margin will compensate the effect of an intense illumination of the region in front. When a fly is moving along a beam of light the posterior edge of neither eye gets much light and one gets as little as the other. When it is deflected to the right, the posterior margin of the left eye gets more light (Fig. 495) and this brings about the tilting of the body to the left. Its direction of movement is at once restored, so that the eyes are illuminated symmetrically. This is only realized when the axis of the body is in line with the source of light.

The majority of animals are not predominantly influenced by any single

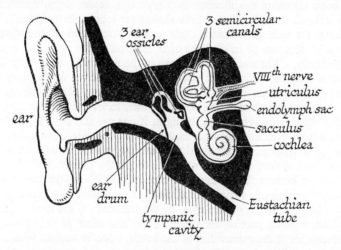

FIG. 496.—SECTION THROUGH RIGHT HUMAN EAR SEEN FROM THE FRONT. VERY DIAGRAMMATIC

Each semi-circular canal is really completely surrounded by bone. Just as any movement in space can be represented on three rectangular co-ordinates, so any movement of the head is represented as component movements of the endolymph of the three canals. These movements of the endolymph stimulate sensory structures in the canals and so produce impulses in the auditory nerve, leading to reflex muscular movements tending to bring the head back to its normal position. Sound vibrations are transmitted to the cochlea via the eardrum, the auditory ossicles (which magnify the vibration of the ear drum) and the fluid surrounding the labyrinth.

type of external stimulus. To identify one form of receptivity and its appropriate field it is necessary to exclude the influence of the others. This is done by removing the stimulus itself when the stimulus is light, or by removing the receptor organs when the stimulus is gravity. The majority of animals retain their characteristic bodily orientation in complete darkness or after removal of their photoreceptive organs. Stereotactic reactions are seen in their most pronounced form in animals which live in crevices and under rocks and stones. Geotactic reactions usually play an exceedingly important role in the bodily orientation of aquatic animals. A blinded dogfish swimming in very shallow water will right itself even when deprived of its georeceptors. The tactile areas associated with the activation of the appropriate groups of muscles brought into play in the movement of equilibration, which the dogfish executes each time it touches the bottom with its fins or belly, have been mapped out by Maxwell.

It is fairly obvious that neither photoreceptivity nor tactile receptivity explains how a blind cat falls on all fours, how a blinded dogfish swims with perfect propriety in deep water, or how a blind bird maintains its natural posture in flight. Movements of this sort involve a special type of receptor organ. In vertebrate animals it is part of the ear. If the portion of the internal ear (labyrinthine organ) (Fig. 496) known as the *utriculus* with its three *semi-circular canals* at right angles to one another is removed on both sides, a fish or frog is quite unable to swim in deep water. The vertebrate labyrinthine organ is an elaborate modification of a type of receptor organ which many aquatic animals possess. Those of the shrimp are located in its feelers.

Shrimps are able to maintain their normal orientation when swimming in complete darkness or in daylight after removal of the eyes, and they can swim normally, if illuminated from above in the usual way, after their feelers have been removed. They will not orientate themselves in darkness after removal of the feelers, and if illuminated from below, they swim on their backs. If deprived both of their eyes and of their feelers, they are incapable of executing righting movements in the light. If one eye and both feelers or one feeler and both eyes are removed they swim on one side. If one feeler and one eye are simultaneously removed they execute spirals. If deprived of both eyes and both feelers a shrimp will still adopt the correct attitude, when resting on the bottom. These facts are explicable on the assumption that the bodily equilibration of a shrimp is sufficiently determined by any one of three agencies: by light acting on the eyes, by the influence of the earth's gravitational field on some part of the feelers, or by the effect of pressure on the tactile receptors at the extremities of the limbs, when in contact with a solid surface. Ordinarily at least two of these three organs of receptivity reinforce one another. Experimentally their effects are separable.

At the base of each of the feelers in the shrimp there is a sac known as the statocyst. Sensory nerves connect it with the brain, and these nerves end in the membrane lining the sac. The membrane itself is covered with sensory hairs on which rests a small mass of chalk and sand (the *statolith*) which is free to move in the fluid interior of the sac, when the body is tilted. The displacement of the statocyst constitutes the reflex stimulus to those movements of equilibration which are determined by the influence of gravity. It is possible to replace the statoliths of a shrimp by iron filings. The experiment was first performed by Kreidl, who investigated the effect of superimposing a very strong magnetic field on the earth's gravitational attraction. By a simple operation the animal is now endowed with magnetic receptivity. It orientates itself with reference to the lines of magnetic force.

The utriculus of the human ear or that of any other vertebrate also contains solid calcareous particles. The effect of a jerky movement is that the statolith hits the wall opposite to that against which it will subsequently lie, as our bodies do when a train starts suddenly. If the internal ear of a dogfish is exposed it will execute the reflex responses characteristic of a tilting movement of the body when the statocyst is gently pushed in the opposite direction. By setting the fluid of the internal ear in motion in turning round repeatedly, we can abolish our own georeceptivity, becoming "dizzy" and losing limb control. If human beings had been endowed with magnetic receptivity the great westerly navigations might not have been postponed till the advent of the mariner's compass and mechanical clocks.

An animal can be subjected to angular acceleration at right angles to gravity by putting it on a revolving turn-table. Its labyrinthine organs initiate reflex movements which give it a definite orientation to rotational displacement. In general vertebrates respond to rotation on a turn-table by a contrary movement of the head during rotation. When rotation stops, the head is deflected in the direction opposite to that which is sustained during rotation. Analogous movements of the eyeball occur. During the rotation the eyes turn in the anti-clockwise direction, if rotation is clockwise, and then in a clockwise direction when the rotation is brought to an end. Postural changes in the limb and trunk muscles also occur. The forced posture of a frog or a lizard initiated at the beginning of rotation is sustained without diminution until the movement stops. An opposite after-effect then supervenes for some seconds.

The posture which some animals adopt during rotation and the after-effect are completely abolished when the labyrinths of both sides are destroyed. If the eyes of other species are removed, or if the animal is rotated within a uniform grey cylinder so that the retinal field of stimulation remains unchanged during rotation, the angle of deflection of the head is smaller during rotation, and the after-effect is exaggerated. There is a retinal component tending to heighten the effect of the labyrinthine reaction during rotation and to diminish the after-effect on account of its much smaller inertia. In some lizards the retinal component has been shown to play a more prominent role. In ordinary rotation the deflection of the lizard's head is pronounced but the after-effect obtained with normal animals is small. In the blinded animal the deflection during rotation is almost abolished; but a very pronounced after-effect ensues. This is not true of the clawed toad which is an aquatic animal living in muddy water. Its normal equilibrating movements depend far more on the influence of gravity than those of a lizard, which crawls on its belly and depends more on its tactile receptivity and the use of its eyes.

In turn-table experiments with mammals and birds, we encounter another feature which introduces a new form of receptivity. Like the labyrinthine function it is one which lies outside the range of the five senses of introspective philosophy. At the beginning of rotation a pigeon executes the same type of head and eye movement as a frog or a lizard, but no stable equilibrium is attained. When the neck has been turned through a certain angle, it jerks back to its original position. This process is rhythmically repeated (nystagmus) during the rotation.

The introspectionist confronted with this phenomenon will find himself on more familiar ground. Here is a tempting opportunity for invoking the exercise of a controlling "will" on the part of the animal which is "consciously" striving to regain its normal posture. There is no objection to using the term "will," if we are quite clear what it means. When we have discovered what is meant by willing, in this context, we also discover that other words can also describe what is taking place. Experimental analysis shows us that the animal *responds to the stretching of its own muscles* by reflex contraction of other ones. When a certain tension is reached, the neck and eye muscles contract reflexly, thus re-establishing the pre-existing posture. In this condition the animal is again free to respond to disturbances of labyrinthine or retinal origin. The head and eyes are again deflected. So the process proceeds rhythmically.

Animals are endowed with receptor organs which register the state of extension of the muscles and their tendons. Reflex activity is initiated both by changes in the external world and changes which have their seat in the body itself. Some fishes possess an elaborate arrangement which records the state of distension of the gas bladder. One would say in the older terminology they have a "sense of depth." Proprioceptive reflexes, i.e. reflexes which arise in the internal receptive fields, were first known to exist in connection with the regulation of the heart beat. The existence of microscopic structures in muscles and tendons,* suggestive of sense organs on account of their con-nexion with nerves entering the spinal cord by sensory roots, was known for some years before Sherrington gave the first experimental demonstration of the existence of proprioceptors in the skeletal muscles. We know (p. 1060) that the spinal nerves of vertebrates are connected with the central nervous system by two roots, one composed exclusively of motor fibres conveying impulses to the muscles, the other known only to contain sensory fibres con-veying impulses to the cord from the receptor organs. Sherrington found that, when muscles are stretched, an opposing tension is superadded to their elastic resistance. This tension, which is of considerable magnitude, is com-pletely abolished after cutting the sensory roots of the nerve which supplies it.

A second method used for exploring the receptive field depends on the *physical nature* of receptivity, and may be illustrated by comparative studies on vision. The octopus and its allies have large and powerful eyes. Observa-tions upon the normal behaviour of the octopus in light do not provide us with definite evidence for their visual function. While it is permissible to entertain the likelihood that the eye of the octopus is a receptor for light, because the structure of the eye of the octopus is very much like that of a vertebrate, anatomical considerations cannot assist us to define the function of the eye with any precision. They do not help us to specify the range or discrimination of vision. They provide us with no reason to suppose that the eye of an octopus is sensitive within the same limits of wave length as our own eye. They do not tell us whether the eye of the octopus, like our own eye, distinguishes between different wave lengths, and if so, what differences. Without recourse to a study of the behaviour of the organism as a whole we can obtain direct evidence concerning the photoreceptive character of the eye of an octopus by the expedient of recording the photo-electric current in the retina. The eyes of some vertebrates give rise to electrical variations which have characteristic features for different regions of the spectrum. Their eyes can distinguish colour.

Closely analogous to this line of attack is a third method which has been

* The knee jerk is a proprioceptive reflex, the sense organs concerned lying in the thick tendon which can be felt between the knee cap and the shin bone. A tap below the knee stretches this tendon and so stimulates the proprioceptors.

employed in the recognition of chemical receptivity and has been used to reinforce earlier methods for the study of the proprioceptors. Although it is difficult to isolate invariable and highly characteristic olfactory or gustatory responses in animals, it is possible to apply a succession of chemical stimuli to different regions of the body and record the discharge of sensory impulses in the afferent nerves arising therefrom, by means of a sensitive galvanometer. The pike, which has a very long and accessible olfactory nerve, has provided suitable material for investigating what chemical stimuli act upon the nasal organ of a fish. Some of the earliest studies on the recording of the nervous impulse in sensory fibres were carried out on the olfactory nerve of this animal. This method will probably be used with increasing confidence as the technique of recording afferent impulses is perfected. Up to the present its most important achievement has been to confirm the existence of the proprioceptors. Einthoven has shown that every heart beat and every respiratory movement discharges a volley of afferent impulses along the vagus nerve to the brain. Jolly, Adrian, Forbes, and others have shown that sensory impulses pass up the spinal nerves when a skeletal muscle is stretched.

Galvanometer records of nerves of which the fibres appear to be of the afferent or sensory type (i.e. nerve fibres whose cell bodies are not located in the central nervous system) can be used successfully to investigate receptivity which does not correspond to any type of human sensation. Thus recent experiments have shown us how *seeing* fishes may be able to respond to very feeble currents in the medium in which they swim. On either side of the body many fishes have a prominent line which marks the position of a system of canals and pits lying in the skin and communicating with the exterior. This *lateral line* system is richly supplied with nerves which would be classified on structural grounds as sensory. It is possible to pick up volleys of electrical disturbances from them, in response to slight variations in the rate at which water can be made to flow in the lateral line canals.

A picturesque application of electrical methods to the analysis of sensation has been made in connexion with the study of acoustical sensation by Wever and Bray, whose work has been confirmed and extended by Professor Adrian and his colleagues. If electrodes are placed upon the auditory nerve, the electric currents which arise when the ear is stimulated by sounds can be amplified so as to reproduce speech as well as notes of high and low pitch. The living cells of the ear of a cat or a guinea-pig record the sound as electrical changes of which the frequency is faithfully reproduced by the physical instrument. Speech is recorded as intelligible speech. This phenomenon can be completely abolished by anaesthetizing the receptive cells of the cochlea (Fig. 496). It can be inhibited by depriving them of oxygen when the circulation of the internal ear is blocked. There is therefore conclusive proof that it is not a physical artifact.

Little is known about existence of special sound receptors outside the vertebrate series. What we know of the phenomenon in vertebrates themselves is also based on a fourth method of investigation. Like the preceding methods, that of *conditioned discrimination* is capable of defining with great accuracy the range and threshold of the effective stimulus as well as the limits of the receptive field. With a few exceptions such as the "pinna reflex" (i.e. pricking of the ears) in the dog, animals show few simple and highly characteristic types of response to sounds unconditioned by training. Consequently observations upon normal behaviour are of little use in the search for receptors for sound. Acoustical receptivity is chiefly found in animals with a well-developed aptitude for the formation of "conditioned" responses. In human beings, among whom acoustical receptivity plays such an important part in the process of communication, it is associated with the most complex characteristics of behaviour which are known to exist.

The method of conditioned discrimination makes use of the possibility of building up new reflexes of the type which Pavlov, their discoverer, calls conditioned reflexes. If any agent to which such an animal as the dog is receptive is applied repeatedly in conjunction with the appropriate stimulus to some simple invariable response, it eventually acquires the property of evoking the response unaccompanied by the original or unconditioned stimulus. In his studies on conditioned reflexes Pavlov has chiefly employed the copious secretion of saliva, when food is presented to a dog, as the basic or unconditioned reflex. The sound of a bell, a metronome, or a tuning fork may be used as the conditioned agent to build up a regular and controllable response to sound.

Pavlov has used this method to test the limits of discrimination of dogs to pure sounds of different wave lengths. It has also been used to demonstrate acoustical receptivity in fishes. Working in Pavlov's laboratory, Andreev employed it to test the theory that different vibrating elements in the *cochlea* of the internal ear act as resonators which pick up individual wave lengths. An experiment of this kind may be quoted in the words of Pavlov himself.

Pure tones were employed, being produced by two sets of apparatus, one giving tones from 100 to 3,000 and the other from 3,000 to 26,000 double vibrations per second. Various conditioned alimentary reflexes were established. . . . The cochlea was first completely destroyed on one side. When tested for the first time six days after operation, all the auditory conditioned reflexes were found to be present. A second operation was now performed on the cochlea on the other side with the object of excluding only the lower part of the tonic scale. The osseous part of the cochlea was opened at the junction of its middle and upper thirds and the exposed part of the membranous cochlea with the organ of Corti was injured with a fine needle. Already on the tenth day of the operation all the auditory stimuli excepting tones of 600 double vibrations per second and lower were found to be fully effective. In the course of three months following the operation, however, the effect of tones from 600 to 300 double vibrations per second became gradually restored. From numerous tests carried out from this period up to two years after the operation, the upper limits of the tones that had disappeared was fixed as somewhere between 309 and 317 double vibrations per second.

This method can be used, as in this experiment, to locate the seat of receptivity with great delicacy. It can be used with great precision to define discrimination, e.g. of pitch and colour in the receptor organ itself. It can also be extended to the study of the way in which stimuli are generalized, selected, and synthesized into effective groupings as signals of response through the activity of the several parts of the forebrain on which the afferent impulses from the receptor organs impinge. Whether he is dealing with the initial activity of the sense organ, the process initiated by the sensory impulse in the brain, or the tuitional aspect of sensation, the experimental biologist communicates discovery without relying on traditional forms of speech. If he is studying the ear, experiment enables him to define the position which an animal will assume, when rotated on a turn-table, to control its posture in swimming by operating upon the labyrinthine organ, to specify the receptive areas in the utriculus and the semi-circular canals involved in the initiation of balancing movements, to detect the range of sounds to which the organism reacts, and the parts of the cochlea which are receptive to different tones. To discuss whether an animal "feels dizzy" or "enjoys" music adds nothing to clarity of exposition or the confidence with which it is possible to control the decisions an animal will make.

LEARNING

Pioneer studies on behaviour were mainly concerned with relatively stable responses to immediate changes in the environment. Such responses of which colour change, balancing movements, or "defence" reactions (e.g. withdrawal of the frog's toes from warm water) are examples, largely determine the pattern of so-called "instinctive" behaviour among such animals as insects or worms. Among the vertebrates, especially the mammals, the behaviour pattern of an individual is less stable, less easy to dissect, and hence more difficult to control. This complexity of behaviour is associated especially with the growth of the forebrain. If the roof of the forebrain (cerebral cortex) of a dog is removed under deep anaesthesia with aseptic precautions, the animal will survive indefinitely, and is able to feed or balance itself, excrete normally, and avoid obstacles in its path. While fully able to carry out these so-called instinctive responses it is unable to form new modes of reaction to its surroundings. It has no power to *learn*.

The word learning is given to at least two distinct processes. One is responding to a new stimulus by an action which formerly required a different signal. For instance, a dog, which will jump on to a table when a lump of sugar is offered to it, may "learn" to do so at the sound of his owner's voice. The other is the evolution of new and more complex modes of action, as when a parrot "learns" to repeat words. So far nothing has been found out about the latter. On the other hand, the experimental researches of Pavlov's school in Russia have led to new discoveries about how to control learning of the first kind. In discovering recipes for doing so we need not depart from the language we use in discussing reflex actions.

Pavlov's investigations began with the study of salivary secretion in dogs. A dog which has been deprived of the forebrain secretes saliva when food is introduced into the mouth. The intact adult can also secrete saliva when food is brought within the range of its eyes or nostrils. In the adult the sight or smell of food is therefore an appropriate stimulus for reflex salivary secretion. The ringing of a bell is ordinarily without effect on the secretion of saliva. If the ringing of a bell is repeated a certain number of times, when food is also presented, it eventually comes to evoke salivary secretion when food does not accompany it. A previously indifferent stimulus applied to the *intact* animal at suitable intervals simultaneously with the application of a stimulus which evokes a reflex response unconditionally acquires the property of evoking the same reflex response when unaccompanied by the original or "unconditioned" stimulus. A new reflex has been built up. This can only happen if the forebrain is present. Dogs without a forebrain do not form new reflexes.

Reflexes of this kind are called *conditioned* reflexes, and the previously indifferent stimulus is called the conditioned stimulus. Any event in the external world which affects a receptor organ may become a conditioned stimulus to the intact animal, provided external conditions are rigidly standardized in other respects. To become one it must accompany the unconditioned stimulus a sufficient number of times, depending on whether the application is precisely simultaneous, whether the conditioned stimulus begins to operate before the unconditioned, overlapping it in duration or separated from it by a short interval. The task of defining the facility with which a conditioned reflex is built up involves a study of the significance of the interval between successive applications of both stimuli and of the juxtaposition of conditioned and unconditioned stimulus. In defining the conditions which bring into being a new reflex system by this method, we are investigating a class of phenomena which would formerly have been attributed to an autonomous "memory." By using experimental methods we can arrive at definite conclusions about when and whether an event will occur without recourse to the usual descriptive epithet.

What it has been the custom to call *memory* is only one aspect of the problem of "conscious" or "voluntary" behaviour, that is to say aspects of behaviour which are spatially referable to reflex paths in the forebrain. Though an animal is constantly subject to the simultaneous application of many indifferent and unconditioned stimuli, its behaviour is selective. This is one aspect of what we call *attention*. To discover the conditions which prevent new reflex systems from coming into being, or extinguish them when they have become established, was perhaps the most important aspect of Pavlov's work, because an understanding of this part of the problem underlies the successful control of experimental procedure. The possibility of isolating a conditioned reflex for study implies the existence of some inhibitory agencies which prevent the normal surroundings of the laboratory from exerting a significant influence on the course of the experiment. The inhibition of conditioned reflexes is a complex question; and its complexity shows that they offer a broad basis for the interpretation of "conscious" behaviour in general and the interpretation of *attention* in particular.

Two important types of inhibition are respectively called inhibition by extinction and conditional inhibition. The first term refers to the fact that an indifferent stimulus which has been converted into a conditioned stimulus, and is then allowed to act repeatedly without the unconditioned stimulus, gradually loses its potency, regaining it after an interval of rest. Conditional inhibition is the extinction which occurs when a new indifferent stimulus is superimposed upon the effective phase of a conditioned stimulus. A third and especially important form of inhibition is the extinction of a state of inhibition by conditional inhibition, or as Pavlov calls it, inhibition of inhibition. Let us suppose that an organ note of one thousand vibrations per second has been made the signal for salivary secretion by repeated application of the stimulus, when food is administered to the animal. If the new stimulus is now administered repeatedly without the accompaniment of food, it suffers inhibition by extinction, recovering its efficacy after a period of rest. If, during the indifferent period, the experimenter superimposes on the now ineffective sound stimulus another indifferent agent such as the flash of a lamp before the dog's eyes, secretion of saliva ensues. The sound regains its power to act as a conditioned stimulus, and the pre-existing inhibition is itself inhibited. An important type of inhibition in everyday life is "generalized

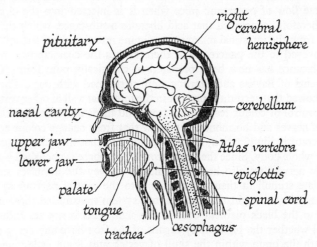

FIG. 497.—VERTICAL SECTION THROUGH HUMAN HEAD

Bones and cartilages are in black. The nasal septum and certain other structures in the nasal cavity are omitted.

inhibition" or elimination of the activity of the forebrain as in sleep or hypnotic trance. It can be brought about by experimental treatment in dogs. Local warming or cooling of an area of the skin induces the torpor characteristic of the decerebrate dog which responds to no conditional stimuli

CHEMICAL CO-ORDINATION

In addition to the action of the nervous system there is a second type of co-ordination in animals. The blood of vertebrate animals plays a part in the telegraphy of the body. So far we have not referred to this at all. We all know that some chemical substances, called *drugs*, when obtained from the tissues of plants, have very characteristic effects on particular organs of the body. For instance, the drug known as caffeine, present in small quantities in coffee, promotes secretion of urine, and aspirin promotes sweating. Some organs of the animal body produce drug-like substances called *hormones*. When carried by the blood stream to other parts, hormones are capable of calling forth very specific responses. In this way the circulatory system plays a part in co-ordinating response and stimulus. This has not been known till recent times. The first discovery of chemical co-ordination was made by Bayliss and Starling in 1902 in researches on the pancreas.

The pancreas does not secrete its digestive juice continuously. Pancreatic secretion is a response to the entry of the acid food from the stomach into the intestine. The secretion of pancreatic juice follows the introduction of food or acid into the intestine, even when all the nerve connexions between it and the intestine are severed. Bayliss and Starling found that if the lining of the intestine is ground up with a little weak acid the concoction produces immediate flow of pancreatic juice when it is injected into the circulation. They, therefore, concluded that acid liberates a substance, which they called *secretin*, from the intestinal mucous membrane into the blood stream. Thence it is conveyed to the pancreas and there evokes the characteristic response. This substance has now been prepared in chemically pure form. The first experiments of Bayliss and Starling were performed with dogs. They afterwards showed that secretin is present in the intestinal wall of other vertebrates.

The control of colour response in frogs and toads illustrates the combined action of nerves and hormones. We know that frogs change colour according to temperature, illumination, humidity, etc., and that they change uniformly over the whole body. Since the "background" response is abolished by cutting the optic nerves, we also know that nerves convey the impulses set up by appropriate stimuli in their surroundings to the central nervous system. It was at one time thought that the nervous system transmitted these impulses directly to the black pigment cells in the skin. This is not so. Indeed, it is doubtful whether the pigmentary organs of the frog have any nerve supply.

Beneath the brain within the skull of vertebrates lies a little gland which has no duct conveying its secretion to the exterior. It is called the *pituitary gland*. Extracts made by grinding up this organ in salt solution have some very remarkable properties. When injected into a pale frog, they bring about a complete darkening of the skin resulting from expansion of the black pigment cells. There is enough of the active constituent in one gland to evoke darkening in a hundred individuals. When the pituitary gland is removed, the frog recovers and survives indefinitely. Though it appears to be healthy and otherwise normal, it will always remain completely pale in whatever circumstances it is kept. Darkening of the skin of a frog from which the pituitary gland has been extirpated will still occur, if a small quantity of the extract of the pituitary gland (about equivalent to one-millionth of a gram of the gland substance) is introduced into the circulation by injection. Thus the nervous system controls the behaviour of the pigment cells *indirectly* by increasing or diminishing the rate at which the pituitary body pours its secretion into the blood.

Near the anterior end of the human kidney is an orange-coloured mass of tissue, the *adrenal body*. This "ductless gland" contains a drug-like substance that acts on plain muscle, in some cases relaxing and in others inducing contraction or increased rapidity of an inherent rhythm (e.g. it accelerates the heart of the frog). It is called *adrenaline*. Adrenaline can now be manufactured in pure form in the laboratory. It is liberated into the circulation in small quantities, but we are not yet certain under what conditions. Like the thyroid gland (p. 886), the adrenal and pituitary bodies are sometimes spoken of as *ductless glands*.

THE PUBLIC WORLD OF THE SCIENTIFIC OUTLOOK

During the two centuries which preceded the publication of Darwin's *Descent of Man*, the prevailing idealism which provided a rationale for the rights of the individual conscience in Protestant countries had accepted Platonic metaphysics, as Catholicism had accepted Platonic physics. Self-knowledge was assumed to be reliable, indeed more reliable than knowledge based on observation. The Platonists subscribed to the dictum of the Delphic oracle. They believed that every man carries within himself the secret of his own nature. The most important result of experimental research of the kind with which we are now dealing has been the discovery that "Know Thyself" carries with it the prior injunction "Know others first."

Like the self-evident principle that the sun rotates over the horizon, the belief that self-knowledge is more trustworthy than the collective testimony of different observers is hard to eradicate. "Surely," says the introspectionist, "you yourself know best when you have a pain in your stomach." Do we really? Hospital practice no longer takes such statements at their face value. Data collected at operations and post mortems have taught us that any statement which a patient makes about himself needs to be confirmed by observations made by somebody else. For instance, the presence of a stone in the bladder is described by the patient as a pain in the right shoulder. What is called a pain in the groin may be due to an inflammatory condition of the kidneys. There is no short cut to knowledge of human nature. Painstaking observation of the behaviour of inanimate objects is the necessary basis of knowledge which can show us how to control the material resources of external nature, and painstaking observation of the behaviour of human beings and other animals is the only basis for knowledge which can show us how to control ourselves.

The Cartesian compromise divided the field of human enquiry into two domains. One, the external world of science, included dynamos and digestion, mercaptan compounds and the Milky Way, potato virus and the petroleum engine. To the other, the internal world of introspective philosophy belonged devotion and duty, melancholia and mathematical intuition, patriotism and piety. We are now beginning to realize that the expanding universe of useful knowledge defies any boundary which can be fixed for all time. Naturally, the disappearance of the old landmarks leads to much hesitation and inconsistency. In discussing the problems of human behaviour we have just begun to lisp a few syllables of a new language, and much of what has been written in this chapter will seem childish to our grandchildren. Meanwhile we may concede to one another the private prerogative of contemplative introspection, so long as it does not interfere with the social programme of discovering how the human brain can be regulated or how social institutions carry on.

Biology and sociology are beginning to undertake this programme. The following sentence taken from the Gifford Lectures of Sir Arthur Eddington illustrates the contrast between the new outlook and the old:

A mental decision to turn right or left starts one of two alternative sets of impulses along nerves to the feet. At some brain centre the cause of behaviour of certain atoms or elements of this physical world is directly determined for them by the mental decision.

It seems that the external world of Professor Eddington is the material world —the *shadow* world of physics as he calls it elsewhere. His internal world is the mental world—the "real" world of religious experience and artistic insight. Professor Eddington's external world, therefore, ends where an important part of the external world of a psychologist or a biologist begins. He takes no account of the fact that mental decisions are matters about which human beings can make, and are making, discoveries. Within its domain a mental decision is a final cause. It flashes like a meteor into the shadow world of common experience trailing clouds of glory from the *Ewigkeit*. Then like a bubble it vanishes, returning to the abode where the eternals are. The onlooker is no longer the physicist. He lays aside his recording instruments and abandons himself to the rapture of the poet.

The new outlook is that science is not exclusively occupied with the behaviour of nebulae, nasturtiums, internal combustion engines, and the indigo dyes. It is also engaged in discovering how to control the behaviour of the lower animals, and may eventually extend its scope to include that of archbishops and dictators. One of the problems which biologists have already investigated is how the behaviour of a dog is influenced by the way in which it has been treated. In the language of everyday life we describe what happens at this level of behaviour by saying that dogs can remember or that they make mental decisions. Patient experiments such as those which have been made by Pavlov's school have made it possible to specify rules about how dogs "remember." Those who carry them out can dictate "mental decisions" which a dog will make. If the behaviour of human beings and of the lower animals is really determined by "mental decisions," mental decisions, as Professor Eddington defines them, are part of the external world which the biologist and the psychologist investigate. If mental decisions can interfere with the functions of the central nervous system, as Professor Eddington suggests, they are not merely the private affair of the isolated philosopher. They are too important to be that.

As we approach the conclusion of the narrative pursued in this book, we can distinguish in retrospect three aspects of the progress of science. One is the enlargement of experience by patient observation. A second is the extension of observation by the improvement of material instruments. The other, which is the co-ordination of experience by the introduction of new symbols to communicate discoveries, is of special interest in connexion with the problems dealt with in this chapter. From time immemorial the progress of science has been obstructed by the poverty of language and the need for what Sir William Petty called a "dictionary of sensible words."

Petty proposed a self-denying ordinance to prohibit the use of words which, having too many meanings, have no meaning at all. Few words have a better claim to such treatment than the word *explanation*. What some people mean by an explanation is labelling a natural phenomenon with a word which makes it a thing apart. The "mental decision" of Professor Eddington, when he writes as a Gifford Lecturer, is an explanation of this sort. It is an object of awe, sufficient in its own right. As such it is a survival of the emotive use of language as verbal ritual to propitiate the unspeakable by incantation. Scientific explanation is altogether different. It exposes the connexions between different things, and thus gives us recipes of conduct. The language in which the isolated philosopher describes "causation," when he is passively contemplating his own "mental decisions," has nothing in common with the language in which scientific workers communicate rules for regulating behaviour. Such rules must include how sense organs signal changes which occur in our surroundings and in our own bodies, how the nervous impulse traverses the synapses of the brain, how previous stimulation affects the ease with which they do so, and many other cognate topics which are omitted in Professor Eddington's pronouncements on biological problems.

Biologists who are studying these problems are not complacent about our ignorance and the need for more knowledge. The most they ask is that we should now judge the respective claims of collective scientific observation and the self-knowledge of introspective philosophy by their fruits. That the comparative study of animal behaviour has taught us far more about our own sensations than the combined efforts of moral philosophers is difficult to dispute, if we compare the present state of knowledge with what was known when Kant wrote the *Critique of Pure Reason*. All that we then knew about sensation was circumscribed by the five senses—sight, sound, smell, taste, and touch, which severally signal changes in the "external" world around us. Nothing was known of the receptors which record changes in the internal field of our own bodies, and there were no known facts to contest the assertion that our recognition of space is independent of our sense organs.

Before Flourens carried out his experiments on the semi-circular canals of Birds (1828) a blind man's knowledge of space was *a priori*. That is to say, it belonged to the province of moral philosophy, and there was nothing more to be said about it. Since then experiments on animals have shown us that the body has receptor organs which record orientation to the earth's gravitational field, receptor organs which register rotational displacement and receptor organs which signal the relative position of individual parts to the body as a whole. Surgical practice has shown that much of our new information about how animals can balance themselves is also relevant to the perception of space by human beings. We can therefore add several new items to our dictionary of sensible words. Nowadays we do not say that a blind cat falls on all fours because it has an *a priori* knowledge of space, or because it has made a "mental decision" to do so. When Professor Eddington himself makes a "mental decision" to use Riemann's geometry his behaviour seems to be more closely connected with experiments on the speed of light than with statements about *a priori* space perception.

In some of his experiments Pavlov made dogs secrete saliva by repeated stimulation at regular intervals. In certain circumstances they would continue to do so at regular intervals, when no external stimulus was applied. A philosopher might say that they have a sense of time, and nothing which introspective philosophy can tell us about the "five senses" can throw any further light on how they get it. We can now connect the dog's perception of time with other things about a dog's make-up, because we know that *proprioceptive* sense organs, which register the relatively quick movements of the heart and the relatively slow pulsations of the bowel, the bladder, and other organs with a muscular rhythm, are stimulated at regular intervals like the ear of a dog, when an alarm clock is set to ring every ten minutes. The sound of an alarm clock may be made the conditioned stimulus for salivary secretion, if food is given to a dog, whenever the clock rings. If it is timed to ring at regular intervals, response will eventually recur at regular intervals when no food is given. If a repetitive stimulus which normally excites salivary secretion is timed to take place whenever the gut muscle contracts, stimulation of the proprioceptors of the gut will coincide with the unconditioned stimulus. From this point of view the proprioceptors of the gut and its own muscular rhythm take the place of the dog's ear and the alarm clock set to ring every five minutes. The dog's *a priori* perception of time is its proprioceptive recognition of its own muscular movements.

How human behaviour depends on characteristics of the human brain and sense organs such as those which have been outlined in this chapter is the least important contribution of biology to a scientific study of human nature. Its most important lesson is the danger of self-deception when we assert our claims to self-knowledge. Human behaviour has many peculiarities which we cannot connect with any characteristics of behaviour in other animals or with anything we as yet know about the properties of the nervous system. It may be more profitable to study how different characteristics of human behaviour are connected with one another than to study how they are connected with the process of nervous co-ordination. In that sense psychology is a study in its own right, and most psychologists are behaviourists nowadays. It is rather a pity that the word *behaviourism* has become identified with a school of psychologists who pay more attention to the common characteristics of animal and human behaviour than to the special characteristics which distinguish human behaviour from that of other creatures. It is possible that we might find out more about how babies learn to talk if we first discovered how parrots can be taught to talk; but it is not certain. What is certain is that we could not find out how parrots learn to talk by asking them; and it is at least likely that we shall not learn much about how children learn to talk by the same method.

CHAPTER XXIV

NATURE AND NURTURE

Superstitions of Our Own Time

"Until lately," says J. L. Gray in his book *The Nation's Intelligence*, "man was regarded pre-eminently as the 'knowing agent,' the province of knowledge being *external* to him. The decline of this anthropocentric view is associated both with the rise of rationalism and humanitarianism and with the expansion of organized social and economic activities. At a time when the growth of capitalist enterprise in democracies with rapidly increasing populations called for new knowledge concerning men as workers and citizens, experience in the physical and biological sciences had already suggested that human behaviour itself be explicable in terms of orderly observation and inference."

We have now seen how biological progress in the social context of telegraphic communications weakened the traditional distinction between an external province of science and man the knowing agent of introspectionist philosophy. In the present state of knowledge it would be unwary, if not presumptuous, to undertake a conspectus of significant lines of enquiry into human nature. Till it is possible to approach the study of human behaviour as a history of human achievement, it is fruitless to express any opinion about the relative importance of the problems which occupy psychologists today. In historical retrospect many issues which claim the attention of contemporary psychologists may seem utterly trivial. Seemingly dull and unimaginative studies may be recognized as growing points for a luxuriant output of fruitful endeavour. Six thousand years elapsed between the determination of the year of 365 days and the completion of the Newtonian synthesis. The determination of the Sirius year was itself the culmination of centuries—perhaps millennia—of painstaking observation stretching back beyond the beginnings of a grain-growing and pastoral economy. While we welcome the fact that psychology has passed beyond the stage of mere star-gazing, and is now beginning to make use of measurement and enumeration, we may also recall how little importance we now attach to the hypotheses with which the priestly pioneers of metrical star-lore were preoccupied.

If any lesson has clearly emerged from this book, it is surely this. Contemporary judgments upon the importance of new theories are ephemeral. The pre-eminent criterion of abiding achievements in the realm of theoretical science is their social fruitfulness, and this we can only recognize in retrospect. The army of science marches like that of Napoleon, on its belly. If we are permitted to make a plausible guess about the future of psychology we can only venture the suggestion that the growing points of modern psychology lie in the recorded observations undertaken to meet a specific social demand.

The social demand for detailed observation on factory welfare and efficiency, business advertisement, native administration, the prevalence of mental defect, urban neurosis and falling fertility has promoted the foundation of new institutes for disciplines variously called industrial psychology, psychiatry, anthropology, demography, and so forth. The demand for such knowledge has been prompted by the conflict of opposing tendencies within the framework of capitalist civilization—missionary effort and imperial exploitation, philanthropic enterprise and the burden of taxation for the upkeep of institutions for the socially defective, the need for universal education at a high level of industrialization and the determination to maintain the social prestige of privileged occupations.

It may be too early to judge how far the new humanistic studies are destined to progress without the further impetus of a new social economy or the contribution of a new personnel. What we can say at present is that some genuine advance has been made in amassing detailed observations, and that no co-ordinating principles, analogous to those of the more advanced departments of science, have as yet emerged. Problems arising in connexion with social institutions, educational technique, backward races, industrial efficiency, delinquency, and population converge at one common focus of interest. This may be called the problem of nature and nurture. In general terms it may be stated thus: to what extent and in what circumstances do the observed differences between the social performances of human beings depend on a different equipment of genes or different circumstances to which the individual reacts at some stage after the fertilization of the ovum? This question impinges on the correct interpretation of nearly every class of problems which engage the attention of students of behaviour, and since it is prompted by conclusions derived from rigorous experimental studies on living organisms, it is important for the student of human nature to grasp its implications clearly. Our concluding chapter will be devoted to an examination of them.

For the social roots of the Nature-Nurture problem we need not go farther back than the intellectual ferment of the French Revolution. Issues of social status in the earlier Protestant democracies were contested against a more primitive background of belief. The Reformers were a chosen people. Augustine's doctrine of predestination, supported by St. Paul's assertion that an omniscient deity foreordained who should be predestinated and only called those who had been, was fitting to the temper of the Reformation struggle. During its first phase of piracy and slave-raiding English and Dutch colonial policy was reassured by the scriptural curse on the descendants of Ham. At the beginnings of the seventeenth century a Dutch divine, Arminius, gathered around him a small following favourable to the Pelagian heresy that salvation is an act of free choice, and supported this conviction with scriptural testimony quite as unequivocal as that of its opponents. In Holland Calvinism remained the official creed of the richer merchants, who adhered to the Reformed persuasion. In contemporary England it received support from the Laudian Churchmen who were antagonistic to the new plutocracy. During the eighteenth century Wesley's doctrine of free grace carried on the Oxford tradition of Wycliff's poor priests and the Laudian

Churchmen. A mass movement, which coincided with the declining influence of the merchant princes, was the signal of a humanitarian revival rooted in the belief that all men are eligible for salvation. The abolition of slavery in the British possessions was one act of a drama which unfolded with the impeachment of Warren Hastings by Burke. That Burke became a vehement antagonist of the Jacobins reminds us how little the peculiarly religious ideology of the Industrial Revolution was fostered by the influence of secularist controversies on the continent. English humanitarianism was led by men and women who had come under the influence of the Quakers and the Methodist Revival.

French humanitarianism, on the other hand, was essentially secular, and as such more closely reflects the stage which biological science had then reached. The class structure of pre-revolutionary France was far less flexible than that of England where nobles had invested and merchants had been knighted from the beginnings of the wool trade with the Low Countries. The divine right of British kings had been settled once for all by a decisive experiment in 1648. The maintenance of the French nobility as a caste, by social and legal conditions of marriage, carried with it the doctrine of fixed estates, ordained by providence. Against a gratuitous assumption which placed the majority of Frenchmen under the same curse as Ham's descendants, the forerunners of the French Revolution advanced the doctrine of *natural rights*, associated especially with the name of Rousseau. The doctrine of natural rights rested on the assertion that social organization involves an implicit undertaking on the part of human beings to satisfy their common needs. This so-called *"social contract"* has been rightly ridiculed in so far as it was put forward as a satisfactory description of the psychology of social evolution. None the less, it embodied the important truth that no public symposium on social conduct is possible, unless individuals who participate forgo supernatural and egotistic claims for preferential treatment, and recognize that the satisfaction of common needs is the only rational basis for co-operative activity. A corollary to the social contract, that the different political privileges which men enjoyed have no basis in their inborn aptitudes, has been criticized with less regard for what the authors of the doctrine stated. Rousseau's views are expressed with the utmost clarity at the beginning of his essay entitled *The Origin of Inequality*:

I conceive that there are two kinds of inequality among the human species: one, which I call natural or physical, because it is established by nature and consists in a difference of age, health, bodily strength, and the qualities of the mind or of the soul; and another, which may be called moral or political inequality, because it depends on a kind of convention and is established or at least authorized by the consent of men. This latter consists of the different privileges which some men enjoy to the prejudice of others, such as that of being more rich, more honoured, more powerful, or even in a position to exact obedience. It is useless to ask what is the source of natural inequality because that question is answered by the simple definition of the word. Again it is still more useless to enquire whether there is any essential connexion between the two inequalities; for this would be only asking in other words, whether those who command are necessarily better than those who obey, and if strength of body or of mind, wisdom or virtue, are always found in particular individuals in proportion to their power or wealth; a question fit perhaps to be discussed by slaves in the hearing of their masters but highly unbecoming to reasonable and free men in search of the truth.

Since there is a fashion of referring to the "mystical equalitarianism" of the French Revolution, it may be pointed out that Rousseau himself does not depart a hairsbreadth from the established biological knowledge of his own time or that of the ensuing century and a half. Indeed, his choice of words shows more discrimination than that of some biologists still living. It is admittedly true that some of Rousseau's successors expressed views which would now be regarded as giving undue emphasis to the effect of the environment and too little attention to the genetic equipment of the individual. On the other hand, it is an error to suppose that the earlier socialists, whose views on economic equality are traced to the influence of the French materialists, embraced the *tabula rasa* as held by some of the educational reformers of the same period. For instance, Robert Owen expressly repudiated any mystical views about individual differences.

"The organization of no two human beings is ever precisely the same at birth," he writes in *The New Moral World*, "nor can art subsequently form any two individuals from infancy to maturity to be the same. . . ." He adds, "nevertheless, the constitution of every infant, except in case of organic disease, is capable of being formed or matured either into a very inferior or very superior being, according to the qualities of the external circumstances allowed to influence that constitution from birth."

In the language of his own time this was an optimistic way of saying that the existence of genetic differences does not entitle us to set any future limit to the educability of the individual. We may correlate observed genetic differences with limits of educability in response to existing methods of education. We cannot say how far those limits may be altered by an extensive change in our methods of education. So soon as we do so we commit ourselves to what Jennings calls "the fallacy that showing a characteristic to be hereditary proves that it is not alterable by environment."

The common sense of Rousseau and of Owen appears all the more commendable if we compare their views with those of the leading biologists during the reaction which followed the death of Robespierre. During the first two decades of the nineteenth century the French evolutionists concocted a doctrine which is devoid of any plausibility as a scientific hypothesis, and may now be consigned to the museum of extinct political rationalizations. The Lamarckian teaching, as it is called after its principal protagonist, set forth two propositions. One was that animals possess a will which continually spurs them on to more strenuous efforts, the results of which accumulate in their offspring. Perhaps because Lamarck's followers declined to stomach a vegetable will, the Lamarckian view of evolution was also supplemented by a second or vegetative process of passing from parent to offspring the direct effect of the environment on the body of the parent.

It is sometimes said that Lamarck's views represent beliefs which had always prevailed among biologists from Aristotle to his own time. Since most superstitions can be unearthed in the works of Aristotle, this may be true. What requires an explanation is why Lamarck took so much trouble to elaborate and define a doctrine which ceases to be credible when it is stated in explicit terms, and why it was widely accepted by his contemporaries. Perhaps the answer is that the political deductions to be drawn from it invested the privileges of the wealthy with the verisimilitude of natural law. According to the Lamarckian view, social and biological evolution are co-extensive and interdependent processes. So the existence of social classes, like the classes of the taxonomist, reflects the accumulated advantages of thrift, perseverence, and a beneficent environment. In fairness to Lamarck, St. Hilaire, and those who embraced their doctrine, it should be recognized that some zoologists still regarded the sperm as a parasitic organism, others professed to detect the complete homunculus within it, while pre-formationists, who taught that the egg was a miniature adult complete in all its parts, were still vocal. In this setting it was not difficult to persuade oneself that biological and legal inheritance resemble one another as closely as the conventions of English spelling suggests, or that parents do, in fact, hand on their noses to their offspring in much the same way as they hand on their belongings.

The discredit of a doctrine so plausibly adapted to the maintenance of social privilege was not accomplished till the compound microscope had revealed the details of sexual union in animals. The challenge which Weismann issued to the Lamarckian doctrine immediately followed the work of Boveri and van Beneden, the first zoologists to discover that the only necessary contribution of the male parent to the hereditary make-up of its offspring is the chromosome complex of the sperm. These discoveries have been summarized in Chapters XVIII and XXII, where we have seen that our parents do not endow us with characters. They endow us with genes which cannot carry their cheque books into the next life. Although some time elapsed before biologists were reconciled to a 100 per cent death duty on improvements to surgical property, experimental biologists are now agreed that Weismann performed a genuine service when he pointed out that the state of death claims all our accumulated anatomical earnings. Since Weismann's time experiments published by the few survivors of the Lamarckian tradition have been repeated again and again with contrary results. The clock-like regularity with which a new *experimentum crucis* has been demolished by subsequent enquiry has deprived the issue of further interest. The evolutionary controversy then at its height in England and Germany gave the problem of nature and nurture a new interest and a new bias. The Descent of Man from a stock of arboreal mammals implied a fundamental unity in the mechanism of human and animal behaviour. Inevitably the opposition which this view encountered sometimes tempted its supporters to emphasize similarities rather than to probe differences.

The genes which an individual receives determine what sort of neuromuscular organization it will develop in its usual conditions of growth. Certain features of neuromuscular organization are characteristic of the individuals of a species or genus and as such depend on idiosyncrasies of what we should now call the gene complex of different species. Broadly two kinds of difference in the neuromuscular organization of different species may be distinguished. One includes differences in the character of relatively stable responses to external influences, as, for instance, whether bodily orientation is mainly determined by light or gravity, and if by the latter whether it is positively or negatively *geotactic* (see p. 1063). The other includes differences in the extent to which the pattern of behaviour is modifiable by previous experience, as, for instance, a difference between sheep-dogs and snails. Pure lines of individuals, distinguished by their normal responses to light or by their ability to learn how to thread a maze, have now been separated within the limits of a single species. There is therefore no obstacle to the conclusion that inter-specific behaviour-differences have arisen by selective survival of mutations which turn up within the confines of a single species.

In Darwin's time such enquiries had not been undertaken. Studies on animal behaviour had been chiefly concerned with elucidating differences of the first type, and biologists were less alert to the difficulties of detecting genetic differences affecting the educability of animals. Galton, whose *Inquiry into Human Faculty* focused attention on the problem of the contribution of heredity to differences of human behaviour, showed himself to be aware of the difficulties when he wrote—

Man is so educable an animal that it is difficult to distinguish between that part of his character which has been acquired through education and that which was in the original grain of his constitution.

THE SOCIAL BACKGROUND OF EUGENICS

The light-heartedness with which his followers shouldered the difficulties, which Galton himself recognized, is less perplexing when we consider the material and intellectual context in which the "eugenic movement" started. In the material context of the Darwinian controversy the geographical aspect of evolution was the predominating issue. Naturalists were specially interested in patterns of behaviour which distinguish animals living in different territories, and such differences are mainly dependent on the hereditary equipment characteristic of a species. Being at the same time preoccupied with defending the doctrine of human descent from an anthropoid stock they were not encouraged to examine the credentials of analogous beliefs about human beings. Contemporaneously the exploitation of peoples at retarded culture levels powerfully influenced the intellectual temper of a period which witnessed the abolition of negro slavery in America and an unprecedented, if unobtrusive, expansion of the British Empire.

Thus it was that the "missing link" provided the occasion for one of the most heroic sociological exploits of anatomical science. There is an account of the incident given in Dr. Haddon's *History of Anthropology*. Three years after *The Origin of Species* was published Dr. James Hunt, President of the Anthropological Society, read his paper on "The Negro's Place in Nature." In it he maintained that "the analogies are far more numerous between the ape and the negro than between the ape and the European." In 1866 he recorded a further contribution to the detection of the missing link by asserting that "there is as good reason for classifying the negro as a distinct species from the European as there is for making the ass a distinct species from the zebra."

In this discussion Huxley gave the exponents of the missing link a half-hearted support tempered somewhat by his humane and sceptical disposition. An obituary notice of Dr. Hunt in a New York paper announced in 1870 the "Death of the Best Man in England." Sixty years after the publication of Hunt's first communication, a leading American anthropologist, Professor Kroeber, summed up the present state of knowledge in the following terms:

> The only way in which a decision could be arrived at along this line of consideration would be to count all features to see whether the Negro or the Caucasian was the most unapelike in the plurality of cases. It is possible that in such a reckoning the Caucasian would emerge with a lead. But it is even more clear that which ever way the majority fell, it would be a well-divided count.

To many of Darwin's contemporaries Natural Selection was at once a sufficient justification for reviving the Calvinistic curse on the descendants of Ham and an alternative to Lamarckism as a plausible rationale for the inherent superiority of the newly enriched manufacturer and entrepreneur. The distaste of the latter for undertaking obligations accepted by an older aristocracy was reassured by such pronouncements as the ensuing passage written in 1876 by St. George Mivart, a noteworthy zoologist, who defined natural selection as a process

> which under bracing climates, rough living, and absence of medical aid (is) beneficial to a community however fatal to individuals by killing off weak members and reducing to a compact community of hardy and vigorous survivors.

By the end of the nineteenth century the demand for educational expansion, sponsored in the early stages of industrialization by a social class which was largely excluded from the older seats of learning, had become a challenge to their privileges as a new hereditary caste. Galton's plea for a science of *eugenics* to study "those agencies under social control which may improve or impair the racial qualities of future generations" bore fruit in a movement for obstructing the general enlightenment of mankind. Eugenics became identified with a system of ingenious excuses for combating the amelioration of working-class conditions. This temper is well illustrated by the following quotation from Dr. Schuster's *Eugenics*, one of the first books on the subject to appear in this country:

> The London County Council sets up educational ladders in all parts of the Metropolis, but finds it difficult to get boys to go up them. The number of children in the schools maintained by the rates who are bright enough to make it worth while to give them the scholarships provided by the London ratepayer is hardly enough to fill them. No difficulty is experienced in filling those at the Public Schools or the Universities with boys of a very respectable level of intelligence, whose fathers belong mostly to the professional classes.

A quotation from *The Family and the Nation* by the Whethams illustrates the same bias:

> Better that an able carpenter should develop slowly into a small builder leaving six tall sons to play their part manfully and, perchance, rise one step

more, than that he should be converted by a County Council Scholarship into a primary schoolmaster, or second-grade Civil Service clerk. . . . They were good sociologists as well as good divines who taught "to learn and labour truly to get mine own living, and to do my duty in that state of life into which it shall please God to call me. . . ." Scholarships have their dangers when used to raise those who win them too suddenly and completely out of their *natural* class. . . . In the matter of education there is a tendency to attribute far too much effect to outside and expensive environment and to lay too little stress on heredity and the traditions of the family. . . . (Italics inserted.)

The intervention of the deity in this passage suggests that it is intended as a pious reflection rather than the disclosure of a scientific discovery. Dr. Whetham and his wife envisage limits to the blessings of competition.

The policy of competitive examination, when driven to excess, has resulted in closing partially the doors of various honourable professions to those who in due course of time would have been best fitted to excel in them. During the last two centuries the landed and official classes could be certain of obtaining for many of their sons posts in which, at all events, a living wage was secure. Now the posts are filled by competitive examination from a wider sphere. . . ."

The same authors sum up the eugenic diagnosis of the national education problem thus:

Our public and elementary schools have been much to blame, the one in that they failed to modify the type of education to suit the altering conditions of national life, the other that they tended to depreciate manual activity and craftsmanship, and over-supplied the ranks of the clerks and penmen. The great public schools go on training their boys chiefly in classics and ancient literature, when the demand has been for men of science, for economists, engineers, and scientific agriculturalists, of the same class and breeding as the men supplied by the public schools. *The classically trained men have difficulty in finding openings in after life, owing to their type of education. The men educated scientifically in schools of other types are often rejected because their heredity and training leave them unfit to deal with men, especially with workmen, foreigners, and natives. Moreover, from the employer's point of view, they often lack the guarantee of character and the intuitive sense of masterfulness that are the usual concomitants of the man of good family.* . . . (Italics inserted.)

A quotation from Major Darwin's book, *Eugenic Reform*, may reinforce the suspicion that eugenic propaganda has been motivated less by a disinterested concern for the advancement and application of scientific knowledge than by the resentment of a certain section of the privileged class towards the disconcerting results of competition arising out of the extension of educational opportunities.

"It may be suggested," writes Major Darwin, "that the award of scholarships would result in the picking out of the best of each social class; and that by thus giving advantages to a selected few over their early associates, they would be made more likely to marry with eugenic consequences. This beneficial effect of scholarships is, however, in my opinion, likely to be outweighed by influences acting in the opposite direction. . . . Scholars certainly form a carefully selected and valuable group of the community, and if it be true that on the whole scholarships tend to diminish the fertility of their recipients, their award must be held to produce eugenic consequences. To aid a few exceptional persons to mount to the top of the social ladder by the award of valuable scholarships would probably be *less harmful* to the race than to aid a *larger number of persons* to climb up a single step by the award of many minor scholarships. . . . There is, however, yet another side of this question which has to be taken into account, and that is the effect of the award of scholarships to members of a lower stratum on the fertility of potential parents belonging to the higher strata into which these selected scholars would enter as recruits. The effect on potential parents of any increase in competition from outside their own social stratum must be to make them feel less secure in regard to the prospects of any children they might have in the future, and this feeling of insecurity would tend to make them less fertile. Hence the award of scholarships tends to produce infertility not only in the social stratum primarily affected, but also in all the strata above it. And the only complete remedy for the harm done by scholarships—and also by educational facilities generally—in promoting infertility by facilitating the transfer between classes would be by the introduction of a caste system so rigid as to prohibit all movement between the different social strata. . . ."

Another issue which helped to thrust the problem of nature and nurture into the foreground of social controversy was the emergence of new social machinery for dealing with a special class of human behaviour. In the eighteenth century the idiot and the lunatic were objects of derision and abhorrence, roaming at large or confined in conditions similar to the worst jails of the time. In England and America their condition was forced on the attention of the legislature by the growth of humanitarian sentiment and the exigencies of urban concentration. Those who took an active part in promoting new institutions for the care of the mentally defective or deranged were generally inspired by a philanthropic zeal which drew little inspiration from scientific knowledge. The following quotation given in Penrose's book on *The Mental Defective* conveys an attitude which was commonly accepted by them. It is taken from one of the earliest reports of Park House, Highgate, the first asylum for "idiots" in Great Britain:

We ask that he may be elevated from existence to life—from animal being to manhood—from vacancy and unconsciousness to reason and reflection. We ask that his soul may be disimprisoned; that he may look forth from the body with meaning and intelligence on a world full of expression; that he may, as a fellow, discourse with his fellows; that he may cease to be a burden on society, and become a blessing; that he may be qualified to know his Maker, and look beyond our present imperfect modes of being to perfected life in a glorious and everlasting future!

No form of piety has done more to discourage the study of how individual conduct is moulded by its surroundings than the faith that providing a "good" environment is the way to produce a "good" character. When the course prescribed by the pious founders of the new institutions failed to reinstate the victims of their benevolence as acceptable members of society, opinion swung to the opposite extreme. The naïvely optimistic view that defective neuromuscular development can be cured by kindness prepared the way for a fatalistic insistence on sterilization as a panacea for social betterment, and the voluptuous enthusiasm with which the Eugenic movement espoused the cause of mutilation is attested by a flood of literature too copious to merit citation.

The truth is that the new fashion had as little foundation as its predecessor in firmly established scientific knowledge. In different departments of social discussion both views continue to flourish. Educational reformers with radical views often justify them by arguments which suggest that cater-pillars of the cabbage butterfly will take to a mixture of pollen and honey. Their opponents appear to hold that Newton would have written his *Principia* if he had been born in Tasmania.

While recognizing the cross currents of prejudice in the social background of the Nature-Nurture problem we need not fall into either of two errors, which are all too common. One is the naïvely rationalistic view that science only advances in an atmosphere of complete detachment from social objectives. The other is the adolescent delusion that beliefs are necessarily wrong, if persons who hold them are encouraged to do so by unworthy considerations. The truths of science are recipes for human action, and science flourishes when it is actively ministering to social needs. It advances conspicuously in periods when men and women are actively engaged in rational endeavour to change their social environment, and is held back when those who partici-pate in it are too anxious to find rationalizations for privilege or political strategy. The complete detachment sometimes associated with an idealized scientific worker is not an attribute of human behaviour. New social cir-cumstances conspire to focus interest on new problems and on fresh aspects of old ones, or to deflect enquiry from fruitful themes which might well be pursued—and endowed—if human beings were always reason-able, considerate, uniformly curious and unselfish. Since human beings are not always reasonable, considerate, uniformly curious and unselfish, they are generally compelled to pursue the search for truth within limita-tions which self-interest or the interests of a narrow social group impose. One social economy will tend to encourage some lines of enquiry neglected by another. Conversely it may neglect a type of research encouraged else-where or at another time. So also the social upbringing of the scientific worker helps him to concentrate on some aspects of the manifold reality or makes it difficult for him to recognize truths easily accessible to mediocre powers of observation and inference.

THE MEANING OF "NATURE AND NURTURE"

A large body of data dealing with the influence both of nature and of nurture has accumulated since Mendel, Darwin, Weismann, Galton, and their generation first discussed these questions. We are now able to be more clear about what we mean by differences due to genes and differences due to environment with greater precision. That is to say, we can state in what situations such differences can be distinguished. Two examples from the scientific study of animal breeding will clarify the distinction.

If chickens are fed on yellow corn or given green food, we can distinguish between some varieties which breed true for yellow shanks and others which breed true for colourless shanks. This is a *genetic difference*. Crosses between such varieties, when all the progeny are fed on yellow corn or given green food, yield numerical ratios of the two types in conformity with Mendel's principle. If chicks of the variety with yellow shanks are fed exclusively on white corn they grow up with colourless shanks. The difference between a fowl of the yellow variety fed on yellow corn and a fowl of the same variety fed on white corn is a *difference due to environment.* If we crossed fowls of the yellow variety with fowls of other varieties, giving some of the progeny yellow corn and others white corn, we could not expect to obtain constant numerical ratios such as Mendel's principle prescribes. If two poultry farms, both using yellow corn for food, specialized respectively in birds with black plumage and yellow shanks and in birds with barred plumage and white shanks, we should call *both* differences genetic differences. If both farms decided to use white corn, we should only be able to recognize the plumage difference as a genetic difference. If both farms varied their procedure quite promiscuously, we should not be able to tell whether the difference between one bird with yellow shanks and another bird with colourless shanks was a genetic difference or a difference due to environment.

Rabbit husbandry provides another illustration of the same issue. Some rabbits deposit yellow fat when fed on green-stuffs. Most rabbits have white fat, whether given greens with their food or not. Yellow fat is a serious carcase defect from a commercial point of view, because purchasers object to it. Rabbits which have white fat when fed on green food possess a liver enzyme which breaks down xanthophyll, thus preventing it from reaching the fat deposits. Rabbits which deposit yellow fat lack this enzyme. Michael Pease has shown that when rabbits of both kinds are crossed and back-crossed, the absence of the enzyme behaves like an ordinary "recessive character." It is only recognizable as such if the rabbits are given green food containing the yellow pigment. In a group of rabbits of both types we can recognize the gene difference by giving them all green food. In that case the biological environment is *neutral* and the gene difference is the *isolate* which we are investigating. If none of our rabbits possesses the enzyme which breaks down xanthophyll, we can make their fat white by feeding them on mash and potatoes, or yellow by feeding them on mash and cabbage. The genetic constitution is then *neutral*, and the biological environment is the *isolate* of the investigation. The practical breeder has therefore two remedies from which to choose. He may put the blame upon the biological environment and cut off the supply of green food. He may put the blame upon heredity and breed for white fat.

In the practice of medicine the same choice may confront us. In some situations the doctor can put the blame for a particular disease on heredity and in others upon environment. An exact biological parallel to *cretinism,* a disease included under the general term *amentia* (idiocy, imbecility and feeble-mindedness), illustrates this very clearly. Cretinism is a condition of stunted growth and a childish level of intelligent behaviour. It turns up occasionally in all communities, and is specially common in certain localities. For this reason doctors sometimes distinguish between a *sporadic* and an *endemic* type of the disease. In the same way we may distinguish between *genetic* and *ecological* neoteny in Amphibia. Cretinism is due to insufficient quantity of the iodine compound manufactured by the thyroid gland. Insufficiency of the same hormone in Amphibia prevents the aquatic tadpole from transforming into the terrestrial adult. This may be because the thyroid gland is incapable of doing its proper work, but even when it can do so, it cannot make thyroxine without iodine. So if tadpoles are kept in water with no trace of iodine and fed upon a diet free of iodine compounds, they fail to transform into frogs.

The European salamander normally completes its development and breeds in the adult form. In certain mountainous districts, where *endemic* cretinism is reported among human beings, the newts commonly fail to undergo metamorphosis, or do so after great delay. This is probably because the iodine content of the waters in which they live is low. A similar explanation does not apply to a local race of the American salamander (*Amblystoma tigrinum*) in the neighbourhood of Mexico City. Individuals belonging to this race never grow up. Though they breed from generation to generation in the aquatic form, they will grow into the terrestrial salamander if fed on thyroid gland, and they will not do so if given iodine compounds. They possess a thyroid gland which does not release its secretion into the circulation. Failure to undergo metamorphosis in the presence of sufficient iodine sometimes occurs *sporadically* in the Colorado variety among individuals living side by side with others which complete their development, but the Mexican variety breeds true for its inability to undergo metamorphosis when kept in aquaria with access to an abundance of iodine compounds.

Human beings do not hatch out as free-swimming larvae in fresh water. They spend the first nine months of their lives nourished by the maternal circulation. A human foetus which receives its nourishment from a mother whose thyroid secretion is deficient is therefore analogous to a tadpole reared in iodine-free water with food containing little iodine. It is important to remember this, because the term "environment" is sometimes circumscribed by a false delicacy. In the discussion of "mental inheritance" the term *environment* is sometimes equated to training, and even to training at so late a stage as when school education begins. This is very misleading. The fact that a condition is congenital provides no presumptive evidence for the view that differences of environment play little part in its occurrence. At the time of birth a human being has already completed about nine months of its existence as a separate individual. During that time its environment is the womb (uterus) of its mother, and her physical condition is relevant to the sort of environment in which the most formative stages of development occur. The fact that a disease is congenital is compatible with three possibilities: that genetic differences account for its occurrence, that it is determined by idiosyncrasies of the uterine environment, or that both these agencies play their part in its manifestation. Several things point to the importance of studying the influence of the uterine environment upon the characteristics of individuals. One is the high incidence of certain conditions among firstborn children. Another is the high incidence of various malformations among offspring of women approaching the end of the child-bearing period.

A previous example to illustrate the meaning of a genetic difference drew attention to a distinction which is of fundamental importance both for the theory and practice of medicine. In contrasting variations in plumage colour with the colour of the shanks we are not separating a class of phenomena to which the Mendelian principle applies from a class of phenomena to which it does not apply. We are distinguishing between a class of phenomena

FIG. 498.—ON THE RIGHT, AXOLOTL, LARVA OF MEXICAN SALAMANDER. ON THE LEFT, SAME SIX WEEKS AFTER FEEDING WITH THYROID GLAND—IT HAS NOW ASSUMED THE ADULT FORM

which are easy to study and a class of phenomena which demand more careful control of the environment. There is no hard-and-fast line between the two. Genetic differences which distinguish plumage colour in fowls are recognizable over a very wide range of environment. This does not mean that they are just as big in every environment which human ingenuity can devise. The difference between the pure black plumage of the Langshan and the mottled plumage of the Light Sussex is a genetic difference. By thyroid feeding, the extent of the black areas in the Light Sussex can be very considerably extended. In short, no statement about a genetic difference is clear, *unless it includes or implies a specification of the environment in which it manifests itself in a particular manner.*

Characteristics of organisms are the result of interaction between a certain genetic equipment contained in the fertilized egg and a certain configuration of extrinsic agencies. The last include the conditions of life in the human uterus and the external environment in which man's social existence is carried on. Differences between individuals may arise from differences in the kind of genes present in the fertilized egg and from differences in the uterine or post-natal environment. Differences of the first kind, that is to say, differences due to a different equipment of genes, may be of two types: (1) differences which are recognizable in almost any environment in which the fertilized egg will develop and continue to grow; and (2) differences which are only manifest within a fairly restricted range of environment. In the human species examples of the first type are the difference between a haemophiliac (*bleeder*) and an adult whose blood coagulates in the normal way, or between an amaurotic family idiot and an ordinary infant. Medical examples of the second type are less easy to cite because they are less easy to detect. That does not mean that they are less numerous. Probably the best case is the type of mental defect called *Mongolism*. Whatever gene differences are involved in the appearance of this condition appear to require a special pre-natal environment to make them recognizable.

The distinction between the two classes is of the utmost importance from a preventive point of view. When we have to deal with the first, we can readily determine the type of transmission involved, and if we know it, we can estimate the rate at which affected individuals can be eliminated by discouraging parenthood. It is more difficult to determine the method of transmission when a disease belongs to the second class. Unless affected individuals are extremely rare, it is rarely possible to do so, and only so if we can specify with some precision the kind of environment in which the manifestation of the gene is recognizable. So we cannot give a certain answer to the question: what would be the result of selective interference with parenthood? Usually we could deal with the matter without recourse to selection, if we had the kind of knowledge which tells us how much effect selection would achieve. For instance, we know sufficient today about the way in which people get cholera to study the genetic factors involved in susceptibility to the disease among a group of individuals equally exposed to the danger of contracting it. The fact that we have the knowledge to study the problem is the reason why it is of no practical importance to do so. To understand the environmental situation is to be able to control it.

When we understand the *modus operandi* of the gene, we can state the kind of knowledge we need in order to control the conditions in which its presence will be recognized. A variety of the domestic fowl known as the Frizzle has defective plumage. Frizzle crossbreds are characterized by curling of the feathers upwards and outwards. The pure-bred Frizzle remains practically bare throughout its first year of life, appearing to be in a state of perpetual moulting. It is extremely delicate and difficult to rear. When newly hatched, the down feathering is fragile and breaks off. The exposure of the skin so produced leads to a great loss of bodily heat from the surface, calling forth increased basal metabolism, increased heat production, increased heart rate, lack of fat deposits, and diminished haemoglobin content of the blood. American biologists have now studied the genetic physiology of this breed, and have shown that the pure Frizzle chick will develop a complete plumage over the whole body within three weeks, if protected from heat loss by enclosure in a woollen jacket and confined to a warm room.

Thus knowledge of the way in which a single dominant gene substitution produces its deleterious manifestations teaches us how to prevent their appearance. Researches of this kind have emphasized three important conclusions. One is the need for defining the kind of environment in which a given gene substitution manifests itself in a particular way. A second is that one and the same gene substitution may be responsible for many and various manifestations, depending upon the kind of environment in which development occurs. In the fruit fly *Drosophila* one gene is predominantly effective in the production of eye colour but has an accessory effect upon the wings. Another influences the number of bristles but has measurable effects upon at least a dozen other characteristics to a less noticeable extent. For convenience we usually define a gene substitution by the most striking effect which it produces in some specified environment or by the single effect which it produces in the widest range of environment in which its effects can be recognized. In reality no gene can be supposed to have a single and absolutely specific effect.

The effect of a gene substitution depends on all the other genes with which it is combined. An example from the pathology of fishes will illustrate this. Two American biologists have recently made a study of intergeneric crosses between different varieties of two kinds of fish kept for ornament in aquaria. Their popular name is the Mexican killifish. Varieties of *Platypoecilus* differ in possessing large black pigment cells, small black pigment cells, or no black pigment cells at all. In inter-specific crosses, the occurrence of the two kinds of black pigment cells can be shown to depend respectively upon a sex-linked and an autosomal dominant gene substitution. Crosses between the genus Xiphophorus and varieties of Platypoecilus having large black pigment cells result in the production of offspring with tumours. Thus a gene substitution whose effect is merely ornamental and, as such, of commercial value, when accompanied by one combination of genes, is definitely pathological in its effect in the presence of another.

When we are dealing with gene differences which only manifest themselves within a very narrow range of environment, we may be able to recognize them as average measurements of individuals belonging to different stocks, even though we cannot decide whether an isolated individual belongs to one stock or the other. One of the most fruitful results of modern genetic analysis is the conclusion that a close system of inbreeding separates a mixed stock into genetically pure lines. This is implicit in the mathematical form of Mendel's principle, and has been abundantly proved to be true by such experimental work as that of Johannsen on beans and Helen Dean King on rats. So, when the difference between two pure lines can only be expressed in terms of two average measurements for overlapping populations, it is likely that individual variation in each stock is the effect of environment, unless the spread is of the same order of magnitude as the errors of measurement.

When we are studying animals in the laboratory we can arrange the conditions of an experiment so as to isolate gene differences or differences due to environment for separate treatment. We can use a highly inbred stock of rats to find how body weight varies with the vitamin content of the food or whether they form tumours when the skin is treated with pentacyclic hydrocarbons. If we keep all our rats on the same diet, we can also separate pure lines with different growth rates and greater or less resistance to tumours. With human populations the unaided investigator cannot do this sort of thing, and when we speak of heredity or environment as more or less *important* in connexion with any differences between human beings, *our criterion of importance is relative to the historic environment in which the differences themselves are measured.* Two hundred years ago the majority of Englishmen ran the risk of smallpox infection. No doubt gene differences played a large part in deciding whether a particular Englishman succumbed to the disease or escaped. No biologist or clinician would argue that gene differences provide the main reason why modern Englishmen are less likely to get smallpox than their great-grandfathers or than Esquimaux communities at the present day. We have created an environment in which it does not matter either way. In the course of millennia it is not unlikely that European communities could evolve a high degree of immunity to smallpox through uncontrolled selective elimination of the less resistant. The African peoples have probably evolved their high immunity to malaria in this way. Thanks to human inventiveness, we have not had to wait several millennia to get rid of smallpox.

Practical husbandry and scientific crop production provide various examples of how human valuations placed upon genetic differences are relative to the environment in which they are recognized. In his book *The Causes of Evolution,* Haldane cites two botanical illustrations. Engledow (1925) found that when two varieties of wheat known as Red Fife and Hybrid H are spaced at 2 inches by 2 inches, Red Fife yields the larger crop. At 2 by 6 inches the yields are almost equal, and at greater distances Hybrid H yields a better crop than Red Fife. Sax (1926) has compared the crop of two colour varieties of the bean. Generally the white of his experiments yielded a smaller crop, but in exceptionally favourable conditions their yield was better than that of the coloured variety. So also at different temperature levels the white-eyed mutant of the fruit fly may be less or more viable than the wild (red-eyed) stock. Many of our best pedigree stocks of cattle and garden plants would have no chance of survival in nature in competition with their less specialized progenitors. Their superiority for specific uses depends on the existence of a man-made environment.

The recognition of a genetic difference thus implies one of two things: (*a*) that the difference is one which manifests itself in almost any environment suitable to the survival of the individuals concerned, or (*b*) that we can reproduce the kind of environment in which it will be recognizable. The last statement is illustrated by the improvement of livestock in the eighteenth century. This happened because the introduction of root crops made it possible to standardize methods of feeding. Thus Ernle (*English Farming— Past and Present*) tells us:

Bakewell's success and the rapidly increasing demand for butcher's meat raised up a host of imitators. Breeders everywhere followed his example; his standard of excellence was gradually recognized. The foundation of the Smith-field Club in 1798 did much to promote the improvement of livestock. Some idea of the effect produced may be gathered from the average weights of sheep and cattle sold at Smithfield Market in 1710 and in 1795. In 1710 the average weight for beeves was 370 lb., for calves 50 lb., for sheep 28 lb., for lambs 18 lb. In 1795 beeves had risen in average weight to 800 lb., calves to 148 lb., sheep to 80 lb., lambs to 50 lb. This enormous addition to the meat supply of the country was due partly to the efforts of agriculturists like Tull, Townshend, Bakewell, and others, partly to the enclosure of open fields and commons which their improvements encouraged. On open fields and commons, owing mainly to the scarcity of winter keep, the livestock was dwarfed in size and weight. Even if the number of animals which might be grazed on the commons was regu-lated by custom, the stint was often so large that the pasture could only carry the smallest animals. Where the grazing rights were unlimited, as seems to have been not unusually the case in the eighteenth century, the herbage was neces-sarily still more impoverished, and the size of the livestock more stunted. On enclosed land, on the other hand, the introduction of turnip and clover husbandry doubled the number and weight of the stock which the land would carry, and the early maturity of the improved breeds enabled farmers to fatten them more expeditiously.

Just as centuries of experience in mining, dyeing, and medicine were necessary to clarify the concept of a pure substance before theoretical chemistry could begin to flourish, centuries of experience in agriculture, stockbreeding, and horticulture preceded and contributed to the recognition of those so-called unit characters with which the pioneers of animal and plant genetics occupied themselves. Historically the recognition that certain characteristics regularly reappear in certain stocks and do not do so in others went hand in hand with the practical task of designing the most favourable conditions for their appearance. The geneticist makes his appearance when that task is accomplished.

INHERITANCE IN HUMAN DISEASE

The stud-book method of Bakewell furnished the raw materials of the first and still the most successful discoveries about human inheritance. They were made by collecting family pedigrees of individuals with congenital deformities and diseases of the body. The data contained in pedigrees can yield valuable information, if the mutant genes responsible for an idiosyn-crasy exert their effect throughout a wide range of environment. It is then possible to apply numerical tests to detect their presence; and a large list of physical conditions pass the tests satisfactorily. Thus red-green colour blindness and haemophilia (inability of the blood to clot) are due to recessive genes located on the X-chromosome; albinism, alkaptonuria (black urine), and a paralysis known as Friedreich's ataxia are due to recessive genes, which are not located on the X-chromosome; brachydactyly (dwarfed fingers), and "lobster claw" are due to dominant genes.

In studying inheritance in human beings, it is not possible to start with pure-bred stocks. So if a human trait is recessive, that is to say, if it is only manifest when the individual receives a particular gene from both parents, a certain proportion of individuals who do not manifest the same trait receive the gene from one but not from the other parent. Similarly, if the trait is dominant, that is to say, if it is recognizable when the individual who shows it receives a particular gene from one parent only, it may not be possible to tell from the appearance of any given individual whether he or she has received it from one or both parents. This is no longer an insuperable difficulty. Marriage is a lottery. The natural history of lotteries, or, as we more usually call it, the theory of algebraic probability, shows us how to calculate what proportion of individuals will derive a given gene from both parents or from one parent only, if we know the proportion who do not possess it. Thus the net expectation for different kinds of offspring of parents of a specified type can easily be calculated if mating occurs at random. Allowance can be made for the fact that strictly random mating does not occur by studying the correlation between husbands and wives.

If mating occurs at random, a simple arithmetical calculation shows that the number of individuals who carry a rare gene on only one chromosome is twice the square root of the number who carry it on both members of the same pair of chromosomes. What this means may be illustrated by albinism. Albinism is a recessive condition. In Britain the proportion of albinos in the community is about one in twenty thousand. According to the principle of random mating, one in every seventy individuals who are not albinos should therefore carry the gene for albinism on one of their chromosomes. For the same reason individuals who display a very rare dominant condition will nearly always possess the gene which determines it on one chromosome only. Genetic theory therefore demands that half the offspring of such individuals, if married to a normal person, will have the dominant trait. This is easy to test in the numerous pedigrees of what medical men refer to as "hereditary" diseases or disfigurements. Such are brachydactyly, a congenital absence of one of the joints of the fingers, one form of night blindness, a somewhat repulsive abnormality known as lobster claw which is a deformity of the lower limb, the disease known as diabetes insipidus, Huntingdon's chorea, and the eye defect called aniridia. The observed proportions in families with one affected parent agree with numerical calculations based on Mendel's law. Such diseases could be eliminated in a generation if individuals suffering from them were not allowed to reproduce. While diseases of this class are incurable, this is the only effective method of prevention.

An individual who exhibits a "recessive" condition must receive the gene from both parents. He or she may thus be the offspring of one of three types of marriage: a marriage between two recessives; a marriage between a recessive and an apparently normal individual who carries the gene; or a marriage between two carriers neither of whom exhibit the trait. What has been said about albinism shows that marriages of the last type will be vastly more common than the other two. In other words, recessives are generally offspring of parents who are not themselves recessives and have no near ancestors who are recessives. They cannot be detected by collecting long pedigrees. We have to resort to other means.

Genetic theory tells us that, if two parents are carriers, one-quarter of their offspring will be recessives. Thus recessive conditions tend to turn up among several brothers and sisters in a family. In the language of the medical profession they are "familial." The proportion calculated from genetic theory is easily tested by collecting sufficient cases. A second test is still more valuable, especially if the recognition of a recessive gene depends on conditions which are not always present in the family environment. Consanguineous parentage will always be more common among parents of recessives than among the general population. The proportion of consanguineous parentage can be stated precisely if we know of the rarity of the recessive condition. About 15 per cent of the parents of albinos and of children who die of amaurotic family idiocy are first cousins. The percentage of all marriages between first cousins in the population at large generally varies between 0·5 and 1·5 per cent in European communities.

Without recourse to mathematics, the reason for this is easy to grasp. Taking at their face value the figures already cited, the square root rule means that if I carry the gene for albinism on one of my chromosomes, the chance that I shall marry an unrelated individual who is likewise a carrier is only one in seventy. If I marry my cousin, I am marrying an individual who has received a certain proportion of her chromosomes from the same pair of grandparents as myself. The chance that the offspring of two grandparents will both receive a particular chromosome from one of them is one in eight. Hence, if I am myself a carrier for albinism, the odds in favour of marrying another carrier would be nearly nine times greater than if I married someone who was not related to me.

About a dozen of these recessive conditions are now well established. One is an eye disease, called *retinitis pigmentosa*. Amaurotic family idiocy and juvenile amaurotic idiocy are two other examples. These are familial diseases in which symptoms of arrested mental development are associated with physical degenerative changes in the central nervous system and eyes. Death preceded by wasting takes place in one during infancy and in the other about the age of puberty. If two parents produce an amaurotic child, the odds are that one-half of their offspring will carry the gene and one-quarter will exhibit it. It is difficult to justify the English law which does not permit such parents to avail themselves of a very simple operation to prevent the *further spread* of the unwelcome genes which are responsible for these two formidable and at present quite incurable diseases. On the other hand, the advantages of sterilization as applied to diseased people can be greatly exaggerated. Sterilization of the individuals directly affected is often undertaken by nature. All amaurotics die before they can propagate their kind. The fact is that selection eliminates rare recessive conditions very slowly. If all albinos were sterilized in every generation it would probably take several centuries to reduce the incidence of albinism to half its present dimensions.

Recessive genes borne upon the sex chromosomes are easily recognized by the fact that recessive females are much rarer than recessive males. Red-green colour blindness is a case of this type of inheritance. Colour-blind males are at least ten times as common as colour-blind females. Recessive genes known to be located on the sex chromosomes are more numerous than all the recessive genes at present known to be located on the remaining twenty-three pairs of human chromosomes. Perhaps this is because the peculiar type of inheritance to which they give rise attracted medical interest more than a century ago in connexion with the study of haemophilia. There is a strain of haemophilia in the Royal Houses of Europe. No eugenist has publicly proposed sterilization as a remedy for defective kingship.

PATERNITY TESTS

The tendency of traits to stick together in the same pedigree has made it possible to construct maps of the chromosomes in animals and plants (p. 1036). All the distinguishable genes of the fruit fly and the sweet-pea can be assigned to their respective chromosomes and to a particular locus relative to other genes on the same chromosomes as themselves. Most of the genes whose manifest effects are easy to distinguish in human beings are rare. It is therefore exceedingly unlikely that we should encounter two in the same pedigree. For this reason the possibility of constructing a chromosome map of the human species seemed quite fantastic ten years ago.

Today the prospects are very hopeful. The possibility of doing so has emerged from the study of the blood groups.

The discovery of the blood groups which are now used in testing paternity was made in connexion with the practice of blood transfusion. This is sometimes necessary after severe haemorrhage. When it was first undertaken the results were enigmatic. Sometimes it was beneficial, sometimes followed by collapse. The blood of the recipient might become curdled. The circulation was obstructed. It slowed down and soon ceased. The danger was removed by the discovery that clumping of blood corpuscles may occur when blood from different individuals is mixed in a tube. From this point of view the blood of some individuals is incompatible with that of others. Individuals can thus be classified in groups according to their compatibility. Provided the test has shown that the donor's blood is compatible with the blood of the recipient, all is well.

It is easy to separate the red cells of the blood from the clear fluid (serum) left after normal coagulation by means of a centrifuge. Red cells in saline solutions cannot be made to clump by adding serum from blood of the same individual. They will often do so if serum of another individual is added. This shows that the clumping of the blood cells depends on a reaction between substances "agglutinable" in the corpuscles and agglutinating substances (agglutinins) in the serum of another individual. There are two of each of them. If an individual has both agglutinins, he can have neither of the agglutinable substances. If he has both the latter he can have neither of the agglutinins. If he has one of the agglutinins he can only have one agglutinable substance, the one which does not react with it. Classification of all possible types of reaction between sera and red cells of different persons shows that there are only these four classes.

Class A has an agglutinable substance A and an agglutinin *b*. Class B has an agglutinable substance B (which reacts with *b* to produce clumping) and an agglutinin *a* (which reacts with A to produce clumping). Hence individuals belonging to group A are incompatible with individuals belonging to group B. A third group is called group O because its red cells will not clump when treated with serum of any individuals. It has no agglutinable substance. Since its serum will make the red cells of group A or group B clump, it has both agglutinins *a* and *b*. A fourth group called AB has red cells which clump when serum of individuals belonging to any one of the three other groups is added to them. The serum of individuals who belong to this group will not produce clumping of red cells from individuals of any group. Thus it contains neither *a* nor *b*.

Partly because relatives are often willing to act as donors when transfusion is necessary, simple rules of inheritance were detected at an early stage in the study of blood groupings. Tests on over quarter of a million individuals and over five thousand families have now been placed on record. So our knowledge about the genetic basis of the blood groups is comparable to our knowledge of inheritance in animals which can be kept for experiment. The following rules have now been established: (*a*) if both parents belong to group O all the offspring belong to group O, (*b*) if one parent belongs to group O and the other belongs to group AB, the offspring belong either to A or to B, (*c*) if one parent belongs to A and the other belongs to B the offspring may belong to *any* of the four groups, (*d*) if one parent belongs to group A and the other belongs to either group O or to group A the offspring must belong to A or O, (*e*) if one parent belongs to group B and the other to O or B, the offspring must be B or O, (*f*) if one parent is AB and the other either A or B, the offspring cannot belong to group O.

For various reasons, which cannot be stated briefly, the few exceptions to these rules are due to the fact that biological and legal paternity do not always coincide. Hence blood tests can sometimes be used to show that a particular male is not the parent of a child. For instance, a male belonging to group O cannot be the father of a child who does not belong to group O, if the child's mother herself belongs to group O. If the child belongs to group A, his father must have belonged to group A or to group AB. Needless to say, the fact that his putative father does belong to one of these two groups would not prove that he was the real father. It merely proves that he may have been. In certain circumstances a test of this kind may prove that an individual is *not* the father of a particular child. It can never prove that he is.

All the rules stated may be explained by regarding group O as the basic stock in which two dominant mutations have arisen independently at the same locus R on the same pair of chromosomes. One dominant gene A is responsible for the manufacture of the agglutinable substance A and the elimination of the agglutinin *a*. The other dominant gene B is responsible for the manufacture of the agglutinable substance B and the elimination of the agglutinin *b*. Thus the genetic formula for group O is RR, for group A it is AA or AR, for group B it is BB or BR, and for group AB, it is AB.

Recent research has led to the discovery of other blood groupings based on the compatibility of human blood with that of various animals which have been previously immunized to the blood of other individuals. If blood-group testing were carried out in all records of clinical pedigree, it would be possible to ascertain whether rare genes responsible for diseases like amaurotic idiocy or night blindness reside on the same chromosomes as the three genes of the blood groups. People have now been classified for their reactions to immunized sera of other species. It has been shown that the genes involved in one such system of blood groups are not located on the same pair of chromosomes as the three genes of the A and B blood groups, and there is a very hopeful prospect that we shall soon be able to test for a blood grouping referable to every one of the twenty-four pairs of human chromosomes. Recently it has been shown that about a quarter of the population are incapable of tasting a group of substances allied to the organic compound called phenyl-thiourea. This substance is exceedingly bitter to those who can taste it. Ability to taste is determined by a single dominant gene. About as many people have the dominant gene as lack it. Like the blood-group test, this reaction may play a part in the mapping of the human chromosomes.

HEREDITY AND SOCIAL BEHAVIOUR

Several defects of neuromuscular organization, such as *amaurotic family idiocy*, all of them associated with detectable physical symptoms, are included in the list of established diseases which depend on a gene difference which is recognizable in all customary conditions of development. When the geneticist is confronted with a discontinuous character which only manifests itself in special circumstances, his first line of attack is to find out everything he can about how nurture controls its appearance.

There is a mutant of the fruit fly which is deformed in the hindmost part of the body. It is usually referred to as "abnormal abdomen." Flies of the pure mutant stock regularly exhibit the deformity when grown in moist cultures. They are perfectly normal when grown in a stale dried-up culture. So long as the experiments are carried out in fresh cultures, matings with wild-type stock yield numerical ratios in keeping with the supposition that the difference between the mutant stock and the wild type is due to a single gene substitution. If the cultures are allowed to become stale and dry, no consistent numerical results can be obtained for an obvious reason. Had the geneticist no means of preventing his cultures from drying up, he would have to confine his counts to larvae which hatch out while the culture is still moist.

A type of feeble-mindedness known as mongolism provides an example of how medical science can apply a similar method. Mongols rarely have young mothers. A high percentage of mongols have mothers about forty years of age or more. Since the genetic constitution of the mother is not affected by her age, the environment of the womb must have something to do with whether an individual is a mongol. By studying families born after the mother has passed a certain age, Dr. Penrose has been able to show what part heredity plays in producing mongolism.

Mongolian idiocy is associated with well-defined physical characteristics, to some of which it owes its name. So far the comparison of pedigrees containing feeble-minded or mentally deranged individuals with no distinctive physical stigmata has not yielded information which satisfies any numerical criteria based on genetic theory. This may be because the occurrence of imbecility and lunacy is due to a combination of genes too complex to detect without recourse to experimental mating which is impracticable. It may be because a particular combination of genes and a particular kind of environment are jointly responsible for producing them.

Of its very nature social behaviour depends on an environment complex which cannot be standardized. Individual differences of social behaviour, as we observe them, are generally differences to which differences of environment and gene differences jointly contribute. When differences of environment and differences of gene equipment jointly contribute to observed differences between human beings it may be that the responsible genes are rare (or are mainly confined to a small group of people), while the conditions of nurture on which their detection depends are relatively common. Heredity is then the more significant source of variation. Conversely it may be that the responsible genes are widely distributed in the population, while the relevant conditions of nurture are rare or very unevenly distributed. The more important source of variation then resides in the environment. In this sense we are entitled to ask whether nature or nurture is the most *important* agency which determines individual differences. The question can be investigated on a statistical scale when it is not possible to find out which decides the fate of a particular individual. Of several methods which can be used the three most important ones are (*a*) the method of twin resemblance, (*b*) the method of adoption, (*c*) the method of consanguinity.

The method of twin resemblance was first suggested by Galton. Partly because the pertinent facts were not fully established and partly because there were insufficient endowments to support large-scale research, it has not been applied extensively till recent years. Embryological research has shown that when mammals produce several offspring together the same result may be produced in different ways. Most species have litters of several offspring because several egg cells are set free into the womb when the mother is on heat. A few multiparous species liberate only one egg at a time. The mass of cells produced from the fertilized egg then splits at an early stage of development to form several embryos. When multiparous pregnancies occur in human beings and in cattle either process may be responsible. Hence human twins are of two kinds. *Identical* twins, being descended from the same fertilized egg, have the same set of genes and are necessarily of the same sex. *Fraternal* twins, being descended from different eggs, have sets of genes which are no more alike than those of ordinary offspring of the same parent. Such twins may be of like sex or unlike sex. They can now be distinguished from the other type by reliable tests.

This fact may be used to investigate the relative importance of nature and nurture in two ways. We may compare the degrees of similarity shown by identical twins, fraternal twins, and ordinary "sibs" (brothers or sisters) brought up together in the same family, and we may compare the resemblance of identical twins reared apart with that of identical twins brought up together. If identical twins are decidedly more alike than fraternal twins in the same family, we may conclude that heredity plays a large part in deciding the difference between individual members *of a single family*. If fraternal twins are decidedly more alike than ordinary sibs we may conclude that the differences of environment to which children of different ages, brought up in the same family, are exposed, play a large part in deciding the characteristics of individual members. Since the environment of a family at one social level may be very different from that of a family at another, the discovery that heredity is the chief agency which decides what the characteristics of different members of the same fraternity will be, does not necessarily imply that it is the chief agency which decides differences between individuals belonging to different social classes, races, or religions. This can be settled by comparing the degrees of similarity shown by identical twins reared together and identical twins reared apart in totally different social circumstances. It happens when they are adopted at birth, because their parents die or desert them.

The practice of adoption can also be used in another way. If true sibs reared together are decidedly more alike than true sibs reared apart, or if foster sibs are more alike than pairs of individuals taken at random from similar homes, differences of home environment may be inferred to play a decisive role.

A third method of investigating the role of nature and nurture depends on the theory of inbreeding. Inbreeding results in separating *pure* stocks from a hybrid population. Hence it increases the amount of variety. It is not difficult to see that this is true where the number of genes involved is small. The reason for it is the same as the reason for the high proportion of albinos whose parents are first cousins. Hence a high measure of variability among children whose parents are consanguineous, when compared with children whose parents are not related, points to the influence of nature rather than of nurture.

These methods of attack have been elaborated within the last twenty years. That they have been applied to the study of comparatively few aspects of man's social behaviour is chiefly due to two circumstances. The first is the persistence of the stud-book mentality. The overwhelming majority of publications ostensibly dealing with human heredity are collections of pedigrees. The analysis of pedigrees can supply useful information when the data supplied by them satisfy numerical tests suggested by the known behaviour of genes. The fact that they pass the tests justifies the suggestion that ordinary differences of environment do not interfere with the expression of the gene difference, and the conclusions drawn from them are then irresistible. When the data supplied by pedigrees fail to do so we are in doubtful territory, and the more so when we are studying social characteristics such as temperamental traits and intellectual performance, which are known to demand certain limiting circumstances of upbringing. The stud book is a reliable guide to the inborn qualities of pedigree cattle, because the farmer aims at equalizing the environment of individuals selected for parenthood.

For two reasons it is not a reliable guide to the contribution which heredity makes to differences of behaviour. One is that the human family transmits a certain social tradition, i.e. a particular sort of environment as well as a certain equipment of genes. The other is that equality of environment is not yet the recognized goal of social organization, least of all by most eugenists. The stud-book method is used because those who profess to accept the stud farm as a model for human betterment shrink from promoting the social arrangements which would make the analogy pertinent to the circumstances of social life.

Another serious obstacle to progress is the paucity of methods for measuring and describing differences of social behaviour. A beginning has been made with the intelligence tests of Binet, Terman, Burt, Spearman, and others. When people apply the word intelligent to a person they do not mean something as definite as black, freckled, or intoxicated. This does not imply that no useful meaning can be attached to the word *intelligent* as a description of the characteristics of human beings. Different observers can arrange a group of individuals in a scale of what they call greater or less intelligence. They can then see whether their arrangements tally and whether it is possible to devise some independent test by which the same group can be arranged in a way which corresponds fairly closely with independent estimates based on personal impressions. This is what an intelligence test does. Extensive and careful statistical researches have been undertaken to devise a scale which will record what is *common* to the various ways in which people use the word *intelligent*, when they apply it to the social behaviour of children and adolescents. It does not necessarily follow that the intelligence tests give a just measure of all that we commonly mean by the adjective intelligent when we apply it to adults. Probably the intellectual performance of adults depends quite as much on temperamental characteristics ordinarily described by alertness, persistence, curiosity, or a sense of humour as on the type of facility which intelligence tests assess. Hence proposals to limit educational facilities to children who get high scores in such tests are exceedingly dangerous. It is never suggested that the education of the prosperous classes should be limited in the same way. So the political motive is not far to seek.

The great advantage of the tests on which such scales are based is that they yield very constant results for the same individual examined on successive occasions, if the intervening period is short. They also give fairly constant results for the order of individuals within a group when it is tested successively over a period of several years. What is important for our purpose is that we now have a method of describing one aspect of human behaviour with some precision and reliability. It can be passed from the hands of one observer to another. So we can pool the results of intelligence tests as we could not do if we had to rely on any customary scale such as teachers' estimates, examination results, or employers' testimonials.

This means that the biologist can investigate to what extent differences of intelligence are associated with the fact that different children are born with different genes, and how far the manifestation of such gene differences is independent of maternal health in pre-natal existence, other conditions of uterine environment, a poorly nourished body, over-indulgent parents, over-bearing brothers and sisters, sympathetic teachers, and an infinite variety of other circumstances which distinguish the physical and social environment of one individual from another. The most definite conclusion which has yet been reached is that the average differences between the intelligence quotients (IQ) of identical twins brought up together are small in comparison with average differences between intelligence quotients of fraternal twins brought up together. In fact they are no larger than average differences between successive tests on the same individuals.

While this shows the influence of heredity on differences between individuals who enjoy the benefits of the same home environment and the same uterine environment, it does not tell us anything about individuals who belong to families at different social levels. Identical twins reared apart are difficult to find, and the social machinery of adoption usually places them in homes *at the same social level*. The fragmentary evidence available shows that the average IQ difference of 10 pairs of identical twins reared apart is 7·7 points. The average IQ difference for fraternal twins reared together is only 8·4 points. If we had a large sample of identical twins reared apart in homes at different social levels the difference might well be greater than 7·7. Even so, the citizen may judge for himself whether scare headlines about the decline of the nation's intelligence belong to the province of science.

In the Middle Ages the advance of physical science was held in check because Catholicism refused to countenance any challenge to its intellectual pretensions. Today the advance of human genetics is held back because the prosperous classes refuse to tolerate any challenge to their intellectual privileges. The natural mission of the middle class or of the Aryan race has now replaced the divine mission of the Church militant. There is no need to ransack Nazi publications for illustrations of a temper which exists elsewhere. In the official organ of the English Eugenics Society which he rightly remarks "has always been especially interested" in "that portion which is popularly called the upper and middle classes," an English biometrician, also a prominent eugenist, propounds the question "who are the middle class?" The answer he gives is this:

In consequence of this selective process this class has necessarily become differentiated in certain hereditary respects from the general body of the population from which it is continually recruited. In the case of intelligence this difference is readily demonstrable by applying the psychological tests to the children of different occupational groups. But we should be altogether mistaken if we took it that the only important difference lay in intelligence. There must be at least a dozen other psychological characters of importance governing self-control, ambition, judgment of character, aesthetic taste, foresight, *grasp of moral principle* which have been at least as influential as intelligence in guiding the process of social promotion during the last two centuries of which our class is the product.

Perhaps no better word than *grasp* could have been chosen for this context.

When human genetics is subsidized to advance the fullest use of human talents without regard to social class, it may be possible to detect and measure racial differences of intelligence depending upon differences of genetic constitution. One difficulty of treating group differences of this kind in a genuinely scientific temper will be less when psychology can equip biological research with a sufficient variety of similar methods for the precise description of other aspects of social behaviour. One can assert that deaf-mutism is commoner among Jews than among Gentiles without incurring the charge of anti-Semitism. With so many diagnosable physical ailments to choose from, it is possible for normal people to discuss the occupational or racial distribution of any single disease of the body without assuming a tone of impudent superiority. No single race, class, or nation has the monopoly of all the virtues.

Hitherto the only social impetus to the study of human genetics, especially in so far as it is concerned with the part played by heredity in social behaviour, has come from proposals for restricting educational expenditure and public money spent on institutions for the care of its defective members, from policies concerned with ruthless exploitation of backward peoples, and from the psychological frustration which has accompanied the acceptance of sterility as the cardinal virtue of the middle classes. The eugenic movement has recruited its members from the childless rentier–twentieth-century bourbons who have earned nothing and begotten nothing. Its voluptuous insistence on mutilation as the goal of applied genetics has borne fruit in no outstanding discoveries. Human genetics has not yet discovered an incentive sufficient to guarantee its further progress. It will not do so while the selfishness, apathy, and prejudice which prevent intellectually gifted people from understanding the character of the present crisis in civilization remains a far greater menace to the survival of culture than the prevalence of mental defect in the technical sense of the term.

This does not mean that the study of human inheritance is unimportant. On the contrary it has everything to gain by out-growing the castration complex. With the prospect of a spectacular decline of population in the near future constructive statesmanship will be more and more preoccupied with ways and means to encourage parenthood. Consequently it will be less and less favourable to drastic proposals for sterilizing the harmlessly unfit. For the same reasons it will be more and more committed to an active policy of preventive medicine. As part of an active policy of preventive medicine the future of human genetics is assured. No community is likely to sterilize people who suffer from frontal sinus infections, or to subsidize research which leads to the conclusion that people who suffer from sinus infections should necessarily be sterilized. What makes it important to know everything which can be found out about the contribution of heredity to such diseases is that if we have such knowledge we can forewarn people who are liable to contract them against exposing themselves to the dangers of infection. So long as sterilization is the goal of human genetics, its scope must be limited to the study of comparatively serious disorders. As a department of preventive medicine it embraces the whole field of disease.

Analogous remarks apply to education. Eugenists are never tired of talking about the "waste" of expenditure on those who are "by nature" unable to benefit from it. Naturally this does not engage the sympathy of educationists who take their job seriously. Nor does it enlist the support of intelligent citizens, who realize that no society is safe in the hands of a few clever people. If knowledge is the keystone of intelligent citizenship, the fact that many people do not benefit from existing provisions for instruction is less a criticism of themselves than a criticism of educational machinery. The possibility that heredity plays a large part in such differences is only relevant to public expenditure, when we have already decided whether we want more or less education. We do not need biologists to tell us that any subject can be made dull enough to defy the efforts of any but a few exceptionally bright or odd individuals. By exploring individual differences human genetics might help us to find out how to adapt our educational technique to individual needs. It will do so, and gain prestige in consequence, when it ceases to be an apology for snobbery, selfishness, and class arrogance.

SELECTED REFERENCES FOR PARTS IV AND V

As an elementary introduction to general biology *The Science of Life,* by H. G. Wells, J. S. Huxley, and G. P. Wells is specially recommended. Palmer's *Living Things* (George Allen & Unwin) and Fox's *Biology* are good for those who want something more compact. For further reading on the subject-matter of Chapters XVII, XX, and XXIII *Human Physiology* by Winton and Bayliss, and Russell's book (*vide infra*) are comprehensive texts. Crew's *Animal Genetics* and a more general treatment by Babcock and Clausen, *Genetics for Students of Agriculture,* are admirable. For Chapter XIX two books by Campbell and Browning cited below are specially relevant as sources of further information. For systematics (Chapter XXI) the reader may consult Strasburger's *Text Book of Botany* and the *Text Book of Zoology* by Parker and Haswell. British readers may extend their knowledge of plant life by getting a copy of Bentham and Hooker's *British Flora* for use when hiking. Holmes's *The Age of the Earth* is an excellent survey of new geological knowledge. The following list contains works cited in connexion with the social background of biology:

AMHERST, ALICIA (HON. MRS. EVELYN CECIL): *A History of Gardening in England.* (Quaritch.) 1896. 3rd Edition. (Murray.) 1910.

BAYNE-JONES, STANHOPE: *Man and Microbes.* (Baillière.) 1932.

BIDWELL, P. W., and FALCONER, J. I.: *History of Agriculture in Northern United States.* Carnegie Inst., Washington. 1925.

BREMNER, DAVID. *The Industries of Scotland, their Rise and Progress and Present Condition.* (Longmans.) 1869.

BROWNING, C. H. *Bacteriology.* (Home University Library. Williams & Norgate.) 1935.

CAMPBELL, D. *Handbook of Therapeutics.* (Livingstone.) (Edinburgh.) 1934.

COLE, F. J. *Early Theories of Sexual Generation.* (Oxford: Clarendon Press.) 1930.

CUTLER, W. H. R. *A Short History of English Agriculture.* (Oxford: Clarendon Press.) 1909.

CRANE, M. B., and LAWRENCE, W. J. C. *The Genetics of Garden Plants.* (Macmillan.) 1934.

ERNLE, LORD (PROTHERO). *English Farming Past and Present.* (Longmans.) 1932.

FISHBEIN, MORRIS. *Frontiers of Medicine.* Century of Progress Series. (George Allen & Unwin.) 1933.

FLINT, W. P., and METCALF, C. L.: *Insects—Man's Chief Competitor*. Century of Progress Series. (George Allen & Unwin.) 1932.

FURNAS, C. C.: *The Next 100 Years*. (Cassell.) 1936.

GOTHEIN, MARIE LUISE: *A History of Garden Art* (2 vols.). Trans. by Laura Archer-hind. (Dent.) 1928.

GRAS, N. S. B.: *A History of Agriculture in Europe and America*. (Pitman.) 1926.

HARVEY, W.: *On the Circulation of the Blood*. (Everyman's Library. Dent.) 1907.

KNIGHT, THOMAS A.: *Collected Papers*. (Royal Horticultural Society.) (Longmans.) 1841.

LAWRENCE, W. J. C.: *Practical Plant Breeding*. (George Allen & Unwin.) 1938.

LILLIE, F. R.: *Problems of Fertilization*. (Univ. of Chicago.) 1929.

LYELL, SIR CHARLES: *Principles of Geology*. (Murray.) 1872.

PLAYFAIR, JOHN: *Illustration of Huttonian Theory*. (Cadell.) 1802.

ROBERTS, H. F.: *Plant Hybridisation before Mendel*. (Princeton Univ. Press.) 1929.

ROGERS, I. E. T.: *A History of Agriculture and Prices in England* (7 vols.). (Oxford: Clarendon Press.) 1866–1902.

RUSSELL, SIR E. J. *Soil Conditions and Plant Growth*. (Longmans.)

SAND, RÉNÉ. *L'Economie Humaine par la Médecine Sociale*. Pp. vii and 305. (Paris.) 1934.

SAVOY, E. *L'Agriculture a travers les ages*. (Paris: Boccard.) 1935–1936.

SIMON, JOHN: *English Sanitary Institutions*. (Cassell.) 1890.

SINGER, CHARLES. *The Evolution of Anatomy*. (Kegan Paul.) 1925.

SINGER, CHARLES: *Greek Biology and Greek Medicine*. (Oxford: Clarendon Press.) 1922.

SMITH, SIR FRED. *The Early History of Veterinary Literature and its British Development*. Reprint from *Vet. Journal*. 1929–30. (Baillière.)

SPALLANZANI, THE ABBÉ. Trans. by R. HALL: Experiments upon the Circulation of the Blood throughout the vascular system: on languid circulation: on motion of the blood independent of the action of the heart: on the pulsation of the arteries. (Ridgway.) 1801.

STERN, BERNHARD J.: *Social Factors in Medical Progress*. (Columbia University Press.)

STUBBS, S. G. B., and BLIGH, E. W.: *Sixty Centuries of Health and Physick*. (Sampson Low.) 1931.

VALLERY-RADOT, RÉNÉ: *Life of Pasteur*. (Constable.) 1910.

WILLCOX, O. W.: *Reshaping Agriculture*. (George Allen & Unwin.) 1934.

WOODWARD, H. B.: *The History of the Geological Society of London*. (Longmans.) 1907.

ZIRKLE, CONWAY: *The Beginning of Plant Hybridisation*. (Univ. of Pennsylvania Press.) 1935.

CHAPTER XXV

ATOMS IN THE SERVICE OF MAN

WE relinquished the story of the atom (p. 806) with a vista of vast stores of untapped energy, but as yet no prospect of using it constructively—or destructively. In outline, we are familiar with conclusions already established in 1920 by direct experiment on particles of atomic or subatomic size, in particular through the study of: (*a*) ionization of gases by a current and by radiation; (*b*) deflection of ions or of emissions from radioactive elements in a magnetic or electrostatic field; (*c*) the photoelectric effect. At a more speculative level, we have seen how such measurements throw light on properties of matter presumptively associated with peculiarities of atomic structure; and we have dealt with these under three headings: (*a*) the periodic properties of the elements in their compounds; (*b*) the line spectra characteristic of the elements; (*c*) the existence of isotopes.

The last of the above invites further comment before we recall the picture of the atom which has emerged from assembling the pieces of the jig-saw puzzle. An element defined as such by its unique chemical properties is a mixture of substances which have the same *atomic number*; but it is a mixture of substances of different mass. The ratio of the mass of any one of these isotopes to that of any other is itself a whole number in a very small range; and what chemists have hitherto called its atomic weight is the mean of the mass of its stable isotopes as found in nature. The heaviest elements (from A.N. 86 onwards) have no stable isotopes. They are radioactive. Only stable isotopes of elements of lower A.N. occur in nature; but radioactive isotopes of a few of them turn up in disintegration of native radioactive elements. Many others are now producible by artificial means. As its name suggests, the Atomic Number of an element is a whole number, and as such it corresponds to the charge of the nucleus of the atom, if the unit of charge is that of the positively charged ion of hydrogen (*proton*).

Since we express its atomic weight as the ratio of the mass of an isotope to that of the hydrogen ion, one way of looking at the new classification of the elements is to say that the nucleus of any one of them consists of *a* protons (hydrogen ions) associated with *b* or more uncharged particles of equal mass. On this assumption, addition of such a particle to the nucleus of an element will step up the atomic weight by unity; but it will not affect its chemical properties. We must likewise assume that such addition is consistent with few stable arrangements, that some combinations of such particles with a fixed number of protons will be unstable (i.e. radioactive) though recognizable as such and that others in effect are too unstable to exist. We now call these electrically neutral particles *neutrons*. Their existence was a topic of speculation before there was direct evidence of their existence. At the stage when we left the structure of the atom in Chapter XVI, we may therefore summarize our knowledge in the following terms. In so far as it is picturable, our present picture of the atom is as follows:

(1) At the centre is a dense core with a positive charge and around it revolve in orbits situated at fixed distances satellite electrons of which the number in the outermost orbit does not exceed 8. The positive core (*nucleus*) of the atom consists of gross particles of two sorts, each of mass approximately equivalent to the hydrogen ion: (*a*) positively charged (*protons*); (*b*) without charge (*neutrons*).

(2) The atomic number (A.N.) of an element corresponds to the number of protons in its nucleus, its atomic weight (A.W.) to the combined number of protons and neutrons. Since more or less stable combinations are possible between a given number of protons and two or more numbers of neutrons, whence there may be two or more isotopes of different A.W. corresponding to one gross chemical element of fixed A.N.

(3) Unstable combinations of protons and neutrons (i.e. radioactive elements) may break down or reform to make stable ones in two ways:

    (*a*) with emission of an *alpha* particle (positively charged *helium* ion) involving loss of whole protons, whence the formation of a product of lower A.N. and of lower A.W.;

    (*b*) with emission of a *beta* particle (*electron*) from the nucleus involving *in effect* the replacement of a neutron by a proton with increase of A.N. but no change of A.W.

If $_nE^w$ represents the isotope with atomic weight w of an element whose atomic number is n, we may thus represent the two processes as:

$$(a)\ _nE^w - \alpha = {}_nE^w - {}_2He^4 = {}_{n-2}E^{w-4}$$
$$(b)\ _nE^w - \beta = {}_{n+1}E^w$$

(4) The mass of the electron is about a two-thousandth (0·00054) of the mass of the hydrogen ion. The empty space within the outermost atomic orbit and the empty space between atoms is immense. All the protons and electrons in the body of an average man would occupy a space barely visible as a speck, if closely packed. Hence the probability that a sub-atomic or atomic particle projected into matter at high speed will eventually collide with an atom of the latter is minute.

SPLITTING THE ATOM

Between 1919 and 1939 much knowledge accumulated to reinforce confidence in these conclusions; but there was little outcome in terms of realizing the promise of harnessing the stored energy of the atom on a scale of human usefulness. Meanwhile, a succession of discoveries on small-scale break-down of atoms, demonstrated as such by cloud chamber photographs and scintillations on fluorescent screens, reinforced confidence in the broad outlines of the foregoing picture of the structure of the atom and of eventual success in mobilizing its resources for human use. Many workers contributed to these advances. It will suffice to distinguish three main themes; and since we have acquainted ourselves in outline with the methods used by nuclear physicists to investigate emanations and individual particles of atomic or subatomic dimensions, it will not be necessary to emphasize details about the techniques employed in such discoveries.

(i) In 1919 Rutherford discovered that the passage of alpha particles (*helium* ions) from radium through nitrogen produces occasional scintillations on a fluorescent screen at distances about six times beyond their normal range. By magnetic deflection, he was able to show that the particles responsible had the dimensions of hydrogen ions, i.e. protons. In the symbolism of (3) above, we can represent the only straightforward explanation of this by means of a new sort of chemical formula:

$$_2He^4 + {}_7N^{14} \rightarrow {}_8O^{17} + {}_1H^1$$

To make the equation balance, we have here assumed that the production of hydrogen by the interaction of nitrogen atoms and swiftly moving helium ions leads to the production of the heavy oxygen isotope. This received confirmation from photographs of the tracks of alpha particles through nitrogen in the Wilson cloud chamber. In the latter, an alpha particle pursues a straight path up to the point where it bombards a nitrogen atom. Two tracks then appear, one less oblique of shorter range, and one more oblique of longer range. By the laws of impact it has been possible to calculate from the observable range the ratio of the kinetic energy of one particle to that of the other, and hence to check the conclusion that the production of a proton goes with the production of an ion of heavy oxygen.

(ii) The likelihood that a relatively slow-moving positively charged particle will collide head-on with a nucleus, the positive charge of which will repel it and hence deflect it from its course, will be less than the likelihood that a swift one will do so. It is possible to increase the speed of such particles greatly in an electric field of high potential, and the exploitation of this possibility led to an important discovery by Cockroft and Walton. In 1932 they subjected lithium (A N 3, A.W. 7) to bombardment by positive rays (*protons*) accelerated in a field of 60,000 volts. The outcome was the liberation of alpha particles recognized as such by the helium spectrum in accordance with the equation:

$$_3Li^7 + {}_1H^1 \rightarrow 2 \, . \, {}_2He^4$$

Devices such as the *cyclotron*, for accelerating protons in a strong magnetic and in an electrostatic field of very high potential, have led to the discovery of other reactions, including:

(*a*) conversion of an atom of boron into an atom of beryllium by a process of *recombination*;

(*b*) conversion of an atom of carbon into nitrogen by a process we may call *capture*.

Examples of one or other are the following:

$$(a) \; _5B^{11} + {}_1H^1 \rightarrow {}_4Be^8 + {}_2He^4$$
$$(b) \; _6C^{12} + {}_1H^1 \rightarrow {}_7N^{13}$$

(iii) Subsequent study of the impact of alpha particles from radioactive substances on the atoms of light elements led to the discovery of many similar transmutations of elements on an ultra-microscopic scale. The most important discovery was the occasional production of carbon atoms by alpha particle bombardment of the light metal beryllium. A by-product of this reaction is a highly penetrating emanation with properties common to radium emanations, i.e. ionization, fluorescence and excitation of a light-sensitive film. The new emanation suffers no deflection in a magnetic nor in an electrostatic field, and cannot therefore be a stream of electrically charged particles. On the other hand, its behaviour during passage through a cloud chamber is essentially different from that of gamma rays or X-rays, in that photographs show evidence of tracks signifying *collisions* with atoms of the gas in the chamber. Seemingly, as Chadwick concluded, the emanation must therefore consist of electrically neutral particles. If we denote such particles by the symbol $_0n^1$, the atomic equation of the reaction which gives rise to them must be:

$$_2He^4 + _4Be^9 \rightarrow _6C^{12} + _0n^1$$

In the same way the boron atom breaks up under bombardment by alpha particles in accordance with the nuclear equation:

$$_2He^4 + _5B^{11} \rightarrow _7N^{14} + _0n^1$$

PARTICLES IN COLLISION

In following the track of discovery in the atomic realm, our main concern has hitherto been with particles, more especially gaseous ions and electrons, which carry an electric charge. Our so far suppositious neutron carries no charge, and it can fulfil the expectation encouraged by the study of isotopes only if we can show that its mass is equivalent to that of the proton. We are able to measure (pp. 786–793) the mass of a charged particle such as a gaseous ion or electron, and likewise its speed, by studying its deflection both in a magnetic and in an electro-static field; but this procedure can throw no light on the mass or speed of a neutron. The only clue we have as yet for a recipe is the supposition that it can impart speed to a gaseous ion with which it collides.

No rule precisely describes what happens at collision of bodies large enough to see and to handle; but two simple rules fit fairly closely with what occurs when: (*a*) bodies move without spinning; (*b*) friction during motion is as small as may be; (*c*) impact between them generates very little heat. Such is the situation when two discs of ivory collide on a flat surface of highly polished glass; but we have no reason to believe that any visible or tangible bodies can move wholly without friction unless they move like planets in empty space. Nor have we direct experience of bodies which collide without generating some heat. On this understanding, we can get a useful preview of the problems of collision, if we assume provisionally that such bodies do indeed exist.

If a body of mass m is moving without friction at speed v_1 in a straight line in empty space and without spinning in its course, the energy it releases as heat when brought to a standstill is $\frac{1}{2}mv^2$ (p. 612). For that of another body of mass M and speed V_1, the corresponding measure of its energy is $\frac{1}{2}MV_1^2$. If collision between two such bodies occurs, we may represent their corresponding velocities after impact as v_2 and V_2. If we assume that the impact generates no heat, the principle of the *conservation of energy* (p. 595) signifies that the so-called joint *kinetic* energy of the two bodies must be the same after impact as before, i.e.

$$\tfrac{1}{2}mv_1^2 + \tfrac{1}{2}MV_1^2 = \tfrac{1}{2}mv_2^2 + \tfrac{1}{2}MV_2^2$$

A second principle, known as the *conservation of momentum*, follows from the definition of mass consistent with Newton's treatment of motion. If we define force as the product of mass and acceleration, we may also define mass in the following terms: *when bodies repel or attract one another without friction or deformation the accelerations they experience are inversely proportional to their masses.* If a particle of mass m undergoes an acceleration a by collision with a particle of mass M, the latter undergoes acceleration of opposite sign, whence we may represent it as $-A$. Our definition of mass then implies:

$$m \div M = -A + a \text{ or } ma + MA = 0 \tag{i}$$

Let us now suppose that the particle of mass m moves before impact with velocity v_1 and thereafter with velocity v_2 in the same straight line as a second particle of mass M itself moving initially with velocity V_1 and afterwards with velocity V_2. In the short interval i during which the change occurs, the corresponding changes of velocity are $(v_2 - v_1)$ and $(V_2 - V_1)$ so that

$$a = \frac{v_2 - v_1}{i} \text{ and } A = \frac{V_2 - V_1}{i}$$

When from (i)

$$\frac{m(v_2 - v_1)}{i} + \frac{M(V_2 - V_1)}{i} = 0$$

$$\therefore MV_1 + mv_1 = MV_2 + mv_2 \tag{ii}$$

As used in mechanics, the term *momentum* signifies the product of mass and velocity. Thus we may express (ii) by saying that the sum of the momenta of the particles has the same value before and after impact. An important consequence of this is easy to see when two particles of equal mass (w) collide head-on without spinning. In the absence of friction, they will jointly lose no kinetic energy, so that

$$\tfrac{1}{2}wV_1^2 + \tfrac{1}{2}wv_1^2 = \tfrac{1}{2}wV_2^2 + \tfrac{1}{2}wv_2^2$$

$$\therefore V_1^2 + v_1^2 = V_2^2 + v^2 \tag{iii}$$

For particles of equal mass, we may likewise write (ii) as

$$V_1 + v_1 = V_2 + v_2 \tag{iv}$$

$$\therefore V_1^2 + v_1^2 + 2V_1v_1 = V_2^2 + v_2^2 + 2V_2v_2$$

By substituting from (iii), this reduces to

$$2V_1v_1 = 2V_2v_2 \text{ or } V_2 = \frac{V_1v_1}{v_2} \tag{v}$$

Whence (iv) is equivalent to

$$V_1 + v_1 = v_2 + \frac{V_1 v_1}{v_2}$$

$$\therefore v_2^2 - (V_1 + v_1)\, v_2 + V_1 v_1 = 0$$

$$\therefore v_2 = \frac{(V_1 + v_1) \pm \sqrt{(V_1 + v_1)^2 - 4V_1 v_1}}{2} = \frac{(V_1 + v_1) \pm (V_1 - v_1)}{2}$$

$$\therefore v_2 = V_1 \ or \ v_1 \qquad\qquad\qquad\qquad\text{(vi)}$$

From (iv) we see that the second solution $(v_2 = v_1)$ signifies that $V_2 = V_1$ in which event there is no acceleration and no collision. The first solution $(v_2 = V_1)$ signifies that $V_2 = v_1$.

Two situations then arise:

(i) one particle A overtakes another B initially moving more slowly;

(ii) two particles collide after moving in opposite directions.

If (i) holds good, the signs of v_1 and V_1 are both positive, those of v_2 and V_2 being also positive. Thus A moves after collision with the speed B had before impact in the same direction, and *vice versa*. If (ii) holds good the signs of v_1 and V_1 are opposite, that of V_2 being the same as that of v_1 and that of v_2 being the same as that of V_1. Thus the particle which was initially the slower one travels after impact in the opposite direction with the speed of the other particle before impact, and the one which was initially the faster recoils with the initial speed of its partner.

We have seen that the foregoing rules can apply exactly to collision of bodies only if three conditions hold good. One is realisable when sliding motion occurs, i.e. there is no spin. One is realisable when bodies move like planets without contact in empty space, i.e. there is no friction. One is quite outside our experience inasmuch as impact of visible or tangible bodies always generate some heat. Our picture of collision will therefore help us to learn more about the neutron only if we can furnish good reasons for believing that impact without generation of heat may indeed occur in the ultramicroscopic domain. Accordingly, we must now ask why physicists believe that they have reasons for believing that ultramicroscopic bodies with this property do indeed exist.

Since the introduction of powerful microscopes, biologists and physicists have been familiar with a phenomenon called *Brownian motion*. If suspended in a still liquid, very fine particles of soot, just visible under high magnification, execute jerky movements to and fro in all directions; and the same is true of the fine particles of cigarette smoke in air protected from disturbance by currents. A striking feature of such motion is that it becomes more lively as the temperature of the medium rises; and a hypothesis which fits all the observable facts is that: (*a*) molecules of a fluid are in constant randomwise movement; (*b*) their impact on sufficiently small solid particles is sufficient to displace the latter; (*c*) the mean speed of the molecules themselves depends on the temperature. This tempts us to regard the temperature of a gas or of a liquid as the tangible measure of the total kinetic energy of its molecules in agitation. While a body insulated from surrounding bodies registers the same temperature, the total kinetic energy of its molecules must then remain the same in spite of their repeated collisions. On this view friction is not a property of the sub-microscopic world. It is relevant only to the behaviour of bodies with which we can make direct contact through our sense organs. Whereas heat and kinetic energy appear as separate entries in the balance sheet of power for matter in bulk, the hypothesis stated signifies that they are merely different ways of labelling referable to different ways of measuring the same phenomenon in the accountancy of the ultramicroscopic domain.

The reader may rightly feel that this conception of matter is paradoxical. It is. None the less, its adoption provides a basis for reasoning which leads to the disclosure of a variety of known laws of chemistry and of physics. Such reasoning relies on the assumption that the motion of molecules is random. Hence it is not possible to do justice to the remarkable conclusions which the so-called kinetic theory endorses, unless we invoke the mathematical theory of probability. Here it must suffice to state that the outcome does confirm physicists in the conviction that collision of molecules occurs in accordance with assumptions that are never exactly realisable with respect to matter in bulk. Since atoms are the bricks for the build-up of molecules, we may now assume that the two fundamental principles of impact apply to atoms likewise. Since we also postulate that neutrons, if such there be, are bricks in the build-up of atoms, we may likewise apply the same principles without inconsistency to the bombardment of atoms by neutrons.

At this stage, we are therefore ready to examine some important consequences of the foregoing rules of collision, as they bear on the natural history of the neutron. If the neutron of the penetrating radium–beryllium or radium–boron emanation is to fit into the scheme suggested by our knowledge of isotopes, it must have the same mass, or almost the same mass, as that of the hydrogen atom. Let us then suppose that we allow a pencil of the emanation to pass through a substance containing a high proportion of hydrogen atoms, e.g. water or paraffin wax. If the speed of a particle of mass equal to that of the hydrogen atom is very high compared with the speed of what we may now call *thermal agitation* in terms of the foregoing interpretation of temperature change, the result of its head-on collision with a hydrogen atom will be either recoil or continued motion in the same direction at a greatly reduced speed equivalent to the previous speed of the particle with which it collides. What happens will indeed tell us whether the speed of the suppositious neutron of our emanation is high or otherwise. If its speed is very high, the range of ionised particles produced in a gas by impact after passing through a so-called *moderator* such as paraffin wax will be much less that it would otherwise be.

We now hold all the clues to measurement of the mass of the neutron and to that of the speed of neutrons from a particular source. With information from the source last mentioned at our disposal, we may legitimately assume that the initial speed (v_1) of the suppositious neutrons in the emanation is indeed high, so high that we can regard speed of a nitrogen or oxygen atom of mass A at thermal level as negligible $(V_1 = 0)$ in comparison with it. If the mass of the neutron is N and the corresponding final speeds are v_2 and v_4, we may then write, for head-on collision in the same straight line:

By the Conservation of Momentum

$$Nv_1 = Nv_2 + A.V_a \text{ and } v_1 = v_2 + \frac{A}{N}V_a \tag{vii}$$

$$\therefore v_1^2 = v_2^2 + \frac{A^2}{N^2}V_a^2 + 2\frac{A}{N}v_2V_a \tag{viii}$$

By the Conservation of Energy

$$\tfrac{1}{2}Nv_1^2 = \tfrac{1}{2}Nv_2^2 + \tfrac{1}{2}A.V_a^2$$

$$\therefore v_1^2 = v_2^2 + \frac{A}{N}V_a^2 \tag{ix}$$

If we combine (viii) and (ix) we get

$$\frac{N-A}{2N}V_a = v_2$$

If we substitute this value of v_2 in (vii), we get

$$v_1 = \frac{N+A}{2N}V_a \tag{x}$$

In this equation v_1 on the left stands for the speed of the neutron and V_a for the speed of any atom of mass A. If we denote the speed of an atom of mass B by V_b we have:

$$\frac{N+A}{N+B} = \frac{V_b}{V_a}$$

Now the speed of a gaseous ion produced by bombardment with a neutron is determinable from measurement of its range by methods already indicated in Chapter XVI; and our assumptions imply that V_a or V_b each stand for the maximal value of speed of an ion after collision. So they are referable as such to the maximum range. On that assumption we may obtain V_b and V_a from observation. If we denote by R_{ab} the ratio $(V_b + V_a)$ based on measurements of maximum range, we can then assign a value to N. For instance if the two gases are oxygen $(A = 16)$ and hydrogen $(A = 1)$, we have:

$$(N + 16) = R_{ab}(N + 1)$$

Values for other pairs of gases are obtainable, and the results, within small limits of error, confirm the supposition that $N = 1$, i.e. that the mass of the neutron is almost exactly the same as the mass of the hydrogen atom. The speed (v_1) of neutrons (from a particular source) is likewise obtainable by substitution in (x), i.e.

$$v_1 = \tfrac{1}{2}(A + 1)V_a$$

NUCLEAR FISSION

Chadwick's particles therefore answer to the hypothetical *neutrons* whose possible existence we invoked to account for the occurrence of isotopes. They owe their high penetrating power to the fact that electrical repulsion does not deflect them in their course. By the same token, they are vastly more liable to head-on collision with atomic nuclei in their tracks. If so, they should be particularly good missiles for disintegrating atoms. Small-scale experiments with the penetrating emanation of neutrons produced by bombardment of light elements such as boron and beryllium by alpha particles soon showed that they can indeed bring about results of both types already mentioned in connexion with bombardment of matter by accelerated alpha particles, *viz.*:

(*a*) *recombination*, as in the break-up of the silicon atom to form one of aluminium and one of hydrogen or of nitrogen to form one of boron and one of helium:

$$_{14}Si^{28} + {_0}n^1 \rightarrow {_{13}}Al^{28} + {_1}H^1$$
$$_7N^{14} + {_0}n^1 \rightarrow {_5}B^{11} + {_2}He^4$$

(*b*) *capture* as in the formation of a radio-active isotope of sodium:

$$_{11}Na^{23} + {_0}n^1 \rightarrow {_{11}}Na^{24}$$

Study of the impact of neutrons on uranium during the three or four years before the outbreak of the Second World War showed that both processes occur in the native metal. One involves a break-down into unequal fragments of (i) atoms of lighter elements in the range including Bromine (A.N. 35) and Molybdenum (A.N. 42); (ii) atoms of heavier ones in the range including Antimony (51) and Cerium (58). The balance sheet suggested that such fragmentation must set free other (*fission*) neutrons. If the disintegration itself involves production of neutrons, as happens in the reaction between swift alpha particles and beryllium, it should be possible to set going a chain of reaction involving an ever-increasing number of atoms. Should this happen in an atomic reaction accompanied by liberation of heat, it would entail the release of atomic energy on a large scale. Such was the prospect at the outbreak of war in 1939. In that year, study of the action of neutrons on the uranium isotope of atomic weight 235 had shown Hahn and Meitner that neutrons can indeed split the atom of this element with the release of other neutrons as a by-product.

The fact that a neutron can break an atom of U235 into unequal fragments with the liberation of one or more neutrons signalized a new prospect. Once started, such a process will lead to production of neutrons which can break down other atoms and so on *ad infinitum*. At first sight, we might therefore conclude that the release of a gargantuan amount of heat must inevitably accompany the impact of neutrons on the fissionable isotope. Were this so, it would never have been possible to demonstrate the possibility; but one good enough reason why the possibility is indeed demonstrable without blowing up the laboratory is intelligible in terms of the last entry in our composite picture of the atom. Because there is so much empty space within and between atoms, there is a very minute chance that a liberated neutron will ever collide with one before it escapes from the material. If so, the chance that a chain reaction can get going depends on the mass of U235 exposed to the first neutron impact. Below a certain critical size, the chance is unimaginably small.

Once the possibility of starting a chain reaction was demonstrable, the efforts of nuclear physicists converged on every aspect of what happens when neutrons bombard matter. By then it was already clear that neutrons in collision with an atom may produce either of two results already illustrated, i.e.: (a) *capture* by the nucleus with the production of a higher isotope of the same atomic number; (b) *fission* with the release of one or more neutrons which may start a chain reaction. Whether the first or second of these possibilities takes place depends partly on the speed of the neutron missile and partly on the nature of the nucleus itself. In nature, Uranium (A N. 92) consists of three isotopes of A.W. 238, 235 and 234 in proportions roughly equal to 10,000 : 70 : 6. Of these, U238 undergoes fission in appreciable frequency only if bombarded by very swift neutrons. Otherwise, it captures with the formation of U239. The isotope U235 undergoes fission when bombarded with neutrons of relatively low speed in a wide range. It then liberates neutrons at a speed which ensures a high frequency of fission of its own atoms when a collision occurs.

Fermi discovered that the capture of a neutron by U238 produces a radioactive isotope. By successive elimination of two beta particles, it gives rise first to Neptunium (A.N. 93, A.W. 239), then to Plutonium (A.N. 94, A.W. 239). Neither of these occurs naturally in detectable quantities; and the discovery of the last was a windfall. Like U235, it is readily fissionable; and it is separable by chemical methods from native uranium at much less cost than the fissionable isotope in the latter. Since each fission of U235 liberates in the long run more than one neutron to continue the chain reaction with other atoms of U235, it liberates enough—in the long run—to make a new fissionable atom of Plutonium from U238 in a native mixture of the two isotopes. Another readily fissionable substance which does not occur in nature in hitherto detectable quantities is the Uranium isotope of A.W. 233. Like Plutonium 239 this is obtainable by fission. The parent atom is the chief native isotope of Thorium and production of a Protoactinium isotope occurs as an intermediate step in the following sequence:

$$_{90}\text{Th}^{232} + {_0}\text{n}^1 = {_{90}}\text{Th}^{233} - \beta = {_{91}}\text{Pa}^{233} - \beta = {_{92}}\text{U}^{233}$$

The practical consequences of such new creations are stupendous and were scarcely imaginable in the lifetime of any reader of this book. Though the store of energy in the atom of radioactive elements has tantalized the physicist for fifty years (p. 797), a balanced view of the long-term possibilities of harnessing atomic energy to human use had first to take stock of the fact that radioactive elements are rare constituents of the earth's crust and latterly of the fact that few isotopes are fissionable by artificial means without recourse either to the use of radioactive particles or to the expenditure of a large output of energy for the production of swift particles of an ionized gas as in the experiments of Cockroft and Walton. Neither of these considerations now sets a limit to the resources of power man can create for human use. In splitting the atom, we can now make more and more atoms which split spontaneously and more and more atoms which we ourselves can also split.

Some simple arithmetic will here help us to get into focus the conditions which are essential to starting a chain reaction. We shall suppose that a piece of natural uranium releases in a second (no matter how) N_1 neutrons travelling at speeds consistent with response of the U235 nucleus by fission. Some of these will escape from it. Some will undergo capture by U238. Others will split U235 with the production of N_2 neutrons in the same speed range as the parent neutron. Let us call the ratio of parent fission neutrons to their marriageable (fission) offspring $k = N_2 \div N_1$. If the birth-rate k is less than 1, the rate of release will slow down to a standstill. If it is greater than 1 the population of neutrons will increase in geometrical progression. In other words, a chain reaction will occur. Without intervention of some sort, the situation will then be soon beyond control, and the release of a vast store of heat will be the outcome. Briefly, therefore, we may state the problem of using atoms for peace and atoms for war as follows. If all we ask is to destroy others, and inescapably ourselves as well, we have to arrange to make k greater than unity. If we seek to realize for ourselves and others a hitherto unrealized prospect of prosperity, we must be able to release energy at a steady rate by keeping k near enough to unity to ensure that the reaction neither comes to a standstill nor gets beyond control.

If our choice is universal extinction, the problem is relatively simple. As we increase the size of a body its mass increases in proportion to surface from which escape is possible. Consequently, there will be a *critical size* at which the escape of neutrons from a fissionable mass such as U235 does not suffice to ensure against a rate of impact sufficient to start the chain reaction. A very small initial input of energy in terms of neutron supply (as from a minute quantity of radium and beryllium or boron) will then suffice to start it. Any mechanism which can keep apart and bring together as required two masses of the fissionable material jointly in excess of the critical size but individually less than it, will accomplish the end in view. The constructive use of nuclear energy sets us a harder task. Since it is not practicable to plan things so that our reproduction factor k will remain exactly equal to unity, the gradual release of heat as a source of constructive power requires *both* some means of slowing down the reaction when it begins to exceed unity *and* some means of speeding it up when k falls below unity. Research stimulated by the prospect of initiating a chain reaction soon disclosed two practicable ways of doing the first and one way of doing the second. The practicability of one or the other is because:

(*a*) Some substances, especially heavy water (p. 803) and graphite, slow down the speed of swift fission neutrons to the level at which fission of U235 is most frequent;

(*b*) Some substances, expecially cadmium and boron, can capture neutrons which escape from a fissionable mass, whence adjustable rods of such material within a fissionable mass of critical size can serve to slow down or speed up the spread of the chain reaction within it.

THERMONUCLEAR ENERGY

Our discussion of the release of energy stored in the atom has hitherto taken within its scope only: (*a*) breakdown of heavier into lighter atoms, in nature by emission of alpha particles and in the laboratory by bombardment with such particles or with artificially produced particles (*protons* and *neutrons*); (*b*) increase of the atomic number of an isotope by emission of a beta particle (*electron*). We have spoken of the proton and the neutron as particles of equal mass. We have likewise assumed that the atomic weight of an isotope is necessarily a whole number. Both the last statements are true within limits of error scarcely exceeding one in a thousand; but technical improvements of the so-called *Mass Spectrograph* (Fig. 397) more especially by Aston in Britain and Bainbridge in America has now made it practicable to measure the mass of atomic particles with five-figure precision. This has led to the discovery that the A.W. of an isotope is the sum of a whole number (now called its *mass number*) and a minute but measurable *binding fraction* which may be positive or negative. If the mass balance sheet of a nuclear reaction involves a net loss of binding fraction, there is release of energy as heat. In the nuclear reaction which Cockroft and Walton discovered, such a net loss of mass does occur. We can now set out the balance sheet as follows:

	Mass number	Binding fraction
$_3Li^7$	7	0·0180
$_1H^1$	1	0·0081
Total	8	0·0261
$2(_2He^4)$	$2(4) = 8$	$2(0·0039) = 0.0078$
Difference		$0·0183 = (0·0261 - 0·0078)$

In whatever way we explain this loss of mass by the nucleus, it appears in the outcome as *release of heat*. Such co-called *thermo*-nuclear phenomena can occur only in special circumstances. Any such reaction signifies that two or more nuclei come into contact to combine. Being of light charge, nuclei of any atoms repel one another. It is therefore difficult to ensure contact by collision, and we know how to do so in two ways only. The experiments of Cockroft and Walton illustrates one, i e. that occasional collisions between hydrogen ions and nuclei of another element may occur if we greatly accelerate the motion of a stream of protons in a very powerful electric or magnetic field. Spectrographic and pyrometric study of the sun suggests another possibility.

We now explain increase of gas pressure in response to heat on two assumptions: (*a*) the molecules of a gas move about randomwise at a mean speed which depends on the temperature of the gas; (*b*) the greater kinetic energy of the molecules at a higher temperature increases frequency of collision with the surface of the container, whence greater force thereon exerted per unit area At very high temperatures, the speed might conceivably be sufficient to bring nuclei into contact; and this may well be what happens in collision in the interior of the sun, where the temperature is about 20 million degrees centigrade. Astro-physicists have long suspected that this is so. As we now know, experiment disastrously confirms their suspicion. The immense fission heat which a chain reaction can liberate can produce a rise of temperature great enough to bring about combination of lighter atoms on a large scale with loss of binding mass and release of stupendous stores of heat energy in the process. Such is the theory of the hydrogen bomb.

ATOMIC ENGINES

In theory, any source of heat can be made available as a substitute for human labour, but the undertaking is not necessarily economical if it entails,

as is true of proposals to trap solar energy, outlay for equipment disproportionate to the small output available for use. Needless to say, this dilemma
does not arise in connexion with nuclear energy. Thus the various ways in
which a heat engine of one sort or another can mobilize heat conveyed from
a device which releases atomic energy by a cooling fluid which circulates
therein need not concern us. The use of fuel by the essential part of the engine
as such does deserve attention, but it would still be premature to say much.
In 1940 atomic engineering was a pipe-dream, and the next fifteen years
may witness achievements no less dramatic than those of the immediate past.
Details which now seem to be important may then seem to be trivial. It must
suffice to indicate the three main types of atomic engines in production to
date (1956).

What we here mean by the essential mechanism of an atomic engine
(*reactor* or *pile*) is the way in which it uses fissionable fuel to supply heat for
any other mechanism capable of exploiting it. We have seen that a chain
reaction can occur in a mass of fissionable material only if it exceeds a certain
critical size; and we have also seen that the frequency of collision between a
nucleus and a neutron with the alternative consequences of capture and
fission depend on the speed of the neutron itself. Relatively slow neutrons can
start a chain reaction in U235 above the critical size limit because each of two
conditions holds good: (*a*) slow neutrons from an outside source can bring
about fission; (*b*) swifter neutrons released by fission can also do so. The
isotope U238 which accounts for slightly more than 99 per cent of the mass
of natural uranium responds to neutron bombardment in a different way. It
is fissionable only by very swift neutrons; and it captures most of the swifter
neutrons released by fission from U235. Thus it damps down to a standstill
the process of starting a chain reaction in the latter. It is therefore impossible
to start up a chain reaction in natural uranium by introducing a few slow
neutrons at trivial initial cost.

First attempts to bring about a chain reaction for merely destructive ends
sidestepped this difficulty by the costly process of separating U235 from its
partner; but this is not necessary if the end in view is a regulated chain
reaction for constructive use. Such a regulated reaction is possible only
if we can slow down the process before it gets out of control; and it happens
that slow neutrons readily capable of bringing about fission of U235 have
much less risk than faster ones of capture by U238. Thus any device which
reduces the speed of fission-neutrons within a mass of natural uranium will
increase the survival rate of fission neutrons themselves available to bring
about fission of U235 within the native mixture of the two isotopes.

(1) *Thermal Reactors.* In this type of Atomic Engine, the fuel is pieces of
natural uranium dispersed in a *moderator* such as heavy water or graphite
to slow down the speed of the fission neutrons without capture. The problem
of designing such an engine involves specification of the arrangement of the
uranium embedded in the moderator with a view to ensuring a high probability that the appropriate reduction of speed will occur. To prevent the
chain reaction from getting out of hand adjustable cadmium rods project
into the substance of the composite fuel. As we have seen, this metal absorbs
neutrons readily. By projecting such rods more deeply into fuel, it is therefore

possible to reduce the survival rate of fission electrons capable of continuing the fission process. Conversely, their withdrawal makes more fission electrons available to continue it.

(2) *Fast Reactors*. Native U235, the artificial isotope U233 and plutonium undergo fission by relatively swift neutrons liberated in the fission process. If used as fuel, it is therefore possible to dispense with a moderator. A cadmium rod mechanism suffices to control the speed of reaction. Complete separation of U235 from natural uranium is costly, but it is possible at much less cost to concentrate it sufficiently to ensure the possibility of a chain reaction beyond an appropriate critical size limit. The special interest of this type of atomic engine arises from the possibility of using U233 and plutonium for fuel as indicated below.

(3) *The Breeder Pile*. Like the last, the breeder pile is a fast reactor which makes use of *enriched* natural uranium (i.e. with artificially high concentration of U235) as its fuel; but it also takes advantage of the capture of neutrons by the residual U238 to produce—and to conserve for use the end-products of—the isotope U239 (p. 1117) of which the atom yields Plutonium 239 by successive emission of two beta particles. Native Thorium 232, which is much more abundant than native uranium, if embedded in the fuel of a fast reactor is also utilizable as a source of fissionable U233. Since fission liberates more than one neutron it is thus possible to produce one or more atoms of plutonium (or U233) for every neutron which brings about fission. This signifies that the breeder can produce as much new fuel as it consumes. Whereas the simple fast reactor or the thermal reactor consume fissionable fuel present in relatively small amounts in the earth's crust, the breeder pile therefore makes enough fuel to keep itself going while it generates heat for useful work in the process.

NO PLACE TO HIDE

This book first appeared as a *Primer for the Age of Plenty* on the eve of the Second (and last-but-one possible) World War. The Western scene was then a spectacle of mass unemployment and poverty in the midst of available plenty; but orthodox economic doctrine still dismissed the possibility of planning our resouces to take advantage of the prosperity scientific discovery can offer mankind. At the end of hostilities, the West began to be aware of an awakening of human aspirations in Asia and Africa. To some, it seemed that the Age of Plenty was as far off as ever before. When the spectacles of Hiroshima and Nagasaki appalled and numbed our faith in the future of mankind, only those behind an Iron Curtain of military secrecy which enveloped the swift advances of nuclear physics between 1940 and 1945 could confidently forecast that power to destroy life on a scale so unprecedented could also become the means of realizing a hitherto unimaginable prospect of human prosperity on a global scale. When the curtain went up in 1955, the Breeder Pile was a reality.

History offers no parallel to what had happened in the preceding fifteen years. Today, we can say that the human race as a whole has now at its disposal unlimited sources of power to replace irksome toil; and no rationalization of privilege can henceforth justify poverty in any part of our planet. According to an authoritative statement issued by one of our leading nuclear physicists, less than twenty thermonuclear bombs each enclosed in a cobalt shell could release enough radioactive dust to extinguish human life on our planet. For the first time in the 25,000 years of its story, the human race thus faces the immediate possibility of total extinction. Such is the choice before us, while we can still hope. Since it is easier to conceive grounds for pessimism than for confidence in the future of mankind, there is no intellectual merit in disillusionment; but the only rational basis for continued hopefulness in a situation which leaves us with so much left to hope for is the possibility that an informed public opinion will force into retirement trigger-happy demogogues boastful because still able to lead us to the brink of thermonuclear annihilation. After an ephemeral outbreak of sanity in the fateful August of 1945, the leaders of all the major political groups in Britain and America have lapsed with sinister and sententious levity into slogans which have lost any similitude of relevance to the prospect ahead. Only a few laconic headlines greet the event when a British Minister of Defence announces a project to evacuate from its major cities to the countryside 12,000,000 mothers, children and old folk of Britain. Whether comedians, our political comedians, will go down to history as crooks or cretins, history alone will decide, but only if history takes our destiny out of their hands.

Under a stable system of world government, to which all nations, kindreds and tongues must surrender a measure of national sovereignty, we can assuredly enter into the Promised Land of Plenty. If we decline to make so small a concession to our traditional ways of life, the alternative is an end like to the end foretold by the writer of the Apocalypse:

There was a great earthquake; and the sun became black as sackcloth of hair, and the moon became as blood; and the stars of heaven fell upon the earth, even as a figtree casteth her untimely figs, when she is shaken of a mighty wind. And the heavens departed as a scroll when it is rolled together; and every mountain and island were moved out of their places. And the kings of the earth and the great men and the rich men and the chief captains and the mighty men, and every bondman and every freeman hid themselves in the dens and in the rocks of the mountains; And said to the mountains and rocks, Fall on us, and hide us from the face of him that sitteth on the throne

EPILOGUE

A NEW SOCIAL CONTRACT

Two questions assert themselves as we take leave of one another. One is whether the present tempo of scientific progress will continue, or whether we are living in the twilight of a culture to be followed by dreary centuries of commentaries and imitators. The other is whether the bulk of mankind will reap the benefit of the new powers and inventions which advancing scientific knowledge has placed at our disposal, or whether the vast destructive instruments which it has also created will be used by power-seeking men to destroy any immediate hope of a brighter future for the human race. To the extent that our own conduct can contribute to the answers we give they are not unconnected. *Science for the Citizen* began with a quotation in which the great German chemist Liebig declared that "only the freeman has a disposition and interest to improve." Inescapably it ends on the same note. The further progress of science depends on how far the scientific worker and his fellow citizens co-operate with one another in applying scientific knowledge to the satisfaction of the common needs of mankind.

Before discussing the first question it is important to clarify a distinction which is commonly taken for granted. The separation of human societies into social classes which enjoy abundant leisure, or are deprived of it, has encouraged a superficial and arbitrary division of science into two branches, *pure* and *applied*. According to a view which has survived from the time of Aristotle, pure science is science sought for its own sake. Its sufficient justification is the individual satisfaction it brings to those who are in the fortunate position to pursue it. In contradistinction to pure science, so defined, applied science is science adapted to the discovery of material amenities which benefit mankind in general or those who patronize the pursuit of it. The sense in which science is worth studying for its own sake has been discussed at length elsewhere (p. 741). Here we may content ourselves with a single comment which has been emphasized repeatedly in what has gone before. From the craftsmen navigators of the Mediterranean in the seventh century B.C. to the researches of Pasteur on silkworm disease, science has advanced conspicuously when it has been actively in contact with the world's work. From the astronomer priest of Gizeh to the priestly astronomer of the Gifford Lectures, science has declined when it has taken refuge in prophecy. The veritable orgy of publicity with which the Press Lords have rewarded astrophysical extrapolations is the proper corollary of the proposal for a moratorium on scientific inventions.

Science is not cosmic prophecy. True science, in the words of Robert Boyle, is such knowledge "as hath a tendency to use." A scientific law embodies a recipe for doing something, and its final validification rests in the domain of action. The immense confidence which certain scientific generalizations rightly command depends on large-scale opportunities for testing their capacity to bear fruit in the commonplace activities of everyday life. Speculative extrapolations concerning the age of the universe change from day to day as astronomical knowledge advances, and we should be justified in treating astronomers with the same suspicion as politicians if the credentials of astronomy had no firmer basis. Our reliance on astronomy is justified by the fact that it provides the farmer with a calendar of the seasons, the fisherman with a table of tides, the statesman with a map, the Union Castle Line with the means of navigating a ship into port, and the Minister of Transport with fines from motorists who fail to light up after civil twilight ends. The only valid distinction between pure and applied research in natural science lies between inquiries concerned with issues which *may eventually* and issues which *already do* arise in the social practice of mankind. Consequently, the pure scientist knows that he has everything to gain from encouragement of applied research, and if the last survivors of Darwin's generation still murmur doubts about Mendelism, the experimental geneticist goes on his way serenely confident that the *Feathered World* will continue to advertise day-old sex-linked chicks, or that rabbit furriers now know how to make pure lilac from blue beveren-chocolate havana crosses, or how to fix "Rex" on any colour pattern in two generations.

Pure and applied science are not independent social phenomena. They are inextricably related as shoot and root in the process of healthy growth. Growing science is the unity of theory and practice. Without its roots firmly planted in the moist soil of social practice the green shoot of pure science withers and becomes the dead trunk of metaphysics. Without the aspiring shoot of theory sustaining it with the nutriment of air and sunlight, the root of applied science degenerates into the dry wood of empirical repetition. This is no new truth, nor paradox. It has been stated and restated anew in every age of rebirth. Hear, for instance, Sir William Petty in whose rooms the Invisible College held its first meetings:

Hindrance of the advancement of learning hath beene because thought, theory, and practice, hath been always divided in severall persons; because the ways of learning are too tedious for them to be joyned. And whereas all writings ought to be descriptions of things, they are now onely of words, books know little of things, and the practicall men have not language nor method enough to describe (them) by words.

The superficiality of this dualism, which we perpetuate in our universities and technical colleges to the detriment of both, may be illustrated by reverting to another metaphor used elsewhere. Science is not a photograph of the real world. It is a map, in which mountains, rivers, and valleys are variously coloured not to represent their actual tints, but because the colours can give us useful directions. It is one thing to say that a discipline can only rank as genuine science when it can also supply us with recipes for the practical conduct of affairs, and it is another to say that scientific research is and must always be confined to topics of immediate social value. If you have to build a railway you need a map. It is obviously superficial to draw a sharp distinction between the work done in mapping the actual track traversed as *useful* work in contradistinction to all the *useless* work of mapping the part of the territory over which no rails are laid down. One reason is that you cannot know what you will have to scrap till your task is finished. Another is that the existence of the railway may make it necessary or desirable to have a water supply, town, or sanatorium in the vicinity. What is easily overlooked is that the part of the map where no rails are laid down, where no town is built, where no wells are tapped, and where no sanatorium is erected would not have been prospected *unless there had first been a definite social reason for constructing the map.*

Among the few who realize the vast expense at which modern scientific work is conducted some will here put forward an objection such as this. So far, so good. We recognize that the average citizen, still less the average capitalist, will not be induced to subscribe voluntarily, or from taxation, to the upkeep of scientific research, unless he foresees the prospect of some material benefit. We recognize also that theoretical advances often arise as a by-product of research conducted in this way. What we assert is that the social value of knowledge is not exclusively circumscribed by its *material* rewards, and that socially useful knowledge which confers no material benefits is necessarily nursed by the existence of a class with leisure to occupy themselves with its pursuit. Although it is not often stated, this embodies a view which is held by many thoughtful citizens.

As did Lucretius, the writer of this book believes that one of the benefits science bestows, and not the least of them, is to liberate mankind from the terror of the gods. Scientific knowledge gives us the means of planning for plenty and also helps to free us from habits which prevent us from doing so. The dividing line between progress in science and progress in morals is not clear cut. Our moral attitude to witch-burning (Chapter VII) is not unconnected with advancing scientific knowledge of chemistry, and advancing scientific knowledge of medicine (Chapter XVII) is not unconnected with social mores concerning the health of the masses. So the social use of science is not exhausted by material welfare, as the term is ordinarily defined. In the words of Robert Boyle we are not entitled to expect that the "goods of mankind will be much increased" by the archaeologist's "insight into the trades." None the less, lack of archaeological knowledge may prevent us from using "the naturalist's insight into the trades," or from continuing to exist long enough to use any sort of knowledge at all. A little instruction in elementary archaeology would have made it far more difficult to spread the doctrines which have been used to bolster up the war madness of Hitler's Europe. The view stated in the preceding paragraph therefore deserves sympathetic attention.

It is always wiser to be guided by the experience of the human race than to be circumscribed by the limitations of our reasoning and imaginative endowments. Before we are driven to conclude that essential unity of theory and practice in scientific progress applies only to such branches of positive knowledge as minister to man's material needs, we should therefore be guided by the history of sciences which do not conspicuously do so. In the light of current events archaeology claims a prominent place among the latter. It is therefore instructive to ask in what circumstances the science of archaeology advances. We have, in fact, a noteworthy illustration in our own generation. The search for new mutations as a basis for selective stock or crop improvement is now based on outbreeding to wild populations which have not been exhausted by previous selection. In connexion with its plans for increased cereal production the Soviet Union recently financed the most ambitious scheme of archaeological research yet undertaken. The objective of this expedition, in which the geneticist Vavilov played a leading part, was to ascertain the focal localities of cereal origins.

It would be unwise to cite the grandiose scale of this inquiry as an isolated case. So we may also recall the circumstances which gave birth to Egyptology. Our knowledge of the early history of Egypt begins with the Rosetta stone. For long the inscriptions in picture-writing on Egyptian tombs were an impenetrable mystery to which classical literature furnished no clue. The Rosetta stone of basalt stele, $3\frac{1}{2}$ by $2\frac{1}{2}$ ft. in size, was inscribed with a decree of Ptolemy V in hieroglyphics, demotic and Greek. By all appearances it was like the trilingual notices which are often seen at money exchange bureaux in ports, and the Greek version therefore provided the key which eventually enabled Champollion to decipher the script of priestly Egypt. It was discovered in 1799, and completely elucidated in 1831, since when a new field of historical science has been explored.

The discovery of the Rosetta stone was the result of an expedition in which science was faced with a new and imperative social demand. The story of the expedition in which Napoleon was accompanied by a veritable galaxy of French scientific men, including Fourier, the mathematician, to survey the country, with Berthollet, the chemist, to study the Nile inundations, is told by A. G. Macdonell (*Napoleon and His Marshals*):

> The wreckage of dead Admiral Bruix's Line of Battle was still drifting in the Bay of Aboukir when Bonaparte flung himself buoyantly into a thousand details of organization. Nine days after the news of the Nile he was establishing the Institute of Egypt in Cairo, accepting its vice-presidency under presidency of the great mathematician Monge, and setting a number of little problems to the savants at their first session. (A new regime was beginning, under which *even professors had to mingle the practical with the abstract*.) "Can the baking ovens of the army be improved?" he demanded of the men of science? Could any substitute for hops be found for the brewing of beer? Was the windmill or the water-mill the more suitable for milling at Cairo? How could the army establish a powder-factory, and did Egypt possess any of the ingredients for the manufacture of gunpowder? On the less utilitarian side, the demoniacally energetic Commander set the professors to work to study and measure ruins, decipher hieroglyphics, and make drawings of statues. It was inconvenient that Nelson should have destroyed the French fleet, and severed all communications between 40,000 Frenchmen and France, but that was no reason why the Sphinx should not be measured, the Rosetta stone deciphered, the land surveyed, the soils analysed, and the inundations of the Nile determined. At Suez Bonaparte himself found the canal of Sesostris, half as old as time, and followed Mahomet and the great Saladin in signing his name in the visitors' book of the monks of Sinai.

The questions which we have set ourselves in these concluding comments can only be answered in a very limited sense. The best answers we can hope to find for them are merely statements about the limitations which our own conduct imposes. Beyond that, anything we might say would usurp the prophetic prerogatives of the astronomer priests and the priestly astronomers. To our first question, whether science will continue to progress at the tempo of recent years, our narrative has already supplied two such reservations. If the physicist capitulates to the frozen patents of monopolistic capitalism and seeks refuge from reality in speculations about the future of the universe five million million years hence, if the geneticist accepts the lop-sided mechanical technology of today and is content to culture his fruit flies in the laboratory, cut off from the urgent problems of crop and stock, if our biologists use their knowledge to concoct ingenious excuses to defend educational privileges and imperialistic exploitation of backward cultures, physics and biology will lose the driving force which science has always derived from living contact with the world's productive work, and the satisfaction of man's common needs. If the chemist devotes his ingenuity to making gases and sprays to blind and suffocate the inhabitants of great cities, and bacteriologists consent to spread plagues to infect the reservoirs and stock of enemy populations, the survivors of our civilization will declare that our science has exacted too high a price for its benefits. Even if science and civilization do not perish together, both will suffer a heavy setback for many years to come.

We turn now to our second question, the immediate prospects for extending the benefits of science to the service of mankind. This is not a primer of politics, and it would be immodest of the author to attempt a complete analysis of the impediments which prevent us from realizing the new potentials of social well-being, except in so far as problems which perplex the citizen of today are specially relevant to its theme. In some of what will be said subsequently the writer is drawing what he believes to be inescapable conclusions from the record of scientific progress. Elsewhere opinions advanced are those of one fellow citizen communing with another.

During the past century scientific knowledge has created new potentials of social organization vastly in excess of anything for which the political education of mankind is prepared. Seventy years ago it was still possible to discuss whether poverty was morally tolerable or materially inevitable. It was still possible to discuss whether war was spiritually edifying or socially escapable. All this is changed. Poverty in the sense in which it was then defined, the sense in which the word is intelligible to the social biologist, is not materially inevitable. The only obstacle to removing it is lack of social initiative. War is not a moral picnic. It threatens to destroy the entire fabric of our civilization, if we do not eradicate it with as much promptitude and ruthlessness as we have eradicated, or are eradicating, smallpox, malaria, and yellow fever.

The power to shape the future course of events so as to extend the benefits of advancing scientific knowledge for the satisfaction of common human need may now be ours in so far, and only in so far, as our conduct is guided by an understanding of the impact of science on human society. During the latter half of the nineteenth century a powerful school of political thought was led to advance three main conclusions from a study of the influence which changing technology was then exerting on the social superstructures of the time. One was that nations were becoming economically more interdependent. A second was that skilled and privileged workmanship and the standard of life of the employed classes as a whole would continue to decline. The third was that the militant opposition of the employed classes to the existing economic system would continue to increase. On these conclusions they based a social policy which has outlived the impulse to searching examination of current events from the same standpoint.

As a description of dominant tendencies in the first phase of modern power production when steam was replacing water, no exception need be taken to the statements made above. They make up a penetrating analysis of what was happening in 1870, when such doctrines took root. Steam navigation and telegraphy were speeding up international trade. The old style craftsman was making way for the machine minder, and universal schooling had not been introduced. Radio and cinema had not placed new instruments for moulding mass opinion in the hands of Government, and there was as yet no popular Press.

Salient features which distinguish the initial and the present phases of modern power production have emerged in Chapters VIII, XII, and XIV The first phase began about 1780. Initially the owners of the larger industries were often men like Roebuck, Boulton and Wedgwood. Themselves inventors or actively sympathetic to the advancement of talent, they participated directly in the task of administration and truly contributed to the production of wealth by their labours. The inventor and technical expert could still anticipate advancement leading to partnership, and lower managerial posts were filled by promotion from the general body of workmen. This alluring picture has little resemblance to the conduct of large modern industries. In the second phase of power production, that is to say from about 1880 onwards, technical improvements of industry have been largely due to *discoveries made in laboratories supported from public funds* by men such as Faraday and Henry (see pp. 715–16). The ownership of industry has passed more and more into the hands of an amorphous parasitic army of shareholders who exercise no creative function in their capacity as such. The actual labour of administration and technical control has passed into the hands of a growing class of salaried officials whose employment is determined partly by special educational qualifications and partly by social influence. At the apex of the hierarchy are the financial conjurers who can manipulate a system of costing with no relevance to the balance sheet (Chapter XII, p. 626) of human effort and materials made available for the satisfaction of common human needs. They exercise credit power to buy up new patents which might otherwise be used by weaker competitors. As often as not the patent is put into cold storage—the "ice-box."*

The belief that increasing scientific knowledge makes for closer economic interdependence, and, what was often stated as a corollary to this, the belief that this increasing interdependence provided a guarantee of world peace, was a dogma universally held by progressive thinkers in the nineteenth century. This was not unnatural in the first flush of surprise which followed the introduction of steam navigation, transcontinental railways, and oceanic telegraphy. Our own perspective is different. We have seen that

* Vide ,B. J. Stern, *Restraints upon the Utilisation of Inventions.* Am. Acad. Pol. Soc., November 1938.

Chile saltpetre can now be made out of atmospheric nitrogen, that *Cheddar* cheese can now be made anywhere, that hospitals are using radio-active sodium prepared from ordinary salt instead of having to import the rare radio-active minerals, that the Channel Islands are no longer regarded as a sufficient guarantee of the genetic credentials of cattle, that we may soon be making most of our machinery of aluminium from the clay of our soils and magnesium from sea salt, that we are already beginning to feed our pigs on the disintegration products of wood pulp, to grow several crops of tomatoes a year by tank gardening, and to produce sugar by the agency of bacteria from vegetable waste matter. Without committing ourselves to any dogmatic assertions about how far this will go on, what we can say is this. The practical outcome of some of the major achievements of scientific discovery during the past two centuries has been to increase the potential local self-sufficiency consistent with the satisfaction of fundamental human needs.

Where social policy becomes alert to the new powers and inventions available for human well-being, the satisfaction of basic human needs will take precedence over the multiplication of useless commodities to distract neurotic urban populations, and the merits of more or less industrial specialization will be examined with proper regard to the distribution of population in congenial and healthy surroundings. The doctrine of Free Trade was sustained by the moral conviction that the greatest good of the greatest number is the same as the greatest number of goods available to the greatest number of people. For privacy and serenity of life, the satisfactions of parenthood and the graces of human fellowship in modest communities Free Trade offered the compensations of the Department store and labour-saving flats in flowerless streets. Free Trade accepted the urban squalor of a coal economy as the price for its own definition of prosperity. Today scientific knowledge offers us the possibility of a new plan of social living more akin to the Utopia of a William Morris or an Edward Carpenter. Mobile power, aviation, and electrical communications make it possible to distribute population at a high level of productive capacity without the disabilities of cultural isolation. The beehive community of Free Trade has robbed the citizen of a lively interest in his immediate social relations without promoting the will to peace abroad. Co-operative organization in the age of hydro-electric power, of light metals, of artificial fertilizers and applied genetics offers us the use of new means of transport and new means of communication both to restore the serenity of small community life and to promote a lively sympathy with folk who live in other lands. Broadcasting has now brought the cultural benefits of travel to the bedside; and scientific horticulture offers us a programme of bio-aesthetic planning which may prove more congenial to basic human needs than the spectacle of Woolworth's building.

A second doctrine which seemed to be supported by the advent of modern power production was the progressive degradation of skilled work during a period which witnessed a great reduction of highly skilled handicraft. Even before the introduction of electricity as a source of power, the conduct of a mechanized and more highly urbanized society had initiated changes which counteracted the cultural process of levelling down. Universal schooling, a popular Press, free libraries, succeeded one another in countries with a democratic constitution. With the coming of electricity as a source of power industry came under the impact of new problems of costing and new technical advantages of mobility. Where it has been introduced into the factory, it has created a demand for a new type of skill and special training, while dispensing with a large volume of unskilled and casual labour which can be done by machinery. To see the impact of the new technical forces most clearly we need to examine the statistics of a country which is in a more advanced state of technical development than Britain. In his book *Insurgent America,* Alfred Bingham has made an analysis of the growth of social classes in the United States during recent years, and finds that the new type of skilled and administrative employee has steadily increased in proportion to labourers performing heavy unskilled work.

Thus modern technology has brought into being a social group with social aspirations and a social status of its own. Its social aspirations for further opportunity of employment can be realized only by the further extension of technical improvements which have encouraged its growth. For the time being, at least, it is still growing and, at present, politically inarticulate. It may therefore play a decisive role in the success of any social movement which can claim its allegiance. In a period of social crisis its importance should not be judged by its numerical strength, because its personnel commands resources against which mere man power is helpless and barricades are literary illusions. If it can be enlisted in a task which will offer it far greater opportunities of creative service than it now enjoys, the transition from a discredited and demoralized competitive to a rationally planned industrial system is assured. If it is driven by fear of chaos to support any dictator movement which offers the prospect of breathing space, it may become the instrument for destroying democracy, freedom of discourse, and the hope of peace.

In the economy of private enterprise the use of science is primarily directed to increase profits for shareholders even at the price of recurrent unemployment, depressions, and national distress. It is secondarily applied to the welfare of the worker, where civic organization undertakes the responsibility of planning its use through such instruments as the Industrial Health Board of the British Medical Research Council. Inescapably on that account, the wage earner and his representatives have been hostile or suspicious in their attitude to technical innovations, while disposed to sympathize indiscriminately with proposals for extending the scope of public enterprise. So the social aspirations of the highly trained worker and of the wage earner had little in common while private enterprise could guarantee the continued expansion of industry with new opportunities of advancement and promotion for special skill and training. The prospects of the salaried worker in highly industrialized countries such as Britain and America become less reassuring as the domain of private monopoly extends. In Britain large-scale unemployment has produced a drift of the working population from depressed areas to localities where no pre-existing tradition of organization safeguards their own interests. Their representatives are now compelled to examine proposals for creating new industries with a progressive technical outlook.

For both reasons a new sympathy of outlook is uniting different sections of the productive population in a common endeavour to prevent the frustration of science by social parasitism.

Advancing scientific knowledge has swept away many beliefs which sustained popular aspirations in the formative stages of modern democracy. The providential dispensation which endorsed the same plan of governance for Church and State, the mythology of the Beautiful Savage and metaphysical libertarianism with its hypertrophied insistence on the diversity of personal preference, do not belong to the century in which we are living. In their place modern science offers us a NEW SOCIAL CONTRACT. The social contract of scientific humanism is the recognition that the sufficient basis for rational co-operation between citizens is scientific investigation of the common needs of mankind, a scientific inventory of resources available for satisfying them, and a realistic survey of how modern social institutions contribute to or militate against the use of such resources for the satisfaction of fundamental human needs. The new social contract demands a new orientation of educational values and new qualifications for civic responsibility. In so far as our narrative has exhibited the place of advancing scientific knowledge in the progress of civilization and the impetus which science has received from expanding opportunities for the satisfaction of common human needs, *Science for the Citizen* is a modest contribution to the new orientation.

ANSWERS TO EXAMPLES

CHAPTER I

2. November 4th.
3. 74½° S.
4. July 3rd.
11. (a) 73½° N.   (b) on equator.
12. (a) 16½° N.   (b) 11½° N.   (c) 73½° N.
13. (a) 73½° S.   (b) 73½° S.
16. (a) Oct. 15th, Nov. 22nd.   (b) Oct. 7th, Nov. 28th.
    (c) Jan. 6th, March 25th, July 17th, Aug. 4th.
17. 1.30 p.m., 1.18 p.m., and 1.22 p.m.

CHAPTER II

1. Declination: 0°, 23½° N., 0°, 23½° S. R.A.: 0 hour, 6 hours, 12 hours, 18 hours.
3. Lat. 50° N., Long. 5¾° W. approx.
4. 2 hours 28 mins., 8.12 p.m., 48½° W.
5. 46° N.
6. 48° 15′ W., 57° 24′ N.
7. Sept. 23rd.
8. Thin, waning crescent, 5.8 a.m., 11.8 a.m.
10. 7,900 miles approx.
11. N. Devon.
12. About Sept. 24th.
13. Yorkshire.

CHAPTER III

1. Just within principal focus, $25\frac{1}{16}''$ from mirror.
2. To 12″ from lens.
3. Both distances 16″.
4. Book from lens 40″, plate from lens 10″.
5. 9″.
6. 15° 53′.
7. 14 ft., 6 ft.
8. (a) 3.   (b) 5.
9. (a) 6·006″.   (b) 4·908″.   (c) 5·264″.   (d) 5·919″.
10. 83° 36′.
11. 44° 59′ approx.
12. Converging, 100 cm.
13. Diverging 166⅔ cm.
14. Diverging 250 cm.
15. $+ 2, - 3\frac{1}{3}, - 5$.
17. $43\frac{1}{6}°$.
18. 1·59.
19. 40·5′.
20. 2·4″.
21. 49.

22. 50·6 cm. from the 16 c.p. lamp towards, and 32·5 cm. from the 16 c.p lamp away from the other lamp.
23. 2·41 to 1.
24. 1 × 10¹⁷ candles.

CHAPTER IV

1. 3,460, 1,550, and 180 land miles.
3. 57·7°, 7.33 p.m.
4. Rising: 6.40 a.m., 7 a.m., 7.28 a.m. Setting: 5.20 p.m., 5 p.m., 4.32 p.m.
5. London: 7.32 a.m., 4.56 p.m., 66° from S.; New York: 7.7 a.m., 5.21 p.m., 70° from S.; Cape Town: 5.33 a.m., 6.55 p.m., 72° from S.
6. Before: Vega sets 6.30 p.m., rises 7.35 p.m., 6° from N.; Sun rises 6.23 a.m., sets 5.56 p.m., 86° from S. After: Vega sets 5.35 p.m., rises 6.40 p.m., 6° from N. Sun rises 5.52 a.m., sets 6.19 p.m., 86° from N.
8. 78°, 53°.
9. 0·375 to 1.
10. 225 days, 687 days, 0·475 to 1.

CHAPTER V

1. 7 m.p.h.
2. 20 yds.
3. 3·83 m.p.h., $30\frac{11}{12}°$ W. of N.
4. 18° W. of S.
5. 1·104 miles.
6. 36·04 cm.
7. 5 ft., $2\frac{1}{2}$ ft., $1\frac{1}{4}$ ft., $\frac{2}{3}$ ft.
8. 77·48 gm.
9. 512 poundals. 140·143 × 10⁵ dynes.
10. 6 cwt., 10 cwt.
11. $37\frac{1}{2}$ lb.
12. 210 lb., $\frac{3}{7}$ of distance along pole from the stronger.
13. 8·68 lb., 25 lb., 35·35 lb., 43·3 lb., 50 lb.
14. 90°.
15. 5·556, 10·94, 16, 20·57, 24·51, 27·71, 30·07, 31·52, 32.
16. 8 ft., 16 ft./sec.; $\frac{8}{9}$ ft., $\frac{1}{9}^d$ ft./sec.; $\frac{8}{3}$ ft., $\frac{1}{3}^d$ ft./sec.
17. (a) 0·465 sec.   (b) 103·52 ft.   (c) 4·714 ft./sec.   (d) 8·368 ft./sec.
18. 30°.
19. 975 cm. per sec.², 13,826 dynes, 4·424 × 10⁵ dynes.
20. 128 lb.
21. (a) 4·6 tons.   (b) 5·04 tons.
22. $\frac{1}{2}$ ton, 4 lb.
23. $58\frac{2}{3}$ ft./sec.
24. 2,200 ft., 0·44 ft./sec.².
26. 256 ft., 4 secs.
27. 3 secs., 30 yds.
28. 43·8 ft./sec., 1·37 secs.
29. 6 ft. 3 in., 7 ft. 10 in.
30. 30 m.p.h., 0·183 ft./sec.².
31. 3,500 ft.
32. $34\frac{2}{3}°$.
33. 39° 12′ or 50° 48′.
34. After 1 or 5 secs., $16\sqrt{133}$ ft. or $80\sqrt{109}$ ft.

35. (a) 14·34 ft./sec.².   (b) 0·1112 ft./sec.².
36. 49° 3′, 66° 33′.
37. 2¾ in.
39. 21⅔ in., 5 ft.
40. 32·16 ft./sec.².
42. 40·3 in.
43. Loses 18 secs.
44. 0·4 per cent.
45. 8·3 lb.
46 1·372 cm., 0·0245 cm.
47. 2·43 ins. per lb.
48. 1⅕ secs.
49. 32·214 ft./sec.², 32·204 ft./sec.², 32·176 ft./sec.².
50. 9·981 lb., 10·002 lb.
51. 32·1185 ft./sec.².
54. 2,444·5 ft., 5 secs.
55. 4888·3 ft., 0·015 ft./sec.².
56. Radii: 2,179, 2,237, 2,490, 2,571, 2,624, 3,064, 3,464, 3,985 miles. Speed: 570, 586, 652, 673, 687, 802, 907, 1,043 miles per hour.
57. (a) 32·227, 32·225, 32·217, 32·214, 32·212, 32·194, 32·176, 32·149 ft./sec.².
    (b) 39·183, 39·181, 39·171, 39·167, 39·165, 39·144, 39·122, 39·089 in.
58. (a) 17½.   (b) 84.   (c) 24½.   (d) 11 seconds.
59. 178 sec. slow. (The oblateness of the earth also causes a variation of *g*, in the same direction and about half as big as the variation due to latitude. The answers to the last three examples neglect this. To get answers nearer the truth, multiply the latitude variations of *g*, pendulum, and clock by 1·52.)
60. 45·6 feet West.
61. 35° to his path.
62. 10 m.p.h.
63. 14·14 m.p.h. S.E.

CHAPTER VI

1. 2·5 ft.
2. 18,300 and 36·7.
3. 132·8 cm.
4. 4,495 feet, 3·75 ft./sec.
5. 0·85 mile.
6. 2,240 ft.
7. 34·54 secs.
8. 542·6, 463·6
9. 50 m.p.h.
10. 651, 556.
11. 598·3 yards.
13. 365·3.
14. 60·6 feet.
15. 2.
16. 260.
17. 517.
18. 6, 4.
19. 1,037.
20. 68·2 m.p.h.

21. 201,600 miles per sec.
22. 327,458 radians per sec.
23. 8·33 revs. per sec.
24. 4·63 revs. per sec.

<h2>CHAPTER VII</h2>

1. < 0·69, 0·87, 0·97, 1·1, 1·26, 1·37.
2. (a) − 23·38, 9·62, − 6·06, − 9·13, − 128,   216·2 ft./sec.^{2}.
   (b) 25·93, 29·55, 27·83, 27·49, 14·46, 4·78 ft. sec
   (c) 27·90, 30·34, 29·18, 28·95, 20 15, 13 60 ft./sec. .
   (d) 29·17, 30·86, 30·06, 29·90, 23·82, 19·31 ft./sec.^{2}.
3. 102·5 kg. per sq. cm
4. 11·1 c.c.
5. 60°.
6. 1 to 3.
7. 15·8 tons.
8. 25 tons.
9. 26·88 ft./sec.^{2}, 27·94 ft./sec.^{2}, 28 78 ft./sec.^{2}.
10. 3·6 tons, 0·09 inch.
11. 1,210 cm.
12. 9·97 lb. per sq. in.
13. 1,800 feet.
14. 104.
15. 53,370 dynes per sq. cm.
16. 150·6 c.c., 57·24 cm.
17. 11 to 1.
18. 28·6 cm.
19. 30·7 inches.
20. 74·1 cm.
21. 2·7 feet.
22. 1·68 litres.
23. P − 1·54 cm., $5 - \dfrac{100}{13P}$ cm. where P is the barometric pressure.
24. 13·92, 12·42, and 9·21 ft./sec.^{2}.
25. 5·2 cm.
26. 8·76 cm.
27. (a) 0·00499 inch.   (b) 0·0497 inch.   (c) 0·472 inch.
28. (a) 1.   (b) 1·014 × 10^9.
29. 0·000089 gm./c.c., 0·00143 gm./c.c., 0·00125 gm./c.c., 16, 14.
30. 1,324·5 c.c., 518·7 c.c., 342·7 c.c.
31. In hydrogen: 31·99979, 31·99712, 31·9958, 31·9885 ft./sec.^{2}. In air: 31·99757, 31·9582, 31·9527, 31·833 ft./sec.^{2}. On SO$_3$: 31·99153, 31·8848, 31·8355, 31·539 ft./sec.^{2}.
32. (a) 1·00003023 sec.   (b) 1·00002092 sec.   (c) 1·0008371 sec.

<h2>CHAPTER VIII</h2>

1. 10·5 cm.
2. 15 cm., 195 cm.
3. 177·2 c.c.
4. 805 mm.
5. 70·8° C.
6. 1 to 1·002.

7. 2,422 inches.
8. 11·04 gm.
9. 108 c.c.
10. 22·02 gm.
11. Densities in gm. per litre: 1·429, 0·7708, 1·251, 3·22, 0·0899. Relative densities: 16, 8·5, 14, 35·5, 1.
12. 2 vols. to 1 vol., 1 gm. to 7·948 gm
13. 1 vol. in 5.
14. 1 to 1.
15. 1 to 2·67.
16. 0·0821 gm.
17. 11·64.

CHAPTER IX

1. (*a*) 650 c.c.   (*b*) 550 c.c.
2. 700 c.c.
3. 100 c.c., nil, 585 c.c., 677·5 c.c., 1,300 c.c.
5. 7·5 cm.
6. (*a*) 0·08205.   (*b*) $8·3135 \times 10^7$.   (*c*) 6,236.
7. HCN; CO.
8. CO_2, 27·27 per cent C, 72·73 per cent O; N_2O, 63·63 per cent N, 36·37 per cent O.
9. H_2S, NH_3.
10. 950 c.c., 16·74 per cent O, 83·26 per cent N.
11. At 140° C. = NO_2, on cooling N_2O_4 is formed. At 28° C. $N_2O_4:NO_2$ = 70:30.
12. See Index.
13. 3 vols. O_2 form 2 vols. O_3, 2 per cent ozone.
14. 15 gm.
15. H: 1, Cl: 35·62 (mean), O: 7·93, S: 15·95, Ag: 108·6 (mean), Hg: 99·42 (mean), Cu: 31·93 (mean), Fe: 27·79, Mg: 12·04.
16. CS_2.
17. 7·838 gm., 5,761 c.c.
18. 0·59.
19. H_2CO.
20. H: 134 cm., O: 67 cm.
21. 15·38 litres.
22. 2·88 atmos.
23. 50·9 mm.
24. 62·05.
25. 5·56 atmos.
26. 56·6 per cent.
27. (*a*) 74·4 gm.   (*b*) 47·8 gm.   (*c*) 40·9 gm.
28. 202·2 cm.
29. Steam: 0·0457 atmos., hydrogen: 0·9543 atmos.
30. 0·174 mol acid, 3·654 mol alcohol, 0·826 mol ester.
31. 3×10^{-6}.

CHAPTER XI

1. (*a*) 36·89° C.   (*b*) 309·89° Abs.   (*c*) 29·51° R.
2. 24⅕° F., 221° F., − 6⅔° C., 101⅕° C.

3. 80° C., 95° C.

4. 0·2424 cm., 0·2835 cm., 0·0105 cm.

5. 177·4 c.c.

6. (*a*) 0·62.   (*b*) 0·88.

7. 79·65 cm.

8. 0·075 cm.

9. 22·1 cm.

10. 174° C.

11. 0·46 inch.

12. 20 miles 58·4 feet.

13. 5·65 secs. lost.

14. 0·137 cm. and 0·341 cm.

CHAPTER XII

1. 0·094.

2. 0·497.

3. 3·12 gm.

4. 0·489.

5. 31° C.

6. 533·3 cals.

7. 12 gm.

8. 0·068.

9. 0·112.

10. 246·9° C

11. 0·11.

12. 28·8° C.

13. 7,962·5 gm.

14. 80·4 cals.

15. 630.

16. 0·495.

17. 2·2° C.

18. Substance (d).

19. 0·447 cals. per sq. cm. per sec.

20. 612 cals.

21. $1·357 \times 10^7$ ergs, $4·24 \times 10^5$ ergs, $1·0476 \times 10^{10}$ ergs.

22. 11,027 cals.

23. (*a*) 2,990,088 ergs, 7·05 foot poundals;
    (*b*) 11,350,000 ergs, 26·915 foot poundals.

24. 1·06° C.

25. (*a*) 3,459,048 cals.   (*b*) $1·384 \times 10^4$ B.Th.U.

26. (*a*) 0·306 therms.   (*b*) 964¾ gm.   (*c*) 68 cub. ft.   (*d*) 2·72 pence.

27. 58,430 ft. lb.

28. 15·8 h.p.

29. 410⅔ h.p.

30. 1,056 cub. ft.

31. 228° C.

32. (*a*) 6·001 ft., (*b*) 0·0367 B.Th.U.

33. British units: 168, $92·12 \times 10^4$ ft. lb., 37·002 B.Th.U.
    International units: $7·086 \times 10^7$, $3·8856 \times 10^{11}$ ergs, 9,250·7 cals.

34. $3,714 \times 10^3$ ergs.

35. 2·56 cub. ft.

36. (*a*) 114 cm.   (*b*) 134·6 cm.

CHAPTER XIV

1. $\frac{1}{6}$ amp.
2. $\frac{1}{3}$ amp., 3 volts.
3. $\frac{1}{3}$ ohm.
4. (a) 0·142 amp.   (b) 0·1 amp.
5. (a) 0·4 amp.   (b) 0·364 amp.
6. 1$\frac{3}{7}$ ohms, 0·35 amp.
7. Current is halved.
8. 1$\frac{1}{3}$ volts.
9. 8·3 ohms, 7 ohms.
10. 18.
11. 127·2 metres.
12. (a) 1·84 ohms.   (b) 1·321 ohms.
13. 0·004394 amp.
14. 0·09868 amp., 0·986 volt.
15. 1 : 4.
16. (a) 0·952 amp.   (b) 1·917 gm.   (c) 1·9048 volts.
17. (a) 0·55 amp.   (b) 0·44 amp.
18. (a) 0·283 amp.   (b) 7 ohms.
19. 0·000001628.
20. 1 amp., 4 volts.
21. A tenth.
22. 1·5 volts.
23. 1,136 ohms.
24. 58.
25. (a) 0·416 amp., 0·0832 amp.   (b) 0·1113 amp. in each.
26. 0·051 amp., 0·0065 amp.
27. 0·0414 amp., 0·029 amp.
28. 46·4 ohms.
29. 12·3 ohms.
30. 1·5 amps., 4 per cent error.
31. 0·05 per cent error.
32. $\frac{1}{7}$ ohm.
33. (a) 7·595.   (b) 30·5 ohms.
34. 3·417 ohms, 3·783 ohms.
35. 0·202 ohm, current increased in ratio of 40 : 20·2, 19·8 ohms.
36. 1·51 ohms, 2·26 ohms.
37. 0·66 × 10^{-6} amp. per scale division.
38. 29 min. 49 sec.
39. 2·68.
40. 91·48 ohms.
41. (a) 4,995 ohms.   (b) 9,995 ohms.
42. (a) 1·344 pence.   (b) 0·48 pence.   (c) 0·36 pence.
43. 72·19° C.
44. 16·47° C.
45. 3 mins. 42 secs.
46. 0·174 amp., 0·27 pence.
47. 1,562$\frac{1}{2}$ ohms.
48. (a) 1 amp.   (b) 4 volts.   (c) 4 watts.
49. 0·26 pence.
50. (a) 862·2 ohms.   (b) 62·87 watts.   (c) 0·827 c.p. per watt.
     (d) 0·377 pence.
51. 4° C. above surroundings.

52. (*a*) 107·5 ohms. (*b*) 558·6 watts. (*c*) 0·5586 pence.
53. 0·000284.
54. 103·4 calories per minute.
55. (*a*) 513·1 ohr ɔ. (*b*) 103·9 watts. (*c*) 1·924 c.p. per watt.
    (*d*) 0·623 pence.
56. 1·46 watts. 0·001957 h.p.
57. (*a*) 26 ohms. (*b*) 1,840 watts. (*c*) 176 watts.
    (*d*) as heat in resistance.
58. 1,600 to 1.

INDEX

GEORGE ALLEN & UNWIN LTD
London : 40 Museum Street, W.C.1

Auckland : 24 Wyndham Street
Bombay : 15 Graham Road, Ballard Estate, Bombay 1
Calcutta : 17 Chittaranjan Avenue, Calcutta 13
Cape Town : 109 Long Street
Karachi : 254 Ingle Road
New Delhi : 13-14 Ajmeri Gate Extension, New Delhi 1
Sao Paulo : Avenida 9 de Julho 1138-Ap. 51
Sydney, N.S.W. : Bradbury House, 55 York Street
Toronto : 91 Wellington Street West

THE BEQUEST OF THE GREEKS

by Tobias Dantzig

Demy 8vo.   18s. *net*

In mathematics all roads lead to Hellas, and any attempts
to study the historical development of modern mathematics
must make a thorough examination of the Greek contribution. This volume deals therefore with the ideas and issues
which agitated the Greeks from Thales to Pappus and
which have survived and are still alive to-day. Professor
Dantzig envisages two later volumes : *Centuries of Surge*
will describe the rebirth of mathematics and its prodigious
progress in the seventeenth and eighteenth centuries, and
The Age of Discretion will cover developments in the nineteenth century.

Professor Dantzig's brilliantly organised work grew out
of his experience with *Number: the Language of Science.*
This earlier book gained immediate recognition as an
exceptionally clear account of a vital mathematical problem
and has been revised and enlarged three times. His new
historical survey exhibits the same stimulating qualities of
lucidity and thoroughness.

SCIENCE MAKES SENSE

by Ritchie Calder

Demy 8vo.   12s. 6d. *net*

Written by Britain's leading scientific writer, this unusual
book has a wide, popular appeal. It presents in lively
fashion the great scientific advances of today, from the use
of atomic energy to Space travel. But it is something more;
it gives a fresh insight into the processes of scientific
thought and development.

It reconstitutes science as one of the humanities, relates
it to religion, literature and the arts, and to the social
problems of the world today. It tells the general reader
what he ought to know about science with freshness and
humour, and without technicalities. It is also intended as
a serious contribution to education, providing students,
who have not had a scientific training, with an appreciation
of the developments which are changing the nature of our
society. *Science Makes Sense* will give the reader a proper
sense of proportion about science and help him to form
judgements about its use.

GEORGE ALLEN AND UNWIN LTD